The Good Food Guide *1986*

The Good Food Guide *1986*

Edited by Drew Smith

Published by Consumers' Association
and Hodder & Stoughton

The Good Food Guide 1986 is published by
Consumers' Association
14 Buckingham Street, London WC2N 6DS and
Hodder & Stoughton Ltd
47 Bedford Square, London WC1B 3DP

British Library Cataloguing in Publication Data
Consumers' Association

The Good food guide.—1986
1. Restaurants, lunch rooms, etc.—Great Britain—Directories
I. Smith, Drew II. Consumers' Association
647'.9541'05 TX910.G7

ISBN 0 340 38157 4

Special thanks for this year's *Guide* to Mon Mohan for the cover design, Sue Huntley for the front cover illustration, James Ainsworth for the wine coverage, Jeremy Round for organising the inspections, Jenny McCallion for the section on diners' rights, Barbara Fraser for editing the entries, Tim Higgins for the typographic design . . . and to all the inspectors who must remain anonymous. The maps are by Cartographic Services (Cirencester) Ltd

Photoset in Monophoto Photina
by Vantage Photosetting Co. Ltd, Eastleigh and London
Printed and bound in The Netherlands
by Rotatie Boekendruk B.V., Krommenie

Contents

The Good Food Guide

The Good Food Guide is compiled from unsolicited reports on restaurants sent in by readers during the last year. A list of everyone who wrote to the *Guide* appears at the back of this edition.

Each nomination is checked by one of the *Guide*'s inspectorial team and the restaurant is asked to give details of its menus, wines and suppliers before a final decision on inclusion is made. In nine out of ten cases the restaurants appearing in these pages will have been nominated separately by at least half a dozen people. In some cases they have been nominated by as many as fifty readers and more; this figure may include a number of inspections.

The Good Food Guide was founded in 1951 and has been published annually since 1969.

No more frozen broccoli, please . . .

Drew Smith

This is a book about good food, the restaurants that serve it, how it is prepared and where it comes from.

All the restaurants included have been spontaneously and independently recommended by readers – in the case of Gastronome One in London, for example, by 46 different people in the three months up until the chef – last year's Young Chef of the Year – left, or in the case of John Tovey's new venture, Uplands, at Cartmel, by 18 people in the first six weeks. The restaurants have then been checked anonymously by *Guide* inspectors who have eaten a typical meal and paid their own bill. The proprietors are then sent a six-page questionnaire on their business; on return, the questionnaire is checked against the information already held by the *Guide* office. The sum of all these recommendations, inspections and details, gleaned throughout 1985, provides the entries. In total, 3,735 restaurants were shortlisted and 1,764 were visited by inspectors. Five out of eight readers supplied details of the prices of meals eaten during the first six months of the year. They spent £186,000 in that time.

We have found 277 restaurants that were not listed last year and lost 228, either because they have closed, changed their kitchen arrangements, or else dropped their standards. We have expanded into areas of the country where we had poor coverage before, but a general tightening of our standards has also meant that we have not increased the number of entries dramatically. The implications of the Real Food campaign have been significant. Where we have found processed food we have marked down restaurants, and in some cases dropped them altogether.

Money talked

Nineteen eighty-five was a year when money talked. The growth of the luxury restaurant catering for the international tourist has been remarkable. At times there has seemed to be a concerted attempt by the top end of the catering trade to take over the pages of the *Guide*. Our files are bursting with lavish and expensively produced brochures, letters from public relations companies, and offers of free meals for inspectors (always declined).

A disproportionate amount of the inspection budget seems to have been taken up by these restaurants. In far too many places the bills are astronomical – certainly well outside the reach of the vast majority of people in this country except once in a blue moon. Prices are now so high that it is quite possible for visitors with a strong dollar in their pocket to spend weeks eating their way around parts of Britain that few born here have ever seen or are ever likely to afford to see. Ten years ago I remember being offered a house for sale in Boldon, Tyne and Wear, for about the same amount that four people would need now to have dinner and a bottle of good claret on Park Lane, Mayfair.

The cost of eating out at the top end of the market now beggars belief. Tickets for the finals of Wimbledon cost £18. A season ticket to watch 50-plus games at Stamford Bridge is, on average, £154. Yet restaurant bills for £40-plus a head are now almost commonplace, often without pushing out the boat at all. It is interesting to note that of the 20 great French restaurants we have listed this year, very few are actually as expensive as similar places in the UK.

It is unfortunate that the two restaurants getting the highest *Guide* rating this year – Le Gavroche and Le Manoir Aux Quat' Saisons – are in this high price-bracket. But we make no apologies for them because we believe that in both cases the money is well spent on achieving standards of excellence that are unparalleled – and they offer something that cannot be found anywhere else. But that should not distract us from the sheer arrogance of restaurants charging high prices. The time has come to consider introducing legislation to stop this spiralling of prices, as has been done in France. Arreté 854/A on restaurant prices forbids increases of more than three per cent a year.

High prices are no guide to good food any more. For example, there is a Mayfair restaurant, where the average amount spent is £30-plus a head, which serves smoked salmon from Young's that can be bought for about £10 a pound in a supermarket. Three slices here cost £6. Then there is a country-house hotel in Kent which has spent tens of thousands of pounds redecorating and publicising its high-class restaurant but the kitchen cannot even make a proper vinaigrette and uses meats of a quality that any decent butcher would mark down as second-rate. Another example is a hotel in Knightsbridge where the inspection bill for one person was £37.40 (including half a bottle of house wine), where 'the sweets had been made last week and were stale and the pastry leaden'.

With this in mind we have summarily dismissed any restaurant charging these kinds of prices which cannot earn a rating of 14.

It may not taste good but it looks good

The one area in which the luxury kitchens have advanced is in the *presentation* of food. Levels of fancy garnishing and Miró-esque design have reached new heights, as if every chef's greatest ambition in life is to have his food photographed for a colour magazine with little regard for what it tastes like.

Presentation is a basic misconception about the nature of *nouvelle cuisine* which leads to many failures. Ingredients are separated from the very things that give them their flavour: fish is taken off the bone, duck breasts are removed from their carcase (in fact it is possible to buy packets of duck breasts). In the best kitchens the flavour is then put back by using the bones to create a sauce. But too often a bit of cream, a slug of alcohol and a tropical fruit for garnish are used instead. The result is four unamalgamated ingredients and a culinary diaspora.

Nouvelle cuisine has almost become the trademark of the second-rate. It is misunderstood because it is not really a *cuisine* at all but essentially a style. Its lessons with regard to presentation and the quality of the ingredients are of use only within the context of the whole sum of traditional cookery knowledge.

In the best restaurants – those rating 14 and above – *nouvelle cuisine* is only one line of thought among many. The best kitchens transcend dogma. Good cooking is not rhetoric but a language of self-expression that changes from day to day – according to the materials available in the market.

A striking exercise is to compare the inspection meals at Le Gavroche and at the Riverside in Helford, two restaurants that would seem to be at opposite ends of the spectrum – Le Gavroche a temple of French cuisine and luxury, the Riverside a small country restaurant cooking to the principles expounded by Elizabeth David in the 1950s and 1960s. In fact it might almost be possible to interchange the dishes without noticing any great difference (indeed, lobster bisque and watercress soup are on both menus) because the cooking at both places derives from the same source – the ingredients available.

Value for money?

Not all the restaurants listed are expensive. We are proud of the fact that the tier of restaurants rated 14 and over encompasses such differing styles as the great classical hotel cooking of Michel Bourdin at the Connaught as well as David Adlard's tiny cottage in Wymondham, Bistro Twenty One in Bristol, which is what its name implies, and David Wilson's extraordinary, inexpensive high-class French cooking at the Peat Inn.

If it is luxury that you want then do not follow the rating system but read the text – a high rating does not necessarily mean pomp and circumstance. The entry is earned by a restaurant for its food alone. It is important that we do not stereotype our ideas as to what a good restaurant should or should not be. The fish in the fish and chip shops listed in these pages should be as good as the fish served in a luxury hotel, and it may well be better than in those luxury hotels not listed this year.

To compensate for the horrific inflation in restaurant prices, we have increased the number of inexpensive eating places in the 8–9 range on the rating system. This is a theme we will return to early in 1986 with the publication of a guide to places to eat for around £5.

In the middle price range – where the UK lags so lamentably behind France – there is no doubt that for value, quality of food and even service, ethnic restaurants are now head and shoulders above European restaurants. Italian food is in the main stuck to the bottom of the pan, like so much soggy pasta. French food is the major area of activity for the processed food industry, and English food is confused and in search of an identity.

The best restaurant in our view in Liverpool is Lebanese, the best restaurants in Manchester Chinese. In Birmingham it is hard to recommend any of the big European restaurants over and above the inexpensive Chinese restaurants and even a little South American cafe. In Bradford it is possible to eat at any number of tiny curry and sweet houses for less than £3 a head, while the Michelin-recommended restaurant in the city is notable mainly for the fact that it has a bottle of wine for sale at more than £1,500 (fifteen hundred pounds!). In London the emergence of the Japanese restaurant is one of the most exciting culinary events of the last few years – and if you choose carefully it is possible to eat for less than at most French restaurants. At the Yakitori Kitchen (see London) it is possible to eat for less than £10 a head.

With this in mind, the feature Eating Ethnic (see page 609) is a series of articles on many of the ethnic cuisines. These try to put the cooking into context and to guide the inexperienced diner through the obstacles of confronting a new cuisine. Many, many readers who have gone on such voyages of discovery report back enthusiastically, even, perhaps surprisingly, about foods as apparently alien as raw fish.

To eat ethnic does require a degree of tolerance on the part of the diner but, at the same time, proprietors should not exploit their customers' ignorance. Some Japanese restaurants indulge in shady practices to jack up the bill and people new to the cooking would do well to stay within the safe confines of the set menu until they are familiar with them. Examples are VAT not being included in prices, items left unpriced on the menu, and too many dishes brought.

A new way of thinking?

Diners must also have respect for other customs, though. One couple protested to the *Guide* that they had gone to a restaurant at 11.45 pm and demanded a five-course meal, only to be told the chef wanted to go home. Just because it was a Chinese restaurant does not mean it should have been expected to co-operate. If it had been a French restaurant the waiter would have told the couple where to get off in much more graphic style.

The emergence of the ethnic restaurant has been symptomatic of the crucial change of thinking in catering over the last 10 years which has contributed enormously to improved standards. The idea of canning, packaging and warehousing foods that dominated the post-war period is being eroded by the technology of transport that can take goods from one corner of the country or even the world (Waitrose now flies in its New Zealand lamb chilled) means that produce can arrive at the kitchen in peak condition. Those caterers whose larders are still filled with packets and tins are living in the 1950s and 1960s. It is now feasible for a kitchen to be completely emptied (stocks and casseroles excepted) at the end of the evening and to be freshly stocked the following day. It is a tricky stock-taking arrangement, but this principle opens new avenues – and creates new jobs too, not in the traditionally hated packing factories but in the supply industries.

This increased availability of fresh foodstuffs tallies with much current thinking on nutrition. Where nutritionists are saying that packaged foods should be treated with caution because the number of preservatives and colourings disguise the quality of the basic ingredients, so chefs have reached similar conclusions as to what is regarded as good food. The chefs have the know-how, the nutritionists the theory. That good food, in the gastronomic sense, might be good for you is a seductive idea. To an extent it is possible to eat now at most of the restaurants in the *Guide* without necessarily going on a calorific blow-out. Anton Mosimann at the Dorchester has even developed a style of cooking for people suffering from heart condition. The cartoon of the Voluptuary Under The Horrors of Digestion that hangs in Lichfield's restaurant in Richmond may truly be representing a thing of the past.

The need for new teaching . . .

A kitchen can develop and progress only by daily contact with the raw materials in their unadulterated state. With quality wine the label clearly states the vintage, the vineyard, the maker and the bottler – an exemplary form of presentation of the product – whereas with food we are content to talk about a tomato or a potato as if the strain, where they were grown, how long they have been unearthed matters not a jot. The EEC insistence on labelling fruit and vegetables with their varieties is a major breakthrough. Consumers are going to have to arm themselves with this kind of knowledge if they want to eat well.

. . . and for a college of ideas

Many of the catering colleges are teaching recipes and techniques that are hopelessly out of date and using second-rate produce. Is it not extraordinary that domestic science pupils in schools are still being taught to make profiteroles as if they were a lynchpin of understanding cooking when in reality they are a frippery? Not that rigorous, self-defeating cant should be taught; more a new approach to food. The best advice to anyone in the food trade, young or old, wanting to learn would not be to cook so much as to eat. See how the Japanese treat fish, the Chinese vegetables, the Indians pulses . . . Understand why salt is used to draw out the juices before reaching either for the Maldon or the Saxa.

There is a very great need for a new catering school where the current knowledge and expertise demonstrated in kitchens across the country can be brought together into a programme to consolidate standards. (In France, one such establishment is being opened in Lyons.) This applies not just to cooking but also to waiting, which is the final link in the restaurant food cycle. The trade of being a waiter has been neglected and is still too often regarded as a worthless job. But any chef ought to spend at least a year front of house to see how the dining-room operates and to have contact with the customer. How else is he or she to understand what happens to his food? And appalling things do happen.

At the Best of Both Worlds in the Britannia Hotel, London, the chef had neatly plated his sea-bass with a carrot sauce and adjusted the seasoning only for the waiter to loom up over the customer wielding a foot-long peppermill and start grinding it furiously. At the Westbury Hotel, London, the chef had neatly plated some turbot over shredded vegetables and glazed the sauce under the grill only for the waiter to come along and plonk great dollops of vegetables all over it as if the place were a canteen.

The responsibility for such acts clearly lies with restaurateurs, not necessarily with the staff themselves. In some cases restaurateurs have been known to exploit their staff, and the murky practice of tipping hides many a rapacious practice even now. Owners split tips between the staff but include themselves and their wives and probably their mothers-in-law too in the share-out; in some cases they refuse to pay wages at all and expect the customer to pay for the staff as if service were nothing to do with the restaurant.

The sooner restaurateurs accept the idea that all the niggling little extras that seem such good money-making wheezes at the time – like the cover charge, a selection of vegetables priced as extras, the greed with which water is priced – just reinforce the notion that the catering industry is dominated by a bunch of scoundrels and philanderers. The way out of such charges is to move to the all-inclusive price, even including half a bottle of house wine, so that the customer knows precisely how much an evening will cost. Otherwise the customer will not return and sooner or later the restaurant will go bankrupt.

Flashes in the pan

Restaurants do go bust, too. The most frustrating aspect of editing the *Guide* is the number of restaurants that come and go from one year to the next. Catering is the most volatile of businesses. Standards cannot improve while restaurants come and go apparently in the middle of the night. It takes time to build up quality suppliers, to establish good service, to get the money-making right . . . and finally to get the rewards. A good example of the time-scale involved occurred last summer. Le Gavroche was booked up 10 weeks in advance at night; nearby Ninety Park Lane, where Louis Outhier from La Napoule was guiding the kitchens and serving food of a quality no more than a point or two from Le Gavroche, were taking bookings for the same evening. The difference is that Le Gavroche has built its reputation over 20 years.

It is a fair criticism of the *Guide* to say that many of the restaurants listed are packed and therefore it is difficult to book tables. This underlines the point that people will pay for good food when it can be found. But in most cases, except perhaps in the tourist centres of London, restaurants have to build up their clientele over a period of years rather than months.

What of the new technology?

One depressing conversation this year was with a *maître d'* in an expensive London restaurant. He was extolling the virtues of blanching vegetables in the morning and then popping them in the microwave a minute before serving them 12 hours later. He obviously never ate them himself, or if he did then we should all feel sorry for the state of his tastebuds. The real failing in this scenario is not the microwave but that the *maître d'* did not care that vegetables taken out of their natural state, peeled, sliced and left hanging around would deteriorate from that moment and were by the time they were served nowhere near the quality that they were when first blanched.

The herbalist Jill Davies makes the point concisely: food when it is cooked is live. From that moment on, with only a few exceptions such as preserved foods or stocks, it starts to die. The longer the time-span between the moment it is cooked and the moment it is eaten the closer to death it will be. In the case of fish left in the hot cupboard that time-span is measured in minutes.

But not all the technology is to be sneezed at. The menace of boil-in-the-bag dishes seems to have been dented by a general acceptance in the catering trade that freezing is an inferior means of packaging. Even Rocco Forte has said as much. The new alternative in the pipeline is vacuum packing. In principle, by vacuum packing it is possible to hold a product at a state of ripeness for a longer period than normal. Some supermarkets already do such things with fresh fruit and vegetables. To get the best produce to the kitchen at its peak, vacuum packing may prove to be a significant breakthrough. Whether or not it will work so well with pre-prepared dishes is another matter: probably not, in restaurant terms, but almost certainly yes in terms of canteens and fast food which could, and hopefully will be, revolutionised.

The principle behind vacuum packing is not vastly different from the principles of cooking en papillote or in silver foil. The heating up process becomes part of the cooking. Expect a chain of new restaurants serving these kind of dishes made up in a central kitchen to open in 1986, with any luck at a reasonable price.

So much for the future. What of this year?

Are standards the same across the country?

Last year we criticised the standards of quasi-French restaurants in London and that criticism seems to hold good – high prices and inferior food. But at least now there is an enormous range of ethnic eating available. The Bombay Brasserie is now talked of in much the same endearing tones as Langan's Brasserie, which is a fair indication of the state of play.

East Anglia is emerging as an area in which some of the best British cooking is being done, mainly thanks to a clutch of small, excellent family-run restaurants.

The food in Scotland is still given a rosy gloss by the many luxury country-house hotels that have emerged to take advantage of the American visitors who can afford to pay the prices. It is encouraging, though, to see Glasgow threatening Edinburgh's long-standing dominance. But out of town some inspection meals were pretty dreadful.

Wales remains a problem. Quite why it has not spawned a country-house hotel industry like Scotland is not clear.

The rise of the vegetarian restaurant seems to gather momentum from month to month, and many are starting to knock on the door of the *Guide*. The two strongest points in their favour are that usually they serve Real Food and are cheap, even if the decor tends to be limited to dried flowers in mineral water bottles.

The most noticeable north–south divide is in the dining-rooms themselves. The northern fashion is for restaurants to be like discotheques, with loud music and some with even flashing lights. Such places would most likely be empty in the south. Sloans in Birmingham, for instance, with its fountain, wickerwork chairs and background music, is heartily endorsed by northern readers but rather more sceptically by southerners.

The picture in Ireland is bleak, as our Irish inspector explains (see page 634). Inspections are expensive because of the vast distances between restaurants and because of the high cost meal for meal – more expensive than France. But both these countries are to some extent outside our purview and the inspection budget must remain primarily in Britain.

What other comings and goings?

We are very sorry to lose Doreen Readshaw's Oak Tree Inn (at Hutton Magna), with her amazing collection of chamberpots. And of major casualties from last year, Anna's Place in London has undergone a metamorphosis and survives in this *Guide*, but Gastronome One, after a succession of alternately brilliant and all right meals last winter, lost its chef, who has now gone to work under Raymond Blanc.

By way of compensation, three restaurants will undoubtedly be the big news of 1986 – Michael Quinn's new venture at the spectacular Ettington Park (see Alderminster), the revamped Tante Claire in Chelsea and Nico Ladenis' new restaurant at Shinfield, Berkshire.

A point or two on wine

For the third year running we have concentrated the wine coverage on a single region. This year it is Alsace, the youngest of the major appellations, which produces superb white wines that complement a wide variety of foods and cooking styles, including, unusually, ethnic food. It is also relatively good value, especially compared to the prices of vintage claret and burgundy which have spiralled with the international money markets. They are becoming increasingly hard to recommend for restaurant drinking given the size of the mark-ups. The lesser regions like the Rhône, the Loire and Spain offer the real value. And roll on Australia and New Zealand too – both countries produce excellent wines that are starting to appear on wine lists.

Every restaurant ought to have a wine on its list at around £5, otherwise it is tantamount to saying that ordinary people on ordinary wages cannot eat there. Any restaurateur who cannot find a decent wine to sell around this price probably shouldn't be let near good clarets anyway. It is encouraging that even Le Gavroche now has a half-bottle of wine on its list at £4, which is a salutary lesson to those restaurants who think their food is so wonderful that only wines of £10 and more can match it.

The campaign for Real Food

We have had to drop a number of restaurants because of the amount of processed food they use. Often restaurateurs stated on the questionnaire we sent that they 'only use fresh produce' – patently untrue, as frozen frogs' legs, canned snails and frozen prawns on the menus testify.

Let us accept that raw ingredients arrive in the kitchen at the peak of condition. But those restaurants bearing the Real Food stamp do more than just shop well. They go out and sponsor cottage food industries and husband an improvement in standards.

Indeed, the principles of Real Food go further than the kitchen and reach into other trades, encouraging higher standards among greengrocers, butchers, fishmongers and on to farmers and even haulage companies. If anyone has any doubt about the need for action, then this letter from a restaurateur makes the point succinctly: 'Because of the apparent lack of demand in Sheffield for fish and herbs we have to struggle to find reliable sources of supply. Fresh fish is very erratic. We are swimming against the tide because we do not offer boil-in-the-bag meals, ready-made sauces, and all the other things which are presented as standard fare. On one occasion we prepared fresh dates, stuffed them with our own almond and liqueur filling, dipped them in chocolate and served them free with coffee. It was not encouraging then to be asked for After Eights.' The customer, too, has to understand what is happening and get involved.

In another Yorkshire town the fish merchant will tell you that only one of more than fifty fish and chip shops sells quality fresh fish. That one is in the *Guide*; the other forty-nine-plus are not.

The only way that the customer is not going to be robbed of the quality of foods available is to demand Real Food. We should just not accept frozen fish, for instance. It is a lazy convenience that suits the trader and makes a good profit for the manufacturer but gives the consumer a poor deal.

The rating system – a success?

Seventy five per cent of readers cottoned on to the new rating system immediately and have given ratings when reporting on restaurants. So the system is here to stay.

It is meant to make the *Guide* easier to use. Those people who write in to say the *Guide* should be a slim volume composed of only the very best restaurants should eat at places earning more than 12 points. Those who complain the *Guide* restaurants can be too expensive should eat in the 8 to 9 category. In an ideal world, every town would have at least one of each, but to artificially aim for that coverage would mean dropping *Guide* standards.

We have not made many adjustments from last year except where necessary to reward those who had persevered with standards and to drop the rating at those establishments that have let standards slip. It will be surprising if we have to make wholesale changes in the future, except for new places and places whose standards increase or fall.

On page 18 is a list of salient points that have been crucial in rating the restaurants.

What else is new?

The names of readers who have made especially helpful contributions to the *Guide* are printed at the end of the book instead of under the relevant restaurants. In the past, many people who have done heroic work have never been credited because the restaurant did not earn a high enough rating for it to be included. The list is a thank you to those people whose opinions form the basis of the entries.

We have also printed the names of the chefs and owners so that it is now easier to check whether or not a restaurant has changed hands. And, for better or worse, we now have a computer which allows us to up-date entries up to the last day before going to press. The computer will hold information, in an instantly accessible format, on the 100,000 or so businesses that might be candidates for inclusion.

And finally . . .

My thanks to everyone who wrote in during 1985 and helped to make the *Guide* what it is. If there are restaurants that are not included that you think should be, or ones that are that shouldn't, or if you visit a restaurant that is in the *Guide* and want to confirm its merits, then please put pen to paper – there are report forms at the end of the book (a sheet of writing-paper will do perfectly well), and we do try to acknowledge all correspondence personally. The *Guide* is a democracy and everyone's views are treated with equal respect. Just by writing in you will be helping to improve the standards of food in this country. I look forward to hearing from you.

Good eating for 1986!

DREW SMITH
September 1985

Notes for restaurateurs

Ups and downs

In applying the grading system, various criteria have been considered. Some are common – and less common – faults – the 'downs'; others are positive points – the 'ups'. They are listed here, but this is not a complete list nor does it follow that one failing necessarily means that the rating will be lowered or that serving canapés or petits fours or warm fresh bread or using expensive ingredients will lead to an increased rating. The list is meant to help raise standards.

DOWN: All tinned produce including tomatoes and artichokes

UP: All produce served in season

DOWN: Garnishes that bear no relation to the dish they appear on. Everything on the plate should be meant to be eaten

UP: Bread freshly baked

DOWN: Waiters interrupting conversation

UP: Waiters who know the dishes they serve

DOWN: Fish served on plates that are so hot that it goes on cooking

UP: The ability to handle complaints correctly

DOWN: Dishes not cooked to order. This includes sweets and terrines not made on the same day or as near as possible

UP: Strength in all sections of the menu

DOWN: Poor-quality house wine

UP: Greeting diners at the door, not leaving them standing around without a welcome

DOWN: Dried herbs instead of fresh, except in special dishes (for example, lamb in a salt crust)

UP: Not using commercial stock cubes

DOWN: Aerosol creams

UP: Ripe cheeses

DOWN: Coffee that has been left around to stew, a very common fault

UP: Good-quality butters and oils used in the cooking as well as for the table

DOWN: Leaving dishes in hot cabinets, which dries them

UP: A positive vegetable policy

DOWN: Serving unnecessary sorbets in the middle of meals

UP: Menus that change

DOWN: Watery, i.e. incorrectly drained, fish

UP: Dishes, and wines, accurately described in English

DOWN: The same sauce on different main dishes

UP: Not using gelatine

DOWN: Sharp practices, including a) the bottom line of credit card slips left blank b) a selection of vegetables charged to each diner as if they were individual portions c) a cover charge d) specials of the day recited without any mention of their price e) VAT not included in the price f) extortionate charges for mineral water g) profiteering charges on taxis ordered h) non-itemised bills

UP: All-inclusive menus

DOWN: High mark-ups on wine and other drinks

UP: All items made in-house

DOWN: Unpriced menus for 'ladies' and other guests

UP: Waiters who do not insist on pouring the wine at a rate of knots to ensure the diners order a second bottle

DOWN: Reheating meats and vegetables

UP: Ethnic restaurants that do not compromise to Western tastes

DOWN: Short cuts taken in stuffings, like foie gras pâté

UP: Simplicity of dishes – no over-elaboration

How to use this guide

All the restaurants listed in this book serve good food and have done so consistently. That it is good food is testified to by the people who wrote in to the *Guide* over the last year (a list appears at the back of the *Guide*) and also by our network of inspectors, who check each establishment.

To say that the food is good means that it must be a) judged to be well above the local standard and b) of a quality conventional wisdom lays down as being better in both its uncooked and cooked state. For instance, the fish served in a fish and chip shop listed in these pages ought to be of the same quality as that served in a luxury hotel. The difference may be that one serves cod and the other turbot, that one serves it wrapped in paper and the other in a well-appointed dining-room, but in terms of freshness, handling in both the markets and the kitchen, and the time of year, the basic quality will be on a par. That is the basis for inclusion irrespective of fashions. To this end we have downmarked every time we have been served processed food.

The points system

All the restaurants are graded out of a possible maximum of 20 points. Those that do not score at least 8 are automatically excluded; and the highest score this year is 17. The points system is meant to make the *Guide* more accessible to readers by putting restaurants in an overall context, and also to set the standards which will encourage the catering trade to go on to greater things.

This is how it works:

8–9 These places *may not be restaurants at all* but nevertheless still serve good food. They may be cafes, pubs, small hotels or even small bistros. Each in their own way will serve *food that is more than adequate* and provide an invaluable service for locals and travellers. At this level we would not judge too harshly either the decor or a lack of good wines provided the food is up to the mark most of the time.

10–11 These restaurants will be *the best in the locality*, definitely worth seeking out if you are nearby, serving good food in a fitting setting. Some dishes may be as good as those served in a restaurant with a higher rating, but *these places may not have the ambition* to bake their own bread, make their own pasta or develop their menu daily according to market. They will, however, cook to order.

12–13 Here you will find the best restaurants in the county or region. They will have shown *consistently* that they are prepared to scour the markets for the best ingredients, which will be served with flair and imagination not just in four or five dishes but *right through the menu*. Here, expect the staff to be aware of what the kitchen is doing and be able to communicate it, expect the surroundings to be in keeping with the cooking, expect to find a **Real Food** denotation because this restaurant ought to be encouraging local cottage food industries, and expect *the cooking to allow the ingredients to taste of themselves*.

14–15 These are, in our view, *the best restaurants in the country* – the finest ingredients will be cooked with *consummate skill*. In these restaurants, expect the bread and the biscuits to be baked in the kitchen or especially for the restaurant, expect most of the menu to be prepared freshly each day, expect wines (or in the case of ethnic restaurants other drinks) to be taken seriously. At this level we do not expect to eat frozen fish, to find inferior oils or butters used in the cooking and nor do we expect to find chefs using commercial ingredients which dilute the individuality of their work. At this level a chef will have convinced us that he has a special talent and also that the staff and the restaurant itself are organised enough to get his or her food to the table at its prime.

16–17 The top marks, given to only 5 restaurants. Each will have shown that, over and above the qualities required for a score of 15, *it has been a positive influence on eating out in this country* either by example, or by its ideas or by training other chefs. These restaurants can and do hold their own against the best in the world.

New entry, zero rated Restaurants on which we have sufficient information to be confident enough to recommend but have not been able to assess as fully as we would have ~~liked~~ are zero rated for this year. This would also apply to a restaurant where a fundamental change in the kitchen or the business partnerships has made it difficult to predict how it will behave in the coming year. We are especially interested in reports from readers on these places so that we can build up as full a picture as possible.

Other signals

▲ This restaurant has rooms.

This restaurant has an exceptional wine cellar, not disproportionately priced.

CELLARMAN'S CHOICE This is a good wine which the restaurant ought to have stocks of during 1986 and which we recommend as suitable to go with the food, although it is likely to be more expensive than the house wine.

Real Food This restaurant does not use processed food. It will have given us a list of its suppliers for checking and will have shown that it is actively encouraging the growth of local cottage industries.

How to read a Guide entry

TORQUAY Devon [1] map 1[2]

▲ *Fawlty Towers* [3] [12/20] [4]

16 Elwood Avenue, Torquay TQ98 4DZ [5]
TORQUAY (0803) 777 [6]
behind Scala Cinema [7] [8] **Real Food** [9] £11–£18 [10]

(main text) [11]
CELLARMAN'S CHOICE: [12]

CHEFS: Kurt and Terry PROPRIETOR: Basil Fawlty [13]
OPEN: Mon to Sat [14] CLOSED: Aug [15] MEALS: 12 to 2, 7 to 9 [16]
PRICES: £13 (£19), Set D £10·50 (£15), Bar meals from £1·50 (£1·65). [17] Service 10% [18] CARDS: Access, Amex, Diners, Visa [19]
SEATS: 72. 4 tables outside. Private parties: 26 main room, 10 private room. [20] Car-park, 40 places. Vegetarian meals. [21] Children's helpings. No children under 10. [22] Jacket and tie preferred. [23] No-smoking area. [24] Wheelchair access (2 steps; also wc). [25] Classical music. [26] One sitting [27]
ACCOMMODATION: 14 rooms, all with bath/shower. B&B £20 to £40. [28] No pets. [29] Afternoon teas. [30] Garden. Indoor swimming-pool. Tennis. [GHG] [31]

[1] The town and county (in the London section, restaurants are listed alphabetically by name rather than geographically).

[2] The map number. The maps are at the end of the *Guide*.

[3] The name of the restaurant. ▲ by the name denotes that it offers accommodation too.

[4] The *Guide* rating out of 20. A zero rating may be given when an entry has not yet been thoroughly inspected; it may be a new entry or have new management or a new chef.

5 The restaurant's address, with post code whenever possible.

6 The restaurant's telephone number, including its STD code.

7 Any special directions in case the restaurant is difficult to find.

8 This symbol is awarded only to restaurants with outstanding wine cellars.

9 **Real Food** denotes a restaurant that does not use processed food, but it indicates more than just good shopping: these restaurants are actively encouraging the growth of cottage industries.

10 This is the price range for three-course meals including half a bottle of house wine, coffee, service and any hidden extras, such as a cover charge, as calculated by the *Guide*.

11 The text is based on reports sent in by readers during the last *Guide* year, confirmed by commissioned, anonymous inspections.

12 Some entries conclude with a CELLARMAN'S CHOICE. This is a wine, usually more expensive than the house wine, that the restaurateur assures us will be in stock during 1986, and that we recommend as suitable for the kind of food served, if you do not want to order the house wine.

13 The names of the chef and the owner, so that any change in management will be instantly detectable.

14 This indicates the days of the week the restaurant is open.

15 This indicates any annual closures.

16 These are the times of first and last orders for meals. It is always advisable to book before going to a restaurant. If you book and then cannot go, please remember to phone the restaurant to cancel.

17 These are calculations of typical prices for three-course meals, giving the à la carte price and variations for set lunch (L) and dinner (D) where applicable. The initial price represents the prices on the menu; the second price, in brackets, is the real cost when the extras of wine, coffee and service (at 10% unless otherwise specified) have been added.

18 This indicates that a fixed service charge will be added to the bill. Where service is included in the menu prices this is specified. When service is not mentioned, it is at the discretion of the customer.

19 These are the credit cards accepted by the restaurant.

20 Not all restaurants will take private parties. The maximum number of people in a party is given.

21 Many restaurants claim to cater for vegetarians but in fact do not. It is always advisable to explain when you book if you do not want meat.

22 Many restaurants and hotels are not keen on children. Where it says children welcome or children's helpings it indicates that they don't mind. Any limitations on age are specified.

23 Jackets and ties are compulsory in very few restaurants and this is specified; otherwise it means the proprietor prefers jacket and ties, or smart dress.

24 The no-smoking arrangements as given to us by the restaurants.

25 Wheelchair access means that the entrance is 33 inches wide and the passages four feet across. Where there are steps it will say so. If it says 'also WC', then the toilet facilities are suitable for disabled people.

26 If a restaurant plays music, this is indicated.

27 This means the restaurant serves a single sitting at a specific time.

28 The price for rooms as given to us by the hotels. The first price is for one person in a single room, the second price is for two people in a double room.

29 Some hotels will not take pets; others prefer to be asked. Best to check first.

30 This indicates teas are served to non-residents.

31 [GHG] denotes that this establishment is also listed in the 1986 edition of our sister guide. *The Good Hotel Guide*.

The Good Food Club

To join The Good Food Club you need a pen. Take out one of the report forms (or use a plain sheet of paper if you prefer) and, in as much detail as you can, describe your last meal in a restaurant and state whether or not you think it should be included in the next *Guide*. It is helpful for us to know precisely what you ate, the style of the dining-room and whether or not you thought the food good value. Mentions of poor restaurants and also well-established places are just as valuable as writing about new finds.

Reports are particularly useful in the spring when we will be planning the 1987 *Guide*. All reports and letters are acknowledged with a list of changes to and up-dated information on this edition of the *Guide*.

Cartographic Services (Cirencester) Ltd.

The best of the year . . .

17/20

Le Gavroche, London
Le Manoir aux Quat' Saisons, Great Milton

16/20

Carved Angel, Dartmouth (*West Country restaurant of the year*)
Riverside, Helford
Tante Claire, London

15/20

Box Tree, Ilkley
Connaught Hotel, London
Croque-en-Bouche, Malvern Wells
Ettington Park Hotel, Alderminster (*Newcomer of the year*)
Gidleigh Park, Chagford
Inigo Jones, London
Miller Howe, Windermere
Peat Inn, Peat Inn (*Scottish restaurant of the year*)
Le Petit Blanc, Oxford
Restaurant 74, Canterbury
Rue St Jacques, London
Walnut Tree Inn, Llandewi Skirrid
Waterside Inn, Bray
Weeks Restaurant, Glemsford

14/20

Airds Hotel, Port Appin (*Scottish hotel of the year*)
Altnaharrie Inn, Ullapool
Aye, Edinburgh (*Scottish newcomer of the year*)
Beechfield House, Beanacre
Bistro Twenty One, Bristol
The Black Boys, Thornage
Capital Hotel, London
Champany Inn, Linlithgow
Corse Lawn House, Corse Lawn
Cromlix House, Dunblane
Dorchester Hotel, London
Hambleton Hall, Hambleton
Hilaire, London
Hill's, Stratford-upon-Avon
Interlude de Tabaillau, London
Kenwards, Lewes
Lichfield's, Richmond
Mallory Court, Bishops Tachbrook
Manleys, Storrington
Morels, Haslemere
Partners 23, Sutton
Plough Inn, Fadmoor
La Potinière, Gullane
Provence, Bournemouth
Restaurant Bosquet, Kenilworth
Rhyd-Garn-Wen, Cardigan
Seafood Restaurant, Padstow
Les Semailles, Bristol
Sharrow Bay Hotel, Ullswater
Sloans, Birmingham
White's, Lincoln

Restaurants

Afric-Carib [8/20] map 9

1 Stroud Green Road, Finsbury Park, N4 2DQ
01-263 9859 £12

This is a Nigerian restaurant with a menu much like that of a Lagos eating-house. There are half a dozen dishes at each course and any could be had as starters or as main. The most striking aspects of Nigerian food are the size of the portions and the heat of the food: dishes are offered at optional strengths of hot, medium and mild. The moi-moi (a bean paste with fish) is authentic and excellent of its kind; there are usually plantains; and the fish pepper soup is very hot. Chicken is cooked with agbonor (mango seed and okra sauce) and served with eba (ground cassava root, dried and reconstituted). Beef is cooked in egusi (ground melon seeds with oil and spinach and with a distinct nutty flavour) and served with West African yams. These can be over two foot long and eight or nine inches in diameter, with tough skin that is peeled off before the fruit is sliced, boiled and pounded (traditionally done by women in a huge wooden mortar with a three foot-long pestle, though there are machines now). There are wines, including palm wine at £3.50.

CHEF: Mrs Osor PROPRIETORS: Mr and Mrs Isebor
OPEN: all week MEALS: 11.30am to 11.30pm (10.30 Sun)
PRICES: £8 (£12). Service inc CARDS: Access, Visa
SEATS: 40. Private parties: 40 main room. Children welcome. African music. Air-conditioned

Al Diwan [10/20] map 10

61–69 Edgware Road, W2 2HZ
01-724 1161 £20–£23

An Arab/Gulf restaurant with smoked-glass mirrors, flashing lights and Saudi-style paintings and coffee-pots. As well as the array of grilled meats that typically make up a Lebanese main course there are nine specifically Gulf dishes. Standards seem to fluctuate but the dish of the day is worth asking for. It is the starters that distinguish both the cuisine and this dining-room – green olives and a bowl of chilled salad are put on the table before hummus, moutabel (aubergine dip), sojok (dry, crusted spiced beef sausages), and falafel (fried broad bean and

If you cannot honour a restaurant booking, always phone to cancel.

chickpea balls). Our inspector who ate the poached lamb's testicles reports: 'The texture was a cross between cod's roe and sweetbreads. They tasted very mild and not as delicious as brains. A bit boring.' Arak is £2·25 a glass; you could drink water.

CHEF/PROPRIETOR: S. Al-Mazidi
OPEN: all week MEALS: noon to 11.30
PRICES: £13 (£23). Set L and D £12 (£20). Cover £1·50. Service 15% CARDS: Access, Amex, Diners, Visa
SEATS: 200. Private parties: 150 main room, 70 private room. Vegetarian meals. Children's helpings. Wheelchair access. Oriental music. Air-conditioned

Al Hamra [12/20] map 12

31–33 Shepherd Market, W1Y 7HR
01-493 1954 £21

A spacious, corner-building restaurant with the feel of a top-class French place, though it is in fact Lebanese. Boxes of plants divide the tables, there are chandeliers, and the blue and white curtains are pelmeted round the windows on three sides. The waiters have good English and welcome Westerners. It is a big, typical menu with the historic 40-item meze divided into hot and cold. Most main courses are grilled meats and there are some dishes of the day that are worth pursuing. Chillis lurk in the vast bowl of salad that arrives as a standard offering and excellent black and green olives come separately. If a Lebanese restaurant is judged on its hummus then this is the best place in town, barring only perhaps the Maroush. Of an equal standard are the ful medames, the beans lifted by infusions of coriander and garlic and lemon; the traditional kibbeh; and a huge dish of stuffed lamb baked with cinnamon, pine kernels, toasted almonds and brown rice, served with a huge bowl of yoghourt. The sweets trolley is loaded with fruits and Lebanese confectionery and the cardamom coffee tastes authentically of cardamom. Lebanese wine is £9 but the arak is cheaper.

CHEF: Mr Hassan PROPRIETOR: Mr Nabolse
OPEN: all week CLOSED: 25 Dec MEALS: noon to midnight
PRICES: £10 (£21). Cover £1. Minimum £5 CARDS: Access, Amex, Diners, Visa
SEATS: 73. 8 tables outside. Private parties: 50 main room. Children welcome. Wheelchair access. Music

Al Khayam [10/20] map 10

27–29 Westbourne Grove, W2 4UA
01-727 2556 £10

Probably the best among many Indian restaurants in the Westbourne Grove area, although not as swanky as it used to be. Meat dishes include fruit and nuts; lobster tandoori is flavoursome; and murgh masala is big on tomato taste. Aloo nan is an Indian version of a chip butty; channa, bhindi and sag are good. Basmati rice is flecked and fragrant. Licensed.

PROPRIETOR: F.H. Vhatti
OPEN: all week MEALS: 12 to 2.30, 6.30 to 11.30 (12 Sat and Sun)
PRICES: £5 (£10). Minimum £4·50. Service 10% CARDS: Access, Amex, Diners, Visa
SEATS: 90. Private parties: 40 main room. Vegetarian meals. No children under 5. No-smoking area. Wheelchair access (also WC). Indian music. Air-conditioned

L'Amico [10/20] map 10

44 Horseferry Road, SW1P 2AF
01-222 4680 £20

This is where Neil Kinnock took Mr Gorbachov to eat when he was in London – it is on the division bell and so well used by MPs and civil servants. It is a classical, conservative Italian restaurant with well-spaced tables and a safe menu of lamb cutlets and boneless duck à l'orange. The bresaola and Parma ham are of good quality; tortelloni with pesto sauce is reliable. Hopefully MPs are normally better briefed than you are after reading the wine list here. Judging from their names the wines probably come from somewhere south of Brighton, but more than that is difficult to say.

CHEF: Nicola Sorrenti PROPRIETOR: Bruno Carini
OPEN: Mon to Fri CLOSED: Aug MEALS: 12 to 2.30, 6.15 to 11
PRICES: £12 (£20). Cover 90p. Service 12.5% CARDS: Access, Amex, Diners, Visa
SEATS: 70. Private parties: 55 main room, 16 and 4 private rooms. Children welcome. Smart dress preferred. Music. Air-conditioned

Anarkali [11/20] map 9

30–35 King Street, W6 9MH
01-748 1760 and 6911 £9–£12

Recently redecorated with an extraordinary slatted brass ceiling and mythological paintings, all of which produces a feeling of space and calm. The smart menu runs to quail cooked with mild spices; marinated leg of lamb or chicken; vegetable, as well as Persian chicken, pilaus; plus more usual items. Tandoori lamb chops are pink and subtly flavoured with only a dash of coriander on top; Goa fish curry has used halibut steak, lightly spiced with turmeric and fennel. Roti bread has an earthy, wholemeal taste about it; potato with cauliflower is richly spiced; and rice is fragrant. Pickles and relishes are lifted from supporting to starring role and have included an orange-coloured coconut paste; fresh green coriander cream; lime pickle; mango pickle and chutney. The restaurant is licensed and there are dozens of cocktails, but spiced tea is wonderfully aromatic.

CHEF/PROPRIETOR: M. Miah
OPEN: all week CLOSED: 25 and 26 Dec MEALS: 12 to 2.30, 6 to 12
PRICES: £7 (£12). Set L £6·50 (£10). Set D from £5·50 (£9). Service 10% CARDS: Access, Amex, Diners, Visa
SEATS: 90. Private parties: 70 main room, 40 private room. Vegetarian meals. Children welcome. Wheelchair access (also WC). Indian music. Air-conditioned

Anna's Place [12/20] map 10

90 Mildmay Park, N1 4PR
01-249 9379 £14

'I am going back to my roots,' said Anna Hegarty when she re-opened last December with a blackboard menu and the kitchen moved downstairs. Now it is largely Swedish dishes that she offers, such as herring marinated in different ways, but the gravlax has been retained from the days she and Redmond Hayward ran this as one of the best restaurants in London. Any thoughts on the new place are tinged by memories of what it used to be, which was a rare combustion of superb food, theatre and friendliness. Now we have in its place Anna's diner – lime-green walls relieved by rubber plants, a collection of American 1950s metal signs and an enormous ornate cash-register guarding the bar. The menu has eight dishes per course, which are pruned back as the evening goes on. There has been good eating in the lax pudding (potatoes, onion and salted salmon, baked with cream); the beef fillet sauté with mustard and onions; and veal with dill sauce. Fish is consistently good. Apple crumble is all of two inches high, with another inch of crumble and chopped hazel-nuts, while whole burgundy pears are served with a sharp cinnamon ice-cream. The excellent house wine, Vin de l'Ecaillière at £4·50, survives.

CHEFS: Paul Sykes, Mark Ashley and Elizabeth Kennedy PROPRIETOR: Anna Hegarty
OPEN: Tue to Sat CLOSED: 1 week Christmas and Easter, Aug MEALS: 12.30 to 2.30, 7.15 to 10.15
PRICES: £10 (£14). Service 10%
SEATS: 52. 5 tables outside. Private parties: 10 main room. Vegetarian meals. Children's helpings. Wheelchair access. Music

Arirang [10/20] map 12

31–32 Poland Street, W1V 3DB
01-437 6633 and 9662 £10

Arirang means mountain top, though the simulated stone boulder that protrudes into this bamboo-roofed Korean restaurant gives you the impression of being rather further down the slope. The menu gives a few pointers to ordering, recommending soup, appetiser, a special, side dish, and rice or noodles. The Korean way is for all the dishes to come to the table at once. The house soup is a thin chicken broth; the fiery kim-chee is made with Chinese cabbage; and skikumchee, a dish of cold spinach, is flavoured with sesame oil and garlic. The national dish of bulgogi (marinated beef) is delivered on a shield-like pan with holes and kept warm over a candle burner, the pieces of beef flavoured with a little sweet soy, sesame and garlic sauce. The waiters show how to roll the kim (seaweed wafers) around rice. The one-plate lunch special is good value at £3·50, and service is excellent. Barley tea is 50p.

CHEF: S.D.Choi PROPRIETORS: Mr and Mrs Eric Wee
OPEN: Mon to Sat CLOSED: 25 and 26 Dec and Easter Monday MEALS: 12 to 3, 6 to 11
PRICES: £6 (£10), Set L and D from £8 (£10). Cheaper set L available. Service 10%
CARDS: Access, Amex, Diners, Visa
SEATS: 80. Private parties: 40 main room. Vegetarian meals. Children welcome. Wheelchair access. Oriental music. Air-conditioned

Restaurants are graded on a scale of 1–20. In the region of 8–9 expect to find places that may not be restaurants but cafes, pubs, bistros and small hotels. In the category of 10–11 you can expect to find the best food in the locality. Ratings of 12 or more are given to restaurants we regard as serving the best food in the region.

An index of restaurants by name appears at the back of the Guide.

The Guide *does not accept free meals.*

The Ark [9/20]

map 10

35 Kensington High Street, W8 5BA
01-937 4294

£16

A garlicky place. The bistro menu has not changed much since the restaurant opened in 1968, but it is inexpensive for onion soup, coq au vin, gigot of lamb with haricots, sole meunière. The cooking medium is butter and a lot of it. The basement has a little more space than its counterpart (see below) and there are also white linen cloths. House French is £4·45.

CHEF: René Montagnon PROPRIETORS: Michael Witt and Colin Harris
OPEN: all week, exc Sun L CLOSED: 4 days at Christmas, 4 days at Easter MEALS: 12 to 3, 7 to 11.25
PRICES: £10 (£16). Cover 80p. Service 10% on parties over 3 CARDS: Access, Diners, Visa
SEATS: 95. Private parties: 20 main room. Children welcome. Wheelchair access. Music

The Ark [10/20]

map 10

122 Palace Gardens Terrace, W8 4RT
01-229 4024

£12

Informal, cramped but good-value bistro with a homely air, still popular after 24 years. The kitchen is well organised and can produce good crab soup with croûtons; duck pâté; half a dozen lamb cutlets with a spread of fresh vegetables; pheasant in red wine. To finish, the ice-cream with chocolate sauce and the apple crumble are dependable. The house claret is very drinkable at £4·25, or try the CELLARMAN'S CHOICE: Brouilly, Château des Tours '83 at £7·95. The place gets busy and they like people to book.

CHEF: Sabina Polese PROPRIETORS: The Harris family
OPEN: all week, exc Sun L MEALS: 12 to 3, 6.30 to 11.15
PRICES: £8 (£12) CARDS: Access, Amex, Visa
SEATS: 80. 6 tables outside. Private parties: 16 main room, 26 private room. Vegetarian meals by arrangement. Children's helpings. Wheelchair access

L'Arlequin [14/20]

map 9

123 Queenstown Road, SW8 3RH
01-622 0555

£13–£35

Christian Delteil's little restaurant is run like a hotel. The tablecloths are ironed crisply, tables are set with fresh flowers, and there are enough waiters to start a trade union. He cooks carefully and inventively. Fish is usually excellent – turbot is poached with wild mushrooms; the salmon cooked in a paper bag is punctured by the waiter at the table, so the smells of the wine and vegetables erupt; half a dozen langoustines are picturesquely alternated with vegetables round the plate. The saucing of some of the game and duck dishes does not seem to be quite so acute. Vegetables are sparing. The chocolate marquise is excellent, as are the pastry tuiles filled with strawberries and ice-cream (Mr Delteil surely makes the

'The waiters refill your glass as they pass, even when asked not to. "But your bottle not finished," explained one puzzled waitress.' (On eating Chinese in North London)

best sorbets in London). There are plentiful canapés and petits fours. A good but expensive wine list.

CHEFS/PROPRIETORS: Mr and Mrs C. Delteil
OPEN: Mon to Fri CLOSED: 1 week winter, 3 weeks Aug MEALS: 12.30 to 2, 7.30 to 11
PRICES: £27 (£35), Set L £11·50 (£13), Set D from £30 (£32). Service inc
CARDS: Access, Diners, Visa
SEATS: 32. Private parties: 30 main room. Vegetarian meals. Jacket and tie. Wheelchair access (also wc)

L'Auberge [new entry, zero rated] map 9

44 Forest Hill Road, SE22 0RR
01-299 2211 £8–£15

There are shades of Nice in the greenery bedecked courtyard and the peppermint and white plastered facade, though the restaurant is in a delapidated arcade of shops. Inside the bourgeois interpretation of the Mediterranean continues with some primitive portraits and floral still-lifes, and sombre, brooding washes of voluptuous nudes for contrast. The set dinner has started with Kir and excellent hummus and taramosalata canapés, but then Sami Youssef's cooking is at its strongest with traditional French dishes – fish soup; eggs Benedict with tongue; the calf's liver with lime; the charcoal-grilled lamb with béarnaise. A few modern touches creep into the repertoire, such as scallops in a warm vinaigrette. There has been a menu paysan offering mussel stew at £1·95 and cassoulet at £3·15. Sunday lunch is inexpensive, more relaxed and children are welcome. 'The best thing to happen to south London since the Victoria Line,' is one comment. Well-chosen, good-value wines, including Vacqueyras '83 at £5·60 and Pinot Blanc '83 from Preiss-Henny at £5·80. More reports, please.

CHEF/PROPRIETOR: Sami Youssef
OPEN: Tue to Sat D, plus Sun L CLOSED: 2 weeks Aug MEALS: 12 to 2.30, 7 to 10.30
PRICES: Set Sun L £4·95 (£8), Set D £11·95 (£15). Service 10% CARDS: Access, Visa
SEATS: 34. Private parties: 25 main room. Children's helpings. Wheelchair access (also wc). Classical music

Au Bois St Jean [11/20] map 10

122 St John's Wood High Street, NW8 7SG
01-722 0400 £13–£14

Some of the tables, by London standards, are actually quite big in this French restaurant in a white basement decorated with poles of dried flowers and with a few horse-box-style cubicles. Both the service and the menu are plus points, the latter being a typically Gallic arrangement of, for example, duck pâté, pigeon with wild mushrooms, and crème de cognac aux amandes. Dishes taste good even when they are subjected to some pre-preparation. Fish terrine comes with an excellent mint sabayon, and that old cliché of vegetable terrine is for once done with some verve and given a red pepper sauce. Duck is either a magret with lime and orange, or else braised with garlic and a little bitter chocolate, which

▲ *This restaurant has rooms.*

has been first-class. The sauces are adept and hold up the sweets, too, such as the iced nougat with raspberry sauce. Cafetière coffee is freshly made. The restaurant is related to Porte de la Cité in WC1. The 30 French wines are imported direct.
CELLARMAN'S CHOICE: Coteaux du Tricastin '83 at £6·75.

CHEF: Jacques Giron PROPRIETORS: Cellier du Midi Ltd
OPEN: all week, exc Sat L MEALS: 12 to 2.30, 7 to 11.30
PRICES: Set L from £9 (£13), Set D from £10·50 (£14). Service inc CARDS: Access, Visa
SEATS: 65. Private parties: 18 main room. Vegetarian meals. Children welcome. French popular music

L'Aventure [10/20]

map 10

3 Blenheim Terrace, NW8 4JS
01-624 6232

£15–£19

A small, established French restaurant. Inside is rustic, with a stripped pine grandmother clock and stripped pine dresser, though there is also a terrace outside with room for four tables. The menu is short and sensible. Good dishes are courgette and anchovy mousse; spinach and bacon salad; côte de boeuf; and excellent lamb cutlets with garlic. Fish dishes may be less carefully done but have tasted fine at inspections. To finish there are fresh figs in season or golf-ball-sized chocolate truffles. The specials of the day are read out quickly without mention of the prices, which can be embarrassing. A short, well-chosen list of French wines. House vin de table is £5·45.

CHEF: Pierre Guth PROPRIETOR: Catherine Parisot
OPEN: all week, exc Sat L MEALS: 12.30 to 2.30, 7 to 11
PRICES: £12 (£19), Set Sun L £10·50 (£15). Cover 60p CARDS: Amex, Visa
SEATS: 38. 4 tables outside. Private parties: 40 main room. Vegetarian meals. Children welcome. No cigars/pipes in dining-room. Wheelchair access. French music

Aziz [10/20]

map 9

116 King Street, W6 0QP
01-748 1826

£16

One of the best Indian restaurants in Hammersmith, with good kebabs, prawns with spinach, and niramish – an Indian version of ratatouille. Dhal is oily, and tomato purée dominates the prawn patia. Speciality moghlai dishes for four at £30 require 24 hours' notice and a deposit. Drink lassi.

CHEF/PROPRIETOR: M.D.Patel
OPEN: Mon to Sat CLOSED: 25 and 26 Dec MEALS: 12 to 2.15, 6 to 11.45
PRICES: £9 (£16). Cover 50p. Minimum £6. Service 10% CARDS: Amex, Diners, Visa
SEATS: 60. Private parties: 24 main room. Vegetarian meals. No children under 6. Wheelchair access. Indian music

Bagatelle [12/20]

map 10

5 Langton Street, SW10 0JL
01-351 4185

£14–£20

A smart little French restaurant decorated with Brassai's photographs of Parisian low-life. Chefs Osamu Ono and Y.Masumoto are Japanese, and their influence is seen in the thinly sliced raw marinated fish as a starter and in the picturesque presentation of the vegetable terrine with tomato coulis which is one of the better versions of this modern cliché. Notably good have been the panaché of fish; the turbot wrapped in lettuce on a bed of mushrooms with a beurre blanc sauce; or the more provincial noisettes of lamb with sauté potatoes and French beans. Steak is unusually poached in stock and served rare with a white wine and shallot sauce. Vin de pays de Vaucluse is £5·80 and there's a short, changing list of better wines.

CHEFS: Osamu Ono and Y.Masumoto PROPRIETORS: D.Marrocco and J.Chiesa
OPEN: Mon to Sat CLOSED: bank hols MEALS: 12 to 2, 7 to 11
PRICES: £14 (£20), Set L £10 (£14). Cover £1 CARDS: Access, Amex, Diners, Visa
SEATS: 60. 11 tables outside

Bahn Thai [13/20] map 10

35A Marloes Road, W8 6LG
01-937 9960 £15

The Thai food is marked by subtle, barely perfumed flavours combined with startling hot dips – when the Thai cook wants something hot he does not mess about. Spare ribs are meaty and the garlic and spring onion dip with the fillet steak is fiery, as is the dip with the honey chicken. Squid salad is very hot. The fish may not be quite as fresh as it would be in Bangkok, but in other respects this basement restaurant (underneath the Singing Bamboo) is as good as you might find in Thailand – peeled crab claws in sweet-and-not-very-sour sticky sauce, fish cakes, startling but excellent pomfret crisply wok-fried with chillis. The dim-sum and the satays are also well done, and to finish there is superb coconut ice-cream or the rare, expensive, but uniquely flavoured durian fruit turned into ice-cream. The Gewürztraminer '82 from Hugel at £4·55 for half a bottle goes uncannily well with the food, or else there is Thai beer and, for the adventurous, Mekhong Thai whisky.

CHEF: Penn Squires PROPRIETOR: Philip Harris
OPEN: Mon to Sat CLOSED: Christmas, 2 weeks in summer MEALS: 12 to 2.15, 6 to 11.15
PRICES: £9 (£15). Cover 75p. Service 10% CARDS: Access, Amex, Visa
SEATS: 32. Private parties: 30 to 40 main room. Vegetarian meals. No cigars/pipes in dining-room. Children's helpings. Thai music

Balzac Bistro [10/20] map 9

4 Wood Lane, W12 7DT
01-743 6787 and 5370 £14–£17

The last of the 1960s-style bistros. The place is painted bright red, with pictures of stars, and has French waiters who get the food to you quickly and top up your wine glass at a rate of knots. The menu is over-long, with three set-price meals featuring familiar dishes, such as onion soup and boeuf bourguignonne. Wild oyster mushrooms have been fried in a lot of butter; lamb is cooked rare on request; sauces tend to be sticky. The vegetables are excellent – red cabbage,

This restaurant has an exceptional wine cellar.

Brussels sprouts and sauté potatoes come in individual bowls. Sorbets to finish. Passable house wine at £5.

CHEF: Julien Cheveau PROPRIETORS: Lorenzo Bucciol and Dominic Cheveau
OPEN: Mon to Sat, exc Sat L CLOSED: 10 days at Christmas, 3 days at Easter, bank hols
MEALS: 12 to 2.30, 7 to 11
PRICES: Set L and D from £9 to £12·50 (£14 to £17). Service 15% CARD: Access
SEATS: 70. Private parties: 25 main room. Vegetarian meals. Children welcome. No pipes in dining-room. Wheelchair access (1 step). French popular music

Bambaya [new entry, zero rated] map 9

1 Park Road, Crouch End, N8 8TE
01-348 5609 £13

This is a Caribbean/African/black American restaurant. It is not as funky as you might expect, though later in the evening Bob Marley takes over from the traditional African music on the sound system. The split-level dining-room, separated by a wooden railing, is white, with large framed graphic posters and helpful waitresses. The menu takes in peanut soup, spinach-based fish stew, and southern beans and cornbread, with a strong leaning to vegetarian dishes. First-class have been the sopito, a fish chowder with a coconut base; the sweet king prawns, shelled apart from the heads and tails and served in a juice of coconuts, allspice and chopped spring onions; and the rice and peas. There is also ackee, either with salt fish or as Hoppin' John (with black rice, peas, pimentos, allspice and tomatoes), and plantain dishes. To finish there is pumpkin pie or a more European trolley. Limited wines. House wine is £4.

CHEFS: Rosamund Grant and Jenny Agada PROPRIETORS: Bambaya Restaurant Ltd
OPEN: Tue to Sun, D only MEALS: 6.30 to 11 (6 to 10.30 Sun)
PRICES: £7 (£13) CARDS: Access, Visa
SEATS: Private parties: 20 main room. Vegetarian meals. Children's helpings. Wheelchair access. African music

Barnaby's [11/20] map 9

39B High Street, Barnes, SW13 9LN
01-878 4750 £16

Good old-fashioned country bistro cooking in a dining-room that uses the fire extinguisher as part of the decor. Dried flowers are suspended from the archway; the walls are a lipstick-coloured mauve; the large tables covered with floral cloths, and by the door is an album of photographs of Claude Harry's most picturesque dishes. The menu works hard to avoid the modern bistro clichés and is faithful to classic regional French cooking. Consommé is served either hot, thickened with cream, egg and sorrel, or cold with a slug of sherry to bring out the flavour. Calves' brains are sliced and arranged on a purée of spinach and mint sprinkled with paprika. Other good dishes have been the brochette of monkfish with beurre blanc served in a side dish; cassoulet; and sweetbreads in a bourguignonne sauce on fresh noodles. Vegetables are presented in the *nouvelle*

Restaurants rating 10 and 11 serve the best food in the locality.

cuisine manner but in generous and varied portions. Of many good sweets the tarte Tatin is nearly all apples with only a little pastry, or there is chocolate bavarois. Coffee and bread could be improved. The red wines are better than the whites on a list of around 25. House vin de pays is £5·65.
CELLARMAN'S CHOICE: Bourgogne Rouge '81, from Boisset, at £9·85.

CHEF: Claude Harry PROPRIETORS: Mr and Mrs Claude Harry
OPEN: Mon to Sat, exc Mon and Sat L CLOSED: 3 weeks in Sept, bank hols
MEALS: 12.30 to 1.30, 7 to 10.15
PRICES: £11 (£16). Service inc CARDS: Access, Amex, Diners, Visa
SEATS: 24. Private parties: 24 main room. Children welcome

Bayleaf Tandoori [11/20] map 9

2 North Hill, N6 4PU
01-340 1719 and 0245 £11–£13

A workers' co-operative runs this up-market Indian place, which bears more than a passing resemblance to Lal Quila (see entry) and is in what used to be an Italian restaurant. The dining-room is elegant, spacious, neat as a new pin, and offers trend-setting quail; fish, well handled as tandoori and curry; kebabs spiced with cardamom and coriander; and good peshwari nan and pilau rice. Puddings are the weak point; kulfi comes with a cherry on top. Service is attentive.

CHEF: Hamid Ali PROPRIETORS: A.A.Khan and B.U.Ahmed
OPEN: all week MEALS: 12 to 2.15, 6 to 11.15
PRICES: £8 (£13), Set Sun L £6·95 (£11). Service 10% CARDS: Access, Amex, Diners, Visa
SEATS: 80. 4 tables outside. Private parties: 22 main room, 22 private room. Vegetarian meals. Children's helpings. Indian music

Beau-Rivage [10/20] map 10

248 Belsize Road, NW6 4BT
01-328 9992 and 625 6786 £10–£18

The basement is calmer than the upstairs in this blue and plant-filled fish restaurant. The menu seems as long as *War and Peace*, which suggests either the use of a freezer or that a lot of the ingredients end up in the bouillabaisse. There is plenty of à la Marseillaise about the dishes, though in the end you may have to hum some of the tune to convince yourselves. Portions are big – more than half a dozen whole scallops come on a bed of spinach as a starter, and there are giant steaks of halibut and turbot for main courses. Some dishes are modern, such as salmon in champagne sauce, or pan-fried Dover sole fillets with mange-tout. The number of favourable reports on file – more than 37 individual dishes recommended – underlines how popular a good fish restaurant can be. Nearly 40 wines.

CHEF/PROPRIETOR: George Njyutin
OPEN: all week, exc Mon D, Sat and Sun L MEALS: 12 to 2.30, 5.30 to 12.30
PRICES: £11 (£18), Set L £6·75 (£10). Cover 45p. Service 10% CARD: Visa
SEATS: 65. Private parties: 30 main room. Vegetarian meals. Children's helpings. Music

Restaurants rating 12 or more serve the best food in the region.

Beccofino [11/20] map 11

100 Draycott Avenue, SW3 3AD
01-584 3600 £15

A suave, well-run Italian restaurant as opposed to a trattoria. The carpaccio is first-class and the pasta is freshly made – tagliatelle with Dolcelatte is usually very good, as are the bagna cauda and the chicken Kiev. Standards are consistent, from the poached salmon with an hollandaise through to the crème brûlée. Service is professional. There are tables on the pavement for hot days. Good Italian wines.

CHEF: Marco Varela PROPRIETOR: Dante Betti
OPEN: Mon to Sat MEALS: 12.30 to 2.30, 7.30 to 11.30
PRICES: £10 (£15). Cover 90p CARDS: Access, Amex, Visa
SEATS: 60. 7 tables outside. Private parties: 10 main room, 16 private room. Vegetarian meals. Children's helpings. Wheelchair access. Air-conditioned

The Bengal Lancer [10/20] map 10

253 Kentish Town Road, NW5 2JT
01-485 6688 £7–£15

The photographs of Indian army officers cover the flockless walls of this cool, comfortable room with overhead plants and a profusion of cane and greenery. Jolly pukka are the fresh spicy poppadums; the chicken and lamb tikkas; karahi josh; and the chicken chaat with its lemon and chilli sauce. Sheek kebab can also be tip-top – unlike the service, which can be slow.

PROPRIETORS: Stanley Krett and Akram Ali
OPEN: all week MEALS: 12 to 3, 6 to 12 (12.30 Fri and Sat)
PRICES: £9 (£15), Set L from £3·50 (£7), Set D from £4·50 (£8). Cover £1 CARDS: Access, Amex, Diners, Visa
SEATS: 55. Private parties: 25 main room. Vegetarian meals. Children's helpings. Wheelchair access. Popular music. Air-conditioned

Beotys [10/20] map 13

79 St Martin's Lane, WC2N 4AA
01-836 8768 £14–£19

Beotys opened the year the Second World War ended. Chef Stelios Sparsi is a bit of a new boy – he only started in 1952. It is an old-school restaurant, but the Greek dishes can be first-class, the service is friendly and all round it is good value for where it is and ideal for business or pre- or post-theatre meals. Especially good are the kleftiko, and the squid in red wine and their own ink. House Greek is £5.

CHEF: Stelios Sparsi PROPRIETOR: Theodore Frangos
OPEN: Mon to Sat CLOSED: bank hols MEALS: 12 to 2.30, 5.30 to 11.30
PRICES: £13 (£19), Set L £9·90 (£14), Set D £10·90 (£16). Cover charge 80p
SEATS: 80. Private parties: 50 main room. Children welcome. Wheelchair access (also wc). Air-conditioned

All letters to the Guide *are acknowledged with a list of changes since we went to press.*

▲ *Best of Both Worlds, Britannia Hotel* [new entry, zero rated] map 12

Grosvenor Square, W1A 3AN
01-629 9400 £15–£25

The Best of Both Worlds means the best of America and Britain, but to put it another way there is a good-value buffet at a set £13·80 that includes wine, in what is called the cafe, plus some extremely polished cooking on the *carte* which works out at a lot more in the restaurant proper. Chef Michael Coaker has trained with Peter Kromberg at the Hotel Inter-Continental, and the impression is that he thinks on his feet. It is a modern, zippy menu, not going overboard for the latest hellzapoppin chic, but not scrabbling around in the mud of pre-*nouvelle*, either. For instance, to show the disregard for fashion, carrot sauce is served over, not under, a slab of turbot. And the sauces are exceptionally fine – witness the deeply reduced stock with cream served with the pancakes filled with chicken, oysters and morels secured by a filament of leek; or the mustard sauce with crab-burgers (really crab fishcakes). Salads come on a trolley laden with mâche, frisée, endive, radicchio, tomato and onions, which are mixed and dressed in a wooden bowl to order. Sweets could be improved, and the service, although professional, does not seem to be in step with the kitchen. It is unlikely Mr Coaker would approve of the swirl of the black-pepper mill offered over the above dishes. There is a fistful of English and plentiful California wines – including the big names, such as Firestone, Mondavi and so on – and a connoisseur's list of clarets and burgundies. The mark-ups are not generous and there is little relief in the shape of half-bottles. House wine is £7·50. Hopefully Grand Met/ICH will not institutionalise Mr Coaker's menu, but let him move with the markets and so not have to rely on inferior, out-of-season produce for the sale of what appears to be, but isn't, luxury. More reports, please.

CHEF: Michael Coaker PROPRIETORS: Grand Metropolitan/Inter-Continental Hotels
OPEN: all week, exc Sat and Sun L MEALS: 12.30 to 2.30, 6.30 to 10.30 in restaurant, 12 to 3, 6 to 10 in cafe
PRICES: £18 (£25), Set L £15.50 (£21), Set D £18.50 (£24) in restaurant. £12 (£19), Set L and D £13·80 (£15) in cafe. CARDS: Access, Amex, Carte Blanche, Diners, Visa
SEATS: 50. Private parties: 90 and 40 private rooms. Car-park. Vegetarian meals by arrangement. No children in restaurant. Jacket and tie. Wheelchair access. Music. Air-conditioned
ACCOMMODATION: 356 rooms, all with bath/shower. B&B £100 to £110. Children welcome. Baby facilities. Afternoon teas. Air-conditioning. Lift. TV. Phone

Le Bistroquet [11/20] map 10

273–275 Camden High Street, NW1 7BX
01-267 4895 and 485 9607 £9–£13

Well-run, noisy, busy brasserie. The provincial dishes are well handled, from ballotine of duck to mussels with garlic butter to steak béarnaise. Good charcuterie, Toulouse sausages and Bratwurst served with potatoes give an extra dimension, and the pastries and ice-creams are made in-house; the floating

The Guide *does not accept free meals.*

islands are exceptional and the cheeseboard heroic. There is ratafia de champagne and de bourgogne as an aperitif, and half a dozen house wines including CELLARMAN'S CHOICE: Marquis de Saporta at £5·65.

CHEF: Paul Whitaker PROPRIETOR: Russel Joffe
OPEN: all week MEALS: 12 to 2.15, 7 to 11.30 (11 Sun)
PRICES: £8 (£13), Set L from £5·50 (£9). Minimum £3. Service 12.5%. CARDS: Access, Amex, Visa
SEATS: 120. 10 tables outside. Private parties: 30 main room, 10 private room. Vegetarian meals. Children's helpings. Wheelchair access. Music

▲ *Blakes Hotel* [13/20]

map 11

33 Roland Gardens, SW7 3PF
01-370 6701

£42

Anouska Hempel Weinberg's basement restaurant to her exclusive hotel is still one of the most chic and seductive in London, with its bowls of flowers, black lacquer, mirrors and glass-topped tables. The menu is eclectic and flirts with all kinds of cuisines – Russian for borshch or blini with beluga (£22); Italian for pasta; Japanese for beef teriyaki; heaven knows where for calf's liver seared on lava rock. Good dishes have been lobster and salmon terrine; quails' eggs with Jerusalem artichoke; veal with Brazil and pine-nuts, and the ever-popular Szechuan duck. Sweets are expensive and with other items charged as extras can launch the bill into the financial stratosphere. House white, a Chardonnay from the Loire, and red, Raimat Abadia from Spain, are £8·50 each, and there is good drinking around the £10 mark. CELLARMAN'S CHOICE: Crozes-Hermitage, Domaine de Thalabert '82, from Jaboulet, at £10·50.

CHEF: James Robins PROPRIETOR: Anouska Hempel Weinberg
OPEN: all week CLOSED: 25 to 26 Dec MEALS: 12.30 to 2.30, 7.30 to 11.30, snacks all day
PRICES: £29 (£42), Snacks from £2·75 (£3). Service 15% CARDS: Access, Amex, Diners, Visa
SEATS: 45. Smart dress preferred. No pipes in dining-room. Children's helpings. Air-conditioned
ACCOMMODATION: 50 rooms, all with bath/shower. B&B £89·25 to £119. No pets. Afternoon teas. Sauna. Lift. TV. Phone [GHG]

Bloom's [9/20]

map 10

90 Whitechapel High Street, E1 7RA
01-247 6001

£11

The salt beef, of course, is among the best in London. The waiters have character and the portions are enormous. House Israeli wine is £4.

PROPRIETORS: Bloom & Son Ltd
OPEN: Sun to Fri, exc Fri D MEALS: 11.30am to 10pm
PRICES: £6 (£11) CARD: Access
SEATS: 150. Private parties: 150 main room. Car-park. Vegetarian meals. Children's helpings. Wheelchair access

'I said: "Have you forgotten us?" She said: "No," and walked off to take the order of someone who had arrived half an hour after us.' (On eating in London)

Bombay Brasserie, Bailey's Hotel [13/20] map 11

Courtfield Close, SW7 4QH
01-370 4040 £12–£21

The dining-areas recreate the magical feeling of Anglo-Indian opulence as depicted in the spate of films set in the sub-continent: pastel fabrics, tent-like awnings, polished dark wood, brass light-fittings, huge potted palms, a conservatory. . . . The tables are large and set comfortably apart. It is difficult to find more skilfully prepared and cunningly spiced Indian food elsewhere in Britain. Portions are not the size of a high-street 'Ruby Murray', but with one or two side dishes and a starter you should leave satisfied. The relatively extensive menu shows a careful selection from different regions and styles of Indian cookery. From the north there are moghlai dishes – mutton rogan josh and biriani; Parsi dishes include mutton with apricots, and pomfret with mint chutney; from Goa there is chicken with coconut, and masala prawns. There is also lamb with chilli, cinnamon and cloves from Kashmir; chicken with black peppercorns from Kerala; lamb cooked with spicy pickle from Hyderabad; a mustard-leaf side dish from the Punjab; a lobster curry from the Konkan coast near Mangalore; and a puri starter from the seaside of Bombay. The sheer enthusiasm of the readers who have written in suggests that the Brasserie warrants a high rating, though the buffet lunch is not what it was and nor is the service – hence the drop in the rating. A short wine list includes a Gewürztraminer for £8 along with other bottles suited to such strongly flavoured dishes, or there is Kingfisher beer, fruit juices such as pear and cherry, or lassi – both salt and sweet. The mango (not fresh) and champagne aperitif is a winner.

CHEF: Sandeep Chatterjee PROPRIETORS: Taj International Hotels
OPEN: all week MEALS: 12.30 to 2.30, 7.30 to 12
PRICES: £13 (£21), Set L £7·95 (£12). Minimum £10. Service 12.5% CARDS: Access, Amex, Diners, Visa
SEATS: 175. 23 tables in conservatory. Vegetarian meals. Smart dress preferred. Children welcome. Wheelchair access (also WC). Piano player. Valet parking D

Boot and Flogger [8/20] map 10

10–20 Redcross Way, SE1 1TA
01-407 1184 £13

A dark but handy bar south of the river and busy at lunch-time. It has an outstanding collection of claret, with 20 vintages of Ch. Latour going back to 1881 and other good Châteaux from years such as '70, '66, '61, '59 and '45. The port list, too, has big names and vintages. All these need at least 24 hours' notice. Otherwise the wine list is short and most bottles are under £10. The brief menu is unchanging, apart from salmon and game in season, and includes

The 1987 Guide *will appear before Christmas 1986, so reports are particularly important in the spring. Report forms are at the back of this book, but just write a letter if you prefer. Address them to* The Good Food Guide, *Freepost, 14 Buckingham Street, London WC2N 6BR. No stamp is necessary if you post in the UK.*

Parma ham with melon, cold roast beef with pots of mustard and horseradish, smoked salmon, cheese, and apple pie.

PROPRIETOR: J.Davy
OPEN: Mon to Fri MEALS: 12 to 2.30, 5.30 to 7.30
PRICES: £8 (£13). Cover 50p CARDS: Access, Amex, Diners, Visa
SEATS: 100. Self-service in evening

Boulestin [11/20]

map 13

1A Henrietta Street, WC2E 8PS
01-836 3819 £22–£30

The head chef here, Ken Whitehead, along with a number of other chefs, last year lent his name to a big advertising campaign for Uncle Ben's rice. That points to the problem we have with this most elegant and expensive of London dining-rooms. Admitting to using Uncle Ben's is tantamount to saying that the cooking will be bland. It is a rice that is designed not to separate or stick, but will look fluffy; it is a real aid to the home cook who might feel like using it in paella one day, then simply as an alternative to potatoes the next. Like tomato ketchup, it is the child of commerce and has no obvious place in any serious *cuisine*. Rice has many nuances – the Chinese and Japanese use different strains; Basmati is a cornerstone of much Indian cooking; and a few blocks away from here it is possible to buy a number of different types of Italian rice. None of this fancy foreign stuff for Ken, though. He's got his packet, for which he charges customers a packet. Worse still, he lends his name to the notion that Uncle Ben has got something to do with *nouvelle cuisine*. Come on, old son. Do you really believe that Michel Guérard, Raymond Blanc, or Frédy Girardet use it? We know the trouble and expense you go to find beef and lamb of the highest quality and how the langoustines come from Scotland. Your food should be the best of British produce and match the grandness of your spectacular dining-room. How is it justifiable to sell Ch. Mouton-Rothschild '70 for £75 in the same restaurant? Throw away the conveniences, get the stock-pots bubbling, and we'll give you back the rating.

CHEF: Kevin Kennedy PROPRIETORS: Grand Metropolitan plc
OPEN: Mon to Sat, exc Sat L CLOSED: 3 weeks Aug, 1 week at Christmas
MEALS: 12.30 to 2.30, 7.30 to 11.15
PRICES: £20 (£30), Set L £14 (£22). Service 15% CARDS: Access, Amex, Diners, Visa
SEATS: 70. Private parties: 24 main room. Children welcome. Jacket and tie

Brasserie St Quentin [11/20]

map 11

243 Brompton Road, SW3 2EP
01-589 8005 and 5131 £14–£21

Alors, St Quentin, êtes-vous une brasserie ou un restaurant? La *nouvelle cuisine*, oui, ça va, mais avec tout ce fracas – ooh là là! Vous êtes bien placés, certes, à Knightsbridge – chic, tout près de Harrods. Et oui, bien sûr, votre nouveau delicatessen (256 Brompton Road) est bien supérieur à celui de Harrods. On y trouve les beaux fromages de Philippe Olivier, de vraies baguettes, et les desserts sont fantastiques – formidable. Le déjeuner n'est pas trop cher. Il y a toujours les rognons à la moutarde de Meaux. Extra! À part ça, quoi de nouveau? Une belle bisque de crabe, de plus en plus de poisson – très à la mode. Et les vins ne sont pas mal, mais les prix!

CHEF: Marc Legros PROPRIETOR: Hugh O'Neill
OPEN: all week MEALS: 12 (11.30 Sun) to 3 (4 Sat), 7 to 12
PRICES: £13 (£21). Set L £8·50 (£14). Set D £12·90 (£19). Cover £1 alc only
Service 12.5% CARDS: Access, Amex, Diners, Visa
SEATS: 85. 3 tables outside. Private parties: 30 private room. Children's helpings. Wheelchair access. Air-conditioned

Brewer Street Buttery [9/20] map 12

56 Brewer Street, W1R 3FA
01-437 7695 £5

A smart, clean cafe run by a group of Polish women. All the food is fresh and some of it exceptionally good – piroshki; ravioli stuffed with cheese and warmed with plenty of butter; roast chicken or fine veal rissoles with mushroom sauce. Everything comes with freshly mashed potato and fat peas. There is no licence, but the orange juice is freshly squeezed, coffee comes out of a Gaggia machine, and there is apple tart or strawberries and cream to finish. The music is 1950s and everything is served with a big smile.

PROPRIETORS: Bradmix Ltd
OPEN: Mon to Fri MEALS: 9 to 6
PRICES: £4 (£5). Unlicensed
SEATS: 30. Private parties: 30 main room. Vegetarian meals. Children's helpings. Wheelchair access. Music. Self-service

▲ *British Harvest, Hilton Hotel* [new entry, zero rated] map 12

Park Lane, W1A 2HH
01-493 8000 **Real Food** £16–£27

The first-floor restaurant at the Hilton, round the corner from the disco, has spent the last two years building up a network of suppliers across the country to provide the best of British produce. The fruits of their labours are piled high on the sideboard – unpasteurised cheeses, organically grown vegetables and so on. The level of enthusiasm from the waiters and kitchen is remarkable for an international hotel and is reflected in the boldness of the menu – venison with sloe gin sauce; black and white pudding with apple sauce; pan-fried skate wings with pickled nasturtium seeds. Hops turn up as a vegetable. It is a valiant attempt to reverse the trend in catering and deserves support. It also tastes good – fine terrine of Cornish red mullet and crab with tomato garnish is dressed with walnut oil, and there is superb glazed rare-breed ham, and impeccable vegetables. The cheeseboard of Bozeat, Alston, Satterleigh and Hawkstone is a revelation and about as blistering an indictment of the Milk Marketing Board's policy of cheese standardisation over the last 20 years as is imaginable. To finish, the strawberry cheesecake is well executed. There are English wines, too, of which the Lamberhurst Müller-Thurgau '83 at £7·80 and the Adgestone '82 at

All inspections are carried out anonymously as we accept no handouts.

£9·70 are the best examples. We have left the rating for a year in the hope that standards will continue to improve and we can award thumping high marks next time. More reports, please.

CHEFS: O.Mair and A.Neil PROPRIETORS: Hilton International
OPEN: all week MEALS: 7 to 10.30, 12 to 2.45, 6 to 10.30
PRICES: £16 (£27), Set L £14·50 (£16), Set D £14·50 (£20) CARDS: Access, Amex, Carte Blanche, Diners, Visa
SEATS: 85. Private parties: 20 private room. Car-park, 200 places. Vegetarian meals by arrangement. Children's helpings by arrangement. Smart dress preferred. Wheelchair access (also wc). Classical music. Air-conditioned
ACCOMMODATION: 503 rooms, all with bath/shower. Rooms for disabled. B&B £144 to £167. Children welcome. Baby facilities. Pets by arrangement. Afternoon teas. Air-conditioning. Lift. TV. Phone. Confirm by 6

Bunny's [12/20] map 10

7 Pond Street, NW3 2PU
01-435 1541 £11–£17

Now something of a Hampstead institution. The basement is romantic, with candles on the tables, pink cloths, comfortable chairs and portraits on the walls. It is not over-expensive, though there is a cover charge and vegetables are extra. The cooking is interesting, always artistically presented and sometimes very good. Mousses, such as the duck liver and crab, are served warm, as is the avocado with hot smoked trout, before fine quails en croûte or picturesque salmon with seafood sausage. Sunday lunch doesn't change and revolves around roast beef, pork or lamb, all of good quality. Service is willing. Some better cheeses would be nice, and some Alsace might help the wine list, which opens with more than half a dozen house wines around £5.

CHEF: Keith Shudall PROPRIETORS: Roy and Sue Winston
OPEN: Tue to Sun, D only, and Sun L MEALS: Sun L 12 to 3, 7 to 11
PRICES: £11 (£17), Set Sun L £8·25 (£11). Cover 70p alc only. Service inc set L only
CARDS: Amex, Visa
SEATS: 65. Children's helpings. No pipes in dining-room

Le Café du Jardin [10/20] map 13

28 Wellington Street, WC2E 7BD
01-836 8769 and 8760 £7–£14

A busy, unpretentious French cafe serving thick soups and stews, spiced sausages in split peas, carré d'agneau, and so on. There is a marvellous cheeseboard with Brie, Chaume, bleu d'Auvergne, chèvre de Poitou and others; espresso coffee too. Even the waiters admit that some nights 'zee serveese is terreeble'. The pre-theatre menu from 6 to 7.30 is good value. Not as polished as

Entries are compiled from the unsolicited reports from readers and are checked by inspectors; each restaurant is asked to supply details of its operation. Report forms can be found at the back of the Guide.

Prices quoted are for an average three-course meal including service and VAT and half a bottle of house wine (or the equivalent in an ethnic restaurant).

its parent, Magno's Brasserie, but it is easier to get a table. House burgundy is £4·75.

CHEF: Ian Loffel PROPRIETOR: N. Coliadis
OPEN: Mon to Sat, exc Sat L MEALS: 12 to 2.30, 6 to 11.30
PRICES: £9 (£14), Pre-theatre menu £6·45 (£7). Service 10% CARDS: Access, Amex, Diners, Visa
SEATS: 116. Private parties: 120 main room. Vegetarian meals. Children's helpings. Wheelchair access (also wc). Music. Air-conditioned

Café Pélican [9/20] map 13

45 St Martin's Lane, WC2N 4TJ
01-379 0309 and 0259 £14–£19

The Pélican swallows 250 diners in a single go. Its heart is in the right place and it stands in the right place, too. Formerly a set of electricity showrooms but redesigned on the lines of a bar in the rue Vieille du Temple in Paris and with some original 1920s and 1930s posters, on the West End's doorstep and open 15 hours a day from 11am to 2am. Everything is made on the premises and the menu is bistro and not expensive – just as likely as sirloin steak is *bavette*, the equivalent French cut of blade. The cooking ebbs and flows with the tide of customers and the service is pot luck, depending on the waiter/waitress. House French is £5·50.

CHEF: Gerard Mosiniak PROPRIETORS: Carolyn and Richard Lewendon
OPEN: all week MEALS: 11am to 2am
PRICES: £14 (£19), Set L and D £9·95 (£14). Snacks from £1·50 (£1·65) CARDS: Access, Amex, Diners, Visa
SEATS: 250. 5 tables outside. Private parties: 250 main room. Vegetarian meals. Children's helpings. Wheelchair access (also wc). Jazz. Air-conditioned

Café Rouge [13/20] map 10

2C Cherry Tree Walk, Whitecross Street, EC1Y QNX
01-588 0710 £16–£23
In shopping-precinct near Safeway

Not so much a cafe but very rouge, with a tricolour hanging down from the ceiling to head height. It is handy for before, during or after a trip to the Barbican centre, which is only two minutes' walk away, and it is particularly welcome in this part of the City. A three-course pre-theatre dinner is sensibly limited in choice. The short, modern, well-balanced menu offers cassoulet de langoustines, beef with wild mushrooms, and chocolate marquise. Fish, particularly, demonstrates careful handling of good ingredients, from turbot with salmon mousse and champagne sauce, to a baked scallop starter that comes like a St Jacques-in-the-box – the two shells are sealed with pastry, the juices collect in the bottom, and a sprinkling of julienne vegetables with chervil and chives does not overpower the fragrance of the plump scallops. Attention to detail also shows in the skinned breast of guinea-fowl with longer-cooked leg meat, sitting on a big heap of thin strips of cabbage with lime sauce. Vegetables are spot-on. Service is bow-tie but unpretentious and chirpy. A Toulouse-Lautrec of a wine list, short and French, and just as dapper. House wine is £5·65. CELLARMAN'S CHOICE: Pouilly Fumé '83, Domaine Conneau at £9·50.

CHEFS: Bryan Webb and Ian Bennett PROPRIETORS: Danny and Bettie Murphy
OPEN: Mon to Sat, exc Sat L CLOSED: 1 week at Christmas, bank hols MEALS: 12 to 2.30, 6 to 11
PRICES: £15 (£23), Set L and D £8·55 (£16). Cover £1. Service 12.5% CARDS: Access, Amex, Diners
SEATS: 36. 4 tables outside. Private parties: 20 main room. Vegetarian meals by arrangement. Children's helpings by arrangement. Wheelchair access. French music

▲ *Capital Hotel* [14/20] map 11

Basil Street, SW3 1AT
01-589 5171 **Real Food** £19–£31

The nice thing about the Capital Hotel is that, although it is expensive, no one is trying to tell you that what you are eating is the best British cooking since Eliza Acton's *Modern Cookery* came out in 1845. Everyone just gets on with the job without too much fuss. In that sense, at least, it is English rather than French, though the menu persists in using only French. Anyone who could afford to treat London hotels and luxury restaurants as bistros would eat here a lot, because the food is very good but does not scream of there being a big ego in the kitchen. The beef and lamb are interesting – Charolais and Soay breeds respectively, neither usually reared in Britain. The langoustines come from Scotland and become a creamed sauce for crab, or are served as a salad with baby turnips. There are other elegant touches, such as sea-urchin sauce for the scallop mousse, and smoked chicken wrapped in a cabbage leaf. Offal dishes have been notable this year – sweetbread terrine and kidneys with a sauce of cream and morels. There are grills, too, and to finish a fine chocolate marquise. Last year we recommended the restaurant as the best executive lunching place in London and that still holds good. There is a fabulous range of '70s clarets, with many in the £20 to £30 range. The Alsace section is mainly of '79s, but most have the maker's endorsement and should therefore still hold their own. It is a pity that the cheapest wine appears to be Tavel Rosé '82 at £8·50 – that must preclude many non-expense account diners. CELLARMAN'S CHOICE: Ch. Haut-Bailly '79 at £24. Old ports and cognacs, too.

CHEF: Brian J. Turner PROPRIETORS: Capital Hotels Ltd
OPEN: all week MEALS: 12.30 to 2.30, 6.30 to 10.30 (12.30 to 2, 7 to 10 Sun)
PRICES: £23 (£31), Set L £14·50 (£19), Set D £16·50 (£21). Service inc CARDS: Access, Amex, Carte Blanche, Diners, Visa
SEATS: 35. Private parties: 10 main room, 24 private room. Car-park, 12 places. Children's helpings. No children under 4. Jacket and tie preferred. No pipes in dining-room. Wheelchair access (also WC). Air-conditioned
ACCOMMODATION: 60 rooms, all with bath/shower. Rooms for disabled. B&B £94 to £108·50. Deposit: one night's accommodation. Children welcome. Baby facilities. Pets by arrangement. Afternoon teas. Air-conditioning. Lift. TV. Phone [GHG]

'The information which you provide in the Guide *does not mention the £1.50 cover charge nor the 15 per cent service charge. You do suggest that dinner may cost an arm and a leg. The arrival of the bill nearly resulted in paraplegia.'* (On eating in London)

Le Caprice [9/20]

map 12

Arlington House, Arlington Street, SW1A 1RT
01-629 2239

£17

Well, it's not quite Langan's. For a start there is less colour about the place: black walls, mirrors, waiters in black, a long sleek shiny bar, black and white pictures – chic in monochrome. But there are faces to gasp at and friendly catering-style service and even the Perrier gets poured with a flourish. The *carte* is eclectic, from bang bang chicken and salmon fish cakes to onion tart with fettuccine. The calf's liver isn't bad. The shortish, chic-ish wine list has fair prices for the set-up. House Trebbiano di Romagna white is £4·75; red country wine from the Rhône, Principauté d'Orange, is £5.

CHEF: Charles Fontaine PROPRIETORS: C.J.Corbin and J.R.B.King
OPEN: all week, exc Sat L MEALS: 12 to 2.30 (3 Sun), 7 to 12
PRICES: £10·50 (£17). Cover 75p CARDS: Access, Amex, Diners, Visa
SEATS: 70. Private parties: 8 main room. Vegetarian meals. Children's helpings by arrangement. Wheelchair access. Piano music. Air-conditioned

▲ *Cap's, Pembridge Court Hotel* [10/20]

map 10

64 Pembridge Road, W11 3HN
01-229 5177

£14

The decor is a cross between a steak house (brick walls, tiled floor, Sinatra on tap) and an antique shop (lots of old wooden signs dusted off) but the cooking is straightforward and honest. Good dishes have been cream of leek soup, duck pâté, and roast best end of lamb with herbs, which is oddly 10p cheaper than calf's liver lyonnaise. Vegetables come on a side-plate and sweets taste less dull than they look – thick slices of apple pie with vanilla ice-cream, and crème brûlée in an earthenware crock. Espresso coffee and a short, trendy list of wines all under £10, including white Beaujolais and red Sancerre.

CHEF: Nikki Rajakul PROPRIETOR: Paul Capra
OPEN: Mon to Sat, D only MEALS: 6 to 11.15
PRICES: £10 (£14) CARDS: Access, Amex, Diners, Visa
SEATS: 60. Private parties: 40 main room; 15 private room. Vegetarian meals. Children's helpings. Music. Air-conditioned
ACCOMMODATION: 34 rooms, 33 with bath/shower. B&B £39·10 to £52·90. Children welcome. Baby facilities. Pets welcome. TV. Phone

Il Cavaliere [9/20]

map 9

14 North End Road, NW11 7PH
01-455 3849

£14

If you are in NW11 this trattoria has freshly made pasta, generous minestrone, veal with sage, and zabaglione. House Merlot is £4·80.

CHEF/PROPRIETOR: Pietro Matraxia
OPEN: Tue to Sun CLOSED: 2 weeks July to Aug MEALS: 12 to 3, 6 to 11.30
PRICES: £8 (£14). Cover 60p. Service 10% CARDS: Access, Amex, Diners, Visa
SEATS: 48. Private parties: 60 main room. Vegetarian meals by arrangement. Children's helpings. Wheelchair access (also WC). Music

Chaglayan Kebab House [11/20] map 9

86 Brent Street, NW4 2ES
01-202 8575 £11

The menu is typical of Turkish restaurant food in England, from patlican salatasi to prawn cocktail and grilled Dover sole. But this does not mean that the Turkish food is a compromise – far from it: authenticity runs from kitchen-made starters and sweets to throbbing, cochlea-crunching music. To start there is excellent nutty hummus; pale smoky taramosalata; vine-leaves packed with rice, pine nuts, small 'bird-currants' and spices; stiff cacik; and proper imam bayeldi – a whole aubergine cooked in good olive oil with tomatoes, onions, garlic and parsley – tangy and smooth. A mixed charcoal grill brings lamb chops, and fillet in chunks and minced, with rice strongly flavoured with turmeric and stock, and a wonderful roast potato. Kleftiko is garlicky, herby, and as good as you'll find. As for the sweets, Ekmek Kadayif Kaymakli – two layers of firm, dark sponge soaked in lemony syrup and filled with clotted cream – would not disgrace the smartest place in Istanbul. Baklava is crisp and nutty, and a big meringue has a stiff chocolate and nut filling. Coffee comes with proper Turkish delight. The gloaming is relieved by candlelight on the table, the ceiling is hung with ropes like a tent, and service makes sure everything runs smoothly. Wines include Yakut, Sungurlu, Papazkarasi and Buzbag.

CHEF/PROPRIETOR: Ata Chaglayan
OPEN: Mon to Sat MEALS: 12 to 2.30, 6.30 to 12
PRICES: £7 (£11). Cover 40p. Service 10% CARDS: Access, Diners, Visa
SEATS: 40. Private parties: 45 main room. Vegetarian meals. Children's helpings. Wheelchair access. Music

Chalcot's [new entry, zero rated] map 10

49 Chalcot Road, NW1 8LS
01-722 1956 £11–£17

Colin and Lynn Thompson's husband-and-wife partnership gives a homely feel to this small, friendly restaurant in a parade of arty shops and three-storey Regency houses. Despite the brick walls being hung with pictures and posters it has outgrown the bistro image it had when opened in 1981. There are no frills, no nibbles, no petits fours, no doyleys, but prices are reasonable. The style is French, the menu mostly simple but occasionally imaginative, using fresh ingredients: sardines come with mustard hollandaise, and rabbit is lightly casseroled with white wine and grapes. Coriander is used with restraint in a dish of green beans, prawns and limes; sea-bass is wrapped in lettuce leaves and sports both a tomato coulis and a cream sauce; and saddle of lamb is covered in puff pastry, given a forcemeat and spinach stuffing and served with a watercress and cream mint sauce. A sextet of vegetables come on a separate plate. Crème brûlée is very

'The business lunch was in the private room. The waiters went round and served the meat and the vegetables. Half way through they realised they had run out of vegetables and so went back and took the vegetables off the first plates to serve the other diners.' (On eating in a luxury London hotel)

custardy, and apple pie has a clafoutis-type batter. Service is quiet and pleasantly efficient. A minuscule wine list, with house French at £4·60.

CHEF: Colin Thompson PROPRIETORS: Colin and Lynn Thompson
OPEN: Tue to Sun, exc Sat L and Sun D. CLOSED: Christmas and Easter
MEALS: 12.30 to 2.30, 7.30 to 10.30
PRICES: £11 (£17), Set L £6·80 (£11). Cover 50p CARDS: Access, Diners, Visa
SEATS: 35. Private parties: 40 main room. Children's helpings (Sun L only), Wheelchair access

Champagne Exchange [new entry, zero rated] map 12

17C Curzon Street, W1Y 7FE
01-493 4490 £20

'A super hole for a spot of bubbly. There are simply oodles of them – Bolly, the Widow, the Boy, and they're not dear. Lalou's '79 is only just over £50. And as for the caviare – it's a good job there are still some of us around who can tell sevruga from osciotre. It's also good to see waiters dressed as they should be, in morning suits. They are a bit slow, but that makes more time for another beaker. Mind you, one doesn't go a bundle on the fish soup, nor on the plate of smoked fish, I mean if God had meant fish to be smoked . . . But then the jolly old smoked sprats with blinis *is* a good wheeze. And the strawberry tart is just biffo.'

PROPRIETORS: Champagne Exchange Ltd
OPEN: all week MEALS: 11.30 to 3.30, 5.30 to 12 (12 to 2, 7 to 11 Sun)
PRICES: £12 (£20). Cheaper set brunch at weekends. Service 12.5% CARDS: Access, Amex, Diners, Visa
SEATS: 80. 2 tables outside. Private parties: 80 main room. Vegetarian meals. Children's helpings. Jazz. Air-conditioned

Chanterelle [12/20] map 11

119 Old Brompton Road, SW7 3RN
01-373 5522 and 7390 £10–£14

This may not be the best restaurant in London – or even in Old Brompton Road – but it is one of the most popular with readers. It is austerely elegant, with big mirrors, small tables and a lot of varnished wood on the walls. The set menus are good value and well balanced. The variety of the endorsed dishes eaten emphasises the kitchen's skill – soups of salsify or mussels and saffron; a salad of jambon cru with mushrooms and cherries; cassoulet; rare steaks; venison with chestnuts; jugged hare. Vegetables are usually good, but sweets more erratic. Most of the wines on the sensible, good-quality wine list are under £10.
CELLARMAN'S CHOICE: Quincy, Domaine de la Maison Blanche '83 at £6·95.

CHEF/PROPRIETOR: Fergus Provan
OPEN: all week CLOSED: 4 days at Christmas MEALS: 12 to 2.30, 7 to 11.30
PRICES: Set L £6·50 (£10), Set Sun L £10 (£14), Set D £10·50 (£14). Cheaper supper after 10.30. Minimum £8·50. Service 12.5% for parties of 6 or more CARDS: Access, Amex, Diners, Visa
SEATS: 45. 3 tables outside. Private parties: 20 main room. Children welcome. Wheelchair access

Charco's Wine Bar [8/20] map 11

1 Bray Place, SW3 3LL
01-584 0765 £8

The atmosphere is of a 1960s coffee bar, but this is a reliable wine bar on two levels, with some tables outside when the sun shines. There is big spread of cold food from salads to roast beef to salmon. The varied wine list starts with house Rhône at £4.

CHEF: Jao Nunes PROPRIETORS: Searcey's Ltd
OPEN: Mon to Sat CLOSED: Christmas, Easter, bank hols MEALS: 11 to 2.45, 5.30 to 10.45
PRICES: £6 (£8) CARDS: Access, Amex, Visa
SEATS: 80. 4 tables outside. Private parties: 30 main room. Vegetarian meals. Children welcome. Music. Self-service

Le Chef [10/20] map 10

41 Connaught Street, W2 2BB
01-262 5945 and 402 7761 £14–£20

Reliable, unpretentious little bistro which does not change with fashions but stays with what it does well – fish soup with rouille; bourride provençale; boeuf bourguignonne. Alan King has cooked here since 1968, which is an endorsement in itself. He hopes to bring in some more vintage wines this year. CELLARMAN'S CHOICE: Ch. Millet '76 at £12·15 – it improves dramatically when warmed to room temperature.

CHEF/PROPRIETOR: Alan King
OPEN: Tue to Sat, exc Sat L CLOSED: mid-Aug to mid-Sept MEALS: 12.30 to 2.30, 7 to 11.30 (11 Sat)
PRICES: £12 (£17), Set L £13·25 (£14), Set Sat D £16·75 (£20). Cover 50p. Service inc
CARDS: Access, Visa
SEATS: 50. 5 tables outside. Private parties: 20 main room, 20 private room. Vegetarian meals. Children's helpings. Wheelchair access (2 steps). Music

CHELSEA and KENSINGTON

BACKGROUND BRIEFING: *Waitrose on King's Road has a fine fruit and vegetable section. In Farmer's Market, Sydney Street, there is a branch of Neal's Yard Wholefood Warehouse and a dairy with good English cheeses. On Chelsea Green, the Pieman sells freshly made steak and kidney pies. For fish cross the river to behind the Battersea bus garage, next to Majestic Wines, where there is fish straight off the boats – including live crabs and lobsters – even on Sunday mornings. La Vigneronne in Old Brompton Road holds regular tutored wine tastings in a nearby hotel. For Chinese food, the Ho Ho, 11A King's Road (not related to the other two listed in London), opposite Peter Jones, is above average. Zen Too has now become Pun, but the I Ching in Earls Court Road is now again under the ownership of Zen (see entry) and we have a number of nominations for it. We also have nominations for Frobishers, 242 Old Brompton Road.*

'I would rate the enjoyment of this restaurant alongside holding a wedding reception in an abattoir.' (On eating in London)

Cherry Orchard [9/20]

map 9

241–245 Globe Road, Bethnal Green, E2 0JD
01-980 6678

Real Food £4

The Orchard is run by four women with a divine interpretation of Real Food – 'to create a livelihood in accordance with Buddhist principles, to provide a service to one of London's poorer boroughs and, through example, show how a balanced and nutritional meal can be had with a limited budget'. Naturally it is vegetarian, and it take its name from the flourishing garden at the back. Service is canteen-style queuing, with the menu written on the blackboard – leek and potato soup, quiche, hearty seaweed stew with rice, busy salads. Portions are generous. To finish there are good fruit crumbles and a rather strange trifle. Half the menu is vegan. Juices, mineral waters and infusions to drink. Corkage 50p.

CHEF: Co-operative PROPRIETORS: Pure Land Co-operative
OPEN: Tue to Sat, exc Thur D CLOSED: 10 days Christmas, Easter, bank hols, 1 week Aug
MEALS: 12 to 3 (2.30 Thur), 5.30 to 8.30
PRICES: £3 (£4). Unlicensed, but bring your own: corkage 50p
SEATS: 76. 5 tables outside. Private parties: 15 main room. Vegetarian meals. Children welcome. No smoking. Wheelchair access. Music. Self-service

Chez Gerard [9/20]

maps 12 (1 and 2) and 10 (3)

(1) 8 Charlotte Street, W1P 1HE
01-636 4975
(2) 31 Dover Street, W1X 3RA
01-499 8171
(3) 119–120 Chancery Lane, WC2A 1PP
01-405 5761

£17–£20

This trio of formula French restaurants provide good steaks, excellent French-style chips, and there are interesting cheeses. House French is £5·50.

OPEN: (1) all week, exc Sat L. (2) Mon to Sat. (3) Mon to Fri, breakfast and L only
MEALS: (1) 12.30 to 2.30. 6 to 11. (2) 12 to 2.45, 7 to 11.30. (3) 8 to 11, 12 to 2.45
PRICES: £11 (£17), Set L from £15 (£20). Cover 70p. Minimum £10. Service 10%
CARDS: Access, Visa
SEATS: (1) 80 (2) 100 (3) 120. Private parties: (1) 30 (2) 100 (3) 80. Children's helpings. No pipes in dining-rooms. Wheelchair access. Music

Chez Moi [12/20]

map 9

1 Addison Avenue, W11 4QS
01-603 8267

£24

An old-style French restaurant which is expensive, but where the quality of the established dishes remains high. Lamb is always excellent, whether grilled and served with mint butter and fresh figs, or the rack roasted with a crust of mustard, breadcrumbs and herbs. To start, both the Oursins Chez Moi – scampi, prawns and scallops rolled in vermicelli and deep-fried – and the snails with almonds are reliable. New additions to the repertoire are canapés and home-made chocolates with coffee. The restaurant's greengrocer is a customer, so the vegetables tend to be good, but are charged as an extra item on the bill. An upper-class wine list strong in '76 and '78 claret in the £15 to £20 range. Cheaper are the '83 Beaujolais around £10, or house red at £6.

CHEF: Richard Walton PROPRIETORS: Richard Walton and Colin Smith
OPEN: Mon to Sat, D only CLOSED: 2 weeks Aug, 2 weeks Christmas, bank hols
MEALS: 7 to 11.30
PRICES: £17 (£24) CARDS: Access, Amex, Diners, Visa
SEATS: 45. Children's helpings. No babies. No pipes in dining-room. Wheelchair access. Air-conditioned

Chiang Mai [11/20] map 13

48 Frith Street, W1V 5TE
01-437 7444 £14–£15

One of a number of smart new restaurants that have helped to set up a culinary renaissance in Soho over the last couple of years. The cooking is northern Thai and the decor designed to look like a Thai wooden house with fat, polished wooden pillars and a woven ceiling. Supplies are flown in from Bangkok every Thursday, though at other times of the week there may be a few shortcuts taken. Especially enjoyable have been the very hot dishes, such as beef with Kaffir limes; the sublime soup of chicken, coconut and galanga; fried beef balls and chilli dip; also, the fish dishes and the pork with ginger. To finish there are exotic fruits. The Thai Singha beer is a pricey £1·80 a bottle, but a good match. Service is disarmingly charming.

CHEF/PROPRIETOR: Vatcharin Bhumichitr
OPEN: all week MEALS: 12 to 3, 6 to 11.30
PRICES: £10 (£14), Set L and D from £12·70 (£15). Service inc set only
CARDS: Access, Amex, Diners, Visa
SEATS: 60. Private parties: 12 main room, 20 to 25 private room. Vegetarian meals. Children welcome. Thai music

Christian's [10/20] map 9

1 Station Parade, Burlington Lane, W4 3HD
01-995 0382 and 995 0208 £15

One of a very rare and select band of restaurants. Outside it has no sign and no awning. Instead there is a shop-front with plants in the window; peer through and the inside looks like a farmhouse. Christian Gustin runs this useful neighbourhood bistro with hardly any help, which can make meals very slow – you could possibly eat somewhere else between courses. Nevertheless, M. Gustin makes good use of the time and has turned out very fine fish quenelles; pheasant with cream, apple and cognac; banana with white rum and blackcurrant sauce. Cream is his right-hand man for saucing main dishes, but less so for sweets, which can be impeccable – witness the pears in red wine with a kiwi sauce. If he had a little help in the kitchen to speed things up we would happily consider a rating of 12 or even more. House claret is £4·50.

CHEF/PROPRIETOR: Christian Gustin
OPEN: Tue to Sun, D only MEALS: 7.30 to 10.15
PRICES: £9 (£15). Cover 65p. Service 10%
SEATS: 30. 4 tables outside. Private parties: 8 main room. Vegetarian meals. Children welcome. Wheelchair access. Classical music

Chuen Cheng Ku [9/20]

map 13

17 Wardour Street, W1 3HD
01-437 1398 and 734 3281

£5–£15

This huge Cantonese canteen with its dragon pole outside seats 400 people at a go and at lunchtime, when the dim-sum trolleys are wheeled through its three cavernous rooms to the sound of Hong Kong's 20 greatest country and western hits, there are three sittings. That's how it makes a profit when lunch can be less than £3 a head. For dim-sum, served until six, it is rivalled in London only by its new venture, the New World (see entry). There is a pictorial menu, or else stop a trolley and have a look in the bamboo steam-baskets. Favourites are the pork dumpling topped with carrot, cheung-fun, the prawn dumplings, and the whelks with chilli. Main meals from the long menu can be less successful, but even so there are some dishes worth picking out – lobster with ginger and spring onions (the cheapest in London); steamed scallops; duck with lemon; or braised lamb with bean curd. Licensed.

CHEF: S.W.Lai PROPRIETORS: K.W.Choi and K.Au
OPEN: all week MEALS: 11am to 11.30pm (11.45 Sat, 11 Sun)
PRICES: £8 (£15), Set L from £2 (£5), Set D from £4·50 (£8). Service inc. Licensed, plus bring your own: corkage £1 CARDS: Access, Amex, Diners, Visa
SEATS: 400. Private parties: 100 main room. Vegetarian meals. Children welcome. Wheelchair access. Music

Ciboure [13/20]

map 10

21 Eccleston Street, SW1 9LX
01-730 2505

£18–£25

An impressive, smart, modern French restaurant on the edge of Belgravia. The cooking is light and dishes pretty – terrines of sweetbreads and guinea-fowl; trout; salmon and turbot; baskets of deep-fried courgette sticks; breast of chicken with mango and coriander sauce; venison with apple, kiwi and pear. The waiters are just the right side of rude. The set lunch is only two courses, and be warned that service at 10 per cent is added but VAT, ridiculously, isn't included. Even so, from the soft jazz to the shining white damask to the overall feeling of discreet glamour, the rise in the rating to 13 is well earned. There are some interesting wines beyond the vin de pays at £5·90, notably CELLARMAN'S CHOICE: Viña Albina Gran Reserva '73 at £7·90.

CHEF: Richard Price PROPRIETORS: Jean-Louis Journade and Marcello Vargiu
OPEN: Mon to Sat, exc Sat L MEALS: 12 to 12.30, 7 to 11.30
PRICES: £16 (£25), Set L £10 (£18). Service 10% CARDS: Access, Amex, Diners, Visa
SEATS: 36. No cigars/pipes in dining-room. Wheelchair access. Jazz. Air-conditioned

Clarke's [13/20]

map 10

124 Kensington Church Street, W8 4BH
01-221 9225

£12–£18

This has the style of a country restaurant, with high ceilings, cream walls, flowers, and no choice on the menu, which changes daily. Sally Clarke arrived via Croydon Technical College, Paris and Michael's in Santa Monica. The

Californian influence is the most noticeable with a strict use of fresh ingredients, plenty of charcoal grilling, marinating, and no vinegar in the dressing of the salads. Typical are the chicken soup with a tapénade, and duck marinated in red wine, grilled but still pink, and served with its reduced marinade and home-made noodles. Fish features strongly, from marinated salmon and monkfish, to char-grilled salmon, to kebabs served with an anchovy and black olive purée, to skate in black butter. The third course is always a fine, cottage-made cheese. Often these are rare; a Satterleigh, an Exmoor, a Devon Garland, and a Belvoir Blue were served on successive nights one week, all with home-made bread and biscuits. Sweets range from chocolate cake to blood oranges with a slice of Sauternes and olive oil cake. The developing menu means that standards are not yet sufficiently consistent for a rating of 14. There is usually an alternative in the kitchen if there is something you don't like. Upstairs is said to be better than down, which echoes cavernously because of the hard floors and where you can get some of the cooking smells. Sally Clarke's eye for detail in all things extends to the wines. The list is also evolving but includes quality bottles at a reasonable price. The house aperitif is blood oranges with champagne. There is also Exshaw cognac.

CHEF/PROPRIETOR: Sally Clarke
OPEN: Mon to Sat, exc Sat L CLOSED: Christmas and Easter MEALS: 12.30 to 2, 7.30 to 10.30
PRICES: Set L from £8·50 (£12), Set D £15 (£18). Service inc CARDS: Access, Visa
SEATS: 60. Private parties: 10 main room. Children welcome. Wheelchair access

Colombina [9/20] — map 12

5 Duke of York Street, SW1Y 6LA
01-930 8279 and 839 3240 — £15

A friendly, crowded, fast Italian restaurant. The offal in kidney and liver dishes has been very good and the sweets trolley is above average. Pasta is made daily and the cheeses are from the excellent Paxton & Whitfield round the corner. House Sangiovese or Trebbiano is £4·25.

CHEF: Vincenzo Ferraris PROPRIETORS: Ferraris brothers
OPEN: Mon to Sat MEALS: 12 to 3, 6 to 11
PRICES: £10 (£15). Cover 80p CARDS: Access, Amex, Diners, Visa
SEATS: 85. Private parties: 26 main room. Vegetarian meals. Children's helpings. Wheelchair access. Music. Air-conditioned

▲ *Connaught Hotel* [15/20] — map 12

Carlos Place, W1Y 6AL
01-499 7070 — **Real Food** £23–£45

'What has become dangerous in France is that more and more people are learning specialities and fewer and fewer are learning to cook.' Michel Bourdin's shrewd pronouncement is as true for Britain, and would serve as a quick guideline as to why some restaurants in this *Guide* rate 14 points and others don't. Bourdin himself has become the curator of the great hotel cooking of 100 years ago. He is the true inheritor of the traditions laid down by Soyer at the Reform Club and Escoffier at the Ritz. His adaptations of the classic cuisine are subtle – a new sauce for the chicken pie; a rendezvous of fish for starter or as a main course, though not of the lightness and mild cooking of Mosimann at the Dorchester, but a soup plate filled with a beige-green cream sauce with hunks of white fish, shellfish and salmon unashamedly cooked more than rare. But for the main course the menu stands by its roasts – sometimes as many as nine at a time – its consommé filled with pieces of meat, and its superb fish quenelles. It earns its rating as the best of the London luxury hotels because it is above all reliably good throughout the length of the menu. It is in some ways a definitive restaurant. The entrance has none of the Dorchester/Savoy/Ritz grandeur but an understated English classiness. The corridor to the dining-room has a line of assembled cold dishes – a big pie, a pillar of crayfish, rows of melons, and artichokes with slices of lemon. The French-polished panels run half up the white walls, and there is a lot of silver both on the tables and on the trolleys, plus silver heating lamps over which everything gets a quick go, for better or worse, before coming to table. Service is in tails and bow-ties, apart from the boys in white tunics who are the young chefs doing their obligatory six months front of house. Typical of the cooking style is the quail belle époque – the breasts from four or five birds served in a savoury demi-glaze with generous slices of black truffle scattered about the plate and in the centre a single, fat, boiled quail egg, its yolk still soft. More extravagant is the lobster grilled with herbs. The sweets have brought a host of compliments – trifle, bread-and-butter pudding, the crêpes flambé, summer pudding and sorbets. Drinking is more of a problem unless the Ch. Latour is in your financial orbit, though the sommelier has positive advice. Some better choices in the less expensive regions could be a wise move and might see the reinstatement of the bottle symbol. A few more half-bottles would be useful, too. House French is £6.75.

CHEF: Michel Bourdin PROPRIETORS: Savoy Hotel plc
OPEN: Rest all week, Grill Room Mon to Fri MEALS: 12.30 to 2, 6.30 to 10.15 (6 to 10.30 Grill Room)
PRICES: Rest Set L from £17·85 (£26), Set D from £15·60 (£23). Service 15%. Grill Room £31 (£45). Minimum £15. Service 15% CARD: Access
SEATS: Rest 80, Grill Room 35. Private parties: 10 Rest, 8 Grill Room, 20 private room. No children under 6. Jacket and tie. No jeans. No pipes in dining-room. Wheelchair access (also men's WC). Air-conditioned
ACCOMMODATION: 90 rooms, all with bath/shower. Rooms for disabled. B&B £88 to £132. Children welcome. No pets. Afternoon teas. Lift. TV. Phone [GHG]

La Corée [11/20] map 12

56 St Giles High Street, WC2H 8LH
01-836 7235 £7–£18

In the shadow of Centre Point and well used by Koreans. The waitress tends to shove everyone to the set meals. Menu A begins with a lacquered box of deep-fried courgettes, prawn, and pork cooked two ways. Then there is chicken, deep-fried and covered in sesame seeds and served with a trio of Korean dates. The bulgogi is excellent, on a less ostentatious shield than in the Arirang (see entry) and cooked as fast or slowly as you want. With this come pickled spinach, celery with cayenne pepper, bean sprouts and carrots. Good fluffy rice with frozen carrots and peas. The kim-chee is potent and other good individual dishes are fried meat dumplings; Korean pizza, here called pa jeon; and octopus in green and yellow pepper sauce. Barley tea comes free, but coffee with a bowl of instant milk. Jungjong (Korean saké) is £2·50 a carafe.

CHEF: Mr Nho PROPRIETOR: Mr Choi
OPEN: Mon to Sat MEALS: 12 to 2.45, 6 to 10.15
PRICES: £12 (£17), Set L and D from £4·50 to £14·50 (£7 to £18). Service 10%
CARDS: Access, Amex, Diners, Visa
SEATS: 61. Private parties: 45 main room. Vegetarian meals. Children welcome. Wheelchair access. Oriental music

Cork & Bottle Wine Bar [8/20] map 13

44–46 Cranbourn Street, WC2H 7AN
01-734 7807 £10

The overnight sleeper from Glasgow to Euston brings langoustines, oysters and gravlax from Loch Fyne to this ever-popular and consistent wine bar on the doorstep of theatreland. The menu has a strong provincial European strain, which has produced good lamb with garlic and rosemary or chicken with herbs and tomatoes. Three-quarters of the sweets are chocolate. The rating is lowered because a lot of the *élan* has disappeared from the cooking. A challenging spread of wines has intriguing showings from lesser areas, such as New Zealand and northern Italy. The four Alsace wines include Gewürztraminer, Les Archenets '79, from Jos Meyer, at £8·95.

CHEF: Camilla Rainey PROPRIETOR: Don Hewitson
OPEN: all week MEALS: 11.30 to 2.45, 5.30 to 10
PRICES: £7 (£10) CARDS: Amex, Diners, Visa
SEATS: 100. Vegetarian meals. Classical music and jazz. Air-conditioned. Self-service

Corney & Barrow [10/20] map 10

118 Moorgate, EC2M 6UR
01-628 2898 £23

A small, blue-rimmed shop-front conceals the wine shop (where Ch. Pétrus '70 is £234) and a big, Hollywood-style staircase leads down to a black and red bar/dining-room which bulges and bustles like the Stock Exchange. You can have one course at the high bar or eat properly at tables neatly laid with flowers. The fashionable, pricey menu can take a bashing by the evening, but there are good things to be had – grilled red mullet with an egg and wine sauce; steak and kidney pie; duck with armagnac and green peppercorns; smoked sturgeon with crab and horseradish mousse. The trimmings, such as the bread, the nut-oil dressing on the salad, and the petits fours, are of a class restaurant. The wine list is Corney & Barrow's full range: strong on claret, burgundy and champagne, which is to say not cheap. House St Emilion is £7.

CHEF: James Rice PROPRIETORS: Corney & Barrow Restaurants Ltd
OPEN: Mon to Fri MEALS: 11.30 to 3, 5.30 to 8
PRICES: £14 (£23). Cover £1·75. Service 12.5% CARDS: Access, Amex, Visa
SEATS: 100. Private parties: 150 main room, 20 and 4 private rooms. Vegetarian meals by arrangement. Children welcome. Music. Air-conditioned

Reports on good shops, small hotels and cafes in your area are welcome.

Country Life [8/20]

map 12

123 Regent Street, W1R 7HA
01-434 2922

£3–£5

In the heart of W1 (the entrance is in Heddon Street), this vegetarian buffet offers all you can eat for £3·50. There are a variety of soups; breads (rye, wholemeal or black) with spreads (peanut butter, sunflower seed, tahini or hazel-nut); a vast range of salads and dressings; and spaghetti with vegetarian meatballs – a mixture of ground nuts and breadcrumbs. Baked potatoes are also available. Spectacular puddings can be chosen from the fresh-fruit counter or the dried-fruit counter and there is rich almond purée to pour over. Children are served half-price. Unlicensed.

CHEF: Loland Moutray PROPRIETORS: Country Life
OPEN: Mon to Fri, L only CLOSED: bank hols MEALS: 11.30 to 2.30 (3 Fri)
PRICES: £3 (£5), Set L from £2·50 (£3). Service inc. Unlicensed
SEATS: 100. Private parties: 100 main room. Vegetarian meals. Children's helpings. No smoking in dining-room. Self-service

La Croisette [11/20]

map 10

168 Ifield Road, SW10 9AF
01-373 3694

£24

Eleven years ago Mr Bracci and Mr Martin opened this basement on the principle that it would look like a restaurant in the south of France and serve the kind of fish dishes normally found in Brittany. It is cramped, gets hot, and the waiters do not speak English, but the fish van comes from Brittany three times a week loaded with shrimps, mussels, oysters, lobsters and so on. The set price for lunch and dinner includes everything from a Kir onwards – apart from the wine, which is £6·50 a bottle. As well as the massive shellfish platters there are pastry cases filled with cream sauces and fish and, for main courses, fillets of white fish in wine and cream sauces. There is a rumour that the vegetables and sweets may be improving, but we reserve judgement. The success of the restaurant has spawned Le Suquet, Le Quai St Pierre and L'Olivier (for meat), all in London, all run on similar lines and all included in the *Guide*.

CHEF: David Laurent PROPRIETORS: A. Bracci and P. Martin
OPEN: Tue to Sun, exc Tue L CLOSED: 2 weeks at Christmas MEALS: 12.30 to 2.30, 7.30 to 11.30
PRICES: Set L and D £18 (£24). Service 15% CARD: Amex
SEATS: 55. 4 tables outside. Children welcome. Music

Crowns [9/20]

map 12

3–4 Crown Passage, Pall Mall, SW1 6PP
01-839 3960

£12

A useful wine bar, open for food from half-past nine in the morning to eight at night. The atmosphere is low-key and unfussy. The floor is parquet, there is a Gaggia coffee machine for espresso, and a counter display of food. Everything is home cooked: they even bake their own hams. The raised pies are exceptionally good, with crisp, brown pastry and beef, ham, chicken, hard-boiled egg, and mushroom fillings. There is usually a pasta dish as well. Ten wines by the glass and some interesting drinking beyond. CELLARMAN'S CHOICE: house claret at £4·75.

CHEFS/PROPRIETORS: Mary and Mario Ghirardani
OPEN: Mon to Fri MEALS: 9.30 to 7.30
PRICES: £8 (£12) CARDS: Access, Amex, Visa
SEATS: 60. Private parties: 40 main room. Vegetarian meals. Wheelchair access. Music

Crowthers [12/20] map 9

481 Upper Richmond Road West, East Sheen, SW14 7PU
01-876 6372 £18–£20

An upper-class, husband-and-wife-run bistro. Philip Crowther has produced some very good dishes, from Basque tart to mussel soup, to calves' kidneys with mustard. It is a short menu with five choices at each stage, and takes in provincial French styles, such as pork stuffed with prunes and given a plum sauce, or quail périgourdine, as well as modern styles, such as brochette of beef teriyaki using good quality fillet, or a timbale of cauliflower, carrot and spinach. The sweets are consistently well reported, from crème brûlée with raspberries to Mozart torte – chocolate and walnuts with cream. An interesting range of aperitifs and well-chosen list of 60 wines. CELLARMAN'S CHOICE: Quincy '83 from Raymond Pipet at £8·25.

CHEF: Philip Crowther PROPRIETORS: Philip and Shirley Crowther
OPEN: Tue to Sun, exc Sat L and Sun D MEALS: 12 to 2, 7 to 11
PRICES: Set L £13·50 (£18), Set D £15 (£20) CARDS: Access, Amex
SEATS: 30. Private parties: 20 main room. Vegetarian meals. Children welcome. Wheelchair access. Music

Daphne [new entry, zero rated] map 10

83 Bayham Street, NW1 0AG
01-267 7322 £8–£12

On the site of what used to be Moditis, a well-loved if rather greasy Greek cafe, but now spruced up and the kitchen moved upstairs. Nothing screams: this is a Greek/Cypriot restaurant, though the white stucco and the murals give a romantic, Mediterranean feel. The familiar menu of taramosalata and stifado is supplemented by blackboard specials. The olives on the table are flavoured with coriander and garlic and notably good have been tsatsiki, cuttlefish in wine, afelia, roast potatoes, and aubergine salad. To finish, the baklava is of a good standard. Ten Greek wines. CELLARMAN'S CHOICE: Lion of Nemea at £5·25.

The irony of the name of the restaurant will not be lost on regulars to the Moditis a decade ago, when the daughter of the owner would be whisked away in a Jaguar every night around nine o'clock. Her beauty once inspired a column by Angus McGill in the *Evening Standard*. More reports, please.

CHEF: Mr Charalambos PROPRIETORS: A. Evangelou, A. Lymbouri and S. Stavrou
OPEN: Mon to Sat MEALS: 12.30 to 3, 6 to 12
PRICES: £7 (£12), Set L £4·75 (£8), Set D £5·50 (£10) CARD: Access
SEATS: 85. 10 tables outside. Private parties: 30 main room. Vegetarian meals. Children welcome. Wheelchair access (also WC). Music

Daquise [8/20] map 11

20 Thurloe Street, SW7 2LT
01-589 6117 £4–£7

An unpretentious Polish cafe not unlike an Eastern Europe railway station. It is cheap, open from 10am to 11.30pm, and some of the Polish dishes are well done – stuffed cabbage, ox tongue with beetroot, black sausage, tripe à la polonaise. It's handy for the museums. 'We desire gentlemen to remove headgear whilst dining.'

CHEF: Zygmunt Ponitka PROPRIETORS: S.Ganjou and C.Z.Konarski
OPEN: all week MEALS: 12 to 3, 6 to 11.20
PRICES: £5 (£7), Set L from £2·50 (£4)
SEATS: 100. Private parties: 30 main room. Children welcome. Wheelchair access

D'Artagnan

As the Guide *went to press this restaurant moved to 50 Greek Street W1, where from October 1985 it will operate under the name La Bastide.*

Defune [10/20] map 10

61 Blandford Street, W1H 3AJ
01-935 8311 £20

The main plus here is the long sushi bar with at least 20 varieties of fish kept in a glass cabinet. The mixed sushi at £8 is a good introduction to the cuisine and makes an ample meal for one. Served at the table in a deep, round lacquered wooden box, it comprises half a dozen tuna rolls wrapped in green nori (seaweed); a roll of cold omelette; slices of salmon, squid, cooked prawn and tuna (both standard and belly-cut), each sitting on small blocks of rice, with some salmon-pink slices of vinegared ginger as pickle. Other dishes in other parts of the restaurant tend to be as expensive as in the high-status Japanese restaurants, but not really of comparable quality. There's a wide range of whiskies – the place is well used by Japanese businessmen as a drinking club.

CHEF: Mr Nabgaura PROPRIETOR: Mr Moyafhta
OPEN: Mon to Sat CLOSED: 25 to 27 Dec, 1 Jan MEALS: 12 to 2.30, 6 to 10.30
PRICES: £16 (£20) CARDS: Amex, Diners
SEATS: 30. Private parties: 10 main room. Vegetarian meals. Children's helpings. Jacket and tie. Music. Air-conditioned

Desaru [new entry, zero rated] map 13

60–62 Old Compton Street, W1V 5PA
01-734 4379 £12–£13

This has the feel of an up-market Malaysian restaurant but it is not expensive and the service is first-class. The menu has many Indonesian influences. Notably good is the satay; the beef rendang heavily flavoured with cumin; tahu telor (bean curd dipped in egg, fried and served on bean sprouts with a tamarind and soy sauce); and the vegetables in the sajor lodeh, liberally flavoured with coconut and lemon grass. The sauces all round are first-class. The mangga kachang is an odd sweet of mango juice with coconut milk and shaved ice, otherwise there are banana fritters. Tiger beer. More reports, please.

CHEF: Yurnas Zainudin PROPRIETOR: Michael Gan
OPEN: all week MEALS: 12 to 3, 6 to 11.45
PRICES: £6 (£13), Set D £10.50 (£12). Cover 30p. Minimum £10 per person on parties over 7 CARDS: Access, Amex, Diners, Visa
SEATS: 60. Private parties: 50 main room. Vegetarian meals. No children under 10. Music. Air-conditioned

Dewaniam [10/20] map 9

133–135 Stanstead Road, SE23 1HH
01-291 4778, 4477 and 1218 £9–£18

A long, narrow restaurant with closely packed tables and a bar at one end. As well as a lengthy list of customary dishes, including good tandoori king prawns and medium-hot chicken dopiaza, there are specialities using pheasant, partridge, quail, goose, duck, venison and hare. Venison might benefit from marinating longer in its vinegar, red wine, olive oil, yoghourt and spices, but it is flavoursome enough and comes with a sauce of cream, almonds, pistachios and sultanas. Lamb's brains are cooked with tomatoes, chilli, garlic and herbs. Service is courteous and helpful; hot towels come after the main course.

CHEFS: Fozlu Miah and Ahmed Ali PROPRIETORS: Rashid Ali and Fozlu Miah
OPEN: all week MEALS: 12.15 to 2.15, 5.30 to 11.45
PRICES: £12 (£18), Set L from £6 (£9), Set D from £9 (£13) CARDS: Access, Amex, Diners, Visa
SEATS: 52. Private parties: 56 main room. Vegetarian meals. Children welcome. Indian music. Air-conditioned

'The diners looked uneasy and spoke in whispers: "How's the venison?" "Venison is venison, deer."' (On eating French in London)

The Diamond [10/20] map 13

23 Lisle Street, WC2H 7BA
01-437 2517 £10

No longer the best restaurant in Chinatown, but the classics of Cantonese cooking – steamed sea-bass; roasted salted king prawns with garlic, ginger and peppers; and crab in black bean sauce, for example – are still of above-average standard. Ask for the Chinese vegetables in oyster sauce. Functional decor and service. House French is £5·30.

CHEF/PROPRIETOR: Harry Lee
OPEN: all week MEALS: noon to 3am
PRICES: £4 (£10), Set L and D £6·50 (£10)
SEATS: 100. Private parties: 40 main room. Vegetarian meals. Children welcome. Wheelchair access

Dining Room [new entry, zero rated] map 10

1 Cathedral Street, SE1 9DE
01-407 0337 £11

This would get laurels in a guide to vegetarian restaurants, though meat eaters might find some of the cooking bland. The menu is imaginative and constantly changing; eclectic if a bit heavy. Walnut cake with apple and mint sauce, and the copious plantain and pepper soup thickened with coconut milk are both excellent. Sweets tend to be gooey and sharing one between two is often a good move. The atmosphere is relaxed. Do not be deterred by the cement hallway and uninviting exterior. The wine list has been expanded recently – from two bottles to six. The best bets are the elderflower wine and the gooseberry champagne. Good herbal teas. More reports, please.

CHEF: Sandra Cross PROPRIETORS: William English and Sandra Cross
OPEN: Tue to Fri MEALS: 12 to 3, 7 to 10
PRICES: £7 (£11). Service 10%
SEATS: 32. Private parties: 35 main room. Vegetarian meals. Children's helpings. Music

Don Pepe [10/20] map 10

99 Frampton Street, NW8 8NA
01-262 3834 and 723 9749 £20

A noisy and convivial Spanish place with authentic dishes, especially if you stick to starters (Serrano ham is not always on the menu but you might be able to persuade the waiter to bring you some) and fish – Galician octopus, monkfish in garlic and butter, and crawfish. Tripe with a spicy sauce is very good. Main meat courses, such as huge veal chops with lots of vegetables, tend to be bigger on quantity than quality. The restaurant imports its own Rioja and the house wine is £4·05. CELLARMAN'S CHOICE: Solar de Samaniego, Reserva '78 at £6·50.

CHEF: Alex Garcia PROPRIETOR: Jose Garcia
OPEN: all week MEALS: 12 to 2.30 (2 Sun), 7 to 12.15 (10 Sun)
PRICES: £14 (£20). Cover 50p at L, 95p at D CARDS: Access, Amex, Diners, Visa
SEATS: 50. Private parties: 70 main room. Children welcome. Spanish music

▲ *Dorchester Hotel* [14/20] map 12

(1) Terrace Restaurant
(2) Grill Room
Park Lane, W1A 2HJ
01-629 8888 £17–£42

Anton Mosimann's reputation precedes his restaurants. A great chef he is, as anyone who has eaten with him will testify, but his dining-rooms lag behind. The Terrace has entered an era of dance-band middle-age, waltzing – not that merrily – to tunes from the BBC Light Programme. The kitchen needs a traffic controller to spot details, for instance unripe gooseberries going out with the vanilla ice-cream with mango sauce, or the coffee beans that have been burned in the roasting. The malaise stretches to a wickedly overpriced and unbalanced wine list. For all its mirrors and carpets and gazebo the Terrace is edging ever closer to the style of a grand seaside hotel, rather than moving into the culinary overdrive that might earn a rating of 15 or 16, of which many might consider Mr Mosimann deserving. The hotel has still, as we go to press, to give its full endorsement to the much-publicised *cuisine naturelle* that is Mr Mosimann's newest style – ideal for those prone to heart disease. Only half a dozen of these dishes appear on each menu, looking conspicuously out of place – rather like Buddhists at a Jewish wedding – amid the flamboyance of the Terrace and the sobriety of the Grill Room. At its most simple, as served to a dozen visiting top French chefs including Girardet and Troisgros, the cuisine may produce a single plate of sliced black and white truffles. At the other end of the spectrum it is oysters wrapped in caul poached and served with a saffron sauce and the ink from a squid. Mr Mosimann has apparently spent much of the year following a regime of cottage cheese and jogging, which may account for such foibles. But *cuisine naturelle* is not to be dismissed lightly. At its best the finest ingredients are allowed to shine without hindrance. The results can be startling – a steaming of pieces of sea-bass, salmon, red mullet, lobster claw, scallop and so on with herbs, such as dill, fennel and some samphire (similar to the red mullet and vegetable soup served at Le Gavroche) or fillet of beef poached in stock and served with clumps of half a dozen shredded vegetables in subtle dressing – raw carrot with thyme and a dribble of lemon; blanched yellow peppers with yoghourt; red cabbage lightly poached in a vinegar stock. Steamed chicken may sound dull, but it is stuffed with white mushrooms and white pepper and lifted by a bottle-green sauce of purée watercress made with chicken stock. The garnish is turned vegetables, plus asparagus. The cuisine is still in the prototype stage and needs to develop with its dishes.

Beside all this still appear the good old indulgences: salmon with a butter sorrel sauce; superlative chicken liver pâté set in aspic with three flowers made with cucumber stems, French parsley tips as leaves and tomato rose heads (a different, but equally good pâté is served in the Grill); and lamb wrapped with cabbage in pastry, a frequent centrepiece to the *menu surprise*, which costs £60 for two. The cheeses are English in the Grill and European in the Terrace (Lymeswold excepted – 'we have to put it on because American visitors ask for it'), and there is a powerful goats', which is marinated in olive oil and wrapped with garlic, bay, chilli and herbs for up to two months. A quartet of sweets is shown plated for you to choose – the vanilla ice-cream displayed, though, is made out of margarine and gelatine. Look for the chocolate and hazel-nut cake, which, like other desserts, is presented dusted with icing-sugar and sauced by an apprentice Miró.

Three years ago we called the Dorchester the best London extravagance and that remains the case, because it is an expensive treat for an occasion but, as a restaurant – either plain and English in the Grill or *nouvelle* in the Terrace, with dancing – does it compete at the highest level? The wine policy is scandalous. Under no circumstances allow the waiter to choose your wine for the *menu surprise* without finding out how much you are spending, or you may be in for a very nasty surprise. It is a swanky, vintage claret-ridden list that is vastly overpriced with virtually no reasonably priced wines at all, while the level of wine knowledge would not grace a bistro. The 'sommelier' has been known to suggest the Mateus Rosé, and although Ch. Pichon-Lalande '78 is very fine, it really should not be for sale as yet, as it has not matured – certainly not enough to justify £12-plus for a half-bottle. House wine may seem an innocuous £3·40 a carafe, but the carafe is only 25cl so the wine costs over £10 a bottle. These criticisms, though, are not true of the cocktail bar, which does immaculate Margaritas and inexpensive snacks – inexpensive for this kind of cooking on Park Lane, at least.

CHEF: Anton Mosimann PROPRIETORS: Dorchester Hotel Ltd
OPEN: (1) Mon to Sat, D only; (2) all week MEALS: (1) 6.30 to 11.30; (2) 12.30 to 3 (2.30 Sun), 6.30 to 11 (7 to 10.30 Sun)
PRICES: (1) £33 (£42), Set D from £24 (£30); (2) £21 (£32), Set L and D £15·50 (£17 and £24). Service inc CARDS: Access, Amex, Diners, Visa
SEATS: (1) 100; (2) 85. Private parties: 14 main room (1). Car-park, 40 places. No children under 9 (1). Jacket and tie. No pipes in dining-room (1). Wheelchair access (2, also wc) Music (1). Air-conditioned
ACCOMMODATION: 280 rooms, all with bath/shower. Rooms for disabled. B&B £128 to £171. Children welcome. No pets. Afternoon teas. Air-conditioning. Lift. TV. Phone. Confirm by 6

Dragon Gate [12/20]

map 13

7 Gerrard Street, W1V 7LJ
01-734 5154 £9–£16

The only authentic Szechuan restaurant in London. Of the 114 dishes, 90 per cent have a Szechuan ring. There is not much atmosphere to speak of, apart from the carved wooden panels lining the top parts of the wall, but the cooking is fiery. Meals open with plates of pickled cabbage with chilli and chilli oil, and peanuts. Typical of the cooking is the cold tripe in Szechuan pepper and ginger sauce which is lip-numbingly hot, the sauté shredded pork with aubergine with fish flavour, and sauté shrimp with hot garlic sauce. The tea-smoked duck is a feature and the set dinner includes starters of fine hot-and-sour soup, prawns with cashew and chilli, beef in oyster sauce, and a sweet-and-sour dish. To finish there are red bean paste pancakes which taste, according to one reporter, like a raspberry omelette. The service is helpful though there can be a culture gap. Chinese beer, or Blanc de Blancs at £4·80.

CHEF: Tse Bin PROPRIETORS: Chun-Lin Man and others
OPEN: all week MEALS: 12 to 2.15, 5.15 to 11.15
PRICES: £9 (£16), Set L and D from £5 (£9). Service 10% CARDS: Amex, Diners
SEATS: 50. Private parties: 50 main room. Children welcome. Music

DRUMMOND STREET, NW1

BACKGROUND BRIEFING: *The sign definitely says Drummond Street but it could be Tiruchirapalli. On one side of the road is a shop selling pan and another with a cold cabinet piled high with mangoes, pineapples and sugar cane which are made into fresh juice as you watch. There are two Diwana Bhel Poori restaurants (related to 50 Westbourne Grove). Number 121 looks a bit brighter than number 114 although the menus are similar. Thali Annapurna is the speciality, or there are other south Indian vegetarian dishes: bhel poori, masala dosai, and so on. At 133–135 there is another Bhel Poori house, the Ravi Shankar. The Mysore thali is not as painful as it sounds, but is four small dishes of varying hotness with rice, four puffed-up, crispy puri breads, plus a little torpedo of an Indian doughnut in sweet syrup for dessert. All for £3·25.*

Ealing Tandoori [10/20] map 9

9–10 High Street, The Green, W5 5DA
01-567 7606 and 840 0818 £13

Service is courteous, helpings are large, and the cooking is north Indian and Nepalese: butter chicken and chicken tikka masala are the specialities. Plenty of space. Standard wines.

CHEF/PROPRIETOR: K.B.Thapa
OPEN: all week MEALS: 12 to 2.45, 6 to 11.45
PRICES: £10 (£13) CARDS: Access, Amex, Diners, Visa
SEATS: 185. Private parties: 100 main room. Vegetarian meals. Children welcome. Wheelchair access (also WC). Indian music

Eatons [12/20] map 11

49 Elizabeth Street, SW1 9PP
01-730 0074 £16

As neighbourhood bistros go, this is very sharp – a long narrow room in white hessian leading to a small back room extension with white walls, a skylight and plants. Half the short menu changes every week, but the old favourites of blinis with smoked salmon and sour cream, trout Colbert, lamb fillet and its kidneys in a provençale sauce remain of a standard. Vegetables are fresh, and the sweets have plenty of cream. It's reliably good all round: hence the high rating. House red is £5·50. CELLARMAN'S CHOICE: Ch. Millet '76 at £10·75.

CHEF: Santosh Bakshi PROPRIETORS: Shayne Pope and Dieter Vagts
OPEN: Mon to Fri CLOSED: bank hols MEALS: 12 to 2, 7 to 11.15
PRICES: £10 (£16). Cover 70p. Service inc CARDS: Access, Amex, Diners, Visa
SEATS: 40. Private parties: 14 main room. Wheelchair access. Light classical music

Ebury Wine Bar [8/20] map 11

178 Ebury Street, SW1W 8UP
01-730 5447 £10--£15

Handy for Victoria coach station. The wine bar has celebrated its first 25 years by expanding into another room. Food at the long green and white bar is kept simple, but is a step above the chilli-and-lasagne level. Thick steaks are griddled in view; daily dishes include salmon in puff pastry with ginger and currants; and there is spicy lamb, and kidneys Turbigo. There are soups, terrines or a hot special to start; cheese or a couple of puddings to finish. A sensible list with a lot under £10, and over 20 wines by the glass. Excellent Gewürztraminer '83, from Willy Gisselbrecht, is £7·50.

CHEF: Caroline Glanty PROPRIETORS: The Ebury Wine Co.
OPEN: all week CLOSED: 25 and 26 Dec MEALS: 12.15 to 2.45, 6 to 10.30 (7 to 10 Sun)
PRICES: £9 (£15), Set L £5·95 (£10). Cover 50p. Minimum £5 CARDS: Access, Amex, Diners, Visa
SEATS: 60. Vegetarian meals. Children's helpings. Air-conditioned

Efes Kebab House [10/20]

map 12

80 Great Titchfield Street, W1P 7AF
01-636 1953

£12

The multi-coloured Turkish lamps create an atmosphere here, though they don't work so well as lights. The waitresses wear braided waistcoats, and no less than seven chefs work behind the take-away counter, charcoal-grilling the meats and assembling mezes. The quality of the meats distinguishes the kitchen – kebabs of chicken and lamb and the speciality of grilled nuggets of lamb, doner and chicken are of a high standard. The meze is authentic but can be less impressive. Coffee is strong and grainy. Avoid the house wines in favour of the Turkish Villa Doluca '78 or Buzbag, both £4·95.

CHEFS/PROPRIETORS: Kazim Akkus and Ibrahim Akbas
OPEN: Mon to Sat MEALS: noon to 11.30
PRICES: £8 (£12) CARDS: Access, Amex, Visa
SEATS: 100. Private parties: 50 main room. Children welcome. Air-conditioned

Equatorial [10/20]

map 13

37 Old Compton Street, W1V 5PL
01-437 6112 and 6093

£7–£13

On two floors with large round tables in the basement and waitresses in regional dress. Some say this Singapore restaurant is one of the best in town, but it pays to know your way around the menu. Avoid the batter and the nasi goreng and concentrate on the satay and the fresh vegetable dishes with a hot chilli dip. Rice is excellent, especially early in the evening, as are the noodle dishes. As well as the usual toffee apple and banana fritters to finish, there is a coconut-milk concoction with jelly bean that looks hard to swallow but cools after all the chilli. Tiger beer goes better than wine, and green tea is served anyway. Good value. The men's toilet is probably the smallest in London.

CHEF: Henry Tan PROPRIETORS: Henry Tan and Henry Ling
OPEN: all week MEALS: 12 to 2.45, 6 to 11.15 (noon to 11.30 Sat and Sun)
PRICES: £6 (£13), set L £4·10 (£7), Set D from £9 (£13). Service 10% CARDS: Access, Amex, Diners, Visa
SEATS: 70. Private parties: 30 main room, 22 private room. Vegetarian meals. Children welcome. Wheelchair access. Chinese music

L'Estanquet [10/20]

map 11

158 Old Brompton Road, SW5 OBA
01-373 9918 £20

Very French. Francophiles treat it as a reasonably priced bistro and love the fish, whether in soup or with vegetables in a pie; accept that confit is fatty; and prefer upstairs to downstairs because it is cheaper. Others find the service indifferent, the wine temperatures all wrong, and the bill, at £20 a head, rather expensive. The music may be loud, but it doesn't start until midnight. House wine is £7·50.

CHEF: Mr Nandez PROPRIETORS: Mr Laughenie and Mr Andrew
OPEN: Mon to Sat CLOSED: bank hols MEALS: 12 to 3, 7.30 to 2
PRICES: £10 (£20). Cover 60p. Service 15% CARDS: Access, Amex, Visa
SEATS: 60. Private parties: 45 main room, 18 private room. Vegetarian meals. Children's helpings. Live guitar music. Air-conditioned

Fleet Tandoori [10/20]

map 10

104 Fleet Road, NW3 2QX
01-485 6402 £8–£10

A solitary, Constable-type reproduction watches over the brown and tan dining-room of this popular, if spartan, local Indian restaurant. Mr Abdur Rahman Khan gets upset that people fill themselves with the savoury dishes at the expense of the puds. Follow his advice and try the nutty kulfi or home-made yoghourt, for which the milk is heavily reduced before the culture is added. Nearly all dishes are listed as specialities but we have eaten good 'kebab roll', a paratha-type pancake wrapped around a spicy lamb sausage; chicken tikka and chaat; muttar paneer; palak (medium-hot dry spinach); nan-e-mughziat (with sultanas); and bhindi bhaji. There is lassi to drink or house French at £4.

CHEF: Abdul Shahid PROPRIETOR: Abdur Rahman Khan
OPEN: all week MEALS: 12 to 2.30, 5.30 to 11
PRICES: £5 (£10). Set L and D from £5 (£8) CARDS: Access, Amex, Visa
SEATS: 34. Private parties: 36 main room. Vegetarian meals. Children's helpings. No-smoking area. Wheelchair access

Food For Thought [10/20]

map 13

31 Neal Street, WC2H 9PA
01-836 0239 **Real Food** £4

Long queues form at this old banana warehouse, now one of the better London vegetarian restaurants. The basement seats are where the hands of fruit were left to ripen. Plates are filled to overflowing and the mega-salad at £1·70 is virtually a meal in itself. Bread is wholemeal and freshly baked. Main courses of stir-fried vegetables and either the bean-based or vegetable-based casseroles seasoned with fresh herbs are excellent. Shepherdess pie is leeks and aduki beans in a mushroom sauce, covered with mashed potato. Yoghourts and cheeses come

'French waiters . . . have an extra dimension of being nearly as rude as possible without actually being it.' (On eating in London)

from the nearby Neal's Yard, and the flapjacks are gigantic. No licence, but no corkage charge.

CHEFS: Siriporn Duncan, Steve Wilcox and Kit Norman
PROPRIETORS: John and Jane Damant
OPEN: Mon to Fri CLOSED: 2 weeks at Christmas MEALS: 12 to 8
PRICES: £3 (£4). Snacks from 20p. Unlicensed, but bring your own: no corkage
SEATS: 50. Vegetarian meals only. Children welcome. Self-service. No smoking. Air-conditioned

Fox and Anchor [9/20] map 10

115 Charterhouse Street, EC1M 6AA
01-253 4838 £12

For steak and chips, or massive mixed grills, this pub off Smithfield meat market takes some beating. It is open for breakfast from six in the morning. There's no fuss, just a lot of food.

CHEF: Julian Wrighton PROPRIETOR: Peter Zeid
OPEN: Mon to Fri CLOSED: 10 days at Christmas, last week Aug MEALS: 6am to 3pm
PRICES: £7 (£12)
SEATS: 70. 3 tables outside. Private parties: 70 main room. Vegetarian meals. Children's helpings

La Frimousse [new entry, zero rated] map 10

75 Fairfax Road, NW6 4EE
01-624 3880 £13–£22

Owned and run by a trio out of the Savoy Hotel. An all-inclusive set menu that changes every Tuesday has put a rein on the prices. The service and the cooking are old school – consommé, salmon quenelles, lamb en croûte, and Grand Marnier soufflé have all been good. There are some old-fashioned descriptions on the menu, too, that conjure up characters in a romantic novel – demoiselles de la mer; tasse Lady Curzon; tortellini à la Joseph Mazzini. Stray from the inclusive half-bottle of wine and the high mark-ups will take you into a realm of unrequited loves. More reports, please.

CHEF: J.Eza PROPRIETORS: A.Toma, M.Trompetto and J.Eza
OPEN: Mon to Sat CLOSED: 1 week at Easter, 3 weeks Aug MEALS: 12 to 3, 7 to 11
PRICES: £14 (£22), Set L £8·75 (£13), Set D £19·50 (£20·50). Cover £1. Service inc set only, alc 15% CARDS: Access, Amex, Diners, Visa
SEATS: 48. 4 tables outside. Private parties: 40 main room. Children welcome. No pipes in dining-room. Wheelchair access. Music. Air-conditioned

Frith's [12/20] map 13

14 Frith Street, W1V 5TS
01-439 3370 £16

More formal than a bistro with its starched cloths, propeller fan and chamber music. Tables are well spaced and there is a tiled floor, bright-red blinds, house plants, plus fresh cut flowers on every table. The two set-price menus are modern and fashionable, leaning heavily on the food mixer and lots of last-minute preparation, for instance in scallops with mange-tout and hazel-nuts. Some of the more adventurous combinations, such as avocado and crab soup, and smoked chicken mousse salad, don't work as well as others, like the stunning caramel syllabub. Plainer dishes seem more solid, such as extremely well-hung mallard garnished with an apple filled with fresh cranberries. Game in general seems to get stuffed – boned goose with wild rice and nuts, pheasant with oatmeal and a flavoursome sauce that is really just a gravy. Cheeses come from Androuët in Paris. Bread is home-made mixed plaits of strong white and nutty wholemeal, and comes with unsalted butter. Perfect chocolate truffles accompany the coffee, which is served in a big china pot and left on the table. A short, reasonably priced wine list, with good showings of half-bottles.

CHEF: Carla Tomasi PROPRIETORS: Mr and Mrs Quarticelli
OPEN: Mon to Sat, exc Sat L MEALS: 12 to 2.30, 6 to 11.30
PRICES: Set L and D from £11·50 (£16) CARDS: Access, Amex, Diners, Visa
SEATS: 60. Private parties: 50 main room, 30 private room. Vegetarian meals. Children's helpings. Wheelchair access (1 step). Music

Fuji [11/20] map 13

36–40 Brewer Street, W1R 3HP
01-734 0957/8 £15–£29

A small Japanese cafe that does not give the same attention to detail as you might find in Tokyo, for example, but the sashimi is of high quality, if expensive. The clear soups and the tempura, notably the prawns, are excellent, and for dessert fresh pineapple is served with a glass of plum wine. The full range of cooking is done, including shabu-shabu, teriyaki and sushi. Good saké at £1·80 a flagon. There is also an unusual lemon liqueur called Midori.

CHEF: Shoji Kuroyanagi PROPRIETOR: Hisashi Taoka
OPEN: all week, exc Sat and Sun L MEALS: 12.30 to 2.30, 6 to 10.45
PRICES: £11 (£15), Set L and D £12 to £26 (£15 to £29). Cover 20p L, 40p D. Minimum £8 at D. Service inc CARDS: Access, Amex, Diners, Visa
SEATS: 55. Private parties: 20 main room. Vegetarian meals by arrangement. No children under 5. Wheelchair access. Music

Fung Shing [13/20] map 13

15 Lisle Street, WC2H 7BE
01-437 1539 £11–£18

Of all the Cantonese restaurants in London this is the one in which we have most confidence. There are carnations on the table and *Danny Boy* is likely to come round a couple of times on the sound-system. The long menu is supplemented by specialities written in Chinese that the waiters are happy to explain. Order in advance and chef Fu Kwun will prepare magical winter melon soup, filled with a profusion of meats and fish. Of the many, many alpha dishes eaten, the ones that stay in the mind are the powerful one-pot roast dishes, such as braised belly-pork in winter, or chicken with preserved clam; and the more delicate dishes, such as diced quail with water-chestnut to wrap up in iceberg lettuce leaves. Even the old cliché of sweet-and-sour pork has contrast in texture and taste. Fish is the mainstay of any Cantonese restaurant: scallops are fresh – still alive in their shells in the fridge of the supermarket next door – and steamed with garlic, while huge crabs come with chilli and black bean sauce. Most spectacular of all is the steamed whole sea-bass. Eel is another favourite of the kitchen – grilled and served dry with salt and chilli, or else with coriander. The salt-baked chicken is the finest we have found in London. House French is £4·80 or try the CELLARMAN'S CHOICE: Quincy '83 at £8·20.

CHEF: Fu Kwun PROPRIETORS: Traceflow Ltd
OPEN: all week MEALS: noon to 11.45
PRICES: £10 (£18), Set L and D from £7 (£11). Minimum £6·50 at D. Service 10%
CARDS: Access, Amex, Diners, Visa
SEATS: 85. Private parties: 50 main room, 30 private room. Children welcome. Music. Air-conditioned

Ganpath [10/20]

map 10

372 Grays Inn Road, WC1 8BB
01-278 1938 £4·50–£6

An unpretentious spartan Indian restaurant with one wall oddly decorated with turn-of-the-century French posters. The carefully prepared dishes on the limited menu are served promptly. The onion bhajias are crisp and dry enough to need the accompanying coconut-based yoghourt, but the sag josh and the lemon rice are excellent, so too the masala dosai, and bhuna chicken with lemon rice, green bananas and bhindi. Poppadums to nibble, and coconut, lime and mango chutneys. The kulfi is smooth, and there is black tea or draught Stella Artois to drink. The atmosphere is convivial.

CHEF: K.Gopal PROPRIETOR: Mr Ramalingam
OPEN: Mon to Sat MEALS: 12 to 3, 6 to 10.15 (10.45 Fri and Sat)
PRICES: £4 (£6), Set L from £4 (£4·50), Set D from £4 (£4·50). Minimum £2. Service inc, set only, alc 10% CARD: Access
SEATS: 44. Private parties: 100 main room. Vegetarian meals. Children welcome Wheelchair access. Music. Self-service

Le Gavroche [17/20]

map 12

43 Upper Brook Street, W1Y 1PF
01-408 0881 and 499 1826 **Real Food** £24–£46

Like some maturing boxing champion, Le Gavroche shuffles around the ring taking on all comers, amid speculation that it is over-the-hill or out of condition. And then bang – it releases the explosive, knockout punch. Make no mistake, this restaurant is in its prime and if it only fights for high stakes, that's the champion's privilege. There are no tricks, just an honest attempt to serve the finest food in the finest restaurant. The style of cooking is interesting. It is cream and butter-based but hardly bears the description of *nouvelle cuisine* at all. Its parentage is closer to the style of George Perry-Smith (see Helford) than, say, one of the modern French chefs. Its roots are in the farmhouse and the market. Yes, there is lobster and foie gras, but these are just part of the repertoire and not the be all and end all, or even particularly significant lynch-pins, any more than the watercress soup or the kidneys and sweetbreads with thyme. Typical is the guinea-fowl. The waiter brings it on a huge silver tray, the plate covered by a silver dome. Another waiter removes the dome to show the dish to the whole table, then puts it back. It is a big driving-wheel of a plate. The neatly sliced breast is laid down one side, still with its skin on and crisp, like a Cantonese version. The boned thigh sits on the other side covering a cake of potato and surrounded by a garden of turned vegetables. A little juice flavoured with an igniting basil and lemon sauce is on the plate, and a small sauceboat with more is left on the table. There are no frills. Everything is meant to be eaten.

The prices are fantastic. One bottle of wine went up £40 in a couple of months – Ch. La Mission-Haut–Brion '61, now £840 for a magnum – and fish soup or cheese are both £8-plus. But is a mark of respect that people are actually prepared to pay for this kind of food and wine. The five-course *menu exceptionnel,* at £30 a head inclusive of VAT and service, is now the cheapest way through a meal at night, though lunch is only £19·50 and tables are easy to get without booking months ahead. An unfortunate by-product of the restaurant's fame is that it has been hijacked by its own reputation and has lost many of its regulars – eased out by pressure on tables. It would be a great thing if bookings were restricted to a week ahead to let back in the faithful, rather than the sightseers. Because this is not a museum, but a place to eat.

Nonetheless, sights there are to see – a turban of sole and salmon fillets wrapped together with, in the centre, a ragout of shellfish; a lobster mousse wrapped in a leaf of spinach with a beurre blanc and garnished with lobster and beluga caviare; more simple, but no less effective, cotelettes d'agneau à la milanaise; or blanquette de veau à l'estragon. The specials of the day are where the real creative force takes off, and they lend the menu an acceleration that would not be there if it stayed with the old, established and rather rich vein of the caneton Gavroche (a variation on pressed duck) or soufflé suissesse (a cheese soufflé on cream). For all the fuss made of other places using lighter, 'healthier' cooking it is interesting to note the theme that appears here which would follow the guidelines from either the National Advisory Committee on Nutrition Education or the Committee on Medical Aspects of Food Policy – sea-bream with a vinaigrette with tarragon, coriander, basil and served with fresh fennel. And then there are the sweets which ought to be eaten, even by people who do not usually eat sweets. The assiette du chef is a wonder of vivid colours and microchip-sized culinary technology – a tiny sablé aux fraises (sometimes not as good as the eight-inch diameter big brother version); délice aux cassis; chocolate truffle cake; tartelette framboise; cape gooseberry; and, in the centre in an almond tuile, the smoothest scoop of honey and cognac ice-cream. The petits fours follow on with macaroons, tuiles, brandy-snaps, chocolate truffles and orchids. All the while the service is unobtrusive – but borders on the smile of someone who knows they are just about to give something you have never had before.

Perfection it is not quite – the lamb could usefully be hung a week longer, and there is a young kitchen brigade, which can mean that some parts of the menu do not have the same technical verve, but above all the restaurant has retained its personality; its notoriety has galvanised rather than corrupted it. Albert Roux is still in the kitchen most nights and not gallivanting around the world or at some lucrative publicity gambit. Even the wine list now has half-bottles at £4, £5 and £6, which means that it is possible to dine without a financial Exocet missile coming in the shape of an overpriced vintage claret. All things considered, the mark-ups are not unfair and the sommelier gives sound advice without playing roulette with your money. And there are some wonderful wines in the £20 bracket. If vintage calvados and cognac at £8 a go sound exorbitant, at least a measure is poured in the glass for smelling and tasting like wine, and then the glass is properly filled – as a friend would do, with a measure that is twice as much as you wanted.

CHEF: A.H. Roux PROPRIETORS: Le Gavroche Ltd
OPEN: Mon to Fri CLOSED: 23 Dec to 2 Jan MEALS: 12 to 2, 7 to 11
PRICES: £39 (£46), Set L £19·50 (£24), Set D £30 (£37). Minimum £30 at D. Service inc
CARDS: Access, Amex, Carte Blanche, Diners, Visa
SEATS: 60. Private parties: 10 main room, 20 private room. No children under 8. Jacket and tie. No pipes in dining-room. Air-conditioned

Gavvers [12/20] map 11

61–63 Lower Sloane Street, SW1W 8DH
01-730 5983 **Real Food** £18·25

The KGB probably don't use Gavvers very much – the tables are close together and it's difficult not to be overheard. But it's still one of the most popular French restaurants in London. The tan and brown low-ceilinged dining-room feels smart despite the crush, and the menu – inclusive of Kir, half a bottle of wine and petits fours – is varied and good value. Some dishes are often out-takes from a higher level of cooking; the black pudding from Normandy served with apples; duck breast with cherries soaked in alcohol; pigeon with prunes; and the chocolate truffle cake to finish. Other dishes are in the more fashionable vein of, say, salmon with sorrel. The service is young, French and in training for Le Gavroche. The wines included in the price make good drinking. Cheese is extra.

CHEF: Denis Lobry PROPRIETORS: Roux Restaurants Ltd
OPEN: Mon to Sat, D only MEALS: 7 to 11
PRICES: Set D £18·25. Service inc CARD: Diners
SEATS: 80. Children welcome. Wheelchair access. Air-conditioned

Gay Hussar [13/20] map 13

2 Greek Street, W1V 6NB
01-437 0973 **Real Food** £13–£20

After 33 years it is easy to overlook the fact that the Hungarian cooking here is not just exceptional value for money but of exceptional quality. More than a hundred dishes – which is virtually the whole menu – were recommended by readers and inspectors in three months last winter – quenelles of hare with game sauce; grilled brill with tartare sauce; liver with onions and paprika; roast suckling pig. Victor Sassie is increasingly taking a back seat to enjoy his well-earned retirement, otherwise the rating would have been raised to 14. The principles on which the restaurant is run are the best – goose is smoked in-house, the service is helpful without being fussy, and the menu changes with the markets. Mr Sassie has kept alive a cuisine that might otherwise have vanished. As well as the red cabbage and the lentils that hold up the cuisine, there is a subtlety amid the big portions that is the mark of a great kitchen: breast of wild duck is served sliced on pâté on toast with the legs on the side of the plate, and hare is cooked as a fillet, seared quickly for four and a half minutes, then sliced and served rare. Regulars take some dissuading from the jellied borshch and the cold pike with beetroot sauce and cucumber. To finish at Christmas, handsome pudding; otherwise the poppyseed strudel and the hot lemon dumplings with plum sauce are both excellent. Clarets are of good vintages, the Tokays go back to the 1900s, but for everyday drinking the CELLARMAN'S CHOICE is Cabernet Sauvignon, from Vilányi in Hungary, at £5.

CHEF: Leslie Hollecz PROPRIETOR: Victor Sassie
OPEN: Mon to Sat MEALS: 12.30 to 2, 5.30 to 10.30
PRICES: £14 (£20), Set L £9 (£13). Cover 50p
SEATS: 35. Children's helpings (Sat L only). Wheelchair access. Air-conditioned

Genevieve [10/20]

map 12

13 Thayer Street, W1M 5DL
01-935 5023

£14–£19

Good plain food is to be found in this pleasant restaurant. Any temptation to tart it up is resisted, which works well – eggs Benedict have been poached precisely, placed on a toasted muffin with, usually, a slice of tongue and covered with a sharp hollandaise; watercress soup tastes authentic without being adulterated with cream. Fish has been conspicuously well reported – brill with an hollandaise, and sea-bass with fennel. Sometimes dishes seem to have been left waiting in the kitchen, which does not help the vegetables or the pastry – but for this the rating would be higher. A trip to the merchant to lay in a few more wines would be welcome. House Blanc de Blancs from Duboeuf is £5·50.

CHEFS: Graham Kitch and Lawrence Benson PROPRIETORS: Kennedy Brookes plc
OPEN: Mon to Fri MEALS: 12.15 to 3, 6 to 11
PRICES: £12 (£19), Set L £9·50 (£14), Set D £9·50 (£14). Service 15% CARDS: Access, Amex, Carte Blanche, Diners, Visa
SEATS: 50. 4 tables outside. Private parties: 10 main room. Children welcome. Wheelchair access (also ladies' WC). Air-conditioned

Ginnan [new entry, zero rated]

map 10

5 Cathedral Place, EC4M 7EA
01-236 4120

£9–£20

Classical Japanese cuisine of the highest order, using immaculately fresh ingredients cooked with great care and beautifully presented, is found here. There are unusual variations on standard dishes, particularly on the daily menu written in Japanese. Chef Mr Shimakage cooks to banquet standard but as a restaurant it is relatively cheap, the atmosphere is relaxed, and non-Japanese are welcome. The £18 set meal is almost enough for two – a rectangular plate of five appetisers; clear picturesque soup; sashimi; a fat slice of grilled salmon brushed with a sweet brown glaze and served on a lettuce leaf with a pink turnip cut into a chrysanthemum shape; simmered fish and aubergine; tempura; and finally rice

'We both ordered artichoke hearts filled with asparagus tips and sauce hollandaise. The waiter brought it and, on seeing there were two of us, gave me the artichokes and my friend the asparagus. We shared the hollandaise.' (On eating in a luxury London hotel)

with three pickles. Also notable have been the eel sushi; raw beef; and the fried oysters. Lunch is a bargain but the alcohols are not. More reports, please.

CHEF: Mr Shimakage PROPRIETOR: Mr Togo
OPEN: Mon to Sat, exc Sat D CLOSED: bank hols MEALS: 12 to 2.30, 6 to 10
PRICES: £13 (£18), Set L £5 (£9), Set D from £16 (£20). Service inc set only CARDS: Access, Amex, Diners, Visa
SEATS: 50. Private parties: 20 main room, 10 private room. Children welcome. Japanese music. Air-conditioned

Golden Chopsticks [new entry, zero rated] map 11

1 Harrington Road, SW7 3ES
01-584 0855 and 581 8951 £14

Mr Choy, who was the guiding hand behind the Diamond in Lisle Street when it was one of the first and best Cantonese restaurants in Chinatown, seven or eight years ago, is involved in this fashionable Chinese restaurant. It is a smart box of a room with ice-blue carpet and matching upholstery, and the tables are laid with big claret glasses and golden dragon chopstick rests. It is an ambitious menu, roaming across China with the emphasis in the south, but taking in the famous north and western dishes, such as duck, which is served both Peking-style and tea-smoked in the Szechuan manner. Two of three inspection meals were brilliant and it is to be hoped the influence remains Hong Kong and not South Kensington. The chefs, at least, are from Hong Kong and the non-westernised dishes are best – seafood and silver fungus soup; fried Peking dumplings (being the kind that are stuffed with pork, half steamed, then sauté on the other side, sometimes known as Shanghai dumplings); spare ribs with salt and pepper; excellent stir-fried shredded crispy beef in chilli; and equally good stewed bean curd with crab-meat. The Yam Bird's Nest is filled with whole prawns, thick pieces of scallop, large black Chinese mushrooms, and carrots cut into butterfly shapes, all stir-fried to get the fragrant effect that only restaurants with their fierce burners and constant wokfuls of hot oil can achieve with any ease. Ask for the seasonal vegetables in oyster sauce. The mixed rice has been first-class. Finish with a small glass of potent Mei Kuei Lu, rose petal alcohol. More reports, please.

CHEF: Mr Wong PROPRIETORS: Elbest Ltd
OPEN: all week MEALS: 12 to 2.30, 6 to 11.30 (11 Sun)
PRICES: £6 (£14). Cover 50p. Service 15% CARDS: Access, Amex, Diners, Visa
SEATS: 75. Children welcome. Music. Air-conditioned

Gonbei [10/20] map 10

151 Kings Cross Road, WC1X 9BN
01-278 0619 £16

A middle-range Japanese restaurant close to the Scala cinema, with paper lanterns lit up in the window at night. The dining-room is small and divided by wood screens, and there are large traditional comic masks on the walls. The waitresses have good English and are welcoming to non-Japanese customers. It is a good place to eat inexpensive noodle dishes, though the fact that it is not as expensive as other Japanese restaurants is reflected in the quality of the ingredients. Nevertheless, the food is more than acceptable. The miso soup is freshly made with cubes of white tofu, fine slices of spring onion, and a cloud of sweet/salty white miso. Tempura is served in a wicker basket on a white napkin folded into a crane. Assorted sushi – there is a bar at the back chiefly of interest for its variety – is eleven pieces of different raw fish pressed on to white rice. Lunch is cheaper than dinner. Japanese tea. Licensed.

CHEF: Mr Ogura PROPRIETOR: Uno Toyana
OPEN: Mon to Sat, D only CLOSED: 2 weeks at Christmas MEALS: 6 to 10.30
PRICES: £11 (£16)
SEATS: 26. Private parties: 10 main room, 16 private room. Children welcome. Wheelchair access. Japanese music

Good Friends [9/20]

map 9

139 Salmon Lane, E14 7PG
01-987 5541 and 5498

£15

Adjacent to nineteenth-century dockland in London's original Chinatown, source of Sherlock Holmes's opium. The Good Friends has been here since 1963 but is now run by the young brothers of the original owner and has been revamped and expanded. The menu has not changed and still offers 150 Cantonese dishes in a choice of sizes. The soups and the fish dishes are noticeably the best, especially the stuffed bean curd with prawns. The Singapore noodles are Anglicised but there is crystallized ginger to finish. A little less monosodium glutamate would help. Jasmine tea.

CHEFS: Wah Moon Cheung and Wah Tong Cheung PROPRIETORS: Cheung Brothers Co. Ltd
OPEN: all week MEALS: noon to midnight
PRICES: £10 (£15). Minimum £6. Service 10%. Unlincensed, but bring your own: corkage 25p CARDS: Access, Amex, Diners, Visa
SEATS: 100. Private parties: 80 main room. Vegetarian meals. Children welcome. Wheelchair access. Music. Air-conditioned

Gordon's Wine Bar [9/20]

map 12

47 Villiers Street, WC2N 6NE
01-930 1408

£7

If this is not the oldest wine bar in London it certainly feels like it, tucked up in the dark cellars under Villiers Street with bottles stored behind a locked grille that looks like something out of Madame Tussaud's and with dusty memorabilia that harks back to the 1940s and before. It gets very crowded and the tables wobble, but the food, prepared by Michael Smith, is a model of what can be done in a small area – smoked chicken, genuine terrines, hams, Spanish omelettes, vegetable moussaka, and good cheeses are laid out for show, much as food would have been dispensed here 100 years ago. Half a dozen fresh salads and dressings are there for you to help yourself, the only limitation being the size of the plate. Tables are put outside the moment the sun shines. They owe themselves a few better bottles of wine, but the white Rioja at £5·35 is good drinking.

CHEF: Michael Smith PROPRIETOR: Luis Gordon
OPEN: Mon to Fri MEALS: 12.15 to 2.45, 5.45 to 8
PRICES: £5 (£7)
SEATS: 80. 12 tables outside. Private parties: 24 main room. Vegetarian meals. Children's helpings. Self-service

Govinda's [8/20] map 13

9 Soho Street, W1V 5DA
01-437 3662 £5

There are no onions in the salad in case they incite passions, but this International Society for Krishna Consciousness self-service restaurant is remarkably cheap and centrally placed. There's no smoking, no meat, no fish, no eggs, no alcohol, but the vegetarian dishes are imaginative. The pizzas and salads are good, and, to finish, the fruit salad and the orange cake would not disgrace a proper restaurant. The chanting is unobtrusive and calm prevails. Service is thoughtful and does not try to convert.

CHEF: Christine Forster PROPRIETORS: Intl Soc. for Krishna Consciousness
OPEN: Mon to Sat CLOSED: Christmas MEALS: 11.30 to 8
PRICES: £4 (£5). Unlicensed
SEATS: 80. 3 tables outside. Private parties: 80 main room. Vegetarian meals. Children's helpings. No smoking. Wheelchair access. Indian music. Self-service

Grahame's Seafare [8/20] map 12

38 Poland Street, W1V 3DA
01-437 3788 and 0975 £14

A popular Jewish restaurant two minutes' walk from Oxford Circus. The fish comes from Billingsgate daily: 70 per cent is fried, and the smoked salmon is excellent. Frascati is £5·20.

CHEF/PROPRIETOR: Robert Dehaan
OPEN: Mon to Sat CLOSED: 2 weeks at Christmas MEALS: 12 to 2.45, 5.30 to 8.45 (7.45 Sat)
PRICES: £10 (£14). Cover 50p at D CARDS: Amex, Visa
SEATS: 90. Vegetarian meals. Children's helpings. Wheelchair access. Air-conditioned

Green Cottage II [new entry, zero rated] map 10

122A Finchley Road, NW3 5HT
01-794 3833 £14–£15

The only restaurant in London serving wholly vegetarian Chinese food. It offers a representative selection of dishes found in China and Hong Kong restaurants, most of them with meat substitutes (Buddhist monks are forbidden meat) made of gluten, bean curd and bean curd skin. The cooking is inventive and makes use of unusual ingredients, like dried fungi. The surprising thing is the lack of vegetables. Good dishes have been vegetable sausage; sweet-and-sour 'pork' which is in fact gluten; My Favourite Tofu; and fried noodles with mixed vegetables. It is not exactly healthy food, given the colouring agents, levels of monosodium glutamate and the amount of oil in use. Service can be off-hand. More reports, please.

CHEFS: Mr Wong and Mr Lok PROPRIETORS: Brunelcrete Ltd
OPEN: all week, exc Tue MEALS: 12 to 3, 6 to 11.30
PRICES: £9 (£15), Set L and D from £8 (£14). Service 10% CARDS: Access, Amex, Diners
SEATS: 80. Private parties: 100 main room. Vegetarian meals. Children welcome. Wheelchair access (also WC). Music. Air-conditioned

The Greenhouse [12/20]

map 12

27A Hay's Mews, W1X 7RJ
01-499 3331

£18

The reassuring thing about the food here is the feeling that it is meant to be eaten and not photographed. None of the chairs match, and an old upright piano has been disembowelled and is used for cutlery – nonetheless the table settings are smart and it is a pretty room. The menu is essentially franglais with warming soups for winter, such as red lentil with diced bacon; whole racks of lamb ('we serve it pink, sir, is that all right?'); and ragout of langoustines, scallops and mussels with baby vegetables and a sauce that owes more to cream than alcohol. The salads are excellent and there is traditional rice pudding with strawberry jam to finish. The short wine list owes a lot to northern France (Muscadet, Chablis, Pouilly-Fumé), while the reds are classically clarets and burgundies.
CELLARMAN'S CHOICE: Ch. du Lyonnat, Lussac-St Emilion'79 at £10·75.

CHEF: Nigel Davis PROPRIETORS: Capital Hotels (Mayfair) Ltd
OPEN: Mon to Sat, exc Sat L MEALS: 12 to 2.30, 7 (7.30 Sat) to 11
PRICES: £12 (£18). Cover 50p CARDS: Access, Amex, Diners, Visa
SEATS: 85. Private parties: 12 main room. Children welcome. Smart dress preferred. Wheelchair access (also WC). Air-conditioned

Green Leaves [11/20]

map 10

77 York Street, W1H 1PQ
01-262 8164

£14–£25

Mr Tao makes his own wine from glutinous rice, which gives the sauces an unusual slant in his small, quiet Peking/Szechuan restaurant. The set meals are good value but especially fine are the lobster, crab, or prawns in garlic and ginger sauce. Other good dishes have been the crispy fried beef with carrots, crispy duck, and diced chicken with chilli sauce. House French is £4·80.

CHEF/PROPRIETOR: H.S.Tao
OPEN: Mon to Sat, exc Sat L MEALS: 12 to 2.30, 6 to 11
PRICES: £9 (£17), Set L and D from £10 to £20 (£14 to £25). Service 10% CARDS: Access, Amex, Diners, Visa
SEATS: 32. 2 tables outside. Vegetarian meals. Children welcome. Music. Air-conditioned

Green's Champagne and Oyster Bar [12/20]

map 12

36 Duke Street, St James's, SW1Y 6BR
01-930 4566 and 1376

£24

Dwarfed by the grey, modern monolith of the Cavendish Hotel and no further from Fortnum and Mason than a dozen hampers laid end to end, are the cream Edwardian pillars and elegant gold and black insignia of this haunt of the racing fraternity. Green's is a public club – a pin-striped atmosphere as old-fashioned English as Osbert Lancaster, but run with the panache of a modern French restaurant. The mahogany panelling around the walls is decorated with old cartoons such as 'May the pleasures of the evening bear the morning's reflection'. To one side is the marble-topped bar for champagne and oysters, to the other is the airy, if tightly packed, dining-room where the cooked lobsters are piled high on the bar. The white-jacketed waiter asks casually if sir/madam would like a glass of champagne? There is a short, English menu of bangers and mash, fish-cakes and treacle tart as well as the fish on which its reputation rests – crabs, oysters and salmon, all fresh, un-messed about, and of a very high standard. The place is crowded at lunchtime but less so at night. House Blanc de Blancs is only £3·80, or try the CELLARMAN'S CHOICE: Ch. de la Rivière '79 at £8·50.

CHEFS: Beth Coventry and Amanda Mathews PROPRIETOR: Simon Parker Bowles
OPEN: Mon to Fri MEALS: 11.30 to 3, 5.30 to 10.45
PRICES: £19 (£24) CARDS: Access, Amex, Diners, Visa
SEATS: 110. Private parties: 60 main room, 20 and 10, private rooms. Children welcome. Wheelchair access. Air-conditioned

Hana Guruma [12/20]

map 10

49 Bow Lane, EC4M 9DL
01-236 6451

£17–£28

This is a very fine restaurant and is purposefully Japanese, from the whisky bottles kept for regulars (with their names written on them) to the fact that you have to say goodbye to everyone as you leave. There is a sushi bar and the sushi is spectacular, especially the roe of salmon set on rice and wrapped in seaweed, and the prawn eggs. Eat at the bar overlooking the kitchen or at a table. The dozen set meals appear more daunting than they are, because the only variations tend to be at main course. Eels are a speciality and fish soup is served in a kettle. Fresh orange to finish. Service is impeccable.

CHEFS: A. Takeuchi and S. Ohshima PROPRIETOR: S.Hyodo
OPEN: Mon to Fri CLOSED: 25 Dec, Jan MEALS: 12 to 2.30, 6 to 11
PRICES: £9 (£17), Set L from £22 (£28) CARDS: Access, Amex, Diners, Visa
SEATS: 172. Private parties: 45 main room, 10 private room. Children welcome. Wheelchair access. Japanese music. Air-conditioned

Han Kuk Hoe Kwan [10/20]

map 12

2 Lowndes Court, Carnaby Street, W1V 1PP
01-437 3313

£6–£13

In Korea the kim-chee – Chinese cabbage pickled in chilli and garlic – is marinated for two to three months, but at this small restaurant it is kept for only a couple of days. Even so, the Mint Imperials with the bill are a needed antidote to its pungency. For the main the food is not overly spicy by Korean standards, and the classic cornerstones of the cookery are well handled – bracken shoots in sesame and soy; Korean pizza with oysters and spring onions; bulgogi, the beef cooked in a flat, ribbed iron pan over a gas stovelette; sauté vegetables with shrimps and beef. The rice is gummy and comes in lidded stainless-steel dishes. There is barley tea to drink or jungjong, the Korean version of saké.

CHEF: K.C.Park PROPRIETOR: W.C.Park
OPEN: Mon to Sat MEALS: 12 to 2.30, 6 to 11
PRICES: £8 (£12), Set L from £3 (£6), Set D from £10 (£13). Service 10% CARDS: Access, Amex, Diners, Visa
SEATS: 100. Private parties: 15 main room. Vegetarian meals. Music

Hard Rock Café [10/20]

map 12

150 Old Park Lane, W1Y 3LN
01-629 0382

£12

The queues are extraordinary – even in the pouring rain. The Hard Rock has earned cult status among teenagers with the opening of the New York branch, and almost as many T-shirts as hamburgers are sold. The buns have changed, not necessarily for the better, but between them is charcoal-grilled prime beef – still undisputed as the best hamburgers this side of the Atlantic. A new addition is the pork sandwich, from the Deep South. Sweets are from the soda fountain. The waitresses, the rock-and-roll memorabilia and the loud 1960s and 1970s music are an irresistible force. The good times roll.

PROPRIETORS: Hard Rock Café plc
OPEN: all week MEALS: noon to 12.30am (1am Fri and Sat)
PRICES: £9 (£12). Minimum £3·05. Service 10%
SEATS: 100. 12 tables outside. Vegetarian meals. Children welcome. Smart dress preferred. Wheelchair access. Rock music. Air-conditioned

Hee's [9/20]

map 9

27 The Broadway, NW7 3DA
01-959 7109 and 0028

£15–£18

The specialities in this smart Peking restaurant are crispy lamb with lettuce, deep-fried shredded beef with chilli, and sizzling fillet steak. Handy after a hard drive down the A1. House French is £5·50.

CHEF: Man Ching Ma PROPRIETOR: Thony Lee
OPEN: all week MEALS: 12 to 2, 6 to 11
PRICES: £10 (£18), Set L and D from £9·50 (£15). Service 12.5% CARDS: Access, Amex, Diners, Visa
SEATS: 120. Private parties: 150 main room, 50 private room. Vegetarian meals. Children welcome. Jacket and tie preferred. Music. Air-conditioned

Hiders [new entry, zero rated]

map 9

755 Fulham Road, SW6 5UU
01-736 2331

£15–£17

This is a good business – fast, fancy *nouvelle cuisine*-style dishes artfully presented in spacious, Edwardian-style dining-rooms at the set price of £11 for two courses, but including canapés and coffee with chocolate truffles. Duck breast is elegantly fanned out with a sauce of its juices; noisettes of lamb are served with a wine sauce flavoured with basil and lemon. To finish there is a symphony of white, milk and bitter chocolate mousses. Service is fast and friendly and the dozen wines will be familiar. House French is £4·95.

CHEFS: Paul Duvall and Andrew George PROPRIETORS: Richard and Hilary Griggs
OPEN: Mon to Sat, exc Sat L CLOSED: Christmas, bank hols, 2 weeks Aug
MEALS: 12.30 to 2.30, 7.30 to 11.30
PRICES: Set L and D £11 to £12·50 (£15 to £17). Service 12.5% CARDS: Access, Amex, Visa
SEATS: 70. Private parties: 40 main room. Children welcome. Wheelchair access. Music

Hilaire [14/20] map 11

68 Old Brompton Road, SW7 3LQ
01-584 8993 £15–£24

Now that Chez Nico has left town this is the clear alternative. Simon Hopkinson's joy in cooking manifests itself in a set-price menu that changes almost daily with the markets. If he does not always succeed by the standards of a 15-point calibre restaurant it is because he is off on to a new dish before finalising an old. Hilaire would not be out of place, or empty, in Paris. Typical of the cooking – which is a mix of the classical, regional, and modern, indeed just about anything French – was the New Year's Eve dinner, a simple unfestive night without the seasonal trimmings but a six-course menu of duck consommé, reduced over five days to an almost black intensity; scallops with a sweet, fish stock sauce, truffles and cream; marinated salmon with pickled vegetables; a single, very rich roundel of foie gras pâté; venison, served rare with chestnuts, or guinea-fowl with cranberry; finishing with Stilton and sweets off the usual menu. A glass of champagne and one of port were included in the £30 price. On other days the menu stays at three courses, with lunch half the choice, and almost half the price, of dinner. Dishes are allowed to taste of themselves – foie gras terrine with a mâche salad dressed in walnut oil; breaded and fried sweetbreads; Challans duck with lime. In the fish department a mustard sauce has been served with John Dory, salmon and brill. Sometimes the combustion of dishes just does not happen, but on the other hand the diversity is remarkable. To finish, the bavarois still wobble and the chocolate marquise is intense. The calm, unhurried atmosphere can sometimes extend to the service and some of the waiters for reasons best known to themselves insist on talking French. The good wines can push up the bill, but the list has been galvanised and now includes some cheaper bottles.

CHEF: Simon Hopkinson PROPRIETORS: Kennedy Brookes plc
OPEN: Mon to Sat, exc Sat L MEALS: 12.30 to 2.30, 7.30 to 11.30
PRICES: Set L £10·50 (£15), Set D £18·50 (£24) CARDS: Access, Amex, Diners, Visa
SEATS: 50. Private parties: 16 main room. Children's helpings. Classical music. Air-conditioned

R.S. Hispaniola [10/20] map 12

Victoria Embankment, WC2
01-839 3011 £17–£25

The best restaurant on a boat in the capital. Sometimes the food is surprisingly good and the kitchen keeps working until 1.30am – for the disco that starts at 10pm. The menu is fashionable and, apart from one disastrous Sunday lunch, all reports are in favour. Notable have been the vegetable feuilletés to start; the excellent rack of lamb garnished with oysters and served with a shiny sauce of reduced lamb stock with eau-de-vie; and the fine sweets. Granary rolls are freshly baked. When the sun comes out a table outside offers one of the most pleasant

'The meringue was standard high street cake shop – the texture of sweetened pumice stone.' (On eating in London)

vantage points on the Thames. Service is slow and there is no great understanding of wine. House Spanish is £5.

CHEF: Mark Lindsay PROPRIETORS: Yardarm Club Ltd
OPEN: all week, exc Sat L MEALS: 12 to 2, 7 to 10 (1.30 Upper Deck)
PRICES: £16 (£25), Set L £11·50 (£17). Cheaper set L & D available for parties over 8. Cover £1. Minimum £15. Service 12.5% on parties over 6 CARDS: Access, Diners, Visa
SEATS: 180. 10 tables outside. Private parties: 200 main room, 100 private room. Vegetarian meals. Children welcome. Smart dress preferred. Pianist. Air-conditioned

Hodja Nasreddin [9/20]

map 10

53 Newington Green Road, N1 4QU
01-226 7757

£11

An inexpensive little Turkish cafe doing authentic dishes, such as sucuk in hot sauce. The wines are Turkish, too, and there is raki to drink as well as Turkish coffee liqueurs.

CHEF/PROPRIETOR: Halil Bedir
OPEN: all week MEALS: noon to 2.30
PRICES: £6 (£11). Minimum £2·75 CARDS: Access, Amex, Diners, Visa
SEATS: 45. Private parties: 20 main room, 25 private room. Children's helpings. Wheelchair access. Turkish music

Ho-Ho [11/20]

map 9

20 High Road, South Woodford, E18 2QL
01-989 8021 and 1041

£8–£18

Still looks like the Italian restaurant it used to be – black-beamed roof, white walls and arches – but with a few Chinese pictures among the greenery as reminders of the origins of the food. The menu is Peking/Szechuan with a few Nonya dishes thrown in for good measure, including a spicily hot version of laksa soup. The cooking is not as classy or as consistent as the excellent service and the decor promise it to be but even so there are interesting and well-judged dishes to eat. Orange chicken; prawn wun-tun; crispy duck; spectacular Shantung, shredded, pan-smoked chicken with garlic sauce; and toffee apples, have all been good. Fish is fresh and a speciality, and there is a range of vegetarian dishes. House French is £4·95.

CHEF: Yuk Chu PROPRIETOR: Steve Man
OPEN: all week MEALS: 12 to 2.30, 6 to 11
PRICES: £10 (£18), Set L from £4·50 (£8), Set D from £10 (£14). Service 12.5%
CARDS: Access, Amex, Diners, Visa
SEATS: 80. 2 tables outside. Private parties: 60 main room. Vegetarian meals. Children welcome. Jacket and tie preferred. Wheelchair access (also wc). Chinese music. Air-conditioned

Ho-Ho [11/20]

map 12

29 Maddox Street, W1R 9LD
01-493 1228

£12–£19

A jack-of-all-trades, inter-regional Chinese restaurant of the new school. The decor has been revamped with polished wooden floor, tall standing 1930s-style spot-lights, pink table-cloths and framed photographs of 1920s and 1930s China. The 80-item menu emphasises Peking, Szechuan and Singapore dishes. The food suffers from some Westernisation – the drunken fish is really just tipsy, but even so the food is good, from hot-and-sour soup to fried beef with carrots and chilli; scallops in black bean sauce; or shredded pork in a fragrant sauce; to glazed toffee bananas. The wine list has been assembled with an eye to the cuisine and includes two '83 Alsace wines from Willy Gisselbrecht that go well with the food for £6 and £8.

CHEF: Lok Sing Yuen PROPRIETORS: Simon Tong and Hiu Fei Yuen
OPEN: Mon to Sat MEALS: 12 to 3, 6 to 10.45
PRICES: £11 (£19), Set L £8 (£12). Service 12.5% CARDS: Access, Amex, Diners, Visa
SEATS: 80. Private parties: 60 main room, 40 private room. Children welcome. Wheelchair access. Music. Air-conditioned

Hoults [new entry, zero rated]

map 9

20 Bellevue Road, SW17 7EB
01-767 1858

£15

A popular wine bar-cum-restaurant with some unusually ambitious dishes – wild duck with cassis and raspberry sauce; salmon hollandaise; crab with lime mayonnaise; and chicken with mango and ginger. There are even tomato-skin rose garnishes. Vin de pays is £4·50. More reports, please.

CHEF: Richard Crisp PROPRIETORS: Alex Campbell and Richard Hoult
OPEN: all week CLOSED: Christmas MEALS: 12 to 2.30, 7 to 10.30
PRICES: £9 (£15). Special daily bargain dish. Service 12.5% CARDS: Access, Amex, Visa
SEATS: 115. 8 tables outside. Private parties: 8 main room, 10 private room. Vegetarian meals. Children's helpings. Wheelchair access. Music

Hung Toa [10/20]

map 10

54 Queensway, W2 3RY
01-727 6017

£9–£14

Rather than order a selection of dishes stay with the roast meats, rice and noodles if you want a very cheap meal. The roast duck is said to be as good as in Hong Kong. Also good are the pork dishes with fine crackling, and the spare ribs. Licensed.

CHEF: Mr Wong PROPRIETORS: Geron Glen Ltd
OPEN: all week MEALS: noon to 11
PRICES: £7 (£14), Set L from £5·50 (£9). Service 10%. Licensed, plus bring your own: corkage £1
SEATS: 65. Private parties: 30 main room. Vegetarian meals. Children welcome. Wheelchair access

Ikkyu [new entry, zero rated]

map 12

67 Tottenham Court Road, W1P 9PA
01-636 9280

£8–£13

This is an unusual Japanese restaurant in that it only does evening meals and offers a menu with fine grilling and some interesting individual dishes, rather than the usual cornerstones of the repertoire. In a basement, it is lit by big square paper lanterns. Part of the room is cut off by a large counter where the chef prepares the food; behind him are a long grill, a saké heating machine, bottles of whisky and beer and a glass case of raw fish. There are high straight-backed stools round the counter, or screened tables. Especially interesting are the tofu steaks for vegetarians; a salad of three kinds of seaweed with prawns and squid, over which the chef pours a dressing of water, bonito, vinegar, soy and saké out of a huge saké bottle; grilled aubergines; and the rolled five-colour vegetables. Meals end with bowls of black cherries or other fresh fruit, and mugs of barley tea. More reports, please.

CHEF/PROPRIETOR: M. Kawaguchi
OPEN: all week, D only MEALS: 6 to 11
PRICES: £7 (£13), Set D £4·50 (£8). Service 10% CARDS: Access, Amex, Diners, Visa
SEATS: 50. Private parties: 50 main room. Vegetarian meals. Children welcome. Wheelchair access. Japanese music. Self-service

India Palace [9/20] map 9

305 High Street North, Manor Park, E12 6SL
01-470 6245 and 4453 £11–£12

On the main street with estate agents and a launderette. As well as tandooris, curries, minced scampi and sizzling dishes there is a good vegetarian thali including bhindi bhaji, muttar paneer and Basmati rice. Bombay mix and orange segments for all.

CHEF: Abdul Malik PROPRIETORS: S. Uddin and R.Uddin
OPEN: all week MEALS: 12 to 3, 6 to 12 (1 Fri and Sat)
PRICES: £7 (£12), Set D from £7 (£11) CARDS: Access, Amex, Diners, Visa
SEATS: 28. Private parties: 28 main room. Vegetarian meals. Children welcome. Music

Inigo Jones [15/20] map 13

14 Garrick Street, WC2E 9BJ
01-836 6456 **Real Food** £23–£40

The 15 per cent service charge added to the bill would buy a meal in more than half the other restaurants in the *Guide*. And yet in a six-month period 107 different dishes were eaten and recommended by readers and inspectors. As a chef Paul Gayler has emerged as one of the few to have fully absorbed the implications of *nouvelle cuisine*. There is a debt to Anton Mosimann at the Dorchester, but in terms of consistency in the dining-room night after night Gayler has the edge on his former teacher. As a restaurant Inigo Jones runs like a finely tuned engine. For that 15 per cent there is no who's-having-the-duck-soup interrupting of conversations. The waiters behave more like doctors at a consultation. And there is a set lunch and pre-theatre dinner up to 7, when it is possible to eat and drink for around £20, which is the smart thing to do.

The food is refined. Everything is served filleted, out of its shell, off the bone. As a style this can lead to a lack of vigour in tastes – a frequent and well-justified criticism of most *nouvelle cuisine*. It requires the flavours to be put back on to the plate via the sauces, made from unsightly items such as bones. Naturally, all this behind-the-scenes activity puts up the bill, but Gayler's skill is in the sauces. He does not mince around – salmon has come with a cream sauce lightly flavoured with smoked bacon; there is a hint of curry to the mouclade of fish; orange and mint flavour a medley of white fish; duck is with nutmeg. Mussels are taken out of their shells and served in a copper pan with a tomato sauce. The portions are small, precise and pictorial – four grilled scallops in a wine reduction sauce come in a bowl with its saucer filled with blue sea-salt for effect. For all the innovation, the cooking very much has its feet on the ground, and there are alpha dishes from other repertoires – fillet steak with oysters, kidneys with juniper berries, and lamb cutlets. Much attention has gone into the minor details – four kinds of fresh bread, including excellent black bread; different vegetables depending on the main course; a pungent, heroic cheeseboard. For sweet the house gives a tiny mousse or sorbet before the main event of mango bavarois with blackcurrant sauce or roast pear in a pastry tuile. One dish that does not make the grade is the apple and raisin pancake, which has tasted as if it has been lying around drying out somewhere before hitting the pan. Mr Gayler's absences from the kitchen are too noticeable, which is a pity, although they do not happen that often. The wine list starts at £9·20 for the house burgundy, rotates regularly, and is an entertainment – albeit at a price – rather than a dusty tome of museum claret meant to impress.

CHEF: Paul Gayler PROPRIETORS: J. Kaeser and P. Ward
OPEN: Mon to Sat, exc Sat L MEALS: 12.30 to 2.30, 5.30 to 11.30
PRICES: £28 (£40), Set L and early D £12·75 (£23). Cover £1·50. Service 15%
CARDS: Access, Amex, Diners, Visa
SEATS: 70. Private parties: 35 main room. Vegetarian meals. Children welcome. Smart dress preferred. Air-conditioned

Interlude de Tabaillau [14/20] map 13

7–8 Bow Street, WC2E 7AH
01-379 6473 and 836 9864 **Real Food** £18·50–£23

Back on form. The loss of a Michelin star and the chastising from this *Guide* last year have improved the service no end. No longer is it reminiscent of a Feydeau farce – instead, waiters fall over themselves to be of use. One black mark remains for some unnecessarily hard selling of the drinks – which are included in the price, but often no one tells you so. Jean-Louis Taillebaud's cooking seems also to have caught a new breath, no longer noticeably relying on just two sauces but showing all the signs of a kitchen in creative overdrive; the liver mousse brought to the table still warm and surrounded by a crayfish mousse; an intense red pepper mousse with a basil sauce. Most of Mr Taillebaud's skill is as a *saucier* – there is nothing prissy about the fillets of turbot, red mullet and sole surrounded by a Sauternes cream sauce and garnished with carrots that are still untopped and untailed. The restaurant does not have the pretensions or the polish of the other big three Roux places, but nor does it have the prices. When things go wrong it is, as at Langan's, mostly due to pressure at tables. And for a restaurant doing 130-plus meals a day the level of sophistication is incredible – inlaid tables set with grey floral plates and a jug of water; an array of canapés that included, one night, chicken liver mousse topped with a shrimp in all its armour; the intensity of the chocolate truffles with coffee; not to overlook the chocolate gateau with coffee sauce and a bitter chocolate tuile that is perfection (albeit so rich that it can be a feat to finish it) or the cheeses from Philippe Olivier, their aroma shuffling around the tables like some smelly dog. A lot of cream is used, but not ostentatiously, and the old brickbat concerning the tiny portions of vegetables has also been dealt with – you don't get a lot, but some. The inclusive Muscadet or Côtes du Ventoux are good examples of their species, and presumably only for the purposes of holding a Michelin star is there a swanky, massively expensive list of historic names and vintages which is mercifully academic.

CHEF: Jean-Louis Taillebaud PROPRIETORS: Mr and Mrs Jean-Louis Taillebaud
OPEN: Mon to Sat, exc Sat L CLOSED: 10 days Christmas, Easter, 3 weeks Aug
MEALS: 12 to 2, 7 to 11.30
PRICES: Set L £18·50, Set D £23. Service inc CARDS: Access, Amex, Diners, Visa
SEATS: 45. Children welcome. Smart dress preferred. Wheelchair access (2 steps). Air-conditioned

Jack's Place [9/20] map 9

12 York Road, SW11 3QA
01-228 8519 and 1442 £13

A steak house with quarry-tiled floor and gingham table cloths, situated near the heliport. The portions are enormous and the value for money a big plus – 12oz steaks are served on large platters with a good pepper sauce, or there is equally gigantic grilled Dover sole. Whole trout are served as starters. Bread is ready sliced and buttered. House French is £4·50.

CHEFS/PROPRIETORS: The King family
OPEN: Tue to Sun, exc Sat L and Sun D MEALS: 12 to 2.30, 6.30 to 11
PRICES: £9 (£13). Service 10% CARDS: Access, Diners, Visa
SEATS: 60. Private parties: 30 main room. Vegetarian meals. Children's helpings. Music

Jason's [9/20] map 9

50 Battersea Park Road, SW11 4JP
01-622 6998 £9–£10

A reliable, cheap, hessian-walled Greek restaurant that has been in the family for 13 years. It is good value. The pitta bread is served hot, the afelia is excellent, salads are dressed with good oil and the baklava can be very good. Turkish coffee is 40p; Demestica is £4·35.

CHEF: Mr Michael PROPRIETORS: Costas Georgiou and Nigel Blundell
OPEN: Mon to Sat, D only CLOSED: 2 weeks Aug MEALS: 6.30 to 11.45
PRICES: £5 (£10), Set D £5·35 (£9). Cover 20p
SEATS: 55. Private parties: 35 main room. Children's helpings. Wheelchair access. Greek music

Joy King Lau [new entry, zero rated] map 13

3 Leicester Street, WC2H 7BL
01-437 1132 and 437 2629 £9–£20

An up-market version of the Wong Kei and the bill is proportionately higher. It holds its own in Chinatown without being a star. Standards go up and down through the 200 or so dishes on the menu. Of the dim-sum, the cheung-fun stands out as being good, though it is short on sauce. The sweet-and-sour pork is commendable in that it achieves a contrast of textures, though the vivid appearance suggests the use of artificial colourings. Better is the rather messy-looking chicken with black beans, chillis and green peppers. The service frowns a lot for 12.5 per cent. More reports, please.

CHEF: Lee Ming PROPRIETORS: Mr Ho, Mr Man and Mr Yau
OPEN: all week MEALS: 11am to 11.20pm (10.30am to 10.30pm Sun)
PRICES: £11 (£20), Set D from £5·50 (£9). Service 12.5% CARDS: Amex, Carte Blanche, Diners
SEATS: 250. Private parties: 60 main room, 60 private room. Vegetarian meals. Children welcome. Wheelchair access (also WC). Music

Justin de Blank [9/20] map 12

54 Duke Street, W1M 5DS
01-629 3174 £11

The self-service counter and uncomfortable chairs in Justin de Blank's cafeteria belie the quality of the food. From half-past eight in the morning, when you can have good breakfasts, to nine at night (with only one hour off in the afternoon) the kitchen produces spinach and sorrel soup, carrot loaf in tomato sauce, lamb's kidneys with marjoram and madeira, and fruit tarts. Notably good have been the lamb casseroles; the fishcakes; and the fruit brûlées. The bread, from Mr de Blank's bakery at Vauxhall, is, of course, first-class; salads are too generous for the small plates; and there are at least five cups of tea per pot. Vegetarian dishes are always available. House Rhône is £4·10 or try the CELLARMAN'S CHOICE: Greystone Zinfandel at £4·96.

CHEF: Edwina Gaisford-St Lawrence PROPRIETOR: Justin de Blank
OPEN: Mon to Sat, exc Sat D CLOSED: bank hols MEALS: 8.30 (9 Sat) to 3.30, 4.30 to 9
PRICES: £6 (£11)
SEATS: 60. Private parties: 14 main rooms, 14 and 8 private rooms. Vegetarian meals. Children's helpings. Air-conditioned. Self-service

Kalamaras [12/20] map 10

76–78 Inverness Mews, W2 3JQ
01-727 9122 £15

Greek food in London is being eclipsed by its near-cousin, Lebanese. Stelios Platonos's old favourite, down this quiet mews away from the cosmopolitan hurly-burly of Queensway, stands out as a confident and authentic taverna producing dishes of rather more imagination than a dollop of dyed pink taramosalata. The waitress sits at the table and reels off the menu, which can be perplexing, but beyond the stream of 'Psaria diafora fournou and soutzoukakia Smyrnaikas' come freshly fried aubergines with a powerful garlic dip, slices off a baby lamb cooked with oregano, garlic and lemon, or squid cooked in their own inks. When in doubt, the kitchen usually throws in a bit of nude garlic. To finish there can be bougatsa (filo pastry filled with egg yolk flavoured with vanilla and

'Service: marvellous, happy, cheeky London women; better than any cabaret.'
(On eating in London)

cloves). 'We cook the way our grandmothers cook.' Greek wines and retsinas. It is possible to spend rather more than you expected, but there is a cheaper version down the mews at No. 66 that does inexpensive mezes: it has no licence so take your own bottle.

CHEFS: Stelios and Penelope Platonos PROPRIETOR: Stelios Platonos
OPEN: Mon to Sat, D only MEALS: 6.30 to 12
PRICES: £9 (£15). Cover 95p CARDS: Access, Amex, Diners, Visa
SEATS: 96. Private parties: 12 main room, 28 private room. Vegetarian meals. Children's helpings. Wheelchair access. Greek music. Air-conditioned

Kettners [10/20] map 13

29 Romilly Street, W1V 5TQ
01-437 6437 £9

The most elegant pizza restaurant in the country. The champagne bar has 25 kinds of bubbly. Pizzas are freshly made for the three dining-rooms – one modern and jazzy, the other two discreet and Edwardian. There are steaks and hamburgers too. House Italian wine is reliably good.

CHEF/PROPRIETOR: Peter Boizot
OPEN: all week CLOSED: Christmas Day MEALS: 11am to midnight
PRICES: £8 (£9) CARDS: Access, Amex, Diners, Visa
SEATS: 200. Private parties: 50 private room. Vegetarian meals. Children welcome. Wheelchair access. Pianist

Kitchen Yakitori [12/20] map 12

12 Lancashire Court, New Bond Street, W1Y 9AD
01-409 1303 £4–£12

Good-quality Japanese food is served in this basement at a price which, by Japanese standards, is ridiculously low. The set meals consist of a succession of dishes cooked by different methods – grilling, simmering and so on – in the traditional Japanese order, and offer particularly good value. One meal is almost enough for two. The emphasis is less on fancy cutting methods and rare ingredients, as is often the case in the more expensive Japanese restaurants, and more on flavour, making it particularly suitable for non-Japanese. The atmosphere is pleasant and friendly. Dishes to look for include grilled eel (the speciality); grilled mackerel; fish salad; and tofu steaks served on a hot, black cast-iron plate shaped like a cow. Saké is £2 a tokkurai.

CHEF: George Takabayashi PROPRIETOR: Mr Okada
OPEN: Mon to Sat, exc Sat D CLOSED: bank hols MEALS: 12 to 2.30, 6 to 9.30
PRICES: £7 (£9), Set L from £3·80 (£4), Set D from £8·50 (£12). Service 10%
SEATS: 25. Private parties: 10 main room. Vegetarian meals. Children welcome. Japanese music

'Why does one put up with certain "idiosyncrasies" here that anywhere else would be unacceptable? i.e. a cup of tea brought lukewarm, very milky and swimming with aniseed, flowery bits and other eastern paraphernalia, by a very wobbly waiter, smirking uncontrollably.' (On eating in London)

Knoodles [8/20] map 10

30 Connaught Street, W2 2AF
01-262 9623 £15

A small pasta bar on two floors in a quiet street off Edgware Road, with parquet tiles, paper tablecloths and hanging ferns. It is rather cramped, with the kitchen downstairs. Pasta ranges from spaghetti to North African couscous to Chinese noodles. Have fun with delicately flavoured orange tagliatelle with mushrooms, or chicken and broccoli lasagne. Pasta stir-fried with a lot of vegetables comes with an oyster or fresh ginger sauce; Knoodle roll is a speciality. Pasta is hand made on the premises daily, using a softer flour than is usual in commercial pastas, and items tend to run out late in the evening. Dishes change daily and weekly and include a meat main course, although it is not difficult to be a vegetarian here. The take-away service is well used by locals for dinner parties. House wine is £4·95. CELLARMAN'S CHOICE: Italian Chardonnay '83 at £6·95.

CHEF: Frank Dardenne PROPRIETORS: Loghatch Ltd
OPEN: Mon to Sat MEALS: 12 to 3, 6 to 10.45
PRICES: £9 (£15). Minimum £2. Service 10% CARDS: Access, Amex, Diners, Visa
SEATS: 46. 1 table outside. Private parties: 30 main room. Vegetarian meals. Children's helpings. Music

Korea House [new entry, zero rated] map 12

10 Lancashire Court, New Bond Street, W1Y 9AD
01-493 1340 £9–£22

Bottled ginseng roots are on display at the back of the bar of this downstairs Korean restaurant in the orbit of the Korean embassy. The menu is long and in English with much squid and octopus as well as Korean steak tartare and the usual dishes found in other London Korean restaurants. It is expensive, but portions are large. The kim-chee tastes as if it has fermented for a long time (a compliment) and the beef for the bulgogi is cooked rare – 'the best way to show off the quality of the meat,' the waiter explains encouragingly as he cooks it at the table. There are good fish cakes and rice, though we have been less impressed by the pizza. Excellent service. More reports, please.

CHEF: Mr Song PROPRIETOR: Y.S.Rhee
OPEN: all week, exc Sat L MEALS: 12 to 3, 6 to 11
PRICES: £5 (£10), Set L from £5 (£9), Set D £17 (£22). Service 12.5% CARDS: Access, Amex, Diners, Visa
SEATS: 60. Private parties: 35 main room. Vegetarian meals. Children's helpings. Korean music. Air-conditioned

Koto [10/20] map 10

75 Parkway, NW1 7PP
01-482 2036 and 2876 £8–£17

An accessible Japanese restaurant with the accent on modern cookery, that is, post-Second World War. Dishes include deep-fried mackerel, tempura made up of deep-fried vegetables and fish, and sukiyaki cooked at the table. The inside is bright and clean, though it gets cold in winter; service is friendly even if the

English is not fluent. Well patronised by Japanese businessmen. Carefully arranged fruit to finish. Saké for £1·90.

CHEF: M.Hirose PROPRIETOR: H.Arai
OPEN: Mon to Sat CLOSED: Christmas, bank hols MEALS: 12.30 to 2.30, 6 to 11.30
PRICES: £13 (£17), Set L from £4 (£8), Set D from £11 (£14). Service 10% CARDS: Access, Amex, Diners, Visa
SEATS: 50. Private parties: 16 and 8 private rooms. Vegetarian meals. Children's helpings. Wheelchair access. Japanese music. Air-conditioned

Lal Bhag [9/20]

map 10

51 Kilburn High Road, NW6 5SB
01-624 5289

£9–£11

Dishes done best are chicken tikka masala, rogan josh, and unusual fish, such as mahi surma and moali ramna. House French is £4·25.

CHEF: Sahid Waheed PROPRIETORS: Haque and Sahid Waheed
OPEN: all week CLOSED: 25 Dec MEALS: 12 to 2.30, 6.15 to 11.45
PRICES: £6 (£11), Set L and D from £6·50 (£9). Service inc set only, alc 10% CARDS: Access, Amex, Diners, Visa
SEATS: 44. Private parties: 44 main room. Vegetarian meals. Children's helpings. Wheelchair access. Indian music

Lal Qila [11/20]

map 12

117 Tottenham Court Road, W1P 9HL
01-387 4570 and 5332

£11–£14

Comparing this with other top-level Indian restaurants in the London area it is fair to say that the food is better than at Last Days of the Raj, on a par with the Bayleaf, and the Moghul Brasserie (see Wembley), but not as good as at the Red Fort or Bombay Brasserie (see entries). The decor is elegant, with flowers on the crowded tables, pale linen napery, tinted mirrors, but there is too much incense-scented air-freshener for comfort. Big meaty chunks of sizzling lamb tikka are a winner, though, and shami kebab is well spiced with ginger, garlic and coriander (in fact this place would be a strong contender for a Coriander Award of the Year). Rather ragged pieces of chicken in murgh chaat come in a numbingly hot-and-sour sauce which needs the nan to mop it up. Thalis are balanced and substantial, but fish is less successful. Aromatic Basmati rice sports a buttery sheen; spinach is smooth without being mushy; and puddings are adequate. The food is worthy of a rating of 12, but the appalling service brings it down: although the enterprise is a co-operative, the waiters aren't.

CHEFS: Ayub Ali and Anuarol Haque PROPRIETORS: Amin Ali and A.Kalam
OPEN: all week CLOSED: 25 and 26 Dec MEALS: 12 to 2.45, 6 to 11.30
PRICES: £7 (£14), Set Sun L and D £6·95 (£11). Minimum £6. Service 12.5%
CARDS: Access, Amex, Diners, Visa
SEATS: 68. Private parties: 75 main room. Vegetarian meals. Children's helpings. Jacket and tie preferred. Indian music. Air-conditioned

'The mainstay of the Caesar's salad was Safeway's blue-cheese dressing. Of course, I could be wrong. It might have been Sainsbury's.' (On eating in London)

Lampwicks [12/20] map 9

24 Queenstown Road, SW8 3RX
01-622 7800 £15–£21

The grey brickwork facade belies Alan and Ann Bennett's aspirations for this French restaurant which has large well-spaced tables, a panelled ceiling and a two-tier dining-room. The short, fashionable set menu usually features beef and lamb and a fish of the day. Canapés, in the style of top restaurants in France, are a warm plate of mussels, avocado, and quails' eggs in mussel sauce. The cheeseboard is a fixture after the main course and is generously covered with French specimens. Good dishes have been the calf's liver with onions; spätzli, venison, hare and quail neatly sliced together on a thin sauce of madeira and truffles; and sole with mussels and crab glazed under the grill. To finish, the passion fruit bavarois is as white as a Persil advertisement, surrounded by a green, syrupy kiwi sauce. Coffee comes in gold cafetières with almond tuiles and a single fruit pastry. The wine list is evolving, and, interestingly, the house wine is an Alsace, a Pinot Blanc from Hugel at £6.

CHEF: Alan Bennett PROPRIETORS: Alan and Ann Bennett
OPEN: Tue to Sat CLOSED: last 2 weeks Aug MEALS 12.30 to 2.30, 7.30 to 10.30
PRICES: Set L £10·50 (£15), Set D £16·50 (£21). Licensed, plus bring your own: no corkage CARDS: Access, Amex, Diners, Visa
SEATS: 34. Private parties: 12 main room. Smart dress preferred. Children's helpings (L only). Wheelchair access. Air-conditioned

Langan's Bistro [12/20] map 12

26 Devonshire Street, W1N 1RJ
01-935 4531 £17

There's something up with Mrs Langan's famous chocolate cake. The thin sandwich of chocolate sponge filled with a finger of whipped cream is now served as two slices on a plate covered with chocolate sauce – *nouvelle cuisine*-style with the sauce underneath – and is a bone of contention in many reports, not just of here but also of Odins next door. Is it as good as ever? Is it better? Well yes, but it's also surpassed by the Roux brothers' chocolate truffle cake these days, according to other reports. Times change. This is not as expensive as Langan's Brasserie but the food can be as good, albeit the surroundings lacking the other's razzamatazz. Excellent plates of charcuterie, monkfish, pork with honey and ginger, and lambs' kidneys in mustard sauce feature on the short, sound menu. Good wines, though the house French is £5·25 a bottle and £1·95 a glass.

CHEF: David Bickford PROPRIETOR: Peter Langan
OPEN: Mon to Sat, exc Sat L MEALS: 12.30 to 2.30, 7 to 11.30
PRICES: £10 (£17). Cover 75p. Service 10% CARD: Amex
SEATS: 40. Private parties: 7 main room. Wheelchair access. Air-conditioned

The 1987 Guide *will appear before Christmas 1986, so reports are particularly important in the spring. Report forms are at the back of this book, but just write a letter if you prefer. Address them to* The Good Food Guide, *Freepost, 14 Buckingham Street, London WC2N 6BR. No stamp is necessary if you post in the UK.*

Langan's Brasserie [12/20] map 12

Stratton Street, W1X 5SD
01-493 6437 and 491 8822 £20

On the fringe of Mayfair, although Mayfair still goes to Langan's, not the other way round. And so does Hollywood and a few other media areas. The 1920s atmosphere fizzes like a speakeasy: the waiters usually have a sense of humour and the food is exceptionally good, considering the numbers catered for – 400 in a day is a conservative estimate. The menu evolves rather more than most brasseries because of the number of regulars. Typical of the many good dishes are the famous spinach soufflé with anchovy sauce; stuffed aubergine; sea-bass with a nantaise sauce; navarin of lamb; braised duck; and salmon or turbot with hollandaise sauce. Offal is always a strong point. The cheeses are usually in good condition and the crème brûlée is always a safe sweet. Peter Langan's eccentric behaviour has led one night to him tearing up the booking sheets and trying to close the restaurant, which is less funny than some of his other antics and hence the drop in the rating. Good house wines.

CHEF: Richard Shepherd
PROPRIETORS: Peter Langan, Michael Caine and Richard Shepherd
OPEN: Mon to Sat, exc Sat L MEALS: 12.30 to 2.45, 7 to 11.45 (8 to 12.45 Sat)
PRICES: £13 (£20). Cover £1. Service 12.5% CARDS: Access, Amex, Diners, Visa
SEATS: 200. Private parties: 12 main room. Children's helpings. Wheelchair access. Jazz. Air-conditioned

The Lantern [9/20] map 10

23 Malvern Road, NW6 5PS
01-624 1796 £9

Sweaters and jeans are the order of the night in this dimly lit, lively bistro staffed by a cosmopolitan gaggle of waiters who are likely to bring your coat before the bill. It is good fun, not expensive and the food is different – choux pastry filled with crab and covered with hollandaise; pork with a cheese and chive sauce; lamb steak marinated in lemon and served with what is called a vegetable caviare sauce. The house vin de pays de l'Hérault is £3·90 and fine.

CHEF/PROPRIETOR: Peter Ilic
OPEN: all week MEALS: 12 to 3, 7 to 11.45 (11 Sun)
PRICES: £5·25 (£9). Service 10%
SEATS: 48. Private parties: 20 main room. Vegetarian meals. Children's helpings. Classical music

Last Days of the Raj [10/20] map 13

22 Drury Lane, WC2B 5RH
01-836 1628 £11–£14

It could be the last days for the Last Days, as far as the *Guide* is concerned. Indian cooking in this country has moved on since this place opened in 1980 and introduced a new style of Indian restaurant to the capital, successfully matching elegant decor to fresh and vivid flavours. But the standards of cooking and service have fallen. It is still a useful curry house but its successors (see entries for

Lal Qila and Red Fort, for example) have outstripped it. Still reliable dishes include the nan, lamb tikka and prawn masala. Others are less impressive.

CHEF: Mr Hamif **PROPRIETOR:** Mr Ali
OPEN: all week, exc Sun L **MEALS:** 12 to 2.15, 6 to 11
PRICES: £7 (£14), Set L £6·90 (£11). Service 12.5% **CARDS:** Access, Amex, Diners, Visa
SEATS: 60. Private parties: 40 main room. Vegetarian meals. Children welcome. Air-conditioned

Lemonia [11/20] map 10

154 Regent's Park Road, NW1 8XN
01-586 7454 £10–£12

A remarkable restaurant for reliability, warmth of atmosphere, high-quality Greek cooking and well-organised, fresh food. Notably good dishes beyond the array of hummus, tahini and so on are the chicken shashlik; the kleftiko; prawns and aubergine salad; the stew of marinated lamb with onions, casseroled in an earthenware pot for hours and hours before being served up with rice. The baklava is made in-house, or else there is fruit to finish. It's a good retsina at £4·95, or there are a couple of very drinkable French wines, as well as Demestica.

CHEF: George Ioannou **PROPRIETOR:** Antony Evangelou
OPEN: Mon to Sat, D only **CLOSED:** 1st 2 weeks Aug **MEALS:** 6 to 11.30
PRICES: £7 (£12), Set D £5·50 (£10)
SEATS: 70. Private parties: 10 main room. Vegetarian meals. Children welcome. Wheelchair access (also WC). Greek music

Light of Kashmir [9/20] map 10

98 Fleet Road, NW1 2QX
01-485 6908 £9–£13

A cosy, club atmosphere, despite the decor. Good dishes eaten have been moist and spicy chicken tikka, meat Darjeeling (lamb) with onion rings and raisins, or sag josh, all at under £3, as is most of the menu apart from Persian dishes with pilau rice, and curry specials. Drink Dortmunder Union beer at 60p.

CHEF: Nawor Miah **PROPRIETOR:** Amin Uddin
OPEN: all week **MEALS:** 12 to 2.30, 5.30 to 11
PRICES: £8 (£13), Set L and D from £5·50 (£9). Service 10% **CARDS:** Access, Amex, Diners, Visa
SEATS: 36. Vegetarian meals. Children welcome. Indian music

All restaurants listed in the Guide *have been independently nominated by a number of readers and have been checked by inspectors.*

The Guide *accepts no advertising and does not allow restaurants to use their inclusion for publicity.*

New restaurants that we have not been able to assess completely are given a zero rating for this year. We are particularly keen to have reports on these places.

Luigi's [10/20] map 9

129 Gipsy Hill, SE19 1QS
01-670 1843 and 1396 £16

A useful little white trattoria with macho waiters, a conventional antipasti, pasta and veal menu, and good oil in the dressing. The house wine comes from Luigi Paglierani's own vineyard and is £6·50.

CHEF: Battista Donghi PROPRIETOR: Luigi Paglierani
OPEN: Mon to Sat, exc Sat L CLOSED: bank hols, Aug MEALS: 12 to 2.30, 6.30 to 10.30
PRICES: £9 (£16). Cover £1 CARDS: Access, Amex, Diners, Visa
SEATS: 40. Private parties: 20 main room. Vegetarian meals

Mabileau [11/20] map 10

61 The Cut, SE1 8LL
01-928 8645 £14–£20

Very popular with readers. The big, calm dining-room has archaeological-style relics framed on the walls and it feels like a good restaurant. The staff are eager and friendly, by London standards, and the menu is fashionably *nouvelle*-out-of-bistro. Fish is the best thing – salmon en croûte with tarragon sauce; plaited salmon and brill with a vegetable purée; and ragout. Vegetables are very good; sadly though, cheeses come ready-portioned out of the fridge. But sweets are of a standard. The restaurant is related to RSJ (see entry). Superb Loire wines. Anjou Gamay at £5·95 is a fine house wine.

CHEF: David Martin PROPRIETORS: Nigel Wilkinson and David Martin
OPEN: Mon to Sat L, exc Sat CLOSED: 1 week at Christmas MEALS: 12 to 2, 6 to 11.15
PRICES: £14 (£20), Set D £12·25 (£14). Service 12.5% CARDS: Access, Amex, Diners, Visa
SEATS: 40. Private parties: 20 main room. Vegetarian meals. Children welcome. Wheelchair access. Music. Air-conditioned

Ma Cuisine [11/20] map 11

113 Walton Street, SW3 2JY
01-584 7585 £21

The tiny cramped room offers a direct insight into classical French cookery – there is an extraordinary array of terrines and pâtés, including neck of duck with prunes; elegant presentation; plus fleet-footed service, all at a price that is not exorbitant. Some of the ingredients are not of the standard we expect, which undermines dishes – hence the drop in the rating – but the chocolate truffles, when fresh, are the best in London.

CHEF: Jean-Claude Aubertin PROPRIETORS: Mr and Mrs Guy Mouilleron
OPEN: Mon to Fri CLOSED: mid-July to mid-Aug MEALS: 12.30 to 2, 7.30 to 11
PRICES: £12 (£21). Cover £1 CARDS: Amex, Diners
SEATS: 33. Children's helpings. No pipes in dining-room. Wheelchair access (also wc)

Entries are compiled from the unsolicited reports from readers and are checked by inspectors; each restaurant is asked to supply details of its operation. Report forms can be found at the back of the Guide.

Magno's Brasserie [12/20]

map 13

65A Long Acre, WC2E 9JH
01-836 6077 £10–£18

When the sheer pressure on tables does not undermine this ever-popular brasserie, some very good dishes are produced. Claude Monsérat does not cut many corners and has been adding more refined fish dishes than the average bistro: fresh prawns (there's a thing) with crayfish in a herb sauce; fillets of sole grilled and served with a tomato sauce flavoured with herbs; and monkfish in a mustard sauce. A starter of raw fish marinated in lime, lemon, herbs and red and green peppercorns features regularly. Duck with a fruit sauce is usually very good, and the vegetables have been improved. To finish, all things chocolate are good, as is the apple tart. The pre-theatre dinner is a snip; in an ever more cynical area like Covent Garden the effort to give value for money is valiant. The house Bordeaux are £5·45 or there's the CELLARMAN'S CHOICE: Sancerre, Les Monts Damnés '83 from the Cotat brothers at £10·45.

CHEF: Claude Monsérat PROPRIETORS: E.Coliadis and A. Wastell
OPEN: Mon to Sat, exc Sat L CLOSED: 24 Dec to 2 Jan MEALS: 12 to 2.30, 6 to 11.30
PRICES: £12 (£18). Pre-theatre menu £7·45 (£10). Cover 50p. Service 12.5%
CARDS: Access, Amex, Diners, Visa
SEATS: 50. Private parties: 60 main room. Vegetarian meals. Children welcome. Wheelchair access. Classical music

Maharajah [10/20]

map 10

50 Queensway, W2 4QH
01-727 1135 £11–£12

Plenty of tandooris, from duck to lobster; a good selection of curries for under £3; kulfi to follow. Generous helpings.

CHEF: Kazi Abdul Goni PROPRIETOR: Quazi Abdul Khali Que
OPEN: all week MEALS: 12 to 3.30, 4.45 to 11.45
PRICES: £7 (£12). Set L for 2 from £14·50 (£22). Set D for 2 from £16·80 (£24). Minimum £3·75. Service 10% CARDS: Access, Amex, Carte Blanche, Diners, Visa
SEATS: 55. Private parties: 33 main room, 22 private room. Vegetarian meals. Children's helpings. Wheelchair access. Indian music. Air-conditioned

Malabar [10/20]

map 10

27 Uxbridge Street, W8 7TQ
01-727 8800 £13–£16

Jo Chalmers and Anil Bist's attempt to provide a range of dishes normally found in Indian homes rather than restaurants is refreshing and welcome. It throws up grilled chicken livers in yoghourt and spices, venison marinated with tamarind, prawns in dhal batter, as well as unusual vegetables: sliced green banana cooked with ginger and spices, and pumpkin fried in butter and herbs. Chicken tikka, minced lamb kebab, and mango fool are enjoyed, too. There is fish curry on

All inspections are carried out anonymously as we accept no handouts.

Friday, and a vegetarian thali for £8. Kingfisher lager is £1, Sylvaner d'Alsace, from Beyer, is £6·75, and house wine is £5·10.

CHEFS/PROPRIETORS: Jo Chalmers and Anil Bist
OPEN: all week CLOSED: 1 week Aug MEALS: 12 to 3, 6 to 11.30
PRICES: £9 (£16), Set L and D from £8 (£13). Cover 50p. Service 12.5% CARDS: Access, Visa
SEATS: 56. Private parties: 12 main room. Vegetarian meals. Children welcome. Self-service buffet Sun L

Malean Chinese Restaurant [12/20]

map 9

1585 London Road, SW16 4AA
01-764 2336 £6–£14

The brown decor matches the toffee apples in this well-liked Szechuan/Peking restaurant. The list of dishes enjoyed is long, from crispy fried beef with chilli, to three-flavour mixed noodles with fat prawns and chicken, to fresh crab with black pepper, ginger and garlic, to Mongolian crispy lamb. The highlights of the Szechuan set meal, which is not small, have been the Szechuan duck, which has converted people who find European ducks too fatty, and the crunchy French beans with a lot of garlic. The service is pleasant and helpful. There are some Chinese/French wines, of which the Wan Fu at £5·50 goes well enough with the food, though some Alsace wines would be a good addition to the list. Mei Kew Lu liqueur is 85p a glass, with the more subtle version, Mou Tai, at £1 a glass.

CHEFS: K.S.Lau, S.Y.Tse and S.Y.Cheung PROPRIETOR: Koon Sang Lau
OPEN: all week, exc Sun L MEALS: 12 to 2.20, 6 to 11.45
PRICES: £8 (£14), Set L from £3 (£6), Set D from £7·50 (£11). Minimum £6 CARDS: Access, Amex, Diners, Visa
SEATS: 40. 11 tables outside. Private parties: 40 main room. Children welcome. Classical music

Mandalay [9/20]

map 9

100 Greenwich South Street, SE10 8UN
01-691 0443 £12

A more unlikely restaurant you will not find in the *Guide*. Up until the food arrives you will be convinced we have gone mad. We have not. Sit down and wait. The Burmese cooking – this is the only Burmese restaurant in the country – is a delight: freshly cooked, vividly spiced, unusual and prepared with knowledge and care three nights a week. Suzy Andrews explains the complexities and suggests extra dishes. Especially good are the mohinga (a fish-based soup), sauté fish, chicken nun-nun-bin, and the coconut rice. To finish, the fuluda, a sort of Burmese knickerbocker glory, is quite simply extraordinary – not good, just extraordinary. Licensed.

CHEF: Gerald Andrews PROPRIETORS: Gerald and Suzy Andrews
OPEN: Thur to Sat D MEALS: 7.30 to 10.30
PRICES: £7 (£12). Cover 60p. Service 5% on parties over 7 CARDS: Access, Visa
SEATS: 32. Private parties: 32 main room. Vegetarian meals. Children welcome. Music

An index of restaurants by name appears at the back of the Guide.

Mandeer [10/20] map 12

21 Hanway Place, W1P 9DG
01-323 0660 £9

The location gives a new meaning to the phrase 'tucked away' – only half a minute's walk from Tottenham Court Road and Oxford Street. Inside, low hanging lamps are ringed with Christmas tree bulbs and give out just enough light to examine the vegetarian menu. Spicing is varied and nothing is very hot: patra is aravi leaves layered with chickpea paste, steamed, sliced and fried; there is slightly sweet, thin yoghourt soup; and muttar paneer is gently flavoured with cumin. Rice and raita are good. Sweetly lemony shrikand, and carrot halva, are better than kulfi. Ice-creams are from Losely Park Farm. Mrs Patel will come and explain a dish, from its ingredients and preparation to the philosophy behind it. Drink plain, salt or sweet lassi, or fruit juice.

CHEFS/PROPRIETORS: Mr and Mrs Patel
OPEN: Mon to Sat MEALS: 12 to 3, 6 to 10.15
PRICES: £5 (£9), Set D from £5·25 (£9). Minimum £2 CARDS: Amex, Visa
SEATS: 60. Private parties: 30 main room. Vegetarian meals. Children welcome. Classical music. Self-service at L. Licensed

Maroush [11/20] map 10

21 Edgware Road, W2 2JH
01-723 0773 £14

The Arabian music can be pretty thunderous in this dark, artificial brick-walled, Middle Eastern restaurant that stays open from noon to five in the morning. Plants in copper troughs are precariously anchored to the wall by wires, but the cooking is sensitive and, if you choose carefully and concentrate on the 20 starters, good value. The £1 cover charge brings warm, puffed-up pitta bread (baked on the premises) plus green olives and a bowl of salad that includes cos lettuce, radishes, spring onions, green chilli, green pepper and huge beef tomatoes. The meze comes liberally sprinkled with fresh mint, chopped flat-leaf parsley and wedges of lemon. The baba ghannoush has been a classically executed marriage of garlic, lemon, sesame oil and aubergine flesh still smoky from grilling. Other very good dishes have been hummus decorated with chopped, cooled chickpeas; brains fried in the thinnest of batters; makaneh (tiny, untidy Lebanese sausages) spiced with chilli and cardamom; and kibbeh, the national dish of both Lebanon and Syria, being deep-fried lamb mince encased in cracked wheat. Main courses rely on chunks of plain or spiced char-grilled meat; their cost inflates the bill. Some of the economics are strange – cardamom coffee is 75p, against Nescafé at £2; stuffed lamb is £5 but stuffed cabbage is the same!

'It is difficult to ruin smoked salmon, but the smoked mountain ham popped over a chunk of fresh pineapple was certainly not inspired by the Roux brothers.' (On eating in Liverpool)

Restaurants rating 12 or more serve the best food in the region.

Sweets come from the House of Lebanon in Knightsbridge who deliver a range of filo pastry to be served with honey. Arak is £1·25 for a small glass.

CHEF/PROPRIETOR: M.C.Abouzaki
OPEN: all week MEALS: noon to 4.30 am
PRICES: £7 (£14). Cover £1. Service 15% CARDS: Access, Amex, Diners, Visa
SEATS: 80. Private parties: 60 main room, 60 private room. Vegetarian meals. Children's helpings. Music. Air-conditioned

Maroush II [new entry, zero rated] map 11

38 Beauchamp Place, SW3 1NV
01-581 5434 £22

Plusher than the original Maroush (see above) with a rockery, goldfish pond and even, at inspection, two belly-dancers, which pleased the waiters no end. The menu has the classic range of meze, though the standard dishes have been less good than at the parent branch. On the other hand the moutabel (aubergine dip); the chickpeas with yoghourt and calf's tongue; and the baked aubergines with well-flavoured firm rice, have been excellent. Arak is £8 for a quarter-bottle and Côtes du Rhône an astonishing £13. Even so, pick carefully and a meal need not be expensive. Attentive service. More reports, please.

PROPRIETOR: Mr Abouzaki
OPEN: Tue to Sat CLOSED: 26 Dec MEALS: noon to 1am
PRICES: £13 (£22). Cover £1·50. Service 15% CARDS: Access, Amex, Diners, Visa
SEATS: 50. Private parties: 50 main room. Vegetarian meals. Children welcome. Smart dress preferred. Arabic music. Air-conditioned

Martin's [13/20] map 10

88 Ifield Road, SW10 9AD
01-352 5641 £22

The tables are set with fat silver cutlery and thin, large-bowled wine glasses in this serious, apricot-coloured modern French restaurant. Martin Coldicott runs the dining-room with panache, while John Armstrong cooks a fashionable menu featuring warm salads; asparagus feuilleté; and kidneys and sweetbreads with raspberry vinegar. The Connaught classic of quails' eggs Maintenon has been well executed. Also good is the assortment of poached fish with fresh noodles and a shellfish sauce to start; the fillet of lamb with a charlotte of aubergines; and the boned and rolled quail in pastry. Sweets are extra to the set menu and are skippable, considering coffee – included in the price – comes with a huge tuile and chocolate truffle, though the chocolate marquise and the chaud-froid of different fruits are of a standard. If we have a criticism it is that some of the sauces can be fey, but in general the quality of the ingredients and the cooking is close to a score of 14. The wines have been chosen with care; the list is strongest in burgundy and claret, which makes it expensive, albeit one of quality. House

Restaurants are checked every year and their entries rewritten. The restaurant scene changes very rapidly so don't be caught with an out-of-date Guide.

Sauvignon de Touraine is £7·50. CELLARMAN'S CHOICE: Givry Blanc '81 from Domaine Ragot £11.

CHEF: John Armstrong
PROPRIETORS: Martin Coldicott, John Armstrong and T.A. Northwood
OPEN: Mon to Sat, D only CLOSED: Christmas to New Year MEALS: 7 to 11
PRICES: Set D from £15·50 (£22). Service 15% CARDS: Access, Amex, Diners, Visa
SEATS: 34. 2 tables outside. Private parties: 30 main room. Smart dress preferred. Children welcome. Wheelchair access

Masako [12/20]

map 12

6–8 St Christopher's Place, W1M 5HB
01-935 1579 and 486 1399 £11–£21

Waltzing Matilda played Japanese-style can be a strange experience, but this is a spacious, middle-to-good Japanese restaurant where the raw fish particularly is good value. There are large, practical black melamine tables with comfortable padded chairs and a spartan but pleasing black/white/red decor. The waitresses dress in traditional pink flowery kimonos, white socks and lacquered sandals, their hair tied back; they are attentive and formal. The sashimi is fresh fish even on a Monday – there is cuttlefish, salmon, mackerel and a white fish in generous quantities, arranged with a stand-up daikon (giant white radish) in the centre. The assorted sushi is made up of 10 varieties of fish. Miso soup comes in red lacquer bowls from which to drink it (minding out for the cubes of bean curd). The beef may be tough, as it has been at inspections, but the fried oysters served with a little mustard and a fruity dipping sauce are excellent. Lunch may be less polished than dinner, when everything seems to be freshly cooked. Rice is authentically sticky. Saké is £1·50 a tokkurai, which is not expensive by London standards.

CHEF: Mr Chikira PROPRIETORS: Ninjin Ltd
OPEN: Mon to Sat CLOSED: Christmas to New Year and bank hols MEALS: 12 to 2, 6 to 10
PRICES: £16 (£19), Set L from £8·50 (£11), Set D from £17·50 (£21). Cover charge 20p. Service 15% CARDS: Access, Amex, Diners, Visa
SEATS: 100. 20 tables outside. Private parties: 26 main room, 20 private room. Jacket and tie. Japanese music. Air-conditioned

Maxim [11/20]

map 9

153–155 Northfield Avenue, W13 9QT
01-567 1719 and 840 1086 £11–£23

Mrs Chow, who has the distinction of being one of the few women chef/proprietors in a Chinese restaurant in this country, has cut back the monosodium glutamate and artificial colourings in her Peking-style food. Other Chinese restaurants please note. The menu is pragmatic, concentrating on the more popular dishes for Westerners, but there is a good choice for vegetarians, including red cooked Chinese vegetables and a set menu. With 24 hours' notice the kitchen will do a hot-pot meal for a minimum of five people (£18 a head) or

Restaurants rating 12 or more serve the best food in the region.

the authentic Peking duck (£16). Good dishes have been the safe ones – imperial hors d'oeuvre, seaweed, chicken with cashew nuts, and quick-fried beef. The wine list includes Gewürztraminer, special reserve '82, from Willy Gisselbrecht, at £6·95.

CHEFS: C.B.K.Chow and Y.C.Man PROPRIETORS: Mr and Mrs Tony Chow
OPEN: all week, exc Sun L CLOSED: 25 to 28 Dec MEALS: 12 to 2.30, 6.30 to 12 (12.30 Fri and Sat)
PRICES: £11 (£19), Set L and D £6·60 to £16·50 (£11 to £23). Minimum £5. Service 12%
CARDS: Access, Amex, Diners, Visa
SEATS: 100. Private parties: 100 main room, 25 private room. Vegetarian meals. Children's helpings. Wheelchair access (also WC). Air-conditioned

Maxim Wine Bar [8/20] map 9

7 Boston Parade, Boston Road, W7 2DG
01-567 9708 £10–£14

This wine bar serves Chinese food, which is an unusual combination but it works – rice and pork casserole; crispy duck with pancakes; sizzling dishes. There's 20 per cent off wines before half-past seven in the evening, and some reasonable, cheap wines include Rioja Campo Viejo Gran Reserva '73 at £7·30.

CHEF: Hing Tung Chan PROPRIETOR: T.Chow
OPEN: all week MEALS: 11.30 to 3, 5.30 to 11 (12 to 2, 7 to 10.30 Sun)
PRICES: £8 (£14), Set L and D from £6·50 (£10) CARDS: Access, Amex, Diners, Visa
SEATS: 60. Private parties: 50 main room. Vegetarian meals. Children welcome. Wheelchair access. Music

Le Mazarin [new entry, zero rated] map 10

30 Winchester Street, SW1V 4NZ
01-828 3366 and 834 4366 £23

A razzamatazz, Mexican-style hoarding announces René and Regine Bajard's basement restaurant in the quiet back streets of Pimlico, and a huge model galleon stands by the bar at the bottom of the stairs. The decor is deep-olive and dark-brown and a bit grim. Bajard kept the kitchen at Le Gavroche steady over some tumultuous years and his set menus reveal all the good signs of the Roux brothers' influence: meat from La Martine in Ebury Street, SW1; excellent rolls; expensive Normandy table-butter; beautiful ratatouille canapés; superlative petits fours. First meals have been a bit tentative, which is why we are giving only a zero rating, but we have high hopes. He is not afraid to break away from the usual flamboyance of the Roux manner and to serve straightforward, bistro-style dishes, such as superbly smooth-textured rabbit terrine with cornichons before onglet – the French cut of blade steak. But also there are the dishes of his apprenticeship, such as chicken with a typical Roux brothers' demi-glaze that verges on the sticky and is served with turnips. The presentation would suit a colour supplement centre-fold. A half-bottle of wine is included in the price – and

'Why do some restaurants dress their waitresses in black skirts and white blouses, which show dandruff, odd hairs and spilt soup to great effect?' (On eating in London)

there is excellent Muscadet and Brouilly. There is also a short, carefully chosen if expensive list of fine burgundy and claret. More reports, please.

CHEF/PROPRIETOR: René Bajard
OPEN: Mon to Sat, D only CLOSED: 24 Aug to 16 Sept MEALS: 7 to 11.30
PRICES: Set D £22·50. Service inc CARDS: Amex, Diners
SEATS: 35. Private parties: 12 main room, 12 and 6 private rooms. Vegetarian meals. Children's helpings. Classical music. Air-conditioned

Melati [10/20] map 13

21 Great Windmill Street, W1V 7PH
01-437 2745 and 734 6964 £14

There are some interesting and unusual dishes to be had in this pristine little Malay cafe – pink-coloured drinks and weird ice creams – as well as more conventional spring rolls (vegetarian) with a hot, sweet dip, satay of chicken and beef with rice cakes and cucumber, and delicate beef with Siamese sauce. Best value is the laksa soup – a vast bowl of fish, noodles and coconut milk – or else the noodle dishes with beef and squid. Some dishes are surprisingly hot, but the retoprak and the rendang are as authentic as can be found in London. Helpful, understanding service. Tiger beer is 55p. The rating has dropped a couple of points not because of any criticism but to bring it into line.

CHEFS: S. Alamsjah and H.Hasyem PROPRIETORS: Mrs M.C.W.Ong and S.Alamsjah
OPEN: all week MEALS: 12 to 11.30
PRICES: £8 (£14), Set D for two £21 (£23). Service 10% CARDS: Access, Amex, Diners, Visa
SEATS: 65. Private parties: 30 main room. Children welcome. Wheelchair access. Oriental music

Methuselah's [9/20] map 10

29 Victoria Street, SW1H 0EU
01-222 0424 and 3550 £14–£15

A Methuselah holds the equivalent of eight bottles of wine, the practice having been to name large vessels of wine after Old Testament patriarchs and kings (reputedly according to how long they reigned, though Methuselah lived 969 years, says Genesis). This is a useful wine bar, brasserie and restaurant in the otherwise culinary arid area in the orbit of the House of Commons. It opens for breakfast at nine and serves snacks out of licensing hours. The usual combination of salad and quiche is augmented by some provincial French cooking and the wine list is unusually good for a wine bar.

CHEF: Geraldo Eghan PROPRIETOR: Don Hewitson
OPEN: Mon to Fri CLOSED: 25 and 26 Dec, 1 Jan MEALS: 9am to 11pm
PRICES: £10 (£14), Set L and D £10·50 (£15). Minimum £2·50 at L in brasserie. Service 12.5%, exc in self-service wine bar CARDS: Access, Amex, Diners, Visa
SEATS: 180. 2 tables outside. Vegetarian meals. Children's helpings in restaurant. Wheelchair access (brasserie only). Jazz. Air-conditioned

Places rating 8 or 9 may not be restaurants at all but still serve very good food. In this category expect to find pubs, cafes, small hotels and wine bars.

Le Metro Wine Bar [8/20] map 11

28 Basil Street, SW3 1AS
01-589 6286 £13

There are some good wines to be drunk in this basement bar round the corner from Harrods – including fine labels by the glass out of a cruover machine. The place is neat and busy and there is some fashionable good-looking food, though the simpler the dishes the better they are: casseroles, soups, cheeses, tarts and so on. You can eat a lot worse in many restaurants for twice the money.

CHEF: Brian Turner PROPRIETOR: David Levin
OPEN: all week, exc Sat and Sun D CLOSED: 25 Dec and bank hols
MEALS: 12 to 2.30, 5.30 to 10
PRICES: £8 (£13) CARD: Amex
SEATS: 60. Private parties: 15 main room. Vegetarian meals. Children's helpings. Wheelchair access. Air-conditioned. Self-service

Mijanou [13/20] map 11

143 Ebury Street, SW1W 9QN
01-730 4099 £17–£26

There are two rooms here, one for smokers and one for non-smokers; the first is better. Ring the front doorbell and the door is unlocked for you. Inside is small and plush in red and black. The waiter then presents you with a positive plethora of paper – the menu, the day's specials, the set menu (good value at £24 for two), and the excellent wine list. Neville Blech explains it all with good humour. Some of the cooking can be very clever – sole, salmon and lobster terrine with a lemon grass sauce; barbecued scallops with a cream sauce (it is an odd quirk that so many restaurants poach this fish for a cream sauce when grilling or barbecuing it like this can give it an extra dimension); liver and veal kidneys in a madeira sauce garnished with lime; half a grouse with onion marmalade. Vegetables are *nouvelle* and sweets sweet. The wine list is magnificent, with plenty of half-bottles and a sensibly priced house wine at £5-75. The list of 20 digestifs arrives with cafetière coffee.

CHEFS/PROPRIETORS: Neville and Sonia Blech
OPEN: Mon to Fri MEALS: 12.30 to 1.45, 7.30 to 10 (11 Fri)
PRICES: £17 (£26), Set D £12 (£17). Cover 80p
SEATS: 30. 4 tables outside. Private parties: 24 main room. No-smoking area

Mi-Mi [10/20] map 12

11 Maddox Street, W1R 9HH
01-493 6548 and 6596 £7–£21

Mi-Mi is Korean for beautiful taste. The menu is clearly laid out but some of the descriptions would mislead vegetarians. There is an interesting variation of

The Guide *is always anxious to recruit new inspectors. If you would like to apply, write to the editor enclosing a) a detailed report on a restaurant where you have eaten and b) a comparative study of restaurants known to you.*

bulgogi, using venison instead of beef, and also bibim bab, a do-it-yourself salad which makes a good one-plate meal. The yuk kwe, a Korean variation of steak tartare, is excellent. Service is helpful. House French is £4·50.

CHEF: Mr Suh PROPRIETOR: C.Kim
OPEN: Mon to Sat MEALS: 12 to 3, 6 to 11
PRICES: £16 (£21), Set L from £3·50 (£7) CARDS: Access, Amex, Diners, Visa
SEATS: 80. Private parties: 55 main room. Vegetarian meals. Children's helpings. Wheelchair access (also wc). Japanese music

Monkeys [10/20] map 11

1 Cale Street, Chelsea Green, SW3 3QT
01-352 4711 £10–£17

An unfussy little French restaurant with a sensible menu based on short-order grills, plus daily dishes according to market – including occasional luxuries, such as caviare and foie gras. The decor is a romantic's idea of a Parisian brasserie and the cooking usually above average – potted shrimps, cheese beignets, asparagus vinaigrette, pigeon and bacon salad to start. Of the main dishes the panaché of scallop, cod, sole and monkfish with a nantaise sauce stands out. Vegetables could be better. House French is £6.

CHEF: T.Benham PROPRIETORS: T.andB.Benham
OPEN: all week, exc Sun D CLOSED: 1st week July, 1st 2 weeks Aug MEALS: 12.30 to 2.30 (1.15 to 3 Sun), 7.30 to 11
PRICES: Set L from £6·75 (£10), Set D from £10·75 (£17). Minimum £2 for drinks
SEATS: 70. Private parties: 16 private room. Children's helpings. Air-conditioned

Mon Plaisir [10/20] map 13

21 Monmouth Street, WC2H 9DD
01-836 7243 and 240 3757 £12–£17

By popular demand this established bistro returns to the listings. It is best for its fabulous charcuterie and its pungent cheeses. The French tourist posters are starting to fade, but the service is full of spirit and the set lunch at £7 is especially good value. The French bread is fresh, and main dishes tend to taste better than they look. It is a clever wine list that stays mostly under £10, though there are not many details. Vin de table du patron is £5·30.

CHEF: P. Robin PROPRIETOR: A.L. Hermitte
OPEN: Mon to Sat, exc Sat L MEALS: 12 to 2.15, 6 to 11.15
PRICES: £10 (£17), Set L £7 (£12). Cover 50p. Service 12.5%
SEATS: 53. Private parties: 26 main room, 26 private room. Vegetarian meals. Children's helpings. Wheelchair access. Music

Monsieur Thompsons [10/20] map 10

29 Kensington Park Road, W11 2EU
01-727 9957 £14–£25

Dominique Rocher still hasn't quite got it right in trying to turn his bistro into a high-flying modern restaurant. The prices are still stuck to the ceiling, but the food has risen some way to meet them. The bread is a wonderful improvement.

Good fish starters have included sole and mushroom terrine, and a salad of sole in sherry vinegar with mackerel 'rillettes', crunchy mange-tout and a selection of leaves in a walnut-oil dressing. Main courses at nearly £10 sometimes disappoint – ultra-gamey pheasant and less than top-quality rib of beef. Others have been more successful: duck breast with glazed onion and rhubarb in a light coulis sauce; roast saddle of lamb with a crown of courgette and diced aubergine; salmon with langouste sauce. Lemon puddings, such as sorbet and tarte, work well, as does a rich chocolate mousse, and somebody has done overtime with the excellent petits fours which come with filter or espresso coffee or herbal tea. The wine list, with nearly five-dozen bottles ranging from house wine at £5·50 to Ch. Mouton-Rothschild '71 at £69, is entirely French with little in single figures and few halves. CELLARMAN'S CHOICE: St-Véran '83, Château de Leynes, at £11·80.

CHEF: Aram Atanasyan PROPRIETOR: Dominique Rocher
OPEN: Mon to Sat CLOSED: 1 week at Christmas MEALS: 12.30 to 2.30, 7.30 to 10.45
PRICES: £18 (£25), Set L from £8 (£14), Set D £13 (£19). Service 12.5% CARDS: Access, Amex, Diners, Visa
SEATS: 50. Private parties: 30 main room. Children welcome. No smoking during meal. Wheelchair access

Montpeliano [10/20] map 11

13 Montpelier Street, SW7 1HQ
01-589 0032 and 2753 £20

An up-market trattoria with a sliding roof that is pulled back in summer. The pastas are freshly made and the lamb cutlets served pink with their juices. Service is brusque. House Italian from Venice is £5·50.

CHEF: Nilo Gaetano PROPRIETOR: Antonio Trapani
OPEN: Mon to Sat MEALS: 12.30 to 3, 7 to 12
PRICES: £15 (£20)
SEATS: 100. 20 tables outside. Private parties: 25 and 20 private rooms. Vegetarian meals. Children welcome. Wheelchair access (also WC)

Mr Fish [8/20] map 9

393 Upper Richmond Road, SW15 5QL
01-876 3083 £10

An upper crust fish and chip shop that even runs to bottles of Meursault. The oil is ground-nut and the fish, fresh from Billingsgate daily, is priced according to market. It is cooked to order so there is a short wait but the candles on the tables give the feeling of a proper restaurant and it is worth booking at weekends. There is a take-away next door. House French is £3·85. CELLARMAN'S CHOICE: Sancerre '83, from Jean Beauquin, at £7·95.

CHEFS: Louise Lawrence and Geoffrey Hopwood PROPRIETORS: Planebyte Ltd
OPEN: all week, exc Mon L MEALS: 12 to 2, 6.30 to 10.30 (1 to 2.30, 6.30 to 9.30 Sun)
PRICES: £6 (£10). Cheaper set L available. Minimum £1·50. Service 10% CARDS: Access, Amex, Diners, Visa
SEATS: 40. Private parties: 40 main room. Children's helpings. No cigars/pipes in dining-room. Wheelchair access (also WC). Music

Mr Kong [12/20]

map 13

21 Lisle Street, WC2H 7BA
01-437 7341

£9–£10

In a blind tasting it would be difficult to tell the difference between the dishes in this modern Cantonese restaurant and those in the Fung Shing, a few doors up. Both restaurants have green facades and smart, westernised interiors and the menus are nearly identical. Especially good are the hot-pot dishes, such as duck with yams; and also the picturesque potato baskets filled with scallops or else stir-fried vegetables. Mr Kong – he's the chef – tends to get the vote from English readers, while Fung Shing is preferred by the Chinese and, marginally, by us. Licensed.

CHEFS/PROPRIETORS: K.Kong, Y.Lo, W.Lee, M.Lee and C.Chau
OPEN: all week CLOSED: Christmas MEALS: noon to 1.45am
PRICES: £7 (£10), Set D from £5·50 (£9) CARDS: Access, Amex, Diners, Visa
SEATS: 115. Private parties: 50 main room. Vegetarian meals. Children welcome. Wheelchair access. Music

Mr Liu [10/20]

map 9

148 Lordship Lane, SE22 8HB
01-693 8266

£9–£14

Probably the best restaurant in Dulwich. The crispy dishes are Mr Liu's forte, from the seaweed to the sweet deep-fried beef with chilli sauce. The Cantonese dishes are not as good as the Pekinese. The sesame prawn toasts, hot-and-sour soup, and aromatic crispy duck are all of a standard. The sizzling dishes turn heads and the steak is good. The Singapore fried noodles are excellent, always a good sign in a Peking restaurant. House French is £4·60.

CHEF/PROPRIETOR: K.S.Liu
OPEN: Wed to Mon, D only MEALS: 5.30 to 10.45 (11.45 Fri and Sat)
PRICES: £8 (£14), Set D £7·50 (£9). Minimum £7·50. Service 10% CARDS: Amex, Diners, Visa
SEATS: 65. Private parties: 50 main room. Vegetarian meals. Children welcome. Oriental music. Air-conditioned

Mr Lu [10/20]

map 9

374 Upper Richmond Road West, SW14 7JU
01-876 2531 and 4508

£11–£13

A workmanlike Peking restaurant. Some unusual dishes have been added to the conventional menu, for example braised prawns with chilli, fried chicken with vinegar sauce and bean curd family-style. The popular dishes, like shredded beef with chilli and the Peking duck, are consistently good. Licensed.

CHEF: David Lu PROPRIETOR: Johnny Lu
OPEN: all week, exc Mon L, Sun D CLOSED: 25 and 26 Dec MEALS: 12.15 to 2, 6.15 to 11
PRICES: £7 (£13), Set L and D from £6·50 (£11). Minimum £6·50. Service 12%
CARDS: Access, Amex, Diners, Visa
SEATS: 48. Private parties: 48 main room, 24 private room. Vegetarian meals. Children welcome. Smart dress preferred. Wheelchair access. Music

Mr Tang [new entry, zero rated] map 13

61–63 Shaftesbury Avenue, W1V 7AA
01-734 4488 and 5001 £11–£20

Downstairs is a pizza place. Mr Tang occupies the upstairs two floors, the upper one being more for parties. The decor is the usual Chinese commercial rococo. A gilded dragon and phoenix hover above the tables at one end, otherwise there are turquoise tiles and gold, black and red motifs. The menu is pages of Cantonese dishes augmented by a few famous Szechuan dishes. At lunchtime there is dim-sum with less common items, such as silver needle noodles. The rice is excellent – steamed and served in individual clay pots for each table. Also notable are hot-and-sour soup; minced quail meat wrapped in lettuce (the current rage in virtually all Chinese restaurants); braised duck with mixed vegetables; and stir-fried Chinese broccoli with scallop. In all, not too different from places in Hong Kong. Licensed. More reports, please.

CHEF: Pang Sing PROPRIETORS: Bill Tang and Raymond Short
OPEN: all week MEALS: noon to midnight
PRICES: £11 (£20). Set D from £7 (£11). Minimum £6·50 after 7pm. Service 10%
CARDS: Access, Amex, Diners, Visa
SEATS: 200. Private parties: 100 main room, 25 private room. Vegetarian meals. Children's helpings. Chinese music. Air-conditioned

M'sieur Frog [12/20] map 10

31A Essex Road, N1 2SE
01-226 3495 £17

As bustling and thriving as ever, with bags of atmosphere, good will and large portions of good food. The emphasis is still on such provincial dishes as duck with sauerkraut; bouef en croûte; and gratin dauphinoise. Frogs' legs have been dropped because the restaurant disapproves of the way they are processed and because they are inevitably frozen. All the herbs are fresh. The waitresses are now in uniform – jeans and a white shirt. Plenty of enthusiasm for sweets as diverse as sorbets and calvados pancakes. Fitting wines to match including CELLARMAN'S CHOICE: Ch. du Rocher '79 from St-Emilion at £9·75.

CHEF: Phillippe Signolet PROPRIETORS: Howard and Tina Rawlinson, Philip Snuggs
OPEN: Mon to Sat, D only CLOSED: 1 week at Christmas, 3 weeks Aug MEALS: 7 to 11.30
PRICES: £11 (£17). Service 10% CARDS: Access, Visa
SEATS: 63. Private parties: 12 main room. Vegetarian meals. Children's helpings. Wheelchair access

M'sieur Frog's Bistro [10/20] map 9

36 Hornsey High Street, N8 7NX
01-340 2116 £12–£15

More a bistro compared with the paternal Frog (see preceding entry) – moules marinière; poussin stuffed with spinach; cassoulet served with garlic mashed

All letters to the Guide *are acknowledged with a list of changes since we went to press.*

potatoes. It is good value, and there is some good drinking in the short list of wines. CELLARMAN'S CHOICE: Ch. Lamothe '78 from Haut-Médoc at £8·90.

CHEF: Thierry Barranger PROPRIETORS: Howard and Tina Rawlinson, Philip Snuggs
OPEN: Tue to Sat, D only CLOSED: 1 week at Christmas, 3 weeks Aug to Sep
MEALS: 6.30 to 11
PRICES: £10 (£15), Set D from £7·95 (£12). Service 10% CARDS: Access, Visa
SEATS: 44. Private parties: 12 main room. Vegetarian meals. Children's helpings. Wheelchair access

Le Muscadet [12/20] map 10

25 Paddington Street, W1M 3RF
01-935 2883 £16

Like an old-fashioned French restaurant. Tapestries hang in the box-like room, tables are solid, and the holes in the top of the salt and pepper make the letters 'S' and 'P' in case you get confused. The cooking is not a million miles from what you would find in a good bistro in France – mushroom vol-au-vent with a lovely wine sauce; boudin noir in the French style with a compote of apples; excellent trout in white wine sauce; and satisfying cassoulet or choucroute. The blackboard menu changes daily. Cheeses come from Philippe Olivier in Boulogne, and have been in very good condition. A short, well-chosen list of wines with house Muscadet at £5·20.

CHEF: Alex Grant PROPRIETORS: J.F.Bessonnard and Alex Grant
OPEN: Mon to Sat, exc Sat L CLOSED: Christmas, bank hols, 3 weeks Aug
MEALS: 12.15 to 2.30, 7.15 to 11
PRICES: £11 (£16) CARDS: Access, Visa
SEATS: 36. Private parties: 40 main room. Children welcome. Wheelchair access. Music. Air-conditioned

Nanten Yakitori Bar [new entry, zero rated] map 12

6 Blandford Street, W1H 3HA
01-935 6319 £9–£20

Highly regarded by the Japanese community as somewhere inexpensive (relatively, for Japanese food) to relax. It is more of an eating-house than a restaurant, with an enormous bar/counter and rough-and-ready grill and steaming-pans. Yakitori is the main business – stick-like grilled variations on the kebab. These are not only based on chicken, but include asparagus wrapped in bacon with a dab of mustard dip, and skewers of mushrooms brushed with a sweet brown sauce of saké, soy, sugar and dashi. There are a few more homely dishes, as found in other restaurants, but these are not really special given the quality of the ingredients and the price. Two kinds of saké. More reports, please.

CHEF: K.Deguchi PROPRIETORS: Ninjin Ltd
OPEN: Mon to Sat, exc Sat L MEALS: 12 to 2, 6 to 10
PRICES: £9 (£16), Set L from £4·80 (£9), Set D £15 (£20). Minimum £7 at D. Licensed, plus bring your own: corkage half value of wine CARDS: Access, Amex, Diners, Visa
SEATS: 31. Private parties: 25 and 4 private rooms. Children welcome. Wheelchair access. Japanese music

Neal Street Restaurant [13/20] map 13

26 Neal Street, WC2 9PH
01-836 8368 **Real Food** £26

This is the place to eat white truffles; their aroma permeates the bar in autumn. They are brought over from Alba by the manager, Antonio Carluccio, a passionate expert and the Svengali behind the scenes. They are grated on the fluffiest of scrambled eggs, or on the carpaccio (cut thickly because he refuses to freeze it), or on the superb game ravioli with a *Boletus edulis* sauce. Wild mushrooms are another sideline, gathered through a network of enthusiasts; usually they figure as a soup, but on occasions rare black chanterelles have been served with turbot. The restaurant is not cheap but over the last three years it has impressed the toughest inspectors time and again, so the rating is raised to 13. You sit by a row of original Hockneys, and the duck breast with either green olives or mango is executed with considerably more *élan* than is usual in London. To finish, the crème brûlée is first-class, or else the array of berries – black, red, blue – with cream. The wine list has some expensive clarets, but more affordable are the quintet of Beaujolais. House Frascati is £6·30. CELLARMAN'S CHOICE: Domaine Richeaume '78 from Provence at £12.

CHEF: Santiago Gonzalez PROPRIETOR: Sir Terence Conran
OPEN: Mon to Fri CLOSED: Christmas to New Year MEALS: 12.30 to 2.30, 7.30 to 11
PRICES: £16 (£26). Cover £1·10. Service 15% CARDS: Access, Amex, Diners, Visa
SEATS: 65. Private parties: 90 main room, 20 private room. Children's helpings. Wheelchair access. Air-conditioned

New Bengal [9/20] map 10

187–189 Queensway, W2 5HL
01-229 1640 £13

A small and busy Indian restaurant at the northern end of Queensway, with main courses from about £2. King prawn patia with coriander, chicken moghlai with plenty of coconut, spinach bhajia, and highly spiced tarka dhal are all better than the mixed grill. Service approaches at the bat of an eyelid, but can't elaborate on the bare bones menu. Gulab jamun is the only pudding.

CHEF: M.Miah PROPRIETOR: Kaptan Ullah
OPEN: all week CLOSED: 25 and 26 Dec MEALS: 12 to 3, 6 to 11.30
PRICES: £7 (£13) CARDS: Access, Amex, Diners, Visa
SEATS: 46. Private parties: 25 main room. Vegetarian meals. Children's helpings (L only). Wheelchair access. Indian music. Take-away service

New Friends [9/20] map 9

53 West India Dock Road, E14 8HN
01-987 1139 and 3440 £12

Time was, in the early 1960s, when this was considered the only authentic Cantonese restaurant in London, while the West End was for foreign devils. The roles are reversed now, yet the food is pretty good, from the capital spare ribs to the lemon chicken, to generous amounts of crab with the sweetcorn soup. It gets packed on Saturdays. House French is £3·90.

CHEF/PROPRIETOR: Tony Chung
OPEN: all week CLOSED: 25 and 26 Dec MEALS: noon to 11 (11.30 Thu to Sat)
PRICES: £7 (£12), Set D £8·50 (£12). Service 10% CARDS: Access, Amex, Diners, Visa
SEATS: 65. Private parties: 65 main room. Vegetarian meals. Children's helpings. Wheelchair access (also wc)

New World [11/20] map 13

Gerrard Place, W1V 7LL
01-734 0677, 734 0396 and 434 2508 £6–£15

The new operation spawned by Chuen Cheng Ku – a massive 550-seater eating-house, just like in Hong Kong. Throughout the day the dim-sum trolleys are wheeled around the cavernous rooms at a rate of knots, stacked high with pork dumplings, beef and ginger dumplings, shark's fin dumplings or more exotic whelks with chilli, or duck's feet. The noodle soups with roast duck provide the cheapest and most sustaining one-plate meals. From the long Cantonese menu it is possible to eat excellent fish – lobster with spring onions and ginger for under £7; soft-shelled, deep-fried crabs; mussels in a potent black bean sauce; prawns steamed with garlic. Good poultry, pork and hot-pot dishes too. Value for money compensates for lack of decor. The place is less busy at night because most Chinese tend to eat in the daytime. House French is £4·50.

CHEFS: K. Tang and C. Poon PROPRIETORS: Honsway Ltd
OPEN: all week MEALS: 11am to 11.45pm
PRICES: £9 (£15), Set L £3 (£6), Set D £5 (£9). Service inc CARDS: Access, Amex, Diners, Visa
SEATS: 550. Private parties: 200 main room, 80 and 60 private rooms. Vegetarian meals. Children welcome. Wheelchair access (2 steps, also wc). Music. Air-conditioned

▲ *Ninety Park Lane, Grosvenor House*
[promotional menu, zero rated] map 12

90 Park Lane, W1A 3AA
01-499 6363 £24–£48

For the time being Trusthouse Forte is in cahoots with Louis Outhier, who has three Michelin stars for his restaurant at La Napoule in the south of France, and as long as that continues expect to eat some sensational dishes here – as good as anywhere in London. It is a big, long, low dining-room hung with thick-framed oil paintings and with a micro-pattern zig-zagging its way across the carpet and up on to the buxom sofa. The waiters have a chatty line in patois. Stains on the tablecloth are explained away with 'there must have been a hole in the plate'.

Little rolls of smoked salmon the size of a 50p piece, filled with salmon mousse and with an asparagus and cream sauce, come as an appetiser. For the main business there is foie gras – two pieces served on a huge plate, one poached inside a transparent cabbage leaf with sweet-sour sauce and the other grilled and placed on a salad and garnished with a little pile of sea-salt and another of crushed peppercorns. But also there are farmhouse dishes, such as pigeon with a lentil soup, or lamb cutlets, still on the bone, criss-crossed in the centre of the plate with a cream and juice sauce and, at the edge, three fat garlic cloves poached in milk ('if madame likes garlic, she can press the heart out with the side of her knife'). Most striking of all are the scallops, laid on a plate of the most intense, sticky beef demi-glaze. The vegetables served with this are baked in an egg custard to form a cake. Vegetarians have done well – wild mushrooms with pastry, or another pastry coffin lined with a spinach purée, filled with turned vegetables and served with a beurre blanc with chives. The sweets are spectacularly displayed on a five-feet-tall table that swivels round, though the quality varies according to how old they are. The waiters insist on serving slices of three or four. The house wine is £12·50, which sums up a list that is top heavy in expensive classed-growth clarets. Some decent half-bottles would help.

CHEFS: Vaughan Archer and Stephen Beehag PROPRIETORS: Trusthouse Forte Ltd
OPEN: Mon to Sat, exc Sat L MEALS: 12 to 2.30, 7 to 10.45
PRICES: £34 (£42), Set L £17·50 (£24), Set D £29 to £40 (£37 to £48). Service inc
CARDS: Access, Amex, Carte Blanche, Diners, Visa
SEATS: 85. Private parties: 100 main room, 1600 private room. Car-park, 85 places
Vegetarian meals by arrangement. Children's helpings. Jacket and tie. Pianist. Air-conditioned
ACCOMMODATION: 471 rooms, all with bath/shower. Rooms for disabled. B&B £95 to £110. Baby facilities. Pets welcome. Afternoon teas. Indoor swimming-pool. Sauna. Air-conditioned. Lift. TV. Phone. Confirm by 6

Nontas [10/20] map 10

16 Camden High Street, NW1 0JH
01-387 4579 £10

The Vassilakas family run their Greek/Cypriot restaurant like racecourse bookies – orders and bookings are taken on scraps of paper which are passed through to the kitchen at the back. It's odds-on for the meze (the only outsider is avocado) at £5·15 – it runs to nearly 15 plates with a paddockful of grilled meats as the focal point. Favourites are the spicy sausages; the smoked sausage and pork marinated in red wine and served on a bed of pourgouri, barring the usual field of moussaka, kleftiko and stifado. All the meat and vegetables are fresh. The dining-room has hoops of Greek etchings around the walls and clean, cafe-style tables. Starting price on the Cypriot wines is £4·05. CELLARMAN'S CHOICE: Domaine d'Ahera at £8·20.

CHEF/PROPRIETOR: Nontas Vassilakas
OPEN: Mon to Sat MEALS: 12 to 2.45, 6 to 11.30
PRICES: £6 (£10) CARDS: Access, Amex, Diners
SEATS: 50. Private parties: 25 main room. Children's helpings. Wheelchair access. Greek music

The Nosherie [8/20] map 10

12–13 Greville Street, EC1N 8SB
01-242 1591 £10

Don't bother to travel all the way from Sheffield just to eat here but, as many readers who work in EC1 know, this offers the best-value quick lunch in the area

The Guide *does not accept free meals.*

and the salt beef is some of the best in London. It opened in 1960 as a kosher cafe and serves typically wholesome Jewish soups, grilled chicken and fried fish, too. Budweiser beers and a minimum charge of £1·95.

CHEF: Mr David PROPRIETOR: Mrs E. Berner
OPEN: Mon to Fri, daytime only MEALS: 8 to 5
PRICES: £6 (£10). Minimum £1·95
SEATS: 80. Private parties: 80 main room. Vegetarian meals. Children welcome

Odins [12/20] map 12

27 Devonshire Street, W1N 1RJ
01-935 7296 £20–£27

An array of paintings covers virtually every inch of the dining-room walls. The place is refreshingly individual and shows a healthy disregard for fashion. The menu too, although modern, has a mind of its own – red mullet pâté or foie gras with sherry vinegar, before fine fish main courses or else noisettes of veal with wild mushrooms, not with a sauce but just a juice. Finish with lemon mousse with raspberry coulis, individual hot apple tart, or Mrs Langan's legendary chocolate pudding (this is Peter Langan's original restaurant – see Langan's Brasserie and Langan's Bistro, which is next door). It is not cheap but it has got style, though service can be casual. Good wines, from house Blanc de Blancs at £5·75, upwards.

CHEF/PROPRIETOR: Christopher German
OPEN: Mon to Sat, exc Sat L MEALS: 12.30 to 2.30, 7 to 11.30
PRICES: £17 (£27), Set L £12·50 (£20). Cover £1. Service inc CARD: Amex
SEATS: 65. Children welcome. Wheelchair access

Oh Boy [10/20] map 9

843 Garratt Lane, SW17 0PG
01-947 9760 £13

The concertina menu is a fun read in this little Westernised Thai restaurant, tucked away in rows of Wandsworth shops. It is a long way from traditional Thai fare, but at least there are dishes for virtually everyone; if you don't find anything you fancy among the satay, dim-sum, tempura, Fighting Chicken, Prawn Sky, Wimbledon Balls and steak Diane, the kitchen will prepare something else. They like to flambé at the table, but it is not ostentatious and the Volcano Poussin is a winner – charcoal-grilled with a garlic, chilli and tomato sauce and flamed with brandy. The Pu Cha has been good too – a well flavoured mixture of crab-meat, potato and pork firmly stuffed into a crab shell. Deep-fried foods have been heavy and oily and the tiny Thai pots of sauces can be similar. Sixteen wines. House white is £4·20 and drinkable.

CHEF: C. Pantana PROPRIETOR: Paranee Pokavanit
OPEN: Mon to Sat, D only CLOSED: 2 weeks Aug MEALS: 7 to 10.30 (10.45 Fri and Sat)
PRICES: £8 (£13). Service 12.5% CARDS: Access, Amex, Diners, Visa
SEATS: 40. Private parties: 25 main room, 15 private room. Children welcome. Music

Reports on good shops, small hotels and cafes in your area are welcome.

Old Budapest [new entry, zero rated] map 13

6 Greek Street, W1V 5LA
01-437 2006 £11–£18

An offshoot of the Gay Hussar (see entry). Lunch is a set £8 and the portions are large. The menu is similar to the Hussar and has included good jellied carp, Hungarian-style liver, cold herrings in apple cream sauce, and Transylvania stuffed cabbage. Cold pike with beetroot sauce is a speciality. The decor is functional. Bull's Blood is £6. More reports, please.

CHEF: A.Tyàk PROPRIETOR: J.Friedman
OPEN: Mon to Sat MEALS: 12 to 3, 6 to 11
PRICES: £12 (£18), Set L £8 (£11) CARDS: Access, Amex, Visa
SEATS: 55. Private parties: 30 main room. Vegetarian meals. Children's helpings. No children under 10. Wheelchair access. Music. Air-conditioned

Olive Branch [new entry, zero rated] map 9

267 Kilburn High Road, NW6 7JR
01-625 8734 £5–£12

Interesting new venture – a vegetarian cafe with fish. The decor is, naturally, green and pine. The menu hitch-hikes round the globe for Aubergine Imam Bayeldi; Thai vegetables; moussaka; and cold mackerel marinated in soy wine and ginger. There are also some dishes that might be found in French restaurants, like herb mousse and quenelles, which have been less good. But on the other hand the garlic mayonnaise with fried avocado, the spinach pancakes and the carrot cake are well above the usual standard for vegetarian restaurants. Minimalist wine policy. More reports, please.

CHEF/PROPRIETOR: S.Demetrou
OPEN: all week, exc Sun and Mon L MEALS: 12.30 to 3, 6 to 11.30
PRICES: £8 (£12), Set L £2·25 (£5). Service 10% CARD: Access
SEATS: 55. 2 tables outside. Private parties: 60 main room. Vegetarian meals. Children's helpings (weekends only). No-smoking area. Wheelchair access (also WC). Music

L'Olivier [13/20] map 10

116 Finsborough Road, SW10 9ED
01-370 4183 and 4199 £23–£25

One of the best undiscovered restaurants in London. It is the meat division of the fish chain of La Croisette, Le Suquet, and Le Quai St Pierre (see entries). Brown awning: ring bell, door answered. The restaurant is in the basement. Floral paintings run around the room, and a great pile of charcuterie stands on the central table. It is smart and club-like, probably because the tables are so close together that conversation drifts from one to the other. The set meal is a big business of no less than five starters of cochonnaille, saucissons and excellent soupe au pistou before the meat of the day; the *carte* has some fish as well as rack of lamb, rôti de boeuf, and magret with peppercorns. Olives, asparagus tart, and a Kir come for the price of the cover charge. Particularly good have been the offal dishes of sweetbreads in pastry, and veal tongue with a sauce ravigote. Steaks, too, are first-class, as is the ratatouille. To finish there is peach soup with raspberries or fruit tarts. Service is efficient and chatty. House Provence is £6·50 off a short, perfunctory list. Perrier, mind, is £1·50.

CHEF: Philippe Moron PROPRIETOR: Pierre Martin
OPEN: Mon to Sat, exc Mon L CLOSED: 2 weeks at Christmas MEALS: 12.30 to 2.30, 7.30 to 11.30
PRICES: £17 (£25), Set L and D from £17 (£23), Cover £1·50. Service 15%
CARDS: Amex, Visa
SEATS: 50. Children welcome. Music

One Hampstead Lane [11/20]

map 9

1 Hampstead Lane, N6 4RS
01-340 4444

£13–£22

Formerly a garage it is now a spacious, noisy place with tables far enough apart to give a bit of privacy. The menu is sensibly split between classic grills and some *nouvelle* dishes – spinach, mushrooms and bacon salad; trout baked with sorrel; 24-ounce ribs of beef grilled on the open fire and served with a béarnaise sauce. Vegetables are minuscule, but the almond torte is excellent – you get up and choose from the sweets table. Ther rating is dropped one point because standards, especially the service, have been inconsistent, and extras push up the bill. Thirty well-chosen wines start with vin de pays de Vaucluse at £5·95.

CHEF: Les Alexander PROPRIETOR: Paul Michaels
OPEN: all week, exc Sun D MEALS: 12.30 to 3.30, 7.30 to 11
PRICES: £14 (£22), Set L from £6·95 (£13). Cover 95p CARDS: Access, Diners, Visa
SEATS: 160. 16 tables outside. Private parties; 300 main room 70 private room. Vegetarian meals. Children's helpings. Wheelchair access (also WC). Live jazz. Air-conditioned

192 [10/20]

map 10

192 Kensington Park Road, W11 2JF
01-229 0482

£15

The fashion-magazine decor of this basement bistro under the wine bar has been looking a bit worn, which is hardly surprising given the number of people who crowd in. The atmosphere is usually fairly manic, but the waitresses manage to keep on top of the din. There is a brilliant cheeseboard and the menu is freshly cooked – asparagus quiche is served still warm; watercress soup catches the taste of the leaves rather than the stock; new season's lamb is served pink with its own juice. Pineapple cheesecake may sound unlikely, but it works well. Not a place for smokers. Alastair Little, who started this restaurant, has gone to his own place in Soho's Frith Street. There are 50 wines, though the Alsace section may be past its prime, and there are some fanciful descriptions. Perhaps someone should tell Monsieur Jaboulet that his Crozes-Hermitage '82 (at £8·50) 'hints of violets, vanilla, blackcurrants, tar and woodsmoke'. Geddaway.

CHEFS: Adam Robinson and Angela Dwyer
PROPRIETORS: A.Mackintosh, M.Chassay, J.Armit and B.Wordsworth
OPEN: all week, exc Sun D CLOSED: 25 Dec, most bank hols MEALS: 12.30 to 2.30 (3 Sat and Sun), 7.30 to 11.30
PRICES: £11 (£15) CARDS: Access, Amex, Visa
SEATS: 32. Private parties: 12 main room. Vegetarian meals. Children welcome. Wheelchair access. Jazz. Air-conditioned

One Two Three [13/20] map 12

27 Davies Street, WIY 1LN
01-409 0750 £14–£27

This is one the best Japanese retaurants in the country, and it has earned high prestige among native businessmen with its combination of carefully cooked dishes and impeccable service, as well as the picturesque arranging of the food and the calm dining-room that are typical of the genre. The set meals, particularly at lunchtime, are not as expensive as sallying into the *carte*. There is sashimi – including salmon, which is not usually served raw in Japan but simmered because it is rarely considered fresh enough, and also a choice of back or belly of tuna – and sushi. The plate of pickled turnip, cabbage and carrot looks prettier than it tastes, but a consolation is the superb dish of belly-pork simmered in saké for five hours and served as a single piece the size of a matchbox, topped with some green leaves and in a sauce of soy and saké. The soups are also good. The atmosphere is not overwhelmingly foreign and the waitresses manage a little English, such as, 'Would you like another beer?' Drink the warm saké or Suntory whisky.

CHEF/PROPRIETOR: S. Ikeda
OPEN: Mon to Fri, and Sun D MEALS: 12 to 2.30, 6.30 to 10.30
PRICES: £16 (£27), Set L from £7·50 (£14), Set D from £18·50 (£27). Cover 50p at L, £1 at D. Service 15% CARDS: Access, Amex, Diners, Visa
SEATS: 50. 8 tables outside. Private parties: 50 main room. Vegetarian meals. Children welcome. Japanese music. Air-conditioned

Ormes [9/20] map 9

67–69 Abbeville Road, SW4 9JW
01-673 2568 £13

The kitchen runs on a stock-pot, making up sauces with wines from the bar, and only prawns and whitebait will be frozen. The decor is rather basic and standards fluctuate, but we have eaten good grilled mushrooms and haddock roulade, and griddled lamb steaks taste better than they look. Sweets are convincing, and include Pavlova and chocolate fudge cake. Some interesting wines, especially from the south west of France, for about £6·25. CELLARMAN'S CHOICE: house claret.

CHEF: Vivian McCann PROPRIETORS: Claire and Derek Orme
OPEN: all week CLOSED: 4 days at Christmas MEALS: 12 to 2.45, 6.30 to 11
PRICES: £8 (£13). Cover 50p CARDS: Access, Amex, Diners, Visa
SEATS: 120. 4 tables outaide. Private parties: 12 main room. Vegetarian meals. Children's helpings (weekends only). Music

Le Papillon [11/20] map 9

57 Greenwich Church Street, SE10 9BL
01-858 2668 £9–£21

Marc Sheridan tends to pop out of his kitchen to deliver Chinese-style bamboo steamers filled with vegetables, or main dishes. It is a small, ground-floor nineteenth-century-style restaurant hard by the *Cutty Sark*. His governing principles are value for money and fresh produce which he buys personally at the market. Game is consistently good, notably saddle of hare and pigeon. Lobster is grilled and served with a squeeze of lime. Grilled ribs of beef are popular. The trimmings are of a very good restaurant – wholemeal rolls; iced water with lemon on each table; a dozen good French cheeses, and so on. A more confident hand with the saucing and with the pastry would raise the rating to 12. The wine list, like the restaurant, has aspirations and includes some good '78 and '79 clarets from around £10 up. House Cuvée de Ropiteau is £4·95.

CHEF/PROPRIETOR: Marc Sheridan
OPEN: all week, exc Sat L and Sun D MEALS: 12.15 to 2.30, 6.45 to 10.30
PRICES: £14 (£21), Set L from £4·95 (£9). Minimum £4·95 CARDS: Access, Amex, Diners, Visa
SEATS: 40. Private parties: 55 main room, 16 private room. Children's helpings. Wheelchair access. Music. Air-conditioned

Il Passetto [10/20]

map 12

230 Shaftesbury Avenue, WC2H 8EG
01-836 9391

£16

A small, crowded restaurant well situated for the theatres. There are original framed pictures by Italian artists of all styles on the walls above the close-together tables. Crudités are already waiting. Starters from the trolley include aubergine stuffed with tomato and garlic, stuffed mussels, stuffed peppers and a good egg mayonnaise. Choose a steak, or there is garlicky leg of lamb. Vegetables are fresh. Coffee comes with Amaretti biscuits. The Italian wine list stays mainly in the £5 to £7 range, but house Soave is £4·50. CELLARMAN'S CHOICE: Dolcetto d'Alba at £7·80.

CHEF: Jesus Sanchez PROPRIETORS: Lindown Ltd
OPEN: Mon to Sat, exc Sat L MEALS: 12 to 3, 6 to 11.30
PRICES: £10 (£16). Cover 75p CARDS: Access, Amex, Diners, Visa
SEATS: 42. Private parties: 20 main room. Vegetarian meals. Children welcome. Wheelchair access. Air-conditioned

Paulo's [10/20]

map 9

30 Greyhound Road, W6 8NX
01-385 9264

£10

An unsophisticated, fun Brazilian restaurant. The dining-room looks like a converted play-group room – kites hang from the ceiling and so do a pair of hammocks. A table of food stretches the length of the far wall underneath the window and diners help themselves. Typical are the black bean stew and pork soufflé, and there is peanut and shrimp sauce or gari powder to go with rice. There are also robust crab dishes and the sopa-do-dia looks like a Brazilian cock-a-leekie. To finish there is mango fool. Coffee is Brazilian. No licence; no corkage.

CHEF/PROPRIETOR: Paulo Torres
OPEN: Mon to Sat, D only CLOSED: bank hols and a week at Christmas
MEALS: 6.30 to 10.30
PRICES: £8 (£10). Service 10%. Unlicensed, but bring your own: no corkage
SEATS: 40. Private parties: 40 main room. Vegetarian meals. Children's helpings. Wheelchair access. Spanish music

Peachey's [12/20] map 10

205 Haverstock Hill, NW3 4QG
01-435 6744 £11–£20

Here you find *nouvelle cuisine* in decent-sized portions, plus a lot of interesting clutter on the walls – old cameras, mirrors, paintings, old projectors. Good starters are eggs with crab; avocado sliced and fanned across the plate with a raspberry vinaigrette; carrot soup. Meat is reliable – paper-thin slices of beef with a mustard sauce; veal in a mustard sauce; chicken stuffed with broccoli mousse and served with a thin, buttery sauce. Vegetables are served separately, the cheeseboard is magnificent on its good nights and, to finish, there has been wonderful banana brûlée or spectacularly exotic house fruit salad. Regulars say the blackboard menu is sometimes more reliable than the *carte*. Interesting wines – the mark-ups are around 130 per cent – though the waiters tend to top up glasses as if they were working in a petrol station. The music gets louder as the place fills up.

CHEF: Hans Küster PROPRIETORS: Sally Kimbell and François de Kerbrech
OPEN: Mon to Sat, exc Sat L MEALS: 12 to 2.30, 7 to 11.30
PRICES: £13 (£20), Set L from £7·50 (£11). Cover 60p. Service 12.5% alc only
CARDS: Amex, Diners, Visa
SEATS: 38. 2 tables outside. Private parties: 40 main room. Vegetarian meals. Children's helpings. Wheelchair access. Classical music

Perfumed Conservatory [10/20] map 9

182 Wandsworth Bridge Road, SW6 1EX
01-731 0732 £21

A pretty pink dining-room with lots of plants and pictures and a tiny, two-table conservatory with even more plants leaning over your shoulder in summer. The menu makes colourful reading and promises a great deal – game livers with kumquats; scallops with ginger; pigeon breasts with rhubarb – and it's all very idiosyncratic. Wild foods (marsh samphire, nettles, elderflowers and dandelion leaves), exotic ingredients and flowers all find their way onto the plate, but it's more of a flirtation between the kitchen and such things than a deep love affair. Better are the simple items, like admirable, simply cooked vegetables.
CELLARMAN'S CHOICE: Ch. Les Ormes-de-Pez '80, at £14·80. More wines, please.

CHEFS/PROPRIETORS: B.M.Deane and J.J.Hayes
OPEN: Tue to Sat, exc Sat L CLOSED: bank hols MEALS: 12.30 to 2.30, 7 to 11.30
PRICES: Set L and D £14·50 (£21). Service 12% CARDS: Access, Amex, Visa
SEATS: 38. 6 tables outside. Private parties: 26 main room, 20 and 18 private rooms. Vegetarian meals. No children under 4. Smart dress preferred. Music

The Guide *does not accept free meals.*

New restaurants that we have not been able to assess completely are given a zero rating for this year. We are particularly keen to have reports on these places.

If you suspect that a restaurant is using processed food, always ask. It would be a contravention of the Trade Descriptions Act for the restaurant to lie.

Le Petit Prince [9/20] map 10

5 Holmes Road, NW5 3AA
01-267 0752 £12

A warm, extrovert cafe specialising in French/Algerian dishes including authentic couscous. The Algerian Sidi Brahim is £4·85.

CHEF: Sushi Bogdonovich PROPRIETORS: Philip and Farima Smith
OPEN: Tue to Sun, exc Sat L and Sun L CLOSED: bank hols MEALS: 12.30 to 2.30, 7 to 11.30
PRICES: £8 (£12). Service 10%
SEATS: 32. Private parties: 32 main room. Vegetarian meals. Children's helpings. Wheelchair access. Music

Phoenicia [10/20] map 10

11–13 Abingdon Road, W8 6AH
01-937 0120 £12

Lebanese cooking is an exciting new addition to London restaurant eating, and of the Lebanese restaurants in the *Guide* this family-run business is the most accessible to Europeans – well organised and friendly, best suited for eating in groups, and the Arab music more muted. The first courses, of which there are more than 40, offer the most interest, while main courses tend to rely heavily on charcoal-grilled meats. The meze encompasses a good spread, from a rough-and-ready hummus to a brown lentil purée that goes well with the radishes in the statutory salad basket, to mancha, spicy, fatty, cocktail-sized sausages. For the brave there is the Arabic variation on steak tartare – kebbeh nayeh. Sweets are cream cheese, pistachios, spun shredded wheat and superior honey. Service comes with a smile, if not much English, which means it can be fairly tricky finding out what you are eating. The rating is dropped one point because of the stiff competition now available. Arak is £1·80 a measure.

CHEF: Choki Serhal PROPRIETOR: Hani Khalifé
OPEN: all week MEALS: noon to 12
PRICES: £6 (£12), Set L and D from £7·95 (£12). Cover charge £1.10. Minimum £8. Service inc set only, alc 15% CARDS: Access, Amex, Diners, Visa
SEATS: 80. Private parties: 80 main room, 25 private room. Vegetarian meals. Children's helpings. Wheelchair access. Piano player. Air-conditioned

PIZZAS

Pizza is becoming king of the fast foods. The base is as good as bread can be, and the topping can be assembled cheaply from the finest of ingredients. Americans say that no pizza in London is as good as even the dullest specimen in New York, but if you're in the capital make do with the following. For Italian-style pizza the Pizza Express chain is best, with branches all over London and a few beyond. Pizza Hut is more American in style and the product rather better than at the enormous chain, Pizzaland. For the Chicago-style deep-pan pizza there is the Chicago Pizza Pie Factory, 17 Hanover Square, W1, which brought the beast over the Atlantic, or Grunt's, 12 Maiden Lane, WC2, where the wait for a table is worth it and there are cocktails to sip in the interim. Good one-off places also include the Castello, 20 Walworth Road, SE1. See, too, the entry for Kettners, W1.

Pollyanna's [11/20]

map 9

2 Battersea Rise, SW11 1ED
01-228 0316 £13–£19

The main drawback at this excellent modern French neighbourhood restaurant is the tables for two, which are cramped and sited in the slipstream of the waitresses on their way to the kitchen. The tables for four are a better bet. The decor is what you might expect in a restaurant called Pollyanna's – long and lanky with pine and posters. Eamonn Connolly runs a remarkable menu, cooking a wide variety of well-balanced and inventive dishes which arrive at the table remarkably quickly. Notably good have been the chilled radish and Red Leicester soup; smooth duck liver pâté picturesquely set in a Cumberland sauce; excellent liver, not swamped in its sauce of orange and Grand Marnier; seafood ragout in a shellfish bisque filled out with noodles. Vegetables are varied but can disappoint. The eye for the visual extends to the sweets: a slice of summer pudding bisects the plate, with the cream to one side and raspberry sauce to the other. There are usually a couple of cheeses in fair condition to go with a well-chosen and legitimately marked-up wine list that opens with a run of ten Ch. Gruaud-Larose dating from '61. There is a full show of the excellent '83 *cru* Beaujolais and also a trio of '83 Alsace wines from Louis Gisselbrecht. House Loire is £5·50.

CHEF: Eamonn Connolly PROPRIETORS: Gortred Ltd
OPEN: all week, D only, and Sun L MEALS: 1 to 3, 7 to 12
PRICES: £13 (£19), Set Sun L £7·95 (£13). Service 10% CARDS: Access, Amex, Diners, Visa
SEATS: 100. 10 tables outside. Private parties: 14 main room, 38 private room. Vegetarian meals. Children's helpings. Popular music

Ponte Nuovo [12/20]

map 11

126 Fulham Road, SW3 6HU
01-370 6656 and 370 4917 £21

A vast umbrella covers the pavement tables fenced in by shrubbery in front of this swish modern Italian restaurant. Inside, Venetian blinds hang the length of the floor-to-ceiling glass frontage and a strip of mirror about six inches deep runs around the walls at sitting-down-eye-level, giving a false sense of space. The waiters are young and self-assured and the pasta – al dente fettuccine with cream and Gorgonzola sauce – and the fish dishes are well above average. Sea-bass (for two) is cooked in a paper bag; Dover sole is plainly grilled, which is probably the best way to cook fresh sole; and the fish risotto and crab Mornay have been excellent. Also good have been the ribs of beef, though the lamb with rosemary could have been better trimmed at one inspection meal, and vegetables could also be improved. The sweets trolley looks the part and the chocolate truffle cake

Prices quoted are for an average three-course meal including service and VAT and half a bottle of house wine (or the equivalent in an ethnic restaurant).

'The waiters refill your glass as they pass, even when asked not to. "But your bottle not finished," explained one puzzled waitress.' (On eating Chinese in North London)

tastes it. Espresso coffee is £1. House Trebbiano is £6·50 on an exclusively Italian list of 40 or so wines.

CHEF: Guiseppe Canizzaro PROPRIETOR: Walter Mariti
OPEN: all week MEALS: 12.30 to 2.55, 7 to 11.55
PRICES: £13 (£21). Cover £1 CARDS: Access, Amex, Diners, Visa
SEATS: 78. 10 tables outside. Private parties: 14 main room. Vegetarian meals. Children's helpings. Wheelchair access. Air-conditioned

Poons [10/20] map 13

4 Leicester Street, WC2H 7BL
01-437 1528 £14

This is essentially a smart cafe specialising in wind-dried foods, especially ducks and sausages, backed up by more than 200 largely Cantonese dishes. As is often the case in Cantonese restaurants the fish is of a high standard – mussels in black bean sauce; steamed scallops; stewed eel with crispy pork and garlic. The flavours come through crystal clear most evenings, though there are some disappointments on file. The original hot-pot dishes are worth exploring. Fried noodles are an alternative to rice. Service is happy and copes well in a rush; it is probably not worth booking. Licensed, but corkage is only £1 and tea is on the house.

CHEF/PROPRIETOR: W.N.Poon
OPEN: Mon to Sat CLOSED: 25 Dec MEALS: noon to 11.30
PRICES: £9 (£14). Set L and D from £8·50 (£11) for 2. Minimum £2·50
SEATS: 100. Private parties: 30 main room. Children welcome. Air-conditioned

Porte de la Cité [12/20] map 12

65 Theobald's Road, WC1X 8SP
01-242 1154 £16

If all expense-account restaurants were run like this, then British catering would be a lot healthier. This is a smart, well-oiled, not over-expensive French restaurant with set prices for two menus of ten starters and ten main courses with some plats du jour. The pity is, it is open only at lunch, though it has a sister (see Au Bois St Jean). Gilbert Altmeyer cooks an unpretentious range of brasserie food: fish soup with rouille and croûtons; excellent brochette of cheese, deep-fried and served with a mustard sauce; duck with limes; roast rack of lamb. Fish varies according to market, and the proprietors say 'nothing is frozen'. A short, workmanlike list of wines. House French is £5·75.

CHEF: Gilbert Altmeyer PROPRIETORS: Cellier du Midi Ltd
OPEN: Mon to Fri, L only CLOSED: bank hols MEALS: 12 to 2.30
PRICES: Set L from £12 (£16). Service inc CARDS: Access, Amex, Diners, Visa
SEATS: 65. Private parties: 50 main room, 25 private room. Vegetarian meals. Children welcome

'The beef was an alcoholic's version of surf and turf – with port and anchovies.'
(On eating in London)

Ports [11/20] map 11

11 Beauchamp Place, SW3 1NQ
01-581 3837 £10–£17

The place to eat Portuguese in London – a spacious airy basement with panels of tiles similar to those in Lisbon restaurants, plenty of plants and lots of whitewash. The salt cod is outstandingly good, served with boiled potatoes and not-so-good oil. Other interesting tastes are the morcela, an unextended variation of black pudding; fiery piri-piri sauce served with prawns. Fish features strongly, and, as you would expect, it is usually char-grilled. Sweets tend to the standard crème caramel. Service is first-class. There are some fine Portuguese wines, too, and Aguardiente, the Iberian version of grappa, as a digestif.

CHEF: Elio de Andrade PROPRIETORS: Louis Pimentel and Mr Valerio
OPEN: Mon to Sat CLOSED: Christmas, Easter, bank hols MEALS: 12.15 to 2.30, 7 to 11.30
PRICES: £11 (£17), Set L £6·50 (£10). Service 12.5% CARDS: Access, Amex, Diners, Visa
SEATS: 45. Private parties: 45 main room. Children welcome. Music. Air-conditioned

Le Poulbot [13/20] map 10

45 Cheapside, EC2V 6AR
01-236 4379 **Real Food** £30

The Roux brothers' City outlet. Upstairs is a bustling French-style cafe doing mostly sandwiches, with nothing like enough tables to meet demand. Downstairs is the directors' dining-room. It is expensive, but it is good. The posters leading downstairs are adverts for St-Raphael (the drink) and Monaco (the place). There is a lavish use of red velvet braid and the tables are arranged to make mini-rooms for business. The inclusive menu (wine extra) runs happily through the Roux repertoire of potage St Germain; feuilleté of moules and oyster mushrooms; and veal kidneys with basil. The emphasis is on the classic. Salads are dressed in walnut oil. Only four wines are offered, and not cheaply either, but they are of good pedigree – the least expensive is Pinot Noir '80 at £11·70.
CELLARMAN'S CHOICE: Meursault '82 at £18·50.

CHEF: R.R.Leigh PROPRIETORS: Roux Restaurants Ltd
OPEN: Mon to Fri, L only MEALS: 12 to 3
PRICES: Set L £24·50 (£30). Service inc CARDS: Access, Amex, Diners, Visa
SEATS: 50. Vegetarian meals. Children welcome. Jacket and tie. No pipes in dining-room. Air-conditioned

La Preferita [10/20] map 9

163 Lavender Hill, SW11 3QH
01-223 1046 £16

Italian food in Britain is, more often than not, pre-prepared using low-quality ingredients – a bland mix of minced beef, tomatoes and parsley is the base for most saucing; the pasta is over-worked from being left around (which is why Italians ask for it al dente so that it *has* to be cooked to order); the cheapest oils and vinegars are used to dress salads; and sweets are bought in. The Preferita is not completely free of these traits (dried herbs being a particular failing), but the pasta is more than edible – spaghetti cooked in a paper bag; linguine with clams;

spaghetti carbonara – and the lamb cutlets with rosemary and the calf's liver have been solid main courses. The restaurant is smart, with a bustling atmosphere. There is zabaglione to finish and house Verona is £4·50.

CHEF: Olivio Barrosa PROPRIETOR: Alfonso Cretella
OPEN: all week MEALS: 12.30 to 3, 7 to 11.30
PRICES: £9 (£16). Cover 75p. Service 12.5% CARDS: Access, Amex, Diners, Visa
SEATS: 75. 5 tables outside. Private parties: 15 private room. Children welcome

Le Quai St Pierre [11/20] map 10

7 Stratford Road, W8 6RF
01-937 6388 £24

The third fish restaurant from La Francine, who also own La Croisette and Le Suquet (see entries). It is run on the same lines as the other two, with a strong fish menu based on large platters of shellfish, oysters, and white fish in cream and wine sauces. The service is not as good as the other two, but the cooking is on a par and the raw materials come from the same van-run to Brittany three times a week. Downstairs there is a bar where you can eat just one course with a bottle of good Muscadet, or there are tables upstairs where you feel more as if you are in a private house than in a restaurant.

CHEF: Alain Patrat PROPRIETORS: La Francine Ltd
OPEN: Mon to Sat, exc Mon L CLOSED: 2 weeks Christmas MEALS: 12.30 to 2.30, 7.30 to 11.30
PRICES: £15 (£24). Cover 80p. Service 15%
SEATS: 55. 3 tables outside. Children welcome. Music

Quincy's '84 [13/20] map 10

675 Finchley Road, NW2 2JP
01-794 8499 £16–£17

Our initial enthusiasm for this higgledy-piggledy little bistro with a rather classy, fashionable menu has been endorsed by many readers. But we are having second thoughts. Should a restaurant scoring 13 used dried dill for its sauce with gravlax? If the calf's liver with raspberry vinegar is too floured, then surely the flour should be cooked out? There seems to be a hurry in the kitchen that leads to, for instance, stocks being insufficiently intense. Nevertheless there are many good reports on file. The granary bread is first-class, the duck with kumquats and the veal dijonnaise mentioned last year continue to impress, as does a vegetarian pie that had all the qualities of saucing that we did not find at other inspections. And the sweets are a powerhouse, from the chocolate pot made with good chocolate and a dribble of rum, to the rhubarb crumble. The wine list is short and elegant for a neighbourhood restaurant. CELLARMAN'S CHOICE: Bourgogne Pinot Noir, Domaine Parent '82, at £9.

CHEF: Sandy Anderson PROPRIETORS: D.J.C.Wardle and D.A.Anderson
OPEN: Tue to Sun, exc Sat L, Sun D MEALS: 12 to 2, 7 to 10.30
PRICES: £11 (£16) L only, Set D £12·75 (£17) CARD: Access
SEATS: 30. 4 tables outside. Private parties: 30 main room. Vegetarian meals. Children's helpings. No-smoking area. Light and classical music

Quinns [new entry, zero rated] map 10

138 Columbia Road, E2 7RG
01-739 9090 £15

Originally a small shop in a row of terraced houses on the road where the flower market is held on Sunday mornings – one of the smarter pockets of the East End. The colour scheme is grey and pink, from the lettering on the window to the tablecloths. The menu is short and fashionably *nouvelle anglaise*. Good dishes have been leek and mushroom tart; hot chicken livers with basil and grapefruit salad; duck with honeyed kumquats; and pork with peas and mustard. Portions are big and the presentation is a strong point. Fresh fruits have made popular round-offs. A good choice of wines in the £5 to £10 range. More reports, please.

CHEF: Nicholas Atkins PROPRIETOR: Kevin Mangan
OPEN: Tue to Sat, exc Sat L MEALS: 12 to 2.30, 7.30 to 10.45
PRICES: Set L and D £12·50 (£15). Service inc CARDS: Amex, Diners, Visa
SEATS: 30. Private parties: 34 main room. Vegetarian meals by arrangement. Children's helpings. Music

Ragam [9/20] map 12

57 Cleveland Street, W1P 5PQ
01-636 9098 £8–£9

A newly opened classical south Indian restaurant, specialising in Kerala cuisine. As well as kaallan – a curry made with yoghourt, mango, coconut and spices – and uppuma – semolina fried with onions and spices – there are variations on the pancake theme. These include meat or vegetable masala dosai; nai roast, a crispy pancake roasted in ghee; and adai, a spicy one made from rice and lentils. There is a good range of meat dishes, too. Licensed.

CHEFS: J. Dharmaseelan and Mosid Ullah
PROPRIETORS: J. Dharmaseelan, J. Haridas and S. Pillai
OPEN: all week MEALS: 12 to 3, 6 to 12
PRICES: £5 (£9), Set L and D £4·50 (£8). Minimum £3. Service 10%. Licensed, plus bring your own: corkage 50p CARDS: Access, Amex, Diners, Visa
SEATS: 34. Private parties: 34 main room. Vegetarian meals. Children's helpings. Wheelchair access (also WC). Music. Take-away service

Rajput [8/20] map 9

144 Goldhawk Road, W12 8HH
01-740 9036 £10–£11

A comfortable, somewhat colonial restaurant in which to eat the best Indian food at this price in the area. There are tandoori, kebab and curry dishes, including rich butter chicken and a few other dishes using cream, as well as vegetarian thalis, good pickles and chutney, and a Sunday buffet at £5·95 a head. Choose a bottle of Dortmunder Union (65p) in preference to the draught lager.

CHEF: Abdul Aziz PROPRIETOR: Raja Meah
OPEN: all week CLOSED: 25 and 26 Dec MEALS: 12 to 2.45, 6 to 11.20
PRICES: £5 (£11), set Sun D £5·95 (£10) CARDS: Access, Amex, Diners, Visa
SEATS: 50. Private parties: 12 main room. Vegetarian meals. Children welcome. Wheelchair access. Indian music. Air-conditioned

Read's [12/20] map 11

152 Old Brompton Road, SW5 0BR
01-373 2445 £14–£25

A private, quiet and relaxing dining-room decorated in rich colours and mirrors. Caroline Read cooks with the accent commendably on British dishes, while her husband Keith runs the upstairs. Tables are laid with dressed salads and cheese nibbles. The cooking is marked by some ambitious combinations – scallop salad with marjoram; liver with leeks; quail stuffed with pear and cooked with garlic; goats' cheese strudel with artichokes; and avocado and oyster mushrooms with a tomato sauce. Quenelles are a favourite device – smoked haddock with saffron and mussel sauce; rabbit on salmon trout mousse. As we go to press there has been a batch of bad reports about misconceived combinations and too many failures among dishes. Plus points, though, have been the English cheeseboard, home-made chocolates, and the very good-value Sunday lunch with fabulous Angus beef. Wines from Corney and Barrow have been picked with care. House Costières du Gard is £6·50.

CHEF: Caroline Read PROPRIETORS: Caroline and Keith Read and Colin Crewe
OPEN: all week, exc Sun D CLOSED: 10 days at Christmas MEALS: 12.30 to 2.30 (12 to 3 Sun), 7.30 to 11
PRICES: £18 (£25), Set L £9·50 (£14) CARDS: Access, Amex, Diners, Visa
SEATS: 45. 2 tables outside. Vegetarian meals by arrangement. No children under 10. Air-conditioned

Rebato's [10/20] map 9

169 South Lambeth Road, SW8 1XW
01-735 6388 £13

The tapas bar serves callos, pupio, albondigas, tortilla, angulas, sardinas, calamares, gambas al ajilo, champinos, riñones al Jerez, chorizo, and jamon, mostly between £1 and £2. Three-course meals in the restaurant cost £9. The staff are Spanish, wonderfully pleasant, and happy to explain the dishes. There is a guitarist, a well-stocked bar, and plenty of Penedès wines, including Torres at £4·95.

CHEF: Arturo Garcia PROPRIETOR: Dino Rebato
OPEN: Mon to Sat, exc Sat L MEALS: 12 to 2.30, 7 to 11.15
PRICES: Set L and D £9 (£13) CARDS: Access, Amex, Diners, Visa
SEATS: 60. Children welcome. Wheelchair access. Music. Air-conditioned

Red Fort [12/20] map 13

77 Dean Street, W1V 5HA
01-437 2115 and 2525 £11–£14

Smart, new wave Indian restaurant with a well-balanced menu concentrating on Moghul cuisine. The smells of spices and a floral perfume hang in the pink dining-room, which is set with dark cane chairs and a few dark-leaved plants. The menu is built around tandooris of chicken, lamb, and so on (and the misconceived idea of tandoori trout); good vegetarian thalis; and fish. Especially good are the masha; succulent quail in dark brown sauce; lamb korahi with a good acid edge from the coriander; and also chicken korahi. The nan could be improved, and the sag can be reminiscent of a high-street take-away. Other minus points centre on the service, and it is no irony that the sound of the cash till reverberates through the calm. Even so, inspection meals have been impressive enough to raise the rating and suggest that this is the real competitor to the Bombay Brasserie (see entry). The kulfi is excellent and there are some splendid camp cocktails like Peacock Throne – migoti, mango and lemonade – served in tall tumblers with naked women dancing around the sides.

CHEF: N.P.Pittal PROPRIETOR: Amin Ali
OPEN: Mon to Fri, Sat and Sun buffet L CLOSED: 25 to 26 Dec MEALS: 12 to 2.30, 6 to 11.30
PRICES: £8 (£14), Set L £6·95 (£11), Set D £6·95 (£11). Minimum £6. Service 15%
CARDS: Access, Amex, Diners, Visa
SEATS: 150. Private parties: 100 main room, 50 private room. Vegetarian meals. Jacket and tie. Children's helpings (weekends only). Wheelchair access (also wc). Indian music. Air-conditioned

The Restaurant & Brasserie [10/20] map 10

Dolphin Square, Chichester Street, SW1V 3LX
01-828 3207 £13–£25

The feeling here is of eating in the bowels of a half-empty luxury liner – the dining-room is strangely becalmed even though the food can be inventive and good. The difference between the brasserie and the restaurant is imperceptible; the dividing line is a grand piano. Along the walls overlooking the swimming-pool is framed sheet-music of *Ave Maria, Blue Hawaii*, and others, and posters from the Georges Pompidou centre in Paris. Potted plants sprout from the art deco linoleum floor. The menu is modern, usually with some vegetarian dishes, and the cooking sound. Notably good have been the laver-bread soufflé with crab sauce, sole fillets fried in butter and served on a watercress purée garnished with bacon and croûtons, and the excellent petits fours, such as orange-flavoured almond tuiles and fruit filled, bitter and milk chocolate truffles. The Brasserie – turn left as you go in – is significantly cheaper. The wine list tries hard to stay under £10; house Rhône is £5·30.

CHEF: Michel Dubarbier PROPRIETOR: A.L.Hermitte
OPEN: Mon to Sat MEALS: 12 to 2.30, 7 to 11.30
PRICES: £11 (£18), Set L and D from £7·50 to £18 (£13 to £25). Cover £1 at D. Service 10% alc, 12.5% set CARDS: Access, Amex, Diners, Visa
SEATS: 130. Private parties: 200 main room. Car-park. Vegetarian meals. Children's helpings. Wheelchair access. Pianist Fri

Rogues Kitchen [9/20] map 9

St Marychurch Street, SE16 4JJ
01-237 7452 £11–£14

An eccentric, almost unique restaurant with a hotchpotch of furniture and a scolding from the waitress if you don't go for the dishes on the blackboard. The food is Creole, and fresh and varied – stuffed peppered trout to start, steaks or oriental jambalaya (a huge spicy mix of meat and fish) for main course, and tasty, if filling, American apple pie to finish. Good coffee and punctual closing at 10.30. Unlicensed.

CHEF/PROPRIETOR: Audrey Kilpack
OPEN: Wed to Sat, D only MEALS: 8 to 10.30
PRICES: £11(£14). Set D from £8·50 (£11). Cheaper set meals available. Unlicensed, but bring your own: no corkage
SEATS: 32. 3 tables outside. Private parties: 36 main room. Vegetarian meals by arrangement. Children's helpings by arrangement. Music

RSJ [11/20] map 10

13A Coin Street, SE1 8YQ
01-928 4554 £17

In the past we have under-rated this restaurant – within walking distance of the South Bank and London Weekend Television – and have done so again because there are changes going on in the kitchen. It is, however, smartly decorated with art gallery posters and has first-class waiters. The *nouvelle* menu sensibly uses mainly the cheaper ingredients, such as liver, but is not beyond the flourish of serving marinated salmon with scrambled quail eggs topped with the salmon roe inside the quail egg-shell. Onion soup is good, duck breast is fanned out in the *nouvelle cuisine* style – as are the al dente vegetables – and there is an unusual dish of chicken marinated in brandy, pan-fried and served with a little cream sauce and onions and mushrooms. The restaurant is one of the most popular among readers of all the London restaurants. The excellent selection of Loire wines earns the bottle denotation.

CHEF: Ian MacKenzie PROPRIETOR: Nigel Wilkinson
OPEN: Mon to Sat, exc Sat L CLOSED: 1 week at Christmas MEALS: 12 to 2, 6 to 11
PRICES: £12 (£17). Service 12.5%
SEATS: 40. Private parties: 30 main room. Children's helpings. Jacket and tie preferred. No smoking in dining-room. Music. Air-conditioned

Rudland & Stubbs [10/20] map 10

35–37 Greenhill Rents, EC1M 6BN
01-253 0148 and 1534
off Cowcross Street £17

Reputedly once a sausage factory, though now it feels like a market-hall and is an interloper in Smithfield in that it dispenses fish. The single, large, glass-fronted room has pillars, tiles everywhere, a long bar counter, railway and opera posters and a dark sea-green ceiling. The menu relies on plain poaching and grilling, which are probably the best ways of handling prime fish anyway, plus a few meat dishes, including a fine pie made with good pastry and a pair of oysters flavouring chunks of steak and veal kidney. Good dishes are the skate in butter, grilled sardines, the Parson's Hat (a ragout in pastry), superlative smoked eel, and

'The weekly visit to market by one of the chefs has proved a good change. Better, far far better, selection of fresh produce . . . and it has given the kitchen more pride in their product.' (Lakeland restaurateur)

omelette Arnold Bennett. The 30 wines are refreshingly un-French, with quite a few Spanish, German and Italian bottles. House burgundy is £4·95.

CHEFS: N.French and Mr Henry PROPRIETOR: R.Stubbs
OPEN: all week, exc Sat L and Sun D CLOSED: bank hols MEALS: 12 to 3, 6 (7 Sat) to 11.30
PRICES: £11 (£17)
SEATS: 80. Private parties: 20 main room. Vegetarian meals. Children's helpings. Wheelchair access (1 step)

Rue St Jacques [15/20] map 12

5 Charlotte Street, W1P 1HD
01-637 0222 £20–£31

Downstairs for mirrors, upstairs for crushed strawberry and deep forest greens; Rue St Jacques wears its style where you can see it. But Günther Schlender, who cooked at Carrier's for 17 years, is a technician who manages to do the set-piece modern dishes with more *élan* than others – salmon terrine with a mousseline sauce of watercress and leeks, and liver with a raspberry vinegar sauce. His sauces are excellent, as seen in the eel stuffed with a lobster mousseline and served with a chive-flecked sauce, or again in the fricassee of chicken, lobster and crayfish. But with fish, when it is genuinely fresh, instead of cooking he will use limes to marinate and will flavour with coriander, tarragon or saffron. Standing out from many good dishes are venison consommé, quail salad and chicken stuffed with foie gras and spinach. The service has settled down, but there are some unnerving franglais accents brought into play: most people are wished bon appetit more than once. Lunch is a relative snip at £13·50. A doorman parks the car. The wines are expensive – on a par with Paris prices rather than London – but there is a clutch of *cru bourgeois* clarets which are good value. House Sauvignon de St-Bris is £8. Vintage armagnacs go back from 1963 to 1893.

CHEF: Günther Schlender PROPRIETOR: Vincenzo Calcerano
OPEN: Mon to Sat, exc Sat L CLOSED: 25 Dec, Easter, bank hols MEALS: 12.30 to 2.30, 7.30 to 11.15
PRICES: £22 (£31), Set L £13·50 (£20). Service 15% CARDS: Access, Amex, Diners, Visa
SEATS: 70. Private parties: 26 main room, 20 private room. Vegetarian meals. Children's helpings by arrangement. Smart dress preferred. No pipes in dining-room. Classical music. Air-conditioned

Sabras [11/20] map 9

263 Willesden High Road, NW10 2RX
01-459 0340 £5–£9

When the Desais opened a take-away in 1972, there wasn't another Indian vegetarian between Southall and Stoke Newington. There are plenty around now, but only Woodlands and Munbhave (see entries) compete. Ravaiya – vegetables stuffed with ground spices – is still unique. Fresh, delicate flavours are balanced by superb masala dosai, a huge, crispy, puffy pancake folded over a fairly hot mixture of potato, onion and spices, and served with a juicy coconut chutney. There is patia – yam leaves rolled round spices, sliced, steamed and fried – and dhokala – a cake-like mixture of grain flour, lentils and yoghourt, spiced with mustard seeds, coconut and coriander leaves. There are thalis and a range of curries, too, with kulfi and shrikand to follow. The menu helpfully explains the dishes, and prices are nothing short of a bargain. Drink salt, sweet or de luxe lassi, or interestingly flavoured milks.

CHEFS/PROPRIETORS: Hemant and Nalinee Desai
OPEN: Tue to Sun CLOSED: 2 weeks in winter, 2 weeks in summer MEALS: 12.45 to 9
PRICES: £6 (£9), Set L and D from £3·75 (£5). Service 10%. Unlicensed, but bring your own: corkage 40p CARDS: Access, Amex, Diners, Visa
SEATS: 24. Private parties: 28 main room. Vegetarian meals. Children's helpings. Wheelchair access. Music

Saga [14/20] map 12

43 South Molton Street, W1Y 1HB
01-629 3931 £6–£26

This is three restaurants rolled into one small one. Downstairs is a sushi bar and upstairs is a frying-bar, where one of two chefs prepares fillet steaks, salmon and king prawns in front of diners, frying huge piles of diced garlic until brown and then wrapping them inside paper-thin layers of fillet. Upstairs are also some tables for more conventional soups, bean curd and fish dishes. The atmosphere is happy and there are big smiles all round, which usually only happens in the very best restaurants. The waiter has some English, jiggles orders into place and gives diners at the bar big bibs. The food comes fast. Notably good upstairs have been the freshest of salmon roe piled on top of some chopped daikon (Japanese radish); tuna marinated in soy and mirin; grilled asparagus with salt; superb-quality fillet steak; and grilled aubergine with sweet miso spread. The belly-pork is stewed rather than simmered, and served with mustard – not quite as fine as the variation served at One Two Three (see entry). For fish go to the bar, where there can be as many as 20 different specimens, rather than eat at the tables. Sushi is served on oval rolls of vinegared rice in groups of two – grilled eel brushed with dark, sweetened soy; lightly veined raw salmon; raw whites of scallop. Any fish can be served either like this or plain as sashimi. The dark-red belly of tuna has been particularly good. Herb tea is blended in-house, and meals end with ornately carved fruit. Unusually for a Japanese restaurant, dishes are not that sweet. Although a meal can work out as expensive as at a top French restaurant, it is possible to eat reasonably with a bowl of soup and one of the chef's specials of the day. Choice of sweet or dry saké or, of course, Suntory whisky.

OPEN: Mon to Sat MEALS: 12 to 2.30, 6.30 to 10
PRICES: £14 (£26), Set L from £5 (£6), Set D from £14 (£16). Cover 50p at D. Service 15%
CARDS: Access, Amex, Diners, Visa
SEATS: 80. Vegetarian meals. Children welcome. Wheelchair access. Music. Air-conditioned

Saigon [10/20] map 13

45 Frith Street, W1V 5TE
01-437 7109 and 437 1672 £10–£16

Vietnamese food is drier than Chinese – less gravy, less oil. The spring rolls are made with pork and prawn wrapped in rice paper (now found in Chinatown supermarkets), lightly cooked and served with lettuce, mint, coriander and a potent dip. The spicing is vivid in stir-fried fish with peppermint, the rare deep-fried squid cake and excellent lemon grass chicken or duck. Chef Uy Vu Ly came from Paris, where there is a strong Vietnamese community, but the guiding hand is Edward Man from Hong Kong, who has kept the family feeling to this relaxed little restaurant. Good are the satay, the barbecued beef with herbs, vegetables to cook at the table with more rice paper for wrapping, and fresh fruit salad to finish. The chillis are very hot and some of the dips and sauces fiery. House Blanc de Blancs is £4·90.

CHEF: U.V.Ly PROPRIETOR: E.C.L.Man
OPEN: Mon to Sat CLOSED: bank hols MEALS: 12. to 11.30
PRICES: £9 (£16), Set L and D from £6·10 (£10). Service 10%
CARDS: Access, Amex, Diners, Visa
SEATS: 80. Private parties: 40 main room, 40 private room. Children welcome. Vietnamese music

San Frediano [12/20]

map 11

62 Fulham Road, SW3 6HH
01-584 8375 £16

The only trouble here is getting a table. The pressure on space and the buzz in the atmosphere is almost as bad as at Langan's (see entry). San Frediano has had a heavy following for over 18 years. The menu is split into three, with a printed list of regular Italian dishes, a few additions according to the season, and some hand-written dishes according to what is available at the market. The latter are always worth looking at and have, on occasion, included elvers and unusual Italian dishes, such as cold ox-tongue with a fresh herb sauce, or osso buco. The fish dishes, from crawfish to grilled sea-bass, can be excellent and so is the pasta of the day, notably the ravioli stuffed with stinging nettles or with sage. Service is more than efficient, but they don't take complaints with much grace. The 40 Italian wines stay mainly in the £6 range and include Galestro, a dependable white from the normally red Chianti region, or else there is Tignanello at £11·45. This last is a vino da tavola, classed that way because the producers use a small percentage of the un-Italian Cabernet Sauvignon grape, but it merits a much better classification.

CHEF: Bruno Lambi PROPRIETORS: Mr Buonaguidi, Mr Parlanti, Mr Galassi and Mr Bazquez
OPEN: Mon to Sat MEALS: 12. 30 to 2.30, 7.15 to 11.15
PRICES: £10 (£16). Cover 80p. Service 12.5% CARDS: Access, Amex, Carte Blanche, Diners, Visa
SEATS: 85. Private parties: 12 main room. Vegetarian meals. Children's helpings. No pipes in dining-room. Wheelchair access (1 step)

San Lorenzo [12/20]

map 11

22 Beauchamp Place, SW3 1NH
01-584 1074 £23

Some hold that this up-market Italian restaurant is not as good as it was, but we are not so sure. The basement is lined with Marilyn Monroe photos and looks like a greenhouse, there are so many plants. The room is aired every afternoon when the sliding roof is pulled back; on cold evenings bamboo blinds are drawn across. Waiters are swift and helpful. The menu is varied and fascinating and includes three ways with carpaccio; excellent bresaola with ripe avocado; superb pasta with peas and mushrooms; but regional dishes, too, such as pigeon. Trattoria main-course clichés, such as veal pizzaiola, or chicken with a good tarragon sauce, are not quite so good. The place is well-known on the international eating-circuit, which keeps the prices up. House Sardinian is £7·50, but there is a fine Venegazzù, too.

CHEF: Gino Arastelli PROPRIETORS: Lorenzo and Mara Berni
OPEN: Mon to Sat MEALS: 12.30 to 2.30, 7.30 to 11.30
PRICES: £16 (£23). Cover £2. Minimum £2
SEATS: 100. Private parties: 14 main room. Vegetarian meals. Children's helpings. Wheelchair access

Santini [new entry, zero rated] map 10

29 Ebury Street, SW1W 0NZ
01-730 4094 and 8275 £15–£24

A smart Italian restaurant with white walls, London Lighting Company designer lights, artfully framed colour photographs of Venetian lagoon life, and a rack of wines on show – overall the cut is that of a fine Italian suit. The menu is less predictable than the average trattoria. The specifically Venetian dishes rate the highest – polenta served with quails; hot artichokes with garlic, parsley, white wine and Parmesan; gnocchi with a tomato and mushroom sauce; spicy sausages with brown beans; and pistachio ice-cream. Fish has been less good. The waiters are better when they remember they are handling human beings. Espresso coffee. An unvintaged wine list, but there is a fine red Venegazzù in the rack somewhere. House Colli del Trasimeno is £6·50.

CHEF/PROPRIETOR: Mr Santini
OPEN: all week CLOSED: bank hols MEALS: 12.30 to 2.30, 7 to 11.30
PRICES: £16 (£24), Set L £9·50 (£15). Cover £1. Service 12% CARDS: Access, Amex, Diners, Visa
SEATS: 65. Private parties: 25 main room. Vegetarian meals by arrangement. Children's helpings. Wheelchair access. Air-conditioned

Seashell [9/20] map 10

51 Lisson Grove, NW1 6UB
01-724 1063 and 723 8703 £7

This has now moved a few doors up the road. London's best-known and best-liked fish and chip shop is now licensed for beer and wine; otherwise the principles are the same: fresh fish each day; crisp batter; strong tea. There are double the number of seats, but no guarantee that there won't still be queues.

CHEFS/PROPRIETORS: John Faulkner and Mark Farrell
OPEN: Tue to Sat CLOSED: 1 week Christmas to New Year MEALS: 12 to 2, 5.15 to 10.30
PRICES: £6 (£7). Minimum £2·50. Licensed, plus bring your own: no corkage
SEATS: 150. Children welcome. Wheelchair access. Music

We keep files on every restaurant, so reports of poor meals are just as valuable as reports of good meals because they save unnecessary inspections.

Seashell [9/20] map 10

424–426 Kingsland Road, E8 4AT
01-254 6152 £7

The new branch – it is only two years old compared to the Lisson Grove's 18 – has established itself for the same quality fish and chips as its parent. It is marginally cheaper and open throughout the day on Saturdays.

CHEF: Michael Webber PROPRIETORS: John Faulkner and Mark Farrell
OPEN: Tue to Sat CLOSED: 1 week Christmas to New Year MEALS: 12 to 2, 5 to 10 (11.30 to 10 Sat)
PRICES: £6 (£7). Minimum £2·30. Licensed, plus bring your own: no corkage.
SEATS: 45. Children welcome. Music. Air-conditioned

Seashore [8/20] map 10

309 Finchley Road, NW3 6EH
01-431 3239 and 262 2000 £3–£7

A better than average fish and chip shop. The fish is fresh from Billingsgate and the salmon is wild, not farmed. It is fried in egg and matzo batter. Unlicensed.

CHEF: Mr Gamal PROPRIETOR: Mr Ahmed
OPEN: Tue to Sat MEALS: 12 to 2.30, 5.30 to 11
PRICES: £6 (£7), Set L and D from £2·60 (£3). Service inc. Unlicensed, but bring your own: no corkage
SEATS: 45. Private parties: 60 main room. Children welcome

Semiramis [10/20] map 10

4 Hereford Road, W2 4AA
01-727 4272 £16

A small, family-run Greek restaurant offering a good, smart meze that runs longer than *Crossroads* – nine starters, three fish dishes, kleftiko, kebabs, sheftalia, chicken, potatoes, salad. House Santa Laura is £4·95.

CHEF: Evdokia Sergides PROPRIETOR: Andreas Sergides
OPEN: all week, exc Sat L and Sun L MEALS: 12 to 3, 7 to 12
PRICES: £11 (£16). Minimum £10. Service 10%
SEATS: 24. Private parties: 30 main room. Vegetarian meals. Children welcome. Smart dress preferred. Wheelchair access (also WC). Greek music

Seoul [new entry, zero rated] map 10

89A Aldgate High Street, EC3N 1LH
01-480 5770 £11

Cheap, unpretentious, lunchtime only Korean cafe where regulars go for just a bowl of soup. The menu is short and well explained, with the emphasis on battered and fried dishes. Apart from the Han Kuk Hoe Kwan (see entry) it is the only Korean restaurant we have seen in which bulgogi is listed without the words, 'Korea's most famous dish.' The spinach soup with beef and sesame is excellent; the kim-chee tasty; and the deep-fried fish with rice and vegetables has been as good as any Korean dish we have tasted. Mints come with the bill to counteract the spices. More reports, please.

OPEN: Mon to Fri, L only CLOSED: bank hols MEALS: 10 to 3
PRICES: £7 (£11)
SEATS: 35. Children welcome. Wheelchair access. Music

Shapla [new entry, zero rated] map 9

380 Brixton Road, SW9 7AW
01-733 7053/4 £9–£11

Once a cheap shoe store but now boasting white Doric columns and tubs of burgeoning flowers on the pavement. The leafy walls inside make this look more like a grotto in the forest of Arden than an Indian restaurant in Brixton. The tandoori dishes and rogan josh are tender and aromatic; the bhindi bhaji is moist, fresh and hot, lacking both slime and grease. Reasonable prices for such an up-market feel. More reports, please.

CHEF: M.Miah PROPRIETOR: Ranu Miah
OPEN: all week MEALS: 12 to 3, 6 to 12
PRICES: £6 (£11), Set L and D from £5·95 (£9) CARDS: Access, Amex, Visa
SEATS: 80. Private parties: 70 main room. Vegetarian meals. Children welcome. Wheelchair access (also WC). Indian music

Sheekeys [11/20] map 13

28 St Martin's Court, WC2N 4AL
01-240 2565 £26

Until Sheekeys was refurbished a few years ago the only man in evidence was the manager. All the service was by brusque but madly efficient waitresses in black and you had to be out by eight o'clock. The steamed fish came in one of two sauces – lobster or parsley – and the turbot usually ran out and was substituted by haddock later in the day. The room is still the same and the autographs on the walls are the originals, but the waiters are male and the still fishy menu has a more modern style (though the bread and butter cannot be said to have improved). The main fish dishes, like grilled Dover sole, skate in black butter, and mussels in cream sauce are, as a rule, well handled and come with first-class vegetables. The oyster bar will serve a dozen with a bottle of the house white, which is £5·50. Turnover of tables is fast enough to ensure getting to the theatre or opera.

CHEF: Keith Phillips PROPRIETORS: Scotts Restaurant plc
OPEN: Mon to Sat MEALS: 12.30 to 2.45, 6 to 11.15
PRICES: £18 (£26). Daily bargain dish. Cover 75p. Minimum £8. Service 12.5%
CARDS: Access, Amex, Diners, Visa
SEATS: 90. Private parties: 30 main room, 15 private room. Children's helpings. No babies. No pipes in dining-room. Wheelchair access. Music. Air-conditioned

The Guide *is always anxious to recruit new inspectors. If you would like to apply, write to the editor enclosing a) a detailed report on a restaurant where you have eaten and b) a comparative study of restaurants known to you.*

Shireen Tandoori [11/20] map 9

270 Uxbridge Road, W12 7JA
01-743 6857 and 749 5927 £12

Although short, the menu offers variety, ranging from diced aubergine with eggs in yoghourt, to lamb's liver marinated with onion and spices and cooked in an iron karahi; from tandoori dishes of chicken, beef and lamb, to kulfi and gajarka halwa, a sweet carrot pudding with nuts. Surroundings are smart, service attentive. Licensed.

CHEF: A. Shaheed PROPRIETORS: M.A.Qureshi and M.R.Choudhury
OPEN: all week CLOSED: 25 and 26 Dec MEALS: 12 to 3, 6 to 11.30
PRICES: £7 (£12). Cover 40p. Service 10% CARDS: Access, Amex, Diners, Visa
SEATS: 35. Private parties: 40 main room. Vegetarian meals. Children's helpings. Wheelchair access (also WC). Indian music. Air-conditioned

Sidi Bou Said [9/20] map 10

9 Seymour Place, W1H 5AG
01-402 9930 £9

A Tunisian restaurant with bird-cages, near Marble Arch, and offering good value. The menu has couscous with harissa; spicy merguez sausages; brik à l'oeuf; and sweet pastries. Drink mint tea, Turkish coffee, or bring your own wine.

CHEF: Mr Amroussi PROPRIETORS: Sidi Bou Said Ltd
OPEN: Mon to Sat MEALS: 12 to 3, 6 to 12
PRICES: £6 (£9). Cover £1. Service 13%. Unlicensed, but bring your own: corkage £1
CARDS: Access, Amex, Diners, Visa
SEATS: 28. Private parties: 28 main room. Children welcome. Music

Simpson's in the Strand [11/20] map 13

100 The Strand, WC2R 0EW
01-836 9112 £16–£17

The return to the listings of this old giant reflects the changing context of the London restaurant scene and marks the opening of a period of detente. Omission has certainly done nothing to improve the appalling vegetables or the institutional nature of the soups. On these points we have given up for the time being and can only advise readers quite simply not to eat them. However, eat the roasts of beef or lamb, finish with treacle roll and custard, or bread-and-butter pudding, soak in the atmosphere of an aspect of English society that has otherwise disappeared, and we promise that it will deliver. Simpson's is an institution and the *Guide* is glad to have it back. Five trolleys are usually in operation, looking like something Leonardo da Vinci invented but could not find a use for – four little wheels supporting the truck and big silvery dome, pushed along by a staffer: they have one each and stick to it. The choice is a thick or a thin slice of roast meat, off this end or that. Occasional subtleties creep in, like carving a bit off the top or side, but that's very flash. The beef is an enormous rib that gives the impression that *nouvelle cuisine* here probably means anything after Henry VIII. Be prepared for four slices, a piece of Yorkshire pudding, and a ladleful of juices from around the meat. The reason they seem to be able to offer the meat more or less well done is because the flame is only under one end. Of course it is a moot point whether it is roast beef at all, as it is virtually braised: roasted to begin with, but then kept covered, with steam coming out of the meat. This may account for the moistness. The service is Italianate in a way that is in fact peculiarly English. Senior staff are dressed in morning coats, one with a wing collar, and the rest in kitchen whites with long tablecloths down to their ankles. The downstairs dining-room is very much on the lines of the Junior Common Room, while upstairs is airier and more Continental. House claret is de rigueur at £5·70.

CHEF: J.Curley PROPRIETORS: Savoy Hotel plc
OPEN: Mon to Sat MEALS: 12 to 2.45, 6 to 9.45
PRICES: £12 (£17), Set Sat L and Set D £12 (£16). Cheaper set L and D available. Cover £1. Service inc CARDS: Access, Amex, Diners, Visa
SEATS: 350. Private parties: 120 main room, 120 private room. Vegetarian meals by arrangement. Children welcome. Jacket and tie. Air-conditioned

69 Westow Hill [new entry, zero rated] map 9

69 Westow Hill, SE19 1TX
01-670 6661 £16

A large, airy Italian restaurant with striped sofa, parquet floor and 1930s-style mirrors. The pasta has been well sauced using chilli in the penne matriciana and the quality of the fish and meats, for grilled Dover sole and entrecôte pizzaiola, for example, has been good. French wines. More reports, please.

CHEF: Benito Pallini PROPRIETORS: Novelbright Ltd
OPEN: all week, exc Sat L and Sun D MEALS: 11.30 to 3 (12 to 2.30 Sun), 6.30 to 11
PRICES: £9 (£16) Cheaper set Sun L available. Cover 60p. Service 10% CARDS: Access, Amex, Diners, Visa
SEATS: 80. Private parties: 80 main room. Vegetarian meals by arrangement. Children's helpings. Wheelchair access. Music

SOHO, W1

BACKGROUND BRIEFING: *Still one of the food centres of the capital. Berwick Street market has fine fruit and vegetables at good prices. For meat there is the high-quality butchers Slater & Cooke, Bisney & Jones, 67 Brewer Street; Randall and Aubin at 16 Brewer Street, especially good for poultry and game; and Bifulco Stores on Old Compton Street. Richards in Brewer Street is one of the best fishmongers in London. In the same street is Lina's for Italian oils, cheeses and charcuterie, or try Vinorio, Camisa or Torino, all in Old Compton Street. For coffee the Algerian Coffee Stores, also on Old Compton Street, are the experts. The cakes at Maison Bertaux at 28 Greek Street are excellent, and the satay at Rasa Sayang in Frith Street almost gained the restaurant an entry in the main listings.*

Restaurants are graded on a scale of 1–20. In the region of 8–9 expect to find places that may not be restaurants but cafes, pubs, bistros and small hotels. In the category of 10–11 you can expect to find the best food in the locality. Ratings of 12 or more are given to restaurants we regard as serving the best food in the region.

Soho Brasserie [11/20] map 13

23–25 Old Compton Street, W1V 5PJ
01-439 9301 £15

Ind Coope would transform British catering if they opened a chain of brasseries of this standard. The decor is unpromisingly chilly and as you go in you might dread finding a three-day-old, dried-up fish terrine – but not at all. David Schwartz cooks some surprisingly adept dishes and is even able to use local suppliers, thanks to Soho's culinary renaissance – Bifulco Stores, the butcher in Old Compton Street and E & G Provisions in Frith Street. The menu is a sensible mix of the modern, as in the salads, and the traditional, as in steak tartare. There are also some down-to-earth dishes, such as home-made sausage with onion and sage compote. Omelettes are well judged and the squid provençale has been excellent. They buy fresh from the market daily. The cover charge of 65p is a rapacious practice, but it is possible to eat a bar snack for under £3. A sensible wine list. CELLARMAN'S CHOICE: Sauvignon du Haut-Poitou '83 at £7·25.

CHEF: David Schwartz PROPRIETORS: Ind Coope Ltd
OPEN: Mon to Sat MEALS: 10am to 11.30pm
PRICES: £9 (£15), Bar meals from £1·35 (£1·50), Daily bargain dish. Cover 65p
CARDS: Access, Amex, Diners, Visa
SEATS: 75. 5 tables outside. Private parties: 20 main room. Vegetarian meals. Children's helpings. Wheelchair access. Jazz and classical music. Air-conditioned

▲ *Le Soufflé, Inter-Continental Hotel* [new entry, zero rated] map 11

1 Hamilton Place, W1V 0QY
01-409 3131 £25–£33

Perhaps more a dining-room for people used to luxury than somewhere for a once-in-a-while treat. The set lunch is good value amid the snazzy art deco red, black and silver, where roses float on water and there are balloon burgundy glasses that would represent a manor house to a goldfish. Peter Kromberg has done a lot of good work behind the scenes training other chefs, some of which gives rise to our caution in recommending the expense of the full blown *carte*. The menu is a tantalising arrangement of what is best described as modern French *haute cuisine*. The combinations are extravagant: quails, 'comme chez nous', are roasted, stuffed, served with a red wine sauce with crème de cassis and poached quails' eggs; and sole is filled with lobster mousse and glazed with a port and truffle cream sauce. Other fish have been served with foie gras, but the caviare is caviare – red keta and sevruga.

The restaurant takes its name from its speciality, which may be made with crab and avocado (helped a lot by lobster sauce); salmon with chicken, oysters and leeks; chestnuts with kirsch; or excellent chocolate with crème de cacao. There are further varieties. If all this movement in the culinary stratosphere is too much, the lunch includes excellent saddle of lamb carved off the trolley (boned and stuffed, of course, because this is not a kitchen that believes in leaving

Reports on good shops, small hotels and cafes in your area are welcome.

things alone). But the chariot des desserts is fantastic, and so is the spread of cheeses. The wine list is encyclopaedic and priced for Mayfair, though at lunch there is a sommelier's choice starting at £8·50.

CHEF: Peter Kromberg PROPRIETORS: Intercontinental Hotels Corp.
OPEN: all week, exc Sat L MEALS: 12.30 to 3, 7 to 11.30
PRICES: £22 (£33), Set L £16 (£25), Set D from £24 (£33) CARDS: Access, Amex, Diners, Visa
SEATS: 76. Private parties: 15 main room, 700 private room. Car-park, 100 places. Children welcome. Smart dress preferred. No-smoking area. Wheelchair access (also WC). Air-conditioned
ACCOMMODATION: 500 rooms, all with bath/shower. B&B £132 to £150. Rooms for disabled. Children welcome. Baby facilities. No pets. Afternoon teas. Sauna. Air-conditioning. Lift. TV. Phone

South Kensington Pasta Bar [9/20] map 11

60 Old Brompton Road, SW7 ADY
01-584 4028 £11

The pick of a small chain of pasta bars that includes the Chelsea (opposite the ABC in Fulham Road) and the Covent Garden. The pasta is as good as in most top trattoria, the sauces mainly good – the garlic and chilli better than the bolognese, which can taste boiled – and with half a bottle of house red it is possible to eat for about £5. Service is quick and friendly. It is unbeatable for value in SW7.

CHEF: Marco Lozada PROPRIETOR: Claudio Pulze
OPEN: all week MEALS: 12 to 3, 5.30 to 11.45 (12 to 11.30 Sat and Sun)
PRICES: £6 (£11). Service 12.5% CARD: Access
SEATS: 60. Private parties: 12 main room. Vegetarian meals. Children's helpings. Wheelchair access. Music. Air-conditioned

Spread Eagle [12/20] map 9

2 Stockwell Street, SE10 9JN
01-692 1618 £13–£16

The Victorian atmosphere is more convivial upstairs while downstairs offers more privacy. On its day this restaurant can compete with the best in south-east London. There is plenty of choice among sound ingredients – including free-range eggs – partnered with contrasting sauces: skate with black butter; pink rack of lamb with curried parsnip sauce; calf's liver with mustard sauce. The steak tartare is good, too, and al dente vegetables come in generous portions. Sometimes the sweet course seems to have had more items off than on. Service is friendly and professional; some evenings there may be live jazz. House Loire is £6·20 a litre, or try the CELLARMAN'S CHOICE: Morgon Charmes '83, from Georges Duboeuf, at £9·80.

CHEF: Martin Heap PROPRIETORS: Richard Moy and Martin Heap
OPEN: Mon to Sat, exc Sat L MEALS: 12 to 2.30, 6.30 to 11
PRICES: £11 (£16), Set L £9·75 (£13), Bar meals at L from £2·50. Service inc
CARDS: Access, Amex, Diners, Visa
SEATS: 60. Private parties: 30 main room, 55 and 10 private rooms. Vegetarian meals. Children's helpings. Wheelchair access (also WC). Classical music. Air-conditioned

Sree Krishna [10/20] map 9

194 Tooting High Street, SW17 0SF
01-672 4250 and 6903 £9

Mr. Ramanarayanan's South Indian restaurant continues its refurbishment, with extra seating planned for the large numbers who recognise a bargain when they see one. It is clean, welcoming, bustling, and looks after vegetarians particularly well. Everything on the list of specialities (maximum £1·25) is good value: masala dosai (pancakes with potatoes and fried onions); avial (vegetables with coconut and yoghourt); egg biriani; uppuma (semolina with onion and spices); and wonderful parathas. Carnivores share the value too: chicken, beef, lamb and prawn dishes don't go above £3. Service is efficient and informal. Drink salt or sweet lassi.

CHEF/PROPRIETOR: R. Ramanarayanan
OPEN: all week MEALS: 12 to 2.45, 6 to 10.45 (12 Fri and Sat)
PRICES: £4 (£9). Minimum £2·50. Service 10%
SEATS: 68. Vegetarian meals. Children welcome. Wheelchair access (also WC). Music

Le Suquet [12/20] map 11

104 Draycott Avenue, SW3 3AE
01-581 1785 £25

The atmosphere is Cannes, from the framed portscapes through the blue and white sailing boats etched on the plates to the young French staff in red Levi's. But the cooking owes more to Brittany, most ostentatiously in the magnificent seafood platters – two kinds of oysters; langoustines; the small whelks you find in France; winkles; a whole crab; brown and pink shrimps; clams; raw mussels piled high on a cork board. The waiter serves a dollop of mayonnaise from a big bowl, and there is vinegar, pins and crackers on the table. Other good to excellent dishes to follow are the sea-bass with bordelaise sauce and the turbot with champagne sauce. A speciality, on request only, is a court bouillon of fish and vegetable stock in which there's a whole lobster. Vegetables are poor but sweets have improved. It is a tight fit and sometimes the service is off-hand, but a little more consistency in the standards of the fish would raise the rating to 13. There is Muscadet to drink, of course.

CHEF: Jean Yves Darcel PROPRIETORS: A.Bracci and P.Martin
OPEN: all week CLOSED: 2 weeks at Christmas MEALS: 12.30 to 2.30, 7.30 to 11.30
PRICES: £18 (£25). Cover 95p. Service 15% CARD: Amex
SEATS: 45. 4 tables outside. Private parties: 8 main room, 21 private room. Children welcome. Wheelchair access. Music

Tante Claire [16/20] map 11

68 Royal Hospital Road, SW3 4LP
01-352 6045 and 351 0227 **Real Food** £19–£34

'Almost uniquely . . . in this country it can hold its place beside the present great French restaurants by being consistently excellent. It has the rare and all too elusive quality of perfect service, which again one expects to find only in France: deferential but not obsequious; unostentatious; efficient; charming, and expertly knowledgeable.' That testimonial was for the old dining-room, closed for the entire summer in 1985 while the dining-room was expanded into the house next door and redecorated. We have not been able to eat in the new room before going to press. But the team is the same, there is more space, which was always at a premium before, and refreshed after a summer away from the range the brilliant Pierre Koffmann is back in action with dishes that have a unique subtlety and power and which have impressed time and again – chicken mousse in pastry with a red pepper sauce; hare medallions ranging from pink to well done served with a burst from the peppermill in a caramel-coloured sauce; or more provincial carré d'agneau. Fish is his main subject – monk with saffron and cream, and red mullet with basil and noodles or in a number of other ways (mullet has become a favourite in all the Roux restaurants) – and the sauces are of an elusive, explosive potency. The list of endorsed sweets runs the gamut of the menu – pavé au chocolat; caramelised peach tart; the spectacular array of sorbets; and of course the armagnac ice-cream with prunes. The exceptionally good-value set lunch at £12 remains, and the wine list is an expensive but a fitting foil for cooking of this stature. Book well in advance.

CHEF: Pierre Koffmann PROPRIETORS: Mr and Mrs Pierre Koffman
OPEN: Mon to Fri MEALS: 12.30 to 2, 7 to 11
PRICES: £25 (£34), Set L £12 (£19). Minimum £25 D CARDS: Amex, Diners
SEATS: 36. Vegetarian meals by arrangement. Children welcome. Wheelchair access (also WC)

Tate Gallery [10/20] map 10

Millbank, SW1P 4RG
01-834 6754 £16

What a model for institutional caterers – a fine setting with quixotic English food and magnificent wines at competitive prices. The basement is surrounded by the mural 'The Expedition in Pursuit of Rare Meats' by the then student, Rex Whistler – a spoof of eighteenth-century hunting landscapes, with castles painted around the real doors. This, with the white pillars down the centre of the room, black leather seats, 'Mind the Mural' signs, and tables packed tightly and served from a bow bar, produces an overall feeling of a restaurant in a briefcase. The cooking is at its best with more simple dishes, such as potted crab, roast beef, skate with black butter, and steak and kidney pie. Other dishes have been less good. The cheeseboard is usually in very fine condition. The wines, although not quite what they were, are still enough to make anyone blink – four Ch. Latour from '58 to '77; minor Ch. Pas-de-Rausan '78 at £6; halves of white burgundy for about £6, or Meursault '78 from Bouchard Père et fils at £9·30 for the whole bottle; and cognacs and eaux-de-vie of the same quality. No wonder there is a note on the list regretting that wines 'can only be purchased for consumption in the restaurant'.

CHEF: Michael Driver PROPRIETORS: Trustees of the Tate Gallery
OPEN: Mon to Sat, L only CLOSED: bank hols MEALS: 12 to 3
PRICES: £11 (£16). Minimum £3·50
SEATS: 130. Private parties: 15 main room. Vegetarian meals. Children's helpings. No-smoking area. Wheelchair access (also WC). Air-conditioned

Thierry's [10/20] map 11

342 King's Road, SW3 5UR
01-352 3365 £10–£20

The social code of Chelsea almost demands that girls do a stint waitressing at Thierry's before coming out at the Chelsea Arts Club ball. Lunch among the handless clocks and rich paintings of the bistro is excellent value. François Rohlion has cooked here since 1974 and buys fresh daily. The soufflés, the quenelles of pike with sauce Nantua, and the carré d'agneau rôti aux herbes are fixtures on a short menu which expands in season with plenty of game. Wines come from a variety of reputable merchants, with Minervois at £5·50 or CELLARMAN'S CHOICE: house claret at £8·95.

CHEF: François Rohlion PROPRIETOR: Thierry Cabanne
OPEN: Mon to Sat CLOSED: last 2 weeks Aug MEALS: 12.30 to 2.30, 7.30 to 11.30
PRICES: £13 (£20), Set L £5·75 (£10). Cover 60p. Service 12.5% CARDS: Amex, Diners, Visa
SEATS: 70. Private parties: 30 main room, 30 private room. Vegetarian meals. Children's helpings. Wheelchair access (also wc). Classical music. Air-conditioned

Tiger Lee [13/20] map 10

251 Old Brompton Road, SW5 9HP
01-370 2323 and 5970 £27

This expensive Chinese restaurant is known chiefly for its fish, but it is also the best place to eat deep-fried crispy chicken, the equivalent of Peking duck for the Cantonese. It arrives, spectacularly, as large pieces of crimson and crisp skin and meat on top of a mountain of shrimp crisps. It is an essential component of any banquet. The bird, after being prepared in similar fashion to Peking duck, is submerged in a wok-ful of hot oil and deep-fried until the skin turns crisp. It is then chopped right through into pieces and served with the flesh still attached to the bone. The menu is relatively short but well-described for other dishes. Also good are the yam deep-fried prawns; stir-fried Cantonese vegetables; braised eel with garlic; and, almost unique in London, stir-fried rice steamed in lotus leaf. The price of the wines suggests that foreign devils should stay with tea.

CHEF: Cheong Hong PROPRIETOR: C. Cassuto
OPEN: all week, D only CLOSED: Christmas MEALS: 6 to 11
PRICES: £15 (£27). Service 15% CARDS: Amex, Diners, Visa
SEATS: 56. Private parties: 36 main room. Vegetarian meals. Children welcome. Smart dress preferred. No-smoking area. Wheelchair access. Air-conditioned

Topkapi [12/20] map 12

25 Marylebone High Street, W1A 3PE
01-486 1872 and 935 3188 £14

The best regarded of London's Turkish restaurants, at least by the Turkish community. Supplies of oils, pulses, and spices come direct via Stoke Newington importers, and everything is prepared daily in-house to order. Notably good are the kebabs; the taramosalata, which is some of the best in town; and the muska boregi (impressive filo pastry filled with cheese). A speciality is kuzu firin (lamb with a spicy sauce of tomatoes and aubergines). The waiters are in uniform and bring chillies and olives for you to nibble; the tables are close together. Turkish wines start at £6. CELLARMAN'S CHOICE: Villa Doluca at £7.

CHEF: R.Kalayci PROPRIETOR: U.Fahri
OPEN: all week MEALS: 12 to 12
PRICES: £8 (£14), Set L and D £9 (£14), Cheaper set L weekdays. Cover 50p. Service 15%
CARDS: Access, Amex, Diners, Visa
SEATS: 50. Private parties: 20 main room. Vegetarian meals. Children's helpings. Wheelchair access (also WC). Music

Tourment d'Amour [12/20] map 13

19 New Row, WC2A 4LA
01-240 5348 £21–£25

The fancy descriptions of the dishes in incomprehensible French – poulet ton sur ton being stuffed, wrapped in pastry and served with orange sauce, or triade marine being three cold fish mousses – do not impress. But the kitchen has stuck firmly to its guns in bringing out different dishes and, by London standards, at reasonable prices. The dining-room is smartly decorated in greys and pinks, and the inclusive menu brings canapés and fresh rolls. Standards vary, but of many good dishes eaten there have been a pair of pastry boats, one filled with Toulouse sausage and the other with chicken liver and port; the steak tartare, an endangered species these days; smoked pheasant with a redcurrant marmalade; and grilled veal with wild mushrooms in an excellent madeira sauce. Sweets put the bill up by £3·50 – the Tourment d'Amour itself is a tart of ground almonds, cream and rum. Service is of the 'I've-only-got-two-hands' type. The 130-strong wine list concentrates on burgundies, with plenty of halves of vintage claret which keep the prices up, and there is not much financial relief in the trio of house wines at £7·50.

CHEF: Chris Bland PROPRIETORS: John Martin, David Owens and Nancy Pigeon
OPEN: Mon to Sat, exc Sat L MEALS: 12.30 to 2, 6.30 to 11.30
PRICES: Set L and D from £14·50 to £18 (£21 to £25) CARDS: Access, Amex, Diners, Visa
SEATS: 46. Private parties: 10 main room. Children's helpings. No children under 10. Smart dress preferred. Wheelchair access. Classical music

Tower Grill Restaurant [new entry, zero rated] map 12

86 Cleveland Street, W1P 5DR
01-387 2375 £10

Where Averof was, and the layout is unchanged, with an open cooking-area on one side of the dining-room. The menu has expanded, with more Turkish dishes added to the otherwise Greek repertoire. As well as the usual taramosalata and hummus there are warm white beans in tomato sauce, and garlic meatballs to start. Lamb is cooked in a number of different ways and the kebabs are good. More reports, please.

CHEF/PROPRIETOR: Yilmaz Altunay
OPEN: Mon to Sat MEALS: 11.30 to 2.30, 6 to 11
PRICES: £6 (£10), Set L and D £6 (£10). Cover 30p CARDS: Access, Amex, Diners, Visa
SEATS: 40. Private parties: 40 main room. Children welcome. Wheelchair access. Greek music. Air-conditioned

Treasure of China [new entry, zero rated] map 9

10 Nelson Road, SE10 9JB
01-858 9884 £10–£15

A Peking/Szechuan restaurant on two floors of a Georgian listed building. The menu is a taster for all regions of China and the staff speak English. Good dishes have been breast of chicken grilled with almonds; Szechuan fish soup; squid with garlic; mandarin beef fillet; and sizzling Hunanese lamb with spring onions and ginger. The steamed rice is leaf-wrapped, and noodle dishes have been recommended, always a good sign. House Italian is £5·50. More reports, please.

CHEF: H.L.Lee PROPRIETOR: Tony Low
OPEN: all week CLOSED: 25 and 26 Dec MEALS: 12 to 2.30, 6 to 11.30
PRICES: £8 (£15), Set L from £6 (£10), Set D from £9 (£14) Cheaper set L available. Minimum £6. Service 10% CARDS: Access, Amex, Diners, Visa
SEATS: 75. Private parties: 40 main room, 35 private room. Vegetarian meals. No children under 4. Chinese music. Air-conditioned

Twenty Trinity Gardens [11/20] map 9

20 Trinity Gardens, SW9 8DP
01-733 8838 £12–£13

The trouble with being one of the few good-value restaurants in the Brixton/Stockwell area is that the pressure on the tables hits the kitchen – some dishes have not been properly cooked and regulars who first found this place with joy have felt let down. But . . . the cassoulet is 'the best I have tasted outside France' . . . and 'restored my faith in duck'. The decor is 1960s with stripped pine, maroon Laura Ashley plastic cloths, posters, and an old horn gramophone in the corner, and there is a conservatory. The menus are set-priced and range from parrot-fish one night, to oriental touches such as untidy-looking but good-tasting pork with lemon grass, ginger and coconut, to vegetarian items such as vegetable and nut terrine. The Sunday lunch at £7·50 is excellent value, finishing with Spotted Dick, 'as delightfully disgusting as I remember from childhood'. Coffee is served with home-made mints. The conservatory is a strictly enforced no-smoking zone. The wine list does not follow the erratic nature of the food and includes some very classy bottles – Ch. Cissac '73 at £12·75; Fleurie, Domaine Thevenet '83 at £7·75; Hermitage '78, from Chave, a youthful snip at £12·50.

CHEFS: Joanna Van Rooyan and Christopher Lock
PROPRIETORS: Jane Mann and David Spence
OPEN: Mon to Sat, exc Sat L MEALS: 12.30 to 2.30, 7 to 10.30
PRICES: Set L from £7·75 (£12), Set D from £8·50 (£13), Snacks from £2 (£2·20) and dish of the day, L only CARD: Visa
SEATS: 50. 3 tables outside. Private parties: 25 main room, 20 and 12 private rooms. Vegetarian meals. No children under 8. No pipes in dining-room. Wheelchair access. Classical music

Entries are compiled from the unsolicited reports from readers and are checked by inspectors; each restaurant is asked to supply details of its operation. Report forms can be found at the back of the Guide.

Upper Street Fish Shop [9/20] map 10

324 Upper Street, N1 2XQ
01-359 1401 £7

'We serve fish and chips, home-made sweets like jam roly-poly and treacle tart, pots of tea, and in season summer pudding and poached salmon.' And jolly good it is too. The Conways are third-generation fryers, and while Alan works away at his magnificant range Olga sends you to the pub next door for a pint until a table is free. She is one of Islington's great characters, a rival to Anna Hegarty (see Anna's Place) and Anna Scher (at the children's theatre), and has made the shop part of the community. Unlicensed, but you can take your own free of charge.

CHEF: Alan Conway PROPRIETORS: Alan and Olga Conway
OPEN: Mon to Sat, exc Mon L CLOSED: bank hols, Christmas MEALS: 11.30 to 2, 5.30 to 10
PRICES: £6 (£7)
SEATS: 28. Children welcome. Wheelchair access. Air-conditioned

Viareggio [10/20] map 10

332 West End Lane, NW6 1RJ
01-794 1444 £11

An above-average trattoria which gets a bit chaotic when busy, but the food is fairly authentic – pasta and bean soup, osso buco, and prawn dishes, as well as the good show of pastas, all stand out. Sweets are poor. Coffee is espresso. A dozen wines.

PROPRIETOR: Jean-Pierre Ballanti
OPEN: all week, exc Sun L CLOSED: bank hols MEALS: 12.30 to 2.30, 6.30 to 11.30
PRICES: £8 (£11). Cover 70p. Service 10% CARDS: Access, Amex, Diners, Visa
SEATS: 50. Private parties: 40 main room. Children welcome

Village Restaurant [new entry, zero rated] map 9

8 High Street, Wimbledon SW19 5DX
01-947 6477 £16–£22

Some of the main dishes in this big, rectangular dining-room lined with modern framed prints have been spectacularly good. The breast of Barbary duck has been rolled and cooked rare as in a true magret, sliced as thin as roast beef, and served with an aromatic demi-glaze, with its crisp legs shredded and made into a salad on a side-plate. Equally good is the salmon mille-feuille, and a dish of lamb with rabbit. There have been other impressive touches – terrines and puff-pastry canapés served warm – though sweets and cheeses have been less acute. It is a short, trendy wine list, well put together with 10 diverse whites, 10 diverse reds and 10 clarets. More reports, please.

CHEFS: N.Rochford and P.Hackett PROPRIETORS: A.Wood, P.Leighton and N.Rochford
OPEN: Mon to Sat, exc Sat L MEALS: 12 to 2.30, 7 to 11.30
PRICES: £14 (£22), Set L £9·50 (£16). Cover 75p. Service 10% CARD: Amex
SEATS: 50. Private parties: 10 main room. Children welcome. Smart dress preferred. Wheelchair access

Wakaba [11/20] map 10

31 College Crescent NW3 5LG
01-722 3854 and 586 7960 £15–£18

A smart Japanese cafe in a brick building, with a wooden-framed entrance which divides the single long room into two. To one side is the sushi bar and to the other are tightly fitted melamine tables and plain white walls. The menu takes in all the major avenues of Japanese cuisine, and the quality of the ingredients, from the sirloin steak for the beef teriyaki to the excellent fish for the sushi, underwrites any weakness in the cooking. Noticeably good is the mixed hors d'oeuvre, which might include as many as eight items on a wooden platter – pickled kelp; dark, sweet pickled ginger; fried prawn; thick slices of cold omelette; cold, battered tofu; a morsel of yakitori; fried pork ball; and some green beans. Also not to be missed is the marinated belly-pork simmered in soy and mirin and served with a dollop of Western mustard. For the conservative there is good tempura and for the adventurous, chawan-mushi, a steamed egg-custard with chicken broth and pieces of chicken, shrimp, mushroom and bamboo shoot. Casual, friendly service. Saké is £1·90, Japanese whisky £1·10. The mark-ups on the other whiskies run to 200 per cent.

CHEF/PROPRIETOR: Minoru Yoshihara
OPEN: Tue to Sun, D only MEALS: 6 to 11
PRICES: £13 (£18), Set D from £13·50 (£15). Service 10%
CARDS: Access, Amex, Diners, Visa
SEATS: 38. Private parties: 20 main room. Vegetarian meals. Children welcome. Japanese music

Waltons [12/20] map 11

121 Walton Street, SW3 2JH
01-584 0204 £17–£41

This is an expensive restaurant, but some meals are not as pricey as others – the set lunch is £11, the late-night supper (after 10pm) is £17·50, and the Sunday roast lunch is £13·50. The decor is overwhelming, with sumptuous fabric on the walls, drapes, and lemon trees, like the bedroom of a French stately home. Each place setting is laid with stainless steel base plates like those used for thalis in Indian restaurants, but otherwise the atmosphere is international. The menu follows suit, leaning heavily on expensive ingredients, such as truffles, wild mushrooms, lobsters, and champagne sauce – the first two not always in the prime condition they ought to be. On the whole the dishes are well executed – vegetable tartlet with thyme pastry and curry sauce; roast duck breast with an orange confit; prime quality veal rolled around a vegetable farce with dried morels; and grilled brill with raspberry vinegar sauce. The beef is of high quality, either as medallions with a Marsala, red wine and shallot sauce, or roast for Sunday lunch before fine chocolate marquise. Some dishes seem to lack purpose, hence the relatively low rating. Service is old school and women get unpriced menus, which does not impress. There are 250 wines listed: house French is

All inspections are carried out anonymously as we accept no handouts.

jugged at £7·50, *cru* Beaujolais and Loires are not much more, but there is a lot of négociant wine. Classed-growth clarets span 25 years, and include Ch. Cissac '79 at £23 the magnum.

CHEF: David Nicholls PROPRIETORS: Waltons Restaurants Ltd
OPEN: all week CLOSED: bank hols MEALS: 12.30 to 2.30 (2 Sun), 7.30 to 11.30 (10.30 Sun)
PRICES: £27·40 (£41), Set L £11 (£17), Set Sun L £13 (£19). Set D available after 10pm. Service 15% CARDS: Access, Amex, Diners, Visa
SEATS: 65. Private parties: 65 main room. Vegetarian meals by arrangement. Children welcome. Smart dress preferred. Wheelchair access (1 step). Air-conditioned

White Tower [13/20] map 12

1 Percy Street, W1P 0ET
01-636 8141 £23

We have forgotten the precise reason for this famous old London Greek being dropped from the listings, but eating here last year it was obvious that with the current state of the London restaurant scene it is a star we have overlooked – unfashionable, old-style, but honest food of a standard that justifies the high prices. It smells of its history (it was founded in 1938). The panelled dining-room is dark and the tables set with olives, radishes and spring onions. It has without doubt the best-written descriptions of any menu in the country. For example: 'Aubergine Imam Bayeldi: Once upon a time there lived in Asia Minor a famous Imam. He was inordinately fond of food. His particular weakness was the aubergine cooked in no matter which of its various delectable forms and one fine day, his Chef excelled himself in the way he served up the Imam's favourite dish. Now, when it came to food, the Imam never erred on the side of moderation and this day he ate so much that he passed out – or to quote the vernacular, he "bayeldeed." He thus (unconsciously) gave his name to an exquisite aubergine dish. The aubergine that made the Imam "bayeldi" was stuffed with onions, tomatoes and garlic, cooked in olive oil and was served cold. This exactly is how we prepare it here; and you should try it as an hors d'oeuvre. It may not be quite so much your undoing as it was the Imam's but you will enjoy it equally.'

Some of the food tastes as good as that reads. The salad of cold turbot trimmings, raw onion, parsley, lemon and oil, for instance; the taramosalata, that is probably the best in London; the boeuf Stroganoff (originally made with trimmings from the tournedos fillets, explains the menu). To finish there are baked apples and fresh fruits or yoghourts. The wine list has one saving grace . . . the house Loire is £5·75.

CHEF: Luigi Contini PROPRIETOR: E. Stais
OPEN: Mon to Fri CLOSED: 1 week Christmas, 3 weeks Aug MEALS: 12.30 to 2.30, 6.30 to 10.30
PRICES: £16 (£23). Cover £1 CARDS: Access, Amex, Diners, Visa
SEATS: 80. Private parties: 10 main room, 16 private room. Children welcome

WIMBLEDON, SW19

BACKGROUND BRIEFING: *Slick fun-food joints with names like Volleys and Rackets were only to be expected. No one stands out. San Lorenzo Fuoriporta, Worple Road Mews, is a fine Italian restaurant related to the San Lorenzo in Knightsbridge (see entry). Another interesting venture in the area is Mustika Rasa, 96 High Street. Run by Sri Owen, whose* Indonesian Food and Cookery *(Prospect Books) is an acknowledged classic, it sells specialist ingredients, books and kitchen equipment as well as prepared Indonesian dishes to eat on the premises or to take away. There are picnic hampers on sale in the summer, cookery demonstrations, subscription dinners and dinner parties provided by private arrangement throughout the year (telephone 01-946 7649).*

Wine Gallery [9/20] map 11

49 Hollywood Road, SW10 9HX
01-352 7572 £11

A first-class wine bar with the same kitchen as Brinkleys next door, but much cheaper. The menu reads better than many a brasserie – soupe de poisson; timbale of scallops with crab sauce; smoked chicken and avocado salad. But there's also sausage, beans and mash for £2·90, and kedgeree too. House champagne is £2 a glass and there is an interesting choice of wines. It gets crowded, especially on Saturdays when Chelsea are playing at home.

CHEF: Graham Day PROPRIETORS: John and Jenny Brinkley
OPEN: all week MEALS: 12 to 3.30, 6.30 to 11.30
PRICES £6 (£11). Cover 50p
SEATS: 60. 9 tables outside. Private parties: 20 main room, 20 private room. Children's helpings

Wong Kei [9/20] map 13

41–43 Wardour Street, W1V 3HA
01-437 3071 and 6833 £4–£8

A noisy, hectic, very cheap Cantonese restaurant on four floors. The lacquered ducks and chickens hanging in the front window make good centre-pieces to proper meals, though it is possible to eat for under £2 if you keep to the set lunch or the one-dish meals. The noodle soups are good, as are things with ginger – baked crab with spring onions, beef with pineapple, liver with pineapple. Tea arrives even as you sit down. Licensed.

CHEF: T.F.Tang PROPRIETORS: E.Liu, M.M.Lo
OPEN: all week MEALS: noon to 11.30
PRICES: £4 (£8), Set L from £1·70 (£4), Set D from £3·50 (£6). Service inc
SEATS: 350. Private parties: 100 main room, 60 private room. Children welcome. Wheelchair access (also WC)

Woodlands [10/20] map 12

77 Marylebone Lane, W1M 4AH
01-486 3862 and 487 4009 £9–£13

One of the top three Indian vegetarian restaurants in the London area, the others being Sabras and Munbhave (see London and Croydon respectively). This is a smart, southern-Indian vegetarian restaurant, part of the Abig chain, and has two-tone brown-stone floor tiles, brown fabric seating, and an array of plants against the off-white walls. The strength of the menu is in the diversity of flavours and textures. Cone-shaped samosas have a hot spicy filling; potato bonda is kinder, but still hot. Both come with a green coconut chutney. Rasa vada (potato rings in a juice of apple and tomato) is a bland relief; as a main course rava masala dosa may be a better bet than the onion version. Lentil sambhar is a velvety accompaniment and the side dish of vegetable korma is perfumed yet not bitter. Sweet lassi is good and thick, or there is saffron-based bhalfi. Keen service.

CHEF: R.D.Bhat PROPRIETOR: Ranjit Sood
OPEN: all week MEALS: 12 to 2.45, 6 to 10.30
PRICES: £7 (£13), Set L and D from £5 (£9). Minimum £4. Service 10%. CARDS: Access, Amex, DIners, Visa
SEATS: 70. Private parties: 70 main room. Vegetarian meals. Children welcome. Wheelchair access. Music. Air-conditioned

Yamato [new entry, zero rated] map 9

51 Church Road, Hendon NW4 4DU
01-203 6010 £5–£13

There is a sizeable Japanese community in Hendon, many of whom eat at this new restaurant in what used to be a boutique. The decor is a tongue-and-groove pine, and the chefs work behind a long counter. You can eat at the bar or at the tables, which have facilities for table-top cooking of excellent sukiyaki or shabu-shabu. Family-style Japanese cooking is served, which means representative selections of popular dishes. Fish is what the kitchen prides itself on, and not just sushi and sashimi but also grilled over charcoal: whole squid have been cooked like this. Of less often found dishes is natto, fermented soya beans. Yamato is the old name for Japan, though the restaurant is not forbiddingly Japanese at all and the prices are cheaper than equivalent restaurants in central London. To drink there is Shockikubai and Ozeki saké or beer.

CHEF: Mr Yoneda PROPRIETORS: Yamato Ya Foods Ltd
OPEN: Tue to Sun D, Sat and Sun L MEALS: 12 to 1.45, 6 to 10.15
PRICES: £11 (£13), Set L from £3·50 (£5), Set D from £9·50 (£11). Service inc
CARDS: Access, Amex, Diners, Visa
SEATS: 65. Private parties: 25 to 150 main room. Car-park, 8 places. Children's helpings. Wheelchair access. Music

Yung's [11/20] map 13

23 Wardour Street, W1V 3HD
01-734 4566 £7–£19

A bustling, smart and small Cantonese restaurant that can be hard to get in to but does authentic dishes, such as chicken blood. The fish dishes are reliably handled, such as steamed scallops and crab in black bean sauce. There are a few Szechuan dishes also, such as twice-cooked pork, and aubergine and pork. The

If you cannot honour a restaurant booking, always phone to cancel.

crispy roast chicken is near perfect, its skin as crisp as the crackling on pork. Rice comes in earthenware pots and is very good. House white is £5·50.

CHEF: Mr Ng PROPRIETOR: Mr Wokiuliu
OPEN: all week MEALS: noon to 4am
PRICES: £11 (£19), Set L £3 (£7), Set D from £11 (£16). Minimum £4·50. Service 10%
CARDS: Access, Amex, Diners, Visa
SEATS: 95. Private parties: 30 main room. Vegetarian meals. Children welcome. Wheelchair access. Air-conditioned

Zaki's [10/20]

map 9

634 Finchley Road, NW11 7RR
01-458 2012 and 9273

£18

Interesting Jewish cooking in the modern sense, that is, Middle Eastern. Plenty of cumin and coriander are used to flavour the likes of kibbeh, ful medames and baba ghanoush. Family-run, friendly and clean. The short wine list includes CELLARMAN'S CHOICE: Gigondas, Cellier des Dauphins '81 at £8·45.

CHEFS: Rachel Pinto, Lily Dwek and Ruth Synett
PROPRIETORS: Zaki and Lily Dwek, and Ruth Synett
OPEN: all week, exc Fri and Sat (open Fri L and Sat D in winter) CLOSED: Jewish hols
MEALS: 12 to 2.30, 6 to 11
PRICES: £11 (£18). Cover 60p. Service 10% CARDS: Access, Amex, Diners, Visa
SEATS: 40. Private parties: 42 main room. Vegetarian meals by arrangement. Children's helpings (L only). Wheelchair access. Oriental music

Zen [11/20]

map 11

Chelsea Cloisters, Sloane Avenue, SW3 3DN
01-589 1781 and 584 9219

£29

The most successful of the Westernised Chinese restaurants, and by far the most outrageous in decor – square mirrors on the ceiling reflect the pink carpet, pink cloths and darker pink chairs. The frosted windows are etched with Chinese characters and animals from the 12-year cycle, while on the other side of the room stands a large rock relief with the Chinese character Zen written on it and a constant stream of water running down. The atmosphere vibrates. The menu is a fantastic read of 120 dishes, combining Szechuan, Hunan, Peking and Cantonese – both regional and *haute cuisine* – but is flawed, as French restaurants have found, in trying to offer too much. Many dishes would just not pass muster in Chinatown (notably an appalling spring chicken at inspection). This is a pity, because some of the food can be very good, such as the boned duck web stuffed with mashed prawn; the appetisers (one is ample per person) of fried, crispy veal sticks, deep-fried vegetable dumpling, and deep-fried paper wrapped tofu; and the rustic Szechuan dish of beef in a lotus leaf. Why, Mr Leung, do you therefore sanction the use of tinned mushrooms in the monk's vegetables? House French is £6.

CHEF: K.S.Leung PROPRIETOR: Lawrence Leung
OPEN: all week CLOSED: 25 to 27 Dec MEALS: 12 to 3, 6 to 11.45 (all day Sat and Sun)
PRICES: £18 (£29). Minimum £8 at D. Service 15% CARDS: Access, Amex, Diners, Visa
SEATS: 130. Private parties: 100 main room, 20 private room. Vegetarian meals. Children welcome. Air-conditioned

England

ALDBOROUGH Norfolk map 6

Old Red Lion [10/20]

The Village Green, Aldborough NR11 7AA
CROMER (0263) 761451
off A140, 5m N of Aylsham £9–£15

A Georgian building on the village green. Some of the cooking is more elaborate than we like, but everything is cooked to order and the kitchen is happy to prepare dishes in more simple ways. There have been recommendations for the avocado and chive omelette; mushrooms cooked with tarragon and cheese; kidneys in madeira; and hake with garlic. The kitchen's favourite is the Barbary duck breast cooked as for a magret. Sorbets and meringues to finish. House French is £4·25, and the house reserve burgundy £7·85.

CHEF: Graham Blackwell PROPRIETORS: Mr&Mrs G.Blackwell
OPEN: Tue to Sat D, Sat and Sun L MEALS: 12 to 1.45, 7 to 9.30
PRICES: £10 (£15), Set L from £5·95 (£9) CARD: Visa
SEATS: 30. Private parties: 36 main room. Car-park, 12 places. Vegetarian meals by arrangement. Children's helpings (L only). Smart dress preferred. Classical music

ALDEBURGH Suffolk map 3

BACKGROUND BRIEFING: *Chiefly notable for a fine fish and chip shop that smokes its own salmon. Nearby Snape has a pub, the Golden Key, that serves good home-made food. The Wine Bar at Woodbridge (see entry) also has a good shop on the ground floor selling game and cheese.*

ALDERMINSTER Warwickshire map 2

▲ *Ettington Park Hotel* [15/20]

NEWCOMER OF THE YEAR GFG '86

Alderminster CV37 8BS
STRATFORD-UPON-AVON (0789) 740740
on A34, 5m S of Stratford-upon-Avon Real Food £19–£30

This is a major new place. It is not finished yet – the gardens along the drive have not all been planted and the tennis courts were still being built last summer – but it has potential as one of the great hotels, not just of Britain but of Europe. It is not hard to see why Michael Quinn MBE gave up the kitchens at the Ritz to come here.

As a building it is on the scale of Boyer at Rheims (see page 587) and our main hesitation, if we have one, is that the sheer grandeur might overshadow the food. But one inspection meal was as perfect a rendition of the virtues of English cooking as we have eaten. Mr Quinn once said, in an unguarded moment, that he intended to be the greatest of all English chefs; that inspection meal suggests it might not be an idle ambition.

First things first. This is necessarily a long entry because there is a lot to discuss. Ettington Park is a Grade I listed building; the estate is mentioned in the Domesday Book. The family motto of the Shirley family, 'Loyal Je Suis', is carved in the old beams around the dining-room; loyal they certainly were, adding to the building in successive generations until it became a unique example of architecture made of different coloured, locally quarried stone. It is set back a quarter of a mile from the main Oxford to Stratford road (ignore the signs to Ettington itself, which is two miles away), a Transylvanian-style building visible through the trees by the long snaking gravel drive. There is some confusion as to which is the front door. The one at the front, between the abbey-style arches, leads into a mediaeval, Italianate conservatory and into the main hall, from which lead off the great staircase and the drawing-rooms. The door at the side leads into a courtyard flanked by the kitchen, a swimming-pool surrounded by glass and with a spa-bath and fountain, a billiard room and the reception desk. The rooms are monuments to Victorian architects (John Pritchard in particular) and are laid with deep-pile patterned carpet (even in the lift) and it is no surprise that the porter is hard to locate. The staff, though, are friendly and helpful and in time will be very good – as they will need to be, because the kind of people who are going to come here are going to know, and expect, the very best. And the best is what the buildings and grounds suggest – and the church, the courtyard around the fountain outside, the lawns, cut as if for a cricket match, and the extension being built, at heaven knows what cost, in precisely matching stone.

Michael Quinn has kept the menu sensibly short, with a set meal plus a *carte* that features crab-filled smoked salmon with yoghourt and chive sauce; lobster beurre blanc; and duck breast with armagnac. The strength of his cooking (often frustrated at the Ritz by the waiters and the length of the menu) is that he isn't always trying to prove something with a sauce. He lets the ingredients taste of themselves, sometimes in the simplest of ways. He is a heroic defender of the English pudding, too. The meal that encapsulated his talents opened with Evesham asparagus chopped on to a bed of radicchio and frisée lettuce and dressed with walnut oil. Then followed a magnificent cup-shaped salmon mousse topped with five beads of sevruga caviare and a chervil leaf, surrounded by a sauce of champagne, chives and cream. The main course was beef: two fat, well-hung fillets, cleverly char-grilled on one side only so the piece went from rare on one side to well cooked on the other, sitting on a deep, classic demi-glaze with wild mushrooms, French beans, and baby carrots untopped so their greenery was strewn across the plate. On the side were two potato pancakes. By-passing the excellent cheeseboard the finale was about 25 raspberries, standing up like soldiers, flanked by two blobs of cream and surrounded by a sweet raspberry syrup. The chocolate truffles with coffee, served in the lounge, were still pliant, they were so fresh. One meal does not make a great kitchen, and a few months – it only opened in April 1985 – is not long enough to establish a great restaurant, but there is further evidence that great it will be: an omelette of sorrel and bacon; seafood sausages with saffron and truffle sauce; a deep gold-coloured consommé;

lamb with scallops; and pommes dauphinoise that reek of garlic.

Breakfasts have been less accomplished but no less interesting with, for example, poached eggs with black pudding. The rooms are fitted out appropriately, but are expensive. The wine list suffers from being a new assemblage, but it is not as overpriced as it might be in the circumstances. It is predictably long on claret and burgundy, and there is a small but well-chosen California section. It would be nice to see the list expand in the less expensive regions over the next few years. The house wine has commendably been kept at £6·50.

CHEF: Michael Quinn PROPRIETORS: Ettington Park Hotel Group plc
OPEN: all week MEALS: 12.30 to 2.30, 7 to 10.30
PRICES: £23 (£30), Set L £12·50 (£19), Set D £21·50 (£29), Snacks from £2·50 (£2·75)
CARDS: Access, Amex, Diners, Visa
SEATS: 70. Private parties: 60 main room, 70, 60, 16 and 14 private rooms. Car-park, 84 places. Children's helpings. No children under 7. Jacket and tie
ACCOMMODATION: 49 rooms, all with bath/shower. B&B £55 to £85. Deposit: 10%. No children under 7. Baby facilities. No pets. Afternoon teas. Garden. Indoor swimming-pool. Sauna. Tennis. Croquet. Fishing. Riding. Snooker. Helicopter pad. Lift. TV. Phone. Scenic. Confirm by 6 [GHG]

ALFRISTON East Sussex map 3

Moonrakers [11/20]

High Street, Alfriston BN26 5TD
ALFRISTON (0323) 870472 £16

Elaine and Barry Wilkinson change the menu monthly in their sixteenth-century oak-beamed cottage, but old favourites, such as Newhaven brill and Burgundy pie, keep cropping up. Fish is fresh, the chickens plump, and thick coriander and carrot soup and chicken liver terrine with ham, pork and bacon show that Elaine Wilkinson knows one end of a spatula from another. Some of the saucing has unfortunately ambled lumpily and greasily downhill, and puddings have been uninspiring. Nevertheless, the combined package of food, atmosphere and service makes for enjoyable, informal evenings. Service is exemplary and the wines are extremely well chosen. Lungarotti's Rubesco di Torgiano '78 is £7·80, López de Heredia's Viña Tondonia Tinto Reserve '70 is £11·10, and CELLARMAN'S CHOICE is Ch. Labégorce-Zédé '78 from Margaux at £12·40.

CHEF: Elaine Wilkinson PROPRIETORS: Elaine and Barry Wilkinson
OPEN: Tue to Sat, D only MEALS: 7 to 9.15 (6.45 to 9.45 Sat)
PRICES: Set D £11·90 (£16)
SEATS: 36. Private parties: 36 main room. Vegetarian meals. Children's helpings

---

The 1987 Guide *will appear before Christmas 1986, so reports are particularly important in the spring. Report forms are at the back of this book, but just write a letter if you prefer. Address them to* The Good Food Guide, *Freepost, 14 Buckingham Street, London WC2N 6BR. No stamp is necessary if you post in the UK.*

This restaurant has an exceptional wine cellar.

ALSTON Cumbria map 7

▲ *High Fell* [11/20]

Alston CA9 3BP
ALSTON (0498) 81597
on A686, 1½m S of Alston £20

After nine years the Chipmans are thinking of retiring from this, the highest hotel in the Lakes, built in 1623 and originally a farmhouse. So long as they are there, the standards will be maintained. They do not use any processed food at all. Specialities include genuine cassoulet, and quail stuffed with goose liver pâté. There are a dozen wines.

CHEF: Patricia Chipman PROPRIETORS: John and Patricia Chipman
OPEN: all week MEALS: 12.30 to 2, 7.30 to 9
PRICES: £17 (£20). Service inc
SEATS: 20. Private parties: 24 main room. Car-park, 12 places. No children under 5
ACCOMMODATION: 5 rooms, 3 with bath/shower. B&B £15·50 to £31. No pets. Garden. Scenic [GHG]

AMBLESIDE Cumbria map 7

▲ *Kirkstone Foot Country House Hotel* [10/20]

Kirkstone Pass Road, Ambleside LA22 9EH
AMBLESIDE (0966) 32232 £15

The name might more properly be Kirkstone Foot Suburban House Hotel as this is in a residential part of town. The five-course dinners are good value and much use is made of fresh produce – fish sometimes excepted – as Jane Bateman likes to point out. Dinner is at eight and everyone sits down together while a bevy of waitresses brings on a procession of food – leek and turkey soup; roast lamb with fresh mint sauce and old-fashioned bread sauce. But the sweets trolley is the thing, with eight or nine items on any evening – pears in cassis; Harvey Wallbanger cheesecake; banana Pavlova; apple and blackcurrant pastry; almond pastry base filled with coffee and chocolate, and so on. Seconds are offered and then there is a range of English cheeses. About 60 wines, among them house Austrian at £6·50 a litre.

CHEF: Jane Bateman PROPRIETORS: Jane and Simon Bateman
OPEN: all week, D only CLOSED: Dec to Mar MEALS: 8 to 10
PRICES: Set D from £10·50 (£15) CARDS: Access, Amex, Diners, Visa
SEATS: 65. Private parties: 15 main room. Car-park, 40 places. Vegetarian meals by arrangement. Children's helpings. No children under 8. Smart dress preferred. No smoking during meals. Wheelchair access (also WC). Music. One sitting
ACCOMMODATION: 14 rooms, all with bath/shower. D, B&B £28, cheaper rates for longer than 3 days. Children welcome. Baby facilities. Pets welcome. Afternoon teas. Garden. Croquet. TV. Scenic. Doors close at 12. Confirm by 6

'We both ordered artichoke hearts filled with asparagus tips and sauce hollandaise. The waiter brought it and, on seeing there were two of us, gave me the artichokes and my friend the asparagus. We shared the hollandaise.' (On eating in a luxury London hotel)

▲ *Rothay Manor* [12/20]

Rothay Bridge, Ambleside LA22 0EH
AMBLESIDE (0966) 33605 £6–£19

English country-house cooking at its best is found in this well-established, family-run hotel. The silverware gleams, candles are lit on each table, and the service from the mob-capped waitresses is usually deft; you are even asked whether you want cheese (excellent choice and quality, including three kinds of Lancashire) or sweet first. The six-course menu includes intriguing suggestions for wines to match, and is cheaper out of season. Especially good have been the smoked mackerel crêpes; the cream of vegetable soups, from parsnip to mushroom; roast mallard with a tart of rowanberry jelly as garnish; huge portions of pork with marjoram and thyme. There is a commendable Englishness about some of the dishes – pork and prune terrine wrapped in bacon or eel pâté. Some of the sweets do not live up to the rest of the meal, though the chocolate rum mousse is reliable and the lemon raisin cheese pie of a similar consistency to Sharrow Bay's famous sticky toffee pudding (see Ullswater). The wholemeal bread is fabulous. The garden gets better every year, but the rooms are no grander. The wine list is poetry – as strong under £10 as over. In the Alsace section there are jewels like Tokay '78, from Hugel, at £8·30, and Gewürztraminer, Vendage Tardive '76, also from Hugel, at £11 for a half, or another Gewürztraminer, Grand Cru Côtes du Brand '81, from Turckheim, at £8·40.

CHEFS: Jane Binns and Bronwen Nixon PROPRIETORS: The Nixon family
OPEN: all week CLOSED: last 3 weeks Jan, first week Feb MEALS: 12.30 to 2 (1.30 Sun), 8 to 9
PRICES: Set L from £3·50 (£6), Set Sun L £8 (£11), Set D from £15·25 (£19) CARDS: Access, Amex, Diners, Visa
SEATS: 70. Private parties: 12 main room, 30 private room. Car-park, 30 places. Vegetarian meals by arrangement. Children's helpings. Smart dress preferred. No smoking in dining-room. Wheelchair access (also WC). Air-conditioned. One sitting. Self-service weekday L
ACCOMMODATION: 16 rooms, all with bath/shower. Rooms for disabled. B&B £42 to £60. Deposit: £40. Children welcome. Baby facilities. No pets. Afternoon teas. Garden. Croquet. TV. Phone. Scenic. Doors close at 12. Confirm by 12 [GHG]

Sheila's Cottage [9/20]

The Slack, Ambleside LA22 9DQ
AMBLESIDE (0966) 33079 £10

Stewart and Janice Greaves' little daytime cafe in this early-nineteenth-century cottage has been going since 1965. The stoneground flour for the granary bread comes from the Watermill at Little Salkeld, Penrith; Cumbrian ham is air cured; and the Cumberland sausages are from Claytons in the town, and are served en croûte. It gets fraught when busy, but the menu – with Alpine overtones that range from a main-course vegetable and ham soup with Swiss cheese to Austrian

Many of the better restaurants offer bargain lunches for half the price of a meal in the evening. Details are given in the text.

Real Food *denotes that the restaurant does not use processed food.*

Sachertorte – remains of a standard. Also good is the Westmorland walnut and raisin tart. Afternoon teas are popular. House French is £5.

CHEFS: Janice Greaves and Vicki Rasmuss PROPRIETOR: Stewart Greaves
OPEN: Mon to Sat, daytime only CLOSED: 1 Jan to mid-Feb MEALS: 10.15 to 5.30 (L 12 to 2.30)
PRICES: £6 (£10), Teas from £2 (£2·20)
SEATS: 38. Private parties: 38 main room. Children's helpings. No-smoking area. Wheelchair access. Classical music

▲ *Wateredge Hotel* [new entry, zero rated]

Borrans Road, Ambleside LA22 0EP
AMBLESIDE (0966) 32332 £17

Originally two seventeenth-century fisherman's cottages. The emphasis is on fresh produce where possible, and bread, croissants and jams are all made in-house. Soups, such as watercress and parsnip, and mushroom, have been good, as has been a main course of pork medallions with cream and mushrooms. Desserts are said to be always excellent, notably the egg custard with fruit purée. The garden rooms give superb views over the lake. An interesting, varied list of wines. CELLARMAN'S CHOICE: Juliénas '83, from Bouchard, at £7·60. More reports, please.

CHEF: Chris Edmondson PROPRIETORS: Mr and Mrs Derek Cowap
OPEN: all week, D only CLOSED: 1 Dec to 7 Feb MEALS: 7 to 8
PRICES: Set D from £12·90 (£17) CARDS: Access, Visa
SEATS: 40. Private parties: 30 main room, 30 private room. Car-park, 25 places. Children's helpings. No children under 7. Smart dress preferred. Wheelchair access
ACCOMMODATION: 20 rooms, 12 with bath/shower. Rooms for disabled. B&B £20 to £48. Deposit required: £15. No children under 7. No pets in public rooms. Garden. Fishing. Scenic. Doors close at 11.30. Confirm by 5 [GHG]

ANDOVER Hampshire map 2

The Keys [9/20]

Swan Court, East Street, Andover SP10 1EZ
ANDOVER (0264) 52830 £6–£14

A good wine cellar, backed up with steaks, fish, paella, and young boar cooked in the Vosges style. House wine from £3·90. CELLARMAN'S CHOICE: Vacqueyras '83, from Jaboulet, at £7·20.

CHEFS: Pam Bernard and Dawn Shrapnell PROPRIETORS: Pam and Walter Bernard
OPEN: all week, exc Mon D MEALS: 12 to 2.30, 7 to 10.30
PRICES: £10 (£14), Set L from £3 (£6). Service 10% alc only CARDS: Access, Amex, Diners, Visa
SEATS: 55. Private parties: 32 main room. Children's helpings (L only). Wheelchair access (also WC). Classical music

Entries are compiled from the unsolicited reports from readers and are checked by inspectors; each restaurant is asked to supply details of its operation. Report forms can be found at the back of the Guide.

APPLETHWAITE Cumbria map 7

▲ *Underscar Hotel* [new entry, zero rated]

Applethwaite CA12 4PH
KESWICK (0596) 72469
off A591, 2m N of Keswick £9–£19

This old Italianate Lakeland favourite, tucked up high above Keswick, is under a new regime. Clive Wheeler took over the kitchens in May 1985 and since then the reports have been very positive. Encouraging signs include five local cheeses, home-made bread, and apparently no processed food, apart from the occasional Bath Oliver. Sauces for lamb, duck, and hare have been skilled and judiciously helped by fresh herbs. The five-course set dinners offer a choice at each course apart from the second, which is a vivid vegetable soup. Fine Pavlovas to finish. The hundred or so wines are wide-ranging, although still young. More reports, please.

CHEF: Clive Wheeler PROPRIETORS: Underscar Country House Properties Ltd
OPEN: all week CLOSED: Dec MEALS: 12 to 2, 7 to 9
PRICES: Set L from £3·50 (£9), Set D £14 (£19), Snacks from £1·25 (£1·40)
CARDS: Access, Amex, Diners
SEATS: 70. Private parties: 30 main room. Car-park, 45 places. Vegetarian meals. Children's helpings. No smoking in dining-room. Wheelchair access (also wc)
ACCOMMODATION: 18 rooms, all with bath/shower. Rooms for disabled. D, B&B £40 to £64. Deposit: 10%. Children welcome. Pets welcome. Afternoon teas. Garden. Tennis. Fishing. Golf. TV. Phone. Scenic. Confirm by 3

ARUNDEL West Sussex map 3

Pink 'n' Green [10/20]

Castle Mews, Tarrant Street, Arundel BN18 9DJ
ARUNDEL (0903) 883866 £7–£12

Named after the decor, though the flavour of Ake Olsson's menu is Swedish – big open sandwiches topped with smoked meats and redcurrants feature as part of inexpensive lunches. Other good dishes are the pea and tomato soup, and gammon with cheese. The Swedish platter is made up of gravlax, marinated herring, egg with prawns, and fried potato. Evening set meals offer three choices per course up to the excellent sweets – Pavlovas, fruit flans, and meringues. Service is courteous. The wine list is uninspired, but akvavit is served in frosted glasses.

CHEF/PROPRIETOR: B.A.L.Olsson
OPEN: all week L, Thur to Sat D MEALS: 12 to 2, 7 to 9.30
PRICES: Set L from £3·95 (£7), Set D from £8·95 (£12) CARDS: Access, Amex, Diners, Visa
SEATS: 26. 2 tables outside. Private parties: 20 main room. Children welcome. Smart dress preferred. Music

The Guide *is always anxious to recruit new inspectors. If you would like to apply, write to the editor enclosing a) a detailed report on a restaurant where you have eaten and b) a comparative study of restaurants known to you.*

ASHBURTON Devon map 1

Country Garden [12/20]

22 East Street, Ashburton TQ1 7AZ
ASHBURTON (0364) 53431 **Real Food** £15–£19

More like a decadent, town-house conservatory than a country garden, with its red moiré wallpaper (even on the doors), gilt mirrors, chandeliers and masses of trailing plants. Chef Robert Barnes has cosmopolitan tastes and chooses his raw materials with care: meat is home-killed, fish comes from Plymouth and Brixham, and there are interesting West Country cheeses on offer. He makes unusual sauces: poached salmon comes with smoked oysters and a lemon and green peppercorn sauce; fillet of beef is with prunes, almonds, red pepper, shallots and a strong, dark, red wine sauce. The array of vegetables can't be faulted for quality, while sweets indicate a fondness for nuts. Barnes trained at the Dorchester, and it shows in rather too much complexity. Excellent coffee is accompanied by home-made petits fours which are wonderful concoctions of chocolate, nuts (again) and glorious marzipan. A short, good wine list with the emphasis on white wines.

CHEFS: Robert Barnes and John Dyson PROPRIETORS: Hassan El-Masri and Edward Casassa
OPEN: Mon to Sat, D only CLOSED: 2 weeks Oct, 1 week at Christmas MEALS: 7.30 to 10.15
PRICES: £13 (£19), Set D £10·50 (£15). Cover 60p CARDS: Access, Visa
SEATS: 30. Private parties: 20 main room, 50 private room. Vegetarian meals by arrangement. Children's helpings by arrangement. Wheelchair access. Classical music

ASHBY-DE-LA-ZOUCH Leicestershire map 5

Mews Wine Bar [9/20]

8 Mill Lane, Ashby-de-la-Zouch LE6 5HP
ASHBY-DE-LA-ZOUCH (0530) 416683 £4–£11

A listed Queen Anne building that was a pub and then became a private house. Now it is as much a restaurant as a wine bar, with two distinctly different rooms – one modern with cane and hanging plants, the other older, with beams. The taramosalata is a suspiciously bright pink, but there are large helpings of lamb chops, soups are healthy, the pies good, and sweets traditional – treacle tart and bread-and-butter pudding. The menu changes daily, which is a good sign. The wine list is still rather strange, but ask for the bin-ends, which are more interesting.

CHEF: Janet Rishman PROPRIETORS: I.G.Bridge and Janet Rishman
OPEN: Mon to Sat MEALS: 12 to 2, 6.30 to 10.30
PRICES: D £8 (£11), Set L from £1·95 (£4). Also cut-price menu. Service inc
SEATS: 70. Private parties: 35 main room. Vegetarian meals. Children's helpings. Wheelchair access. Music. Air-conditioned

'The business lunch was in the private room. The waiters went round and served the meat and the vegetables. Half way through they realised they had run out of vegetables and so went back and took the vegetables off the first plates to serve the other diners.' (On eating in a luxury London hotel)

ASHFORD Surrey map 3

Terrazza [10/20]

45 Church Road, Ashford TW15 2TY
ASHFORD (078 42) 44887 and 41732 £12–£24

Attilio Cepollina and Emanuele Maffi run their Italian restaurant rather better than the way we compiled their entry last year. We got the STD code wrong, the phone number wrong, the rating wrong, and the price of the Barolo wrong. Sorry. Sorry. Sorry. Sorry. Let's start again. The pasta and the fish are the things to go for – fettucine with basil, fillet steak and tomato sauce, salmon cooked in foil with white wine and herbs. A little less butter would help the cooking, and extras can add to the bill, as can drinking some of the fine French wines, but there are some interesting Barolos that are less expensive.

CHEF: Andres Gomez PROPRIETORS: Attilio Cepollina and Emanuele Maffi
OPEN: Mon to Sat, exc Sat L MEALS: 12 to 2.30, 7 to 11
PRICES: £14 (£24), Set L and D £9·75 (£12). Cover 95p alc only. Service 10%
CARDS: Access, Amex, Diners, Visa
SEATS: 70. Private parties: 70 main room. Children's helpings. Smart dress preferred. Wheelchair access. Air-conditioned

ASKRIGG North Yorkshire map 7

Rowan Tree [11/20]

Askrigg DL8 3HT
WENSLEYDALE (0969) 50536 **Real Food** £15

Wild rabbit is supplied by a Methodist minister and ends up with apples and prunes in red wine; trout is potted with lemon; haunch of venison is served with a sauce of brandy, port, redcurrant jelly and orange juice; gurnets come with vinaigrette. The Baileys make their own bread, jams, jellies, soft cheese and yoghourt. The style is friendly and informal, and mother waits at table. Saturdays get booked up quickly. A short list of mainly French wines with CELLARMAN'S CHOICE: Brouilly '83, from Duboeuf, at £8·95.

CHEFS: Emma Bailey and Doreen Harvey PROPRIETORS: John and Emma Bailey
OPEN: Tue to Sat, D only (Thur to Sat D Nov and Dec; all week D 26 Dec to 1 Jan)
CLOSED: Sept, Oct, Jan, Feb MEALS: 7.30 to 9.3£0
PRICES: Set D £10·95 (£15)
SEATS: 24. Private parties: 20 main room. Vegetarian meals by arrangement. No children under 10. No pipes in dining-room. Wheelchair access. Music. Air-conditioned

ASTON CLINTON Buckinghamshire map 3

▲ *The Bell* [12/20]

Aston Clinton HP22 5HP
AYLESBURY (0296) 630252 £34

The Bell does not always live up to its reputation as the pick of the old school restaurants, although it is better than it was a few years ago. Meals can veer from the sublime, as in the gravlax, the trio of pâtés, pantoufle périgourdine, **guinea-fowl with wild mushrooms, and ribs of beef on Sunday, to the less so, as** in the three filets Médicis swamped in their sauce, and the occasionally unruly service. It is this inconsistency at these prices that accounts for the demotion to 12. But the wines smooth most edges – a tremendous if hardly cheap list that has grown up over many years and is therefore big on '60s clarets and old Rhônes. CELLARMAN'S CHOICE: Châteauneuf-du-Pape, Domaine Font de Michelle '74 at £13·50.

CHEF: Jack Dick PROPRIETORS: The Harris family
OPEN: Tue to Sun, exc Sun D MEALS: 12.15 to 1.45, 7.15 to 9.45
PRICES: £26 (£34). Service inc CARDS: Access, Visa
SEATS: 140. Private parties: 200 and 20 private rooms. Car-park, 250 places. Children welcome. Wheelchair access (also WC)
ACCOMMODATION: 21 rooms, all with bath/shower. Rooms for disabled. B&B £40 to £78. Children welcome. Baby facilities. Pets welcome. Garden. Helicopter pad. TV. Phone. Scenic [GHG]

BADMINTON Avon map 2

▲ *Bodkin House* [new entry, zero rated]

Petty France, Badminton GL9 1AP
DIDMARTON (045 423) 310 £19

This Grade II listed building on the edge of the Badminton estate is under new ownership again since last year. First meals have included good ceviche, lamb and seafood kebab with buttery rice and crayfish sauce, with assorted al dente vegetables a highlight, followed by home-made ice-cream and hot profiteroles. More reports, please.

CHEF: Glenn Muir PROPRIETORS: Roy and Jean Langley
OPEN: Tue to Sun, exc Sun D MEALS: 12 to 2, 7 to 9.30
PRICES: £14 (£19), also daily bargain dish CARDS: Access, Amex, Visa
SEATS: 40. Private parties: 50 main room, 26 and 14 private rooms. Car-park, 25 places. Children welcome. Jacket and tie. Wheelchair access (also WC). Air-conditioned
ACCOMMODATION: 3 rooms. B&B £15 to £27. Children welcome. Garden. Doors close 11.30

BAGSHOT Surrey map 3

Sultan's Pleasure [9/20]

13 London Road, Bagshot GU19 5HJ
BAGSHOT (0276) 75114 £17

A family-run Turkish restaurant offering excellent kebabs, good salads and pitta bread. Friendly, sympathetic service. A basic wine list with some Turkish reds and whites.

CHEF: Mr Cuzoun PROPRIETORS: Mr and Mrs Cuzoun
OPEN: Tue to Sat, D only CLOSED: 2 weeks Aug MEALS: 6.30 to 10.30
PRICES: £12 (£17)
SEATS: 60. Private parties: 60 main room. Car-park, 100 places. Children's helpings. Smart dress preferred. Wheelchair access (also WC). Turkish music

If you cannot honour a restaurant booking, always phone to cancel.

BAINBRIDGE North Yorkshire map 7

▲ *Riverdale House* [10/20]

Bainbridge DL8 3EW
WENSLEYDALE (0969) 50311 £9–£12

This hotel is a row of converted cottages overlooking the spruce village green. The dining-room's seersucker tablecloths, pot plants and bowls of daffodils give it the air of a tea-shop. Mrs Harrison cooks a different main course each night of the week, with a choice on Saturday: perhaps roast beef and Yorkshire pudding, roast pork, or steak and kidney pie. She also serves a first-class baked York ham with Cumberland and raisin sauce. Soups are good, but puddings are even better: brown sugar meringues with a sharp lemon sauce, or raspberry charlotte in a langue-de-chat case. Service is friendly and willing, although cutlery may be put on the table in a heap. House wine is £3.45.

CHEF/PROPRIETOR: Anne Harrison
OPEN: all week, D only CLOSED: Nov to Apr MEALS: 7 (8 Sat)
PRICES: Set D from £6·50 to £9 (£9 to £12)
SEATS: Private parties: 70 main room. Car-park, 5 places. Vegetarian meals by arrangement. Children's helpings. One sitting
ACCOMMODATION: 14 rooms, 6 with bath/shower. B&B £11 to £22. Deposit: £5. Children welcome. Garden. Fishing. Scenic. Doors close at 10.30

BAKEWELL Derbyshire map 5

Fischer's [13/20]

Bath Street, Bakewell DE4 1BX
BAKEWELL (062 981) 2687 **Real Food** £10–£21

The standards have been consistently excellent in Max and Susan Fischer's stone and beamed restaurant. Dishes are cooked to order and you are expected to stay for the whole evening. His cooking is modern and game is always a strong feature. The mixed game is two slices of pheasant breast, two pink breasts of wild duck and a small venison steak sitting on a game sauce surrounded by tiny chestnuts. The venison is garnished with tart apple. Otherwise pheasant may be offered as two dishes – first the breast in a sauce with apple and caramelised chestnuts, and then the legs. Salmon and sole are plaited; turbot is served with a sauce of herbs from the garden; sea-bass comes with tomato and ginger sauce. An array of vegetables comes on a separate plate. Portions are large and there are many, many endorsements for the crème brûlée, but also the summer pudding and the apple tart. The only niggle of the past year seems to have been the speed with which diners are met, greeted and the meal got under way. The interesting wine list is not greedily priced – Vacqueyras '78 is £7·65, when it was selling retail for £5-plus last summer. A good run of poorly described *cru* Beaujolais, too.

'I drink it when I'm happy and when I'm sad. Sometimes I drink it when I'm alone. When I have company I consider it obligatory. I trifle with it if I'm not hungry and drink it when I am. Otherwise I never touch it – unless I'm thirsty.' (Mme Lily Bollinger on champagne)

House burgundy is £5·50, or try the CELLARMAN'S CHOICE: Mercurey '82 from Michel Juillot at £11·55.

CHEF: Max Fischer PROPRIETORS: Max and Susan Fischer
OPEN: Tue to Sun, exc Sat L and Sun D MEALS: 12 to 2, 7.30 to 9.30 (10.30 Sat)
PRICES: £15 (£21), Set Sun L £6 (£10) CARDS: Access, Amex, Visa
SEATS: 35. Private parties: 40 main room, 12 private room. Vegetarian meals by arrangement. Children's helpings (Sun L only). No children under 12 at D. No cigars/pipes in dining-room. Wheelchair access (also wc)

BALLASALLA see ISLE OF MAN

BARFORD ST MARTIN Wiltshire map 2

▲ *Michels'* [13/20]

Barford St Martin SP3 4AJ
SALISBURY (0722) 742240
6m SW of Salisbury on A30 £14–£21

Erik Michel has an uncanny eye for the visual. Dishes come out of the swing doors of his kitchen with the panache of a private viewing – two spears of chicory with tiny florets of calabrese garnish a pheasant mousse encased in pastry, with a madeira and truffle sauce. His cooking does not lose sight of its main purpose – that the food has to be eaten. Successes have been the boned and rolled widgeon in a deep demi-glaze, its legs served on the side in a busy salad dressed in walnut oil; the eggs of a turbot garnishing pike quenelles in a lobster sauce; and the turbot itself as a main course in a mustard sauce topped with a pair of fat king prawns. To finish there are the three happinesses – a Miró of a dessert comprising praline ice-cream on a coconut biscuit; a star-shaped mousse; and a thick slab of chocolate mousse with a Grand Marnier butter scimitar shaped in the centre and surrounded by colourful fruits. The dining-room has similar artistic touches – claret jugs, a pair of carved wooden elephant tables – one African, one Indian – half dome lights on each table. Service by Karen Michel and her mother is happy and they have picked out some good wines for their short list – Ch. Millet '76 is £9·75. Try the Kir made with elderflower wine.

CHEF: Erik Michel PROPRIETORS: Erik and Karen Michel
OPEN: Mon to Sat, D only MEALS: 7.30 to 9
PRICES: £14·50 (£21), Set D from £10 (£14) CARDS: Diners, Visa
SEATS: 30. 3 tables outside. Private parties: 50 main room. Vegetarian meals. Car-park, 15 places. Children welcome. Wheelchair access. Music. Air-conditioned
ACCOMMODATION: 4 rooms, 1 with bath/shower. B&B £10 to £19. Deposit: 50%

The Guide *does not accept free meals.*

'The other starter was morels stuffed with hazel-nuts on a bed of noodles. It was more like a top-heavy duvet of poor shredded wheat fried to a crisp in left-over soya oil suffocating already half-dead morels.' (On eating in London)

'In my experience, the quality of Chinese food is in inverse ratio to the pattern of the wallpaper.' (On eating in Surrey)

BARKSTON Lincolnshire map 6

▲ *Barkston House* [new entry, zero rated]

Barkston NG32 2NH
LOVEDEN (0400) 50555
on A607, 4m N of Grantham £17

A converted Georgian farmhouse with working fireplaces, Laura Ashley-style decor and expensive matching crockery. There is a small *carte* much in the vein of Delia Smith, Michael Smith and John Tovey recipes. Bread is home made. Good dishes have been the smoked chicken and avocado salad, with dressing served in a separate jug; beef Stroganoff; char-grilled lamb cutlets with mint butter; and steak, mushroom and kidney pie. Vegetables are fresh and come in separate bowls. Ice-cream is served with home-made biscuits and the treacle tart comes with a jug of custard. Sweets are a feature. An improving wine list, on which house Rhône is £4·95. CELLARMAN'S CHOICE: Ch. La Croix de Grézard '81 at £8·95. More reports, please.

CHEF: Paul Godfrey PROPRIETOR: Peter Cochrane
OPEN: all week, exc Sat L and Sun and Mon D CLOSED: 25 to 28 Dec MEALS: 12 to 2, 7.30 to 9.15
PRICES: £12 (£17) CARDS: Access, Amex, Diners, Visa
SEATS: 28. Private parties: 28 main room. Car-park, 16 places. Vegetarian meals by arrangement. Children's helpings. Wheelchair access (also wc)
ACCOMMODATION: 2 rooms, both with bath/shower. B&B £25 to £35. Children welcome. Pets by arrangement. Afternoon teas. Garden. Fishing. TV. Phone

BARNARD CASTLE Durham map 7

BACKGROUND BRIEFING: *W. Kidd, 13 Market Place, watches how the local farmers breed, feed and treat their animals before buying from them, and consequently it has some of the area's best supplies of mountain lamb and local beef. Teesdale lamb is said to be exceptionally sweet. Thompson & Foster, 32 Galgate, is a small, traditional butchers with its own abattoir. Good local cheese can be had from Eggleston Hall, which has a provisions store called Partners joined to the cookery school at 26 Horsemarket. The excellent Blagraves House is up for sale so sadly we cannot give it an entry, but the Davidsons may still be there for a few months.*

Market Place Teashop [9/20]

28 The Market Place, Barnard Castle DL12 8NE
TEESDALE (0833) 37049 £8

Straightforward, excellent food to traditional recipes is served through the day in this stone shop overlooking the old Butter Market. The home-made soups, the breads, pot-roast brisket, and Lancashire hot-pot with red cabbage would not be out of place in a restaurant rating 12 or 13. Haggis is brought down from

'The music is the Tijuana brass played loudly. For some reason northern restaurants seem to regard this as classy now, whereas in the south it would be anathema.'
(On inspecting in Yorkshire)

MacSween's in Edinburgh, venison from Pitlochry. All main dishes come with salads or two vegetables. For children, there is also spaghetti on toast and Bertorelli ice-creams. It's always open, even in the snow. There is Theakston's Old Peculier and vintage cider to drink plus a few token wines.

CHEF: J. Moffat PROPRIETOR: R. A. Hilton
OPEN: all week CLOSED: Sun Dec to Mar, 1 week at Christmas MEALS: 10 to 5.30 (3 to 5.30 Sun)
PRICES: £5 (£8), Set L from £4·50 (£8)
SEATS: 46. Vegetarian meals. Children's helpings. Wheelchair access

BARNET Hertfordshire map 3

Wings [12/20]

6 Potters Road, New Barnet, Barnet EN5 5HW
01-449 9890 £15–£22

Downstairs is what steerage class on the *Titanic* must have been like – crowded, noisy and hot. Upstairs is more like first-class – attractive, with whitewashed and blue-grey walls, wicker blinds, Raffles-type fans and Chinese pictures. The staff hurry and constantly refill glasses in passing, even when told not to. The Peking/Szechuan cooking is fiery: very hot and sour cabbage; chilli and garlic sauce with prawns. Batters and pancakes have been heavy, but the quality of the meats is first-class, particularly the beef and the crispy duck. Specialities are spiced crispy smoked chicken; spicy aubergines; crab with ginger and garlic. The house Italian is pricey at £5·95.

CHEF/PROPRIETOR: Wing Ki Yuen
OPEN: L Wed to Sun, D Tue to Sun CLOSED: last 2 weeks in July MEALS: 12 to 2, 6 to 10 (11 Sat)
PRICES: £11 (£21), Set L £8 (£15), Set D from £12 (£22). Cover 85p. Service 15%
CARDS: Access, Amex, Diners, Visa
SEATS: 80. Private parties: 20 main room. Vegetarian meals. Children welcome. Wheelchair access

BARNSLEY South Yorkshire map 5

▲ *Brooklands* [11/20]

Barnsley Road, Dodworth, Barnsley S75 3JT
BARNSLEY (0226) 299571
500 yds W of M1 exit 37 £8–£13

'. . . 'Tis no sin to ask for more and it shall be freely given' is the inscription written across the top of the lunch menu, and it is no joke. The Grattons have been here since 1967, and the Yorkshire welcome, the value for money, and the wine cellar are larger than life. The three-course lunch is £5·70 off a menu that expands at night and takes in anything from spaghetti bolognese with generous amounts of Parmesan left on the table, through fresh grilled fish from Scarborough, to braised ox-tail with pickled red cabbage. There's always game in season. Wild duck is served with choux cabbage and a reduction of its marinade of burgundy, garlic and vegetables. Help yourself to salad off the trolley. Sweets are plain and plentiful, the apple tart first-class and the napery crisp. Magnificent list of inexpensive fine wines. The clarets of good vintages are bargains, and there are good showings of lesser areas, notably Hungary, and of the five Alsace wines there is the unusual and inexpensive Pinot Noir '81 at £3·90.

CHEF: John Smith PROPRIETORS: Mr and Mrs J. W. Gratton
OPEN: all week CLOSED: 3 weeks in Aug and 25, 26 Dec MEALS: 12 to 2.30 (2 Sat and Sun), 6.30 to 9.30
PRICES: £9 (£13), Set L £5·70 (£8), Set D from £7·90 (£10). Service inc CARDS: Access, Amex, Diners, Visa
SEATS: 110. 6 tables outside. Private parties: 100 main room. Car-park, 300 places. Children's helpings. Wheelchair access (also WC). Two sittings Sat, 7 and 9
ACCOMMODATION: 20 rooms, all with bath/shower. 4 rooms for disabled. B&B £27·50 to £31. Garden. Children welcome. Baby facilities. TV. Phone. Tea and coffee facilities in every room. Confirm by 6

BARNSTAPLE Devon map 1

Lynwood House [11/20]

Bishops Tawton Road, Barnstaple EX32 9DZ
BARNSTAPLE (0271) 43695
on A377 S of Barnstaple £20

Not unlike a French family-run country hotel, with a formal silver service dining-room upstairs and more relaxed eating-areas down. 'We specialise in fresh foods, though in the case of meats and game not too fresh.' Good reports of the seafood thermidor; the dressed crab; grilled mussels; and the excellent seafood platter, for which warm white and brown loaves are wheeled in on a trolley and cut up in front of you. The sweets can be the main event – treacle tart; meringue with kiwi; home-made chocolates with coffee. Mr and Mrs Roberts, who have been here for 17 years, make up for deficiencies by their willingness and friendliness. Good-value wine list.

CHEF: Ruth Roberts PROPRIETORS: John and Ruth Roberts
OPEN: Mon to Sat, exc Sat L MEALS: 12 to 2, 7 to 10 (9.30 in winter)
PRICES: £15 (£20). Bar meals from 95p (£1·05) CARDS: Access, Amex, Diners, Visa
SEATS: 70. Private parties: 80 main room, 24 private room. Car-park, 25 places. Vegetarian meals. Children's helpings. Wheelchair access (also WC). Light classical music

BARWICK Somerset map 2

▲ *Little Barwick House* [12/20]

Barwick BA22 9TI
YEOVIL (0935) 23902
leave Yeovil by A37, take 2nd left
opposite Red House pub, ¼m on left **Real Food** £16

The fading grandeur and timelessness of this Georgian dower-house lend meals here both informality and a sense of occasion. Summer aperitifs are served in the garden or in the cool cellar bar, while in winter, port is offered by the log fire in the lounge after an evening meal of dishes such as cream smokies, hot crab in mustard sauce, Popeye pancakes (spinach and cream cheese) and traditional English puddings. Game is the speciality and is usually excellent. Grouse has been served with slices of fillet steak, roast partridge with a clear orange gravy, and sauté venison with a green peppercorn and port sauce; sometimes there is snipe. Vegetables too are well treated. The Colleys have a good network of local suppliers, vegetables are often home grown, and eggs are from their own hens. Votes for the house wines: Beaujolais Cuvée de l'Amitié from Duboeuf, and Lamblin Blanc de Blancs – both £5 a bottle. CELLARMAN'S CHOICE: Côtes du Frontonnais, Ch. Bellevue la Forêt '82 at £6.

CHEF: Veronica Colley PROPRIETORS: Christopher and Veronica Colley
OPEN: Mon to Sat, D only MEALS: 7 to 9.30
PRICES: Set D from £11·80 (£16). Service 10% CARDS: Access, Amex, Diners, Visa
SEATS: 30. Private parties: 50 main room, 12 private room. Car-park. Children's helpings. Guitar music
ACCOMMODATION: 3 rooms, all with bath/shower. B&B £30. Pets welcome: advance notice. Garden. Children welcome. TV. Scenic. Doors close at 11 [GHG]

BASINGSTOKE Hampshire map 2

BACKGROUND BRIEFING: *Palmer's, opposite the Red Lion Hotel, serves English bistro food. In the new town centre Franco's has a good-value Monday night pizza and pasta evening. Hee's, in Westminster House, is a new Peking restaurant related to the Mill Hill operation (see London). For shopping, a small grocer's called the International Supermarket, 63 Winchester Road, has fresh Indian ingredients.*

BATH Avon map 2

BACKGROUND BRIEFING: *A small restaurant, Tranters, 2 Saracen Street, is the best bet for fish dishes in an area poorly served with fresh supplies; it also has game in season. There is an excellent cheese stall on the market and the Broad Street bakery has five kinds of bread – sunflower, heavy wholemeal, light wholemeal, sour-dough and a cheese bread. For cheap eating there is the Four Seasons in the Pump Rooms, with a splendid Palm Court dining-room and a varied cold table. Rossiters in Broad Street has a short, honest menu, and Sally Lunn's, 4 North Parade Passage, sells sweet and savoury filled buns. There is now a small museum under the shop, exhibiting items found on the site.*

Chikako's [new entry, zero rated]

Theatre Royal, Sawclose, Bath BA1 1ET
BATH (0225) 64125 £11–£12

Excellent value for westernised Japanese food – the ingredients are top quality and the menu easy to understand. The restaurant has moved around over the last eight years, from High Barnet to Melksham to here, beside the theatre. Seating is either on comfortable padded chairs with carved backs, or on low benches around the walls of a separate Japanese room which has a long, low table and straw slippers to change into. It is simple and smart, with black lacquered wood, paper screens, a bamboo ceiling, and hessian on the walls. The menu takes in the range of Japanese dishes, such as sukiyaki, shabu-shabu and teriyaki. Spicing is conservative in starters of gyoza (pork dumplings) and chicken kara-age, where the meat is taken off the wing, reassembled to look like a miniature drumstick, marinated in soy, rice wine and spices, then deep-fried.

Mixed teppan-yaki is a selection from beef, chicken, pork, salmon, scallops, mackerel, squid, prawn and sometimes halibut, with seasonal vegetables. Chikako Cameron starts the cooking on an electric hot-plate at the table, then leaves you to continue; by tradition a male member of the party should cook. A glazed earthenware tray of sauces for dipping is provided. House French is £4·20 or there is saké at £1·30 a flask. Other Japanese drinks are Suntory and Asahi lagers, plum wine, melon liqueur, and calpico – a concentrate of fruit juice and fermented milk, to be mixed with your choice of mineral water.

CHEF: Chikako Cameron PROPRIETORS: Chikako's (T.R.B.) Ltd
OPEN: all week MEALS: 12 to 2.30, 6 to 10.30
PRICES: £9 (£12), Set L and D £7·50 (£11). Service 10% CARD: Access
SEATS: 56. Private parties: 40 main room, 16 private room. Vegetarian meals. Children welcome. Japanese music. Air-conditioned

Clos du Roy [13/20]

7 Edgar Buildings, George Street, Bath BAI 2EH
BATH (0225) 64356 £13–£23

The new star in Bath, a few doors up from the Hole in the Wall. Philippe Roy is from Poitiers and cooks for his bright, rosy dining-room some extraordinary dishes, serving them with an ingenious eye for presentation. Quenelles of smoked chicken appear on a bed of chanterelle mushrooms with a cream sauce that is the colour of buttercups and sharpened with Roquefort. Even more ambitiously, salmon mousse is topped with its roe, bordered by sole fillets and served beside nuggets of Welsh lamb garnished with mange-tout and a sauce flavoured with rosemary. The selection of beans, oyster mushrooms and broccoli is served inside a half-moon-shaped casing of filo pastry. Amid all this extravagance Emma Roy conducts the dining-room with refreshing human candour rather than snobbery. To finish there is Sophie's Choice – a fresh white peach poached in champagne, set on a lemon tuile and served with a kiwi sauce and pistachio ice-cream – the sauce eased with a few drops of raspberry sauce. Quite remarkable. Filter coffee is plentiful and comes with chocolate truffles. The short, sensible and not overpriced selection of wines includes a trio from Alsace and some clever choices from other regions. CELLARMAN'S CHOICE: Santenay '81 from Jaboulet-Vercherre at £13·60.

CHEF: Philippe Roy PROPRIETORS: Philippe and Emma Roy
OPEN: Tue to Sun CLOSED: 2 weeks Jan to Feb MEALS: 12 to 2.30, 7 to 11.15
PRICES: £15 (£21), Set L from £7·95 (£13), Set D £16·50 (£23). Service 10%
CARDS: Access, Amex, Diners, Visa
SEATS: 30. Private parties: 30 main room. Vegetarian meals. Children's helpings. Classical music

▲ *Hole in the Wall* [13/20]

16 George Street, Bath BA1 2EN
BATH (0225) 25242/3 £20–£22

For the last two years we have held faith with Sue and Tim Cumming in the face of many criticisms, but our patience has run out. It is just no good carrying on as if nothing has changed since 1953 and cooking to a recipe book of the same year. If you want to be curator of a culinary museum in memory of the great days here under George Perry-Smith then fine, don't bother to redecorate. What is the point of making your own fresh pasta when you serve commercial chocolates with coffee? Where is the sense in serving terrines when one of them is tired and is probably yesterday's or the day before yesterday's leftover? And is it enough for a serious restaurant with as many as 60 seats to be run furtively from the kitchen, leaving dishes and customers to the mercy of waitresses apparently chosen as much for looks as expertise? How is it that standards, even within a single meal, plummet then soar like a seagull caught in a gale? What credibility is there in our telling people that the scallops in beurre blanc are impeccable, that the guinea-fowl and hazel-nut terrine has masterly contrasts of boozy flavours and of texture, that the chicken in a sauce of lime and cream is exemplary, when the lamb charlotte is bedsitter cookery and the pears with a black goo called blackcurrant sauce has as much delicacy as a pneumatic drill? There are good wines, worthy of a bottle denotation, but no one to serve them.

CHEF: Tim Cumming PROPRIETORS: A.T. and S.C.Cumming
OPEN: all week, exc Sun L CLOSED: 3 weeks Dec and Jan MEALS: 12 to 2, 7 to 10
PRICES: L £18 (£22), Set D from £16 (£20). Cheaper set L for residents. Service inc
CARDS: Access, Amex, Diners, Visa
SEATS: 60. Private parties: 16 main room, 36 private room. Vegetarian meals. Children's helpings. No-smoking area. Wheelchair access. Music. Air-conditioned
ACCOMMODATION: 8 rooms, all with bath/shower. B&B £50 (double). Baby facilities. No pets. TV. Phone. Doors close at 10 [GHG]

Moon and Sixpence [10/20]

6A Broad Street, Bath BA1 5LJ
BATH (0225) 60962 £10–£15

This culinary complex is up a crack off Broad Street, in the old Bath post office buildings. There is a wine bar downstairs, restaurant up, and a sheltered courtyard with fountains, lit up at night by fairy lights. The bar is all greenery, cane chairs, marble-topped pub-style tables, naive prints, wicker birdcages. Daily specials may range from butterbean and tomato soup to home-cooked ham. There is granary bread to mop up the sauce from the marinated mushrooms or to go with the pork terrine, and prices include one of half a dozen first-rate salads. Good dishes served both here and upstairs have been salmon with ginger in pastry; generous portions of devilled kidneys; pork with curry and kiwi. There are some innovative touches, such as a free delivery sandwich service for office workers and a Sunday brunch of Bucks' Fizz and kedgeree. The grading is upped two points because we have been impressed by the whole style of the operation despite the aggressive pop music. The wide-ranging choice of wines is backed up by some 30 monthly specials at cheaper rates. House wines from £4·75.

CHEF: Kevin King PROPRIETOR: Keith Waving
OPEN: all week MEALS: 12 to 2.30, 6.30 to 10.30 (11 Fri and Sat)
PRICES: £11 (£15), Set L £5·95 (£10), Snacks from £1·25 (£1.40)
CARDS: Access, Amex, Visa
SEATS: 70. 15 tables outside. Private parties: 35 main room. Vegetarian meals. Children's helpings. Music. Partly self-service at L

'The service was slow and so laid back as to be almost horizontal.' (On eating in Dorset)

Popjoy's [13/20]

Sawclose, Bath BA1 1EU
BATH (0225) 60494 **Real Food** £18

Beau Nash lived here with his mistress, Juliana Popjoy, who was reputedly a fine cook herself – hence the name. Ring the bell to get in and you are escorted upstairs to the sumptuous drawing-room. For all the professionalism it is still run as a private home. Alison Golden's essentially modern English menus change with the seasons and let the principal ingredients speak for themselves. Sweetbreads have been served with champagne and wild mushrooms, or else in an unusual mix of apple, banana and cognac; rabbit is grilled and served with a sauce of armagnac; fillets of Scotch beef come with a truffle butter. There is a zest about the cooking that indicates a well-organised and creative kitchen, as seen in the goats' cheese profiteroles with cucumber sauce, or fish terrine including smoked eel served with a lightly curried sauce, or syllabub with Sauternes and scented with geranium leaves. Puddings are rich. Tables are given only to bookings and Ms Golden, not unreasonably, insists on punctuality so that meals are staggered. Parking is tricky. The restaurant prides itself on its dry Martini cocktail but the wine list is carefully chosen, with a white VDQS Provence from Loron at £5·40. There is also an interesting Australian wine, Rosemount Chardonnay '84 from the Hunter Valley at £9·70.

CHEF/PROPRIETOR: Alison Golden
OPEN: Tue to Sat, D only CLOSED: 3 weeks after Christmas MEALS: 6 to 10
PRICES: Set D £12·50 (£18) CARDS: Access, Visa
SEATS: 36. Private parties: 36 main room. Vegetarian meals by arrangement. No children under 12. Smart dress preferred. No cigars/pipes in dining-room. Classical music

▲ *Priory Hotel* [12/20]

Weston Road, Bath BA1 2XT
BATH (0225) 331922 £20–£22

The vast sprawling urban house out of the centre of town overlooks the city from the crest of a hill in its own two-acre ornate garden. There are two dining-rooms connected by a corridor filled with china chickens. One is a big comfortable room with a seven-bulbed chandelier, sneering Dutch paintings looking down on varnished tables with straw placemats and doyleys; the other is strikingly covered with a wallpaper of different coloured dried leaves. The menu is short but varied and Michael Collom has produced again this year a few dishes that keep the rating up – superb Jerusalem artichoke soup, venison marinated, roasted and served with a game sauce, and exquisite, delicate passion fruit tart. There's a good choice of English cheeses. Prices crazily do not include VAT, and the bedrooms, lavish as they are, hardly merit the price. Service is from Trusthouse

The 1987 Guide *will appear before Christmas 1986, so reports are particularly important in the spring. Report forms are at the back of this book, but just write a letter if you prefer. Address them to* The Good Food Guide, *Freepost, 14 Buckingham Street, London WC2N 6BR. No stamp is necessary if you post in the UK.*

Forte refugees. An excellent, well-balanced wine list with clarets in abundance and sensible, not overpriced bottles from other regions.
CELLARMAN'S CHOICE: Ch. Cissac '73 at £16·38.

CHEF: Michael Collom PROPRIETOR: John Donnithorne
OPEN: all week CLOSED: 1st 2 weeks Jan MEALS: 12.30 to 2, 7 to 9.15
PRICES: £14 (£20), Set D from £15 (£22). Service inc CARDS: Access, Amex, Carte Blanche, Visa
SEATS: 60. Private parties: 25 main room. Car-park, 25 places. No jeans. No cigars/pipes in dining-room. No children under 10. Wheelchair access
ACCOMMODATION: 21 rooms, all with bath/shower. B&B £41 to £71·50. Afternoon teas. Swimming-pool. Garden. No children under 10. TV. Phone. Doors close at 11.30 [GHG]

Woods [9/20]

9–13 Alfred Street, Bath BA1 2QX
BATH (0225) 314812 £12–£13

Very pretty for a bistro – the big pine dining-room is airy and spring-like, with cord carpet, racing prints, Satchmo blaring out, and cheerful girls in blue overalls serving. The poor man's dishes tend to be the best – sticky lamb stew, chicken with chicken livers, and calf's liver and kidneys with limes and coriander. Plenty of vegetables, banoffi pie and good bread. There is also good grilled lamb with raspberry vinegar, and loin of pork with sesame and garlic. Terrines and bakes have been less successful, while the bread-and-butter pudding is quite unusual. Dull wines.

CHEF: Mary Alley PROPRIETORS: David and Claude Price
OPEN: Mon to Sat CLOSED: 8 days at Christmas MEALS: 12 to 2.15, 6.45 to 10.15
PRICES: £10 (£13), Set D from £8·95 (£12). Service inc CARDS: Access, Visa
SEATS: 100. Private parties: 70 main room, 36 private room. Vegetarian meals. Children's helpings. No cigars/pipes in dining-room. Wheelchair access (2 steps; also WC). Classical music

BATTLE East Sussex map 3

The Blacksmith's [10/20]

43 High Street, Battle TN33 0EE
BATTLE (042 46) 3200 £11–£16

The decor is a bit Berni Inns, but there are good Hungarian dishes prepared by Martin Howe, who has worked at the Gay Hussar in London. Nominations have been received for the chilled wild cherry soup, roast duck with honey and more cherries, and goulash with egg dumplings; other dishes may be more run of the mill. A well-spread list of 40 wines has something from everywhere, except Hungary, and from Alsace there is a Gewürztraminer '82 from Meyer at £7·50.

CHEF: Martin Howe PROPRIETORS: Martin and Christine Howe
OPEN: Tue to Sun, exc Sun D in winter CLOSED: 2 weeks Oct MEALS: 12 to 2 (2.30 Sun), 7 to 10.30 (11 Sat)
PRICES: £10 (£16), Set L £6·90 (£11), Set D £9·90 (£15). Cover 50p
CARDS: Access, Visa
SEATS: 65. Private parties: 75 main room. Children's helpings (L only). Jacket and tie. Wheelchair access (also WC). Music. Air-conditioned

Boxers [new entry, zero rated]

31 Mount Street, Battle TN33 0EG
BATTLE (042 46) 2132 £9–£16

The three-course dinner menu at £8·75 includes half a bottle of house wine, coffee and VAT in this typical Battle timber-framed building. Ingredients are fresh and the cooking is not elaborate: mushrooms with garlic, and entrecôte with a stock and wine sauce. An Italian influence is at work, bringing al dente fettucine, petti di pollo alla Emiliana, and fegato alla Veneziana. Service is speedy, well oiled and careful, but could unwind a bit: take along your own atmosphere. House French is £4·75, CELLARMAN'S CHOICE: St-Véran '82, from Mommessin, at £9·25. There is a wine bar at the back. More reports, please.

CHEF: Edward Wood PROPRIETORS: Edward and Ann Wood
OPEN: Tue to Sun, exc Sun D MEALS: 12 to 2, 7 to 10
PRICES: £10 (£16), Set L £5·50 (£9), Set D £8·75 (£10), Snacks from £1·10 (£1.20)
CARDS: Access, Amex, Visa
SEATS: 36. 4 tables outside. Private parties: 24 main room. No children under 12 at D. Wheelchair access

BEACONSFIELD Buckinghamshire map 3

China Diner [10/20]

7 The Highway, Station Road, Beaconsfield HP9 1LG
BEACONSFIELD (049 46) 3345 £8–£15

The best Chinese restaurant in Buckinghamshire. The dining-room has been given a facelift and the cooking has roamed into the fiery, hotter dishes of Szechuan. The set meal is good value and includes bang bang chicken; dumplings in chilli sauce; and the classic Szechuan dish, twice-cooked pork. Elsewhere, the menu is well balanced with sections featuring sizzling iron-griddled dishes, vegetarian dishes, exotic appetisers, three ways with duck as well as some pop descriptions like squirrel fish (fried fish in sweet-and-sour sauce) or tiger's whiskers (pork shreds in sea spice sauce). Specials are the orange chicken, Manchurian crispy lamb and steamed sea-bass. Finish with the exotic fruit sorbet. The pair of Alsace wines, both from Gisselbrecht, marry well with the food. The Côtes du Rhône '78 from Pascal won't go so well, but it is an excellent wine at £6·75.

CHEF: Tim Lai PROPRIETOR: Shu Fun Li
OPEN: all week MEALS: 12 to 2.30, 6 to 11.30 (12 Fri and Sat)
PRICES: £8 (£15), Set L £4·50 (£8), Set D £9·50 (£14). Service 10% CARDS: Access, Amex, Diners, Visa
SEATS: 80. Private parties: 80 main room. Vegetarian meals. Children welcome. Wheelchair access (also WC). Chinese music

'Why does one put up with certain "idiosyncracies" here that anywhere else would be unacceptable? i.e. a cup of tea brought lukewarm, very milky and swimming with aniseed, flowery bits and other eastern paraphernalia, by a very wobbly waiter, smirking uncontrollably.' (On eating in London)

BEAMINSTER Dorset map 2

Nevitt's [9/20]

57 Hogshill Street, Beaminster DT8 3AG
BEAMINSTER (0308) 862600 £12–£16

Michael Nevitt not only cooks, but also hangs his still-life paintings of food in this Grade II listed building, a conversion from two yellow-stone Dorset cottages. Bistro dishes with lots of battering and grilling are supplemented by the likes of duck breast marinated in honey, with an orange and Grand Marnier sauce. Locally smoked fish and meats from Bridfish at Bridport find themselves on a chock-full plate for hors d'oeuvre, and local Corscombe duckling can be barbecued with 24 hours' notice. Dorset Blue Vinney may occasionally be served, but more likely are Cheddar from Denhay Farm, Blackdown, and Carolina, a ewe's-milk cheese from Higher Holditch Farm near Chard, which won first prize at the Bath and West Country Show in 1985. House claret is £6·50.

CHEF: Michael Nevitt PROPRIETORS: Michael and Carole Nevitt
OPEN: all week, D only, and Sun L MEALS: 12 to 1.30, 7 to 10
PRICES: Set D £8 and £10·50 (£13 and £16), Set Sun L £6·50 (£12) CARD: Visa
SEATS: 30. Private parties: 30 main room. Vegetarian meals. Children welcome. Wheelchair access (also WC). Music. Air-conditioned

BEANACRE Wiltshire map 2

▲ *Beechfield House* [14/20]

Beanacre SN12 7PU
MELKSHAM (0225) 703700
on A350 between Lacock and Melksham **Real Food** £14–£23

The house is made of Bath stone. The drive is lined with mature trees and outside stands a magnificent cedar with its flopping branches held up by poles. There is also a pair of llamas in the grounds. The place has the style of a private country house, with a swimming-pool, a choice of rooms for an aperitif, and then two dining-rooms set with large napkins and good glass. Andreas Antona (ex-Ritz and Dorchester) took over the kitchen of Peter Crawford-Rolt's house last spring, and suddenly meals seemed to go into overdrive. Plaited rolls have arrived hot out of the oven, as have pastry cases filled with sweetbreads and wild mushrooms with a mild mustard sauce. Duck breast with kumquats has been excellent, or else there may be steamed fillets of sea-bass and red mullet on a warm vinaigrette. Vegetables do not appear to have seen the inside of a hot cupboard, and there are supplies of some of the most exotic tropical fruits to finish, splayed out on a plate with a passion-fruit sabayon lightly flamed under the salamander. There are fine cheeses, an abundance of game in season, and the eggs are free-range. An outstanding collection of wines is in the cellar – fine clarets,

'I get to the point of desperation not knowing what to order and that is when pâté comes in. If one has to eat pâté, then this is the stuff to eat. Reminds one of picnic lunches in the countryside of France!' (On eating in the West Country)

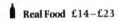

burgundies and Loires especially, but look also for Rhônes from Jaboulet. House Côtes du Rhône is £5·95.

CHEF: Andreas Antona PROPRIETORS: Mr and Mrs P.Crawford-Rolt
OPEN: all week MEALS: 12.30 to 1.45, 7 to 9.15 (9.30 Fri and Sat)
PRICES: £17 (£23), Set L from £9·50 (£14). Service inc CARDS: Access, Amex, Diners, Visa
SEATS: 54. 10 tables outside. Private parties: 50 main room, 50 private room. Car-park, 45 places. Vegetarian meals by arrangement. Children's helpings. No cigars/pipes in dining-room. Wheelchair access (also wc)
ACCOMMODATION: 16 rooms, all with bath/shower. Rooms for disabled. B&B £45 to £85. Deposit: 50%. Children welcome. Baby facilities. No pets. Afternoon teas. Garden. Outdoor swimming-pool. Tennis. Fishing. Croquet. Helicopter pad. TV. Phone. Doors close at 12 [GHG]

BEARWOOD see BIRMINGHAM

BELBROUGHTON Hereford & Worcester map 5

Bell Inn [12/20]

Bell End, Belbroughton DY9 9XU
BELBROUGHTON (0562) 730232
on A491, 6m SE of Stowbridge £12–£21

A long, barn-like room broken up by an open fire in the centre and with green-clothed tables set with fresh carnations. The three-course lunch is good value: fried plaice with chive purée; underdone fillet of beef with al dente vegetables; light grapefruit mousse enlivened with fresh fruit. Flashier dishes pepper the six-course dinner menu: cold trout mousse in a salmon parcel; hot brill cutlet in champagne sauce with cucumber; lamb with redcurrant sauce; tarte au Poire Williams. The service takes itself a mite too seriously, but this is balanced by first-class little extras, such as chicken mousse and asparagus canapés, and petits fours with the coffee. Nearly 100 mostly French wines: no points for the Hirondelle but there are good clarets for £15 to £20, a couple of Alsace wines from Meyer, and the CELLARMAN'S CHOICE: '83 Beaujolais, from Duboeuf for about £8.

CHEFS: Roger Narbett and Idris Caldora PROPRIETORS: The Narbett family
OPEN: Tue to Sun, exc Sat L and Sun D
CLOSED: first week in Jan MEALS: 12 to 2.30, 5.30 to 10.30
PRICES: £16 (£21), Set L from £8.50 (£12), Set D from £13.50 (£19)
CARDS: Access, Amex, Diners, Visa
SEATS: 64. Private parties: 100 main room, 30 private room. Car-park. 110 places. Vegetarian meals. Childrens's helpings. No children under 10 after 9pm. Jacket and tie. No-smoking area. Wheelchair access (also wc). Classical music. Air-conditioned

Freshman's [new entry, zero rated]

Church Hill, Belbroughton DY9 0DT
BELBROUGHTON (0562) 730467 £21

Ignore the sign outside saying, 'a new concept in eating out,' as this restaurant seems to be based on the good old concept of mostly fresh ingredients cooked to order. Annette Wheatley, virtually single-handed, runs this terraced former workhouse and pub in a village once known for its scythe-making industry. The bar is the first thing you see. It leads to a pink dining-room set with those dark tables and place mats beloved of ye olde tea shoppes. The napkins are of the type you feel twice to check they are paper. It is an expensive and rather heavy menu – no one starves, least of all at the vegetable course, which usually includes five kinds in big measure. There is plenty of deep-frying among the starters – mushrooms filled with chicken liver pâté; monkfish – and excellent seafood tagliatelle. Good main courses have been the rack of lamb with a stainless-steel sauce boat of orange, mint and redcurrant jelly; duck with port and black cherry sauce; poached salmon with fresh prawns and asparagus. The raspberry chocolate box is well liked, but better when fresh, otherwise there is lime syllabub or chocolate roulade with Tia Maria. There are two wine lists – look for the Beaujolais from Joseph Vernaison or the burgundies from Champy. More reports, please.

CHEF/PROPRIETOR: Annette Wheatley
OPEN: Tue to Sat, exc Sat L MEALS: 12 to 2, 7 to 9.45
PRICES: £13 (£21), Snacks from £2·75 (£3·50) CARDS: Access, Diners, Visa
SEATS: 50. 4 tables outside. Private parties: 40 main room. Vegetarian meals by arrangement. Children's helpings. Smart dress preferred. Wheelchair access. Music. Air-conditioned

BERKHAMSTED Hertfordshire map 3

La Fiorentina [9/20]

21–23 Lower Kings Road, Berkhamsted HP4 2AE
BERKHAMSTED (044 27) 3003 £15

The only place in the area to get a decent bowl of pasta, fresh mussels or osso buco. Minestrone is fine, too. House Italian is £5·25.

CHEFS: Shaun McCann and Vincenzo Iannone PROPRIETOR: Vincenzo Iannone
OPEN: Mon to Sat CLOSED: 2 weeks Aug MEALS: 12 to 2, 7 to 10
PRICES: £10 (£15). Service 10% at D only CARDS: Access, Amex, Diners, Visa
SEATS: 90. Private parties: 40 main room, 40 private room. Vegetarian meals by arrangement. Children's helpings. Wheelchair access. Music. Air-conditioned

BERKSWELL West Midlands map 5

▲ *Nailcote Hall* [new entry, zero rated]

Nailcote Lane, Berkswell CV7 7DE
COVENTRY (0203) 466174
off A4023, 6m W of Coventry £13–£19

Coventry has an excellent market but little of the produce seems to get into catering circulation in any form to fit these pages. However, what the garden of this originally sixteenth-century building does not provide, the market does. Tony Barnes is a furniture designer and has refurbished the house while his wife Hedy cooks an English/German menu of the old school, in more senses than one – Elizabethan pork is rolled fillets with apricots and almonds and cooked in white wine. Duck has been good, especially with raspberries or orange. Vegetables are served on side plates and, of the sweets, the profiteroles are mentioned frequently. House wine from Georges Duboeuf is £5·75. More reports, please.

CHEF: Hedy Katharina Barnes PROPRIETORS: Tony and Hedy Barnes
OPEN: Mon to Sat MEALS: 12 to 2, 7 to 9.30
PRICES: £12 (£19), Set L £8·50 (£13). Service 10% CARDS: Access, Amex, Diners
SEATS: 50. Private parties: 30 main room, 20 private room. Car-park, 28 places. Vegetarian meals. No children under 10. Jacket and tie. Wheelchair access (also WC)
ACCOMMODATION: 4 rooms, all with bath/shower. B&B £45. No children under 10. No pets. Garden. TV. Confirm by 12

BIDDENDEN Kent map 3

Three Chimneys [8/20]

Biddenden TN27 8HA
BIDDENDEN (0580) 291472
on A62, 2½m W of Biddenden £2–£6

This rustic pub with a bar and restaurant serves more or less the same food in both. Good dishes have been potted shrimps, chunky spinach and pork terrine, steaks, ginger pudding with Jersey cream, and the white Cheddar ploughman's. House wine is £3·95 or there are ales on gravity, such as Godson's Black Horse, Harvey's Best, Fremlins, Adnams' Best, Maidstone Light, and Marston's Pedigree, as well as Biddenden cider and scrumpy.

CHEFS: Jane Studd and Audrey Morris PROPRIETORS: Christopher and Pippa Sayers
OPEN: all week MEALS: 11.30 to 2, 6.30 to 10 (12 to 1.30, 7 to 10 Sun)
PRICES: £3 (£6), Bar snacks from £1·50. Service inc. in bar
SEATS: 100. 40 tables outside. Private parties: 40 main room. Car-park, 50 places. Vegetarian meals. Children welcome

BIRKENHEAD Merseyside map 5

Beadles [10/20]

15 Rosemount, Oxton, Birkenhead L43 58G
051-653 9010 £14

A good-value, unpretentious, French-style neighbourhood bistro in a converted shop, where more attention is paid to the food than the decor. Mrs Gott's cooking reflects seasonal availability and embraces marinated salmon with black peppercorns; duck with apricots; black pudding fried with apples; garlicky cod brandade; a 'Desperate Dan' game pie; and brown bread ice-cream. Some dishes, such as jugged hare with not much in the jug, seem to have been less well thought out. Roy Gott explains the menu and may sit down for a drink with you later. CELLARMAN'S CHOICE: Mâcon Blanc Villages '83, from Antonin Rodet at £6·90.

CHEF: Bea Gott PROPRIETORS: Roy and Bea Gott
OPEN: Tue to Sat CLOSED: Aug MEALS: 7.30 to 9
PRICES: £9 (£14). Service 10%
SEATS: 34. Private parties: 30 main room. Vegetarian meals. Children welcome. Wheelchair access (1 step). Jazz

BIRMINGHAM West Midlands map 5

BACKGROUND BRIEFING: *This year we have been totally exasperated by the standard of European food in Birmingham. At the Plough and Harrow (where the waiter asked our inspector if she wouldn't prefer to wait for her husband before ordering a drink), at Jonathan's and at House of Mr Chan the bills were so large (for unexceptional food in all three instances) that we cannot see any reason for recommending them to readers. TV personality Rustie Lee's restaurant at 192 Soho Hill at least has some pezazz about it, but for real value the Indian food at cafes around the Ladypool Road area in Balsall Heath takes some beating. Try Adil's. Los Canarios, 105 Albert Street. has one or two authentic Spanish dishes such as huevos a la flamenca, but the chief glory is the Spanish wine list. Birmingham's wholesale fish market is possibly the best in Britain, with excellent supplies from all the major ports. Quite why the fish does not appear more on menus in the city's restaurants is a mystery. The trade market also has good meat, fruit and vegetables.*

Los Andes [9/20]

Bristol Road, Selly Oak, B29 6BD
021-471 3577 £10

Reminiscent of one of those small Spanish restaurants where the food is invariably good and the decor a little of whatever is going – netting hangs from the ceiling and there are posters and the cheapest chairs and tables. The music is Andean, with songs from Bolivia, Peru and Chile, and the owners' allegiance is to the last. Prawn cocktail is the only sop to English tastes and the food is at once interesting, edible and a quarter of the price of the big French/Continental restaurants in the city. Not all the ingredients are Real Food, but it is amazing what can be done with tinned tuna and mashed potato covered with a Russian salad. But the real strength is the stews, particularly the chorizo, ham and smoked sausage with kidney beans and rice, or a hot and sweet pastel de choclo, beef and chicken mashed with sweetcorn and baked. To finish there is coconut mousse or brazo da reina, a rolled sponge with cream and alcohol. No licence, but 50p corkage and a good choice of fruit juices.

CHEFS/PROPRIETORS: Roque Milla, Freddy Aburto, Armando Pardo and Greg Grandon
OPEN: Mon to Sat MEALS: 12 to 2, 7 to 11.30
PRICES: £7 (£10). Unlicensed, but bring your own: corkage 50p
CARDS: Access, Amex, Diners
SEATS: 34. Private parties: 34 main room. Vegetarian meals. Children's helpings by arrangement. Wheelchair access. South American music

Le Biarritz [11/20]

148–149 Bromsgrove Street, B5 6RG
021-622 1989 £12–£18

A solid wall of clatter greets you as you enter this corner of France in an unfashionable part of town. The menu has moved more towards fish – huge platters for the crab salad, fine turbot, sea-bass with thyme and butter, mousse of crab with prawn sauce. Soups are reliably good, as is the red wine sauce with the entrecôtes. The rack of lamb is cooked pink. Ducks and pigeons are imported from France. The staff are attentive and tend to wield the pepper mills as if they were in an Italian restaurant. Standards are still too erratic to upgrade to 12, but the good-value set lunch and the wines compensate for the unpredictable. Customers who bring their own wine are not charged corkage so long as the wine is 'venerable French vintages'. House red from Duboeuf is £5·80.

CHEF: Didier Graffin PROPRIETOR: Julien Graffin
OPEN: Mon to Sat, exc Sat L MEALS: 12 to 2, 7 to 10.30
PRICES: £13 (£18), Set L £7·20 (£12), Set D £9 (£14). Service 10%. Licensed, plus bring your own: no corkage CARDS: Access, Amex, Diners, Visa
SEATS: 50. Private parties: 50 main room. Smart dress preferred. Children welcome. Piano player. Air-conditioned. Post-theatre dinner by special booking

Chung Ying [11/20]

16–18 Wrottesley Street, B5 6RT
021-622 5669 and 622 1793 £7–£15

At Sunday lunch this red-brick building of warehouse dimensions takes on the atmosphere of a bustling market-place, with grannies down to the smallest children tucking in to dishes from a Cantonese menu with more than 300 items. There are dim-sum; 15 soups, including hot-and-sour, and wun-tun; and 11 starters, including stuffed crab claw and king prawn toasts. Main dishes are grouped under prawn; chicken; beef; pork; duck; seafood; casseroles; barbecues; specials; grills; noodles; vegetables; and rice. The classic testing dishes of Chinese restaurants – char siu, cheung-fun, and lemon chicken – have been of the high standard usually found only in Manchester. A long wine list, but everyone drinks tea.

CHEF/PROPRIETOR: Siu Chung Wong
OPEN: all week MEALS: noon to midnight
PRICES: £10 (£15), Set L from £4 (£7), Set D from £10 (£14). Service 10% CARDS: Access, Amex, Diners, Visa
SEATS: 200. Private parties: 200 main room, 100 private room. Car-park, 10 places. Vegetarian meals. Children welcome. Music. Air-conditioned

Franzl's [10/20]

151 Milcote Road, Bearwood B67 5BN
021-429 7920 £15

A converted corner shop that Adolf and Valerie Geiregger have run as an Austrian restaurant for the last five years. It is well used by locals and needs booking mid-week. There are some nice touches, such as a choice of butters – plain, anchovy, garlic – with the dark rye rolls with caraway seeds, and some genuine Middle European dishes including the Gulaschsuppe of meat and potatoes spiced with paprika or the fillet steak with a cream sauce flavoured with cucumber and kümmel. The rating is dropped one point because standards don't seem to be consistent. On the wine list the Austrian Gewürztraminer '81 from

Places rating 8 or 9 may not be restaurants at all but still serve very good food. In this category expect to find pubs, cafes, small hotels and wine bars.

Klöch at £7·10 makes an interesting comparison to the Alsace, and from Austria there is the CELLARMAN'S CHOICE: Müller-Thurgau. Beerenauslese Eiswein '75 at £11·65.

CHEF: Adolf Geiregger PROPRIETORS: Adolf and Valerie Geiregger
OPEN: Tue to Sat, D only CLOSED: Aug MEALS: 7 to 10.30
PRICES: £10 (£15) CARDS: Access, Visa
SEATS: 35. Private parties: 35 main room. Vegetarian meals. Children's helpings. Austrian music

Giovanni's [10/20]

27 Poplar Road, Kings Heath, B14 7AA
021-443 2391 £8–£16

Giovanni Butto has been here for eleven years serving freshly cooked food at good-value prices. Rolls are served hot and the platefuls of freshly made tagliatelle matriciana are enormous. Dover sole is always fresh and the quality of the veal is high. The chef's special ice-cream is chestnut with angelica, chocolate sauce and sambouca – very sticky and rich. Italian wines are £5·30 for a carafe.

CHEF/PROPRIETOR: Giovanni Butto
OPEN: Tue to Sat MEALS: 12 to 2, 7 to 10.30
PRICES: £10 (£16), Set L £5·50 (£8). Minimum £8. Service inc set only, alc 10%
CARDS: Access, Diners, Visa
SEATS: 70. Private parties: 70 main room, 25 private room. Vegetarian meals by arrangement. Children's helpings. Smart dress preferred. Wheelchair access (1 step; also WC). Music

Henry Wong [new entry, zero rated]

283 High Street, Harborne, B17 9QH
021-427 9799 £12–£16

Opposite Royalty Bingo is this young, up-market, modern Chinese restaurant in what used to be a bank, now all pinks and whites with the napkins concertinaed into the glasses. The menu is fashionable, drawing on rather more than just Cantonese fare, with an emphasis on fish and sizzling dishes. Some of the cooking has been alpha – fillet steak with ginger and black beans; lemon chicken; pak choy with oyster sauce; sesame prawn toasts. Less inspired are the trendy dishes, such as the diced meats to wrap in lettuce, and the Peking duck. The Mou Tai liqueur is viciously alcoholic at £1 a glass. More reports, please.

CHEF: S.K.L. Yeung PROPRIETORS: H.W. Wong, S.K.L. Yeung and M. Yau
OPEN: Mon to Sat MEALS: 12 to 2, 5.30 to 11 (11.30 Fri and Sat)
PRICES: £9 (£16), Set L and D £8 (£12). Service 10% CARDS: Access, Amex, Diners, Visa
SEATS: 85. Private parties: 60 main room, 40 private room. Children welcome. Wheelchair access. Light music

'The only light relief of the evening was provided by the sight of the two young chefs who occasionally poked their heads out of the kitchen to see whether it was all clear for them to take the two women, who had been previously waiting for them, upstairs for some more satisfying entertainment. Fortunately, their patience was rewarded around 11 o'clock.' (On eating in Warwickshire)

Ho Tung [11/20]

308 Bull Ring Centre, B5 4PY
021-643 0033 £11–£20

Good Chinese restaurants in cities, particularly London and Manchester, have been edging out the competition with their quality and value. This is happening in Birmingham, too, and although the Ho Tung (on the site of the old New World, beside the Nat West bank, opposite the main entrance to New Street Station) is not the cheapest, it still offers affordable Cantonese food with occasional flashes of brilliance. The dining-room is enormous, too stark to be grand, but up-market with cane and black furniture and lots of chrome and brass. Prawns come with a light, crisp batter and delicate spicing; steamed duck's feet are wrapped in a pancake with a strip of duck breast and a piquant honey syrup. At inspection the noodles, with crunchy spring onion, bean sprouts, and a glistening coat of sesame oil, were excellent. Lemon chicken is one of the best in the city. Portions are large, service is impeccable, and tea terrific. Dim-sum are available until 5.30pm.

CHEF: Mr Lai PROPRIETOR: Tony Ho
OPEN: all week MEALS: noon to midnight
PRICES: £12 (£20). Set L and D from £6·50 (£11). Cheaper set L available. Service 10%
CARDS: Access, Amex, Diners, Visa
SEATS: 150. Private parties: 150 main room, 60 private room. Vegetarian meals. Children welcome. Jacket and tie preferred. Wheelchair access (also WC). Chinese music. Air-conditioned

Maharaja [9/20]

23–25 Hurst Street, B5 4AS
021-622 2641 £9–£13

A neat building, decorated in pink; the ceiling is an Indian version of the Sistine Chapel. They serve north Indian and tandoori dishes, raita with bits of pineapple and dried cumin, oily nan, and the best gulab jamun we've eaten for a long time. Maroon-jacketed waiters serve speedily, but give you time to sit back between courses.

CHEF: Bhupinder Waraich PROPRIETOR: N.S.Batt
OPEN: Mon to Sat MEALS: 12 to 2.30, 6 to 11.30
PRICES: £6 (£11). Set L from £5 (£9). Set D from £8·50 (£13). Minimum £4·50. Service 10%
CARDS: Access, Amex, Diners, Visa
SEATS: 65. Private parties: 30 main room. Vegetarian meals. Children welcome. Wheelchair access. Music. Air-conditioned

Rajdoot [9/20]

12–22 Albert Street, B4 7UD
021-643 8805 and 8749 £8–£15

Three shop-fronts joined together. Good Punjabi cooking where the lamb pasanda tastes of lamb and the prawn bhuna tastes of prawn. Quail is served as masala or as excellent tandoori. Chicken moghlai is ordinary, but the nan are glorious: among the best in the business. Take some fudgey, almondy burfi home for tea.

CHEF/PROPRIETOR: B.Mali
OPEN: all week, exc Sun L MEALS: 12 to 2.30, 6.30 to 12
PRICES: £10 (£15), Set L £4·50 (£9), Set D from £8·50 (£13). Cover 50p. Minimum £4·50. Service inc alc only, set 12.5% CARDS: Access, Amex, Diners, Visa
SEATS: 80. Private parties: 40 main room. Vegetarian meals. Children welcome. Wheelchair access (also wc). Indian music. Air-conditioned

Sloans [14/20]

27–29 Chad Square, Hawthorne Road, Edgbaston B15 3TQ
021-455 6697
follow one-way system past Botanic
Gardens: turn left then right £11–£26

The loudest of all the restaurants to rate 14, but although the pink decor is like something Ken Russell might have dreamed up for a 1920s revival or a documentary on northern night-clubs, Carl Timms' cooking of fish bought fresh daily from Birmingham's excellent market is of a very high standard: witness the red mullet fillets on a purée of leeks with a cream sauce made from a reduction of the fish stock and Noilly with chives. The style is both the provincial French of moules marinière or seafood gratin and the modern idiom of pike and salmon terrine with watercress sauce. Lobster is always available but it is expensive with thermidor at £17·50. Dover sole is excellent. There is beef and lamb for meat eaters. Vegetables are pretty – and pretty ungenerous. To finish there are fabulous Grand Marnier or passion fruit soufflés that are worth the 30-minute wait. Other marks of the quality of this restaurant are the fresh rolls, the strong coffee, the plate of prawns with drinks before dinner. The set lunch is remarkably good value and the wine list a treat. Both the Alsace wines would go well with the cooking or else, marginally cheaper, CELLARMAN'S CHOICE: Quincy '83, from Mardon, £7·90.

CHEF: Carl Timms PROPRIETORS: Maine Restaurants Ltd
OPEN: Mon to Sat, exc Sat L CLOSED: bank hols and 2 weeks July and Aug
MEALS: 12 to 2, 7 to 10
PRICES: £19 (£25), Set L £7·50 (£11), Set D £21 (£26) CARDS: Access, Amex, Diners, Visa
SEATS: 60. Private parties: 30 main room. Car-park, 60 places. Smart dress preferred. Children's helpings. Wheelchair access (1 step; also wc). Music. Air-conditioned

BIRTLE Greater Manchester map 5

▲ *Normandie* [11/20]

Elbut Lane, Birtle BL9 6UT
061-764 3869 and 1170
off B6222, 3m NE of Bury £19–£21

The Normandie enjoyed fame in the 1960s and 1970s as the creation of the Champeau family, who ran it as a simple hotel and bistro with excellent food. Since then a company has bought the place, spent a small fortune on alterations and redecoration, and installed a manager, Glenn Davies, to run it. The cooking has varied over recent times, but Mohammed Daho has done much to restore the previous renown. He is still nominally in charge, but the kitchen is now run in practice by Stuart Beard. The menu is mainly modern and heavily French, with such dishes as poussin en cocotte aux gousses d'ail, and filet de saumon aux crevettes. Mousseline of turbot is light with a sharp cream and wine sauce; fillet of lamb comes sliced and pink with crescents of avocado and a few mint leaves. Vegetables include al dente greens. Good raw materials are used, but the large amount of cream that finds its way into sauces for the smoked fish pancake, chicken breast with prawns, and the soup, indicates that one foot is still in the traditionalist camp. Service is scrupulously correct. The wines are extensive and well annotated, but not many are below £8. Although there is no house wine, a non-vintage claret costs £6·80. CELLARMAN'S CHOICE: Côte Rotie '78, from Chapoutier, at £15·30.

CHEFS: Mohammed Daho and Stuart Beard PROPRIETOR: K.W.Foster
OPEN: Mon to Sat, exc Sat L MEALS: 12 to 2, 6.30 to 9.30
PRICES: £14 (£21), Set D £13·50 (£19), L snacks from 90p(£1). Service 10%
CARDS: Access, Amex, Diners, Visa
SEATS: 70. 2 tables outside. Private parties: 80 main room. Car-park, 50 places. Vegetarian meals by arrangement. Children's helpings by arrangement. No-smoking area. Wheelchair access (also WC). Music
ACCOMMODATION: 18 rooms, 16 with bath/shower. Rooms for disabled. B&B £33·50 to £39·50. Children welcome. Baby facilities. Pets by arrangement. Garden. Helicopter pad. Lift. TV. Scenic [GHG]

BISHOP'S CLEEVE Gloucestershire map 2

▲ *Cleeveway House* [10/20]

Bishop's Cleeve GL52 4SA
BISHOP'S CLEEVE (024 267) 2585
on A435, 3m N of Cheltenham £15

A tranquil stone house surrounded by three acres of its own garden with pine trees. From the dining-room it is possible to see the kitchen at work boiling up the lobsters. Some of the cooking is very good – scallops with sweetbreads, huge portions of duck or peppered steak, and plentiful fresh vegetables out of the garden. Sweets, too, such as kiwi sorbet and chestnut mousse, have been up to the mark. Good, if expensive, wine list, but house French is £4·80.

CHEF/PROPRIETOR: John Marfell
OPEN: Mon to Sat, exc Mon L CLOSED: 1 week at Christmas, Easter and bank hols
MEALS: 12 to 1.45, 7 to 9.45
PRICES: £10 (£15)
SEATS: 38. Private parties: 10 main room. Car-park, 50 places. Vegetarian meals. Children's helpings. No cigars/pipes in dining-room. Wheelchair access (also WC). Air-conditioned
ACCOMMODATION: 3 rooms, all with bath/shower. B&B £20 to £35. Children welcome. Dogs welcome. Garden. Helicopter pad. TV. Doors close at 1

Entries are compiled from the unsolicited reports from readers and are checked by inspectors; each restaurant is asked to supply details of its operation. Report forms can be found at the back of the Guide.

BISHOP'S LYDEARD Somerset map 2

Rose Cottage [10/20]

Bishop's Lydeard TA4 3LR
BISHOP'S LYDEARD (0823) 432394
on A358, 1m E of Bishop's Lydeard £13

The Dale-Thomases have been here since 1976. The food is cooked to order, sauces thickened by reduction, rather than with flour, and there is a vegetarian strain to the menu that brings vegetable moussaka alongside rack of lamb with herbs and garlic. Meringues are freshly baked and portions are large. There should be some '78 *cru bourgeois* clarets of interest added to the wine list this year. Dorset IPA or Sheppey's cider.

CHEF: T.Dale-Thomas PROPRIETORS: P. and T.Dale-Thomas
OPEN: Tue to Sat CLOSED: 2 weeks Nov, 2 weeks at Christmas MEALS: 12 to 2, 7 to 10
PRICES: £9 (£13)
SEATS: 45. 5 tables outside. Private parties: 16 main room. Car-park, 20 places. Vegetarian meals. Children's helpings. No-smoking area. Wheelchair access. Classical music

BISHOPS TACHBROOK Warwickshire map 2

▲ *Mallory Court* [14/20]

Harbury Lane, Bishops Tachbrook CV33 9QB
LEAMINGTON SPA (0926) 30214
off A452, 2m S of Leamington Spa £20–£26

As a country-house hotel Mallory Court rates alongside Hambleton Hall and the other heavyweights. Allan Holland has a completely English team in the kitchen, though the unobtrusive waiters are French. The atmosphere is relaxed and unhurried, even though jacket and tie are obligatory. There are touches of a very fine restaurant, from the hot wholemeal rolls and good-quality butter onwards. The short menu encompasses both the traditional – avocado with prawns, first-class roast beef and Yorkshire pudding, and sirloin steak in red wine sauce – and the *nouvelle* – a starter of red mullet and scallop salad, or chicken with wild mushrooms. Good sweets have been English, like jam pudding and treacle tart. Excellent wines are around £10-plus, but a few cheaper bottles would be welcome. The rooms are idyllic, although twin baths, squash courts, ten acres of landscaped garden and swimming don't come cheap: take the helicopter.

CHEF: Allan G.Holland PROPRIETORS: Allan Holland and J.R.Mort
OPEN: all week CLOSED: 26 Dec to 1 Jan MEALS: 12.30 to 1.30, 7.30 to 9.30 (10 Sat)
PRICES: Set L £15·50 (£20), Set D from £21 (£26). Service inc CARDS: Access, Amex, Visa
SEATS: 50. Private parties: 50 main room. Car-park, 50 places. Jacket and tie. No cigars/pipes in dining-room. No children under 12
ACCOMMODATION: 10 rooms, all with bath/shower. B&B from £72. Afternoon teas. Swimming-pool. Garden. Croquet. Squash. Helicopter pad. No children under 12. TV. Phone. Doors close at 12 [GHG]

New restaurants that we have not been able to assess completely are given a zero rating for this year. We are particularly keen to have reports on these places.

BLACKBURN Lancashire map 5

Foxfields [12/20]

Whalley Road, Billington, Blackburn BB6 9HY
WHALLEY (025 482) 2556
M6 exit 31 then A59 to Whalley £13–£19

The truffles and foie gras here come from Vin Sullivan in Abergavenny and the shellfish is from Scotland, but it is good to see Henk van Heumen making use of local suppliers for fish and fowl. Blackburn's excellent fish market puts many others to shame. The French-style menu might include slices of mallard filled with duckling pâté; pink lamb cutlets with rosemary; sole, langoustines and monkfish in a cream sauce flavoured with orange, in puff pastry. Seasonal dishes quite properly vary with what is available in the markets: perhaps Guernsey or Californian asparagus; Scottish langoustines; grouse; breast of pheasant or partridge. Service is smart in immaculate, comfortable surroundings. The *carte* is not cheap, but the simpler, fixed-price three-course lunch, especially on Sunday, is good value. House wine is £6 and there is a clutch of bottles from Alsace, including some from Sipp and Hugel, on an overwhelmingly French list. CELLARMAN'S CHOICE: St-Véran '84, from Duboeuf, at £9·50.

CHEF: Henk van Heumen PROPRIETORS: T.H.Parkinson and K.W.Bradshaw
OPEN: Tue to Sun, exc Sat L CLOSED: bank hols MEALS: 12 to 1.30, 7 to 9.30 (9 Sun)
PRICES: £14 (£19), Set L £8·50 (£13) CARDS: Access, Amex, Diners, Visa
SEATS: 60. Private parties: 20 main room, 120 private room. Car-park, 65 places. Vegetarian meals. Children's helpings (L only). No children under 4 at L, or under 8 at D. Smart dress preferred. Music

BLACKPOOL Lancashire map 5

Danish Kitchen [9/20]

295 Church Street, Blackpool FY1 1HU
BLACKPOOL (0253) 24291 £5

Plentiful open sandwiches, salads, pizzas, biscuits, sweets and pastries are found at this self-service. Presentation is attractive and polite, and smiling staff are on hand if needed. Surroundings are bright and clean; a fiver brings a meal and change. Drinks include fruit juice, tea, chocolate and wine.

CHEFS: Nadine Simister, Sally Dowling, Samantha Carter and Diana Greenhough
PROPRIETORS: Diana and John Greenhough
OPEN: Mon to Sat, daytime only MEALS: 9.15 to 5.30
PRICES: £3 (£5), Set L from £2·15 (£5)
SEATS: 110. Vegetarian meals. Children's helpings. No-smoking area. Wheelchair access. Air-conditioned. Self-service

If you suspect that a restaurant is using processed food, always ask. It would be a contravention of the Trade Descriptions Act for the restaurant to lie.

'Why do some restaurants dress their waitresses in black skirts and white blouses, which show dandruff, odd hairs and spilt soup to great effect?' (On eating in London)

Jasmine Cottage [9/20]

52 Coronation Street, Blackpool FY1 PD
BLACKPOOL (0253) 25303 £6–£11

This Peking restaurant offers a set lunch at £2·20 and also competent individual dishes – prawn toasts, seaweed, Peking duck and so on. The one-plate meals are large and good value. Licensed.

CHEF: H. Yip PROPRIETORS: H.B.Un and Peter Man
OPEN: all week, exc Sat L and Sun L CLOSED: Nov to Feb closed for L MEALS: 12 to 2, 5 to 12 (all day in summer)
PRICES: £6 (£11), Set L £2·20 (£6), Set D £6 (£10). Minimum £2·80 CARDS: Access, Visa
SEATS: 62. 16 tables outside. Private parties: 45 main room. Vegetarian meals. Children welcome. Classical music. Air-conditioned

---

BLANCHLAND Northumberland map 7

▲ *Lord Crewe Arms* [new entry, zero rated]

Blanchland
BLANCHLAND (043 475) 251
off A68 7m S of Corbridge £9–£13

A large, stone-flagged, thirteenth-century inn with thick, castellated walls and huge wood fires. Good-value four-course dinners have included grilled sardines, potted shrimps, smoked quail, and contrefilet of beef in cream and brandy sauce. The bar food, too, has been of a standard – fresh Northumberland cod along with home-made pâtés and soups. The latter come with sippets – small oven cakes, four inches in diameter, crunchy on the outside, soft in the middle. Samson bitter from the Vaux breweries and a good selection of single malt whiskies. House wine is £6·50 a litre. More reports, please.

CHEF: Michael Brookbank PROPRIETOR: E.F.Oretti
OPEN: all week, D only, also Sun L MEALS: 12.30 to 2.15, 7 to 9.15
PRICES: Set L £6 (£9), Set D £9·35 (£13), Bar meals from £1·65, Snacks from 75p. Service inc
SEATS: 50. Private parties: 65 main room, 30 private room. Car-park, 15 places. Vegetarian meals. Children's helpings
ACCOMMODATION: 15 rooms, all with bath/shower. Rooms for disabled. B&B £31·50 to £45. Children welcome. Baby facilities. No pets in public rooms. Afternoon teas. Garden. Phone. Doors close at 12. Confirm by 7 [GHG]

BLOCKLEY Gloucestershire map 2

▲ *Lower Brook House* [10/20]

Lower Street, Blockley GL56 9DS
BLOCKLEY (0386) 700286 £4–£17

A small, pleasant old-world country house. The dinner menu has become increasingly English – good vegetable soups before guinea-fowl with lovage; rack of lamb; pork with sage; and plenty of game in winter. The sweets on the trolley are dressed in Jersey cream – apple pie and coffee and walnut gateau are very good. The young staff are friendly and efficient. The rating is reduced by one

point from last year because of some erratic main courses. Ask about the bin-end wines or there's the CELLARMAN'S CHOICE: Fleurie, Domaine des Quatre Vents '83 from Duboeuf at £9.

CHEF: Sandra Button PROPRIETOR: Ewan Wright
OPEN: all week CLOSED: Jan MEALS: 12.30 to 2, 7.15 to 9.30
PRICES: Set L from £1·50 (£4), Set D £12 (£17) CARDS: Access
SEATS: 38. 2 tables outside. Private parties: 20 main room, 20 private room. Car-park, 12 places. Vegetarian meals. Children's helpings. Wheelchair access (also WC)
ACCOMMODATION: 8 rooms, all with bath/shower. B&B from £27·50 to £56. Pets welcome. Afternoon teas. Garden. Golf. TV. Scenic [GHG]

BODINNICK Cornwall map 1

▲ *Old Ferry Inn* [9/20]

Bodinnick PL23 1LY
POLRUAN (072 687) 237 **£13**

'Old' is right – the building is about 400 years old and the ferry service itself dates from the 1400s. This is primarily a hotel and pub filled with nautical artefacts, but the vegetables are fresh and freshly cooked, and the Farrs buy their own fish from the quay. There are bar meals or a set, varied dinner. Good dishes eaten have been deep-fried Camembert; smoked mackerel pancakes; plaice bonne femme; pork fillets with grapefruit. Non-vintage wine list.

CHEFS: Christine Farr and Mel Burns PROPRIETORS: Kenneth Farr and Simon Farr
OPEN: all week CLOSED: Nov to Mar MEALS: 11 to 2.15 (12 to 1.45 Sun), 7.30 to 8.45
PRICES: Set D £10·50 (£13), Bar meals only at L CARD: Visa
SEATS: 30. Private parties: 25 main room. Car-park. Children's helpings
ACCOMMODATION: 13 rooms, 5 with bath/shower. B&B £16·50 to £33. Deposit: £10. Children welcome. Pets welcome. Scenic

BOGNOR REGIS West Sussex map 3

Costellos [9/20]

Snooks Corner, Felpham Village, Bognor Regis
BOGNOR REGIS (0243) 866124 **£14**

A busy bistro with mirrored walls, hanging plants, and pink seersucker cloths, candles and fresh flowers on squeezed-together tables. Easy to prepare fish and steak dishes chalked on the blackboard include a coquille of crab and mussels; a bit of everything crammed on a plate and called hors d'oeuvre; and scallops on a skewer wrapped in streaky bacon. Pork and duck come with plenty of honey. Puddings vary. House Les Frères is £3 per half-litre.

CHEF: Heinz Schneebecke PROPRIETOR: Simon Cook
OPEN: all week, D only CLOSED: 1 Jan, and Sun in winter MEALS: 7 to 9.30 (10 Fri and Sat)
PRICES: £9 (£14) CARDS: Access, Amex, Diners, Visa
SEATS: 48. 8 tables outside. Private parties: 50 main room. Vegetarian meals. Children's helpings. Wheelchair access (also WC). Music. Air-conditioned

Reports on good shops, small hotels and cafes in your area are welcome.

BONCHURCH see ISLE OF WIGHT

BOROUGHBRIDGE North Yorkshire map 7

Fountain House [11/20]

St James Square, Boroughbridge YO5 9AR
BOROUGHBRIDGE (090 12) 2241 £14–£21

The fish here comes direct from Whitby and the meat from a local farmer/butcher. The Carters' 200-year-old building is well run, with a lounge upstairs for drinks and the dining-room down. The cooking is a good mix of classic and modern styles. Excellent dishes have included langoustines and scallops in puff pastry, grouse with bread sauce, lamb with béarnaise, and the speciality of boned duck breast, roasted and served with a sauce of crème de cassis and orange. Vegetables are well handled and the sweets have included a fine summer pudding, and also brandy snaps with bananas and ginger ice-cream. It is a very clever wine list – strong in France, with clarets from the '70s, but also good in less expensive regions, especially the Rhône. The Alsace wines come from Hugel and Trimbach. House Gamay is £5·80 or try the CELLARMAN'S CHOICE: Ch. Cissac '73 at £15.

CHEFS: J.R.Carter and J.J.Topham PROPRIETORS: Mr and Mrs J.R.Carter
OPEN: Tue to Sat, D only CLOSED: last 2 weeks June MEALS: 7.30 to 9.30
PRICES: £15 (£21), Set D £12·50 (£14) CARDS: Access, Amex, Diners, Visa
SEATS: 45. Private parties: 18 main room. Car-park, 8 places. Vegetarian meals. Children's helpings. Music

BOSHAM Sussex map 3

▲ *Millstream Hotel* [new entry, zero rated]

Bosham Lane, Bosham PO18 8HL
BOSHAM (0243) 573234
off A27 towards Bosham quay £9–£17

Over the last five or six years there have been a couple of consistent nominations for this peaceful hotel. The view is that the food may now be up to the standard of the grand dining-room and the silver service. The set meals are good value. The cooking is old school: crab omelette with orange and grapefruit garnish; chilled consommé with a hint of madeira; duck with cherry sauce; and fillet steak with madeira. The sweets trolley is a pile of cream concoctions. The trifle has jelly (!) but real custard. Coffee in the lounge. A well-spread wine list that is longest in claret. More reports, please.

CHEF: Beverley Boakes PROPRIETORS: Wild's Hotels Ltd
OPEN: all week MEALS: 12.30 to 2, 7 to 9.30 (9 Sun)
PRICES: £12 (£17), Set L from £6 (£9), Set D £9·50 (£13), Bar meals from £1·50 (£1·65)
CARDS: Access, Amex, Diners, Visa
SEATS: 120. 8 tables outside. Private parties: 120 main room, 44 private room. Car-park, 40 places. Children's helpings. Wheelchair access (also WC). Piano music. Air-conditioned
ACCOMMODATION: 22 rooms, all with bath/shower. B&B £32 to £58. Children welcome. Baby facilities. No pets in public rooms. Afternoon teas. Garden. TV. Phone. Scenic. Doors close at 11 [GHG]

BOTALLACK Cornwall map 1

Count House [13/20]

Botallack TR19 7QQ
PENZANCE (0736) 788588
off B3306, 1m N of St Just £10–£15

Take the road beside Manor Farm that leads to the cliff edge and the sea. This is the big toe nail on the foot of Britain, a converted mine workshop, set on the cliff edge near the ruined engine-houses of the old Crown Mines. The Longs have been here since 1976, changing half the menu daily according to market and offering some of the best-value meals in the west. Ann Long's cooking can be rich and main dishes (the £5·50 Sunday lunch excepted) are usually sauced, but she does not lose sight of their purpose. Fillet steaks are marinated and served in sherry and cream sauce or else chopped and sauté with goats' cheese and served with tomato sauce. The short, varied menu always features an adventurous soup – swede, melon and dill one night – and usually a pastry dish, such as pork fillet spread with a vegetable mousse wrapped in puff, served with a red wine sauce and garnished with apple purée. Fish is out of Penzance, vegetables generous and to finish, if you have room, there will be chocolate marquise or raspberries in oatmeal meringue. Service is by the family, and the short wine list continues the value-for-money-first principle with odd bottles from across the globe. Mâcon-Lugny '82 from Paquet is £5·65, which is virtually the retail price of the same wine from Louis Latour.

CHEF: Ann Long PROPRIETORS: Ian, Ann and Suzanne Long
OPEN: Wed to Sat, D only, and Sun L; D also Easter Mon, spring and late summer bank hols
CLOSED: 4 weeks in winter MEALS: 12.30 to 1.45, 7.30 to 10
PRICES: £10 (£15), Set L £6·35 (£10) CARDS: Access, Amex, Carte Blanche, Diners, Visa
SEATS: 35. Private parties: 12 main room. Car-park, 40 places. Children's helpings. Wheelchair access

BOTLEY Hampshire map 2

Cobbett's [10/20]

15 The Square, Botley SO3 2EA
BOTLEY (048 92) 2068 £14–£24

Not so much in the square as in the bulge of Botley's main drag. The dining-room is low, with beams, and light from the windows that look out on to the street. The pink cloths are covered with superior wine glasses, and the menu is heroically French, mixing modern dishes with regional favourites such as the pork pâté with gherkins; a fish soup with a virulent red rouille courtesy of cayenne; and the medallions of steak spiced with herbs, garlic and peppers. Brill with a cucumber cream sauce is just that – a fillet of local fish in a sauce that is virtually all cream.

Many of the better restaurants offer bargain lunches for half the price of a meal in the evening. Details are given in the text.

This restaurant has an exceptional wine cellar.

Service may be slow and standards a bit erratic – hence the drop in the rating. Good Rhônes and Loires to drink.

CHEFS: Lucie Skipwith and Michel le Poidevin
PROPRIETORS: Charles and Lucie Skipwith
OPEN: Mon to Sat, exc Mon L and Sat L CLOSED: 2 weeks summer, 2 weeks winter
MEALS: 12 to 2, 7.30 (7 Sat) to 10
PRICES: £15 (£22), Set L £8·25 (£14) CARDS: Access, Amex, Visa
SEATS: 40. Private parties: 35 main room, 14 private room. Car-park, 15 places. Vegetarian meals. Children's helpings. No cigars/pipes in dining-room. Wheelchair access

BOTLEY Oxfordshire map 2

Bilash Tandoori [9/20]

23 Chapel Way, Botley OX2 9LS
OXFORD (0865) 722527 £12

More popular with town than gown and serving mulligatawny and lentil soup, nargis kofte (Indian Scotch egg), as well as the customary range of samosas, bhajia, tandooris and curries. Choose chicken for tandoori – succulent, well-marinated and tasting of the charcoal oven – but meat for curry: the dhansak has a subtle sweet-sour edge, and vindaloo is red-hot. Nan is light and not greasy. Don't give in to pushy waiters trying to make you order as much as they can get away with. Drink Kingfisher beer or Double Diamond.

CHEF: Mokbul Ali PROPRIETORS: M. Ali and A. Rahman
OPEN: all week MEALS: 12.15 to 2.15, 6.15 to 11.15
PRICES: £8 (£12) CARDS: Access, Amex, Diners, Visa
SEATS: 48. Private parties: 48 main room. Vegetarian meals. Children welcome. Music

Tong San [10/20]

20 The Square, Botley OX2 9LJ
OXFORD (0865) 248230 £7–£22

The door handle is still here from when Mac Fisheries was in the building, but Raymond Mak's little Peking restaurant in the shopping precinct is well established after six years. It is unpretentious and reliable for sesame prawn toasts; spare ribs with black pepper and garlic; vegetable and bean curd soup; and scallops in black bean sauce. The sizzling dishes hiss and spit and the lamb with spring onion is very good. Sweets are completely Westernised. Licensed.

PROPRIETOR: Raymond Mak
OPEN: all week MEALS: 12 to 2 (1 to 2.30 Sun), 6 to 11.45
PRICES: £14 (£22), Set L £3·25 (£7), Set D from £6·50 (£11). Service 10% CARDS: Access, Amex, Diners, Visa
SEATS: 70. 15 tables outside. Private parties: 30 main room. Car-park, 50 places. Vegetarian meals. Children welcome. Wheelchair access. Chinese music. Air-conditioned

The Guide is always anxious to recruit new inspectors. If you would like to apply, write to the editor enclosing a) a detailed report on a restaurant where you have eaten and b) a comparative study of restaurants known to you.

BOURNEMOUTH Dorset map 2

Crust [10/20]

Hampshire House, Bourne Avenue, The Square,
Bournemouth BH2 6ED
BOURNEMOUTH (0202) 21430 £10–£13

The fresh shellfish and the wines characterise this lively bistro which gets its lobsters, scallops, mussels and crabs from the local boats. Service can be slow, but Paul Harper tends to cook to order. Elsewhere on the menu have been meaty and messy spare ribs, five quiches, and plain, well-handled vegetables. An excellent and not expensive list of wines with dry Australian Muscat '82 from Brown Bros at £7·95 and Ch. La Lagune '76 at £14·95.

CHEFS: Paul Harper and Sue Cole PROPRIETORS: Tricia and Paul Harper
OPEN: all week MEALS: 12 to 2.30, 6.30 to 11 (11.30 Sat)
PRICES: £9 (£13), Set L £5·25 (£10) CARDS: Access, Diners, Visa
SEATS: 50. Vegetarian meals. Children's helpings. Smart dress preferred. Wheelchair access. Music

▲ *New Ambassador Hotel* [10/20]

East Cliff, Bournemouth BH1 3DP
BOURNEMOUTH (0202) 25453 £10–£12

This family-run hotel complies strictly with Jewish dietary laws. It is a large, cavernous dining-room, and those dishes that are essentially Jewish are excellent – hamisher cucumber, thick vegetable soup, and ox-tail. The kitchen has more difficulty with spaghetti bolognese. There's plenty of water on the table. Kosher wines.

CHEF: Emil Bekir PROPRIETORS: The Vickers family
OPEN: all week MEALS: 1 to 1.40, 7 to 7.45 (8 on Fri in summer)
PRICES: Set L from £7 (£10), Set D from £9 (£12). Service inc
SEATS: 250. Private parties: 250 main room, 55 private room. Car-park, 60 places. Children's helpings. Smart dress preferred. Wheelchair access (also WC). Live music. One sitting. Kosher cuisine only
ACCOMMODATION: 112 rooms, all with bath/shower. Rooms for disabled. Prices not available. Children welcome. Baby facilities. No pets in public rooms. Afternoon teas. Garden. Outdoor swimming-pool. Lift. Phone. Synagogue on premises. Doors close at 12

Provence [14/20]

91 Bellevue Road, Southbourne, Bournemouth BH6 3DH
BOURNEMOUTH (0202) 424421 £20

Jean-Pierre and Claire Novi started on a shoestring, but as the points show they have not betrayed the confidence we had in them last year. The menus are imaginative in the square dining-room among the bed and breakfasts along the cliffs of this suburb of Bournemouth. The large windows look on to the street, and everywhere is usually jammed with flowers. A little more attention to detail and a score of 15 would be possible. Alpha dishes have been the mussel and vegetable soup; the chicken leg with artichokes, ceps and ginger; more ginger, this time in a mango mousse; turbot in red wine; magret of duck. Classically conceived, if macabre, is the woodcock with tangerines, neatly carved save for the legs, head and beak which are re-formed into the shape of the live bird. Vegetables are small – garlic potatoes, baby beans, baby carrots. To finish there is a quartet of spectacular sorbets – banana, pear, strawberry and lemon – on a single plate, decorated with angelica, kiwi, strawberry and mint leaves, and served with home-made macaroons. Equally decorative is the poached egg-white with a praline sauce garnished with more colourful fruits. Claire is a natural hostess and coffee is by the potful. The wine list matches the food – solidly bourgeois with some subtleties. Three of the four Alsace wines come from different producers – Preiss-Zimmer; Kuentz-Bas; Beyer. CELLARMAN'S CHOICE: Morgon '83 from Duboeuf, at £10·75.

CHEF/PROPRIETOR: Jean-Pierre Novi
OPEN: Mon to Sat, D only CLOSED: Feb MEALS: 7 to 10
PRICES: £17 (£20). Service inc CARDS: Access, Amex, Diners, Visa
SEATS: 30. Private parties: 35 main room. Children's helpings. Wheelchair access. Classical music

Sophisticats [11/20]

43 Charminster Road, Bournemouth BH8 8UE
BOURNEMOUTH (0202) 291019 £17

A small, relaxed restaurant decorated in avocado, peach and bronze, and with a gypsy of a menu that roams from marinated salmon à la Russe to veal cauchoise in the Normandy style. The Javanese fillet steak marinated in soy and wine is the best-seller, and the presentation of other dishes is colourful. Good dishes have been the smoked salmon mousse in all its juices, satay, grilled monkfish with hollandaise sauce, and the warm bread. Sweets are of the meringue school, but there is also chilled cherry soup – cherries poached in claret with orange zest and cinnamon. There are 40 rather unprepossessing wines, or try the CELLARMAN'S CHOICE: Ch. Pindefleurs '81 at £8·85.

CHEF: Bernard Calligan PROPRIETORS: John Knight and Bernard Calligan
OPEN: Tue to Sat, D only CLOSED: last week June and Oct, 2 weeks Jan MEALS: 7 to 10
PRICES: £11 (£17)
SEATS: 32. Private parties: 20 main room. Vegetarian meals by arrangement. Children welcome. Wheelchair access (also WC). Music

BOURTON-ON-THE-WATER Gloucestershire map 2

Rose Tree [11/20]

Riverside, Bourton-on-the-Water GL54 2BX
COTSWOLD (0451) 20635 £13–£19

This picturesque, 300-year-old cottage overlooks the village green and the river Windrush. Val and Chris Grundy's style is an enterprising version of country cooking. Two sets of three courses (the cheaper one is not available on Saturday evening) offer a sensibly small choice that might include breast of duck with armagnac, cream, peppers and apple; chicken breast with whisky and almonds in lightly curried cream; or halibut steak cooked in yoghourt. Vegetables are plain but excellent, as are brown sugar meringues with cream. Service is efficient and attentive. Over three-quarters of the 100-strong wine list is French, with a good showing of claret and burgundy, backed up by the Rhône and Loire, with four from Alsace. Prices are generally reasonable, and from Easter to October there will be bar meals from £1·90. The Grundys' adjoining wine shop is open from 10 to 6, Tuesday to Saturday.

CHEF: Val Grundy PROPRIETORS: Chris and Val Grundy
OPEN: Tue to Sat D and Sun L CLOSED: 14 Jan for five weeks MEALS: 12.30 to 2, 7.30 to 10
PRICES: Set L Sun £8·50 (£13), Set D £8·50 and £14·50 (£13 and £19) CARDS: Access, Amex, Diners, Visa
SEATS: 32. 8 tables outside. Private parties: 35 main room. Vegetarian meals by arrangement. Children's helpings. Smart dress preferred. Wheelchair access. Classical music

BOWNESS-ON-WINDERMERE Cumbria — map 7

Jackson's Bistro [new entry, zero rated]

Bowness-on-Windermere LA23 3EE
WINDERMERE (096 62) 6264 — £14

Frank and Christine Jackson, after ten years at Greenriggs Hotel at Underbarrow, have opened this smart bistro with gas-lamps, single-pedestal tables, flagged floors covered with bright rugs, and lots of plants and flowers in summer. The pâtés and casseroles on the short menu are augmented by plaice fillets stuffed with crab, kebabs, and prawns en cocotte, all of which are praised. To finish there are Lakeland cheeses, vacherins and charlottes. Twenty inexpensive wines. More reports, please.

CHEFS: Michael Thomson and Frank Jackson PROPRIETORS: Frank and Christine Jackson
OPEN: Tue to Sun, D only MEALS: 6.30 to 10
PRICES: £8 (£14) CARDS: Access, Visa
SEATS: 45. Private parties: 30 main room. Children's helpings (until 8.30). Music

BRADFIELD COMBUST Suffolk — map 3

Bradfield House [12/20]

Sudbury Road, Bradfield Combust IP30 0LR
SICKLESMERE (028 486) 301
on A134, 5m SE of Bury St Edmunds — **Real Food** £13–£18

Bradfield Combust gets its name from a village riot in the fourteenth century when the locals burnt down the hall. It is hardly a village at all now, just a few houses on the road to Sudbury. Not far away is Bradfield Woods, the most ancient area of worked woodland in England. Victoria and Michael Stephenson run their seventeenth-century home as a restaurant serving English food not so much as it used to be, but as it should be. The menu is pinned ceremonially to the front door, and there is a taste of the past about it. The almond soup is a sixteenth-century recipe, although its roots are in the early Middle Ages, the dish being a descendant of the ancient blanc-mange. Or there might be chilled sorrel, lettuce and mint soup. Main courses are meaty: ox-tongue is casseroled with red wine and grapes (Victoria Stephenson does the same with ox-tail); rabbit comes with mustard and orange; steak is with anchovy butter or watercress and caper butter. The dining-room is sturdily furnished but has a relaxed, friendly atmosphere. The cooking is at its best with the fundamentals – tomato, orange and basil soup; braised quails set on curly endive with a sauce of port and chanterelles; superb roast sirloin of beef served with head-blowing fresh horseradish sauce *plus* old English mustard *plus* gravy in a separate jug. If people can dismiss the merits of English cooking it is largely because we have pawned our saucing heritage to the commercial relish-makers. Vegetables come out of the garden; meringues are first-class. The wine list is as French as the food is English, and is strongest in burgundy which makes it expensive. House Merlot is £6·50. Interesting aperitifs and digestifs.

CHEF: Victoria Stephenson PROPRIETORS: R.M. and V.Stephenson
OPEN: Tue to Sat D, and Sun L MEALS: 12.30 to 2, 7.30 to 10
PRICES: £12 (£18), Set L £7·75 (£13). Service 10% CARDS: Amex, Diners, Visa
SEATS: 24. Private parties: 32 main room. Car-park, 10 places. Children's helpings (Sun L only). Wheelchair access (also wc)

BRADFORD West Yorkshire map 5

BACKGROUND BRIEFING: *With the exception listed below, first-rate food here invariably falls into the cheap category. Whether it is excellent pie and peas for 37p at Pie Tom, Rawson Market; haddock for 40p at the fish shop at 138 Old Road; breakfast for 95p at Baxendall's on the first floor of the Kirkgate Centre market; or a vegetable curry for £1·20 at Karachi, 15–17 Neal Street, the quality is heartening. Another fish and chip shop is Salty's, 159–161 St Helena Road, which has a small back dining-room like a miniature Harry Ramsden's (drive the short distance to Guisley to see Mr Ramsden's fish and chip shop – 'the most famous in the world'). La Cocina, 66 Oak Lane, is a small Mexican restaurant, and Da Tonino's, 26 Avondale Buildings, Bradford Road, Shipley, uses some fresh ingredients – pasta and fish dishes have been especially good. There are many pizza joints, most serving good specimens, but it is the small Indian and Pakistani cafes that are most memorable. Some of them draw such comments from hardened inspectors as: 'I wouldn't dare recommend this place for any book, but will go back again and again myself.' Three examples are Shah, Carlisle Street; Kebabeesh, 234 Whetley Lane; and Kashmir, 27 Morley Street.*

▲ *Restaurant Nineteen, Belvedere Hotel* [12/20]

North Park Road, Heaton, Bradford BD9 4NT
BRADFORD (0274) 492559 £19

This handsome old corner house that once belonged to a wool-merchant overlooks Lister Park and has a stairwell running up the centre to all three floors. The dining-area is two rooms with mahogany doors, bay windows, and round tables set with napkins starched like a nun's wimple. There are flowers and floral crockery to match the apricot shades of the walls. The menu is French *nouvelle*, short and freshly prepared, offering the likes of cream of scallop soup, various terrines, and sole rolled around smoked salmon butter. Stephen Smith has cooked some alpha dishes, such as fresh chicken livers in a pastry case with a sauce of madeira and curry; scallop mousse with crayfish sauce; pheasant rolled in bacon with a sauce of crème de cassis and four juicy onions. Vegetables are plainly and neatly served and sweets have also been of a standard, notably brandy cake with walnuts and calvados pancakes. It is ironic that after a year Mr

Smith and his partner Robert Barbour – who runs the front of the house with the professionalism you would expect in France, mixed with Yorkshire friendliness – report that no one from Bradford has come to the door offering fresh produce. 'I'm told it is not possible to get fresh ducks in this area' – an appalling indictment on West Yorkshire traders when the Indian community can bring items over from Asia. The well-spread list of wines concentrates on the major regions of Bordeaux and Burgundy, which makes it expensive, but there are cheaper wines of interest from Provence, the Loire and Australia. CELLARMAN'S CHOICE: Chassagne-Montrachet rouge '82, from Clerget, at £11·90.

CHEF: Stephen Smith PROPRIETORS: Stephen Smith and Robert Barbour
OPEN: Tue to Sat, D only MEALS: 7 to 9.30 (10 Sat)
PRICES: £13 (£19). Minimum £10·50 CARDS: Amex, Diners, Visa
SEATS: 40. Private parties: 10 main room. Car-park, 6 places. No children under 14. Jacket and tie preferred. Classical music
ACCOMMODATION: 13 rooms, 3 with bath/shower. B&B £16 to £26. No pets. TV. Doors close at 11.30

Shiraz Sweet House [8/20]

Oak Lane, Bradford BD9 4QU
BRADFORD (0274) 490176 £2–£5

Gaudy-looking sweets are displayed in the window of this popular Muslim cafe, matched by the lighting inside. It is the pick of the many cheap northern Indian cafes and incredibly good value. Chicken and lamb dishes are good, and vegetable dishes include spicy dhal with potatoes and pumpkin bhajia. Chapatis are cooked on a griddle and rasmalai is the texture of coconut fudge, tasting of milk, lemon and cinnamon. Drink lassi.

CHEF: Mr Rashid PROPRIETOR: M. Aslam
OPEN: all week MEALS: noon to 2am (4 Fri and Sat)
PRICES: £3 (£5), Set L and D from £1·20 (£1·50). Service inc. Unlicensed
SEATS: 36. Private parties: 40 main room. Vegetarian meals. Children's helpings. Wheelchair access. Indian music

BRAINTREE Essex map 3

Braintree Chinese Restaurant [11/20]

3 Rayne Road, Braintree CM7 7QA
BRAINTREE (0376) 24319 £12–£21

Kim Man's well-established upstairs Chinese restaurant – you can hear the music as you go up the stairs – has some unusual dishes, such as tea-smoked chicken or clay-pot braised lamb and chilli. At the top end of the set meals is a ten-dish banquet with lobster for £16·50. Notable among the many good dishes we have eaten have been spiced pork with fried seaweed; crispy fried beef; steamed scallops in a strong garlic sauce; and Peking duck. The planning and

'A request for a vegetarian meal was met with tomato soup, a terrine with tomato sauce, and a mushroom and tomato ragout for main course – in short, not a good balance.' (On eating in the Lake District)

presentation of meals is well thought out, and the kitchen is becoming increasingly adept at carving decorative swans, dragons and flowers out of vegetables. House Choix du Roy is £6.

CHEF: K.Tse PROPRIETOR: K.Man
OPEN: all week CLOSED: 25 to 27 Dec MEALS: 12 to 11.30 (12 Fri and Sat)
PRICES: £8 (£15), Set D from £7 to £15 (£12 to £21). Minimum £8·50. Service 10%
CARDS: Access, Amex, Diners, Visa
SEATS: 100. Private parties: 120 main room. Car-park, 10 places. Vegetarian meals. Children welcome. Jacket and tie. Chinese music

BRAMPTON Cumbria — map 7

▲ *Farlam Hall* [10/20]

Brampton CA8 2NG
HALLBANKGATE (069 76) 234
on A689 2½m from Brampton (not at Farlam village) — £13–£16

The Quinions' family-run seventeenth-century country-house hotel is four miles south of Hadrian's Wall and set in half a dozen acres of mature grounds. Country cooking with plenty of wine and herbs might produce hot Morecambe Bay shrimps with cream, mushrooms, garlic and white wine sauce; roast local lamb with onion sauce and thyme jelly; pigeon, port and mushroom pie. From the short wine list, generously endowed with halves, house wine is £4·75 and Müller-Thurgau from Lamberhurst Priory in Kent is £6·50.

CHEF: Barry Quinion PROPRIETORS: The Quinion family
OPEN: all week D, plus Sun L CLOSED: 3 weeks Nov, all Feb, Mon and Tue Nov to Feb
MEALS: 1, 8
PRICES: Set L £9·50 (£13), Set D from £12·50 (£16) CARDS: Access, Amex, Visa
SEATS: 50. Private parties: 30 main room. Car-park, 30 places. No children under 4 in dining-room. Jacket and tie preferred. Wheelchair access. One sitting
ACCOMMODATION: 13 rooms, all with bath/shower. B&B £33 to £66. Children welcome. Dogs by arrangement. Afternoon teas. Garden. Croquet. TV. Scenic. Doors close at 12. Confirm by 2 [GHG]

▲ *Tarn End* [new entry, zero rated]

Talkin Tarn, Brampton CA8 1LS
BRAMPTON (069 77) 2340
off B6413, 2m S of Brampton — £18

A squat, stone building in a remote setting by the tarn. The proprietors, the Hoefkens family, can outnumber the guests out of season, which is a pity because the food is good value and some of the cooking – especially of game, from excellent grouse to jugged hare – very good. There is a sensory overload at the magnitude of the menus, but even so the fish cooking impresses – always the mark of a good kitchen – from salmon gateau to langoustine thermidor, to shellfish feuilleté with lobster sauce. Meals are interrupted by brown rolls arriving on a silver salver; unnecessary sorbets between courses; and cheeses, which include a fine local goats'. All this, plus an enormous sweets trolley, can feel incongruous on quiet nights. The wine list is like the rice fields of China – it covers a huge area, but not in any great depth. Good choice of other alcohols, however, and good breakfasts, too.

CHEF: Martin Hoefkens PROPRIETOR: Mrs M.C. Hoefkens
OPEN: all week CLOSED: 25 Dec, Oct MEALS: 12.30 to 1.45, 7.30 to 9
PRICES: Set L and D £13·50 (£18)
SEATS: 40. Private parties: 40 main room. Car-park. Vegetarian meals by arrangement. No smoking in dining-room
ACCOMMODATION: 6 rooms, 3 with bath/shower. Prices not available. No pets. Garden

BRANSCOMBE Devon map 2

▲ *Masons Arms* [9/20]

Branscombe EX12 3DV
BRANSCOMBE (029 780) 300
off A3052, 5m E of Sidmouth £10–£14

A charming place to stay. Some of the cooking from the varied set menu is well up to scratch – scallops poached with Pernod and fennel, steaks, poached trout. Soups are inventive, such as parsnips and apple, and asparagus and oyster (despite the ingredients for the latter being tinned/frozen when out of season). There are some fair wines, but the minor French regions are poorly described, so you could be forgiven for missing them.

CHEF: J.Kickinger PROPRIETOR: J.Inglis
OPEN: all week D only, and Sun L MEALS: 12.30 to 1, 7.15 to 8.30
PRICES: Set L £6 (£10), Set D from £10 (£14), Bar meals from £1·40 (£1·55), Snacks from 80p (90p) CARDS: Access, Visa
SEATS: 46. 11 tables outside. Private parties: 30 main room, 14 private room. Car-park, 45 places. Children's helpings (high tea). Wheelchair access (also WC)
ACCOMMODATION: 22 rooms, 15 with bath/shower. Rooms for disabled. B&B £16 to £46. Deposit: £20. Children welcome. Baby facilities. Pets welcome. TV. Scenic. Doors close at 12 [GHG]

BRAY Berkshire map 2

Waterside Inn [15/20]

Ferry Road, Bray SN6 2AT
MAIDENHEAD (0628) 20691 and 22941 **Real Food** £36+

Well, well, well. So Michelin finally handed over the three stars. The award can only be a boost for the catering industry, and if they also raise Nico Ladenis, Pierre Koffmann, and Raymond Blanc from two stars this year, then so much the better. But whether most people actually like the rigid ostentatious formula required for the accolade is another matter (it is often said in France, with some reason, that the one- and two-star establishments are more enjoyable). The cooking becomes just one element in a flurry of armagnac bottles and black-suited waiters who put the service into overdrive. The setting is, of course, three stars – overlooking the Thames and with, at the back of the room, a semi-circular arrangement of banquettes, mirror and plastic foliage on trellises, rather in the manner of a painting from the Tate Gallery. Encased in glass on the central table is a confection sculpture of Michel and Albert Roux sitting at a table. The food has not noticeably improved. The menu is exceedingly rich and relies rather too much on the lazinesses of *haute cuisine*, with lobster, black truffles and caviare. The testing dishes, such as soupe de poisson, have on occasion been no better than an average bistro's. It is mostly only at the desserts that Michel Roux's true vocation comes through in spades, with magnificent soufflés, either with the fruit baked inside or else with a fruit sauce that is brought separately and poured into the punctured surface. Equally good has been the nougat cassis tart that looks as pretty as it does in its photograph in the Roux book, *New Classic Cuisine* – the starting-point for many of the menus. The money is not really made on the food. The components of the famous egg dish, oeufs brouillés aux oeufs – a bed of scrambled eggs with a poached egg and quails' eggs on top, garnished with croûtons, beluga caviare and American caviare, must work out at near the £7·80 price. There are some wonderfully sexy Gallic touches: the tree-trunk-sized brioche that acts as a basket for hot rolls; the side fork for the separate plate of vegetables; and, if you want to eat lobster and truffles, the fresh, slightly untidy ravioli that encases them with a sauce vierge – oil, garlic, tomatoes and herbs – courtesy of the master, Michel Guérard. All this is paid for via the high cost of the house aperitif – blood orange, champagne and Cointreau – the coffee, and the armagnac. You can even buy a Waterside Inn plate as a souvenir. It is a connoisseur's wine list, full of subtlety, and although the mark-ups are not kind they have not increased with inflation over three years. The Alsace section holds a full range, not just of grapes but also different growers, and the Beaujolais section is strong on the fine '83s at around £10. On the other hand there is Montrachet '82, from Drouhin, at £100.

CHEF/PROPRIETOR: Michel Roux
OPEN: Tue to Sun, exc Sun D from late Oct to after Easter CLOSED: 25 Dec to 25 Jan
MEALS: 12.30 to 2, 7.30 to 10
PRICES: £27 (£36+)
SEATS: 80. Car-park, 50 places. Children welcome. Smart dress preferred. Wheelchair access (also WC). Air-conditioned

BRIDGNORTH Shropshire map 5

The Haywain [10/20]

Hampton Loade, Bridgnorth WV15 6HD
QUATT (0746) 780404
off A442, 5m S of Bridgnorth £21

Enormous five-course set meals are served in this dining-room dominated by an artificial fire in a large grate, which is flanked by serving tables with a port decanter and glasses. The sorbet in the middle of the meal is, for once, a useful palate cleanser, coming in the midst of warm rolls and soup; a cold table piled high with salmon, prawns, lobster pâté, quiche and salads; spare ribs; game pie or chicken suprême; and quintets of vegetables. And then there is charlotte russe, hazel-nut meringue and trifle; cheeses, coffee and petits fours. There are not quite

'The bill was a stratospheric £129, of which about £33 was for aperitifs and wine. At such prices (I estimate my main dish cost me 50p for each lukewarm forkful) a cover charge of £1.50 seems superfluous.' (On eating in Bedfordshire)

as many wines as there are dishes, but a few interesting '78 clarets or CELLARMAN'S CHOICE: Vacqueyras '78, from Pascal, at £9·50.

CHEF: Johnny Coleau PROPRIETORS: David and Cathy Browning
OPEN: Tue to Sat, D only CLOSED: 2 weeks Jan, 2 weeks Aug MEALS: 7.30 to 9.30
PRICES: Set D £17·25 (£21) CARDS: Access, Amex, Diners, Visa
SEATS: 40. Private parties: 40 main room. Car-park, 20 places. Vegetarian meals. Children welcome. Wheelchair access. Music

The Old Colonial Restaurant [9/20]

3 Bridge Street, Low Town, Bridgnorth WV15 6AF
BRIDGNORTH (074 62) 66510 £9–£11

An up-market Indian restaurant in a 300-year-old, half-timbered black and white cottage, with Laura Ashley wallpaper and a lot of atmosphere. The nan bread is first-class, the tandoori chicken aromatic, and the spices in the prawn bhuna, beef rogan josh and chicken korma are distinct. Good rice and poppadums. The staff are willing; they also have a dial-a-dinner service and will serve the food at your home and wash up. Freshly ground coffee or Darjeeling or Assam tea all come with After Eights. Licensed.

CHEFS: Ali Ahmad and Gulam Hussain PROPRIETORS: T. Ambia, M.E.H. Chowdhury and M. Ahmad
OPEN: all week, D only MEALS: 5.30 to 11.45
PRICES: £6 (£11), Set D from £5·85 (£9) CARDS: Access, Amex, Diners, Visa
SEATS: 28. Private parties: 32 main room. Vetgetarian meals. Children's helpings

BRIDPORT Dorset map 2

BACKGROUND BRIEFING: *Chesil Bank between Weymouth and Bridport has some of the finest sea angling in Britain, including mackerel in abundance and sometimes bream, but little gets to the restaurants. For Dorset baking along the lines of knobs and lardy cakes R. W. Hodges has shops at Bridport and Sherborne, as well as at Crewkerne, Chard and Yeovil nearby in Somerset. In Dorchester the Cookery Nook, 3–4 Agra Place, has votes for its long, eclectic menu, and The Bridge Between, 8 High East Street, has good wholefood dishes at reasonable prices.*

BRIGHTLINGSEA Essex map 3

Jacobe's [10/20]

High Street, Brightlingsea CO7 0AQ
BRIGHTLINGSEA (020 630) 2113 £19

Brightlingsea has always been known for its fish. This originally thirteenth-century hall on the main street provides home-made crab bisque, roast crawfish and a few classical dishes, such as sole Colbert. Lobster is prepared any way you

The Guide is always anxious to recruit new inspectors. If you would like to apply, write to the editor enclosing a) a detailed report on a restaurant where you have eaten and b) a comparative study of restaurants known to you.

like: £6·50 for a half, £12 whole. There are steaks, too. The wine list includes a trio of '76 Meursault, all at £14·25, and CELLARMAN'S CHOICE: Muscadet at £6·05.

CHEF: Brian K. Turner PROPRIETORS: B.L. Lewington and Brian K. Turner
OPEN: Mon, and Wed to Sat, exc Sat L CLOSED: 2 weeks Feb, bank hols
MEALS: 12.30 to 2, 7.30 to 9 (10 Sat)
PRICES: £13 (£19), Bar meals from 70p (80p). Cover 50p CARDS: Access, Amex, Diners, Visa
SEATS: 30. 4 tables outside. Private parties: 36 main room. Car-park, 100 places. Vegetarian meals by arrangement. Children's helpings. No children under 8. Smart dress preferred. No cigars/pipes in dining-room. Wheelchair access. Classical music

BRIGHTON & HOVE East Sussex map 3

Eaton Restaurant [10/20]

Eaton Gardens, Hove BN3 3TN
BRIGHTON (0273) 738921 £14–£18

An English theme runs through the menu of this well-established old-style restaurant that remains faithful to the silver service – triple smoked fish pâté; steak, kidney and mushroom pie; duck and bean casserole; trifle. The fish from Silverthorne's, who have been established for 60 years, is consistently well reported – excellent whitebait; sole and scampi in a herb sauce with wild rice; and roes on toast as a savoury to finish. Other dishes are more continental. Parking is easy, which is saying something in Brighton. House red is £6·25 a litre.

CHEFS: John Stevens and Stanley Rackowski PROPRIETORS: John and June Cutress
OPEN: all week, exc Sun D MEALS: 12.30 to 2.15, 6.45 to 10
PRICES: £12 (£18), Set L from £8·50 (£14), Set D from £9·75 (£15) CARDS: Access, Amex, Diners, Visa
SEATS: 100. 2 tables outside. Private parties: 20 main room, 70 private room. Vegetarian meals. Car-park, 30 places. No pipes in dining-room. Children's helpings. Music

Food For Friends [9/20]

17A–18 Prince Albert Street, Brighton BN1 1HF
BRIGHTON (0273) 202310 **Real Food** £6

Incredibly cheap, chaotic, cramped, vegetarian self-service with flowers on each table and with oil paintings for sale. There are queues most of the day. The vegetables are organic, eggs free-range and the room ionised, but the staff have a sense of humour too – maxistrone soup comes with cheesy garlic croûtons. Good dishes have been the vegetable curry, spinach and cauliflower savoury pies, and the quiches. More innovative are sweet-and-sour courgette and cashew casserole, or stir-fried mange-tout with Swiss chard and rice. Desserts such as madeira cake or apple and apricot charlotte are made with real fruit and served

Prices quoted are for an average three-course meal including service and VAT and half a bottle of house wine (or the equivalent in an ethnic restaurant).

with fresh cream, and the fresh apple juice is delivered daily, so it earns its Real Food denotation. There is cidre bouché, or Loire red at £3·50.

CHEF: Philip Taylor PROPRIETOR: Simon Hope
OPEN: all week MEALS: 11.30 to 3, 5.30 to 10
PRICES: £3 (£6). Service inc
SEATS: 55. Vegetarian meals. Children's helpings. No-smoking area. Wheelchair access. Music. Self-service. Take-away service

Le Français [12/20]

1 Paston Place, Kemp Town, Brighton BN2 1HL
BRIGHTON (0273) 680716 £28–£31

John Brunner does some very good cooking in this restaurant near the seafront. The prices are high, but there is space between the tables, service is first-rate, and the salmon mousse encased in smoked salmon and glazed with a fine fish aspic was one of the best starters eaten at inspection last year. His saucing is adept – garlic for lamb, alcohol and orange for veal, but frustratingly he allows himself to be deflected from the main business that would earn him a higher rating. Garnishing is less than last year but still overdone – a whole head of garlic including stem on the above-mentioned lamb – and while the chocolate truffles are superb, the table butter is blended and the Japanese rice crackers inappropriate. The odd wine list needs some investment which is obviously a problem. In the grand manner of kitchen skulduggery, harking back to Escoffier at the Ritz, Mr Brunner not only has knives and forks from Michelin – but also some from his former bosses at the Hotel Metropole along with 14 dessert spoons, 14 fingerbowls, 12 tables and two ice-buckets – about which the local magistrates took rather a dim view and last May imposed a nine-month suspended jail sentence.

CHEF/PROPRIETOR: John Brunner
OPEN: all week, D only MEALS: 7 to 11.30
PRICES: £20 (£28), Set D from £25 (£31). Minimum £1·50 CARDS: Access, Amex, Diners, Visa
SEATS: 33. Private parties: 36 main room. Car-park, 20 places. Vegetarian meals. Children welcome. Jacket and tie preferred. Wheelchair access. Music

French Cellar [new entry, zero rated]

37 New England Road, Brighton BN1 4GG
BRIGHTON (0273) 603643
on A27 £13–£18

Once a cafe, now a French restaurant with an eye-catching tricolour awning. The walls are rough-cast stone and the tables and chairs Regency style. The menu is classic regional French – bouillabaisse, jambon de montagne and so on. The soups – onion, and chervil – are excellent, as is the pastry for the vol-au-vent filled with shellfish. Main courses of boned poussin in wine, cream and mushrooms, and sole in pastry, have been of a standard. To finish, pears poached

All letters to the Guide *are acknowledged with a list of changes since we went to press.*

in red wine are filled with blackcurrant sorbet. A short, mainly French choice of wines. CELLARMAN'S CHOICE: Ch. La Tour-Carnet '78 at £13·50. More reports, please.

CHEFS/PROPRIETORS: Mr and Mrs Jean-Claude Rozard
OPEN: Mon to Sat MEALS: 12 to 2.30, 7 to 10
PRICES: L £8 (£13), Set D from £13 (£18) CARDS: Access, Diners
SEATS: 42. Private parties: 22 main room, 20 private room. Vegetarian meals by arrangement. Children's helpings by arrangement. No children under 10 at D. Smart dress preferred at D. No cigars/pipes in dining-room. Wheelchair access

La Marinade [11/20]

77 St George's Road, Kemp Town, Brighton BN2 1EF
BRIGHTON (0273) 600992 £10–£17

The upstairs bar here has oak-leaf wallpaper hand-painted in China. Downstairs, the dining-room is smart and comfortable but with tables even closer together than in London restaurants. There is a fashionable slice of modern cooking, and the £6 lunch is a bargain. Good dishes have included: the mushroom soup liaised with eggs and cream; courgettes stuffed with a cauliflower farce; well-trimmed lamb cutlets; and duck, looking splendid on a white plate with a cassis sauce. Portions are large. If the bread, butter and vegetables were more consistently good, a score of 12 would be in order. Service is professional. The sweets are a mixed bag, quality-wise, but the pear and banana crumble stands out. The 16 wines run the length of the French vineyards both in quality and price. House Muscadet is £5.

CHEFS: Jeremy Rudge and Donald Jackson PROPRIETORS: Jeremy and Ruth Rudge
OPEN: Tue to Sat CLOSED: 24 Dec to 7 Jan, last week Aug and first week Sept
MEALS: 12 to 2, 7 to 10 (10.30 Sat)
PRICES: £13 (£17), Set L £6 to £10 (£10 to £14) CARDS: Access, Amex, Diners, Visa
SEATS: 27. Private parties: 30 main room. Children welcome. Smart dress preferred. Music. Air-conditioned

Muang Thai [new entry, zero rated]

77 St James's Street, Brighton BN2 1PA
BRIGHTON (0273) 605223 £11–£12

A new Thai restaurant related to the Chiang Mai in Soho. The decor is as green as the jungle, with a traditional room upstairs and a plainer room and bar down. The spices, like lemon grass and lime leaves, as well as unusual fish, are flown from Bangkok weekly. The cooking provides a good introduction to the cuisine. Hot-and-sour soup is distinctly different from the Chinese variation – a thin broth filled with chicken, coriander, lemon grass and lime leaves. The meat with seven flavours looks deceptively ordinary and is augmented with fish balls, noodles, carrots, and lettuce. The Thai fish comes either with sweet-and-sour sauce or else chilli sauce, and provides handsome centrepieces, especially for groups of four or

'The wine list was comprehensive and there would be no difficulty in choosing something suitable, assuming that one had thought to make previous arrangements with one's bank.' (On eating in London)

even more. The boiled rice is a necessary cooling medium. Thai beers and whiskies, or Muscadet at £4.25. More reports, please.

PROPRIETOR: Stephen Binns
OPEN: all week, D only MEALS: 6 to 12.30
PRICES: £7 (£11), Set D £8.50 (£12). Service 10%
CARDS: Access, Amex, Diners, Visa
SEATS: 45. Private parties: 40 main room, 40 private room. Vegetarian meals. Children's helpings. Wheelchair access (also wc). Oriental music

Restaurant Chardonnay [new entry, zero rated]

33 Chesham Road, Kemp Town, Brighton BN2 1NB
BRIGHTON (0273) 672733 £11–£18

Christian Debu (late of Au Petit Normand at Poynings) has teamed up with Keith and Frances Bartlam (late of the Lido and the Alcazar dancing-clubs in Paris) at this well-set dining-room lined with framed French posters and with an altar-like arrangement of flowers on each table. The set meals at lunchtime are inexpensive, but the *carte*, which changes monthly, is a headier financial proposition. The style is French – snails in pastry cases with a Roquefort sauce; ficelle normande; and a good helping of morels with the veal. There are plenty of vegetables. Sweets are recited at the table and the oeufs à la neige have been notably good. A short spread of French wines. More reports, please.

CHEF: Christian Debu PROPRIETORS: Keith and Frances Bartlam
OPEN: Mon to Sat, exc Sat L MEALS: 12 to 2, 7.30 to 10.45
PRICES: D £11 (£18), Set L £6 (£11). Service 13% alc D CARDS: Access, Amex, Diners, Visa
SEATS: 35. 2 tables outside. Private parties: 21 main room, 14 private room. Vegetarian meals by arrangement. No children under 5 at L, or under 13 at D. No cigars/pipes in dining-room. Wheelchair access (also wc). Music

▲ *The Twenty One* [11/20]

21 Charlotte Street, Brighton BN2 1AG
BRIGHTON (0273) 686450 £19

This has some of the best food in town, but as only residents and their guests may eat, the rating is deceptively low. There are only fourteen seats and six bedrooms – smart locals book in visiting friends and join them in the Wedgwood blue dining-room. It is possible to discuss the menu when you register, according to what the market has produced. Simon Ward's cooking owes its allegiance to the other side of the water. Especially good have been the scallops with leeks or mange-tout and a Noilly sauce; busy warm salads of snails, bacon and walnuts; beautifully trimmed lamb with rosemary; and calf's liver with madeira sauce. Vegetables are handled well, and the chocolate pot is exceptionally good. The tomato skin roses possibly impress others more than they do us, and the same

Restaurants are graded on a scale of 1–20. In the region of 8–9 expect to find places that may not be restaurants but cafes, pubs, bistros and small hotels. In the category of 10–11 you can expect to find the best food in the locality. Ratings of 12 or more are given to restaurants we regard as serving the best food in the region.

could be said of the bought-in chocolate mints with the coffee. Breakfasts are first-class. The 40 wines are all French, with a full range of *cru* Beaujolais. CELLARMAN'S CHOICE: Chiroubles, Château de Raousset '83 at £9·25.

CHEF: Simon Ward PROPRIETORS: Simon Ward and Stuart Farquharson
OPEN: Mon to Sat, D only CLOSED: Christmas and Jan MEALS: 7 to 8.30
PRICES: Set D £13·50 (£19). Service 12.5%. Licensed, plus bring your own: corkage £1
CARDS: Access, Amex, Diners, Visa
SEATS: 14. Private parties: 12 main room. Vegetarian meals by arrangement. No children under 12. No cigars/pipes in dining-room. Classical music
ACCOMMODATION: 6 rooms, 4 with bath/shower. B&B £24 to £30. No children under 12. TV. Phone. Confirm by 5.30 [GHG]

BRIGHTWELL BALDWIN Oxfordshire map 2

Lord Nelson Inn [10/20]

Brightwell Baldwin OX9 5NP
WATLINGTON (049 161) 2497 £11–£15

An old pub, off the beaten track, which does brisk and busy trade at lunchtimes. The menu is essentially a compilation of bar snacks, with main courses of salads or liver and bacon, and the portions are generous. Scotch salmon salad, fresh lemon sole, prawn cocktail, chicken breast with cream sauce, and the apple and raspberry pie all draw enthusiastic reports. Dining-room service is by waitresses in long dresses. House wine is £5·25.

CHEF: B. Allen PROPRIETORS: B. Allen and Mr and Mrs Gomm
OPEN: Tue to Sun, exc Sun D MEALS: 12 to 2, 7 to 9
PRICES: £10 (£15), Set Sun L from £7·25 (£11), Snacks from £2·85 CARD: Amex
SEATS: 70. 16 tables outside. Private parties: 20 main room. Car-park, 35 places. No children under 10. Wheelchair access (also WC). Music

BRISTOL Avon map 2

BACKGROUND BRIEFING: *This city is awash with wine merchants. The family firm of Averys, 11 Park Street, arguably has the edge – at least for red burgundy, claret and fortified wines – over the better-known Harveys, 12 Denmark Street (which has an old school steak-and-claret restaurant). Most Bristol butchers sell excellent pork and lamb but good quality beef is harder to find. So is fish, although the Carrefour hypermarket, near exit 17 of the M5, has a fair range as well as some good cheeses. The canteen is good for children's meals. Of the casualties from last year's* Guide *Keith Floyd has closed, Bouboulina's greatest asset now seems to be its atmosphere and, although the ethnic revolution has not hit the west with full vigour yet, Malacca is an interesting quasi-Indonesian restaurant serving good satay.*

Berkeley Brasserie [10/20]

Berkeley Centre, 15–19 Queen's Road, Bristol BS8 1QE
BRISTOL (0272) 294679 £10–£14

A workmanlike, unpretentious, good-value brasserie. It gets hot and crowded but the service copes. The cooking is French, and you can eat just one course of fish soup or Toulouse sausage inexpensively. Best end of lamb is charcoal-grilled with herbs, sea-bream is baked in salt. The bread is fresh and the butter unsalted. Wines come from solid suppliers in Averys and Eldridge Pope, and there is also cidre bouché from Normandy.

CHEFS: Joel Joubin, Vincent Castellano and Philali Aberkraama PROPRIETOR: Max Raynes
OPEN: Mon to Sat MEALS: 12 to 2.30, 7.30 to 11
PRICES: £10 (£14), Set L £5·95 (£10), Set D £9·75 (£14), Snacks from £1·95
CARDS: Access, Amex, Visa
SEATS: 84. Private parties: 84 main room. Vegetarian meals. Children's helpings. Music

Bistro Twenty One [14/20]

21 Cotham Road South, Kingsdown,
Bristol BS6 5TZ
BRISTOL (0272) 421744 **Real Food** £15

The best cramped restaurant in the country. It is a bistro and proud of it. Hang your coat by the door and take a seat on a wooden chair. Of course, the table is covered with an oil-cloth and has a candle on it. The waitresses know nothing about the wine or the food but they ask when required, worry if you don't finish your food, and smile a lot. Stephen Markwick comes out of the kitchen from time to time to help with the wine. The trimmings may not be all we expect from a restaurant rating 14, but nor are the prices. It's a short menu, with a good range in the George Perry-Smith/Elizabeth David mould. The fish soup is outstanding; the hollandaise with the asparagus is one of the very finest; jugged hare and steak dijonnaise are both excellent. Main dishes tend to come with rather a lot of sauce, be it a rich port with duck, or calvados with guinea-fowl; and one of the fruit sweets, such as poached figs in Pernod, may cut the richness of the first two courses better than the classic chocolate St Emilion. The wine list, like the food, rises above bistro surroundings, concentrating on the cheaper regions, with plenty of half-bottles. CELLARMAN'S CHOICE: Morgon, Domaine des Pillets '83, from Busson, at £6·75.

CHEF: Stephen Markwick PROPRIETORS: Stephen and Judy Markwick
OPEN: Tue to Sat, D only CLOSED: 1 week Christmas, 1 week Easter, Aug MEALS: 7 to 11
PRICES: £11 (£15)
SEATS: 26. Private parties: 8 main room. Vegetarian meals by arrangement. Children's helpings by arrangement. Wheelchair access. Music

Edwards [10/20]

24 Alma Vale Road, Clifton, Bristol BS8 2HY
BRISTOL (0272) 741533 £12

This uncluttered oak-panelled dining-room is rather smarter than the menu, which is a Jacques-of-all-trades. But John and Margot Pitchford are natural hosts. Portions of lamb cutlets with mint and redcurrant sauce are Yorkshire-sized. The crusty brown bread is fresh, and the frying is done in good oil. Mentions for fish in particular, from seafood lasagne to scampi in cream sauce, and also kidneys in Meaux mustard. Sweets are colourful and usually come with cream on top. They cut a few corners – dried herbs; cash-and-carry-bought

The Guide *does not accept free meals.*

ingredients – but there is no pretence, and they are likely to dissuade you from drinking claret in favour of the house red, though it is a good list for a small place.

CHEFS: John Pitchford and G.Perry PROPRIETORS: John and Margot Pitchford
OPEN: Mon to Sat, exc Sat L MEALS: 12 to 2, 7 to 10.30
PRICES: £8 (£12) CARDS: Access, Visa
SEATS: 30. Private parties: 24 main room, 10 private room. Vegetarian meals. Smart dress preferred. Children's helpings. Wheelchair access. Light classical music

The Ganges [9/20]

368 Gloucester Road, Horfield, Bristol BS7 8TP
BRISTOL (0272) 45234 and 428505 £9–£17

An Indian restaurant in startlingly vivid red, blue and green. Inside it is quite dark and the tables are in stable boxes, which makes you want to get up to see who it is you can hear next door. There are three main-course vegetarian dishes and an Afghan chicken on an otherwise standard menu. Lamb could be of better quality, but all vegetables are fresh and the parathas (made unusually with white flour) and gulab jamun have been good. Exceptionally friendly service. There is Kingfisher lager and a take-away service is available.

CHEF: B.Bista PROPRIETOR: Ahmed Chowdhury
OPEN: all week MEALS: 12 to 2.15, 6 to 11.30
PRICES: £9 (£17), Set L from £7·50 (£11), Set D from £5·50 (£9). Minimum £5. Service 10% CARDS: Access, Amex, Diners, Visa
SEATS: 54. Private parties: 30 main room, 24 private room. Car-park, 30 places. Vegetarian meals. Children's helpings. Smart dress preferred. Wheelchair access. Music. Air-conditioned

Michael's [10/20]

129 Hotwell Road, Bristol BS8 4RU
BRISTOL (0272) 276190 £14

The food in this restaurant has improved in the last few years but the service has become slower and slower. The dining-room is warm and decorated in reds in turn-of-the-century-style. Notably good have been smoked haddock and spinach roulade, salmon and avocado mousse, quails, and pheasant. The venison sausages seem a less good bet. To finish there is home-made crème brûlée and damson ice-cream. House wine is £4·25.

CHEF/PROPRIETOR Michael McGowan
OPEN: Mon to Sat, D only MEALS: 7 to 11.30
PRICES: Set D from £8·75 (£14) CARDS: Access, Amex, Diners
SEATS: 40. Private parties: 40 main room, 30 private room. Vegetarian meals. Children welcome. No smoking in dining-room. Wheelchair access

Les Semailles [14/20]

9 Druid Hill, Stoke Bishop, Bristol BS9 1EW
BRISTOL (0272) 686456 £11–£21

René Gaté's cooking in this quiet suburb can be explosive. Dishes are picturesquely arranged on huge 12-inch plates. He mixes the best of modern cookery with some of the complexities of older styles – roast saddle of hare is garnished with pears, caramelised chestnuts and red cabbage and served with a cream sauce; breasts of maize-fed chickens are stuffed with a mousseline of chicken livers and garnished with small mushrooms. His wife Jillian does all the serving in the subdued hessian-walled dining-room lit by wall-lamps and candles. Mousses are a favourite – spinach served with quail breasts as a starter – and in autumn and winter there have been glorious fruit compôtes. The trappings, and the lack of bustle, are of a restaurant of class – unusual salads, warm wheatmeal rolls, and so on. A little more precision in the seasoning and the score would be raised to 15. The large list of aristocratic French wines includes half a dozen Alsace wines which could handle the broad sweep of the menu, but at a price. House Coteaux d'Aix is £5·90. CELLARMAN'S CHOICE: Bourgogne Hautes Côtes de Nuits '78 at £10·10.

CHEF: René Gaté PROPRIETORS: René and Jillian Gaté
OPEN: Tue to Sat CLOSED: bank hols, 1 week Christmas to New Year, 2 wks in Aug
MEALS: 12 to 2, 7 to 10.30
PRICES: £15 (£21), Set L from £6·80 (£11). Cover charge 30p. Minimum £7·50. Service inc
CARDS: Access, Amex, Visa
SEATS: 26. Private parties: 20 main room. Children welcome

Vintner Wine Bar [9/20]

Crusader House, St Stephen's Street, Bristol BS1 1EL
BRISTOL (0272) 291222 £9

This part of Bristol, near the Law Courts, is a nightmare for cartographers and car-parkers, but a haven for drinkers, and worth a visit for those who have lost faith in wine bars. The carpeted stairway sets the tone and downstairs are endless cellars and a hidden garden. There is good solid furniture, with not a bit of pine in sight, and a setting worthy of Bristol's supping history. The simple fare is a change from quiche and plonk: steak and kidney pie, curry, scallops and prawns in a white wine sauce, home-made ravioli, cheese, and good bread. Wonderful salads include sweetcorn with mango and peppers; cabbage, apple, cucumber and raisins; and potato with home-made mayonnaise. There are a dozen wines by the glass – two dozen if you count sherry and port – and a good choice of bottles for around a fiver, supplemented by a few fine wines. Ch. Gloria, St-Julien '70, is £18·90.

CHEF: W.Comstellano PROPRIETOR: Max Baynes
OPEN: Mon to Fri MEALS: 8 to 10, 12 to 2.30, 6 to 8.30
PRICES: £7 (£9)
SEATS: 80. Private parties: 100 main room. Vegetarian meals. Children's helpings. Children under 18 outside. Pianist. Self-service

BROADSTAIRS Kent map 3

Marchesi Bros [9/20]

18 Albion Street, Broadstairs CT10 1LU
THANET (0843) 62481 £10–£15

This restaurant, family-run since 1886, is set in a handsome old building overlooking the bay. The set meals are good value – help yourself to salads from the cold table, then there is good local plaice and steaks. It is professionally run:

an ambitious new *carte* of classical dishes has been introduced, on which we have no reports as yet. The classical French wine list of 200 bottles has an interesting, inexpensive but poorly annotated Alsace section. CELLARMAN'S CHOICE: Lirac '79 at £7.

CHEF: A.Kember PROPRIETORS: The Roger family
OPEN: all week CLOSED: 3 days after Christmas MEALS: 12 to 2 (2.30 Sun), 6.30 to 9.30 (10 Sat)
PRICES: £11 (£15), Set L from £5·95 (£10), Set D £7·95 (£12). Service 10% CARDS: Access, Amex, Diners, Visa
SEATS: 70. 7 tables outside. Private parties: 45 main room, 18 private room. Car-park, 15 places. Vegetarian meals. Children's helpings. Smart dress preferred

BROADWAY Hereford & Worcester map 2

▲ *Collin House* [11/20]

Collin Lane, Broadway WR12 7PB
BROADWAY (0386) 858354
on A44, 1m NW of Broadway £3–£13

A comfortable family hotel out of the town with only a swimming-pool and a bungalow to mar the rural setting. There are good-value bar meals at lunchtime and a generous, imaginative English menu in the evening. The local meat is notably good; chicken liver pâté; rabbit in cider and celery; rare fillet of beef; crisp halves of duck; pigeon and steak pie; and a range of puddings from the adventurous guava and tamarillo ice-cream to apple pie. The wholemeal bread is traditionally baked by Keen & Stock in the town, and the cheeseboard has included Shropshire and Dorset blues and unpasteurised Stilton. Hook Norton beers, eight malt whiskies and a varied wine list with a good Spanish section going up to CELLARMAN'S CHOICE: Reserva 904 '70, La Rioja Alta, at £12·55.

CHEF: Judith Mills PROPRIETORS: John and Judith Mills
OPEN: all week, exc Sun D MEALS: 12 to 1.30, 7 to 9
PRICES: Set Sun L £9 (£12), Set D from £10 (£13), Bar meals, L only, from £1 (£3)
CARDS: Access, Visa
SEATS: 35. 5 tables outside. Private parties: 30 main room. Car-park, 30 places. Children's helpings, L only. No children under 8 at D. Wheelchair access (also WC)
ACCOMMODATION: 7 rooms, all with bath/shower. B&B £26·50 to £48. Deposit: £20. Swimming-pool. Garden. Scenic. Doors close at 12 [GHG]

Hunters Lodge [11/20]

High Street, Broadway WR12 7DT
BROADWAY (0386) 853247 **Real Food** £10–£19

'We try not to have any rules and regulations and do whatever staff, time and tables dictate,' writes Dottie Friedli, which neatly sums up the feeling in her and husband Kurt's Cotswold stone house, to be found on the High Street and with a walled garden at the back. The cooking, though, is exact – a warm salad of genuine *confit* of duck; guinea-fowl cooked in good burgundy; smoked quail with celery. And although it is a serious restaurant there is no problem about slipping in for a £5 lunch or just a sweet. We have eaten excellent leek soup; a shellfish ragout with vegetables and saffron; best end of lamb with mustard and also tarragon. We were harsh last year on the wine mark-up policy – Ch. Pape-Clément '71 is listed at £17·50 though it has sold at auction for £110! It is a solid list with good drinking from the Spanish wines for around £5 and more.

CHEF: Kurt Friedli PROPRIETORS: Kurt and Dottie Friedli
OPEN: Tue to Sun, exc Sun D CLOSED: 2 weeks Jan, 2 weeks Aug MEALS: 12.30 to 2, 7.30 to 9.45
PRICES: L £10 (£16), D £12 (£19), Set L £6·25 (£10) CARDS: Access, Amex, Diners, Visa
SEATS: 40. 6 tables outside. Private parties: 40 main room. Car-park, 20 places. Vegetarian meals. Children's helpings. No children under 8 at D. No cigars/pipes in dining-room. Wheelchair access (also WC)

▲ *Lygon Arms* [new entry, zero rated]

Broadway WR12 7DU
BROADWAY (0386) 852255 £14–£29

The Lygon Arms is a fixture on the international hotel circuit and could be in a Good Architecture Guide. It is one of the grand dining-rooms of the Cotswolds and the service matches. It is possible to eat a cheap light meal of just pâté and a dessert. They say they have the best smoked salmon in the UK. Or just go for tea. There are more elaborate dishes which are well-reported – soufflé of crayfish with watercress purée, noisettes of venison with wild mushrooms, and roast best end of lamb with herb breadcrumbs. The straightforward dishes of traditional English food impress most – roast chicken with bread sauce, steak and kidney pie, and the puddings, particularly butterscotch tart. Wines come from Edward Sheldon in Shipton-on-Stour. House claret is £6·25. CELLARMAN'S CHOICE: Marqués de Cáceres '80 at £7. More reports, please.

CHEF: Alain Dubois PROPRIETOR: Douglas J. Barrington
OPEN: all week MEALS: 12.30 to 2.30, 7.15 to 9.30
PRICES: £22 (£29), Set L £9 (£14), Set D £16 (£21) CARDS: Access, Amex, Diners, Visa
SEATS: 120. Private parties: 90 main room. Car-park, 100 places. Vegetarian meals. Children's helpings. Jacket and tie. No cigars/pipes in dining-room. Wheelchair access (also WC)
ACCOMMODATION: 61 rooms, all with bath/shower. Rooms for disabled. B&B £50 to £86. Children welcome. Baby facilities. Pets welcome. Afternoon teas. Garden. Tennis. Golf. Helicopter pad. TV. Phone [GHG]

BROCKDISH Norfolk map 6

Sheriff House [11/20]

Brockdish IP21 4JY
HOXNE (037 975) 316 £17

Old brandies line the shelf in the dining-room of this eccentric, seventeenth-century timbered restaurant. They start at 1802, with a bit of a gap until 1914, then you find '28, '30, '40, '45, '46, '49 and '66; many are Harveys Frapin, early-landed and late-bottled. The Pichel-Juans like you to order on the telephone, which may be a good move as inspectors have had their doubts as to how Real the food is when ordering on the night. The cooking is classic French, though more on the lines of a *routier* than the old gentleman of a dining-room and the attentive service lead you to expect: excellent hare and chestnut stew; chicken provençale; beef Stroganoff; steak offered with a choice of green or black peppercorns. A simple, set menu would iron out the ruffles. The wine cellar is stocked with classic Bordeaux and burgundies, with a good range of communes, vintages and merchants. Some bottles are old and there are plenty of good ones, even if they are not terribly cheap.

CHEFS: E. and J. Pichel-Juan PROPRIETORS: F. E. and A. Pichel-Juan
OPEN: all week, exc Wed MEALS: 12 to 2, 7 to 9
PRICES: £11 (£17). Minimum £5 CARDS: Access, Visa
SEATS: 32. Private parties: 6 main room, 16 private room. Car-park. No children under 14. Jacket and tie. No pipes in dining-room, no smoking until dessert

BROCKENHURST Hampshire map 2

Le Poussin [13/20]

57–59 Brookley Road, Brockenhurst SO4 7RB
LYMINGTON (0590) 23063 £10–£20

A serious husband-and-wife-run French restaurant doing modern dishes with more than a little flair. The dining-room is smart and remarkably pink – even the napkins folded into the glasses on the table. One wall is taken up with wine bottles. Alexander Aitken has sensibly cut back his *carte* and concentrates on his menus of the day. He has been experimenting with meat and fish variations, such as salmon with a little foie gras stuffing or brill with a mousse of foie gras, chicken and fish. He is an adept *saucier*, as seen in his béarnaise served with asparagus, asparagus mousse and a pastry case, and the cream and meat glaze for lamb fillet with its kidney. Other touches, from excellent brown bread onwards, are those of a confident and improving restaurant. The sweets are works of art – a cassis mousse with a blackcurrant sauce, and his speciality of a fresh fig split open with armagnac ice-cream, spun sugar and a strawberry sauce. Service is friendly and everyone is trying hard. A lot is made of the wines, with bottles being shown and explained, and it is a very strong French list, especially in Bordeaux, and all, from the six good house wines around £5, are chosen with care.

CHEF: Alexander Aitken PROPRIETORS: Alexander and Caroline Aitken
OPEN: Mon to Sat, exc Mon L MEALS: 12.30 to 2, 7 to 10
PRICES: £15 (£20), Set L from £6·25 (£10), Set D from £11·50 (£16) CARDS: Access, Amex, Diners, Visa
SEATS: 35. Private parties: 35 main room. Vegetarian meals. Children's helpings. Jacket and tie. No cigars/pipes in dining-room. Wheelchair access (also WC)

BROMLEY Kent map 3

BACKGROUND BRIEFING: *The south-eastern fringe of London is not rewarding for eating out. The run of Greek, Chinese, Indian, Turkish and fast-food restaurants, steak houses, and the wine bars, function suites, cocktail bars and pubs serving food have, in general, little to recommend them (the entries below are naturally exceptions). Now Le Bon Bec has joined the list of casualties good eating possibilities are reduced. However, Mamma Mia, Bromley, is a small Italian trattoria serving home-made pasta and veal dishes to a young student crowd. It is good value for money and always crowded.*

Capisano's, Westmorland Road, Bromley, is a smarter version of the above, with an older clientele; prices are higher. Giannino's in Keston is similar but there is lobster, and the sweets trolley is perhaps a mite creamier. Guests in Hayes is a small bistro with two set-price menus and a tendency to serve dishes on the lines of duck with black cherries. Bernard's, Barry Road, Dulwich, is a small, family-run place, popular with locals; it has a Franco-Italian menu, cheerful atmosphere, good house wines and friendly owners. Flashmans, Lordship Lane, also in Dulwich, is a small hamburger and steak restaurant in a converted chemist's shop, popular with the local young crowd, good value, and offering well-cooked food and very friendly service. Kate 2 Bistro, 121 Lee Road, is a small, pine-tabled bistro run by a couple of local ladies, with good, reasonably priced lunches cooked by a consortium. The Hollywood Bowl in East Street is Bromley's answer to the Hard Rock Café (see London), and is packed every night for burgers and filled potatoes with a background of loud music. There are some interesting shops within striking distance of Bromley. Apart from the Sainsbury and Safeway in Lewisham and Beckenham one of the great cheese merchants, James, is to be found in Beckenham High Street, with a full range of English and foreign cheeses. J.F. Ayre at Nunhead bakes excellent bread and elaborate gateaux to continental standards; another good bread shop is Keogh's in Lewisham.

Carioca [8/20]

239 High Street, Bromley BR1 1PQ
01-460 7130 — £11

Ken Modi is always up to something. The ground floor is now called Zanzibar Brasserie, and this year he is planning to increase the number of vegetarian dishes available. Ideas come from all points of the compass and current specialities include prawn mini puri (pineapple with a spicy prawn mixture), a thali, lamb cutlet biriani, and mango pancakes. He is also big on presentation, so watch out for frills and parasols. Children are welcome. House Italian is £2·70.

CHEF: Mr Shina PROPRIETORS: Ken and Joanna Modi
OPEN: all week MEALS: 12 to 2.15, 6 to 11 (11.45 Fri and Sat)
PRICES: £7 (£11). Service 10% CARDS: Access, Amex, Diners, Visa
SEATS: 90. Private parties: 50 main room. Vegetarian meals. Children welcome. Wheelchair access. Music. Air-conditioned

Peking Diner [10/20]

71 Burnt Ash Lane, Bromley BR1 5AA
01-464 7911 — £12–£16

There is a lot of propaganda on the menu but the cooking, especially of fish and Peking dishes, is probably still the best in Bromley. Reliably good are the crispy beef with chilli; sizzling scallops with ginger; fried prawns with pickled cabbage;

This restaurant has an exceptional wine cellar.

Restaurants rating 10 and 11 serve the best food in the locality.

All letters to the Guide are acknowledged with a list of changes since we went to press.

and piquant hot-and-sour soup. Good rice and noodles. The waiters have stopped filling up wine glasses every 30 seconds, which is a relief. House French is £5.

CHEF/PROPRIETOR: Mr Kok
OPEN: Mon to Sat MEALS: 12.30 to 2.15, 6.30 to 11.15
PRICES: £8 (£16), Set D from £7·50 (£12). Minimum £7·50. Service 10% CARDS: Access, Amex, Diners, Visa
SEATS: 55. Private parties: 60 main room. Vegetarian meals. Children welcome. Wheelchair access (also WC). Music. Air-conditioned

BROMSGROVE Hereford & Worcester map 5

▲ *Grafton Manor* [12/20]

Grafton Lane, Bromsgrove BG1 7HA
BROMSGROVE (0527) 31525
on B4091, 1½m SW of Bromsgrove **Real Food** £18–£24

Down a rutted lane, only a short distance from the town but appearing to be deep in the countryside, is this sixteenth-century house which has been lovingly restored over the last six years by the Morris family. The front door opens as you open the car door, but the service is refreshingly unfussy. The set, four-course dinners are varied and English, and the supplies of ingredients appear solid. Notably good have been the calves' brains in a port sauce, an unusual pumpkin and duck soup, and gravlax. Main-course meats are not over-sauced, witness the Welsh lamb with béarnaise and the char-grilled sirloin, and herbs from the Morrises' own garden are used liberally. The niggles that dogged last year's assessment seem to have cleared up and we are happy to raise the rating. Sweets tend to the luscious, such as brown bread ice-cream, whisky pudding, chocolate marquise. A thorough wine list. Five of the six Alsace wines bear the maker's (Trimbach and Kuentz-Bas) endorsement stamp of Réserve or equivalent, and there is a respect for diners' purses as well as for quality.
CELLARMAN'S CHOICE: Coteaux du Tricastin '81 at £6·85.

CHEFS: Nicola and John Morris PROPRIETORS: The Morris family
OPEN: all week, D only, and Sun L MEALS: 12.30 to 1.30, 7.30 to 9
PRICES: Set L £12·50 (£18), Set D £17·95 (£24) CARDS: Access, Amex, Diners, Visa
SEATS: 50. Private parties: 14 main room. Car-park, 55 places. Vegetarian meals by arrangement. No children under 12. Jacket and tie. No smoking in dining-room. Wheelchair access
ACCOMMODATION: 6 rooms, all with bath/shower. B&B £45 to £60. No children under 12. No pets. Garden. Fishing. Golf. Helicopter pad. TV. Phone. Doors close at 12. Confirm by 6 [GHG]

BROXTED Essex map 3

▲ *Whitehall* [new entry, zero rated]

Church End, Broxted CM6 2BZ
BISHOP'S STORTFORD (0279) 850603 £17–£28

This is a good one – a twelfth-century manor, formerly the home of Lord Butler, run without pretensions and with big smiles. Chef Gary Rhodes has worked at the Capital Hotel (see London) and produces a menu based on half a dozen stocks.

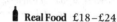

It is modern, the sauces used with restraint and not swamping the plate à la *nouvelle*. It is not cheap because it relies on expensive luxuries such as a starter of guinea-fowl and artichoke, turbot, or grilled Dover sole with herb butter. The menu surprise changes every night. One impressive example opened with a small smoked goose salad before a plate of alternating smoked salmon (excellent) and gravlax. Then came quail filled with foie gras in a little puddle of port and butter sauce; then a pink champagne and grapefruit sorbet; then slices of beef with wild mushrooms and a madeira sauce; cheese; and an elaborate strawberry sponge confection. There are 60 wines carefully chosen from the best vintages and not just at the price level of Bâtard-Montrachet '80 from Leflaive at £34·25 but also at that of Côtes du Rhône '78 from Pascal at £6·50. More reports, please.

CHEF: Gary Rhodes PROPRIETORS: Mr and Mrs G.M.Keane
OPEN: Tue to Sun, exc Sun D CLOSED: 3 weeks Jan MEALS: 12 to 1.45, 7 to 9.30
PRICES: £21 (£28), Set L from £12·50 (£17), Set D £22·50 (£28) CARDS: Access, Amex, Visa
SEATS: 40. 4 tables outside. Private parties: 20 main room, 10 private room. Car-park, 20 places. Vegetarian meals. Children's helpings (Sun L only). No children under 5. Wheelchair access
ACCOMMODATION: 4 rooms, all with bath/shower. B&B £60 to £85. No children under 5. Afternoon teas. Garden. Outdoor swimming-pool. Tennis. Helicopter pad. TV. Phone

BRUTON Somerset — map 2

Clogs [10/20]

95 High Street, Bruton BA1 0AR
BRUTON (074 981) 2255 — £16

Not, as its name might suggest, a purveyor of chip butties and black pudding, but a small Indonesian/Dutch restaurant, whose pièce de résistance is a rijsttafel that needs a day's notice and runs to 15 different dishes, including nasi goreng, atjar, serundeng, gado-gado, bah-pow and two different satays. Regular dishes include quails with strawberry sauce, and steaks stuffed with mushrooms. Vegetables are varied. Cream for coffee comes in little chocolate cups which can be eaten afterwards. House French wine is £5·50.

CHEFS/PROPRIETORS: Mr and Mrs D.F.Ismangiu
OPEN: Tue to Sat, D only; also Mon D June to Sept MEALS: 7 to 10
PRICES: £10 (£16). Minimum £5
SEATS: 25. Private parties: 20 main room, 20 private room. Children's helpings by arrangement. No children under 5. No pipes in dining-room. Music

BUCKDEN North Yorkshire — map 7

▲ *Low Greenfield* [9/20]

Langstrothdale Chase, Buckden BD23 5JN
KETTLEWELL (075 676) 858 — £13

The brochure says you won't find any discos here. You can say that again – this spartan, white Victorian house is a mile and a half along a gated track, as remote as anywhere in England, and 1,200 feet high: the Sedgleys light a fire most evenings to keep the guests warm. Mrs Sedgley cooks (on a coke-fired Aga) a first-class, homely menu made up around locally made sausages, free-range eggs, and wholemeal bread from David Humphrey in Skipton. Breakfasts are therefore excellent, which means the Tiptree preserves do not look so good. In the evening the accessories, such as perfectly cooked jacket potatoes and immaculate blue and white Wensleydales, give otherwise competent meals a lift – there may be mushroom tarts; chicken breasts with sage and cream; braised brisket of beef; gooseberry jelly and strawberries; brandy meringues. Tea is better than coffee. There is a modest wine list and Theakston's beers.

CHEF: Lindsay Sedgley PROPRIETORS: Austin and Lindsay Sedgley
OPEN: Mon to Fri, D only CLOSED: Nov to Mar MEALS: 8
PRICES: Set D from £8·95 (£13). Service inc
SEATS: 10. Private parties: 10 main room. Car-park, 6 places. Children welcome. No smoking in dining-room. Classical music. One sitting
ACCOMMODATION: 6 rooms. B&B £12 to £24. Deposit: £10 per person. Children welcome. Baby facilities. Pets by arrangement. Garden. Sauna. Fishing. Scenic [GHG]

BUCKLAND Gloucestershire — map 2

▲ *Buckland Manor* [12/20]

Buckland WR12 7LY
BROADWAY (0386) 852626 — £14–£23

This old Cotswold manor, surrounded by gardens, paddocks and hills, is usually filled with flowers. Service is professional and of the old school. Chef Robert Elsmore trained at the Dorchester with Anton Mosimann, whose paternal influence is evident in the flamboyance of the dishes. There is a fresh soup each day; also a special dish that is not on the *carte*. Chicken and Brie mousseline has been served with an unusual Sauternes and cream sauce. Fish has been good, notably sea-bass and ginger on a tomato coulis. Other successes include beef with basil; veal with lemon sauce; and grilled duck. Vegetables are varied and are served firm and generously. The New Year's banquet was quite a feast – salad; wild duck soup covered with pastry; hare terrine with pistachio; sorbet; salmon and turbot in a cream sauce: veal; half a dozen cheeses; and vanilla ice-cream with pineapple. This is an emerging country-house hotel of some stature. Traditional breakfast includes home-made jams and marmalades. The wine list is a conservative collection, with mark-ups of over 100 per cent. A braver policy in the less famous regions would find wines of sufficient quality to match the food but at considerably less expense. The house burgundy, though, is commendably only £5·25.

CHEF: Robert Elsmore PROPRIETORS: Mr and Mrs Berman
OPEN: all week CLOSED: 3 weeks in Jan, Feb MEALS: 12 to 1.45, 7.30 to 8.45
PRICES: £15 (£23), Set L Sun £8·75 (£14) CARDS: Access, Amex, Diners, Visa
SEATS: 34. 6 tables outside. Private parties: 34 main room. Car-park, 30 places. No children under 8. Smart dress preferred. No cigars/pipes in dining-room. Wheelchair access. One sitting
ACCOMMODATION: 11 rooms, all with bath/shower. Rooms for disabled. B&B £69·50 to £105. Kennels. Afternoon teas. Garden. Outdoor swimming-pool. Tennis. Croquet. Putting. Riding. TV. Phone. Scenic [GHG]

Restaurants rating 12 or more serve the best food in the region.

BURGHFIELD Berkshire map 2

Knights Farm [13/20]

Burghfield RG3 3XE
READING (0734) 52366
¾m NE of Burghfield, sign to Pingewood — Real Food £17–£20

There is a prosperous air about Knights Farm which makes it feel more like a country manor than a farmhouse, and Charles Trevor-Roper looks more like a bank manager than a restaurateur. Carol Trevor-Roper is joined in the kitchen by Pierre Mathiot from Mijanou (see London) and between them they cook an attractive four-course menu that takes in a wide range of flavours and textures. Pigeon breast for a salad is marinated with garlic and shallots, fried, and given a mango sauce; monkfish is poached and served with a cream and Pernod sauce; quails' eggs come in a strudel pastry nest with beetroot and celeriac. Sometimes duck breast will appear on the same plate as hot duck pâté and sauté livers, together with caramelised blackcurrants; and medallions of venison saddle will accompany pieces of venison casseroled with port and juniper berries. There are generous helpings of organically grown, al dente vegetables. Cream is organic, too; chickens and eggs are free-range; and fish comes from Brixham. Scallops are served with an orange and vermouth sauce; sole and salmon with herbs and cream. A vegetarian dish is available. Patrick Rance's cheeses appear, are taken away, and large slabs return on a plate with Bath Olivers. There is a very fine Sicilian chocolate cake with bitter chocolate sauce. White wines are classified according to sweetness, reds according to body-weight, and there is something to suit every pocket. House wine is £6·50. CELLARMAN'S CHOICE: Rosemount Chardonnay '84, from Australia's Hunter Valley, at £8·25.

CHEF: Carol Trevor-Roper PROPRIETORS: Charles and Carol Trevor-Roper
OPEN: Mon to Sat, exc Sat L CLOSED: 1 week at Christmas, 3 weeks Aug
MEALS: 12.30 to 1.30, 7.15 to 9
PRICES: Set L £13·60 (£17), Set D £16·95 (£20). Service inc CARDS: Access, Amex, Diners, Visa
SEATS: 50. Private parties: 22 main room, 18 private room. Car-park, 30 places. Vegetarian meals. No children under 12. Smart dress preferred. Wheelchair access. Music

BURNHAM MARKET Norfolk map 6

Fishes' [10/20]

Market Place, Burnham Market PE31 8HE
FAKENHAM (0328) 738588 — Real Food £10–£16

At her restaurant some two miles from the coast Gillian Cape uses local fish and shellfish, including mussels from Brancaster, crab from Overstrand, and her own oysters. A three-course lunch menu for around £6 has salmon fishcakes with crab sauce, skate wing with black butter, and crab mayonnaise. Starters include lamb and leek soup, and there may also be apple, nut and date salad, and goats' cheese from Satherleigh in Yorkshire. Sadly, though, gravlax is bought in and

All letters to the Guide *are acknowledged with a list of changes since we went to press.*

may vary from excellent to very poor. There is good brown bread ice-cream, sorbets and coffee. Local wine from Elmham Park ('83) is £7·30, and CELLARMAN'S CHOICE is Anjou Blanc extra sec '82, made from Chardonnay, at £6·25.

CHEFS: Gillian Cape and Carole Bird PROPRIETOR: Gillian Cape
OPEN: Tue to Sun, exc Sun D (open all week in Aug, and Sun D July to Sept)
CLOSED: 24 to 28 Dec MEALS: 12 to 2 (2.15 Sun), 7 to 9.30 (9 Oct to Mar)
PRICES: £11 (£16), Set L from £5·95 (£10) CARDS: Access, Amex, Diners, Visa
SEATS: 48. Private parties: 32 main room, 18 private room. Children's helpings. Wheelchair access

BURNHAM-ON-CROUCH Essex map 3

The Contented Sole [10/20]

80 High Street, Burnham-on-Crouch CM0 8AA
MALDON (0621) 782139 £9–£18

An old-fashioned family-run fish restaurant that takes the pick of the local catch of sole and sea-bass and cooks it in classic sauces, such as Nantua and créole. Scallops come provençale or else in a cream soup. Good dishes have been mussels with a cream sauce in pastry; stuffed mushrooms; the seafood pancake; and apple fritters with apricot sauce to finish. There are steaks and a few equally classic meat dishes too. House Alsace is £4·65. Prices, infuriatingly, still do not include VAT . . . but do include 10 per cent service.

CHEF: Roy Walton PROPRIETORS: Roy, Elaine and Simon Walton
OPEN: Tue to Sat CLOSED: 2 weeks July, 4 weeks at Christmas MEALS: 12 to 2, 7 to 9.30
PRICES: £12 (£18), Set L £4·75 (£9). Minimum £4·75. Service inc
SEATS: 65. Private parties: 40 main room, 28 private room. Vegetarian meals. Children's helpings. Wheelchair access (also WC)

Polash [9/20]

169 Station Road, Burnham-on-Crouch CM0 8HJ
MALDON (0621) 782233 £10–£12

A cut above the usual tandoori/curry house. It is a long, unwieldy menu, but the staff are helpful and the spicing distinct. The strength of the cooking is in the tandoori and the bhuna curries, but there are also some vividly coloured examples from Madras, Ceylon (sic), Malaysia and Kashmir. House Soave is £3·95.

CHEF: Kacha Miah PROPRIETORS: Faruque Ahmed and Kacha Miah
OPEN: all week MEALS: 12.15 to 2.45, 6 to 11.45
PRICES: £6 (£10), Set L and D £8·50 (£12) CARDS: Access, Amex, Diners, Visa
SEATS: 52. Private parties: 40 main room. Vegetarian meals. Children's helpings. Wheelchair access (also WC). Oriental music. Air-conditioned

▲ *This restaurant has rooms.*

New restaurants that we have not been able to assess completely are given a zero rating for this year. We are particularly keen to have reports on these places.

BURY ST EDMUNDS Suffolk map 3

▲ *Angel Hotel* [10/20]

Angel Hill, Bury St Edmunds IP33 1LT
BURY ST EDMUNDS (0284) 3926 £13–£20

Charles Dickens allegedly complained about the plumbing here (a recent revamp should put paid to that) and the literary tradition continues with quarterly bookish dinners and the annual Angel Literary Award for East Anglian writers. This creeper-covered, stately hotel has been an inn since 1452. Now it has two restaurants. The upstairs Regency has the formality of an old, country-town hotel dining-room with silver cutlery and crisp white linen. The menu-style is one of chicken mousseline, egg cocotte with curry sauce, and stuffed loin of lamb, all of which have been good. Specialities include chicken breast cooked with butter, raspberry vinegar, egg yolks and cream, and served with pastry fleurons. Downstairs, in the more informal pink and grey vaults, there are nods towards vegetarianism with such dishes as minced and sliced mushrooms with Stilton cooked in puff pastry. House wines from Lay & Wheeler are £5·95 a litre.

CHEFS: B.Harrison, B.MacCallum and J.Fulcher PROPRIETOR: S.C.Gough
OPEN: all week, exc Sun D MEALS: 12.30 to 2, 7 to 9 (10 Sat)
PRICES: £13 (£20), Set Sun L £8·50 (£13), Snacks from £1·50 CARDS: Access, Amex, Diners, Visa
SEATS: 44. Private parties: 12 main room, 120, 60 and 14 private rooms. Car-park, 20 places. Vegetarian meals by arrangement. Children's helpings. Jacket and tie. No pipes in dining-room
ACCOMMODATION: 38 rooms, all with bath/shower. B&B £44 to £51. Children welcome. Dogs welcome. Afternoon teas. TV. Phone. Doors close at 12. Confirm by 6 [GHG]

Mortimer's [11/20]

31 Churchgate Street, Bury St Edmunds IP33 1RG
BURY ST EDMUNDS (0284) 60623 £15

An attractively straightforward seafood restaurant with excellent wines. Langoustines come from Argyll, live lobsters from a local fisherman, crab from Cromer, and smoked eel from the Fens. Steaming and grilling are the preferred cooking methods, although there must be better things to do with oysters than heating them with cheese. Recommended main courses include brill with wine sauce, mackerel in oatmeal, seafood gratin, and steamed lemon sole with mussels and prawns. Non-fish eaters have to make the best of the run of the excellent desserts, such as chocolate pot or pineapple sorbet. Mr Gooding owns the off-licence next door and his list is remarkable, with four grape varieties from Alsace alone, and four Chablis as well. CELLARMAN'S CHOICE: Mâcon Prissé '83 from Gonard at £7·75 and Magdalen Rivaner '83 from Norfolk at £5·95.

CHEF: K.A.Ambler PROPRIETOR: M.H.Gooding
OPEN: Mon to Sat, exc Sat L CLOSED: 24 Dec to 5 Jan and bank hols MEALS: 12 to 2, 7 to 10 (9.30 Mon)
PRICES: £11 (£15), Snacks from £1·95 (£2·15) CARDS: Access, Amex, Diners, Visa
SEATS: 60. No pipes in dining-room. Children's helpings. Wheelchair access. Music

The Guide *does not accept free meals.*

BUXTON Derbyshire map 5

Nathaniel's [new entry, zero rated]

35 High Street, Buxton SK17 6HA
BUXTON (0298) 78388 £8–£16

The dining-room of this bistro has solid tables, a marble floor, heavy maroon curtains, lace, and green-patterned wallpaper. Cooking is honest – mushrooms on toast with mustard, pork normande, chicken chasseur, steak pie, all served with generous amounts of vegetables. Sweets tend to the traditional, like Bakewell tart or bread-and-butter pudding. House French is £5.
CELLARMAN'S CHOICE: Bulgarian Cabernet Sauvignon at £4·95. More reports, please.

CHEFS: Michael Jordan, Mark Gilbert and Andrew Webster
PROPRIETORS: Michael and Margaret Jordan
OPEN: Tue to Sun, exc Sun D MEALS: 12 to 2.30, 7 to 10.30
PRICES: £11 (£16), Set L £4·75 (£8), Set D from £6·50 (£10) CARDS: Access, Amex, Diners, Visa
SEATS: 50. Private parties: 34 main room, 24 private room. Vegetarian meals. Children's helpings. Wheelchair access (also WC). Music

CAMBRIDGE Cambridgeshire map 3

BACKGROUND BRIEFING: *If Oxford can be described as a city that has a university, then Cambridge is a university round which a city seems to have sprung up. Compared to the former, Cambridge has a paucity of places to eat out, although out of term conferences and private parties are well catered for at some of the colleges. Of places listed in last year's* Guide *the Peking in Burleigh Street has changed hands, Panos in Hills Road has as many votes against inclusion as for, and Xanadu in the university Pitt Club has a wonderful dining-room and weird but not so wonderful food. Twenty Two in Chesterton Street is unpretentious and has decent food, as long as you don't mind trying to get your knees under the shared card-tables. It is, though, one of only two restaurants in the country to have its salad ingredients supplied by Joy Larkcom. The Arts Theatre has a good buffet-style restaurant, as has the Joshua Taylor department store ('grab a tray and pay, find a seat and eat'). Next door there is a delicatessen also run by Taylor's which is clean and well stocked with salamis, sausages, loose pasta, cheeses and fresh bread. Indeed, the Cambridge shopping scene is quite healthy. The market has good stalls for fish, cheese, teas and coffee beans. P. Belzano, 204 Cherry Hinton Road, has pasta, pulses, oils, wines, Parma ham and other Italian fare. The notable cake-maker and chocolatier Fitzbillies, 52 Trumpington Street, has opened a new branch at 50 Regent Street. There is an excellent pork butcher, as well as a Chinese supermarket, in Burleigh Street. Two wholefood shops are Natural Selection, Regent Street, and Arjuna, Mill Road, which also does take-away snacks at lunchtime. Other places for cheap eating include Gardenia in Rose Crescent, which specialises in kebabs and has a good atmosphere – especially in the cellar – and the Pizza Express.*

'My friend had five deep-fried sprats on a white plate with tartare sauce. The miracle did not happen.' (On eating in London)

Free Press [9/20]

7 Prospect Row, Cambridge CB1 1OU
CAMBRIDGE (0223) 68337 £5

A tiny Victorian pub with very little space inside. Wooden settees are fixed to the walls, there are small cast-iron tables with polished wooden tops, and rowing memorabilia on the walls. It is one of the few pubs in Cambridge to rise to any degree of imagination in the production of lunchtime food. There are good soups, such as curried apple and spiced carrot, a variety of excellent pies, and other made-up dishes, such as mussels in cider – and all at reasonable prices. The coffee is good, but puddings more variable. Service is good-natured. Go early because it gets crowded. Greene King ales.

CHEF: Karen Barker PROPRIETORS: Chris and Debbie Lloyd
OPEN: all week, L only MEALS: 12 to 2
PRICES: £3 (£5)
SEATS: 45. 2 tables outside. Private parties: 12 main room, 6 private room. Vegetarian meals. Children welcome. No-smoking area. Wheelchair access. Self-service

CAMPSEA ASH Suffolk map 3

▲ *Old Rectory* [new entry, zero rated]

Campsea Ash IP13 0PU
WICKHAM MARKET (0728) 746524
on B1078, 1½m E of A12 £14–£15

Order when you book a table at this big, slightly shabby but charming seventeenth-century rectory. Stewart Bassett, who has had distinctions before when he ran Bassetts at Halesworth, manages to cook and serve on quiet nights. His centrepieces can be very fine – salmon cooked in foil with diced vegetables and champagne; marinated fillet of beef roasted and served with a girolle sauce; guinea-fowl, flavoured beneath the skin with ginger, turmeric, honey, garlic and parsley. Some of his sauces are continuous, evolving from one meal to the next. Maggie Bassett bakes fine brown rolls, which are served hot. Coffee is horrid, as it was at Bassetts. There is no choice on the night, but on the other hand it is possible to agree the inclusive price of a meal on the phone beforehand. Good wines in the cellar, but again no wine list as such. More reports, please.

CHEF/PROPRIETOR: Stewart Bassett
OPEN: all week, exc Sat and Sun L MEALS: 12 to 2, 7 to 10
PRICES: Set L £10·50 (£14), Set D £11·50 (£15) CARDS: Amex, Visa
SEATS: 36. Private parties: 24 main room; 24, 8 and 4 private rooms. Car-park, 20 places. Vegetarian meals. Children's helpings. Wheelchair access
ACCOMMODATION: 3 rooms, all with bath/shower. B&B £15 to £27. No children under 10. No pets. Garden. Helicopter pad. Doors close at 12

CANTERBURY Kent map 3

BACKGROUND BRIEFING: *Inexpensive places to eat include wine bars such as Tascolls, 49 Castle Street, and Alberry's, 38 St Margaret Street. JV's City Brasserie, 4 Church Street, St Paul's, is a wine bar and restaurant where the best of the food (mostly on the hand-written rather than the printed menu) is good – for example, scallops in white wine with cream. Il Vaticano in St Margaret's Street is good for pasta, and for pizzas there is Pizza Place, 87 Northgate, and Manhattan Transfer, 41 Broad Street. Ingrid Eissfeld's Sweet Hearts Pâtisserie, Old Weaver's House, St Peter's Street, continues to serve excellent cakes, pastries, coffee and a small selection of savoury dishes. On the pub front, the Miller's Arms is ever popular among Real Ale enthusiasts. For a wide variety of unusual ingredients start with Gateways, 21 The Borough, where the strength is in herbs, spices, pulses, Greek yoghourt, filo pastry, tahini and so on. Another good wholefood shop is Oasis, 24 Palace Street. For Chinese produce there is Sang Woo Supermarket in St Dunstan's, near the now closed Paradise Cafe. The meats and cheeses at C. R. Townsend, 24 Sun Street, are well kept. Michael Waterfield's Merchant Cook, 4 Best Lane, an ancillary to his restaurant (see entry), sells pies, pâtés and cold meats. Wincheap Butchers, 26 Wincheap, smokes its own chicken and other meats and offers a good range of game hung to order.*

Restaurant Seventy Four [15/20]

74 Wincheap, Canterbury CT1 3RX
CANTERBURY (0227) 67411/2 **Real Food** £13–£23

Nouvelle but not nonsense. Ian McAndrew's cooking can be dazzling – ravioli stuffed with lobster and monkfish set on a mushroom sauce and garnished with scallops; fillet of beef with a fennel sauce; lamb with scallops and a scallop mousseline, and another night with a pimento sauce and a parsley mousse. In three years Mr McAndrew and his wife Jane have developed this into one of the best restaurants in the south. It is a 400-year-old, double-fronted house. The small white-walled lounge is dominated by a huge original fireplace, and the dining-room has imposing dark panels. The tone is both serious and family. There are two set meals at night, with a good balance and elegant touches like the home-made wholemeal rolls and a dozen cheeses in good condition. For dessert there have been pale pear and dark chocolate mousses on a sharp pear sabayon, and brandy snaps filled with rhubarb sorbet. Lunch is very good value. Two well-annotated wine lists, one of half a dozen vintage bottles, the other of 20 upwards from house Provence at around £7, with plenty around £10.

CHEF: Ian McAndrew PROPRIETORS: Ian and Jane McAndrew
OPEN: Mon to Sat CLOSED: bank hols, 2 weeks in summer, 1 week at Easter
MEALS: 12.30 to 2, 7.30 to 9.30
PRICES: £16 (£23), Set L from £8·50 (£13), Set D from £14 (£19) CARDS: Access, Amex, Diners, Visa
SEATS: 34. Private parties: 34 main room. Car-park, 12 places. Smart dress preferred. No smoking. No children under 7. Wheelchair access (also WC)

Tuo e Mio [10/20]

16 The Borough, Canterbury CT1 2DR
CANTERBURY (0227) 61471 £10–£15

This spacious and light Italian restaurant has the smartness of a Gucci skirt. Fish straight up from Folkestone harbour is on display in the dining-room along with other fresh produce. The menu is rather long, but some pasta is made daily and there has been good fish soup. The staple veal and chicken dishes in a variety of sauces have been liked too. Sweets fade by comparison. It's opposite the entrance to King's School in the shadow of the cathedral. Italian wines: house Soave or Valpolicella £4·90.

CHEFS: Bernardino Lombardo and Tino Guzman PROPRIETORS: Mr and Mrs R.P.M.Greggio
OPEN: L Wed to Sun, D Tue to Sun CLOSED: 18 Aug to 6 Sep MEALS: 12 to 2.30, 7 to 10.45 (10 Sun)
PRICES: £10 (£15), Set L £6·50 (£10). Cover 40p. Service 10% L, 15% D CARDS: Access, Amex, Diners, Visa
SEATS: 40. Private parties: 20 main room. Vegetarian meals. No pipes in dining-room. Children welcome. Wheelchair access (also WC). Music

Waterfields [13/20]

5 Best Lane, Canterbury CT1 2JB
CANTERBURY (0227) 450276 **Real Food** £10–£16

Here is Real Food at work. Michael Waterfield's elegant provincial restaurant on the River Stour, with its bare brick walls hung with original paintings, is a positive force in the community. Local Women's Institute members help in the kitchen on a part-time basis, and vegetables, fruit and herbs are grown by a nearby Italian farmer. The aim is to develop English provincial cooking. At present the menu still goes on a cook's tour of Europe and the Mediterranean for pissaladière, Palestine soup, aubergine pâté with dukkah (crushed nuts and spices), but there are solidly British main courses too, even if they are a bit thin on flair and imagination: fillet of venison with chestnut purée and pepper sauce; roast duck with onions glazed in port; and salmon baked in puff pastry with watercress sauce. Not all good intentions work on the plate, however: first-rate lamb has been spoilt by careless saucing, salad has been left in dressing until it becomes inedible, cheeses have not been looked after, and other points have not been attended to with the care one expects of a restaurant of ambition. Nevertheless, vegetables and puddings are fine, and the wine list includes CELLARMAN'S CHOICE: Côtes du Rhône, Cuvée Pascal '78 at £6·50.

CHEF/PROPRIETOR: Michael Waterfield
OPEN: Mon to Sat CLOSED: Feb MEALS: 12 to 2.30, 7 to 10.45
PRICES: £12 (£16), Set L £6·50 (£10). Service 10% CARDS: Access, Amex, Visa
SEATS: 60. Private parties: 12 main room, 24 private room. Vegetarian meals by arrangement. Children's helpings. Wheelchair access (also men's WC)

CARTMEL Cumbria map 7

▲ *Aynsome Manor* [10/20]

Cartmel LA11 6HH
CARTMEL (044 854) 276 £10–£16

The Varleys could be promoting Dairy Crest, judging by the amount of cream they serve in their sixteenth-century house/hotel. It trickles into excellent soups, such as asparagus, and marrow and apricot; runs through main courses, such as the sauce for roast guinea-fowl; and flows like a river through the sweets trolley. The calorie count is high in avocado pear Waldorf, but there are plainer dishes too. Locally caught fish, and a few well-chosen and well-kept cheeses. Latour burgundies and German Spätlesen and Auslesen are welcome among more common wines. The dining-room may get a bit smoky, but service is friendly, and there are spacious and comfortable bedrooms for a quiet weekend.

CHEFS: Ernest Scott, Jennifer Huck, Tony Varley and Suzanne Barton
PROPRIETORS: Tony and Margaret Varley
OPEN: Mon to Sat, D only, and Sun L CLOSED: 1 to 21 Jan MEALS: 1, 7 to 8.15
PRICES: Set Sun L £6·25 (£10), Set D £11 (£16) CARDS: Access, Amex, Visa
SEATS: 35. Private parties: 35 main room. Car-park, 20 places. Children's helpings. No children under 5 at D (but high teas). Smart dress preferred. Wheelchair access
ACCOMMODATION: 13 rooms, 12 with bath/shower. D, B&B £29·50 to £59. Children welcome. Baby facilities. Garden. Doors close at 12. Confirm by 6 [GHG]

▲ *Uplands* [13/20]

Haggs Lane, Cartmel LA11 6HD
CARTMEL (044 854) 248/9 £11–£18

Miller Howe (see Windermere) on a budget. This large, unobtrusive nineteenth-century house overlooking Morecambe Bay has been turned into a hotel by John Tovey, his former number two in the kitchen and his secretary – Tom and Diana Peter. The pastel dining-room, hung with posters (notably Manets) from the Metropolitan Museum of Art in New York, is less ostentatious and more murkily lit than its parent, but otherwise the parallels are evident in the four-course meals based on Tovey's recipes. The difference is that there is a choice of main course and they come with only five vegetables instead of Miller Howe's seven. Soups, such as fennel and almond or pepper, or tomato, apple and celery, arrive in vast tureens. The pastry work has been excellent giving a lift to starters, such as Stilton and onion quiche, as well as sweets, such as the farmhouse pies filled with black cherries and rum. Good main dishes have been the roast Norfolk duck with calvados, apple and green peppercorn sauces, and also fillets of halibut baked with yoghourt, lime, tomato, coriander and turmeric. Plaice stuffed with avocado and smoked salmon has been less successful. Service is eager and unrushed. The concise wine list reflects Tovey's enthusiasm for South African wines but there is a helpful section of half-bottles too. House South African is £5.

CHEF: Tom Peter PROPRIETORS: John Tovey, Tom and Diana Peter
OPEN: all week CLOSED: 2 Jan to 2 Feb MEALS: 12.30 to 1, 7.30 to 8
PRICES: Set L £7·50 (£11), Set D £13·50 (£18). Service 10% CARDS: Access, Amex, Diners
SEATS: 34. Private parties: 34 main room. Car-park, 18 places. Vegetarian meals. No children under 12. No smoking in dining-room. Wheelchair access. Classical music. One sitting
ACCOMMODATION: 4 rooms, all with bath/shower. B&B £40 to £56. No children under 12. No pets in public rooms. Garden. TV. Phone. Scenic. Doors close at 12. Confirm by 3 [GHG]

The 1987 Guide will appear before Christmas 1986, so reports are particularly important in the spring. Report forms are at the back of this book, but just write a letter if you prefer. Address them to The Good Food Guide, *Freepost, 14 Buckingham Street, London WC2N 6BR. No stamp is necessary if you post in the UK.*

If you suspect that a restaurant is using processed food, always ask. It would be a contravention of the Trade Descriptions Act for the restaurant to lie.

CASTLE BOLTON North Yorkshire map 7

Bolton Castle [10/20]

Castle Bolton DL8 4ET
WENSLEYDALE (0969) 23408
off A684, between Leyburn and
Askrigg £10–£12

The Great Chamber in this historic house is now the dining-room, decorated with ferns and stuffed animals. Cooking is Yorkshire-style – black pudding toasties, chilled rhubarb soup, and duck with green-pea sauce. Good dishes have been the herb pâté, pickled herring with home-pickled beetroot, and chicken and mushroom pie. There is Wensleydale cheese served with fresh biscuits and local butter, or good brown bread ice-cream with maple syrup to finish. Lunches are casual and inexpensive. The flat £2 mark-up on all wines makes it possible to explore the finer wines – red Chassagne-Montrachet '76, from Clerget, is £11·30. A little less garnishing and pretention on the menu would put the rating up. CELLARMAN'S CHOICE: Sancerre '83 at £7·85.

CHEF: Caroline Richardson PROPRIETOR: Timothy Fairhurst
OPEN: Tue to Sun, exc Sun D CLOSED: Tue and Wed D, Nov to Apr MEALS: 12.30 to 2, 7.30 to 9.30
PRICES: Weekday L £6 (£10), Set Sun L from £5·50 (£10). Set D from £7·50 (£12)
CARDS: Access, Amex, Diners, Visa
SEATS: 100. Private parties: 100 main room. Car-park, 50 places. Vegetarian meals by arrangement. Children's helpings. Music

CATTAWADE Essex map 3

Bucks [11/20]

The Street, Cattawade CO11 1RG
COLCHESTER (0206) 392571
on A137, 8m SW of Ipswich £17

A converted pub, now half wine bar and half restaurant, with a sensibly short, freshly prepared menu ranging from home-smoked duck breast with onion jam to pork normande. The eight-course tasting menu ambles on for two hours plus, but has featured ballotine of chicken studded with pistachios served with a dollop of excellent mayonnaise, and triumphant salmon with scallop sauce. Service is included in the £11·50 set meal but not VAT – work that one out! Other good dishes have been feuilleté of kidneys and sweetbreads, mussels in cream, and lamb with rosemary. Some interesting wines, though a few more halves would help the tasting menu. There is, however, Muscat Les Amandiers '82, from Dopff & Irion, at £4·65, and also Châteauneuf-du-Pape, Chante Cigale '80 at £6·50. House Bulgarian is £4·95.

CHEFS: Paul Lewis and Anthony Peacock PROPRIETORS: Penny and Paul Lewis
OPEN: Mon to Sat MEALS: 12.15 to 1.45, 7.15 to 9.45
PRICES: £11 (£17), Set L and D £11·50 (£17). Snacks from 80p. Service inc CARDS: Access, Amex, Diners, Visa
SEATS: 32. 4 tables outside. Private parties: 30 main room. Car-park, 50 places. Children's helpings

CHAGFORD Devon map 1

▲ *Gidleigh Park* [15/20]

Chagford TQ13 8HN
CHAGFORD (064 73) 2367 and 2225
2m W of Chagford **Real Food** £19–£35

John Webber and Kay Henderson combine to produce some of the best modern restaurant cooking in Europe. One main dish is a neatly boned eye of lamb served pink, with its kidney fanned out beside it and, as a contrast, two slices of the brain in a white wine sauce with freshly chopped chives added at the last minute. The atmosphere in the dining-room is not so much one of mounting climax as of an evening lull after the storm. A cruover machine will dispense a single glass of fine wine from a small selection that varies each month – Alsace, Ch. Latour vintages, '61 clarets – to drink perhaps as an aperitif or at the end of the meal with one of the lesser-known English farm cheeses that can outshine the continentals on the board. The set menu has been supplemented by a *carte* to bring more lobster and foie gras into play, but the kitchen does not rest on such luxuries. Main courses can employ the range of mediums – lobsters baked with herb butter; duck breast roasted with a lime sauce; veal kidneys cooked with brandy and juniper berries; fillet steak poached in veal stock. The many alpha dishes eaten have varied from seafood ragout, to lambs' brains served in tiny rectangular boxes of pastry with a leek sauce, to home-made fettuccine with smoked salmon and tomato. Devon clotted cream adorns the calorific lemon tart or pear mille-feuille; the kiwi and calvados sorbet is speckled with the fruit to look like a bird's egg. There are more than 400 bottles on a magnificent list of wines: no fewer than eight feature from the great Alsace year of '76 and there are four Sauvignons Blancs from Robert Mondavi in a powerful Californian section. The big money has been spent well – on '78 white burgundies rather than token vintage clarets. There are very few passengers on the list and the Beaujolais Nouveau is £7, which puts the restaurant in reach of everyone at least once in a while . . . unless of course you drink Hugel's eau-de-vie de marc de Gewürztraminer at £3·50 a go.

CHEFS: Kay Henderson and John Webber PROPRIETORS: Kay and Paul Henderson
OPEN: all week MEALS: 12.30 to 1.30, 7 to 9
PRICES: £24 (£35), Set L £13 (£19), Set D £22·50 (£30), Snacks from £3 (£3·50). Service inc CARD: Amex
SEATS: 40. Private parties: 15 main room. Car-park. Vegetarian meals by arrangement. Children welcome. No cigars/pipes in dining-room. Wheelchair access
ACCOMMODATION: 12 rooms, all with bath/shower. B&B £55 to £105. Children welcome. No pets in public rooms. Afternoon teas. Garden. Tennis. Fishing. Helicopter pad. TV. Phone. Scenic [GHG]

'They do a mixed grill which contains 30 ounces of meat, and if you manage to eat it all you are given a signed certificate by the waitress.' (On eating in Greater Manchester)

Restaurants are graded on a scale of 1–20. In the region of 8–9 expect to find places that may not be restaurants but cafes, pubs, bistros and small hotels. In the category of 10–11 you can expect to find the best food in the locality. Ratings of 12 or more are given to restaurants we regard as serving the best food in the region.

▲ *Teignworthy Hotel* [11/20]

Frenchbeer, Chagford TQ13 8EX
CHAGFORD (064 73) 3355
3m SW of Chagford: from Chagford Square take signs to Fernworthy, then Kestor and Thornworthy

Real Food £24

One thousand feet up on the moors the Newells run their oak-panelled, granite-fireplaced, Lutyens-style house as their home. They grow most of their own vegetables and take their pork from Heal Farm at King's Nympton, who rear and cure in traditional ways. The set four-course dinner menu, with four choices per course, is based on Real Food – roast wild goose with apple sauce, or snipe with black olives and cognac. There are some inventive touches, such as scallops with hazel-nuts, or lamb's heart with a curry and lemon stuffing. Good dishes have been crab bisque; roast grouse; and guinea-fowl with tarragon. There is an interesting choice of local cheeses. But standards have been frustratingly erratic, hence the drop in the rating. Breakfasts are splendid. The wine list has been well put together and includes five *cru* Beaujolais from the excellent '83 vintage, and the gold-medal-winning Riesling '83 from Louis Gisselbrecht for £5·95.
CELLARMAN'S CHOICE: Venegazzù Della Casa '74 at £8·50.

CHEF: John Newell PROPRIETORS: John and Gillian Newell
OPEN: all week MEALS: 12 to 2, 7.30 to 9
PRICES: L £16·50 (£24), Set D £19·50 (£24), Snacks from £3 (£3·30)
SEATS: 30. 3 tables outside. Private parties: 30 main room. Car-park. Vegetarian meals. No children under 12. No smoking in dining-room. Wheelchair access (also WC)
ACCOMMODATION: 9 rooms, all with bath/shower. B&B £42·50 to £67. No children under 12. No pets. Afternoon teas. Garden. Tennis. Fishing. Sauna. Helicopter pad. TV. Phone. Scenic. Confirm by 6 [GHG]

▲ *Thornworthy House* [new entry, zero rated]

Chagford TQ13 8EY
CHAGFORD (064 73) 3297
3½m SW of Chagford; follow Thornworthy signs

£13

Thornworthy is a rambling but neatly furnished Victorian house of rough grey stone set in isolated, prehistoric Dartmoor, three and a half miles from Chagford. It feels like a family house, with a warm welcome, wood-burning stove, and dominoes after dinner. Cindy Cull's cooking is homely, too, using some home-grown and local produce. Soups include tomato, celery and apple, or watercress. Avocado is sliced and served with smoked salmon and orange vinaigrette. The main course – there is no choice – is likely to be a traditionally British dish: perhaps game pie, lamb chops or roast pork. Cheeses include Cornish Yarg, named after the producer, Mr Gray. Bread-and-butter pudding is made with local farm cream, or there is sweet mincemeat frangipane tart. At £9·50 for four courses it is good value for money. Service is informal. The wine list is short, well

All letters to the Guide *are acknowledged with a list of changes since we went to press.*

chosen, and good on halves, although a greater variety among the less expensive bottles would be welcome.

CHEFS: Cindy Cull and Robert Young PROPRIETORS: John and Cindy Cull
OPEN: all week CLOSED: Jan and Feb MEALS: 8
PRICES: Set D £9·50 (£13), Snacks from £3 (£3·30)
SEATS: 14. 2 tables outside. Private parties: 40 main room. Car-park, 12 places. No children at D (but high teas). No cigars/pipes in dining-room. One sitting
ACCOMMODATION: 5 rooms, all with bath/shower. B&B £15·50 to £31. Deposit: £25. Children welcome. Baby facilities. Pets by arrangement. Afternoon teas. Garden. Tennis. Fishing. Helicopter pad. Scenic [GHG]

CHAPPEL Essex map 3

Swan Inn [9/20]

Chappel CO6 2DD
EARLS COLNE (078 75) 2353
on A604, between Colchester and Halstead £13

Good plain food is served in this beamed English pub by the river – grilled sole, fried skate, steaks, and good chips. There is a courtyard for the summer and a log fire in the winter. House French is £4·10, and there is Greene King IPA.

CHEF/PROPRIETOR: T.L.F.Martin
OPEN: all week MEALS: 12 to 2 (1.15 Sun), 7 to 10
PRICES: £9 (£13), Snacks from 60p (70p), Bar meals from £1·25 (£1·40)
CARDS: Access, Visa
SEATS: 52. 16 tables outside. Private parties: 50 main room. Car-park, 35 places. Wheelchair access (also wc)

CHEAM Surrey map 3

Mandarin [new entry, zero rated]

481 London Road, North Cheam SM3 8JN
01-337 2768 £10–£13

Another London suburb falls to the troops of the Peking culinary battalions. The battle plan is the same one that has led to success elsewhere – smart up-market decor with white walls and Chinese prints; attentive service that fills both tea and wine cups quickly; a range of exotically named dishes taken from across the mainland of China, adapted according to Surrey taste but reasonably priced. Particular medals for this campaign are awarded to the bang-bang chicken; tiger's whiskers (pork with water-chestnuts, peppers, garlic and chilli oil); squid in black bean sauce; lamb in hot-and-sweet sauce; French beans Peking-style; toffee apples. Witnesses please report on the new rulers following the formal surrender of the French restaurateurs to the Chinese.

CHEF: Shum-Yam Shing PROPRIETOR: Kai-Chun Shing
OPEN: all week MEALS: 12 to 2.30, 6 to 11.30
PRICES: £7 (£13), Set L from £6 (£10), Set D from £7·50 (£12). Minimum £7·50. Service 10% CARDS: Access, Amex, Diners, Visa
SEATS: 50. 11 tables outside. Private parties: 50 main room. Music. Air-conditioned

CHEDINGTON Dorset map 2

▲ *Chedington Court* [12/20]

Chedington DT8 3HY
CORSCOMBE (093 589) 265
off A356 at Winyards Gap, 3½m N of Beaminster
£19

Ten acres of mature garden around the court include a water garden, pond, fine old yew hedge, tall trees and wild flowers, and there is a panoramic view across Dorset and Somerset. The house is also mature and has a big fire burning in the library. Five-course dinners are built around excellent wild salmon with hollandaise or roast duck with Cumberland sauce – the farm birds are dressed and dry-plucked in the traditional manner. Sweets are where Hilary Chapman's cooking comes into its own – the Queen of Puddings is sensational. Some rooms have four-poster beds; all, unfortunately, seem to have UHT milk for the tea-making kit. The wine list is an encyclopaedia: the Alsace section alone includes a choice of producers and vintages in all the four major grape varieties; there are halves of '60s claret for under £15; and even the Spanish section would merit the Bottle denotation. Arrive two hours early so that you can order a vintage cognac in the conservatory and study it at leisure.

CHEF: Hilary Chapman PROPRIETORS: Philip and Hilary Chapman
OPEN: all week, D only MEALS: 7 to 9
PRICES: Set D £16·50 (£19). Service inc CARD: Amex
SEATS: 30. Private parties: 40 main room, 50 private room. Car-park, 20 places. Vegetarian meals by arrangement. Children's helpings (D only). Smart dress preferred. No cigars/pipes in dining-room. Wheelchair access (also WC). Classical music. One sitting
ACCOMMODATION: 8 rooms, all with bath/shower. D, B&B £40 to £94. Deposit: £30. Children welcome. Baby facilities. No pets in public rooms. Garden. Snooker. Croquet. Putting. Helicopter pad. TV. Scenic. Doors close at 12. Confirm by 9 [GHG]

CHELMSFORD Essex map 3

Melissa [9/20]

21 Broomfield Road, Chelmsford CM1 1SY
CHELMSFORD (0245) 353009
Real Food £5

The best food in Chelmsford. The fact that there are recommendations for baked potatoes here says quite a lot about the state of the food supplies in Essex. It is wholefood vegetarian, everything cooked on the premises, and a wide-ranging choice served from behind the counter. Some of the cooking is more adventurous than potatoes – split pea soup, bulgar wheat casserole, spinach roulade with lentil filling, bean risotto, and excellent hummus. To finish there are crumbles, and Greek yoghourt with honey. The posters on the walls seem to support every

'The meringue was standard high street cake shop – the texture of sweetened pumice stone.' (On eating in London)
'The menu said bonemarrow sauce, and that's what we got – a sauce of bonemarrow with bits of the bone in it.' (On eating in Cheshire)

imaginable alternative movement, but everyone is charming. It gets very busy. No licence, but plenty of fruit juices. Related to the Farmhouse Feast at Roxwell.

CHEFS: Rosemary and Melanie Upson and David Burton
PROPRIETORS: Rosemary and Melanie Upson
OPEN: Mon to Sat, L only MEALS: 9 to 4
PRICES: £3 (£5), Set L £3·95 (£5). Unlicensed, but bring your own: no corkage
SEATS: 22. Private parties: 28 main room. Vegetarian meals. Children's helpings. No smoking. Wheelchair access. Self-service

CHELTENHAM Gloucestershire map 2

La Ciboulette [13/20]

24–26 Suffolk Road, Cheltenham GL50 9QT
CHELTENHAM (0242) 573449 £11–£18

This stretch of the A40 is characterised by the frequency with which antique shops come and go, but there is now a culinary infiltration, with a wine shop and The Retreat (see entry) up the road, as well as this very good, well-patronised French restaurant. The emphasis is on the food rather than the decor, which resembles a 1930s Parisian bistro with a garden-centre of plants. Warm onion tarts and brown shrimps with aïoli arrive with aperitifs. Alpha dishes that underline the quality of Kevin Jenkins' cooking have been the baby vegetables served in a pastry coffin as a starter, fish soup, turbot soufflé, duck with blackcurrant sauce, and partridge. The sauces are a strong point. Dishes are colourfully arranged – a hot apple, for instance, is served surrounded by a ring of blackcurrant sauce, and a jug of cream is left on the table. In early summer there is asparagus from Evesham, a rarity these days despite the fact that asparagus from the Vale of Evesham is renowned for its quality. Blandine Jenkins runs the front of house with charm. It's a good house burgundy for £5, too.

CHEF: Kevin Jenkins PROPRIETORS: Kevin and Blandine Jenkins
OPEN: Tue to Sat MEALS: 12.30 to 2, 7.30 to 10.30
PRICES: £13 (£18), Set L from £6·50 (£11) CARDS: Access, Amex, Visa
SEATS: 34. Private parties: 30 main room. Children's helpings. Wheelchair access. French popular music. Air-conditioned

Number Twelve [12/20]

12 Suffolk Parade, Cheltenham GL50 2AB
CHELTENHAM (0242) 584544 £10–£16

Instead of a chandelier a huge basket of ferns hangs over the dining-room of this stylish French restaurant. The raw materials for the menu are excellent and treated with respect, the kitchen saving its inventiveness for the sauces. This can produce superb results. The menu has some clever contrasts which are not beyond the waiters – they have been known to warn of possible conflicts in dishes. Especially good have been the sole ramekin with shrimps; petites fondues à la bourguignonne; and chicken breast with curried mango sauce served with rice flavoured with coriander and cardamom. Pungent garlic bread – the only bread on offer – arrives hot from the oven, in silver foil. Vegetables are plainly cooked, included in the price, and served on a side plate. The lemon mousse comes in a tall glass and is the pick of the sweets eaten so far. Unlimited Cona coffee. The usefully annotated list has 37 mainly French wines, with house French at £4·75.

CHEFS: Norman Young and David Harker PROPRIETOR: Norman Young
OPEN: Tue to Sun, exc Sat L and Sun D MEALS: 12 to 2, 7.30 to 10 (10.30 Fri and Sat)
PRICES: £11 (£16), Set L £6·25 (£10) CARDS: Access, Visa
SEATS: 40. Private parties: 48 main room. Children's helpings. Classical music

The Retreat [9/20]

10–11 Suffolk Parade, Cheltenham GL50 2AB
CHELTENHAM (0242) 35436 £8

A crowded, loud, earthy bar with self-service food. It does not look much from the outside but the garden, which is open in summer, has twice won first prize in the Cheltenham in Bloom contest. Notably good are the steak and kidney pie, stewed with Guinness; soup with granary bread; cold meats and salads; and fruit crumbles. In season there are 'oyster nights' and fresh salmon. Vin de table is £2·95.

CHEF: Lucy Inkpen PROPRIETORS: Michael and Lella Dey
OPEN: Mon to Sat MEALS: 12 to 2.15, 6 to 9
PRICES: £4 (£8). Also cut-price L menu CARDS: Access, Amex, Diners, Visa
SEATS: 60. 8 tables outside. Private parties: 25 main room. Vegetarian meals. Children's helpings. Smart dress preferred. Wheelchair access (1 step). Music. Self-service

CHELTENHAM see also SHURDINGTON

CHESHAM Buckinghamshire map 3

Chesham Tandoori [8/20]

48 Broad Street, Chesham HP5 3DX
CHESHAM (0494) 782669 £10–£11

This family-run, friendly Tandoori with an emphasis on Bangladeshi cooking is opposite the police station. The food is freshly cooked and the flavours are distinct. Good dishes have been the lamb dhansak, butter chicken, and the curries. Poppadums come with a range of chutneys. House Italian is £4·75.

CHEF: Mojibul Hoque PROPRIETOR: Faijul Hoque
OPEN: all week CLOSED: 25 and 26 Dec MEALS: 12 to 2.30, 6 to 12
PRICES: £7 (£11), Set L and D from £6·50 (£10). Service inc alc only CARDS: Access, Amex, Diners, Visa
SEATS: 42. Private parties: 20 main room. Vegetarian meals. Children's helpings. Wheelchair access (also WC). Indian music

The Guide is always anxious to recruit new inspectors. If you would like to apply, write to the editor enclosing a) a detailed report on a restaurant where you have eaten and b) a comparative study of restaurants known to you.

'The fire alarm went off accidentally and no one could stop it for 20 minutes, which resulted in the diners being somewhat neglected!' (On inspecting in Cornwall)

CHESTER Cheshire map 5

Abbey Green [new entry, zero rated]

2 Abbey Green, Northgate Street, Chester CH1 2JH
CHESTER (0244) 313251 £10

Eating out as a vegetarian can make life seem like an everlasting Lent. Julia Lochhead's attempt to introduce a civilising influence which non-vegetarians can enjoy as much as vegans is warmly welcomed. Pre-dinner drinks and coffee are taken in the Victorian/Edwardian withdrawing-room, which has fresh flowers on the table. Quiche, stuffed potatoes, open sandwiches and pizzas during the day give way in the evening to barbecued vegetable kebabs; asparagus crêpes with hot lemon sauce; mushroom and watercress pancakes; and crisp tempura vegetables with peanut sauce. Vegetables are organically grown, tofu is made locally, eggs are free-range, and cheese is free from rennet. House wine is not carrot or parsnip but French, at £3·80. We hope they do well enough to install hot water in the gents. More reports, please.

CHEFS: Christian Irwin and Susan Brassey PROPRIETOR: Julia Lochhead
OPEN: Tue to Sat MEALS: 10 to 3, 6.30 to 10.15
PRICES: £7 (£10), Snacks from 75p (85p)
SEATS: 40. 5 tables outside. Private parties: 8 main room, 20 private room. Car-park, 30 places. Vegetarian meals. Children's helpings. No smoking in dining-room. Wheelchair access. Classical music

▲ *Grosvenor Hotel* [10/20]

Eastgate Street, Chester CH1 1LT
CHESTER (0244) 24024 £13–£25

The old English charm of this hotel, with its clean and bright pillared and pot-planted dining-room, sparkling glass and ornate candles, is well married to modern French cooking, particularly among the starters: chicken and scampi terrine, creamy fish soup with tarragon. There are good sauces, such as redcurrant, to go with light and tangy duck mousse and endive salad, and orange, with chicken suprême on a bed of liver and herbs. Vegetables are nicely varied. Some meat may be overcooked but the creamy, undistinguished desserts are the real weak spot. Service is good. The *carte* is expensive but the fixed-price dinner is better value (though the well-known boxed chocolates with the coffee lower the tone and function dinners are said to have been less good). There is a good buffet at lunch. Interesting bin-end wines. CELLARMAN'S CHOICE: Ch. Trottevieille '66 (St Emilion) at £29·50.

CHEF: Gilbert Schneider PROPRIETOR: The Duke of Westminster
OPEN: all week MEALS: 12 (12.30 Sun) to 2, 7 to 10
PRICES: £19 (£25), Set L £7·95 (£13), Set D £13·50 (£19), Bar meals from £2·50 (£2·75), Snacks from £1·75 (£2) CARDS: Access, Amex, Carte Blanche, Diners, Visa
SEATS: 96. Private parties: 12 main room, 350, 60 and 18 private rooms. Vegetarian meals by arrangement. Children's helpings. Jacket and tie. Wheelchair access (also WC). Air-conditioned
ACCOMMODATION: 106 rooms, all with bath/shower. Rooms for disabled. B&B from £53·50 and £60. Children welcome. Baby facilities. No pets. Afternoon teas. Lift. TV. Phone. Confirm by 4

Pippa's in Town [10/20]

58 Watergate Street, Chester CH1 2LA
CHESTER (0244) 313721 £7–£19

On Saturday nights this is positively jumping as the pianist thumps away at the Scott Joplin. It is exuberant, and the long open dining-room, reached from the vaulted bar up spiral stairs, is popular locally. The menu falls somewhere between French bistro and the international. Duck terrine comes with five fingers of toast set on radicchio and apple; the *fruits de mer* gratin is varied and includes squid, cod, mussels and prawns; chicken liver salad is served with ceps. A variation on a Cornish recipe has produced fillet steak stuffed with smoked oysters and given a red wine sauce; duck is the breast still on the bone, marinated with oil, lemon and garlic and roasted. Chocolate comes in tall fat glasses and the crème brûlée is the hard-topped version. Coffee is left in its pot warming over a candle at the table. A wide-ranging list of wines. House Chardonnay at £5·50 is good drinking and they sell their own burgundies retail.

CHEFS: G. Perkins, T. Lee and J. Lloyd PROPRIETORS: John Burville Ltd
OPEN: Mon to Sat MEALS: 12.15 to 2, 7 to 10.30
PRICES: £14 (£19), Set L from £3·50 (£7), Set D £8·25 (£12). Snacks from 60p
CARDS: Access, Amex, Diners, Visa
SEATS: 75. Private parties: 50 main room, 20 private room. Vegetarian meals. Children welcome. Wheelchair access (also WC). Music

CHESTERTON Oxfordshire map 2

Woods [13/20]

Bignell View, Chesterton OX6 8UJ
BICESTER (0869) 241444 £12–£20

Chesterton may be miles from anywhere, but after Le Manoir aux Quat' Saisons (see Great Milton) and Le Petit Blanc (see Oxford) this has probably the best restaurant food in Oxfordshire. The converted Cotswold barn is smartly turned out, airy, light and decorated in pinks and greys with a hanging carpet, fresh flowers and big glasses on the table. It is set in three acres, whence come herbs and vegetables. What the balanced menu may lack in imagination, the cooking makes up in precision. Fish is good – sea-bass is stuffed with fish mousseline and baked in puff pastry – but meat is better, such as pink rack of trimmed lamb with hollandaise, or large chunks of gamey venison sitting in a puddle of reduced jus slightly sweetened with port and with a scattering of tart cranberries. Pheasant (with apricot and a hint of ginger), duck (with a pistachio mousseline), and quail are treated well, too, and vegetables are first-rate. Puddings, from lemon cheesecake to almond flan to a Guérard-style chocolate marquise with coffee sauce, are excellent. Charming, helpful and knowledgeable service runs

All Guide *inspectors are anonymous. Anyone purporting to represent the* Guide *is an impostor.*

CELLARMAN'S CHOICE: *This is a wine that is more expensive than the house wine but is good value and fitting for the kind of food served.*

smoothly. The short wine list has plenty under £10; house Duboeuf is £4·85. CELLARMAN'S CHOICE: Graves, Ch. Chicane '79 at £9·80 (£5·45 for a half).

CHEF: Robert Harrison PROPRIETORS: David and Georgina Wood
OPEN: Tue to Sun, exc Sat L and Sun D MEALS: 12 to 2, 7 to 10.30
PRICES: Set L from £8·75 (£12). Set D from £15·75 (£20) CARDS: Access, Amex, Diners, Visa
SEATS: 40. 10 tables outside. Private parties: 40 main room, 20 private room. Car-park, 25 places. Vegetarian meals. Children's helpings. Wheelchair access (also wc)

CHICHESTER West Sussex map 3

BACKGROUND BRIEFING: *A good place to stay is Clinch's in Guildhall Street, which has six rooms. The hotel restaurant is open to non-residents and is handy for the Festival Theatre. The cooking tends to be spontaneous according to the market – pancakes filled with crab; steaks; plenty of vegetables; and excellent strawberry Pavlova. It has good vin ordinare to drink.*

Savourie, Little London Restaurant [9/20]

38–39 Little London, Chichester PO19 1PL
CHICHESTER (0243) 784899 £10

The street was christened by Queen Victoria, as it reminded her of London. The upstairs Savourie manages to cook good-quality food without charging the earth for it – mushrooms à la grecque, seafood gratin, and varied salads have all been good. Free-range chicken breasts are served with apricots in a light curry sauce, and the strawberry and apple meringues are excellent, as is the service. House burgundy is £5·95.

CHEF: R.Tooke PROPRIETOR: C.F.W.Miley
OPEN: Tue to Sat MEALS: 12 to 2, 7 to 10 (later post-theatre by arrangement)
PRICES: £5 (£10) CARDS: Access, Amex, Diners, Visa
SEATS: 51. Private parties: 51 main room. Children's helpings. Smart dress preferred. No pipes in dining-room

CHILGROVE West Sussex map 3

White Horse Inn [new entry, zero rated]

Chilgrove PO18 9HX
EAST MARDEN (024 359) 219
off B2141, 3m W of Singleton £13–£17

An up-market country pub/restaurant in a building dated 1756, with a wine cellar that is believed to be among the biggest in Britain. All the available shelf-space is taken up with bottles. Service is first-rate. The menu is classical and there are elegant touches, like canapés of salami and scrambled eggs with drinks and even, one evening, an unannounced second course of asparagus vinaigrette. Good dishes have been wild mushroom and chicken vol-au-vent; veal with a

If you cannot honour a restaurant booking, always phone to cancel.

vermouth and sorrel sauce; and braised Aylesbury duck with black cherries and port. The wine list is divided into two sections which might aptly be labelled 'affordable' and 'not so affordable'. Clarets go back to 1900 and prices top £1,000 but the house French is only £4·95. More reports, please.

CHEF: Adrian Congdon PROPRIETORS: Dorothea and Barry Phillips
OPEN: Tue to Sat CLOSED: 3 weeks Jan to Feb, 1 week Oct MEALS: 12 to 1.45, 7 to 9.30
PRICES: Set L £11·95 (£13), Set D £14·95 (£17). Service 12% CARDS: Access, Amex, Diners, Visa
SEATS: 65. 12 tables outside. Private parties: 65 main room. Car-park, 50 places. Vegetarian meals. Children's helpings. Wheelchair access (also wc). Music

CHINNOR Oxfordshire map 2

Crickets [12/20]

Keens Lane, Chinnor OX9 4PF
KINGSTON BLOUNT (0844) 53566
M40 exit 6, over Chinnor crossroads, 2nd R £12–£16

A drab modern building in the new part of the village, under the Chiltern scarp. The dining-room is pink and suburban but the menu is good value and features many interesting dishes, such as tagliatelle with smoked salmon and walnuts, a starter of pigeon breasts, a salad of red and white cabbage, and sweetbreads with basil and Manzanilla. Cream is the common denominator in Tom Bridgeman's saucing – sometimes a lot of it, just mildly flavoured with an alcohol. Pork is notably good with a wine and Stilton sauce; monkfish carefully done with good puff pastry and cream and Pernod; and the combination of veal kidneys with spinach cream and raspberry vinegar works well. Most people mention the high quality of the potatoes. Of many good sweets the chocolate roulade and the poached pear in a kirsch custard stand out. Service is smooth and thoughtful, as is the wine list – there are carefully chosen bottles from all the major regions and good examples of Muscadet, Sylvaner and Châteauneuf-du-Pape. House wine is £5·50.

CHEF: Tom Bridgeman PROPRIETOR: O.L.Mitchell
OPEN: Tue to Sun, exc Tue L and Sun D CLOSED: 2 weeks in summer MEALS: 12 to 2, 7 to 10
PRICES: Set L and D £7·50 to £12·50 (£12 to £16) CARDS: Access, Visa
SEATS: 100. 4 tables outside. Private parties: 60 main room, 40 private room. Car-park, 30 places. Vegetarian meals. Children's helpings. No jeans. Wheelchair access (also wc). Music

Sir Charles Napier Inn [11/20]

Sprigg's Alley, Chinnor OX9 4BX
RADNAGE (024 026) 3011
M40 exit 6, right at Chinnor crossroads £8–£16

The pheasants and pigeon are shot in the beechwoods at the bottom of the paddock of this remote pub with a restaurant in the Chilterns. In summer, lunch is served on the terrace among the honeysuckle and wisterias, and there is a big fire in winter. The menu takes its inspiration from provincial France – bourride; soupe au pistou; entrecôte Café de Paris. Lamb has been very good either with onion sauce or else with sorrel, mint, beef stock and cream. The quality of the

steaks too is high. Good Stilton and Brie, less good crème brûlée. An elegant, carefully chosen, good-value list of wines, with strong representations from all areas, includes a pair of excellent '83 Alsace and a dozen half-bottles.
CELLARMAN'S CHOICE: Merlot '79 from Firestone's Ambassadors Vineyard in the Santa Ynez Valley at £8·25.

CHEF: Batiste Tollu PROPRIETORS: The Griffiths family
OPEN: L Tue to Sun, D Tue to Sat MEALS: 12 to 2 (3 Sun), 7.30 to 10 (10.30 Fri and Sat)
PRICES: £12 (£16), Set L from £4 (£8), Set D £8·75 (£14). Service 12.5%
CARDS: Amex, Diners
SEATS: 65. 10 tables outside. Private parties: 45 main room, 45 and 25 private rooms. Vegetarian meals. Car-park, 60 places. No cigars/pipes in dining-room. Children's helpings (L only). No children under 7 at D. Wheelchair access. Terrace luncheons in summer. Garden. Croquet. Helicopter pad

CHIPPING NORTON Oxfordshire — map 2

Anarkali [10/20]

6 & 6A West Street, Chipping Norton OX7 5AA
CHIPPING NORTON (0608) 2785 — £10–£13

Better than any of the Indian restaurants in Oxford, with flock walls, proper cloths, and sitar music, in a long, narrow room. A mainly traditional high street menu, with good vegetable or meat samosas, and onion bhajias to start. Both chicken and lamb tandoori come well marinated, moist, and sizzling impressively. King prawn korma is fresh-tasting in a mild creamy sauce; nan is freshly cooked; brinjal is moreish. Licensed.

CHEFS: A.Bari and M.Ali PROPRIETORS: R.Ahmed, A.Bari and M.Ali
OPEN: all week MEALS: 12 to 2.30, 5.30 to 11.30
PRICES: £7 (£13), Set D from £6 (£10), Cheaper set L & D available. Service 10%
CARDS: Access, Amex, Diners, Visa
SEATS: 42. Private parties: 42 main room. Vegetarian meals. Children's helpings by arrangement. Smart dress preferred. Wheelchair access. Music

La Madonette [12/20]

7 Horsefair, Chipping Norton OX7 5AL
CHIPPING NORTON (0608) 2320 — **Real Food** £18

Alain Ritter, a Surf-clean chef's hat lengthening him by two feet, will bring out whole salmon or fillets of beef uncooked for inspection to make guests feel part of the kitchen. He knows his ingredients – there is a family cheese-importing business in London. Standards in his small restaurant do not vacillate. The menu is provincial French. As well as the snails cooked with mushrooms and garlic, there is red mullet baked in foil with tomatoes and fennel, or breast of pigeon pan-fried with chicory and served with a game sauce. Especially good have been mussels with shallots, leeks and cream; the fish soup flamed with Pastis; the fillet steaks and the veal sweetbreads with mushrooms and cream. Four vegetables come in a steaming hot tureen. To finish: apple tartlets with calvados sauce or

Reports on good shops, small hotels and cafes in your area are welcome.

Grand Marnier soufflé. There's a limited but well-kept French cheeseboard. The wine list, like the cooking, is French and has a good pedigree. There is a quartet of Alsace wines showing a good range of the grapes. CELLARMAN'S CHOICE: Saumur Blanc, Caves du Château de Parnay, '83 at £7·20.

CHEF/PROPRIETOR: Alain Ritter
OPEN: Tue to Sat, D only MEALS: 7.30 to 10
PRICES: £12 (£18) CARDS: Access, Visa
SEATS: 32. Private parties: 10 main room. Children's helpings

CHITTLEHAMHOLT Devon map 1

▲ *Highbullen Hotel* [10/20]

Chittlehamholt EX37 9HD
CHITTLEHAMHOLT (076 94) 561
5m SW of South Molton £13

So many readers have been going here for so long that few of them can fairly say they are not connected with the management. However, independent assessment reveals that the menu has not changed – guacamole, crab mousse, though this year has seen the arrival of mussels in cream, which we don't remember from before. Main courses, too, are perennials – loin of pork dijonnaise; Swedish lamb with dill. Of the sweets the hazel-nut and apricot meringue is legendary; drink a glass of Muscat de Beaumes de Venise with it. The wine list is still superb, though not the bargain it was – it repays a look at the less expensive end. The Bordeaux section ('78 – '52) contain what are now some very rare wines.

CHEF: Pam Neil PROPRIETORS: Hugh and Pam Neil
OPEN: all week, D only MEALS: 7.30 to 9
PRICES: Set D £10·50 (£13), Snacks from £1. Service inc
SEATS: 60. 4 tables outside. Private parties: 10 main room. Car-park, 36 places. Vegetarian meals by arrangement. No children under 10. Smart dress preferred. No smoking
ACCOMMODATION: 31 rooms, all with bath/shower. Rooms for disabled. B&B £21·50 to £45. No children under 10. No pets. Garden. Indoor and outdoor swimming-pools. Sauna. Spa bath. Tennis. Golf. Croquet. Fishing. Snooker. Helicopter pad. TV. Phone. Scenic [GHG]

CHORLEY Lancashire map 5

BACKGROUND BRIEFING: *There is a good market on Tuesday, Friday and Saturday with fish from Fleetwood, fruit and vegetables from the Fylde, Lancashire cheese mild, crumbly and tasty, and an excellent tripe stall selling cowheel, manifold, seam, honeycomb and others, as well as elder. Thornley's in Chapel Street sells prize-winning black puddings.*

Places rating 8 or 9 may not be restaurants at all but still serve very good food. In this category expect to find pubs, cafes, small hotels and wine bars.

If you cannot honour a restaurant booking, always phone to cancel.

CHRISTCHURCH Dorset map 2

Splinters [10/20]

12 Church Street, Christchurch BH23 1BW
CHRISTCHURCH (0202) 483454 £16

Twenty thousand bottles of wine are kept in the cellars. From Alsace there are '83s from Kuentz-Bas, from Burgundy the Hospices de Beaune wines, from different vineyards, range from '62 to '73, at around £20, and all the major clarets are there. To go with these is a short menu that may feature rather more capers and peppers than a wine deserves, but the chickens are free-range, the local salmon hollandaise popular and the rösti potatoes good. CELLARMAN'S CHOICE: Ch. La Tour-Gayet '82, £6·90; Saumur-Champigny, Domaine Filliatreau, vieilles vignes '82, £7·50; and rosé Château Millet '82, £8. The house wine, from Anjou, is £4·95.

CHEF: Jua Franke PROPRIETORS: John Carter and Jua Franke
OPEN: Mon to Sat, D only MEALS: 6.30 to 10.30
PRICES: £11 (£16). Cover 50p CARDS: Amex, Diners, Visa
SEATS: 40. Private parties: 20 main room. Vegetarian meals. No-smoking area. Children's helpings. No children under 3 after 8pm. Wheelchair access (also WC)

CIRENCESTER Gloucestershire map 2

▲ *Fleece Hotel* [new entry, zero rated]

Market Square, Cirencester GL7 4NZ
CIRENCESTER (0285) 68507/8/9 £10–£20

A small, country-town hotel which is part of a privately owned chain that includes the Bear at Hungerford and the Copper Inn at Pangbourne. The elegant dining-room is decorated in green and salmon pink with tapestries, an antique sideboard, high-backed upholstered chairs, and hurricane lamps. The set menus are particularly good value. The *carte* offers vegetarian dishes, such as smoked Cheddar and vegetable soufflé, and has some neat touches, such as home-cured duck with avocado salad. Good dishes have been moules marinière; calf's liver with a sauce of celeriac and sherry; and pan-fried chicken with tarragon. Vegetables are varied and have included calabrese with an hollandaise, and potatoes sauté in bacon fat. There are English cheeses and home-made desserts, such as apple and almond pudding. The food is all fresh and cooked to order. The wine list includes good minor clarets and also Gewürztraminer '76, the great year, from Faller, at £10·95. House Gamay is £4·95, or try the CELLARMAN'S CHOICE: Ch. du Clos Renon '76, at £6·95. More reports, please.

CHEF: Clive Southgate PROPRIETORS: Laurella and Andrew Parffrey
OPEN: all week CLOSED: 3 days at Christmas MEALS: 12.15 to 2 (12.30 to 1.45 Sun), 7.30 to 9.30 (10 Fri and Sat)
PRICES: £14 (£20), Set L from £5·50 (£10), Set D £9·45 (£14) CARDS: Access, Amex, Diners, Visa
SEATS: 42. 6 tables outside. Private parties: 40 main room. Car-park, 15 places. Vegetarian meals. Children's helpings
ACCOMMODATION: 19 rooms, all with bath/shower. B&B £37·75 to £47. Dogs welcome. Afternoon teas. TV. Phone. Doors close at 12 [GHG]

Rajdoot Tandoori [9/20]

35 Castle Street, Cirencester GL7 1QD
GLOUCESTER (0285) 2651 and 4083 £10–£12

The ventilation fans are good here, so you aren't much troubled by cigarette smoke. Portions are so generous that you may not want a starter. Lamb is minced and spiced, or marinated in yoghourt and cooked with capsicum. Chicken is spiced with cumin and cooked with onions and peppers. There are vegetarian dishes and good vegetables, such as mushroom, cauliflower or sag bhajias, plus sweets, such as gulab jamun.

CHEF: Mofiz Uddin PROPRIETOR: Faruk Miah
OPEN: all week MEALS: 12 to 3, 6 to 11.45
PRICES: £8 (£12), Set D from £6·95 (£10). Minimum £4·75 CARDS: Access, Amex, Diners, Visa
SEATS: 75. Private parties: 30 main room. Vegetarian meals. Children welcome. Wheelchair access (also WC). Indian music

---

CLUN Shropshire map 4

▲ *Old Post Office* [new entry, zero rated]

9 The Square, Clun SY7 0HG
CLUN (058 84) 687 **Real Food** £6–£12

'South west Shropshire has suffered badly from rural depopulation and decline over the last 20 years, and it is our policy to buy as much as possible locally, thereby keeping the money circulating within the area.' The quality of the ingredients underwrites the meals at the five tables in the dining-room. There is usually a choice of half a dozen dishes at each course. Notably good have been ratatouille soufflé, pigeon or pheasant en croûte, steak and kidney pie, and pork with mustard. Many of the vegetables are organically grown. There is always a vegetarian dish and simpler lunches are on the lines of spaghetti and minestrone. The cheeseboard has Derby and Stilton in prime condition, plus interesting Provençal cheeses, such as mixed goats' and cow. Finish with hazel-nut meringue with whipped cream and damson purée. A well-chosen, not expensive wine list, strong in '83 *cru* beaujolais. House vin de pays de Vaucluse is £2·60 for half a litre. CELLARMAN'S CHOICE: Château du Grand Moulas '84 at £5·40. More reports, please.

CHEFS/PROPRIETORS: Caroline Denham and Martin Pool
OPEN: Tue to Sat CLOSED: Feb, and daytime Nov to Mar MEALS: 12.30 to 2, 7.30 to 9.30
PRICES: L £4 (£6), Set D £9·25 (£12). Service inc
SEATS: 20. 1 table outside. Private parties: 20 main room. Vegetarian meals. Children's helpings (L only). No small children at D. Classical music
ACCOMMODATION: 3 rooms. B&B £10 to £22. Deposit: £10. Afternoon teas. Baby facilities. No pets. Scenic. Doors close at 11.30. Confirm by 4.30

All inspections are carried out anonymously as we accept no handouts.

COATHAM MUNDEVILLE **Durham** map 7

▲ *Hall Garth* [10/20]

Coatham Mundeville DL1 3LU
AYCLIFFE (0325) 313333 £10–£16

Ernest Williamson and Janice Crocker have been at this rambling country house since July 1977. The food is English, the vegetables from the garden, and they now have supplies of fresh crayfish – it appears as a soup or with a cheese and parsley mayonnaise. Other soups, such as pea or mushroom, have been good. Guinea-fowl too is now served. The rating is dropped a point because of a few short cuts and an inconsistency in standards. But the welcome is a big one. A hundred wines, strong in the Rhône, and house California is £4·50.

CHEF: Janice Crocker PROPRIETORS: Ernest Williamson and Janice Crocker
OPEN: all week, exc Sun D CLOSED: 10 days Christmas MEALS: 12.30 to 1.30, 7.30 to 9.30
PRICES: Set L from £6·75 (£10), Set D from £11·95 (£16) CARDS: Access, Amex, Diners, Visa
SEATS: 62. 5 tables outside. Car-park, 65 places. Vegetarian meals. Children's helpings. No smoking. Wheelchair access (also WC)
ACCOMMODATION: 19 rooms, all with bath/shower. B&B £29 to £49. Children welcome. Baby facilities. Pets welcome. Afternoon teas. Garden. Swimming-pool. Tennis. Croquet. Putting. Sauna. Helicopter pad. TV. Phone. Doors close at 11.30. Confirm by 6 [GHG]

COBHAM **Surrey** map 3

Plough [8/20]

Plough Lane, Downside, Cobham KT11 3LT
COBHAM (0932) 62514 £5

The pies are home-made in this cheerful red-brick pub five minutes' walk from the centre of Cobham. Duck is casseroled with onions and olives, and jacket potatoes with various fillings provide cheap meals from 80p to £1·95. Courage beers.

CHEF: Ruth Sears: PROPRIETORS: John and Irene Huetson
OPEN: all week MEALS: 12 to 2, 5.30 to 9.30
PRICES: Snacks from 80p, Bar meals £1·60 to £5. Special bargain dish. Service inc
CARD: Visa
SEATS: 48. 8 tables outside. Private parties: 30 main room. Car-park, 40 places. Children's helpings (L only). Wheelchair access (also WC). Music

COCKERMOUTH **Cumbria** map 7

Wythop Mill [9/20]

Embleton, Cockermouth CA13 9YP
BASSENTHWAITE LAKE (059 681) 394
3m E of Cockermouth, ½m off A66 £8

The dining-room hums to the sound of the water-wheel that powers the woodwork museum up this quiet, winding country lane on the hillside. The cooking equipment is antique and the decor stone and pine. It is open during the day, and on Thursdays for dinner, for tomato and orange soup, moussaka, appetising salads with garlic bread, home-made, garden mint ice-cream, followed by coffee and home-made peppermints. Half-litres of French wine at £2·60.

CHEFS: P.G.Sealby, C.Sealby and E.M.Pammenton PROPRIETORS: Mr and Mrs J.Sealby
OPEN: L Tue to Sun, D Thu CLOSED: mid-Oct to Good Friday MEALS: 11.30 to 2, 7 to 9
PRICES: £5 (£8)
SEATS: 20. Private parties: 20 main room. Car-park, 8 places. Vegetarian meals. Children's helpings (L only). No smoking

COGGESHALL Essex — map 3

▲ *White Hart* [11/20]

Market End, Coggeshall CO6 1NH
COGGESHALL (0376) 61654 — £15–£30

Raymond Pluck assures us that only fresh produce is used, which means that he must have acquired very good suppliers who can get fresh figs in December, unfrozen frogs' legs and, ever rarer, unfrozen prawns. Nevertheless, the lobsters are caught locally and are relatively inexpensive, while the steaks are very good and marry with a superb wine cellar of immense scale – it has no fewer than 20 '70 clarets, including magnums. A fine hotel in which to stay on expense account.

CHEF: John Grimsey PROPRIETORS: Mr and Mrs Raymond Pluck
OPEN: Mon to Thur, exc Mon L; Sat D and Sun L (also Sun D residents); Bar L all week, exc Sun CLOSED: Aug MEALS: 12.30 to 2, 7.30 to 9.30
PRICES: £23 (£30), Set Sun L £9·50 (£15), Bar L from £2·95 (£3·25) CARDS: Access, Amex, Diners, Visa
SEATS: 50. 5 tables outside. Private parties: 75 main room, 20 private room. Car-park, 20 places. Vegetarian meals by arrangement. Children's helpings by arrangement. Wheelchair access (also WC). Live music
ACCOMMODATION: 18 rooms, all with bath/shower. B&B £35 to £50. Children welcome. No pets. TV. Phone. Doors close at 12. Confirm by 6 [GHG]

COLCHESTER Essex — map 3

BACKGROUND BRIEFING: *Lay & Wheeler in Culver Street West is one of the leading wine merchants in the east of England. It always has a selection of wines available for tasting and is worth a browse. Of the town's butchers, C. E. Leeds, 5 Crouch Street is good for lamb, pork and sausages, and Frank Wright, 43 Crouch Street is best for game. Also in Crouch Street is the Golden Crown Chinese supermarket. Jacklin's in the High Street is one of a dying breed of confectioners selling high-class chocolates. The High Street market has good fruit and vegetables. Tillies, a tea-shop in Crouch Street has excellent home-made cakes, scones and open sandwiches. Fifi's Brasserie gets crowded and noisy but serves good simple food, such as fish of the day and salads.*

We keep files on every restaurant, so reports of poor meals are just as valuable as reports of good meals because they save unnecessary inspections.

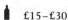

Bistro Nine [10/20]

9 North Hill, Colchester CO1 1DZ
COLCHESTER (0206) 576466 £8–£12

Although a bistro, the menu here takes on board some vegetarian dishes and some traditional English pies as well as the pâté maison and entrecôte with garlic butter. The weekday set lunch at £5 is a snip. Service is by students, and the atmosphere is cheerful and hearty. It's a £5 wine list, with some interesting regional French wines such as Cahors, Cave Co-operative des Côtes d'Olt '81 at £4·95.

CHEF: Penny Campbell PROPRIETORS: M.N.S. and Penny Campbell
OPEN: Tue to Sat CLOSED: Christmas to New Year MEALS: 12 to 1.45, 7 to 10.45
PRICES: £7 (£12), Set L £5 (£8), Snacks from 75p CARDS: Access, Visa
SEATS: 70. Private parties: 35 main room. Vegetarian meals. Children's helpings. Wheelchair access (2 steps)

CONGLETON Cheshire map 5

Odd Fellows [8/20]

20 Rood Hill, Congleton CW12 1QL
CONGLETON (0260) 270243 £12

A wine bar that goes beyond lasagne, chilli con carne and eight bowls of salad is almost certain to make its mark; if it's in Congleton any uncertainty is removed. True, there *are* eight bowls of salad, but the cucumber is gingered up with honey, lemon and dill; tomatoes are dunked in herbs and red wine; and mushrooms are capped with a mustard sauce. There is a tomato, horseradish and yoghourt dressing, and an apricot and curry mayonnaise. Pâté is made by an old friend of the proprietors, but most other things are done in-house: a topside dish is cooked in red wine, barley wine and whisky, not to mention mushrooms, onion, tomatoes, herbs and spices, and there are tandoori pork kebabs, vegetarian lasagne and vegan moussaka, and fondue bourguignonne. There is also 'an unusual vegetable of the week'. Up to 10 wines are available by the glass, from 70p, and 150 bottles come from all the major wine-producing areas of the world, apart from California. Alsace is well represented, and the selection includes a couple of '82s from both Louis Gisselbrecht and Hugel, with the latter's '79 Gewürztraminer Réserve Personnelle at £12·75. Solid choices from the classic regions of France, and Italy is taken seriously with a pair from Abruzzo – white Trebbiano '81 at £8·25 and red Montepulciano '75, which happens to be CELLARMAN'S CHOICE, at £8·95.

CHEFS/PROPRIETORS: The Kirkham family
OPEN: Mon to Sat CLOSED: 24 to 29 Dec, bank hols MEALS: 12 to 2, 6.45 to 10 (10.30 Fri and Sat)
PRICES: £7 (£12) CARD: Amex
SEATS: 136. 8 tables outside. Private parties: 50 main room, 24 private room. Vegetarian meals. Children's helpings (L only). Wheelchair access. Jazz

All Guide *inspectors are anonymous. Anyone purporting to represent the* Guide *is an impostor.*

CONSTABLE BURTON North Yorkshire map 7

Wyvill Arms [8/20]

Constable Burton DO8 5LH
BEDALE (0677) 50581
on A684, 3m E of Leyburn £3

The £3 mixed grill in the bar of this converted farmhouse pub/restaurant arrives piled high on plates 14 inches long – grilled local ham, pig's liver, two eggs, tomatoes, mushrooms, Cumberland sausage, black pudding, chips and carrots. Sweets, such as apple pie and crème caramel, are from the same trolley that serves the restaurant proper (about which we have no reports). To drink there are well-kept McEwan's and John Smith's ales.

CHEF: S.Dean PROPRIETOR: M.C.A.Wyvill
OPEN: all week, exc Sun D MEALS: 12 to 2, 7 to 9.30 (9 Sun)
PRICES: Bar meals from £3. Service inc
SEATS: 45. 12 tables outside. Private parties: 50 main room. Car-park, 50 places. Vegetarian meals. Children's helpings. Wheelchair access (also wc)

COOKHAM Berkshire map 3

Peking Inn [new entry, zero rated]

49 High Street, Cookham SL6 9SL
BOURNE END (062 85) 20900 £15

A cool, white Peking restaurant with starched linen tablecloths and an atmosphere that hums because it is usually packed every night. No wonder. It is good food without pretensions and at reasonable prices. The 50 dishes are not exclusively in Peking tradition but the cooking is adept – prawns in rice-paper with a chilli dip, steamed scallops, and the aromatic duck with all its trimmings have all been excellent. The mixed vegetables owe too much to tins. To finish, the toffee-apples are well done or there are oranges in orange sauce. More reports, please.

CHEF: S.K.Ka PROPRIETORS: W.B.Chan and K.H.Ching
OPEN: all week MEALS: 12 to 2.15, 6.15 to 11.15
PRICES: £8 (£15). Cover 30p. Service 10% CARDS: Access, Amex, Diners, Visa
SEATS: 85. Private parties: 45 main room. Children welcome before 8pm. Smart dress preferred. Wheelchair access

CORSE LAWN Gloucestershire map 2

▲ *Corse Lawn House* [14/20]

Corse Lawn GL19 4LZ
TIRLEY (045 278) 479, 531 and 533
on B4211 5m SW of Tewkesbury **Real Food** £12–£21

Barbara and Dennis Hine have built up a fertile infrastructure of suppliers for their family hotel. As well as using the big suppliers who buy cheeses from the superb Androuët in Paris and fish from Brixham, they get game from the local shoots, and what vegetables they don't grow themselves are supplemented by village gardeners; they gather their own wild mushrooms, and children bring in snails, elderflower and sloes for the kitchen too. All this translates into a mid-Channel menu in the mould of leek soup; brill with watercress sauce; braised ox tongue with madeira sauce served either cheaply in the bar or else more formally in the elegant pea-green dining-room of this Queen Anne house. Especially good has been the hare in puff pastry with a sauce of juniper and sloe gin. The soufflés are a tour de force – off the varied trolley we have eaten orange soufflé with Grand Marnier, raspberry with eau de vie, and passion fruit. Breakfasts too are classy: freshly squeezed orange juice, mango compote, a slice of honeycomb and home-made croissants and preserves. All round it is an irresistible case for an elevation to 14 points. The wine list is strong in Rhônes that can only improve with age, and each of the six Alsace wines represents a different grape variety. Very fine cognacs too. CELLARMAN'S CHOICE: Lirac, La Fermade, '79 from Maby at £7.

CHEFS: Baba Hine and Andrew Foley PROPRIETORS: Dennis and Baba Hine
OPEN: Tue to Sun, exc Sun D CLOSED: 1 week at Christmas MEALS: 12.30 to 2, 7 to 10
PRICES: £15 (£21), Set L £9·50 (£12), Set D £12·75 (£15). Snacks from £1·75. Service inc
CARDS: Access, Amex, Diners, Visa
SEATS: 45. 8 tables outside. Private parties: 55 main room, 24 private room. Vegetarian meals. Car-park, 50 places. Children's helpings. Wheelchair access (also WC)
ACCOMMODATION: 4 rooms, all with bath/shower. B&B £22·50 to £32.50. Pets welcome. Garden. Helicopter pad. TV. Phone. Baby facilities. Scenic. Doors close at 12 [GHG]

COTHERSTONE Durham map 7

Fox and Hounds [8/20]

Cotherstone DL12 3FS
TEESDALE (0833) 50241
on B6277 3m NW of Barnard Castle £9

A spacious, family-run pub with a good local reputation for its steak and kidney pies and well-kept bars. Roast beef Sunday lunches are £3.45. The village post office sells Cotherstone cheese.

CHEF: Helen Cockill PROPRIETORS: Peter and Margaret Cockill
OPEN: Tue to Sun MEALS: 12 to 2, 7 to 10
PRICES: £5 (£9)
SEATS: 72. Private parties: 24 main room, 24 private room. Car-park, 30 places. Vegetarian meals. Children's helpings. Wheelchair access

▲ *This restaurant has rooms.*

CELLARMAN'S CHOICE: *This is a wine that is more expensive than the house wine but is good value and fitting for the kind of food served.*

Many of the better restaurants offer bargain lunches for half the price of a meal in the evening. Details are given in the text.

COVENTRY West Midlands map 5

▲ *Herbs, Trinity House Hotel* [10/20]

28 Lower Holyhead Road, Coventry CV1 3AO
COVENTRY (0203) 555654 £9

A solidly reliable restaurant striving to provide interesting food without using meat or fish. Attached to a modest hotel, the little box-like dining-room has been transformed by a light green decor with pale bamboo-patterned wallpaper and semi-abstract and landscape watercolours on the walls. Robert Jackson hasn't much time for additives, preservatives, chemicals, artificial flavourings or heaps of salt, sugar or fat. If he threw some of his bottles and packets in the dustbin, the food would be even better. Four choices for each course might include acceptable spinach gnocchi, soup, or pâté to start, followed by vegetable and millet Carolina, which reads better than it tastes, or moist, light, pine-nut loaf with lemon and herb stuffing. Salads are well made, puddings rich and creamy, and the ice-cream better than the sorbets. A short wine list, with most bottles under £5.
CELLARMAN'S CHOICE: Chablis '83, from Jean Claude Boisset, at £6·75.

CHEF: Robert Jackson PROPRIETORS: Robert Jackson, Lesley Jackson and Charles Davis
OPEN: Mon to Sat, D only MEALS: 6.30 to 9.30
PRICES: £6 (£9). Service inc
SEATS: 26. 3 tables outside. Private parties: 26 main room. Vegetarian meals. Wheelchair access. Music
ACCOMMODATION: 8 rooms. B&B £12 to £19·50. No pets. Doors close at 12. Confirm by 6

COXWOLD North Yorkshire map 7

▲ *Fauconberg Arms* [new entry, zero rated]

Coxwold YO6 4AD
COXWOLD (034 76) 214
between A19 and A170, 5m SE of Thirsk £9–£17

A well-kept, seventeenth-century inn with rooms, Theakston's beers, bar snacks and a conservative, hotel-style menu that changes daily. Staff holidays are in October and February, when the operation is scaled down, but for the rest of the year the brass gleams and there are fresh flowers everywhere. Waldorf salads are served inside scooped-out apples; smoked mackerel and tarragon ramekins are garnished with a single prawn; and good lamb cutlets are served with a piquant onion sauce. Salads are less good than the vegetables, and sweets, such as apricot tart, are generous. Excellent-value bar food and pretty bedrooms. Fifty unvintaged wines. More reports, please.

CHEF: Robert McQue PROPRIETORS: Mr and Mrs Richard Goodall
OPEN: Tue to Sun, exc Sun D MEALS: 12 to 1.30, 7 to 9.30
PRICES: £13 (£17), Set L £5·75 (£9), Snacks from £1·95 (£2·15)
SEATS: 60. 2 tables outside. Private parties: 60 main room. Car-park, 2 places. Vegetarian meals by arrangement. Children's helpings. Smart dress preferred. Wheelchair access. Music. Air-conditioned
ACCOMMODATION: 4 rooms, 1 with bath/shower. B&B £18 to £30. Deposit: £5. Garden. Fishing. Golf. Snooker. TV. Scenic

CRACKINGTON HAVEN Cornwall map 1

▲ *Crackington Manor* [10/20]

Crackington Haven EX23 0JG
ST GENNYS (084 03) 397
off A39, 10m S of Bude £12

A manor house with five public rooms, set in 11 acres. The dining-room was the billiard room. The menu is conservative, with the accent on pâtés and steaks. There has been good roast lamb and carefully assembled salads. Sweets are displayed on a chest near the kitchen – profiteroles, Pavlova, lemon mousse. Coffee is poor. An adequate wine list, but look for CELLARMAN'S CHOICE: Cabernet Sauvignon '78 at £5·62.

CHEF: Alex Coates PROPRIETORS: Peter and Alex Coates
OPEN: all week CLOSED: Jan and Feb MEALS: 12 to 2.15, 7.30 to 9
PRICES: Set D £7·95 (£12), L snacks from 70p (80p) CARDS: Access, Amex, Visa
SEATS: 38. Private parties: 65 main room. Car-park, 25 places. Vegetarian meals. Children's helpings. Music
ACCOMMODATION: 15 rooms, 8 with bath/shower. Rooms for disabled. B&B £15 to £22. Deposit: £20. Children welcome. Baby facilities. Afternoon teas. Garden. Outdoor swimming-pool. Sauna. Snooker. Scenic

CROYDON Surrey map 3

Hockneys [11/20]

98 High Street, Croydon CR0 1ND
01-688 2899 £10

Hockneys is unlike other vegetarian restaurants. The decor is white with Hockney and Picasso prints, the service is excellent, and the cuisine, as they put it, far transcends the limp lettuce leaf and the nut rissole. Good dishes have been gazpacho, pâtés, aubergine provençale, and vegetable lasagne. There is a speciality dish of almond and aubergine enchiladas, though the really spectacular dish is the mine of serpents – fruit salad with apricot nectar, topped with rum and raisin parfait, peaches, cream, brandy-snaps and strawberry sauce. Sometimes there is a sparkler on top as well! Unlicensed. Corkage is £1·35.

CHEF: Paul Keeler PROPRIETORS: Rainbow (Croydon) Ltd
OPEN: Tue to Sat CLOSED: 2 weeks at Christmas and in Aug MEALS: noon to 10.30
PRICES: £8 (£10), Snacks from £1·35 (£1·50). Special students' dish. Unlicensed, but bring your own: corkage £1·35 CARDS: Access, Amex, Diners, Visa
SEATS: 80. Private parties: 25 main room. Vegetarian meals only. Children's helpings. No smoking in dining-room. Classical music. Self-service at L

Kelong [new entry, zero rated]

1B Selsdon Road, Croydon CR2 6PU
01-688 0726 £11–£25

Locals have taken this Malay/Singaporean restaurant to heart. The decor of slatted ceiling with fans does not really fit the cooking, which is essentially Malay home cooking, but it is apt enough. There is a long menu with some specials of the day on a blackboard. There are seafood satays of prawn, squid and fish, and the meat-ball soup is another good starting point. Good main dishes have been grilled mackerel stuffed with sambal, the lamb curry Kari Kambing, paper-wrapped chicken, and crab with chilli. The waitresses are helpful in guiding novices through their choice of dishes. To finish there are ices or tropical fruit salads. 'We will not Anglicise the food,' says Mr Ho. Quite right, too. Licensed. There are banana and lychee liqueurs. House wines are £4·95. More reports, please.

CHEF: Tom S.L.Ho PROPRIETORS: Tarngrove Ltd
OPEN: Mon to Sat CLOSED: 2 weeks Aug MEALS: 12 to 2.30, 6.30 to 10.45
PRICES: £17 (£25), Set L and D from £7·50 (£11). Also cut-price menu. Service 10%
CARDS: Access, Amex, Diners, Visa
SEATS: 50. Private parties: 60 main room. Children welcome. Music

Munbhave [12/20]

305 London Road, Croydon CR0 3BA
01-689 6331 £8–£11

A little cubby-hole with a big neon sign outside, a fish pond and a 1950s-style bar inside, and a relaxing, homely atmosphere. Here is Gujerati vegetarian cooking with unmatched lightness and elegance. Crispy battering elevates samosas, bhajias, and puris filled with chickpeas and potatoes, served with a sweet-sour sauce of yoghourt and mango chutney. Spicing is multi-layered and subtle, as in masala dosai. The de luxe thali brings fluffy Basmati rice; grilled poppadums; dry chickpea curry with lots of coriander; a soup-like lentil curry; and shrikand for pudding: creamy, lemony, sticky, and scented with cardamom. Service is unfailingly polite and willing to help; if it appears slow, diners are reminded that food is cooked to order. House French is £5·50.

CHEF/PROPRIETOR: Kesh Tank
OPEN: Tue to Sun, D only CLOSED: 3 weeks in Aug MEALS: 6 to 11 (12 Sat)
PRICES: £5 (£11), Set D from £3·90 (£8). Service 10% CARDS: Access, Visa
SEATS: 40. Vegetarian meals. Children's helpings. Wheelchair access. Jazz

Tung Kum [11/20]

205–207 High Street, Croydon CR0 1QR
01-688 0748 and 680 8665 £6–£15

This old favourite, essentially Cantonese despite a few curries, is on the main street through Croydon. Service is friendly and the cuttlefish in black bean sauce, the stuffed bean curd and the stewed pork ribs in plum sauce are of a standard. The noodle and rice stick dishes offer excellent value. House Wan Fu is £5·10.

CHEF: Hung Chiu PROPRIETOR: Tony Lam
OPEN: all week MEALS: 12 to 2.30, 5 to 11.30 (all day Sat and Sun)
PRICES: £9 (£15), Set L from £2·20 (£6), Set D from £6 (£10). Minimum £5 at D. Service 10% CARDS: Access, Amex, Diners, Visa
SEATS: 95. Children welcome. Wheelchair access (also wc). Music

This restaurant has an exceptional wine cellar.

DARLINGTON Durham map 7

Victor's [new entry, zero rated]

84 Victoria Road, Darlington DL1 5JW
DARLINGTON (0325) 480818 £7–£14

A small restaurant with modern decor that puts Cotherstone cheese on the cheeseboard and on turkey, uses local game, makes bread and petits fours in-house, and serves good-value three-course lunches and four-course dinners. A short wine list. More reports, please.

CHEFS/PROPRIETORS: Peter and Jayne Robinson
OPEN: Tue to Sun, exc Sun L MEALS: 12 to 2.30, 7 to 10.30
PRICES: Set L £3·50 (£7), Set D £10·50 (£14). Cheaper set L available CARDS: Access, Amex, Visa
SEATS: 26. Private parties: 26 main room. Vegetarian meals by arrangement. Children's helpings. Wheelchair access. Music

DARTMOUTH Devon map 1

Carved Angel [16/20]

WEST COUNTRY RESTAURANT OF THE YEAR

2 South Embankment, Dartmouth TQ6 9BH
DARTMOUTH (080 43) 2465 **Real Food** £18–£22

Both the Angel and York House next door are intricate, black and white buildings with elaborate coloured carvings between the timber frames – an eagle, flowers, a ship, an 'R' emblem. The view across the road from the front room is to the harbour quay. At the back is the open kitchen hidden by large plants. In the centre stands the carved statue of an angel. Otherwise it is an unfussy beige and white room. Front of house now is the dynamic Meriel Boydon, helped by two young girls who have the eyes and movements of shy deer. If anything, Joyce Molyneux's cooking gets better. The style is classic Elizabeth David, but less orthodox than her partner George Perry-Smith practised at Helford. There is a constant awareness in the menu of the moving seasons. The cheese straws, served with aperitifs like the house mix of raspberry liqueur and champagne, came one night covered with cumin seeds and the next with poppy. In some cases Joyce Molyneux is content to rest on her execution of classic regional dishes, like goujons of Dover sole (in a batter straight out of Elizabeth David's *French Provincial Cooking* recipe for beignets d'aubergine) deep-fried in groundnut oil and served with a delicate and intense mix of onion and lemon. Now, from a spiced lamb dish with aubergines and yoghourt (still practised at the Hole in the Wall in Bath and at the Riverside in Helford) has evolved beef marinated in ginger and orange, threaded on to a skewer with bay leaves, grilled so the smoky flavour is absorbed, and then served with a similar aubergine concoction, cooked ratatouille-style with tomatoes and spiced strongly with cinnamon and cumin eased by a blob of yoghourt and parsley. Such cooking can come only from the principles of Real Food, worked out in the kitchen, and not from a dogma or recipe book. It is the same principle as Frédy Girardet's spontaneous cooking or Raymond Blanc's cooking of today. It is not by any means *nouvelle cuisine*, which is too often hidebound by its own tenets, but it is creative cooking of the highest order. What other dishes have we eaten at the Angel that reach such standards?

Lambs' kidneys and sweetbreads with mushrooms on puff pastry sprinkled with sesame seeds, in a sticky sauce of butter, stock and madeira; roast rabbit served with bread sauce and sloe and apple jelly; Pavlova with pineapple and kirsch cream; a cheeseboard of Stilton, matured Cheddar and local Sharpham, served with freshly made oatcakes – all these compare with the best by any standards. The coffee is excellent and comes with home-made fudge. There are 187 wines chosen with the same care that goes into the food; four house wines figure at £7.

CHEF: Joyce Molyneux PROPRIETOR: George Perry-Smith
OPEN: Tue to Sun exc Sun D MEALS: 12.30 to 1.45, 7.30 to 9.30
PRICES: L £14 (£18), Set D from £18 (£22). Service inc
SEATS: 30. Private parties: 30 main room, 15 private room. Vegetarian meals by arrangement. Children's helpings

DEDHAM Essex map 3

▲ *Marlborough Head Hotel* [9/20]

Mill Lane, Dedham CO7 6DH
COLCHESTER (0206) 323124 and 323250 £10

The knack to eating in this busy, 500-year-old house that once belonged to a weaver but is now a pub with bar, family-room and lounge is to find the custodian of the menus – usually sitting at a table by the bar – and pay in advance. As well as the large selection of sandwiches there are good, hearty English dishes. Soups include a thick vegetable and pulse broth served with a cob roll, and fresh asparagus or mussel chowder. There are handsome stews too – beef carbonnade, beef and mushroom pie, Aga-roasted bacon steaks, and pork provençale. Fish, too, has been good. Portions are generous, and to finish there is fine, traditional, but rich treacle tart. Ind Coope bitter is 78p a pint and house French £6 a litre.

CHEFS: Brian and Jackie Wills PROPRIETOR: Brian Wills
OPEN: all week MEALS: 12 to 2, 7 to 9.30
PRICES: £7 (£10). Service inc
SEATS: 90. 5 tables outside. Private parties: 25 main room. Car-park, 6 places. Vegetarian meals. Children welcome. Wheelchair access
ACCOMMODATION: 4 rooms. B&B £15 to £25. Children welcome. Pets welcome. Garden. TV. Doors close at 11

▲ *Terrace Restaurant, Dedham Vale Hotel* [12/20]

Stratford Road, Dedham CO7 6HW
COLCHESTER (0206) 322273 **Real Food** £16–£20

An attractive, comfortable, well-run hotel. The menu is deceptively conservative, and traditional dishes, such as chicken liver pâté and seafood pancakes, are well handled. Chicken and ducks are spit-roasted, and a genuine steak tartare survives prominently on the menu. Local crabs are served as salad, and the ingredients are Real Food. Wines come from Lay & Wheeler. House French is £5·40.

▲ *This restaurant has rooms.*

CHEF: Terry Barber PROPRIETOR: Gerald Milsom
OPEN: all week MEALS: 12.30 to 2, 7 to 10
PRICES: £15 (£20), Set L £10·50 (£16), Set D from £11 (£16). Service 10% CARDS: Access, Amex, Diners, Visa
SEATS: 110. 10 tables outside. Private parties: 100 main room. Car-park, 80 places. Vegetarian meals. Children's helpings. Smart dress preferred. Music
ACCOMMODATION: 6 rooms, all with bath/shower. B&B £40 to £70. Children welcome. Baby facilities. No pets. Garden. Fishing. TV. Phone. Scenic [GHG]

DERBY Derbyshire — map 5

BACKGROUND BRIEFING: *Derbyshire is not only the home county of J. W. Thornton, whose chocolates sell all over the country, but also of Matthew Walker, who make widely available Christmas puddings and mincemeat; Bakewell pudding (Olde Original Bakewell Pudding Shop, The Square, Bakewell is the best source), and Ashbourne gingerbread (from the shop in St John's Street, Ashbourne). In Derby itself Goodall's, 6 Ashbourne Road sells good pork pies and sausages and also cure bacon and supply good hams. George Stafford, 132 Belper Road, Stanley Common is a champion black-pudding maker and puddings are also good from N. H. Beckett in Derby market hall. The best tripe in the area comes from Sam Adams, also in the market hall; the best fish is from B. & A. Roome, 43 Sadler Gate. Up the road at 37 Sadler Gate Ted Corden is the top greengrocer in Derby, and people drive from all over the city to buy their meat from F. G. Scattergood, 127 Kedleston Road. Another good butcher and not as expensive is H. E. Rawlings, 39 St Chad's Road. G. W. Monk, 28 Stanley Street makes locally famous pikelets (crumpets) which are sold at small stalls on the way into the market hall.*

Golden Pheasant [new entry, zero rated]

221 Chellaston Road, Shelton Lock, Derby DE2 9EE
DERBY (0332) 700112
off A514, 3m SE of Derbyshire — £9–£18

In an area that has been non-*Guide* territory for too long. This large restaurant is well used by executives and does cheap set meals. It serves big portions of steaming steak and kidney pie, moussaka, and pork in cider, as well as plenty of vegetables. Fruits are mostly fresh and there are calorific sweets. Vin de table is £6·60 a litre, Muscadet is £7·25. More reports, please.

CHEF: S. Williams PROPRIETORS: F. Akers and B. M. Skitt
OPEN: Tue to Sun, exc Sun D MEALS: 12 to 2, 7 to 10
PRICES: £13 (£18), Set L from £5·20 (£9), Set D from £7·30 (£11). Minimum £3·50. Service inc CARDS: Access, Amex, Diners, Visa
SEATS: 100. Private parties: 100 main room, 12 private room. Car-park, 50 places. Vegetarian meals. Children's helpings. Wheelchair access (also WC)

Restaurants are checked every year and their entries rewritten. The restaurant scene changes very rapidly so don't be caught with an out-of-date Guide.

Places rating 8 or 9 may not be restaurants at all but still serve very good food. In this category expect to find pubs, cafes, small hotels and wine bars.

Restaurant 524 [13/20]

524 Burton Road, Littleover, Derby DE3 6FN
DERBY (0332) 371524 and 380390
100 metres S of the Derby ring road at
Littleover **Real Food** £8–£28

Originally this building on the old main road was three farm cottages, then three shops. Now, you can see Craig Dent working in his kitchen, surrounded by copper pots, through the plate-glass window facing the street. It is a relaxed but formal French restaurant, heavily beamed and with marble floors. The menu is uncompromising, each meat has its own stock, everything is made in-house, and the flour is used for pastry, not sauces. Notably good are the mussel soup; brill in a fennel sauce; pigeon served with its legs en croûte; noisettes of lamb with tarragon. Vegetables are shown respect. Look for the pear flan and the chocolate mousse to finish. Coffee with petits fours is included at lunch, when they are not usually busy. There is a tasting menu at £15 on request, and Mr Dent is happy to show people around the kitchen. Good wines are bought from auction, and there is also a range of cognac, calvados and vintage armagnac. House claret is £5·80.

CHEF: Craig Dent PROPRIETOR: Freda Dent
OPEN: Tue to Sat MEALS: 12.30 to 1.30, 7.30 to 10
PRICES: £21 (£28), Set L from £3·95 (£8). Also cut-price menu. Licensed, plus bring your own: corkage £3 CARDS: Access, Amex, Diners, Visa
SEATS: 36. Private parties: 40 main room. Vegetarian meals. Car-park, 15 places. Smart dress preferred. No pipes in dining-room. Children's helpings. Wheelchair access

DISLEY Cheshire map 5

The Ginnel [10/20]

3 Buxton Old Road, Disley SK12 2BB
DISLEY (066 32) 4494 and 4409 £9–£16

A small, stone terraced cottage with a Victorian dining-room where the menu with themes seems to go ever more over the top: a Mad Hatter's dinner started with salmon and sharkfish terrine overpowered by red peppers and pink peppercorns. The more simple dishes, on the other hand, are good – a cheese profiterole in a celeriac sauce featured on the same menu, as did excellent jugged hare and jam tarts that signify a cool hand at the pastry table. There has also been good quail, boned, rolled and served with apricots and redcurrants. There are some interesting wines, not overpriced and including some of the better

An index of restaurants by name appears at the back of the Guide.

Restaurants are graded on a scale of 1–20. In the region of 8–9 expect to find places that may not be restaurants but cafes, pubs, bistros and small hotels. In the category of 10–11 you can expect to find the best food in the locality. Ratings of 12 or more are given to restaurants we regard as serving the best food in the region.

English bottles, but from Beaujolais the Brouilly '83 will have the edge on the '84 – both are £7·60. House Loire is £4·75. CELLARMAN'S CHOICE: Lirac Blanc, La Fermade '83, from Yapp, at £7·10.

CHEFS: Jon Holmes and Ian Smith PROPRIETORS: Annette and John Derbyshire
OPEN: Tue to Sat, D only, and Sun L MEALS: 12.30 to 2, 7 to 10.15
PRICES: £11 (£16), Set Sun L £6 (£9) CARDS: Access, Amex, Diners, Visa
SEATS: 48. Private parties: 28 main room, 20 and 10 private rooms. Vegetarian meals. Children's helpings. Wheelchair access (1 step). Music

DISS Norfolk — map 6

▲ *Salisbury House* [13/20]

84 Victoria Road, Diss IP22 3JC
DISS (0379) 4738 — £22

The secluded gardens of this former mill contrast with the long, unattractive approach road. Among the neighbours are petrol stations, small factories, the railway and a transport depot. But there is a croquet lawn in front of the house, and rare breeds of chickens, pigeons, ducks and geese wander among the flower-beds at the back. The front dining-room is a major feature and is decorated with an amazing collection of fans. Anthony Rudge is good with sauces and makes full use of the herbs in the garden. The four-course menu is *nouvelle* in style and presentation – a red soup is made of tomato, orange and carrot, and Brie baked in pastry is given a currant sauce. Main courses are less vivid, such as beef sirloin roasted and topped with herb butter and served on a cream mustard sauce. To finish there is excellent chocolate mousse or claret jelly. Service is good when not petulant. Short, adequate wine-list, though the addition of a few extra bottles would suit the cooking. House claret is £5·60.

CHEF: Anthony Rudge PROPRIETORS: Anthony Rudge and Jonathan Thompson
OPEN: Tue to Sat, D only CLOSED: 1 week at Christmas, spring and autumn
MEALS: 7.30 to 9
PRICES: Set D £16 (£22)
SEATS: 25. 2 tables outside. Private parties: 14 main room, 14 private room. Car-park, 10 places. Vegetarian meals. No children under 12. No cigars/pipes in dining-room. Wheelchair access (also WC). Classical music
ACCOMMODATION: 3 rooms, all with bath/shower. B&B £35·50 to £50. No children under 12. Garden. TV. Doors close at 12. Confirm by 6 [GHG]

DONCASTER South Yorkshire — map 5

BACKGROUND BRIEFING: *The market on Tuesday, Friday and Saturday has plenty of good fresh vegetables, most of them local produce. The fish market is much better than anything Hull has to offer, with more variety and better quality. Grantham & Son, Unit 2, Wheatley Hall Business Centre, Wheatley Hall Road may have fresh Scotch salmon, monkfish and Dover sole. There is brill most days, 'as long as the last of the*

'Evidently, the restaurant itself has some doubts, since the head waiter, the table waiter and the wine waiter all asked if we were enjoying the meal several times each and the chef himself made the same enquiry once.' (On eating in Humberside)

Grimsby in-shore boats have been busy that morning,' and Stuart Grantham can supply fresh turbot with a day's notice. The delicatessen at 46, East Laithe Gate has a fair range.

DONHEAD ST ANDREW **Wiltshire** map 2

Le Radier [12/20]

Donhead St Andrew SP8 9LG
DONHEAD (074 788) 324
3m E of Shaftesbury on A30 £14

Drive slowly, it is an awkward hill and turning is tricky. Margaret and Lucien Voisin are in their third year at this detached seventeenth-century cottage. He is French and cooks, she is English and serves (they used to be at Cookham). The menu is a dash above a good bistro. Snails are unusually cooked with red wine, grapes, garlic and croûtons; the seafood pancakes are thin and generously filled with both shell and white fish; the curried chicken soup is deftly made and different. Good main dishes have been venison with herb and black cherry sauce or, for those in search of lost protein, calf's liver pan-fried with avocado; both have come with good vegetables. To finish, their St Emilion au chocolat is professionally executed and alcoholic. Coffee – with petits fours – could be more virile. A dozen wines.

CHEF: Lucien Voisin PROPRIETORS: Lucien and Margaret Voisin
OPEN: D Tue to Sat, and Sun L MEALS: 12 to 2, 7.30 to 9
PRICES: Set L, D £11·50 (£14). Service inc
SEATS: 25. Private parties: 20 main room. Vegetarian meals. Car-park, 15 places. Children welcome. Wheelchair access (also wc). Music

DORKING **Surrey** map 3

River Kwai [12/20]

274–276 High Street, Dorking RH4 1QT
DORKING (0306) 889053 £11

Every town should have a little restaurant like this. The combination of Thai cuisine and bistro atmosphere (and prices) is remarkable. The ingredients are handled with care and the spicing is ingenious. Satay is excellent – flat squares of well-done beef with a separate plate of sauce made of chopped peanuts, coconut milk and chilli, plus a plate of sliced cucumber and chopped chilli in a vinegar sauce. The menu and staff give helpful advice but it is fairly safe to roam at random through the menu and sample some of the exotic dishes – sai krug pu is crab and onion wrapped in filo pastry and deep-fried; gung pud prik are fried king prawns with chilli; praew wan kai is chicken with onions, cucumber, fresh pineapple, sweet tomatoes and cashews served with a hot sweet-and-sour sauce.

The Guide is always anxious to recruit new inspectors. If you would like to apply, write to the editor enclosing a) a detailed report on a restaurant where you have eaten and b) a comparative study of restaurants known to you.

It is a healthy cuisine with little respect for puddings, though there is an unusual fried green banana with sweet-corn and coconut milk. House Nicolas is £5·60.

CHEFS: Mr Kiat and Miss Malee PROPRIETOR: Mr Kiat
OPEN: Tue to Sun CLOSED: Christmas, bank hols, and 2 weeks Apr MEALS: 12 to 2.30, 6 to 10.30
PRICES: £6 (£11) Cheaper set L available. Service 10% CARDS: Access, Diners, Visa
SEATS: 45. Private parties: 18 main room. Car-park, 20 places. Vegetarian meals. Children's helpings. Wheelchair access (also WC). Music. Air-conditioned

DORRINGTON Shropshire map 4

Country Friends [12/20]

Dorrington SY5 7JD
DORRINGTON (074 373) 707
on A49, 5m S of Shrewsbury £12–£20

An historic, beamed house where Pauline Whittaker cooks a short, country menu that changes with the seasons. From the hot wholemeal garlic rolls to the decorative if rather over-the-top meringue swans that tend to garnish the sweets there is a purpose to her food. The crab soup has depth; the salmon and monkfish in pastry with parsley sauce has continued to impress, as do the sole fillets with chive sauce. In the poultry department the old English technique of using nuts pops up in chicken breast with almonds, or else duck with bacon and walnuts. Fillet steaks are topped with horseradish butter. To finish there is hazel-nut meringue with chestnut cream, and chocolate truffles with coffee. A short, varied list of wines. CELLARMAN'S CHOICE: Château du Grand Moulas '83 at £5·85

CHEFS/PROPRIETORS: Charles and Pauline Whittaker
OPEN: Mon to Sat, exc Mon L MEALS: 12 to 2, 7 to 9.30
PRICES: £15 (£20), Set L and D £9 (£12), Snacks from £1·50 (£1·65)
CARDS: Amex, Diners, Visa
SEATS: 35. Private parties: 45 main room, 10 private room. Car-park, 40 places. Children welcome. Wheelchair access. Classical music

DURHAM Durham map 7

Undercroft Restaurant [8/20]

The College, Durham Cathedral, Durham DH1 3EQ
DURHAM (0385) 63721 £6

Walk through the cloisters to this airy, pine dining-room – still the best place we can find to eat in the city in the daytime. There are excellent pâtés, cold roast beef, large portions of boiled ham, and salads. Home-made lemonade, or wine at 75p a glass.

CHEFS: K. Dixon and V. Beveridge PROPRIETORS: Milburns Rest. Ltd
OPEN: all week, daytime only MEALS: 9.30 to 5, L 12 to 2
PRICES: £3 (£6)
SEATS: 85. Vegetarian meals. Children's helpings. No-smoking area. Wheelchair access (also WC). Self-service

EAST BERGHOLT Essex map 3

Fountain House [10/20]

The Street, East Bergholt CO7 6TB
COLCHESTER (0206) 298232 £11–£13

A family-run, cottage-style restaurant with oak beams, carpeted flagged floors, and paintings for sale. Service is friendly and the menu mid-Channel. There is superb scofa bread made in the village. Starters have been good, from mushroom soup to mixed vegetables à la grecque, but main courses, such as lambs' kidneys with mustard sauce, more erratic. Sunday lunches of roast beef, however, are generous and the restaurant likes to serve families. Wines from Lay & Wheeler include a pair of '83 Alsace wines, from Blanck, for around £8.

CHEF: Wendy Sarton PROPRIETOR: James Sarton
OPEN: Tue to Sun, exc Sun D CLOSED: last 2 weeks Jan MEALS: 12.30 to 2, 7.30 to 10
PRICES: Set L £7·50 (£11), Set D £9·50 (£13) CARDS: Access, Visa
SEATS: 32. 3 tables outside. Private parties: 30 main room. Car-park, 12 places. Vegetarian meals. Children's helpings. No cigars/pipes in dining-room. Wheelchair access. Classical music

EASTBOURNE East Sussex map 3

Byrons [11/20]

6 Crown Street, Old Town, Eastbourne BN21 1NX
EASTBOURNE (0323) 20171 £14

Simon Scrutton has moved into using organic vegetables in this old-style, animated French restaurant he runs with his wife Marian. His meat comes from a butcher who takes lambs and chickens raised in as near an organic way as is possible, and excellent fish is from the local boats. The soupe de poisson arrives complete with croûtons and rouille, and sea-bass has been excellent too. Other main courses are loyal to the best bourgeois principles – poulet au vin de Margaux et au lard fumé; rognons d'agneau à l'armagnac; filet de boeuf à la béarnaise or bordelaise. To finish there is good praline and Tia Maria ice-cream. Cheaper lunches are cooked only for reservations. Two dozen carefully chosen French wines start at £4·25. CELLARMAN'S CHOICE: Ch. Bonnet '83 at £5·85.

CHEF: Simon Scrutton PROPRIETORS: Simon and Marian Scrutton
OPEN: Mon to Sat, exc Sat L (L by arrangement only) CLOSED: 1 week at Christmas
MEALS: 12.30 to 1.30, 7.30 to 10.30
PRICES: D £9 (£14), also cut-price L menu. Minimum £2.85 CARDS: Amex, Diners, Visa
SEATS: 22. Private parties: 10 main room, 10 private room. Children welcome. No cigars/pipes during meals. Classical music

Restaurants are graded on a scale of 1–20. In the region of 8–9 expect to find places that may not be restaurants but cafes, pubs, bistros and small hotels. In the category of 10–11 you can expect to find the best food in the locality. Ratings of 12 or more are given to restaurants we regard as serving the best food in the region.

This restaurant has an exceptional wine cellar.

Qualisea [9/20]

9 Pevensey Road, Eastbourne BN21 3HH
EASTBOURNE (0323) 25203 £3

Michael Cosma has run this fish and chip shop for the last 21 years. It is cheaper than its competitors and a lot better. Cod and plaice are fresh and fried correctly in ground-nut oil. The potatoes, too, are unadulterated. Service is efficient and the shop spotless. By far the best-value place to eat in the town. Tea is 17p.

CHEF/PROPRIETOR: Michael Cosma
OPEN: Mon to Sat MEALS: 11.30 to 8
PRICES: £2 (£3). Unlicensed, but bring your own: no corkage
SEATS: 24. Children's helpings. Wheelchair access

EAST HORSLEY Surrey map 3

Tudor Rose [9/20]

15 Bishopsmead Parade, East Horsley KT24 6RT
EASTHORSLEY (048 65) 4484 £9–£15

Regulars keep coming back for Winnie Chapman's simple but well-prepared food: duck with orange and Grand Marnier sauce, generous vegetables, apple pie and cream, or without cream if you prefer, or with ice-cream – she's very accommodating. CELLARMAN'S CHOICE: Ch. Grivière '79, from the Médoc, at £7·95.

CHEF/PROPRIETOR: Mrs Winnie Chapman
OPEN: Tue to Sat D, Sat and Sun L MEALS: 12 to 2.30, 7 to 10.30
PRICES: £9 (£15), Set Sat L £4·25 (£9), Set Sun L £6 (£11). Special bargain dish. Service 10%
CARDS: Access, Amex, Diners, Visa
SEATS: 36. Private parties: 25 main room, 20 private room. Vegetarian meals. Children's helpings. Smart dress preferred. Wheelchair access

EAST MOLESEY Surrey map 3

The Lantern [11/20]

20 Bridge Road, East Molesey KT8 9AH
01-979 1531 £16–£19

The regularly changing menu might include home-made liver pâté, home-cured salmon, and crab mousse. But it also seems to have changed in other ways since last year, and the fun and zip in the menu seem to have disappeared, accounting for the lower rating. The choice of fish recently has been sole, sole, sole or sole, and meat dishes are dominated by lamb and steak, the latter coming four ways: with peppercorns, three butters, béarnaise, or in a red wine sauce. But vegetables

Entries are compiled from the unsolicited reports from readers and are checked by inspectors; each restaurant is asked to supply details of its operation. Report forms can be found at the back of the Guide.

are fresh and carefully cooked, and there have been additions to the sweets trolley. Service is pleasant. The short list includes house wine at £4·95.

CHEF: P. Morphew PROPRIETORS: Mr and Mrs P. Morphew
OPEN: Mon to Sat, D only CLOSED: Aug MEALS: 7 to 10.30 (11 Sat)
PRICES: £11 (£19). Set D from £10·25 (£16). Cover 75p. Service 12.5% CARDS: Access, Amex, Diners, Visa
SEATS: 50. Private parties: 25 main room. Children's helpings. Music

Vecchia Roma [10/20]

55–57 Bridge Road, East Molesey KT8 9ER
01-979 5490 and 941 5337 £12–£22

By popular vote from readers this old Roman returns to the listings. Bread, pasta, and fennel-flavoured grissini are all home made. Veal, chicken and beef are done simply, and an Italian – or possibly Japanese – style fondue provides a clear consommé in which to cook slivers of beef. House Italian is £5·90.

CHEF: Adolfo Fiore PROPRIETOR: Toni Michele
OPEN: all week, exc Sat L MEALS: 12 to 2, 7 to 11
PRICES: £14 (£22), Set L £6·25 (£12). Cover 75p CARDS: Access, Diners, Visa
SEATS: 90. Private parties: 90 main room. Children welcome. Smart dress preferred. Wheelchair access. Music. Air-conditioned

EASTRY Kent map 3

Coach and Horses [10/20]

Lower Street, Eastry CT13 0JF
SANDWICH (0304) 611692
on A256 3m S of Sandwich, 6m N of Dover £16

If you book, Pearl Long will cook a classical French meal for you in her 300-year-old de-licensed pub. She does not use processed food and you discuss the menu by phone according to what is in the market. Specialities are sole normande and roast duck. Sweets are excellent. Twenty, not overpriced, good-quality wines.

CHEF: Pearl Long PROPRIETORS: M. J. and P. V. Long
OPEN: Wed to Mon, exc Sat L MEALS: 12.30 to 1.30, 7.45 to 10
PRICES: £11 (£16). Service 10%
SEATS: 18. Private parties: 18 main room. Vegetarian meals. Car-park, 9 places. No children under 10. Wheelchair access

EAST STOKE Dorset map 2

▲ *Kemps* [10/20]

East Stoke BH20 6AL
BINDON ABBEY (0929) 462563
on A352 2m W of Wareham £9–£20

The home-made items are the best in this former Victorian rectory on the busy main road – good carrot and excellent watercress soups; roast beef with fresh cabbage; Dover sole with butter and shrimps; excellent venison; and there is fresh brown bread on a Sunday. The desserts from the trolley are lathered in cream, or you can have petits fours with coffee by the log fire amid the Victoriana and Schubert. There is fresh milk for the teamaker in the rooms. Three dozen bottles, mostly French, on the wine list, with house wine at £4·75.

CHEF: Mike Kemp PROPRIETORS: Mike and Valerie Kemp
OPEN: all week MEALS: 12 to 1.30, 7 to 9.30
PRICES: £12 (£18), Set L from £4·60 to £15 (£9 to £20), Set D from £9·60 to £15 (£14 to £20), Bar meals from £2 (£2·20) CARDS: Access, Amex, Diners, Visa
SEATS: 40. 2 tables outside. Private parties: 60 main room. Car-park, 20 places. No children under 7. Wheelchair access (also WC). Classical music
ACCOMMODATION: 9 rooms, 8 with bath/shower. Rooms for disabled. B&B £23 to £36. Children welcome. Baby facilities. No pets. Garden. TV. Scenic. Confirm by 6 [GHG]

EGHAM Surrey map 3

La Bonne Franquette [11/20]

5 High Street, Egham TW20 9EA
EGHAM (0784) 33206 and 34223 £17–£25

A formal French restaurant opposite the Ferrari showrooms. It prides itself on the presentation of its dishes, which are complicated, but mainly consist of good-quality ingredients. Notable have been hare with an alcoholic wine sauce; sea-bass with ginger, pink peppercorns and lime sauce; and the unusual kipper and Drambuie soup. The cooking is extremely sweet, not just in the final course of lemon tart with raspberry purée, but also in starters, such as gravlax. The pastry and the saucing need more care for a higher rating. For some reason that defeats us, owner David Turvey believes that wines under £12 do not particularly complement the food. What funny ideas some people have – after all, there is house wine at £6·50.

CHEF: David Smart PROPRIETOR: David Turvey
OPEN: all week, exc Sat L CLOSED: bank hols MEALS: 12 to 2, 7 to 10
PRICES: £16 (£25), Set L £12·50 (£17). Service 10% CARDS: Access, Amex, Diners, Visa
SEATS: 46. Private parties: 20 main room, 8 private room. Car-park, 14 places. Children welcome. Smart dress preferred. Wheelchair access. Music

ELLAND West Yorkshire map 5

Berties Bistro [10/20]

7–10 Town Hall Buildings, Elland HD1 2TA
ELLAND (0422) 71724 £11

No bookings are taken but prices are kept down and the turnover kept up at this Edwardian-style bistro. The menu changes weekly, ranging from ragout of

'The music is the Tijuana brass played loudly. For some reason northern restaurants seem to regard this as classy now, whereas in the south it would be anathema.'
(On inspecting in Yorkshire)

monkfish with Chablis sauce, to Yorkshire pudding with pink peppercorns and onion gravy, to treacle and orange tart. A short list of pedigree wines.

CHEF: Michael Swallow PROPRIETOR: Brett Woodward
OPEN: Tue to Sun, D only MEALS: 7 to 11 (11.30 Fri and Sat, 5 to 9.30 Sun)
PRICES: £7 (£11) CARDS: Access, Visa
SEATS: 110. Private parties: 40 main room, 40 private room. Car-park, 60 places. Vegetarian meals. Children's helpings. Smart dress preferred at D. Wheelchair access. Music. Air-conditioned

ELLESMERE Shropshire — map 4

▲ *The Grange* [new entry, zero rated]

Grange Road, Ellesmere SY12 9DE
ELLESMERE (069 171) 3495
¼m out of Ellesmere on A528 to Wrexham — £8–£12

Good-value English food, including such old-fashioned items as flummery and more modern apple stuffed with cheese and served with an hollandaise sauce with tarragon, is served in this family-run hotel in a Grade III listed Georgian building. The Huttons have their own Jersey milk and cream and grow their own vegetables; the bantams lay the eggs. Main courses of excellent lamb en croûte or steak and kidney pie come with potatoes, spinach and cauliflower. There is usually a roast. The cheeseboard includes Shropshire blue. Vegetarian dishes on request run to rather more than an omelette. Journeyman wine list, but CELLARMAN'S CHOICE is Gewürztraminer '82 from P. Blanck at £6·80.

CHEF: Phyllis Hutton PROPRIETORS: Peter and Phyllis Hutton
OPEN: D all week, and Sun L MEALS: 12.45 to 2, 7 to 8.30
PRICES: Set L from £5 (£8), Set D from £9 (£12). Bar snacks from £1·50 CARDS: Access, Diners, Visa
SEATS: 50. Private parties: 35 main room. Car-park, 20 places. Children's helpings (Sun L only). Wheelchair access. Light classical music
ACCOMMODATION: 14 rooms, 13 with bath/shower. Rooms for disabled. B&B £21·50 to £35. Children welcome. Baby facilities. Pets welcome. TV. Phone. Snooker. Doors close at 11.30. Confirm by 6

ELSWORTH Cambridgeshire — map 3

Meadow Farm [12/20]

Broad End, Elsworth CB3 8JD
ELSWORTH (095 47) 413
3m off Cambridge–Huntingdon Road (A604) — **Real Food** £13

A small French restaurant found in a flagstoned farmhouse warmed by an open log fire. The raw materials are Real Food – local beef and lamb are hung to Leonora Cooke's specifications; turkey is the now rarely found Norfolk Black; eggs are free-range; vegetables and herbs come from their garden in summer; and cheeses from Patrick Rance. The menu encompasses scallop soup with wine and cream; monkfish tarts with béarnaise; steak with chive and Stilton butter.

Good dishes have been leek and egg vinaigrette, mushroom soup and duck served with red cabbage, salsify and dauphinoise potatoes. Sweets have been emphatically good, particularly the meringues, the blackcurrant sorbet and the crème brûlée. The wine list is young but blue-blooded, with good '79 minor clarets and champagne from Gosset, the oldest wine house in the region, as well as cheaper regional bottles. CELLARMAN'S CHOICE: Crozes-Hermitage blanc '83 from Jaboulet at £8·40.

CHEFS/PROPRIETORS: Leonora Cooke and Nicolas Toke-Nichols
OPEN: Tue to Sat, D only, L, parties only, by arangement CLOSED: 2 weeks Jan, 2 weeks Aug MEALS: 7 to 9
PRICES: Set D from £9·50 (£13) CARDS: Access, Amex, Visa
SEATS: 20. Private parties: 20 main room. Vegetarian meals by arrangement. Car-park, 16 places. Children welcome. Wheelchair access (also WC)

ELY Cambridgeshire map 6

Old Fire Engine House [13/20]

25 St Mary's Street, Ely CB7 4ER
ELY (0353) 2582 £13

No exaggeration, no camouflage, no dressing up – just plain, simple, country style in everything from decor, to food, to service. The fire station doubles as an art gallery and can feel like a vegetarian restaurant with its open-plan kitchen, unclothed wooden tables and uneven, red and yellow tiled floor. Occasionally in season there are some genuine Fenland specialities, such as eel pie or baked zander, but more often the choice is robust and rustic – a rather greasy but home-spun and tasty lamb and barley soup, or else excellent pork terrine or eel in white wine. Main courses lean heavily on pies, stews and game – huge helpings of beef in beer or red wine; whole pigeon, wildly overcooked but all its goodness retained in its gravy; hare with cream sauce. The vegetables are generous and magnificent. To finish there can be hot rhubarb tart straight out of the oven, excellent crumbles, or meringues. In the first four months of last year no less than 54 dishes received nominations from readers. The list of mainly French wines is well chosen and not overpriced, but for the robust food a Bulgarian wine, or the Beaujolais Juliénas '83 at £7·80, may suit better than the delicate clarets. The trio of Alsace wines is well chosen too.
CELLARMAN'S CHOICE: Muscat '83, from Dopff & Irion, at £6·50.

CHEFS/PROPRIETORS: Ann Ford and Michael Jarman
OPEN: all week, exc Sun D CLOSED: 24 Dec to 7 Jan and bank hols
MEALS: 12.30 to 2, 7.30 to 9
PRICES: £9 (£13), Special dish at L
SEATS: 36. 8 tables outside. Private parties: 36 main room, 24 private room. Car-park, 8 places. Vegetarian meals by arrangement. Children's helpings

'The front door was locked – the restaurant advertises a 7 o'clock opening. We rang for four minutes in the biting cold, and the young man who appears to be the head waiter (and is neither as gormless or unhelpful as he first appears) stood in the doorway to say that there was no heating, since Mr X had the key to the boiler and had been away at the races.' (On eating in the Midlands)

EPWORTH Humberside map 5

Epworth Tap [8/20]

9–11 Market Place, Epworth DN9 1EU
EPWORTH (0427) 873333
on A161, 3m from M180 £10

A handy wine bar with a short menu that may include watercress soup, mushrooms with cream and lemon, veal and paprika casserole, and moussaka made with lamb. Portions are small for the price, but the wine list makes up for it – John Wynne has over 150 varied, first-class wines at reasonable prices. CELLARMAN'S CHOICE includes Ch. Les Ormes-de-Pez '79, at £10·50, from a good claret section; and Chablis *premier cru* Vaillons '83, from Michel Remon at £7·95, from a choice of a dozen. Also good are Jaboulet Rhônes; burgundy producers de Villaine, Remoissenet et al; Cavallotto's Barolo; Lungarotti's Rubesco di Torgiano; Viña Ardanza Rioja; a dozen Loires and a page of German wines.

CHEF: Helen Wynne PROPRIETORS: Helen and John Wynne
OPEN: Tue to Sat, D only MEALS: 7.30 to 10.30
PRICES: £7 (£10) CARDS: Access, Amex, Diners
SEATS: 50. Private parties: 18 main room. Children's helpings. Wheelchair access. Jazz

ESHER Surrey map 3

Les Deux Amis [new entry, zero rated]

17 Queens Road, Hersham, Esher KT12 5LS
WALTON-ON-THAMES (0932) 227412 £21

An old-fashioned restaurant where the lamb cutlets have little paper crowns round the bones and the menu leans heavily on the likes of prawns and grilled grapefruit for starters. But the execution has been good, from fettuccine to baked avocado with mushrooms and aubergines with a Cheddar sauce. The half-chicken with tarragon and butter is served with its pan juices. Vegetables are lightly cooked and to finish the omelette surprise is good. Forty basic wines. More reports, please.

CHEF: Mike Bryant PROPRIETORS: M.Frow and Mike Bryant
OPEN: Tue to Sat, exc Sat L MEALS: 12 to 2, 7 to 11
PRICES: £16 (£21). Cheaper set L available CARDS: Access, Amex, Diners, Visa
SEATS: 60. 5 tables outside. Private parties: 70 main room. Vegetarian meals. Children's helpings (exc Fri and Sat after 8). Smart dress preferred. Wheelchair access. Music. Air-conditioned

Read's [new entry, zero rated]

4 The Parade, Claygate, Esher KT10 0NU
ESHER (0372) 65105 £10–£16

A small, family restaurant run with flair and enthusiasm by Stephen, Sheila, Ann and Bill, where good ingredients are cooked to a high standard and attractively presented. Some English and French dishes on the seasonally changing menu avoid richness: home-made gravlax with dill sauce; a salad of avocado, cucumber, tomato and grapes with herby vinaigrette; and plain grilled Dover sole. Others don't: creamy seafood pancake; scallop thermidor; and a generous helping of well-hung fillet steak with mushrooms and a sauce of stock, red wine and bonemarrow. Crème brûlée arrives warm, and tortoni combines ice-cream, macaroons soaked in Drambuie, chopped almonds and cream. Strawberry sorbet has been disappointing. Service is cheerful, even when they're packed. The short wine list has house French at £4·85. CELLARMAN'S CHOICE: Gewürztraminer, La Cigogne '82 at £8·95.

CHEF: Stephen Read PROPRIETORS: Stephen and William Read
OPEN: Tue to Sun, exc Sun D MEALS: 12 to 2, 7 to 10.30 (11 Sat)
PRICES: £11 (£16), Set L £5·95 (£10) CARDS: Access, Amex, Diners, Visa
SEATS: 28. Private parties: 38 main room. Vegetarian meals by arrangement. Children's helpings (L only). Smart dress preferred. Wheelchair access. Music. Air-conditioned

ETON Berkshire map 3

Eton Wine Bar [8/20]

82–83 High Street, Eton SL4 6AF
WINDSOR (075 35) 54921 and 55182 £14

A stripped-pine wine bar with church pews, and with flowers in hanging baskets. The food is above average for wine bars – quiches; smoked mackerel with horseradish; chicken, cucumber and pasta; nut and honey tart. Good wines, too, including St Nicolas de Bourgueil '83 at £8·50.

CHEFS: Amanda Hawkins, Caroline Gilbey and Linda Gilbey PROPRIETORS: William Gilbey, Caroline Gilbey, Michael Gilbey and Linda Gilbey
OPEN: all week CLOSED: 5 days at Christmas, Easter Sun MEALS: 12 to 2.30, 6 (7 Sun) to 10.30
PRICES: £8 (£14). Service 10% CARDS: Access, Visa
SEATS: 75. 5 tables outside. Private parties: 34 main room. Vegetarian meals. Children welcome. Wheelchair access. Music

EVERSHOT Dorset map 2

▲ *Summer Lodge* [12/20]

Evershot DT2 0JR
EVERSHOT (093 583) 424
between A37 and A356, 10m NW of Dorchester **Real Food** £18

The Corbetts claim to have rare supplies of traditionally made Blue Vinney on their cheeseboard. Old farmers who remember this great traditional cheese say that it was drier than this one, making it almost like a Parmesan, but that may be because it had matured longer or they remember one of the failures. The newer Dorset Blue is creamier and very blue, the colour brought about by the injection of penicillin; traditional Vinney is hand-skimmed (and used to be matured for 18 months in vats of cider) and one in four would not take on the colour that John Arlott calls 'the divine accident of the blue'. It should be moist and very rich and eaten not with any roll but with Dorset knobs, as it is here. Summer Lodge is a homely, comfortable hotel but if there are tables free, bookings are accepted from non-residents. There is no choice at the meal but it is honest, careful cooking built around excellent steak en croûte with béarnaise sauce; roast lamb wih redcurrant sauce; soufflé-like onion quiches. The principles behind the kitchen raise the standard of the food – home-made cheese straws; tureens of vegetable soups left on the table; fresh granary rolls; fresh figs served with the cheeses. Sweets are always mentioned in reports – lemon syllabub; almond roulade; chocolate cake. The wine list is varied and strongest in vintage clarets, and is not overpriced. CELLARMAN'S CHOICE: Ch. Pavie (St Emilion) '76 at £17·50.

CHEFS: Margaret Corbett and Anne Knebel PROPRIETORS: Nigel and Margaret Corbett
OPEN: all week, D only CLOSED: Dec and Jan MEALS: 8
PRICES: Set D £14 (£18) CARDS: Access, Visa
SEATS: 28. Tables outside. Private parties: 28 main room. Car-park, 30 places. Vegetarian meals. No children under 8. Smart dress preferred. One sitting
ACCOMMODATION: 9 rooms, all with bath/shower. B&B £30 to £50. No children under 8. No pets in public rooms. Garden. Outdoor swimming-pool. Tennis. Croquet. Games room. Phone. Doors close at 12 [GHG]

EVESHAM Hereford & Worcester map 2

▲ *Cedar Restaurant, Evesham Hotel* [10/20]

Cooper's Lane, Evesham WR11 6DA
EVESHAM (0386) 49111 £8–£15

The Jenkinsons run a comfortable, eccentric hotel. Variety is the keynote of their menu – duck curry and Caribbean kebabs line up alongside boeuf en croûte and sweetcorn fritters. Sweets are as disparate as kiwi and ugli fruit cheesecake, and mulberries from the tree in the garden served with cream liqueur and a burned sugar topping. The buffet/grill lunch is good value. The wine list displays even more of the gipsy, ignoring France in favour of Chile, Russia, Malta . . . Wines from Texas are said to be on the way too. There are three California Gewürztraminers that make an interesting comparison with the Alsace originals, but the real strength is in the up-and-coming Australian wines.
CELLARMAN'S CHOICE: Rosemount Chardonnay '84 at £9.

CHEF: Kathy Young PROPRIETORS: The Jenkinson family
OPEN: all week CLOSED: 25 and 26 Dec MEALS:12.30 to 2, 7 to 9.30
PRICES: £12 (£15), Set L from £5·15 (£8). Service inc CARDS: Access, Amex, Diners, Visa
SEATS: 55. Private parties: 20 private room. Car-park, 55 places. Vegetarian meals. Children's helpings. Wheelchair access (also WC)
ACCOMMODATION: 34 rooms, 33 with bath/shower. B&B £35 to £48. Baby facilities. Pets welcome. Afternoon teas. Garden. Croquet. Putting. TV. Phone. Doors close at 12. Confirm by 6 [GHG]

The 1987 Guide *will appear before Christmas 1986, so reports are particularly important in the spring. Report forms are at the back of this book, but just write a letter if you prefer. Address them to* The Good Food Guide, *Freepost, 14 Buckingham Street, London WC2N 6BR. No stamp is necessary if you post in the UK.*

▲ *This restaurant has rooms.*

EWHURST Surrey map 3

Windmill Inn [9/20]

Pitch Hill, Ewhurst GU6 7NN
CRANLEIGH (0483) 277566
N of Ewhurst, on Shere Road £9

A fine view, fine beers, fine roast-beef salad, and fresh crabs and lobsters up from Selsey Bill in summer.

CHEF: Mrs Holland PROPRIETORS: Mr and Mrs Holland
OPEN: all week MEALS: 12 to 2.15, 7 to 10.15
PRICES: £6 (£9), Snacks from 50p (55p)
SEATS: 40. 19 tables outside. Car-park, 25 places. Vegetarian meals by arrangement. Children's helpings. Wheelchair access. Air-conditioned

EYNSHAM Oxfordshire map 2

Edwards [9/20]

4 Lombard Street, Eynsham OX8 1HT
OXFORD (0865) 880777 £14

An undergraduate of a restaurant. It looks young and fresh-faced but does not yet have all the savoir faire that will come. Nonetheless, there is fine kedgeree for Sunday brunch with the papers and Renny Cope is a flamboyant hostess. Husband Ken is the actor. Ruddles beers. A short wine list with most bottles around £5.

CHEF: Renny Cope PROPRIETORS: Kenneth and Renny Cope
OPEN: all week, exc Sat L and Sun D MEALS: 12 to 2.30, 7 to 10
PRICES: £9 (£14). Cheaper buffet L available. Cover 50p CARDS: Access, Visa
SEATS: 60. Private parties: 50 main room, 20 private room. Car-park, 8 places. Vegetarian meals. Children's helpings. Wheelchair access (also WC). Music. Air-conditioned

FADMOOR North Yorkshire map 6A

Plough Inn [14/20]

Fadmoor YO6 6HY
KIRKBYMOORSIDE (0751) 31515 **Real Food** £11

In spring 1986, after 16 years in their remote pub, the Browns plan to leave and start afresh. In the meantime in the back room, which is set with an old-fashioned dresser, pewter candlesticks, starched linen on polished wooden tables and with a huge tapestry hanging across one wall, it remains possible to eat as well as anywhere in Yorkshire. Half a dozen langoustines arrive in their shells with nutcrackers, a small fork, a small pot of aïoli and warm bread rolls. Duck and steaks are the pillar of the menu, together with handsome bowls of vegetables (including the famous cabbage, onion and garlic salad). Special mentions have been made for the Stilton and walnut pâté, beef collops in madeira sauce, and even the chilli con carne, which was served in the bar to someone who could not get a table in the dining-room – Saturday nights are booked solid for months ahead. To finish there are scoops of coffee and walnut ice-cream, or excellent hazel-nut and chocolate gateau. There is plenty of fine drinking to be found in a cellar that stretches from Bulgarian Merlot '79 at £4 to Ch. Lynch-Bages '75 at £18·50. Many thanks for many fine meals, Mr and Mrs Brown.

CHEF: K.Brown PROPRIETORS: D.P. and K.Brown
OPEN: Tue to Sat, D only. Bar L Sat, Sun, bank hols CLOSED: 1 week Feb, May and Oct; Christmas and New Year MEALS: 12 to 1.30, 7.30 to 8.30
PRICES: Set D from £8·40 (£11). Bar meals from £1·30. Service inc
SEATS: 25. Private parties: 8 private room. Car-park, 15 places. No children under 8. Air-conditioned

FARINGDON Oxfordshire — map 2

▲ *Bell Hotel* [11/20]

Market Place, Faringdon SN7 7HP
FARINGDON (0367) 20534 — £10–£18

The building is in the village square and has character. Behind the bar and lounge and next to the hotel reception is the dining-room, now being renovated. The menu embraces the conservative, such as Mediterranean prawns (although in fact they are local), as well as some promising, if rather elaborate modern dishes. Beef has been good, whether roast, as fillet with green peppercorn and brandy sauce, or stuffed with oysters and a raspberry vinegar and red wine sauce. Another sound pointer to the quality of Steven Williams' cooking has been a terrine of Jerusalem artichokes with a mushroom and truffle cream sauce. Other dishes may be clumsier. The wine list is evolving at a slightly slower pace than the food. House choices of claret, Bergerac and Gros Plant are all £5·85.

CHEF: Steven Williams PROPRIETOR: W.Dreyer
OPEN: all week MEALS: 12.30 to 2, 7 to 9.30 (10 Fri and Sat)
PRICES: £15 (£18), Set L and D from £7·95 (£10), Snacks from 65p. Service inc
CARDS: Access, Amex, Diners, Visa
SEATS: 45. 8 tables outside. Private parties: 55 main room, 18 private room. Car-park, 12 places. Vegetarian meals. Children's helpings. Wheelchair access (also WC). Music
ACCOMMODATION: 11 rooms, 7 with bath/shower. B&B £19·75 to £26·75. Children welcome. Baby facilities. Afternoon teas. Doors close at 11. Confirm by 6 [GHG]

FARNHAM Surrey — map 3

Tirolerhof [12/20]

84 West Street, Farnham GU9 7EN
FARNHAM (0252) 723277 — £14–£17

The atmosphere can lurch into the oompah even though Helmuth Staffler puts on his lederhosen only at weekends. Nonetheless, the cooking of Viennese dishes is some of the best we have eaten in the last few years. The rye bread is baked every day and the matjes herrings, marinated with onions and apples and served with cold schnapps, are first-class, as are soufflés. The Bauernschmauss is a spectacularly large and spicy main course of smoked rib, a pork and a beef sausage, dumplings and sauerkraut. Other European dishes show care, for example the fresh herbs in the vinaigrette for the asparagus and avocado, but the Dover sole has been less impressive. Ice-cream and strudels are home-made, and all round the puddings are excellent. A well-chosen Austrian wine list includes reasonably priced dessert wines by the glass.

CHEF: Gerhard Krug PROPRIETORS: Helmuth Staffler and Gerhard Krug
OPEN: Tue to Sat, D only CLOSED: 7 to 23 July MEALS: 7 to 10.30 (1am Fri and Sat)
PRICES: £11 (£17), Set D from £10 (£14). Service 10% set D only CARDS: Access, Amex, Diners, Visa
SEATS: 100. Private parties: 60 main room, 60 private room. Vegetarian meals. Children's helpings. Smart dress preferred. Music

FARNLEY TYAS West Yorkshire — map 5

Golden Cock [new entry, zero rated]

Farnley Tyas HD4 6UD
HUDDERSFIELD (0484) 661979 and 663563
off A629, 3m SE of Huddersfield — £11–£19

This pub – the building is dated 1740 – has a reputation for serving enormous portions. Orders are taken in the bar and meals served in a relaxed atmosphere in the royal blue and white dining-room. The size of the chateaubriand is staggering. Peter John Midwood trained at Berne and the Swiss influence is evident in curried beef, smoked trout mousse wrapped in smoked salmon and set in aspic, and the calorific sweets trolley. Game is a feature, in season, and there are usually half a dozen vegetables. House French is £5·50. More reports, please.

CHEFS: Peter John Midwood and David Midwood PROPRIETOR: Peter John Midwood
OPEN: all week, exc Sat L and Sun D MEALS: 12.15 to 2, 7.15 to 9.45
PRICES: £12 (£19), Set L £6·95 (£11), Snacks and bar meals from 90p (£1). Cheaper set L and D available CARDS: Access, Amex, Diners, Visa
SEATS: 125. 9 tables outside. Private parties: 24 main room, 40 private room. Car-park, 75 places. Vegetarian meals. Children's helpings. No jeans in rest. Wheelchair access (also wc). Music

FARRINGTON GURNEY Avon — map 2

▲ *The Old Parsonage* [12/20]

Main Street, Farrington Gurney BS18 5VB
TEMPLE CLOUD (0761) 52211
on A37 12m S of Bristol — **Real Food** £17

The Gofton-Watsons' Queen Anne house, with its romantic, well-kept and at night floodlit garden, still provides some of the best honest cooking in the area, though the atmosphere has atrophied some – a few jokes wouldn't go amiss. The napery stars instead – gleaming silver and polished glass. The menu does not change much either, and relies heavily on dairy produce, but the details, from the wonderful hot rolls with unsalted Normandy butter, remain of a standard for 12 points. Trout is lightly smoked; thin pancakes are filled with fresh spinach and cream cheese. The quality of the meat – dressed and hung by a local butcher – is high: lamb comes with herb butter and pork is served with an orange-flavoured demi-glace, though both are cooked well beyond pink, according to local taste. Sweets are either iced or calorific, and the coffee, despite coming in the famous silver jug, may have been left to stew. A clever choice of wines for a short list includes plenty of halves. House claret is £5 or try the CELLARMAN'S CHOICE: Ch. la Bécade '78 at £8·75.

CHEF: H.M.Gofton-Watson PROPRIETORS: W.E. and H.M.Gofton-Watson
OPEN: Tue to Sun, exc Sun D (all week for residents) CLOSED: 25 to 28 Dec and Good Friday
MEALS: 12.30 to 1.30, 7 to 10
PRICES: £12 (£17). Service 10%
SEATS: 26. Private parties: 14 main room, 12 private room. Car-park, 100 places. Vegetarian meals by arrangement. Children's helpings. Wheelchair access (also WC)
ACCOMMODATION: 3 rooms, all with bath/shower. B&B £17·50 to £35. Children welcome. Baby facilities. No pets. Garden

FAVERSHAM Kent map 3

Read's [new entry, zero rated]

Painters Forstal, Faversham ME13 0EE
FAVERSHAM (0795) 535344
2m S of Faversham £12–£19

David Pitchford is thought, in some circles, to be one of the finest chefs in the south east of England, offering as he does good sauces; elegant presentation; adequate portions and food backed by an excellent wine list. The cooking is varied, from mussel soup lightly flavoured with curry to a mousse of maize-fed chicken with wild mushrooms and a provençale tomato chutney. Meats have been excellent – fillet of beef (from the butcher in Wincheap, Canterbury) served with an anchovy sauce, or veal kidneys with mustard sauce and vegetables served from a copper pan on to a side plate. The unusual wine list includes '50s and '60s clarets and also burgundies which may be pricier, but there is also house wine at £4·95. CELLARMAN'S CHOICE: Ch. Durfort-Vivens '70 at £18·60. More reports, please.

CHEF: David Pitchford PROPRIETORS: David and Rona Pitchford
OPEN: Mon to Sat CLOSED: 1st 2 weeks Aug MEALS: 12 to 2, 7 to 10
PRICES: £12 (£19), Set L from £7·50 (£12). Cover 50p CARDS: Amex, Diners, Visa
SEATS: 40. 3 tables outside. Private parties: 72 main room. Car-park, 30 places. Children's helpings. Wheelchair access (1 step; also WC)

FAWLEY Oxfordshire map 2

Walnut Tree [10/20]

Fawley RG9 6JE
TURVILLE HEATH (049 163) 360 and 617
off A4155, between Henley and Marlow £15

The dining-room is calmer than the bar, though the food is the same – honest cooking of whatever the markets supply, such as smoked trout with horseradish, pheasant pâté, enormous portions of venison hiding a bed of sauerkraut, and trout amandine. The smoked dishes are a feature, cured in the Norwegian style.

Restaurants rating 10 and 11 serve the best food in the locality.

Plenty of recommendations for sweets, from treacle tart to lemon syllabub. There are some clarets and burgundies that are not expensive and also some '71 Germans. House wines are £4·75. CELLARMAN'S CHOICE: Muscadet, St Vincent '83 at £5·75, or Ch. Gruaud-Larose '76 at £19·95.

CHEF: Frank Harding PROPRIETORS: W.Brakspear and Sons plc
OPEN: all week MEALS: 12 to 2, 7 to 10
PRICES: £9 (£15) CARDS: Access, Visa
SEATS: 55. 4 tables outside. Private parties: 40 main room. Car-park, 40 places. Vegetarian meals. Children's helpings. Wheelchair access (also wc)

FELIXSTOWE Suffolk — map 3

Andre's [new entry, zero rated]

2 Manning Road, Felixstowe IP11 8AS
FELIXSTOWE (0394) 270199 — £13

'My aim is to fight the war against the ever-increasing fast-food society,' declares Robert Vassili from his small French restaurant. His manifesto is a short menu of classically inclined dishes that changes every five weeks. Fish is a major armament – crab Mornay, sardines, local sole either grilled or meunière, lobster en croûte. There are also good reports of the steaks and Stroganoff and the Dutch apple tart to finish. Service is steady and professional. Thirty wines, with house Italian at £5·30 a litre. More reports from the battlefront, please.

CHEF/PROPRIETOR: Robert Vassili
OPEN: Mon to Sat, exc Mon and Sat L MEALS: 12 to 2, 7 to 10
PRICES: Set L and D £8·50 (£13). Service 10% CARDS: Access, Amex, Diners, Visa
SEATS: 30. Private parties: 36 main room. Wheelchair access. Music

FELSTED Essex — map 3

Rumbles Cottage Restaurant [new entry, zero rated]

Braintree Road, Felsted CM6 3DJ
GREAT DUNMOW (0371) 820996 — £10–£13

Small, intimate restaurant in a sixteenth-century cottage in the village centre. Joy Hadley does all the cooking herself. The menu changes weekly, roaming from garlic soup to Arabian lamb casserole to steak, pigeon and mussel pie. The spicing department has been busy with some dishes, notably the chicken in papillote with cumin, turmeric, ginger, garlic and yoghourt. Sweets have all been liked: honey and whisky ice-cream, plum and port mousse, elderflower cheesecake. Plentiful coffee. The 25 wines are a varied, interesting choice and include a Gewürztraminer '83 at £6·50. House red at £6 or CELLARMAN'S CHOICE: Ch. Caronne-Ste-Gemme '79 at £9·50. More reports, please.

CHEF/PROPRIETOR: E. Joy Hadley
OPEN: Wed to Sun, exc Sat L and Sun D CLOSED: 3 weeks in Feb MEALS: 12 to 2, 7 to 9
PRICES: £9 (£13), Set L from £6·25 (£10) CARDS: Access, Visa
SEATS: 38. Private parties: 24 main room, 10 and 8 private rooms. Vegetarian meals. Children's helpings. Wheelchair access

FELTHAM Greater London map 3

W.R.Grant [9/20]

499 Staines Road, Bedfont, Feltham TW14 8BN
01-890 3845 £2

This is a fish and chip shop serving only take-aways and staffed by people in blue and white striped aprons and straw boaters. The quality of the fish is remarkable. Skate, for example, are Blonde Wings, prized in the trade above other kinds like Roker, Ray, Crownbacks or Thornbacks, and more expensive. Likewise with cod, which is from Peterhead. With Scarborough, Peterhead has the most expensive fish in the trade. Fish is fried in ground-nut oil and the flour used has added rice cones. Potatoes come from the Maris range. Overall the frying technique is first-class, service is fast, and there is a big turnover. Fresh shellfish are sold, too.

PROPRIETOR: W.R.Grant
OPEN: Mon to Sat MEALS: 10 to 2, 4 to 8 (10.30 Thu to Sat)
PRICES: £1·20 (£2). Unlicensed

FLEETWOOD Lancashire map 5

Trafalgar [new entry, zero rated]

42 North Albert Street, Fleetwood FY7 6AR
FLEETWOOD (039 17) 2266 £10–£16

This friendly, rather cramped and good-value-for-money restaurant is on the main street between the betting shop and the launderette. Fish is the main business of the menu – Dover sole, lobster, oysters, mussels. Scallops and queenies are a speciality, as is paella. Vegetables are plentiful, and there are a few classically inclined meat dishes as well. Fundamental wine list. More reports, please.

CHEFS: Michael and Aaron Smith PROPRIETORS: Michael and Dot Smith
OPEN: Tue to Sun, D only, and Sun L MEALS: 12 to 2.30, 7 to 10 (11 Fri and Sat)
PRICES: £11 (£16), Set L £5.50 (£10), Set D £7·50 (£12)
SEATS: 40. Private parties: 20 main room. Vegetarian meals. Children's helpings. Wheelchair access. Music. Air-conditioned

New restaurants that we have not been able to assess completely are given a zero rating for this year. We are particularly keen to have reports on these places.

Restaurant tricks (4): Charging for service but leaving the total on the credit card slip blank, thus inviting an extra tip.

Restaurant tricks (5): Pricing wine to include VAT and then adding another 15 per cent on the total at the end of the meal.

The 1987 Guide *will appear before Christmas 1986, so reports are particularly important in the spring. Report forms are at the back of this book, but just write a letter if you prefer. Address them to* The Good Food Guide, *Freepost, 14 Buckingham Street, London WC2N 6BR. No stamp is necessary if you post in the UK.*

FLITWICK Bedfordshire map3

▲ *Flitwick Manor* [11/20]

Church Road, Flitwick MK45 1AE
FLITWICK (0525) 712242
off A5120, S of Flitwick £12–£25

A Union Jack suitably flies over this classical late-seventeenth-century house set by 50 acres of parkland with a three-acre lake and a 200-yard drive lined with lime trees. Somerset Moore has organised a young team to execute his menus, which lean strongly towards fish – a speciality is a plate of lobster, crab, prawns, langoustines and a Helford oyster. The simpler dishes, such as moules marinière, tend to be good, while the ornately presented gravlax stuffed with a smoked trout mousse impresses less. Some of the saucing and attention to detail is still too unpolished to rate a score of 12, but the sweets are strong, notably the chocolate and Grand Marnier mousse. Coffee with petits fours is served by the fire in the lounge. A blue-blooded wine list draws heavily from the quality merchant Robin Yapp. Mark-ups are just over the hundred per cent line – it is strong in the Loire and the Rhône, but there is a quintet of Alsace with a pair from the characterful Charles Schleret, who has been winning quite a few medals for his quality. House Saumur is £6·80.

CHEFS: Somerset Moore, Alistair Lawton and Sarah Burrows
PROPRIETORS: Mr and Mrs Somerset Moore
OPEN: all week, exc Sun D (residents only) MEALS: 12 to 2, 7 to 9.30
PRICES: £16 (£25), Set L from £7·75 (£12), Set D from £7·75 (£12). Snacks from £1·50 (£3) CARDS: Access, Amex, Diners, Visa
SEATS: 90. 8 tables outside. Private parties: 60 main room; 14 and 45 private rooms. Vegetarian meals. Car-park, 70 places. No pipes in dining-room. Children's helpings. Wheelchair access (also WC)
ACCOMMODATION: 7 rooms, 6 with bath/shower. B&B £55 to £60. Afternoon teas. Children welcome. No pets. Garden. Croquet. Tennis. Darts. Table tennis. Helicopter pad. TV. Phone. Scenic [GHG]

FOLKESTONE Kent map 3

BACKGROUND BRIEFING: *The fishing fleet in Folkestone is just a handful of boats compared to its French counterpart in Boulogne. Most of its catch is sold wholesale at the market on the quay, but fish is available along the coast in Hythe, where Griggs have a fish shop in the High Street and a lock-up garage on the beach (next to the boats), which is open in the week. They smoke their own cod, which is magnificent, and have the pick of the local catch of sole. The Dungeness boats also sell direct. The butchers at Brenzett and Aldington on Romney Marsh both take Romney Marsh lamb, although most of it goes for export. Emilio's, 124A Sandgate Road, Folkestone is an old fashioned flambé restaurant that is not over-expensive, has good fish and does a steak tartare in the traditional manner. Rome House at New Romney has a good £4 set lunch of, for example, crudités, vegetable pancake, lamb Stroganoff, and sponge pudding, with coffee included. Places to eat for under £5 a head in Hythe are Davy's wine bar; the Park Road fish shop (cod is 70p, chips 30p and 40p); and the George.*

Real Food *denotes that the restaurant does not use processed food.*

The India [new entry, zero rated]

1 Old High Street, Folkestone CT20 1RJ
FOLKESTONE (0303) 59155 £7 – £15

This is more than just another curry house. Crab kochin is cooked with ginger and coriander, and lobster with white wine and cognac betrays Ali Ashraf's French background. Partridge is done with saffron, lemon, cream and cardamom; duck with cashew nuts, raisins, cardamom and cinnamon. Both rogan josh, and chicken korma with nuts and cream, are highly rated. Desserts include a small round cake, balushai, made with milk, cardamom and almonds. As well as Kingfisher beer there is an Indian white wine called Beena at £5·25. More reports, not necessarily of the special aphrodisiac sauce, please.

CHEF/PROPRIETOR: Ali Ashraf
OPEN: all week MEALS: 12 to 2.30, 6 to 11.30
PRICES: £9 (£15), Set L £6 (£7). Cover charge 40p. Minimum £4·50 CARDS: Access, Amex, Diners, Visa
SEATS: 52. Private parties: 56 main room. Vegetarian meals. Children's helpings. Wheelchair access. Indian music

Paul's [10/20]

2A Bouverie Road West, Folkestone CT20 2RX
FOLKESTONE (0303) 59697 £14

Clean, relaxed, easy-going restaurant that serves wholesome bistro-style food of casseroles and bakes in a rather smart dining-room. Paul Hagger adds a few unusual dishes, such as asparagus with almond butter or venison sausage with chilli sauce. The varied list of 50 wines is not overpriced and has some good-value bottles.

CHEF/PROPRIETOR: Paul Hagger
OPEN: Mon to Sat CLOSED: 1 week winter, 2 weeks summer MEALS: 12 to 2, 7.30 to 9.30
PRICES: £9 (£14). Service 10% CARDS: Access, Visa
SEATS: 44. Private parties: 50 main room. Vegetarian meals by arrangement. Children's helpings by arrangement

FOTHERINGHAY Northamptonshire map 6

Falcon Inn [10/20]

Main Street, Fotheringhay PE8 5HZ
COTTERSTOCK (083 26) 254 £9

This comfortable village pub by the church gets busy on Fridays and Saturdays. Healthy bowls of French onion soup, ham and pea soup, various pâtés, from crab

'My husband said his coral eggs were too good to eat – they looked like a Cretan lady's bosom.' (On eating in Yorkshire)

Restaurant tricks (1): Charging each person for every serving of vegetables even when the diners have shared portions between them.

to chicken liver, and first-rate cod baked in cheese sauce with prawns are served at tables by the bar. The dinner menu can stretch to cold lobster salad, or rabbit cooked in cider with walnuts, as well as elderflower cheesecake. Plenty of puddings. Real ales or try the CELLARMAN'S CHOICE: Ch. Cissac '79 at £7·20

CHEF: Alan Stewart PROPRIETORS: Alan and Jill Stewart
OPEN: Tue to Sun MEALS: 12.30 to 2, 6.45 to 9.45 (7 to 9 Sun)
PRICES: £6 (£9)
SEATS: 50. 10 tables outside. Private parties: 60 main room, 36 and 12 private rooms. Car-park, 30 places. Vegetarian meals by arrangement. Children's helpings. Wheelchair access (also wc). Air-conditioned

FOWEY Cornwall map 1

Food for Thought [10/20]

Town Quay, Fowey PL23 1AT
FOWEY (072 683) 2221 £20

The old custom-house on the quay is now a long, low-ceilinged room with rough stone walls, brown infilling, beams, and a view on to the estuary. Pastry cases are opened to reveal superb quality Cornish lamb, and the parentage of dishes is declared, as with the terrine of leeks Pierre Koffmann (see Tante Claire in London). The style is *nouvelle* with dishes plated in the kitchen, though the execution is not yet sufficiently consistent for the rating to be raised any further. Good dishes have been the duck with Grand Marnier; the mix of sole, turbot, lobster and scallops on a tart; and chicken stuffed with crab and served with a saffron sauce. Others live more dangerously owing to some cavalier saucing. Forty wines, including the white Châteauneuf-du-Pape, Domaine de la Solitude '83, a snip at £7·95.

CHEF: M.J.Billingsley PROPRIETORS: M.J. and C.M.Billingsley
OPEN: Mon to Sat, D only CLOSED: 22 Dec to 1 Mar MEALS: 7 to 10
PRICES: £12 (£20) CARD: Access
SEATS: 40. Private parties: 22 main room. No children under 10. Smart dress preferred. Wheelchair access

Restaurant Cordon Bleu [10/20]

3 The Esplanade, Fowey PL23 1HY
FOWEY (072 683) 2359 £15

A cheerful meeting place for locals, yachtsmen and holiday-makers, with a Victorian bar constructed from the dock and panelling of an old court-room. Fresh fish includes scallops, Dover sole, lobster cooked five ways, and Fowey sea-trout with a sharp yoghourt and gooseberry sauce. Meat also gets a look in: lamb kidneys are cooked with onion and mushrooms in a white wine, mustard and

'I have had a long flirtation with cuisine nouvelle, *but have found that the public is becoming increasingly disenchanted with small if beautifully prepared dishes that become more and more like a production from Kew Gardens.'* (West Country restaurateur)

Stilton sauce; fillet steak is stuffed with mushrooms, pâté and mustard and served in a red wine sauce. House French is £3·80. More reports, please.

CHEFS: Ann Andrew and Stephen Harris PROPRIETORS: L.D. and A. Andrew
OPEN: Mon to Sat D (Thur to Sat D only, Nov to Mar) MEALS: 7 to 9.45 (L by arrangement)
PRICES: £10 (£15) CARDS: Access, Amex, Diners, Visa
SEATS: 40. Private parties: 26 main room, 12 and 10 private rooms. Vegetarian meals. No children under 7. Smart dress preferred. No cigars/pipes in dining-room. Music

FOWLMERE Cambridgeshire — map 3

Chequers Inn [10/20]

Fowlmere SG8 7SR
FOWLMERE (076 382) 369 — £20

An up-market pub dating from 1675, related to the ever-popular George at Stamford (see entry), and offering excellent bar meals. There is a long and elaborate *carte* for the dining-room, which is more hit and miss – as it must be at such length – but the fish dishes, such as seafood soufflé and the salmon with dill, draw good reports. There is roast beef carved off the trolley to go with some of the good wines in the cellar. The two Alsace wines come from Pierre Sparr, who is well respected.

CHEF: Norman Rushton PROPRIETORS: Poste Hotels & Inns
OPEN: all week MEALS: 12 to 2, 7 to 10
PRICES: £14 (£20) Snacks from £1·40 (£2). Cover 60p. Service inc CARDS: Access, Amex, Diners, Visa
SEATS: 50. 10 tables outside. Private parties: 30 main room. Car-park, 50 places. Vegetarian meals. Children's helpings. Wheelchair access (also wc). Air-conditioned

FRENCHBEER see CHAGFORD

FRESSINGFIELD Suffolk — map 6

Fox and Goose [12/20]

Fressingfield IP21 5PB
FRESSINGFIELD (037 986) 247
next to village church — £16–£23

In the centre of the village by the church and pond is this unpretentious, family-run restaurant with beams and a huge brick fireplace. There is a magnificent wine list and honest – not cheap, but effective – cooking of classical dishes, such as tournedos bordelaise or boeuf en croûte. There is now a set menu at £12, but the Clarkes prefer diners to book in advance and order off the *carte* by phone. Good dishes eaten have been provençale fish casserole with white fish, unshelled crab, langoustine, Dublin Bay prawns and plenty of garlic; gazpacho; veal with cream and tarragon. A little more care in the saucing of otherwise excellent pork en croûte and hot raspberry soufflé could lead to a further upping of the rating next year. In the cellar is a formidable assembly of vintage burgundies and clarets. Ch. Margaux '45 is apparently still drinking well for £300 and the other great vintages of '61, '66, '70, '75 are on offer, although only Ch. Talbot remains from '59. More affordable are eight house wines at about £7 or under. CELLARMAN'S CHOICE: Chambolle-Musigny '79, from Delaunay, at £15·50.

CHEF: A.P.Clarke PROPRIETORS: Mr and Mrs A. P. Clarke, Mr and Mrs P. H. Clarke
OPEN: all week, exc Tue CLOSED: 21 to 28 Dec MEALS: 12 to 1.30, 7 to 9
PRICES: £17 (£23), Set L and D £12 (£16) CARDS: Access, Amex, Diners, Visa
SEATS: 28. Private parties: 32 main room. Car-park, 30 places. No children under 8

GLASTONBURY Somerset map 2

▲ *No. 3* [13/20]

Magdalene Street, Glastonbury BA6 9EW
GLASTONBURY (0458) 32129 **Real Food** £15–£23

This Georgian house is a good place to eat lobster. They come up from Cornwall, are kept in a tank, and are only £1 more than the Somerset lamb with ginger and orange. The hotel is a family operation with Michael Gilliat front of house and his daughter Jillian in the kitchen. The menu is built around good-quality meats and fish with some interesting sauces, such as rhubarb and kirsch for venison, or curried fruits with prawn puffs. Traditional Sunday lunch of roast beef, Yorkshire pudding and fresh, well-prepared vegetables has been excellent. The Gilliats are considering selling up, so check when booking. The wine list has exemplary explanations on each bottle and is carefully chosen. CELLARMAN'S CHOICE: Clos de la Coulée de Serrant '83 at £13. 'In times past', explains the wine list, 'this wine was numbered alongside d'Yquem, Château-Chalon and Le Montrachet as one of the finest white wines in France. The wine is kept in bottles for two years at the Château and is very hard to come by; it is undoubtedly the finest wine of the Savennières vineyard area. Made from the chenin blanc grape, it has an unforgettable flavour and richness. Descriptive wine merchants have found an "apple-like tang" in its full-bodied dry midst.' That's telling it.

CHEFS: Jillian Gilliat and Danielle Barton PROPRIETOR: M.D.A.Gilliat
OPEN: Tue to Sat, D only, and Sun L
MEALS: 12.30 to 2, 7.30 to 10
PRICES: Set D £16 to £18 (£21 to £23), Set Sun L £10 to £18 (£15 to £23) CARDS: Amex, Diners, Visa
SEATS: 24. 3 tables outside. Private parties: 36 main room, 18 private room. Car-park, 8 places. Vegetarian meals. Children welcome. No pipes in dining-room. Wheelchair access (also wc)
ACCOMMODATION: 2 rooms, both with bath. B&B £20 to £30. Children welcome. No pets. Garden

Rainbow's End [8/20]

17A High Street, Glastonbury BA6 9DP
GLASTONBURY (0458) 33896 £5

There are two ways in to this all-day vegetarian cafe – at the back is a garden courtyard with herbs and tubs. Shelagh Spear buys herself, mostly direct from Bristol market. She has her converts among the carnivores for inexpensive bread,

Restaurants rating 12 or more serve the best food in the region.

cheese and wine casserole; pizzas; baked potatoes and salads. Counter service. 'No muddy wellies.' Boxed wines.

CHEF/PROPRIETOR: Shelagh Spear
OPEN: all week, exc Wed and Sun MEALS: 10 to 4.30 (5 Sat), L from 12
PRICES: £3 (£5)
SEATS: 30. 4 tables outside. Private parties: 6 main room. Vegetarian meals. Children's helpings. High-chair available. Classical music. Self-service

GLEMSFORD Suffolk map 3

Weeks Restaurant [15/20]

31 Egremont Street, Glemsford CO10 7SA
GLEMSFORD (0787) 281573 **Real Food** £18

A near perfect cameo of a restaurant in a traditionally styled but modern building on the main road through Glemsford. Sue Weeks is a natural hostess while Ian is a master of sauces – wine and prawn for turbot; burgundy for steak cooked precisely; Gruyère, mustard and celery for chicken. The interior is split into a lounge with sofas and original watercolours and a dining-room with a low partition that masks one table from the next. It is a set menu with a modicum of choice, but the dishes are made of the finest local ingredients – mushroom soup with madeira; sole mousseline; calf's liver with shallots and sherry; marvellously simple vegetables. For sweet there may be claret granita, lychee syllabub, or lemon tarts on freshly made shortcrust pastry with an almond cream. The quality of the beef is noticeably high, and the Weeks report good new supplies of partridge and quails raised for their eggs. The atmosphere is tranquil, and the wine list a fine example of quality at reasonable prices. Minor regions are well shown and there is a trio of Rieslings, from Trimbach's Cuvée Frédéric Emile Vendange Tardive '76 at £20·25, to Réserve Speciale '83 from Blanck at £3·95 for a half. CELLARMAN'S CHOICE: Castello di Fonterutoli, Riserva, Chianti Classico, '77 at £7·30.

CHEF: Ian Weeks PROPRIETORS: Ian and Sue Weeks
OPEN: Tue to Sat, D only MEALS: 7.30 to 9
PRICES: Set D £13·95 (£18). Service 10%
SEATS: 20. Car-park, 6 places. Children's helpings. No smoking in dining-room

GOLCAR West Yorkshire map 5

Weavers Shed [11/20]

Knowl Road, Golcar HD7 4AN
HUDDERSFIELD (0484) 654284
off A62, 3m SW of Huddersfield £9–£17

A village restaurant in an old building with flagged floors and beams on the ceilings. The napery is not up to much but the cooking is honest and the atmosphere relaxed. The home-made bread is dark brown, and comes with the

All letters to the Guide *are acknowledged with a list of changes since we went to press.*

vegetable soups to start. Yorkshire puddings are filled with onion sauce, and lamb and venison have been good, as has the fish pie. Vegetables are served in huge tureens; puddings are good. Fifty not over-priced wines.

CHEFS/PROPRIETORS: Betty and Peter Saville
OPEN: Tue to Sun, exc Sat L and Sun D CLOSED: 1st 2 weeks Jan, last 2 weeks July
MEALS: 12 to 2, 7.30 to 9 (9.30 Sat)
PRICES: £12 (£17), Set Sun L £4·75 (£9)
SEATS: 70. Private parties: 30 main room, 30 private room. Car-park, 40 places. Vegetarian meals by arrangement. Children welcome. Smart dress preferred. Wheelchair access (also WC)

GRANTHAM Lincolnshire map 6

Premier Restaurant [10/20]

2–6 North Parade, Grantham NG31 8AN
GRANTHAM (0476) 77855 £10–£19

Despite all the gimmickry that surrounds this, Margaret Thatcher's birthplace and the fabled grocer's shop, the food is well up to scratch. The reception area is a mock-up of how the shop was in the 1930s – all the tinned and packet goods are in their original wrappers and priced as they would have been then. The lounge is reached through a replica of the front door of Number 10. Close inspection of the menu reveals an agenda that changes monthly and is less conservative than might at first appear. Fish and cauliflower soup makes a successful starter, and the quality of the meats lifts main courses of lamb, either baked in pastry or stuffed with mint and leeks; roast beef and Yorkshire pudding; and sweet-pastry Poacher's Pie. Sweets are more predictable, as is the wine list.

CHEF: Tony Griffiths PROPRIETOR: Rodney Cloke
OPEN: Tue to Sun, exc Tue L and Sun D MEALS: 12 to 2, 7 to 10
PRICES: £12 (£19), Set L £6·95 (£10), Set D £12·50 (£16). Cheaper set L available. Minimum £2·50 at L CARDS: Access, Amex, Diners, Visa
SEATS: 48. Private parties: 50 main room. Car-park, 6 places. Vegetarian meals by arrangement. Children's helpings. No jeans. Wheelchair access (also WC). Classical music

GRASMERE Cumbria map 7

▲ *Michaels Nook* [new chef, zero rated]

Grasmere LA22 9RP
GRASMERE (096 65) 496
off A591, 400 yards from The Swan £22–£29

The picture here is confusing. Some backroom upheavals, poor service, and misunderstandings have put off regulars but, at the same time, inspectors who have eaten here most recently are confident that the food is worth a high rating again. It is, of course, nothing like a nook – a large Victorian house, named after Wordsworth's shepherd, in an isolated setting near Rydal Fell. There is a lot of antiquery around the house, from old gramophones to apothecary jars to Persian carpets. The building itself has oak bannisters and high, Adam-style rooms. The bedrooms are named after birds. It is stylish in a jumbled sort of way, and patrolled by an enormous soppy Great Dane called Sebastian. The menu is an interesting combination of classical and modern: convincing dishes have been a salad of asparagus and chicory with hazel-nuts; consommé mikado; medallions of beef with pickled walnuts; pot-roast pork with orange sauce. Vegetables come in quintets in a stainless-steel dish. Lemon pancakes with strawberry sauce are freshly made, and coffee is served with fanciful petits fours in the lounge. It is a strong wine list, with plenty of Latour burgundies, a good selection from the Loire, and pedigree wines from Alsace, too.

CHEF: William MacLeod PROPRIETOR: R.S.E. Gifford
OPEN: all week MEALS: 12.30 to 1, 7.30 to 8 (7 to 7.15 and 9 to 9.15 Sat in summer)
PRICES: Set L £18 (£22), Set D £24 (£29)
SEATS: 28. Private parties: 28 main room, 20 private room. Car-park, 20 places. Vegetarian meals by arrangement. No children under 10. Smart dress preferred. No smoking in dining-room. Wheelchair access. One sitting
ACCOMMODATION: 11 rooms, all with bath/shower. D, B&B £95. No children under 10. No pets. Garden. TV. Scenic

▲ *White Moss House* [13/20]

Rydal Water, Grasmere LA22 9SE
GRASMERE (096 65) 295 **Read Food** £19

Here is real English food: roast local mallard with sage and onion stuffing and a port, claret and damson sauce, served with a quartet of vegetables; Sussex Pond pudding; chocolate brandy cake. A lightness of touch, informed by *cuisine moderne*, lifts many traditional ingredients, as in curried duck and parsnip soup, and sauces, such as mustard béarnaise with Westmorland roast beef, or fennel cream with terrine of salmon and sole. Other sauces are made with a reduction of the cooking juices enlivened with a little alcohol – madeira, oloroso, calvados – or butter, cream or fruit purée. Potatoes are roasted in the fat from the Cumberland sausages. Sorrel, lovage and fennel are home grown, breakfast kippers are free from colouring, and a fine array of English cheeses comes direct from the farms: Cotherstone, Barac and Allendale (a Cumbrian goats' cheese). There is no choice on the menu before the pudding. The atmosphere is formal, but the service is smooth and efficient. Choose your wine from 150 bottles half an hour before you eat: clarets are strong, Louis Latour supplies a lot of the burgundy, and Hugel provides a few excellent Alsace wines.
CELLARMAN'S CHOICE: Sancerre rouge, Les Belles Dames '82, from Gitton, at £8·50, and half-bottles of Châteauneuf-du-Pape, Les Cèdres '69, from Jaboulet, at £7·30.

CHEFS: Peter Dixon and Jean Butterworth PROPRIETORS: Susan and Peter Dixon, Jean and Arthur Butterworth
OPEN: all week, D only CLOSED: Nov to mid-Mar MEALS: 8
PRICES: Set D £14.50 (£19)
SEATS: Private parties: 18 main room. Car-park, 10 places. No children under 10. Smart dress preferred. No smoking in dining-room. Wheelchair access. Classical music. Air-conditioned. One sitting
ACCOMMODATION: 7 rooms, all with bath/shower. B&B £48. No children under 10. Garden. Fishing. Air-conditioned. TV. Scenic. Doors close at 11. Confirm by 4 [GHG]

Reports on good shops, small hotels and cafes in your area are welcome.

GRAYS Essex map 3

R. Mumford & Son [9/20]

6–8 Cromwell Road, Grays RM17 5HF
GRAYS THURROCK (0375) 374153 £9

When this fish and chip shop opened in 1960 it had just 12 seats. Now it is a proper fish and chip restaurant serving 75 people at a time. Fish comes from Billingsgate every day, and crabs are boiled on the premises. Scampi and prawns are hand-shelled and served on a salad (thanks to Marks & Spencer).

CHEFS: R.Mumford and R.Mumford Jnr PROPRIETOR: R.Mumford
OPEN: Mon to Sat CLOSED: 25 and 26 Dec, bank hols MEALS: 11.45 to 2.10, 5.30 to 11
PRICES: £6 (£9). Minimum £2
SEATS: 75. Private parties: 35 main room. Vegetarian meals. Children's helpings. Music. Air-conditioned

GRAYSHOTT Hampshire map 2

Woods [12/20]

Headley Road, Grayshott GU26 6LB
HINDHEAD (042 873) 5555 £20

On the Surrey/Hampshire border, Grayshott is a satellite of Hindhead and has a street and a tall church. The restaurant reveals its shop history in the tiles and the wooden cash-booth from where the waitresses look out at what is going on among the fug from the paraffin lamps. And fug it is, though you don't notice it once acclimatised. The menu has not changed noticeably, which is a pity, because Eric Norrgren is capable of some very fine cooking indeed. There is still excellent gravlax or its meat equivalent of raw beef marinated in madeira and black pepper, with a horseradish, mustard and chive dip; plus some complex dishes such as kidneys stuffed into a veal parcel and served with a béarnaise sauce. Fish and pastry are the best, such as sea-bass with champagne and leek sauce. Saddle of hare with wild mushrooms – some wilder than others – is also notable. Good vegetables, especially gratin dauphinoise, cost extra. Eric Norrgren's training is as a *pâtissier*, which reflects in the strength of the sweets. A well-chosen list of wines, from the good house vin de l'Ecaillère at £4·80 upwards.

CHEF: Eric Norrgren PROPRIETORS: Eric and Dana Norrgren
OPEN: Tue to Sat, D only MEALS: 7 to 12
PRICES: £15 (£20). Cover 45p CARDS: Access, Diners, Visa
SEATS: 35. Private parties: 12 main room. Children welcome. Wheelchair access (also wc)

GREAT DUNMOW Essex map 3

Indian Village [9/20]

15 High Street, Great Dunmow CM6 1AP
GREAT DUNMOW (0371) 3334 and 3597 £9–£13

The building is 500 years old and was a pub until it became a tandoori restaurant in August 1983. The cooking is a cut above the local average. The vegetarian thali consists of thick and delicious dhal, a trio of curries – one based on aubergine, one on okra and one on swede – and excellent nan. The bhajia and the rice can be greasy. Sweets are the usual commercial ones. The service is friendly: at Christmas regulars were given a brandy, a Christmas card and a calendar!

CHEF: Siddique Ahmed PROPRIETOR: Anwar Hossain
OPEN: all week MEALS: 12 to 2.45, 6 to 11.45
PRICES: £8 (£13), Set D £7 (£9). Service inc CARDS: Access, Amex, Diners, Visa
SEATS: 64. Private parties: 20 main room, 8, 6 and 2 private rooms. Vegetarian meals. Children's helpings. Wheelchair access (also WC). Music

The Starr [12/20]

Market Place, Great Dunmow CM6 1AX
GREAT DUNMOW (0371) 4321 Real Food £18–£24

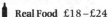

The imposing white building juts into the road. The tarmac outside is adorned with conifers in wooden tubs, and at Christmas a large Christmas tree is hung with fancy lights. There is no menu outside, just a notice to the effect that all the ingredients are fresh so the menu changes, plus an array of awards, in case you didn't think they could cook. This is helpful, because it shields the innocent diner from the full horror of having to read their prices: four new potatoes, £1·15; two calabrese, £1·15. At these prices the waiters make a point of remembering your name and are rather over-chatty. The dining-room is beamed and the variously shaped tables are well distributed around the room. It is an imaginative, largely French-inspired menu with rather too much eye on the presentation, at the expense of the food, to warrant a raising of the rating. Pastry, for instance, appears to be over-kneaded so that it becomes tough enough to cut into heart shapes for the strawberry tart. It looks a picture but does not taste quite as good as it should. Usually, though, tastes do win – witness the robust, English-style terrines; the duck with green peppercorns; the rack of lamb; and the cherry roulade. All red wines seem to be decanted as a matter of course. It is a very fine list, splendidly annotated and with good showings of all the major regions, including Alsace. The mark-ups do not appear to be as greedy as those on the victuals. CELLARMAN'S CHOICE: Australian Cabernet Sauvignon '80, from Brown Bros, at £9·20.

CHEF: Mark Fisher PROPRIETORS: Brian and Valerie Jones
OPEN: all week, exc Sat L and Sun D CLOSED: 3 weeks Aug, 2 weeks at Christmas
MEALS: 12 to 1.30, 7 to 9.30
PRICES: £15 (£24), Set L £12·95 (£18). Service 10% on parties over 6. Licensed, plus bring your own: corkage £4 CARDS: Access, Diners, Visa
SEATS: 60. Private parties: 8 main room. Car-park, 15 places. Vegetarian meals. Children's helpings. Wheelchair access (also WC). Classical music

Restaurants rating 12 or more serve the best food in the region.

'You have to be of a certain disposition to want to drive 100 miles from London to what can sometimes be a Trappist retreat: two visits ago we had the place entirely to ourselves. Mr X can be as elusive as the Loch Ness monster; at other times he appears fleetingly like the white rabbit.' (On a hotel in Hampshire)

GREAT HARWOOD **Lancashire** map 5

Tiffany [new entry, zero rated]

79 Church Street, Great Harwood BB6 7QB
GREAT HARWOOD (0254) 889528 £17

Neil Wigglesworth cooks in view of most of the restaurant to the sound of Dietrich tapes. The decor is pink and grey art deco with a black and white checker-board floor. The staff are handsomely dressed as though they might be working in an American diner, and do a polished job in an atmosphere that is both casual and glamorous. The cooking has been very good, and fish is certainly the highlight: mussel soup, terrine of shrimps, and sole and salmon with three sauces. Beurre blanc is flavoured with lemon to go with poached oysters wrapped in lettuce, and with tarragon to accompany salmon en croûte. Meat, fowl and vegetables have not matched this quality so far and puddings have been unremarkable, except for strawberries injected with Cointreau and dipped in chocolate. There are few wines, but house red and white are £5·25, and CELLARMAN'S CHOICE is Sancerre, Domaine de Sarry '82, for £9. More reports, please.

CHEF: Neil Wigglesworth PROPRIETORS: Brian and Neil Wigglesworth
OPEN: Tue to Sun, exc Sat L and Sun L MEALS: 11.30 to 2.30, 7 to 10.30
PRICES: £11 (£17) CARD: Access
SEATS: 32. Private parties: 16 main room. Vegetarian meals by arrangement. Children's helpings by arrangement. No children under 6. Wheelchair access (also wc). Music

GREAT MILTON **Oxfordshire** map 2

▲ *Le Manoir aux Quat' Saisons* [17/20]

Church Road, Great Milton OX9 7PD
GREAT MILTON (084 46) 8881 and 8803/4 **Real Food** £28–£43

The Manoir is a sensation. To quote from just one report from the correspondents who wrote last year: 'No restaurant will ever be quite the same again – the dishes were exquisite, the portions not big, but we left the table completely satisfied. The rooms are glorious, on a par with The Mandarin in Hong Kong, breakfasts replete with strong coffee, fresh orange juice, Mme Blanc's fantastic brioches and croissants. . . . All round, everyone is made so welcome.' And this is from one of the canniest men in catering: '£75 a head well spent, I reckon. Certainly the best meal I've eaten in Britain, nearly on a par with Girardet in Switzerland.' Raymond Blanc has, miraculously, appeased the money men, ironed out the stiffness in the service and put the kitchen into overdrive. Some of the cooking is simply amazing – orange used with a scallop mousse or with vinegar for one of his light sauces for veal; the old stalwart from the Summertown days of Jerusalem artichoke mousse with an asparagus sauce; breast of pigeon with a nugget of lobster with a red wine sauce, or else the bird baked in salt and served with a sauce perfumed with truffles. Much still owes its allegiance to bourgeois cooking, as in roast milk-fed pork with prunes, or the Bordeaux marriage of lamb with crab served with a lightly curried sauce with basil, or else suckling pig with marjoram. What marks Blanc out is that each dish is designed to show off its component parts so that they taste of themselves. He works as hard finding his ingredients as he does in the kitchen. There is no needless garnishing. Everything on the plate is meant to be eaten and is there for a purpose. There is no over-complication of sauces. Indeed, some dishes are vivid in their simplicity. There is a steak on the menu – well-hung Aberdeen fillet served with its juices bound with a little tomato, caramelised shallots and topped with a herb butter. Of course, other dishes are more sophisticated – the tartare of marinated salmon bound with sour cream, topped with caviare and served with a cucumber salad; pan-fried oysters placed on sliced mango glazed with a curry sabayon; the red mullet given a sauce of veal stock. And for pudding? Soufflés of coconut or apricot; apple tart; chocolate mousse with a caramel. But no, skip the chocolate, for with coffee (at a premium £3) comes a tray of chocolates. All of this is served amid the Englishness of an old manor, with log fires and festooned with flowers, and in summer drinks are served in the surrounding gardens. Of course it is astronomically expensive, but you are unlikely to find ingredients of this quality elsewhere, cooked with such skill and imagination and served with such enjoyment in an historic, elegant building. With all that it is probably good value for money. At lunch, at least, it is just possible to get away for £25, and after all it can cost £10 to watch Tottenham Hotspurs football club these days. In winter there are cut-rate bargain weekend breaks that are less expensive. It is a pity that the cellars have nothing under £10 – the house Sancerre, red or white, is £14·10 – with mark-ups for millionaires, and the list is unbalanced because of it. You could drink the cidre bouché from Normandy or else CELLARMAN'S CHOICE: Domaine de la Bernarde '83, a white from Provence at £15·50, or Volnay, les Brouillards '78 from Rossignol Changarnier at £25.

CHEF/PROPRIETOR: Raymond Blanc
OPEN: L Wed to Sun, D Tue to Sat CLOSED: 4 weeks from 24 Dec MEALS: 12.15 to 2.30, 7.15 to 10.30
PRICES: £31 (£43), Set L from £18·50 (£28). Minimum £15. Service inc
CARDS: Access, Amex, Visa
SEATS: 70. 4 tables outside. Private parties: 10 main room, 35 private room. Vegetarian meals. Car-park, 45 places. Smart dress preferred. No cigars in dining-room. Children's helpings. Wheelchair access (also WC)
ACCOMMODATION: 10 rooms, all with bath/shower. B&B £95 to £180. Deposit: £50. Swimming-pool. Garden. Tennis. Helicopter pad. No children under 7. Pets not allowed, but kennel facilities. TV. Phone. Scenic [GHG]

GRIMSTON Norfolk — map 6

▲ *Congham Hall* [11/20]

Lynn Road, Grimston PE32 1AH
HILLINGTON (0485) 600250 — **Real Food** £12–£24

A fine old Georgian manor house set in 40 acres of parkland with its own orchards, a herb garden that boasts 100 different species, and a kitchen garden for baby vegetables and soft fruit. Chef John McGeever also has the pick of the King's Lynn fishing boats and uses the same game dealer as the Queen. Dinners are showy, running to eight courses including appetiser, a mid-meal sorbet and coffee with petits fours. Dishes veer between the simple and the adventurous – from a herb salad, or Stilton and port pâté, to poached breast of chicken stuffed with Camembert and sorrel mousse, served with onion sauce. Good dishes have

been the seafood ragout and the duck breast with caramelised garlic. Vegetables are firm and neat, and the special Congham Dessert is constructed with fruits, a sorbet and a piece of lemon tart on blackcurrant syrup. Service is relaxed and matches the clean elegance of the surroundings. Concise young wine list.
CELLARMAN'S CHOICE: Gewürztraminer '83, from Sparr, at £9·75.

CHEF: John McGeever PROPRIETORS: T.C. and C.K. Forecast
OPEN: all week, exc Sat L and Sun D MEALS: 12.30 to 2, 7.30 to 9.30
PRICES: Set L from £8 (£12), Set D from £18·75 (£24). Cheaper Set D for residents
CARDS: Access, Amex, Diners, Visa
SEATS: 34. Private parties: 8 main room, 12 private room. Car-park, 50 places. No children under 12. Jacket and tie. No smoking in dining-room. Wheelchair access
ACCOMMODATION: 11 rooms, all with bath/shower. B&B £42 to £52. No children under 12. Pets welcome. Garden. Outdoor swimming-pool. Spa bath. Tennis. Helicopter pad. TV. Phone. Doors close at 11.30. Confirm by 10am

GUILDFORD Surrey — map 3

Rumwong [12/20]

16–18 London Road, Guildford GU1 2AF
GUILDFORD (0483) 36092 — £17

For the last eight years this has been one of readers' favourite places to eat in Surrey. The Thai dishes are helpfully explained and authentically executed. Notable are the todd-mun-pla (fish paste) served with carrot and cucumber sauce, son-in-law eggs and lemon soup, and mussels in brown beans. The menu offers an immense variety of flavours in small portions, and the fish and vegetables are the main pillars. Sweets may not be quite so good. Service is charming. 'We have lots of lovely customers.' Licensed.

PROPRIETORS: Thairama Ltd
OPEN: Tue to Sun MEALS: 12 to 2.30, 6 to 10.45 (later Fri and Sat, 10.15 Sun)
PRICES: £10 (£17) CARDS: Access, Visa
SEATS: 46. Private parties: 20 main room, 25 private room. Children welcome. Smart dress preferred. No-smoking area. Wheelchair access (also wc). Oriental music

Three Kingdoms [11/20]

14 Park Street, Guildford GU1 4XB
GUILDFORD (0483) 61458 and 63902 — £10–£15

Prosperity, health and happiness are the three kingdoms, and Mr Lau's pink Chinese restaurant has the first two in good measure and usually offers the third, except when the service is under strain. It is a seductive menu, strong on centrepieces like Peking duck; steamed sea-bass; Chinese fondue. Many of the accompanying dishes are hard to find outside central London – smoked fish Peking-style or fresh prawns with ginger, garlic and tomato, flambé in Chinese liqueur and served in their shells. Especially good have been the crispy beef with

We keep files on every restaurant, so reports of poor meals are just as valuable as reports of good meals because they save unnecessary inspections.

chilli; grilled chicken with garlic and lemon; and sweet and sour prawns. The waiters are friendly. Some Cantonese dishes have been added with the arrival of a third chef. Good choice of wines by Chinese restaurant standards, though there are no bargains. The Chinese liqueurs Mou Tai and Mei Kwei are £1·40 a glass.

CHEFS: C.H.Wong, E.Chan and Ken Lau PROPRIETOR: Ken Lau
OPEN: all week CLOSED: 25 to 26 Dec MEALS: 12 to 2.30, 6 to 11.15
PRICES: £9 (£15), Set L £6·50 (£10), Set D £10·50 (£14). Service 10% CARDS: Access, Amex, Diners, Visa
SEATS: 130. Private parties: 100 main room; 60 private room. Vegetarian meals. Children welcome. Music. Air-conditioned

GUIST Norfolk map 6

Tollbridge [12/20]

Dereham Road, Guist NR20 5NN
FOULSHAM (036 284) 359
on B1110, 10m SW of Holt **Real Food** £11–£14

The river Wensum runs by this old, red-bricked toll house and supplies a surprising amount for the menu – eels, pike, crayfish. The samphire and the wild mushrooms come from further afield. William and Glynis Stark have built up a reputation over the last nine years for using local produce, though as often as not there will be sophisticated dishes, such as feuilleté of crab with sorrel, or veal sweetbreads with two pepper sauces. Good dishes have ranged from savoury pancakes to ample portions of haddock mousse, to wild mallard with a port sauce. Sweets get their own menu and are usually a variation on fruit ice-cream in a tuile; chocolate mousse; or a gratin of fruits. The cover charge has been dropped – a welcome move to get rid of this archaic habit. If the weather is warm there is a terraced garden for drinks. There are 50 carefully chosen and not overpriced wines. CELLARMAN'S CHOICE: Pouilly Fumé, de Ladoucette '82 at £6 for a half.

CHEF: Wiliam Stark PROPRIETORS: William and Glynis Stark
OPEN: Tue to Sat CLOSED: 3 weeks Jan, 1 week Oct MEALS: 12 to 1.45, 7 to 9.30
PRICES: £10 (£14), Set L £7 (£11). Minimum £7 CARD: Visa
SEATS: 44. 6 tables outside. Private parties: 44 main room. Car-park, 25 places. Vegetarian meals by arrangement. Children's helpings. No cigars in dining-room before 9.30. Wheelchair access (also WC)

GULWORTHY Devon map 1

▲ *Horn of Plenty* [12/20]

Gulworthy PL19 8JD
TAVISTOCK (0822) 832528
off A390, 3m W of Tavistock £14–£23

Half a dozen rooms have been added to the Stevensons' valley-top restaurant, with views, they say, stretching 28 miles towards Bodmin Moor. Regulars report

The Guide *does not accept free meals.*

that Sonia's cooking is recapturing some of its sparkle – excellent salmon and sorrel mousse, that old stalwart of lamb in pastry, guinea-fowl with lentils, and, to finish, Devonshire junket with clotted cream. A strong French wine list has house Côtes du Rhône at £6·85.

CHEFS/PROPRIETORS: S. and P.R.N. Stevenson
OPEN: all week, exc Thu L and D, and Fri L MEALS: 12 to 2, 7 to 9.30
PRICES: £13 (£23), Set L £12·50 (£14)
SEATS: 68. 5 tables outside, L only. Private parties: 48 main room. Car-park, 30 places. Vegetarian meals. Children's helpings (L only). Wheelchair access (also WC)
ACCOMMODATION: 6 rooms, all with bath/shower. Rooms for disabled. B&B £35 to £55. No babies. No pets. Garden. Helicopter pad. TV. Phone. Scenic. Doors close at 12. Confirm by 6

GUNTHORPE Nottinghamshire map 5

Mr Toad's [10/20]

Riverfront, Gunthorpe NG14 7FB
NOTTINGHAM (0602) 663409 £12

An unpretentious and unlicensed bistro. Good dishes have been mushrooms stuffed with celeriac purée, red peppers stuffed with couscous, fillets of lamb with honey, pork in red wine, and poached salmon. Vegetables are well handled. To finish there are fruit mousses.

OPEN: Tue to Sat, D only CLOSED: bank hols MEALS: 7.45 to 9.30
PRICES: £10 (£12). Unlicensed, but bring your own: no corkage
SEATS: 28. Private parties: 28 main room. Car-park, 20 places. Vegetarian meals. Children welcome. Wheelchair access

HADLEIGH Suffolk map 3

Weaver's [12/20]

25 High Street, Hadleigh IP7 5AG
HADLEIGH (0473) 827247 £15

There's a herb garden at the back of these three converted sixteenth-century weavers' cottages which Roy Ghijben makes full use of throughout a solid provincial menu. The small beamed dining-room is hung with trinkets from old Victorian knife grinders to a gamekeeper's copper oven; the walls and cloths are Laura Ashley. One of the two dining-rooms becomes a cheaper bistro mid-week. Of many persuasive dishes that push up the rating there have been excellent tomato and tarragon soup; a white fish and scallop ragout with Parmesan, garnished with a langoustine; guinea-fowl and apple pie; and plainly cooked lemon sole with a tomato concasse with herb sauce. The vegetables are impressive – fried potatoes with crumbled sausagemeat, beetroot, and fried courgettes – as, too, are the desserts, such as mergingues with butterscotch sauce and toasted almonds, fools of elderflower and gooseberry, and even an unlikely sounding chocolate marquise with kiwi and strawberry. Sally Ghijben runs the front of house (and makes the sweets) with a smile and with help from local youngsters. The wine list is a clever working of the less expensive regions with some good bargains, especially from the Rhône. House Bulgarian Chardonnay is

£4·45. CELLARMAN'S CHOICE: Châteauneuf-du-Pape, Domaine du Vieux Télégraphe '81 at £8·35.

CHEF: Roy Ghijben PROPRIETORS: Roy and Sally Ghijben
OPEN: Tue to Sat, D only CLOSED: Christmas to New Year, 2 weeks July MEALS: 7 to 9.30
PRICES: £11 (£15). Cut-price menu in bistro CARDS: Access, Visa
SEATS: 35. 2 tables outside. Private parties: 24 main room. Vegetarian meals. Children's helpings. No children under 5. No pipes in dining-room. Wheelchair access (also WC). Light classical music

HADLOW Kent — map 3

La Crémaillère [10/20]

The Square, Hadlow TH11 0DD
TONBRIDGE (0732) 851489 — £14

Hamson Maillard's pleasant French restaurant with handwoven menus, a vine-covered conservatory for summer eating and a 200-year-old dining-room with large open fires, candles and decanters has improved over the last year. The rolls are served hot, and confit of duck has come in an excellent apple and cider sauce. Vegetables are served in hot copper pots, and the staff are friendly and knowledgeable. It is good value. There are usually around 60 mainly French wines bought from auctions.

CHEF: Michel Maillard PROPRIETOR: Hamson Maillard
OPEN: Mon to Sat, exc Sat L MEALS: 12.30 to 1.30, 8 to 9
PRICES: Set L £10 (£14), Set D £10 (£14) CARDS: Access, Amex, Diners, Visa
SEATS: 31. Private parties: 19 main room. Children welcome

HALIFAX West Yorkshire — map 5

▲ *Holdsworth House Hotel* [new entry, zero rated]

Holdsworth, Halifax HX2 9T4
HALIFAX (0422) 240024 — £18

Holdsworth House is four miles north of Halifax off the Keighley Road. It is an attractive stone building apparently dating from the seventeenth century, with a small but neat grass garden at the front. The entrance lobby has an old world charm with panelled walls, wooden bench seating and a carved wooden staircase. There are three small dining-rooms adjoining, two with stone walls and one with panelling – all of them have a selection of framed paintings. Tables are of polished wood and decorated with fresh flowers and candles. The menu is modern and manorial with well-presented and imaginative dishes. Soups, such as scallop and spinach, and pistou, have been excellent, and main courses on the whole utilise good ingredients, although some of them may not have known each other for very long, which can mean they do not have all the impact we would like. Carp is poached and served with a basil and lemon sauce. Vegetables and sweets are good – especially the poached pears with lime and a peach syrup. The house is rightly proud of its wines – excellent clarets, burgundies, and

An index of restaurants by name appears at the back of the Guide.

Rhônes, albeit at a price that is less than generous. The Beaujolais section offers the best value, but it is a pity the house wine, St-Véran '82, is inflationary at £8·50. More reports, please.

CHEF: Richard Hanson PROPRIETORS: The Pearson family
OPEN: Mon to Sat, exc Sat L CLOSED Christmas and New Year MEALS: 12.30 to 1.30, 7.30 to 9.30
PRICES: £13 (£18). Service inc CARDS: Access, Amex, Diners, Visa
SEATS: 45. Private parties: 100 main room, 14, 10 and 8 private rooms. Car-park, 40 places. Children's helpings. No pipes in dining-room. Wheelchair access (also WC)
ACCOMMODATION: 40 rooms, all with bath/shower. Rooms for disabled. B&B £37 to £55. Children welcome. Baby facilities. No pets in public rooms. Garden. Snooker. TV. Phone. Scenic. Doors close at 1. Confirm by 6

HAMBLETON Leicestershire map 6

▲ *Hambleton Hall* [14/20]

Hambleton LL15 8TH
OAKHAM (0572) 56991
off A606, 3m SE of Oakham **Real Food** £26–£28

The hall looms out of the fog, and pre-dinner drinks are served before the roaring fire. Hambleton combines a relaxed atmosphere with the seriousness of some elaborately presented fine cooking. The menu has taken on a new breath of life with the introduction of a lavish *carte*, using plenty of lobster, as well as a set menu. The ingredients are Real Food brought from across the country and further, though squabs are from their own pigeonhouse and pike are out of the surrounding Rutland Water. Nick Gill cooks with gusto. In the fish department, John Dory fillets are steamed and served with chive or rosemary sauce, and turbot with sorrel and spinach; more typical of his inventions at their best is sole with limes and chives served with new potato and green bean salad. Often he is rightly content to keep it simple – roast sirloin of beef, scallops baked in their shells, or roast lobster with buttered artichokes (£14). Cheese includes a selection of French and English as well as a warm puff pastry pillow of Stilton and walnuts. Desserts are spectacular – Amaretto ice-cream in a brandy-snap basket with butterscotch sauce, and parfait of chestnuts in white chocolate sauce. The wine list is aristocratic, but the best value is in the expensive clarets and burgundies; the Pinot Blanc '82 from Hugel at £8 comes into its own in this context, when house burgundy is £1 more. CELLARMAN'S CHOICE: Ch. Haut-Batailley '71 at £25.

CHEF: Nicholas Gill PROPRIETORS: Timothy and Stefa Hart
OPEN: all week MEALS: 12.30 to 1.45, 7.30 to 9.15
PRICES: £21 (£28), Set D £22 (£26). Service inc CARDS: Access, Amex, Diners, Visa
SEATS: 60. Private parties: 45 main room, 20 private room. Vegetarian meals. Car-park, 40 places. Smart dress preferred. Children's helpings. Wheelchair access (also WC)
ACCOMMODATION: 15 rooms, all with bath/shower. Rooms for disabled. B&B £60 to £100. No children under 9. Pets welcome. Afternoon teas. Garden. Tennis. Helicopter pad. Lift. TV. Phone. Scenic. Doors close at 12.30 [GHG]

Restaurant tricks (2): By law, prices on the menu displayed in the window must include VAT. But no such obligation applies to the menu inside.

HARBERTONFORD Devon map 1

Hungry Horse [10/20]

Old Road, Harbertonford TQ9 7TA
HARBERTONFORD (080 423) 441
on A381, 3m S of Totnes £16

The Jefferies have been building up this little restaurant since 1972. The quality of their meats and fish is high. Special dishes include red bream with lime and anchovy butter, and duck with green peppercorns. Notably good has been the cheese and crab soufflé. There are usually a dozen puddings with cream from Sharpham Dairy. House French is £4·20.

CHEF: Bev Jefferies PROPRIETORS: Bev and Anne Jefferies
OPEN: Tue to Sat, D only MEALS: 7 to 9.30
PRICES: £11 (£16) CARDS: Access, Amex, Diners, Visa
SEATS: 55. Car-park, 10 places. Vegetarian meals by arrangement. Children's helpings. Classical music

HARROGATE North Yorkshire map 5

BACKGROUND BRIEFING: *The fish merchant Ramus, Ocean House, King's Road is Harrogate's chief glory. It would earn a top rating in any Good Shop Guide, and it is the wholesale supplier to almost every restaurant of note in the vicinity. Specialities include live lobsters; live trout; oysters; prawns; crab; and Scotch salmon. This is a conference town and it has spawned many eating-places aimed at the expense account diner. Locals tend to go out to the Dales to eat, instead. Burdekins, 21 Cheltenham Crescent has a pleasant bistro air and good crab mousse, duckling, beef Wellington, and richly sauced kidneys in a pastry shell. Oliver, 24 King's Road, has good main courses; Emilio's, 3 Ripon Road, has good fish; Maddicks, 4 Montpellier Parade, has good, reasonably priced dishes, such as baked king prawns in garlic butter. There is a Dayville's ice-cream parlour near the station. A full range of good cheeses, including Wensleydale, can be found at Cheeseboard in Commercial Street. Ingle's at Scotts Corner, Leeds Road, and Regal in King's Road, next to Ramus, have good fruit and vegetables, as does the market. On the way to Knaresborough Frank Mitchell at Starbeck is a good butcher; alternatively, on the South Drive roundabout at the other end of town is Country Butchers, Leeds Road who specialise in pork, moorland lamb and game in season.*

Bettys [8/20]

1 Parliament Street, Harrogate HG1 2QU
HARROGATE (0423) 64659 £9

The original of the four Bettys tea-rooms, first opened in 1919 (see also Ilkley, Northallerton and York). 'We are our own largest supplier, which perhaps explains how Bettys has survived while most of the other tea-shops from the 1920s have disappeared.' A good point, and not at odds with the principles of Real Food. The decor is mock Victorian, with palms and green carpet but white plastic-topped tables. The waitresses in black uniforms with white aprons come straight to you and wait while you read the menu. The cakes are famous, and the range of unusual teas and coffees – and also '83 Alsace wines – superb. Good breakfasts and other hot snacks, too.

PROPRIETORS: Bettys Ltd
OPEN: all week, daytime only MEALS: 9 to 5.30 (10 to 5.30 Sun)
PRICES: £5 (£9), Snacks from 80p (90p)
SEATS: 147. Vegetarian meals. Children's helpings. No-smoking area. Wheelchair access. Pianist

Drum and Monkey [12/20]

5 Montpellier Gardens, Harrogate HG1 2TF
HARROGATE (0423) 502650 £15–£20

The downstairs here is like a pub, with a smoky room, a bar and some of the fish that did not get away mounted in cases on the green walls. Upstairs is the more sedate dining-room. Despite the crush, fish is cooked with some care and is invariably fresh. There is plenty of cream in the lobster bisque, and the monkfish rolled up in bacon with a smidgen of pâté and good Dijon sauce is an odd mix but tasty. Other good dishes have been crab claws and langoustines in garlic butter; moules marinière; the seafood platter; and lobster thermidor. Service is friendly and lively, and the granary bread is first-class. The atmosphere keeps the rating up. Good, short list of white wines. CELLARMAN'S CHOICE: Muscadet sur lie, Coupe Louis Métaireau '82 at £8·05.

CHEF: Patrick Laverack PROPRIETOR: William Fuller
OPEN: Mon to Sat CLOSED: 25 Dec to 1 Jan MEALS: 12 to 2.30, 7.15 to 10.15
PRICES: L £10 (£15), D £15 (£20) CARDS: Access, Visa
SEATS: 48. Children welcome

▲ *Hodgson's, Russell Hotel* [12/20]

Valley Drive, Harrogate HG2 0JN
HARROGATE (0423) 509866 £14–£21

A family-run hotel in a row of Victorian terraced guest-houses, overlooking the valley gardens. Richard Hodgson is a serious cook in the modern manner. Fish is his favoured subject and he does some inventive dishes, such as skate and sorrel soup with saffron, or salmon and trout in a pastry case with a cider sauce. Diced monkfish in a Marsala cream sauce garnished with mange-tout has been excellent. The quality of the cooking runs through the meals, from the Marie Rose dip with crudités, to the loaves of poppy-seed bread for each table, to plenty of vegetables, to the good pastry for the lemon tart. The duck breast with green peppercorns is a strong version of this now clichéd dish. Service is attentive and the wine list one of quality, with a good showing of '70s clarets. The Alsace

All Guide *inspectors are anonymous. Anyone purporting to represent the* Guide *is an impostor.*

Restaurant tricks (3): The bad practice of making a cover charge is dying out, but please report to us on any restaurant still doing so.

section, supplied via Hugel and Louis Gisselbrecht, includes a Tokay, Cuvée Tradition '82, from Hugel, at £8·10. House Gamay is £5·75.

CHEF: Richard Hodgson PROPRIETORS: The Hodgson family
OPEN: Tue to Sat, D only MEALS: 7 to 10.30
PRICES: Set D £10·25 to £17·50 (£14 to £21), Bar meals from £3·50, Snacks from 80p. Service inc CARDS: Access, Amex, Carte Blanche, Diners, Visa
SEATS: 75. Private parties: 30 main room, 12 private room. No children under 8. Smart dress preferred. No cigars/pipes in dining-room. Wheelchair access (also WC). Music
ACCOMMODATION: 34 rooms, all with bath/shower. Rooms for disabled. B&B £29·50 to £40·50. Children welcome. Baby facilities. No pets in public rooms. Afternon teas. Lift. TV. Phone. Confirm by 6 [GHG]

Number Six [new entry, zero rated]

6 Ripon Road, Harrogate HG1 2JB
HARROGATE (0423) 502908 £24

Good reports have been coming in, as we go to press, on the new owners at this restaurant up the hill from the town centre. The car-park at the back is tricky to negotiate, but the menu is a good read, very much in the modern idiom. Wild mushroom soup, asparagus soup, and a pot-au-feu of lobster and John Dory with ginger stand out, and the saucing is said to be exceptional. Sweets are said to be less good and the wines are not what they were. More reports, please.

CHEF: Simon Gueller PROPRIETORS: Malcolm and Adele Anderson
OPEN: Mon to Sat, D only CLOSED: 1st two weeks Aug MEALS: 7.30 to 10.30
PRICES: £19 (£24). Service 10% CARDS: Access, Amex, Diners, Visa
SEATS: 52. Private parties: 52 main room, 25 private room. Car-park, 25 places. Children's helpings. Wheelchair access. Classical music

Shabab [9/20]

1 John Street, Harrogate HG1 1JZ
HARROGATE (0423) 500250 £6–£12

Once a famous carpet shop, now converted at vast expense and given canopies, a marble fountain and a profusion of ornamental brass. There are plenty of waiters to take orders for finely mixed shami kebab, spiced with chilli, wrapped in pounded lentils and deep-fried; or nargis kofte, a hard-boiled egg wrapped in minced lamb. Many meat dishes also use cream, eggs and nuts. Mango chutney is like jam. Licensed.

CHEF: Ghulam Kadir Darr PROPRIETORS: Patron Services Ltd
OPEN: all week, exc Sun L CLOSED: 25 Dec MEALS: 11.30 to 2.30, 6 to 11.30
PRICES: £7 (£12), Set L £2·95 (£6). Service 10% CARDS: Access, Amex, Carte Blanche, Diners, Visa
SEATS: 130. Private parties: 40 main room. Vegetarian meals. Children welcome. Wheelchair access. Indian music

Restaurants are graded on a scale of 1–20. In the region of 8–9 expect to find places that may not be restaurants but cafes, pubs, bistros and small hotels. In the category of 10–11 you can expect to find the best food in the locality. Ratings of 12 or more are given to restaurants we regard as serving the best food in the region.

▲ *Shrimps, Studley Hotel* [11/20]

Swan Road, Harrogate HG1 2SE
HARROGATE (0423) 60425 £15

The set menu is good value in this smart fish restaurant in a low-ceilinged basement attached to the Studley Hotel. The debt is to the fish merchant – oysters are £6 a dozen and there are Dover sole and lobsters. But the place is well run and there is fresh brown bread on each table, plus the handsome touch of a whole bowl of pickled salad. Especially good have been the monkfish kebabs, sea-trout with tarragon and mushrooms, turbot with leeks and a mustard cream sauce, and seafood paella. The fruit salad has variety but other sweets fade. The list of exclusively white wines includes good names but few details. Music tends to the Tijuana. Bendicks bitter mints come with the Cona coffee.

CHEFS: Michel Boulineau and Michel Mingam PROPRIETOR: G.G.Dilasser
OPEN: Mon to Sat, D only MEALS: 7 to 10.30
PRICES: £10 (£15). Service 10% CARDS: Access, Amex, Diners, Visa
SEATS: 60. Private parties: 20 main room. Car-park, 14 places. Vegetarian meals. Children's helpings. Wheelchair access. Music. Air-conditioned
ACCOMMODATION: 40 rooms, all with bath/shower. Rooms for disabled. B&B £39·50 to £52. No children under 8. Lift. TV. Phone. Scenic. Confirm by 6

William and Victoria Wine Bar [9/20]

6 Cold Bath Road, Harrogate HG2 0NA
HARROGATE (0423) 56883 £10

Victoria Grahem's downstairs Victorian wine bar has a cool, stone-flagged floor, dark wood tables and chairs, lace curtains, and sundry large pots and terracotta jars full of aspidistra. Order at the bar, find a table, and tuck into plain but satisfying vegetable soup; liver and bacon; properly made cheese, tomato and onion flan; roast knuckle of lamb with rosemary and mint sauce; or the pièce de résistance – gooey, nutty-flavoured, latticed treacle tart with a whiff of lemon and a splodge of cream. Real sweet-tooths can take a glass of Muscat de Beaumes de Venise with it. The detailed, balanced wine list includes Hugel's '83 Pinot Noir at £7·35, and plenty of half-bottles, but few wines by the glass, although house French at £3·95 by the bottle is 85p per glass.

CHEF/PROPRIETOR: Mrs V.Grahem
OPEN: Mon to Sat, exc Sat L CLOSED: 25 Dec MEALS: 12 to 2, 6.30 to 10
PRICES: £7 (£10). Service inc
SEATS: 50. Private parties: 30 main room, 30 private room. Vegetarian meals. Children's helpings (L only). Wheelchair access (3 steps). Music

HARWICH Essex map 3

The Pier at Harwich [10/20]

The Quay, Harwich CO12 3HH
HARWICH (0255) 503363 £9–£18

The ground floor Ha'penny Pier has simple meals for around £5 a head. Upstairs overlooks the harbour. The decor is nautical and – surprise! – the strength is fish:

smoked salmon cornets with prawns, grilled halibut, lobsters from April to October, salmon mousse studded with scallops and prawns on a lemon sauce, and sole maharajah for those who like their fish with banana, mango and kiwi. There is also steak and kidney pie, good-value set lunch, a pianist most of the week and an elegant wine list from Lay & Wheeler of Colchester with some magnificent whites.

CHEF: C.E.Oakley PROPRIETOR: G.M.W.Milsom
OPEN: all week MEALS: 12 to 2, 6.30 to 9.30
PRICES: £12 (£18), Set L £5·75 (£9). Also cut-price menu at Ha'penny Pier. Service 10%
CARDS: Access, Amex, Diners, Visa
SEATS: 125. Private parties: 85 main room. Car-park, 12 places. Children's helpings. Piano music

HASLEMERE Surrey map 3

Morels [14/20]

25–27 Lower Street, Haslemere GU27 2NY
HASLEMERE (0428) 51462 £15–£25

A very fine little restaurant. Jean-Yves Morel comes round to talk food at the end of the evening, explaining why he marinates his venison for three days before serving it with a chestnut mousse and a game sauce. He takes on both classical dishes, such as blini with smoked salmon and caviare, and modern dishes, such as the slices of guinea-fowl, quail and rabbit in an orange and Dubonnet sauce. The front of the house is rimmed in blue and white, black-beamed, and run with the precision of a French mother dressing her son. Notably worth the 14 rating are the thick mussel soup with a little saffron, the pig's trotters with sweetbreads, and the saucing. Vegetables are varied and excellent, salads are dressed with nut oil, and cheeses come from Philippe Olivier in Boulogne. The chocolate marquise is pretty close to perfection, but there is also an iced calvados terrine, presented with an outline of raspberry purée in the shape of an apple encircling the cream sauce. The occasional dish, and the bread in particular, have lacked the dazzle we expect at this level, but we are not about to lose faith. The set meals in the week are very good value. The wines are priced to match, but without taking the easy option of expensive vintage clarets or burgundies. CELLARMAN'S CHOICE: Crozes-Hermitage '83, from Barbier, at £8.

CHEF: Jean-Yves Morel PROPRIETORS: Jean-Yves and Mary-Anne Morel
OPEN: Tue to Sat, exc Sat L CLOSED: 3 weeks Feb, 2 weeks Sept MEALS: 12.30 to 1.45, 7 to 10
PRICES: £17 (£25), Set L £10 (£15), Set D £11·50 (£16) CARDS: Access, Amex, Diners, Visa
SEATS: 45. Private parties: 12 main room. Children's helpings. No pipes in dining-room. Wheelchair access (1 step; also wc). Music

The 1987 Guide *will appear before Christmas 1986, so reports are particularly important in the spring. Report forms are at the back of this book, but just write a letter if you prefer. Address them to* The Good Food Guide, *Freepost, 14 Buckingham Street, London WC2N 6BR. No stamp is necessary if you post in the UK.*

HASSOP Derbyshire map 5

▲ *Hassop Hall Hotel* [10/20]

Hassop DE4 1NS
GREAT LONGSTONE (062 987) 488
on B6001, 2m N of Bakewell £12–£17

Hardly a place for feminists – an infant heiress to the hall was sold twice by her wards and betrothed to be married before she was 11 months. The manor, which is mentioned in the Domesday Book, is in the heart of the Peak District National Park. There is a large menu bolstered up by some frozen produce, but the soups have been good and the roasts are popular, although some main dishes tend to be cooked rather longer than conventional wisdom suggests is good for them. A well-kept cheeseboard and the sweets, from chocolate and rum mousse to cherry tart, compensate. Lunch is good value. The 40-odd wines are mostly French and short on detail, but there is English Three Choirs '82 at £8·95.

CHEF: Michael Stone PROPRIETOR: Thomas Chapman
OPEN: all week, exc Mon L and Sun D MEALS: 12 to 2, 7 to 9.30
PRICES: Set L from £8·50 (£12), Set D from £13·50 (£17). Cheaper set L available. Minimum £5·50. Service inc CARDS: Access, Amex, Diners, Visa
SEATS: 160. Private parties: 110 main room, 55, 36 and 16 private rooms. Car park, 120 places. Vegetarian meals. Children's helpings. Wheelchair access (also WC)
ACCOMMODATION: 12 rooms, all with bath/shower. Rooms for disabled. B&B £38·50 to £60. Children welcome. Garden. Tennis. Fishing. Croquet. Helicopter pad. Lift. TV. Phone. Scenic. Doors close at 1. Confirm by 6

HATFIELD Hertfordshire map 3

The Salisbury [new entry, zero rated]

15 The Broadway, Hatfield HL9 5JB
HATFIELD (070 72) 62220
in the Old Town £14–£24

A recent change of ownership has raised ambitions and prices at this four-storeyed building decked out in autumnal colours. Julian and Linda Waterer have come to old Hatfield from Greywalls in Gullane. For starters, slices of smoked goose breast are served with pink grapefruit salad in walnut dressing; terrine of leeks and duckling layered with mushrooms is served with raspberry vinegar jelly and pine kernels; and hot-pot of salmon and scallops in shallot and vermouth sauce is baked under a dome of puff pastry. For mains, saddle of venison is marinated in red wine and served with port sauce, and rosettes of lamb come with a leek and spinach mousse and a rich sherry sauce. Vegetables come in fours. Almond basket and biscuit cups are filled with fresh fruit and ice-cream to finish. Wines, including house wine at £7·95, are expensive. More reports, please.

CHEF/PROPRIETOR: Julian Waterer
OPEN: Tue to Sun, exc Sat L and Sun D MEALS: 12.30 to 2, 7.30 to 9.30
PRICES: £18 (£24), Set L from £8·75 (£14), Set D £18 (£24) CARDS: Access, Amex, Diners, Visa
SEATS: 55. Private parties: 50 main room. Car-park, 20 places. Vegetarian meals. Children's helpings. Wheelchair access. Air-conditioned

HAWES North Yorkshire map 7

▲ *Cockett's Hotel* [12/20]

Market Place, Hawes DL8 3RD
HAWES (096 97) 312 £14–£19

The atmosphere here is reverential, but the restaurant runs smoothly and there is nothing over-elaborate about Cherry Guest's cooking. Fish varies from sole en croûte to cold poached trout with cucumber, prawns and mushrooms. The quality of the meat is evident in steak with green peppercorns; loin of lamb with orange stuffing; local roast grouse with wild rice. There are local cheeses, too, including excellent goats' cheese and Swaledale. The summer pudding is often mentioned. Brian Guest serves promptly and unobtrusively. Breakfasts are first-class and the cramped bar encourages people to introduce themselves. Some good wines figure on the list, including three Alsace from Hugel with Tokay '82 at £7·60 though the CELLARMAN'S CHOICE is Spanish Riojas.

CHEF: Cherry Guest PROPRIETORS: Brian and Cherry Guest
OPEN: all week, D only CLOSED: mid-Nov to mid-Dec, early Jan to Mar MEALS: 7.30 to 9.30
PRICES: Set D £10·50 to £14·50 (£14 to £19) CARDS: Access, Visa
SEATS: 30. 4 tables outside. Private parties: 20 main room. Vegetarian meals by arrangement. Children's helpings. No children under 10. No pipes in dining-room. Classical music
ACCOMMODATION: 5 rooms, 3 with bath/shower. B&B £18 to £31. Children welcome. Baby facilities. Pets by arrangement. Afternoon teas. TV. Doors close at 11.30. Confirm by 5

HAWKHURST Kent map 3

Osborn House [new entry, zero rated]

Hawkhurst TN18 4AG
HAWKHURST (058 05) 3265 £17

The Osborns used to run a delicatessen, which shows in the excellent use of quality cheeses. She serves in the classical, pale green dining-room of their home, while he cooks an eclectic modern menu with a good eye for contrasting flavours – and for expense accounts, judging by the emphasis on luxuries like turbot, or medallions of beef with scallops. Oddities have been the snails in garlic on creamed potatoes and the Szechuan prawns, but very successful is the grilled goats' cheese starter on a salad of spinach, curly endive, chicory and lettuce with a hazel-nut oil dressing. The sauces are excellent, and there are good reports of the lamb noisettes with a white wine and garlic sauce, but the timing of other dishes has made us hesitate to fix a rating. Generous amounts of cafetière coffee. There are 40 or so wines, again leaning towards the expense account, though the house Côtes du Rhône at £4·80 is excellent, or try the CELLARMAN'S CHOICE: Crozes-Hermitage '81, from Chapoutier, at £8·60.

CHEF: Michael Osborn PROPRIETORS: Michael and Diane Osborn
OPEN: Mon to Sat, D only, exc Wed CLOSED: Jan MEALS: 7 to 9.30
PRICES: £12 (£17), Bar meals from £4 (£4.40) CARDS: Access, Amex, Visa
SEATS: 26. Private parties: 26 main room. Car-park, 3 places. Children welcome. Jacket and tie. No pipes in dining-room. Wheelchair access

HAYDON BRIDGE Northumberland map 7

General Havelock Inn [10/20]

Radcliffe Road, Haydon Bridge NE47 6ER
HAYDONBRIDGE (043 484) 376 £6–£15

An unpretentious inn by the Tyne bridge, with a blazing log fire. Angela Clyde's cooking is honest and straightforward – thick meat and vegetable soups, before main-course roasts of gammon or lamb with a large plate of mixed vegetables. Roast duck is a favourite, as are the crab dishes, which also feature on the bar menu. Half a dozen sweets include star attractions in the pies – blackberry or Banoffi. House red is £5·60 a litre. Tetley's beers.

CHEF: Angela Clyde PROPRIETORS: Ian and Angela Clyde
OPEN: Wed to Sun, exc Sun D CLOSED: 1 week Jan and Mar, 2 weeks Sept
MEALS: 12 to 1.30, 7 to 9
PRICES: Set L from £2·50 (£6), Set D from £10·50 (£15)
SEATS: 28. 5 tables outside. Private parties: 32 main room. Car-park, 15 places. Children's helpings. Wheelchair access (also WC)

HEALD GREEN Greater Manchester map 5

La Bonne Auberge [11/20]

224 Finney Lane, Heald Green SK7 3AN
061-437 5701 £10–£16

There are a number of green French restaurants in Cheshire and this is one of the better ones, found in a row of shops, cramped and a little dark but well used by local businessmen. The tournedos with paprika and calvados is excellent, as are the gigot of lamb, langoustines provençale and duck with cider sauce. The service and ambience give a lift to the food too, and the desserts are especially good, notably the apple pancakes, the mille-feuilles and the meringues. The rating is reduced by one point this year because standards are frustratingly erratic at these prices, though the set lunch is good value. The list of 50 wines has been cleverly put together and is not overpriced. If the Côte Rôtie '78 from Chapoutier is still on the list at £14, drink it. Or else CELLARMAN'S CHOICE: Muscadet sur lie '83, Château des Gautronnières, at £5.

CHEFS: Roger Boutinot and Michael Hogg PROPRIETORS: Roger and Cecilia Boutinot
OPEN: Mon to Sat, exc Mon D CLOSED: bank hols MEALS: 12 to 2, 6.45 to 9.45
PRICES: £11 (£16), Set L from £6·50 (£10) CARDS: Access, Amex, Diners
SEATS: 65. Private parties: 35 main room, 25 private room. Car-park. Children welcome. Music

Prices quoted are for an average three-course meal including service and VAT and half a bottle of house wine (or the equivalent in an ethnic restaurant).

All Guide *inspectors are anonymous. Anyone purporting to represent the* Guide *is an impostor.*

Restaurant tricks (1): Charging each person for every serving of vegetables even when the diners have shared portions between them.

HELFORD Cornwall map 1

▲ *Riverside* [16/20]

Helford TR12 6JU
MANACCAN (032 623) 443 Real Food £26

Reputations are fearful things. Some readers have raised eyebrows at the high rating for George Perry-Smith's and Heather Crosbie's white, Mediterranean-looking restaurant in a narrow street above the creek. It is not *nouvelle cuisine*, of course, nor does it have the luxurious pomp of some of the restaurants on the international circuit. But it is ironic that inspection meals here and at Le Gavroche (see London) might almost have been from the same kitchen, as if two totally different strands of cooking – Elizabeth David on one hand and what Albert Roux might call New Classic Cuisine – had met at the very top. The thought reinforces the principle that good food is good food whatever clothes it wears. And this is very good food. One correspondent says he has eaten a better lobster bisque . . . in Munich, and an inspector points out that the cup of deep rich consommé served with rissoles and a glass of Marsala is a gimmick in the same way that the spinach soufflé with anchovy sauce is at Langan's Brasserie (see London). What else suggests that the rating should be this high? The pies, either steak and kidney or chicken, mushroom and madeira; the plate of charcuterie, comprising sweetbread terrine, loin of pork, ham in a green sauce with soft, home-pickled onions; ribs of beef for two with an honest jus rather than a sauce; of course, the perennial salmon with ginger and currants; the treacle tart with chopped walnuts; and the fudge with coffee.

It is a fair criticism to say that the cooking gets better as the season goes on, as the new intake (all girls last year) in the kitchen get into its stride and the niggles in the supply lines (there was poor cream, amazingly, at one meal) are ironed out. It is anybody's guess why Mr Perry-Smith offers Bath Olivers and Ritz crackers with cheeses that are served at the peak of ripeness. Heather Crosbie runs the front of house with all the charm in the world. The wine list is put together with the same enthusiasm for under £10 as over, with some intriguing, lesser-known French regional wines as well as established clarets from throughout the '70s. It is illuminating to see that Mr Perry-Smith has no qualms about offering wines as cheap as £3·50 for a half-bottle, when lesser places go on maintaining the nonsensical position of insisting that their food deserves bottles of £10-plus.

CHEFS: George Perry-Smith and Abigail Iversen
PROPRIETORS: George Perry-Smith, Heather Crosbie and Joyce Molyneux
OPEN: all week, D only CLOSED: Dec to Feb MEALS: 7.30 to 9.30
PRICES: Set D £22 (£26). Service inc
SEATS: 36. Private parties: 20 main room. Vegetarian meals by arrangement. Children's helpings. Wheelchair access (also WC)
ACCOMMODATION: 6 rooms, all with bath/shower. Rooms for disabled. B&B £35 to £60. Children welcome. No pets. Garden. TV. Scenic [GHG]

Entries are compiled from the unsolicited reports from readers and are checked by inspectors; each restaurant is asked to supply details of its operation. Report forms can be found at the back of the Guide.

HEMEL HEMPSTEAD Hertfordshire map 3

Casanova [9/20]

75 Waterhouse Street, Hemel Hempstead HP1 1ED
HEMEL HEMPSTEAD (0442) 47482 £18

A reliable Italian restaurant good for fresh sardines, pasta e fagioli, veal in cream and mushroom sauce, and home-made cheesecake with blackcurrants. Service is courteous, relaxed and unhurried. The short wine list includes house Trebbiano and Sangiovese at £4·95.

CHEF: F.Gonzalez PROPRIETORS: A.Gavira, G.Ventriglia and G.Venigno
OPEN: Mon to Sat, exc Sat L MEALS: 12 to 2.15, 6.30 to 11.30
PRICES: £12 (£18). Cover 50p. Service 10% D only CARDS: Access, Amex, Diners, Visa
SEATS: 55. Private parties: 55 main room. Vegetarian meals. Children welcome. Wheelchair access. Music

HENFIELD West Sussex map 3

Kents [new entry, zero rated]

High Street, Henfield BN5 9DE
HENFIELD (0273) 492872
junction of A281 and A2037 £10–£15

A suburban house where the dining-room has the look and feel of Granny's front parlour. As well as some conventional soups, pâté and steaks, there are more imaginative dishes, such as chicken in a cream sauce with carrots, mushrooms, apple juice and Pernod. We have enjoyed slices of lamb in a delicate tarragon sauce with butter and chopped tomato, and also scampi, coated with a mixture of crab, cream and breadcrumbs, and then deep-fried. Vegetables and puddings are tasty. Service is by the proprietors. The short wine list includes local Downers '83 at £6·65, house white Cante Cigale '83 from the Hérault at £5·60, and CELLARMAN'S CHOICE: Ch. Millet '79 from the Graves, at £9·75, or £5·05 for a half-bottle. More reports, please.

CHEF/PROPRIETOR: Jonathan Kent
OPEN: Tue to Sun, exc Sat L and Sun D MEALS: 12.30 to 2, 6.30 to 9.30
PRICES: £10 (£15), Set L £5·75 (£10) CARDS: Access, Amex, Diners, Visa
SEATS: 40. Private parties: 30 main room. Vegetarian meals. Children's helpings. Wheelchair access (also WC). Air-conditioned

HERSTMONCEUX East Sussex map 3

Sundial [12/20]

Gardner Street, Herstmonceux BN27 4LA
HERSTMONCEUX (0323) 832217 £13–£24

The fish from Hastings underwrites the over-long menu of this old favourite. Giuseppe and Laurette Bertoli have been here since 1966. The dining-room is beamed, smart, cluttered and arranged around a large table of desserts. The petite bouillabaisse is in fact a rather big bouillabaisse, served complete with rouille and croûtons, and the grilled Dover sole has been exemplary. Other dishes are more classically sauced – lamb with a rich madeira, guinea-fowl bourguignonne, entrecôte forestière. Vegetables are generous and plainly cooked. There is a spectacular view and the welcome is always friendly. There is a powerful showing of claret and burgundies of good vintages, and hence expensive; the fine Rhônes are less heady. House Valpolicella is £5·75. CELLARMAN'S CHOICE: Crozes-Hermitage '80, from Chapoutier, at £10·75.

CHEF: Giuseppe Bertoli PROPRIETORS: Giuseppe and Laurette Bertoli
OPEN: Tue to Sun, exc Sun D CLOSED: 25 Dec to 20 Jan, last week Aug and 1st week Sept
MEALS: 12.30 to 2, 7.30 to 9.30
PRICES: £16 (£24), Set L £8·50 (£13), Set D £12·50 (£18). Service 10% CARDS: Amex, Diners, Visa
SEATS: 70. 8 tables outside. Private parties: 50 main room, 22 private room. Car-park. 25 places. Vegetarian meals. Children's helpings. No smoking in dining-room. Wheelchair access (also WC). Music

HESWALL Merseyside map 5

Les Bougies [11/20]

106 Telegraph Road, Heswall L60 0AQ
051-342 6673 **Real Food** £15

Some small converted cottages set back from the road hold this, one of the best of the batch of restaurants that have opened in the area. A short French menu takes in sauté mushrooms with port, and steaks with two-mustard sauce, herbs and cheese. The pigeon wrapped in vine leaves with sultanas and cooked in white wine is good, as are Parkgate shrimps in garlic and wine; and venison in a wine and redcurrant sauce. New potatoes come in their jackets, and carrots come with nutmeg cream sauce. Both can be organic. Choice of about eight or ten desserts. Bread is sliced and fresh, and chocolate mints come with any amount of coffee. The wine list is longer than you might expect in a restaurant of this size. Quite a few of the wines are 'next-to's' . . . the village next to Chablis, and so on. Look for the Riojas, but with Mâcon-Lugny, Les Genièvres '83 from Latour at a mere £6.95, prices are excellent value all round.

CHEF: Anita Jones PROPRIETORS: Alvar and Anita Jones
OPEN: Tue to Sat, D only CLOSED: 1st week Jan, Aug MEALS: 7.15 to 9.45
PRICES: £10 (£15). Service 10% CARDS: Access, Amex, Visa
SEATS: 35. Private parties: 20 main room. Car- park, 10 places. Vegetarian meals by arrangement. Children welcome. Wheelchair access. Music

HETTON North Yorkshire map 5

Angel Inn [10/20]

Hetton BD23 6LT
CRACOE (075 673) 263
½m off B6265, between Skipton and Grassington £10–£14

This 400-year-old Dales pub with pseudo-log fires has a good-value cold table composed of over 14 items. There is also a set menu that has offered good gravlax, fish soup, steak with béarnaise sauce, rack of lamb with rosemary and as many as five different vegetables, and steak and kidney pie. Usually there are around eight sweets and a cheeseboard in good condition. Service is friendly and the music is turned down as the dining-room fills up. House vin de pays is £5, or there's Theakston's Old Peculier. Of interest is a red from Austria, which is the CELLARMAN'S CHOICE: Schloss Gobelsburg Heiligensteiner Blauburgunder '77, at £6·50.

CHEF: Denis Watkins PROPRIETORS: Denis and Juliet Watkins
OPEN: Mon to Sat, D only, and Sun L CLOSED: 1 Jan MEALS: 12.15 to 2, 7 to 9.30
PRICES: Set L from £6·75 (£10), Set D £10·50 (£14) CARD: Access
SEATS: 36. Private parties: 40 main room. Car-park, 17 places. Children's helpings (L only). Smart dress preferred. No pipes in dining-room. Wheelchair access (also WC). Music

HILDENBOROUGH Kent — map 3

Gate Inn [new entry, zero rated]

Rings Hill, Hildenborough TN11 8LX
HILDENBOROUGH (0732) 832103 — £18

Guy and Maggie Sankey serve fish in a Victorian inn that is complete with gas-lamps, maps, brass, a handsome collection of hand-pumps, and waitresses in high-necked blouses. The busy atmosphere has an air of confidence and expectancy. Out at the back is a 3,500 litre seawater tank, stocked with shellfish from Cornwall and Guernsey – Loch Fyne, Rungis and Billingsgate supply the rest. Cooking is admirably minimal, with no frying. Helston oysters from the Duchy of Cornwall oyster farm, and butter clams ('the Rolls-Royce of clams') come straight from the shell. Soft-shell crabs come from Maryland; fish soup is with rouille; gambas are hot with garlic; skate is with black butter. There are puddings, too. Wines are naturally white, with good burgundies and Loires. CELLARMAN'S CHOICE: Muscadet Domaine de l'Hyvernière '83 at £6·50.

CHEF: James Howard PROPRIETOR: Guy Sankey
OPEN: Mon to Sat CLOSED: bank hols MEALS: 12 to 1.30, 7 to 10
PRICES: £14 (£18), Bar meals from £1 (£1.10) CARDS: Amex, Visa
SEATS: 40. Private parties: 8 main room, 14 private room. Car-park, 40 places. Vegetarian meals. Children's helpings

HILLINGDON Greater London — map 3

Ron & Cyn's [8/20]

26 Sutton Court Road, Hillingdon UB10 9HP
UXBRIDGE (0895) 32981
off Long Lane — £1

One of the arts of fish and chip frying is known in the trade as the battering arm – using a rhythmical movement that picks up the flour and lays the fish into the batter gently, as opposed to the dunking-a-doughnut technique. Mr Hoyon has a lovely battering arm and uses excellent fish – not small, immature cod but slices

Reports on good shops, small hotels and cafes in your area are welcome.

cut from a large juicy fillet. He uses vegetable oil rather than ground-nut (which we prefer) but the end product is first-class. The fish is from Grimsby. Take-away only.

CHEF/PROPRIETOR: Mr Hoyon
OPEN: Tue to Sat MEALS: 11.30 to 1.30, 5 to 9
PRICES: £1

HINTLESHAM Suffolk — map 3

▲ *Hintlesham Hall* [new entry, zero rated]

Hintlesham IP8 3NS
HINTLESHAM (047 387) 268
on A1071 W of Ipswich — £18–£23

The story goes that Robert Carrier went round his dining-room one evening only to discover that everyone was either celebrating a birthday or on expenses, and as no one was there solely for the food he decided to sell. The fifteenth-century hall has been decorated by the new owners, Ruth and David Watson, in a less outrageous style than before. The early months have not been without their teething problems but the ambition is there, and probably the expertise too. The menu has some twee touches – 'a little idea from Japan with beef and ginger', or 'venison consommé with madeira under a "thousand leaves"'. Yet some dishes are far from prissy – mussel, garlic and parsley soup; gravlax; duck as two courses, first the breast with calvados and morels (which grow wild in Suffolk) and then the leg on a salad. Other dishes have been let down by a lack of polish in the saucing, and the pastry work needs improving – odd, because chef Robert Mabey has done a year at Le Gavroche, where it is the major subject. His ingredients, though, are first-class and this produces such second courses as superb salads or oysters warmed in red wine vinegar. The sorbets are curious – blackcurrant overwhelmed by Guinness, lemon and ginger – and the sweets showy in the manner of modern restaurants in France. There are some 250 wines, predominantly well-known French ones and, relatively speaking, not that expensive. The house wines are good choices too – Quincy or Château du Grand Moulas, both around £7. More reports, please.

CHEF: Robert Mabey PROPRIETORS: Ruth and David Watson
OPEN: all week, exc Sat L MEALS: 12.30 to 2, 7.30 to 9.30
PRICES: £16 (£22), Set L from £15 (£18), Set D £20 (£23). Service inc CARDS: Access, Amex, Diners, Visa
SEATS: 60. Private parties: 20 main room, 100 and 20 private rooms. Car park, 50 places. Vegetarian meals by arrangement. Children's helpings (Sun L only). No children under 10 (exc babies). Smart dress preferred. No cigars/pipes in dining-room. Wheelchair access
ACCOMMODATION: 10 rooms, all with bath/shower. B&B £48 to £95. No children under 10. Baby facilities. Garden. Tennis. Snooker. TV. Phone. Scenic. Doors close at 1 [GHG]

The 1987 Guide will appear before Christmas 1986, so reports are particularly important in the spring. Report forms are at the back of this book, but just write a letter if you prefer. Address them to The Good Food Guide, *Freepost, 14 Buckingham Street, London WC2N 6BR. No stamp is necessary if you post in the UK.*

HINTON CHARTERHOUSE Avon map 2

▲ *Homewood Park* [13/20]

Hinton Charterhouse BA3 6BB
LIMPLEY STOKE (022 122) 3731
off A36, 5½m S of Bath **Real Food** £17–£24

The old abbot who reputedly lived in this spacious house, set in 10 acres by the now ruined priory, would not have been a fire-and-brimstone man to judge by the decor today – more of a man of letters who liked his tea out of Wedgwood cups. He would have approved of Stephen Ross's menu, which is handsomely written in English – fresh pasta with sweetbreads and oyster mushrooms followed by rib of beef with tarragon butter or breast of maize-fed chicken with a light vindaloo sauce, sultanas and coconut. Soups are a feature, as varied as lobster and pumpkin to leek, chive and yoghourt to crab, cumin and saffron. His ingredients are first class – vegetables, herbs and soft fruit – even lamb – from the garden. Thursday's fish nights have seen ling, monk, and gurnard alongside more common fish. Sweets are unanimously endorsed, from chocolate soufflé to almond tart with a raspberry sauce. A new dining-room and five bedrooms have been added. The wine list keeps an eye on value in the Loire and clarets. A few of the fascinating Australians are starting to show, and there are four Alsace wines including the Tokay d'Alsace, Cuvée Particulière '83, the great year, from Baron de Hoen, at £7·50.

CHEF: Stephen Ross PROPRIETORS: Stephen and Penny Ross
OPEN: all week CLOSED: 2 weeks from 23 Dec MEALS: 12 to 1.30 (2 Sun), 7 to 9.30 (8.30 Sun)
PRICES: £18 (£24), Set L and D £12·50 (£17). Service inc CARDS: Access, Amex, Diners, Visa
SEATS: 50. Private parties: 36 main room (80 if buffet), 18 and 30 private rooms. Car-park, 30 places. No smoking. Children's helpings. Wheelchair access (also WC)
ACCOMMODATION: 15 rooms, all with bath/shower. Rooms for disabled. B&B £40 to £85. Children welcome. No pets. Afternoon teas. Garden. Tennis. Croquet. Riding. Helicopter pad. TV. Phone. Scenic. Doors close at 1 [GHG]

HOLT Norfolk map 6

The Flask [10/20]

7–8 Chapel Yard, Holt NR25 6HG
HOLT (026 371) 3968 £9–£13

Good-value wines are the main asset at this cream-painted bistro. Fifty bottles, mostly classical French, appear on a well-annotated list (Ian McEwan is a former wine-broker). To go with them there is a short, mid-Channel menu of vegetable soup, entrecôte, pork with yoghourt, and good cheeses. The cooking is limited by the quality of the ingredients, hence the fruit salad is better than the ice-creams. Vin de table is £3·50. CELLARMAN'S CHOICE: Ch. Cissac '78 at £8·50.

CHEF: Jackie Chapman PROPRIETOR: Ian McEwan
OPEN: Tue to Sun, exc Sun D CLOSED: mid-Jan to mid-Feb MEALS: 12 to 1.45, 7 to 9.15
PRICES: L £5 (£9), D £9 (£13), Snacks from 60p (65p)
SEATS: 26. 3 tables outside. Private parties: 20 main room. Vegetarian meals. Children's helpings. Smart dress preferred. Wheelchair access (1 step). Music

HOOK Hampshire map 2

Whitewater House [12/20]

Hook RG27 9EH
HOOK (025 672) 2436
1m E of Hook on A30, behind
Crooked Billet pub £21–£23

A trout stream flows under this glorious seventeenth-century mill that originally made paper, then flour, then paper again. Inside is a gracious, much-loved private house, and you are invited to take your drink for a stroll around the gardens. Vanessa Hoare cooks a menu of good length with genuine choices, such as quails' eggs on pastry with hollandaise, hot pigeon breast salad, or tomato and red pepper, to start. Good main courses have been venison with a madeira sauce and side tartlets of wild mushrooms and apple sauce, and pheasant with calvados. Most dishes are allowed to taste of themselves and hence rely on the quality of the ingredients, occasionally helped along with a slug of booze. Vegetables are excellent and unadulterated, and the French cheeseboard has been in magnificent condition. Crème brûlée is flamboyantly topped with sugar and a flame applied. Coffee could be more virile. The list of 70 or so wines has a good showing of half-bottles.

CHEF/PROPRIETOR: Vanessa Hoare
OPEN: Tue to Sat CLOSED: 4 weeks from Christmas MEALS: 12.30, 7.30
PRICES: Set L £16·50 (£21), Set D £18 (£23) CARDS: Access, Amex, Diners, Visa
SEATS: 24. Tables outside. Private parties: 60 main room, 14 private room. Car-park, 25 places. Vegetarian meals by arrangement. Children welcome. Smart dress preferred. Wheelchair access (also WC). One sitting

HOPTON WAFERS Shropshire map 5

Crown Inn [10/20]

Hopton Wafers DY14 0NB
CLEOBURY MORTIMER (0299) 270372
on A4117, 2m W of Cleobury
Mortimer £13–£16

The service is friendly, if a bit slow, in the low, beamed dining-room, but otherwise the food is the same as in the bar – home made, from Stilton soup to steak and kidney pie to excellent steamed treacle sponge. Other good dishes on the menu that changes fortnightly have been prawns with garlic and saffron, calf's liver with bacon, and pancakes with a variety of fillings, including haddock and egg. There can be as many as 20 sweets, with half of them ice-creams. Hopton Wafers, for example, is a banana and praline ice-cream topped with crème Chantilly, kiwi, banana, strawberry, grapes and four wafers, served in a

'You have to be of a certain disposition to want to drive 100 miles from London to what can sometimes be a Trappist retreat: two visits ago we had the place entirely to ourselves. Mr X can be as elusive as the Loch Ness monster; at other times he appears fleetingly like the white rabbit.' (On a hotel in Hampshire)

glass that would put a number of ice-cream parlours to shame. Marston's and Hook Norton beers, or Côtes du Ventoux at £5·25.

CHEFS: L.V.G.Harrison and Julian Harrison PROPRIETOR: L.V.G.Harrison
OPEN: Tue to Sun (plus Mon bank hols), exc Sun D MEALS: 12 to 1.45, 7.30 to 9.30
PRICES: £11 (£16), Set L and D £10 (£13) CARDS: Access, Visa
SEATS: 40. 10 tables outside. Private parties: 40 main room. Car-park, 40 places. Children's helpings. No children under 10 at D. Wheelchair access (1 step; also wc)

HORNCASTLE Lincolnshire map 6

Magpies [10/20]

73–75 East Street, Horncastle LN9 6AA
HORNCASTLE (065 82) 7004 £9–£15

An old, white, cottage-like building opposite the church. The steaks are cooked rare, vegetables are plain, and the sweets calorific. The menu owes a little to bistro cooking, a little to Italy and a little to England. Good dishes have been the seafood ragout with fresh tomatoes and basil; omelette espagnole; veal with cheese; and hot blackcurrants served with vanilla ice-cream and a butterscotch sauce. Sometimes there will be cassoulet, or monkfish marinated in lemon, warmed with butter and served with artichokes and tomatoes. The service is efficient. House French is £5·20.

CHEF/PROPRIETOR: I.E.Jamieson
OPEN: Tue to Sat D only, and Sun L MEALS: 12.30 to 2, 7.30 (7 Sat) to 10
PRICES: Set L from £6 (£9), Set D £11 (£15) CARD: Access
SEATS: 40. 6 tables outside. Private parties: 34 main room. Children's helpings (exc Sat D). Wheelchair access (also wc). Music

HORTON Northamptonshire map 3

French Partridge [13/20]

Horton NN7 2AP
NORTHAMPTON (0604) 870033 £17

At £14 for four courses, the Partridge would be good value even if the food were not as good as it is. Game is a strong feature in winter, and it is possible to eat game and lentil soup, hare mousse in pastry and roast pheasant at a single meal. Other good dishes are: lobster mousse; sweetbread terrine with a tomato sauce; four-pepper steak; and the savoury of roes on toast. Vegetables are better than the salads. There is a superb blackcurrant tart or rum baba to finish. The wine list is magnificent and equally good value. It has an unusually strong German section and includes three Alsace Rieslings, each from a different producer and a different vintage, for around £6·50. Leave the car at home and start with half of the Jacquesson Blanc de Blancs Brut champagne at £8·50.

CHEF: D.C.Partridge and Justin Partridge PROPRIETORS: D.C.and M.Partridge
OPEN: Tue to Sat, D only CLOSED: Christmas and Easter, 3 weeks July to Aug
MEALS: 7.30 to 9
PRICES: Set D £14 (£17). Service inc. Cover 50p Sat
SEATS: 50. Private parties: 10 main room. Car-park. Wheelchair access

HUDDERSFIELD West Yorkshire map 5

Shabab [9/20]

37–39 New Street, Huddersfield HD1 2BG
HUDDERSFIELD (0484) 49514 £6–£12

Start with mulligatawny soup, sharp aloo tikka, or good onion pakora, then try flavoursome prawn masala or creamy chicken dishes. Chapatis are substantial and vegetables are deliciously spiced. Good service.

CHEF: Mahmood Ahmed PROPRIETOR: Mohammed Tanvir
OPEN: all week, exc Sun L CLOSED: 25 Dec MEALS: 11.30 to 2.30, 6 to 11.30
PRICES: £7 (£12), Set L £2·95 (£6). Service 10% CARDS: Access, Amex, Diners, Visa
SEATS: 78. Private parties: 50 main room. Vegetarian meals. Children welcome. Indian music

HULL Humberside map 6

BACKGROUND BRIEFING: *The stalls in the Hull fish market are half given over to frozen chicken legs and pork steaks. The nearest good supplies of fish are at Doncaster market or the fish counter in the Leeds Sainsbury. The search for a Hull restaurant to recommend this year has been fruitless. Ceruttis, by the old ferry pier, loses last year's entry – although the dining-rooms are nice and there is a fine view of the Humber, prices are astronomical. There are several cheerful pizza places – Medio on Anlaby Common is probably better than Pecan, 32 Silver Street. Pasta and veal dishes have been good at Cadora, 425 Anlaby Road. There are one or two diverse glimmers of light: Mrs V. Pickwell's tiny stall in the market sells duck eggs, fresh ducks and chickens, and fresh curds; and people drive miles for a take-away from Greenland Fisheries, 106 Cottingham Road – a spotless chippie run by Chinese. But the general standard is reflected in the fact that one of the city's chop-suey houses has started advertising 'Chinese dishes,' as if this is in some way remarkable. Basic oriental provisions can be bought from Sui Hing supermarket on Story Street, or Indian and Continental Stores on Princes Avenue.*

HUNGERFORD Berkshire map 2

▲ *Bear Hotel* [13/20]

Charnham Street, Hungerford RG17 0EL
HUNGERFORD (0488) 82512 Real Food £12–£19

There has been a coaching-inn on this site since 1250. David Evans, though, has been heavily influenced by the modern French chefs and has built up a good network of suppliers to aid his menus. There have been gastronomic evenings with visiting chefs, but the less ornate dishes still win praise: roast beef, lamb with madeira sauce, and corn-fed chicken with a purée of shallots. Saddle of roe-deer is marinated with juniper and wine, pan-fried in butter and served with a confit of celery and spätzli. The cheese selection is first-class. Tables are well

'The menu said bonemarrow sauce, and that's what we got – a sauce of bonemarrow with bits of the bone in it.' (On eating in Cheshire)

spaced and service eager. House Chardonnay or Gamay is £5 but there is red Sancerre, Clos les Romains '83, from Vacheron, at £9·75, or Montagny, Les Coères '83, from Michel, at £9·50. A good selection of eaux-de-vie, too.

CHEF: David Evans PROPRIETORS: Fine Inns plc
OPEN: all week MEALS: 12.30 to 2, 7.30 to 9.30
PRICES: £14 (£19), Set L from £8·45 (£12), Set D from £8·95 (£13). Service inc
CARDS: Access, Amex, Diners, Visa
SEATS: 55. 4 tables outside. Private parties: 20 main room, 12 private room. Car-park, 40 places. Children's helpings. Wheelchair access (also wc)
ACCOMMODATION: 28 rooms, 24 with bath/shower. Rooms for disabled. B&B £40 to £48. Children welcome. Baby facilities. TV. Phone. Doors close at 12. Confirm by 6

HUNTINGDON Cambridgeshire — map 6

▲ *Old Bridge Hotel* [9/20]

1 High Street, Huntingdon PE18 6TQ
HUNTINGDON (0480) 52681 — £2–£24

If you are in Huntingdon this coaching-inn, related to the George at Stamford (see entry), does good bar food and roasts.

CHEF: Robert Lane PROPRIETORS: Poste Hotels Ltd
OPEN: all week MEALS: 12.30 to 2.15, 7.30 to 10.15
PRICES: £15 (£24), Bar meals from £1·45 (£2). Cover 60p CARDS: Access, Amex, Diners, Visa
SEATS: 50. 14 tables outside. Private parties: 40 main room. Car-park, 100 places. Children's helpings. Jacket and tie. Wheelchair access
ACCOMMODATION: 22 rooms, all with bath/shower. B&B £40 to £60. Children welcome. No pets in public rooms. Afternoon teas. Garden. Fishing. Helicopter pad. TV. Phone. Scenic. Doors close at 12. Confirm by 6

HUSBANDS BOSWORTH Leicestershire — map 5

Fernie Lodge [new entry, zero rated]

Berridge Lane, Husbands Bosworth LE17 6LE
MARKET HARBOROUGH (0858) 880551
on A50 6m W of Market Harborough — £10–£15

The Speights have left but most other things have stayed the same, including the long menu, the chef, the manager and the out-of-tune piano. There's a fire in the bar, fresh flowers are on the dining-tables and coffee is served in the conservatory. Cream runs liberally through the courses. Good dishes eaten here have been as varied as crab and mackerel pâté; smoked chicken and ham salad; roast Aberdeen Angus beef with Yorkshire pudding; and trout stuffed with crabmeat. The sweets make a powerful finale in the shape of treacle tarts; butterscotch sundaes; and profiteroles. 'The best value in striking distance of Wellingborough,' is one summing-up. The list of 100 wines is a joy – well chosen and not greedily priced, with many mark-ups well under 100 per cent:

An index of restaurants by name appears at the back of the Guide.

Gewürztraminer, Cuvée Lupfens '82, from Blanck, is £6·25 and white Crozes-Hermitage, Mule Blanche '83, from Jaboulet, is £6·50. More reports, please.

CHEF: Robert Gilbertson PROPRIETORS: Perry's Restaurants Ltd
OPEN: Tue to Sun, exc Sat L and Sun D CLOSED: bank hols MEALS: 12 to 2, 6.45 to 9.45
PRICES: Set L from £6·75 (£10), Set D £11·50 (£15) CARDS: Access, Visa
SEATS: 90. Private parties: 12 main room, 24 and 18 private rooms. Car-park, 80 places. Vegetarian meals. Children's helpings (L only). Jacket and tie. Wheelchair access (also WC). Pianist. Air-conditioned

HUXHAM Devon map 1

Barton Cross [10/20]

Huxham EX5 4EJ
STOKE CANON (039 284) 245
off A396 at Stoke Canon, 5m N of Exeter £11–£18

With only a farm and green fields for company, this sixteenth-century building, beautifully kept, immaculately thatched, and heavily beamed, serves weekday lunches by reservation only, usually for business people. English cooking dominates the set menu: duck soup, genuine Lancashire hot-pot, grilled lemon sole. The French à la carte dishes display a cavalier disregard for cardiac considerations and have been less well done. CELLARMAN'S CHOICE: Ch. Lynch-Moussas '76 at £13·40

CHEF: Clifford Humphries PROPRIETORS: Mollie and Peter Burman
OPEN: Tue to Sun, exc Sat L and Sun D MEALS: 12.30 to 2, 7.30 to 9.30 (later by arrangement)
PRICES: £11 (£18), Set Sun L from £5·75 (£11), Cheaper set L in July, Aug
CARDS: Access, Visa
SEATS: 42. Private parties: 36 main room, 14 private room. Car-park, 28 places. Vegetarian meals. Children's helpings. Smart dress preferred. Wheelchair access (also WC). Classical music

ILFORD Essex map 3

Bolaka [9/20]

132 Cranbrook Road, Ilford IG1 4LZ
01-554 5395 £11

A standard menu but stylish cooking: onion bhajias, king prawns tandoori and good nan. Drink beer or lager.

PROPRIETOR: S.U. Ahmed
OPEN: all week MEALS: noon to midnight
PRICES: £7 (£11). Service inc CARD: Amex
SEATS: 50. Private parties: 50 main room. Vegetarian meals. Children welcome. Indian music

'Service at the table was by young ladies who were willing and attentive enough but who seemed more at home in the stables. A sort of ham-fisted gentility.' (On eating in Cambridgeshire)

Da Umberto [10/20]

361 Ley Street, Ilford IG1 4AA
01-553 5763 £10–£21

This is a good, unpretentious Italian restaurant. The pasta and lamb dishes are not out of the ordinary, but the daily specials can be – tortelloni, octopus, oysters, partridge with grappa, wild duck and eel casalinga. Calf's liver in wine and onion sauce is tender and not over-rich. They do a very fine zabaglione on request. Of the 34 wines 25 are Italian, but few details are given.

CHEF: Umberto Medaglia PROPRIETORS: Umberto and J.A.Medaglia
OPEN: Mon to Sat, exc Sat L MEALS: 12 to 2, 6.30 to 11 (12 Sat)
PRICES: £15 (£21), Set L £6 (£10). Cover 50p. Service 12% CARDS: Access, Visa
SEATS: 40. Vegetarian meals. Children's helpings. Music. Air-conditioned

Mandarin Palace [10/20]

559 Cranbrook Road, Ilford IG2 6JZ
01-550 7661 and 4882 £7–£27

The grandiose Peking/Cantonese menu runs to 300 dishes and, unusually for such restaurants, includes a vegetarian section with such dishes as sweet-and-sour bean curd and deep-fried milk custard. The 'Floral Hors d'Oeuvre' are seven cuts of assorted meats and fish. There are dim-sum and abalone dishes as well. Fresh lobsters and crabs are brought to the table live before cooking. Good service.

CHEF: Yuk Yip PROPRIETOR: Peter Kwen-Cheung Yeung
OPEN: all week MEALS: 12 to 2.30, 5.30 to 12 (1am Fri and Sat)
PRICES: £18 (£27), Set L from £2·80 (£7), Set D from £8 (£13). Minimum £5 at D. Service 12.5% CARDS: Access, Amex, Diners, Visa
SEATS: 120. Private parties: 120 main room, 25, 15 and 10 private rooms. Vegetarian meals. Children's helpings. Smart dress preferred. Wheelchair access (also WC). Air-conditioned

Sharon's [9/20]

376 Cranbrook Road, Ilford IG1 4UQ
01-554 7097, 554 2471 and 518 0374 £8–£14

An alternative to Bloom's, Sharon's has been serving Ashkenazi-style meals for sixteen years. There is kasha from across the Black Sea, stuffed neck and stomach, and every variation on chicken soup, but it's best to stick to traditional top-class salt-beef, or splendid chopped liver. The lockshen pudding is light and first-class. Great roast potatoes, otherwise take advice on the vegetables.

CHEFS: Mr Abraham and Mr Dominic PROPRIETOR: Mr Zwenber
OPEN: all week, exc Sat CLOSED: all Jewish holidays MEALS: 12 to 3, 5 to 9.30
PRICES: £8 (£14), Set L (exc Sun) £4·50 (£8) CARDS: Access, Visa
SEATS: 120. Private parties: 100 main room. Vegetarian meals. Children's helpings. Wheelchair access (also WC). Air-conditioned

▲ *This restaurant has rooms.*

ILKLEY West Yorkshire map 5

BACKGROUND BRIEFING: *Rombalds Hotel, West View, Wells Road, at the gate to the moor, has a good local reputation and the Sunday Victorian breakfasts are reliable. Up the road from Bettys (see entry), the Ilkley Wine Cellars has an interesting range, while Burrell in Brook Street has supplies of pulses, wholefoods, dried fruits and cheeses, including Swaledale.*

Bettys [8/20]

32–34 The Grove, Ilkley LS29 9EE
ILKLEY (0943) 608029 £9

Fine coffees, fine teas, fine '83 Alsace wines and swift service of freshly made snacks throughout the day.

PROPRIETORS: Bettys Ltd
OPEN: all week, daytime only MEALS: 9 (9.30 Sun) to 5.30
PRICES: £5 (£9), Snacks from 80p (90p)
SEATS: 78. Vegetarian meals. Children's helpings. No-smoking area. Wheelchair access. Baby facilities

Box Tree [15/20]

29 Church Street, Ilkley LS29 9DR
ILKLEY (0943) 608484 **Real Food** £27

For a short period last year the Box Tree had a serious rival in the Mallard Inn across the road, but this corner cottage behind the Masonic Hall sails on. In an era when restaurants come and go, Malcolm Reed and Colin Long survive – 24 years now – and their enthusiasm for recreating their dishes does not diminish. Each night among the red flock, the vases, the oil paintings, the plates and the dalmatian figures the magic returns as if new – the fish soup with a distant edge of fennel; the lightness of the sole mousseline réputation ('it is the basis of our reputation, sir'); the fragility of the almond tuile that holds the strawberries marinated in Grand Marnier, and the rosewater ice. Other dishes come and go with varying degrees of success, and if we wanted to criticise or explain why the rating is not 16 we would point to the inferior foie gras pâté stuffing, to the poached pear, or the demi-glaze that overpowers the guinea-fowl and its asparagus. But the sauces – what sauces. A watercress, chive and yoghourt one with that stuffed pear; the vinaigrette with the salad; and the white wine with a hint of ginger for salmon rolled around a mousse of scallops – these are sublime. The wine list is a lazy collection and heavily priced, which is a pity. If the house wine were less than the £9·95 charged, perhaps the restaurant would be fuller mid-week.

CHEF: Michael Truelove PROPRIETORS: Malcolm Reed and Colin Long
OPEN: Tue to Sat, D only MEALS: 7 to 9.45
PRICES: £17 (£27). Minimum £12·50 CARDS: Access, Amex, Diners, Visa
SEATS: 50. Private parties: 30 main room, 16 private room. Vegetarian meals by arrangement. Children's helpings. Smart dress preferred. No smoking in dining-room. Wheelchair access. Pianist

Olive Tree [11/20]

31 Church Street, Ilkley LS29 9DR
ILKLEY (0943) 601481 **Real Food** £14

This little Greek restaurant is emerging as one of the best in the north. Over and above the usual restaurant dishes they specialise in Greek vegetarian cooking with aubergine dips; tsatsiki; and courgettes cooked with onions, garlic, oregano and free-range eggs. Their taramosalata – sometimes served inside an avocado – is matched only by the White Tower's (see London), and fillet and sirloin steaks are hung for three weeks (paid for at original weight). The Uncle Ben's rice and the frozen red mullet (much cheaper than the steaks) do not come into the definition of Real Food, but the enthusiasm is there and if they explore other avenues of the cuisine to avoid using such things, then another trip up the ratings (two points this year) could be on the cards. To finish there is Greek trifle of honey, rosewater and almonds. Service is well timed. Twenty Greek wines and also Filfar orange liqueur at 95p, or Metaxa 1888 brandy at £1·80.

CHEF: George Psarias PROPRIETORS: George and Vasoulla Psarias
OPEN: all week, D only MEALS: 6.30 to 12
PRICES: £9 (£14). Service 10% CARD: Visa
SEATS: 90. Private parties: 90 main room, 35 and 20 private rooms. Vegetarian meals. Children's helpings. No-smoking area. Wheelchair access. Greek music

Sangster's Wine Bar [9/20]

19–21 Church Street, Ilkley LS9 9DR
ILKLEY (0943) 600566 £11

Looks a bit dull from the outside, but inside is a very good wine bar with three rooms, with cord carpet, wooden pews and tables, candles stuck in champagne bottles and an eclectic collection of old keys and corkscrews fastened to the walls. The blackboard menu features much local produce, such as goats' cheese quiche. Dishes are hearty – good tomato soup is with granary bread; smoked chicken comes as half a bird; and pork dijonnaise is served with good vegetables. There is usually a good choice for vegetarians. A better than average selection of 100 wines includes Tokay, Réserve '81, from Trimbach, at £6·95 and CELLARMAN'S CHOICE: Sauvignon du Haut-Poitou '83 at £5·50.

CHEF: M.D.Sangster PROPRIETORS: H.A. and M.D.Sangster
OPEN: Tue to Sat CLOSED: 25 Dec to 2 Jan MEALS: 12 to 1.45, 7 to 9.45
PRICES: £8 (£11). Service 10% CARDS: Access, Amex, Visa
SEATS: 52. 2 tables outside. Private parties: 20 main room. Vegetarian meals. No children under 16. Smart dress preferred

'Rendezvous des fruits de mer has now become assignation of the sea, not, as our waitress once said, assassination of the seas.' (Midlands restaurateur)

The 1987 Guide *will appear before Christmas 1986, so reports are particularly important in the spring. Report forms are at the back of this book, but just write a letter if you prefer. Address them to* The Good Food Guide, *Freepost, 14 Buckingham Street, London WC2N 6BR. No stamp is necessary if you post in the UK.*

INKPEN Berkshire map 2

Swan Inn [new entry, zero rated]

Lower Inkpen RG15 0DX
INKPEN (048 84) 326 £9–£14

A large pub near the centre of Lower Inkpen redecorated and relaunched last winter by the Grants. It's a family business. The menu is essentially English with some interesting combinations – Stilton and cider, smoked chicken and ham in a yoghourt sauce flavoured with orange. There are grilled meats for main course or a good sauté of beef with red wine and vegetables. Cheeses are from James's of Beckenham, for which there can be no better endorsement, or else to round off there are ices, well-made meringues or old English puddings like crumbles and sticky toffee. Sixteen wines including Fleurie '83 at £8. The back of the menu has a wonderful historic note taken from the *Illustrated London News* of 8 August 1846: 'At the Swan Inn, Inkpen, a small village about three miles from Hungerford, the paper on the walls was in many places completely stripped off: the lightning then followed the bell-wire to the kitchen, where the maid-servant was at work; her clothes caught fire, but her screams speedily brought assistance, and the flames were happily extinguished without her receiving much injury; and a boy, who was standing in a barn near the house, was knocked down by the lightning, but escaped with a few slight scars on the cheek; a great portion of the barn, however, was destroyed by the electric fluid.'

CHEF: Neil Bates PROPRIETORS: Ian, Lotte and Dirk Grant
OPEN: all week, exc Sun D MEALS: 12.30 to 1.45, 7.30 to 9.30
PRICES: £10 (£14), Set Sun L £4·95 (£9), Bar snacks from 75p CARDS: Access, Amex, Visa
SEATS: 35. 8 tables outside. Private parties: 48 main room. Car-park, 40 places. Children's helpings (L only). Smart dress preferred. Wheelchair access. Music

IPSWICH Suffolk map 3

Kwok's Rendezvous [10/20]

23 St Nicholas Street, Ipswich IP1 1TW
IPSWICH (0473) 56833 £8–£12

Parasols hang in the corners of this Peking/Szechuan restaurant. The staff speak English and recommend the tea-smoked duck and the squirrel-fish Peking-style. Rice is well handled, though the bang-bang chicken would be improved by using sesame oil rather than glutinous paste. The rating is dropped one point because the dependency on convenience foods seems to be increasing. There is an extraordinarily long wine list, but who drinks Gevrey-Chambertin with drunken fish? Try the oolong tea instead. A very useful restaurant in the area.

CHEF: Thomas Kwok PROPRIETORS: Lucia and Thomas Kwok
OPEN: Mon to Sat MEALS: 12 to 2, 7 to 10.45
PRICES: £6 (£12), Set L £4 (£8), Set D £7·50 (£12). Minimum £7·50 at D. Service 10%
CARDS: Amex, Diners
SEATS: 50. Private parties: 60 main room. Children welcome. Smart dress preferred. Music

Restaurants rating 10 and 11 serve the best food in the locality.

▲ *The Marlborough* [10/20]

Henley Road, Ipswich IP1 3SP
IPSWICH (0473) 57677 £13–£25

The big English cheeses, swaddled in what look like large nappies, sit on a sideboard, in this smart, pink and green dining-room with reproduction gaslight lamps. There are good roasts and raw materials in use on a *carte* that promises much. Fish is consistently good and may figure as a terrine, quenelles or Dover sole, either poached with a wine and cream sauce or smoked from the Butley-Orford Oysterage (see Orford). Sweets can fade; service is attentive. The set menus are good value. Breakfasts have included scrambled eggs with potted shrimps or Suffolk sweet-pickle bacon. There are over a hundred wines with a good range of prices and regions. House French is £6·75, and there's a trio from local vineyards.

CHEFS: Andrew Townend and John Gear PROPRIETORS: David and Wendy Brooks
OPEN: all week MEALS: 12.30 to 2, 7.15 to 9.30 (12.15 to 2.15, 7.15 to 10 Sat)
PRICES: £18 (£25), Set L from £7·50 (£13), Set D from £10 (£16), Snacks from £1 (£1·10) CARDS: Access, Amex, Diners, Visa
SEATS: 60. 6 tables outside. Private parties: 75 main room, 42 private room. Car-park, 60 places. Vegetarian meals. Children's helpings. No children under 5 at D. Smart dress preferred. Wheelchair access (also WC)
ACCOMMODATION: 22 rooms, all with bath/shower. Rooms for disabled. B&B £20 to £40. Children welcome. Baby facilities. No pets in public rooms. Afternoon teas. Garden. TV [GHG]

Singing Chef [11/20]

200 St Helen's Street, Ipswich IP4 2RH
IPSWICH (0473) 55236 **Read Food** £12–£16

For the last 26 years Kenneth and Jeannine Toyé have figured in these pages with their French country food. Salads provided by Joy Larkcom are prodigious, and a retired builder puts out the lobster pots at Felixstowe. '*Nouvelle cuisine* is mucking about with food. The difficult things to manage are the simple things, like a good soup made from fresh produce,' says Mr Toyé. He concentrates on daubes, bourrides, carbonnades and occasional quenelles. Vegetarian dishes figure even more prominently, and there has been a concentration on individual areas of France, which has led to a big expansion of the champagnes held in the cellar – 25 in all. There's also a short wine list from the classic vineyards. CELLARMAN'S CHOICE: Bourgogne Passetoutgrain '82 at £7·50. Songs by request only.

CHEFS: Kenneth and Jeannine Toyé PROPRIETORS: Cynthia and Kenneth Toyé
OPEN: Tue to Sat, D only MEALS: 7 to 11
PRICES: £12 (£16), Set D £8·50 (£12), Snacks from £2·50 (£2·75). Also cut-price menu CARDS: Access, Diners, Visa
SEATS: 35. 3 tables outside. Private parties: 40 main room, 20 private room. Vegetarian meals. Children's helpings. Wheelchair access (also WC). French popular music

New restaurants that we have not been able to assess completely are given a zero rating for this year. We are particularly keen to have reports on these places.

ISLE OF MAN

map 4

BACKGROUND BRIEFING: *The capital, Douglas, offers the largest choice for eating out, from the usual ice-cream parlours and fast-food outlets to good tea-rooms and hotels serving meals. Good-value set lunches are offered by some of the well-established restaurants and hotels. The Clock Inn of the Villiers Hotel, Loch Promenade has a popular self-service lunch with at least five hot dishes a day, plus salads and desserts. Underneath, in the Clarendon Grill in the evenings, the food is more varied, lavish and expensive. The Ganges Tandoori serves good Manx beef. Outside Douglas, the two establishments most often reported favourably by readers are the Harbour Bistro, 5 East Street, Ramsey – a small, friendly restaurant with good seafood and steaks (sometimes, as with the steak Waleska, together in the same dish) – and the Grosvenor, Kirk Andreas. Prices here are high for dishes in the style of mushrooms stuffed with crab-meat, topped with prawns, surrounded with mashed potato and doused with cream and brandy sauce. The Rowany Room, Ocean Castle Hotel, Port Erin offers fresh local ingredients (vegetables and fish in particular) served in a quiet, attractive room with good service and prices around £6 to £7 for four courses. The Ravensdale Castle, set in a fine glen at the foot of Snaefell, has a manorial atmosphere and has been completely modernised into a hotel popular for its hot bar lunches. The Little Italy, Mannin Hotel, Broadway gives good value with a meal such as minestrone, osso buco, and dessert pancakes for about £5. Generally the quality of local meat is high and local vegetables are good, too, though limited in variety. There are Manx kippers and queenies – small scallops. Simple dishes of these local ingredients are popular as bar meals at pubs such as the Colby Glen, and hotels such as The Shore.*

Boncompte's [11/20]

King Edward Road, Onchan
DOUGLAS (0624) 75626

£10–£19

Local opinion is split as to which is the best restaurant on the island. This elegant, family-run restaurant with a fabulous view over Douglas Bay and excellent service is certainly a contender. There is an hors d'oeuvre trolley before fine steaks, chicken Kiev, or salmon hollandaise. Local queenie scallops are delivered fresh and served with garlic butter and bacon, or else there are oysters from Port Erin served neat on crushed ice. There is good Stilton, and chocolate sweets. Lunch menus are shorter and cheaper. A well-spread choice of wines, with house Sauvignon at £5·90. CELLARMAN'S CHOICE: Beaune Bastion at £5·10 for a half-bottle.

CHEF: Jaime Boncompte PROPRIETORS: Jaime and Jill Boncompte
OPEN: Mon to Sat, exc Sat L MEALS: 12.30 to 2, 7.30 to 10
PRICES: £13 (£19), Set L £6 (£10) CARDS: Access, Diners, Visa
SEATS: 80. Private parties: 80 main room. Car-park, 10 places. Vegetarian meals by arrangement. Children's helpings. Smart dress preferred. Wheelchair access (also wc). Music

This restaurant has an exceptional wine cellar.

Many of the better restaurants offer bargain lunches for half the price of a meal in the evening. Details are given in the text.

La Rosette [new entry, zero rated]

Main Road, Ballasalla
DOUGLAS (0624) 822940 £15

Formerly Ye Olde Bakery Tea Shoppe, this is now a chapel-like dining-room with seats resembling pews. The menu is French bistro and Robert Phillips cooks to order. Soups have been good, and the local scallops are served either grilled in their shells or with Mornay sauce. Other fish, such as monk and brill, has also been well handled. More than half the main courses are variations on beef, from Stroganoff to au poivre, but sometimes there is cassoulet too. There are plenty of trimmings, including complimentary sherry, sorbet and, for women, roses – and you could probably take away the tomato rose garnish, too. There are 20 wines, mostly in the £6 to £9 range. CELLARMAN'S CHOICE: Côtes du Ventoux '81 at £6·50. More reports, please.

CHEF: Robert Phillips PROPRIETORS: Robert and Rosa Phillips
OPEN: Tue to Sat, and Sun L MEALS: 12 to 2.30, 7 to 10.30
PRICES: £10 (£15). Cover 25p at L, 50p at D. Service inc
SEATS: 32. Private parties: 6 main room, 10 private room. Children's helpings (Sun L only). Music

ISLE OF WIGHT

map 2

▲ *Peacock Vane* [11/20]

Bonchurch PO38 1RG
ISLE OF WIGHT (0983) 852019 Real Food £13–£17

The best restaurant on the island may not compete with the increasingly high standards on the mainland at present, but nevertheless the charm of the building and the owners make this a handsome place to stay. The fish dishes are the best, notably fine turbot with well-made hollandaise, or sea-bass, which is carved at the table, or scallops with bacon. Home-made bread is served with the good soups (especially Jerusalem artichoke) and with the cheeseboard, which usually features eight English and French specimens. House French is £5. Poor coffee: might be something to do with the island's water.

CHEF: Rosalind Wolfenden PROPRIETORS: John and Rosalind Wolfenden
OPEN: all week, exc L Mon and Tue CLOSED: 2 Nov to 28 Feb MEALS: 1, 8 to 9.15
PRICES: Set L £10 (£13), Set D £14 (£17). Service inc CARDS: Access, Amex, Diners, Visa
SEATS: 30. Private parties: 30 main room. Car-park, 20 places. No children under 11. Wheelchair access
ACCOMMODATION: 9 rooms, all with bath/shower. Prices not available. Pets welcome. Garden. Outdoor swimming-pool. TV. Scenic. Doors close at 12 [GHG]

The 1987 Guide *will appear before Christmas 1986, so reports are particularly important in the spring. Report forms are at the back of this book, but just write a letter if you prefer. Address them to* The Good Food Guide, *Freepost, 14 Buckingham Street, London WC2N 6BR. No stamp is necessary if you post in the UK.*

IXWORTH Suffolk map 6

Theobalds [11/20]

68 High Street, Ixworth IP31 2HJ
PAKENHAM (0359) 31707 £11–£18

This unpretentious restaurant, in a genuinely old building, is well patronised by locals. Service is by local girls, and Geraldine Theobald greets you. The essentially French menu changes monthly, and has been trimmed back to good effect. It is a good mix between the conventional and the classic with clever touches, such as garnishing the Jerusalem artichoke soup with toasted hazel-nuts. Good dishes have been the pheasant pâté; moules marinière; grilled fillet of lamb with artichoke bottoms and a madeira sauce; and the roast beef for Sunday lunch. Vegetables are varied. The more elaborate concoctions are without exception less successful. The wine list has backbone to it, and the Doudet-Naudin burgundies are worthwhile.

CHEF: Simon Theobald PROPRIETORS: Simon and Geraldine Theobald
OPEN: Tue to Sun, exc Sat L and Sun D MEALS: 12.15 to 2, 7.30 to 10
PRICES: £13 (£18), Set L £7·25 (£11) CARDS: Access, Visa
SEATS: 36. 2 tables outside. Private parties: 36 main room. Children's helpings (Sun L only). No children under 8 at D. No-smoking area. Music

JEVINGTON East Sussex map 3

Hungry Monk [11/20]

Jevington BM26 5QF
POLEGATE (032 12) 2178
turn off A22 at Polegate crossroads and
proceed along B2106 to Jevington £14–£15

It's a bit rough and ready, but the Hungry Monk's enormous portions are ever popular. The three low flint cottages, dating in part from the fourteenth century, have one dining-room and three rooms with roaring fires in winter for drinks and coffee. The set menu includes hot rolls and a free glass of port. Mussel and squid stew is hot and spicy, or there are pâtés and terrines before beef Wellington, excellent duck or rack of lamb with garlic and cream sauce. Finish with the hot chocolate cake with vanilla ice-cream and hot chocolate sauce. An interesting, not overpriced, range of wines and 16 malt whiskies too, including Laphroaig and Macallan at £1·20 a glass. CELLARMAN'S CHOICE: Quincy, Domaine de Maison Blanche '83 at £6·67. No credit cards.

CHEFS: Ian Dowding and Kent Austin PROPRIETORS: Mr and Mrs Nigel Mackenzie
OPEN: all week, D only plus Sun L MEALS: 12.15 to 2.30, 7.15 to 10.30
PRICES: Set L from £10 (£14), Set D from £10·30 (£15)
SEATS: 36. 1 table outside. Private parties: 36 main room. Vegetarian meals. Car-park, 17 places. Smart dress preferred. No cigars in dining-room. Children's helpings. No children under 3. Classical music

Restaurants are checked every year and their entries rewritten. The restaurant scene changes very rapidly so don't be caught with an out-of-date Guide.

KENILWORTH Warwickshire map 5

Diment [11/20]

121–123 Warwick Road, Kenilworth CV8 1HP
KENILWORTH (0926) 53763 £10–£18

The tables are well spaced in this small French restaurant, and the service is unobtrusive. No fewer than nine starters vary from melon with curaçao to herring roes in pastry cases with cream and mustard sauce. Main courses usually include alcohol – chicken with Grand Marnier; venison with red wine and black cherries; duck breast with cassis liqueur. Vegetables have been good, as have sweets, such as coffee ice-cream with walnuts. An interesting selection of wines with some clever choices of vintage, for example, Hermitage '76, from Sichel at £12·95. House Muscadet is £5·50. In the basement is now an attached, good-value bistro with excellent service and robust food. No bookings taken.

CHEF: David Fanshawe PROPRIETORS: Antonio and Jennifer Martin
OPEN: Tue to Sat, exc Sat L CLOSED: 1st 3 weeks Aug MEALS: 12 to 2, 7 to 10
PRICES: £13 (£18), Set L £5·25 (£10), Set D £10·45 (£13) CARDS: Access, Amex, Diners, Visa
SEATS: 40. Private parties: 40 main room. Car-park, 12 places. Vegetarian meals by arrangement. Children's helpings. Music

Portofino [10/20]

14 Talisman Square, Kenilworth CV8 1JB
KENILWORTH (0926) 57186 £7–£16

The pasta is freshly made each day and the menu sensibly restrained in this family-run trattoria. Fish is from the excellent Birmingham market or Grimsby. Both florentine chicken and veal with breadcrumbs and cheese are done with more flair than usual. The Ferros pride themselves on their fresh vegetables and home-made sweets. There's plenty of 'prego' and 'grazie' about the service. House Trebbiano is £5·50.

CHEF: Maurizio Torchia PROPRIETORS: Michele and Vito Ferro
OPEN: all week, exc Mon L and Sun D MEALS: 12.15 to 2, 6.15 to 11
PRICES: £10 (£16), Set L £4·25 (£7). Service inc. set only, alc 10% CARDS: Access, Amex, Diners, Visa
SEATS: 60. Private parties: 90 main room. Children's helpings (Sun L only). Smart dress preferred. Wheelchair access. Classical music

Restaurant Bosquet [14/20]

97A Warwick Road, Kenilworth CV8 1HP
KENILWORTH (0926) 52463 £14–£20

Bernard Lignier is as much an inventor as a cook. 'I want to surprise the mind,' he says. Where this works it works well: witness the trio of vol-au-vents to start, one filled with lobster and spinach, one with sweetbreads on sweet onion pickle, one with soft-boiled quails' eggs (a feat in itself), and each with their own sauce, or the boned ox-tail wrapped in lettuce. His sauces and construction work carry him through, even if some of his combinations verge on the bizarre –

langoustines and sweetbreads? Smoked salmon and smoked goose breast with broccoli and hazel-nut oil? There are more successes than part-failures – home-made ravioli filled with wild mushrooms; roast saddle of lamb stuffed with kidney, aubergine and tomato; coffee and chocolate mousse served in a tall-stemmed glass with an almond tuile. Service from Jane Lignier is personable and relaxed. The excellent '83 vintage of Alsace wines arrived quickly on the list of good-quality, often lesser-known French wines, and suits the extremes of flavours well. Otherwise the house Cahors is £5·80, or try the CELLARMAN'S CHOICE: Fitou '76 at £7·20.

CHEF: Bernard Lignier PROPRIETORS: Bernard and Jane Lignier
OPEN: Mon to Sat CLOSED: last 3 weeks July MEALS: 12 to 1.45, 7 to 10
PRICES: £14 (£20), Set L and D £10·50 (£14). Service inc. set only CARDS: Amex, Visa
SEATS: 28. Private parties: 32 main room. Children welcome

Romano's [9/20]

60 Waverley Road, Kenilworth CV8 1VN
KENILWORTH (0926) 57473 £9–£16

Romano Goldoni treats everyone as his personal guest. His wife Anna prepares a menu deep in the vein of international Italian cooking – Parma ham with melon; Dover sole with asparagus; good pasta with Gorgonzola sauce; fruits with Cointreau. Fish is a strong point. There are good wines from all over to match. Vacqueyras '78 is a snip at £6·90 and Italian wines come from many regions. CELLARMAN'S CHOICE: Barolo '71 at £10·50.

CHEF: Anna Goldoni PROPRIETOR: Romano Goldoni
OPEN: Mon to Sat, exc Sat L CLOSED: Aug MEALS: 12.30 to 2, 7.30 to 10.30
PRICES: £10 (£16), Set L from £4·80 (£9), Set D £12 (£13·50). Minimum £6·20
CARDS: Amex, Visa
SEATS: 30. Private parties: 36 main room. Car-park, 10 places. Vegetarian meals. Children welcome. Smart dress preferred. Wheelchair access. Music

KILDWICK West Yorkshire map 5

▲ *Kildwick Hall* [new entry, zero rated]

Kildwick BD20 9AE
CROSS HILLS (0535) 32244
on A629, 4m NW of Keighley £13–£24

An impressive Jacobean manor with panelled walls, soft drapes, flock wallpaper, Staffordshire figures staring out from a show-case, and an inglenook fireplace big enough to put a car in. There are two dining-rooms, one large and baronial, the other smaller and more like an old-fashioned dining-club. Both are set with starched linen and silver accessories and David Burns cooks a menu to match, with the accent strongly on some picturesque presentation. It is not cheap and the waiters seem to be on piecework rates for filling up the wine glasses, but the ingredients are very good – fish from Harrogate, foie gras from Rungis near Paris, locally raised beef – and they carry meals through with some style. Good dishes have been salmon with asparagus; a generous portion of fanned-out duck breast with a buttery herb sauce; brill with crayfish sauce. The bread rolls could be improved, as could the small portions of vegetables smothered in butter, considering they cost £2·50. A similar level of mark-up operates on the clarets and burgundies. More reports, please, also on the attached steak-bar, Justices, which is open for lunch and dinner all week except Sunday, and is considerably cheaper.

CHEF: David Burns PROPRIETOR: John Sharpe
OPEN: all week, D only, and Sun L MEALS: 12.30 to 2.30, 7.30 to 10 (7 to 8.30 Sun)
PRICES: £17 (£24), Set Sun L £8·95 (£13), Set D £12·95 (£17). Service inc. CARDS: Access, Amex, Diners, Visa
SEATS: 45. Private parties: 65 main room, 25 private room. Car-park, 60 places. Vegetarian meals by arrangement. Children welcome. Music
ACCOMMODATION: 12 rooms, all with bath/shower. B&B from £31·50. Children welcome. No pets in public rooms. Afternoon teas. Garden. TV. Phone. Scenic. Doors close at 12

KILSBY Northamptonshire — map 5

Hunt House [new entry, zero rated]

Kilsby CV23 8XR
CRICK (0788) 823282
2m W of M1 exit 17, in Kilsby, opposite
Red Lion pub — £17

Converted stables next to a Tudor cottage, where Ian Geggie takes orders while wife Jan cooks. The five-course menu lacks a strong stamp of individuality in execution, but there have been good dishes nonetheless. Starters include sardine pâté with lemon; egg en cocotte with chicken livers; seafood pancakes; mushrooms, stuffed with pâté, in madeira sauce; followed by honest, wholesome soups, such as carrot and leek or cauliflower cheese. Main courses enjoyed include fillet of veal with chicken mousse and rosemary sauce, and rack of lamb with redcurrant, orange and mint sauce. Puddings from the trolley have a lot of chocolate. Bread is terrific, Malvern water is brought without asking, and service is pleasant and efficient. The 50 wines are well chosen and good value, and include Ch. Giscours '79 at £9·75, and Gewürztraminer '81, from Hugel, for £6·85. There is also a good choice of half-bottles. More reports, please.

CHEF: Janice Geggie PROPRIETORS: Janice and Ian Geggie
OPEN: Tue to Sat, D only MEALS: 7.15 to 10.15 (11 Sat)
PRICES: Set D £12·50 (£17). Service 10% CARDS: Access, Amex, Diners, Visa
SEATS: 36. Private parties: 12 private room. Car-park, 24 places. Vegetarian meals by arrangement. Children's helpings. Smart dress preferred. Separate smoking area. Wheelchair access (also WC). Music. Air-conditioned

KIMBOLTON Cambridgeshire — map 3

La Côte d'Or [10/20]

19 High Street, Kimbolton PE18 0MB
HUNTINGDON (0480) 861587 — £10–£20

A quaint little note on the top of the menu says: 'Please note: Garlic is used in the cooking'! Barry and Marie Hélène Beever's restaurant is in a listed building: it is claimed that the beams date from 1202, while the dining-room is arranged around a 400-year-old fireplace. The *carte* has rather more commercial things brought in than we approve of (snails, frogs' legs . . . and how can all the steaks weigh out at exactly eight ounces?) but on the other hand Mrs Beever is a good cook – witness the courgette soufflé; duck marinated and cooked with port; her chateaubriand. There is always a set menu of the day, which usually features her best work. A cracking wine list, with good red burgundies from '78 and '79. We make no specific recommendations because the price of last year's CELLARMAN'S CHOICE rose by £2·20 in the year.

CHEF: Marie Hélène Beever PROPRIETORS: Barry and Marie Hélène Beever
OPEN: all week, exc Sun D and Tue MEALS: 12 to 1.45, 7.30 to 9
PRICES: £15 (£20), Set L £5·25 (£10), Set D £14·75 (£20). Also cut-price L menu. Minimum £5·25 L, £10 D. Service 10% CARDS: Access, Visa
SEATS: 30. 6 tables outside. Private parties: 12 main room. No children under 6. Jacket and tie. Wheelchair access

KINGHAM Oxfordshire — map 2

▲ *Mill Hotel* [new entry, zero rated]

Kingham OX7 6UH
KINGHAM (060 871) 8188
off B4450, between Stow-on-the-Wold and Chipping Norton — £12–£18

This comfortable but immaculately run hotel-restaurant on the edge of a peaceful village approaches many people's ideal of an English establishment. Reliably good food is served from a conservative menu including mushrooms in garlic cream, lemon sole stuffed with mushrooms and anchovies, and pan-fried calf's liver with avocado. Service is courteous. Chef John Beach is coming to the end of his tenure and a replacement may be in place early in 1986, but the second chef has worked at Sharrow Bay in Ullswater, Chewton Glen at New Milton, and Le Talbooth in Dedham. A sensible, annotated wine list with four from Alsace and house wine at £5·85. CELLARMAN'S CHOICE: Rioja Viña Pomal '77/'78 at £7·25. More reports, please.

CHEF: John Beach PROPRIETORS: Mr and Mrs John Barnett
OPEN: all week MEALS: 12.30 to 2, 7 to 10
PRICES: £12 (£18), Set L £7·50 (£12), Set D £9·25 (£14), Bar L from £1·85 (£2), Snacks from 85p (95p) CARDS: Access, Amex, Diners, Visa
SEATS: 60. Private parties: 50 main room. Car-park, 40 places. Children's helpings. Jacket and tie. Wheelchair access. Classical music
ACCOMMODATION: 20 rooms, all with bath/shower. B&B £20 to £40. Deposit: £10. No children under 5. No pets. Afternoon teas. Garden. Fishing. TV. Phone. Scenic. Doors close at 11.30. Confirm by 4

KING'S LYNN Norfolk — map 6

Riverside Rooms [9/20]

The Fermoy Centre, 27 King Street, King's Lynn PE30 1HA
KING'S LYNN (0553) 773134 — £14

This is in a 500-year-old former warehouse that is part of a National Trust-maintained complex. The bare brick dining-room overlooks the Ouse. It is an English-style menu, in the sense of having sauté cockles in red wine and parsley, as well as avocado and shrimps with Rose Marie sauce. There is good pastry work and a bit more seasoning would help other dishes. Sweets have been poor. A short and mostly French wine list, with a few bottles from most major regions.

CHEF: Dennis Taylor PROPRIETORS: Michael and Sylvia Savage
OPEN: Mon to Sat MEALS: 12 to 2, 7 to 10
PRICES: £9 (£14). Cheaper set L available CARDS: Access, Visa
SEATS: 65. 24 tables outside. Private parties: 95 main room. Car-park, 10 places. Vegetarian meals. Children's helpings. Pianist

KINGSTON UPON THAMES Surrey map 3

Ayudhya [11/20]

14 Kingston Hill, Kingston upon Thames KT2 7NH
01-549 5984 £12

Ayudhya is the original name for Siam. The brick, cane and stained-wood interior of this Thai restaurant is comfortable; tables are big enough to accommodate the many different dishes; and the menu has descriptions for Western palates. Many of the ingredients and sauces sound similar, but what comes out of the kitchen is varied, interesting and authentic. Spicing is pungent but not overwhelming: real skill has influenced the balance of flavours. Thin, oily sauces are light and not in the least cloying or sticky and, happily, spoons are provided. There are Indonesian and Chinese influences on the starters – dim-sum, pancake rolls, shrimp toast and satay all figure. Main-course dishes of pork, chicken, beef and seafood are cooked with garlic, chillies, coriander, basil, lemon grass, potent fish-paste, and citrus – a typical speciality is the fish curry with coconut cream, citrus leaves and sweet basil. The service smiles and the French house wines, both white and red, are above average, though from a very limited list.

CHEF: Somjai Feehan PROPRIETORS: Somjai Feehan and Charoen Priaynu
OPEN: all week, exc Sat L MEALS: 12 to 2.30, 6.30 to 11.15
PRICES: £6 (£12). Service 12.5% CARDS: Amex, Diners, Visa
SEATS: 80. Private parties: 22 main room, 22 private room. Children welcome. Wheelchair access. Oriental music

KINTBURY Berkshire map 2

▲ *Dundas Arms* [10/20]

Station Road, Kintbury RG15 0UT
KINTBURY (0488) 58263 £13–£22

The butchery policy badly needs rethinking here. Ducks may come from Challans and pigeons from Bresse but they are tough, mangy birds by the time they get on the plate. Time and again potentially very good meals have collapsed at the main course and not even some expert sauces made from veal stocks can save them. Nonetheless, the Arms has enough plus points to rate inclusion – good pastry work, excellent terrine of scallops with herb sauce, and equally brilliant mint and chocolate bavarois with a coffee and chicory sauce all show what the kitchen can do when it has a mind. Add to that a wine list with some rare vintage clarets and good burgundies and there are the seeds, at least, of a restaurant that could rate 13 or 14.

CHEFS: David Dalzell-Piper and Pascal Morelle PROPRIETOR: D. Dalzell-Piper
OPEN: Tue to Sat CLOSED: Christmas MEALS: 12.15 to 2, 7.30 to 9.30 (11 Fri and Sat; 12 to 2 and 7 to 10.30 Sun)
PRICES: £16 (£22), Set L £7·90 (£13) CARDS: Access, Amex, Diners, Visa
SEATS: 36. 8 tables outside. Private parties: 20 main room. Car-park, 50 places. Children's helpings. Smart dress preferred. No cigars/pipes in dining-room. Wheelchair access (also WC)
ACCOMMODATION: 6 rooms, all with bath/shower. Rooms for disabled. B&B £32 to £38. Children welcome. No pets. TV. Phone. Scenic. Doors close at 11. Confirm by 6 [GHG]

KIRKBY FLEETHAM North Yorkshire map 7

▲ *Kirkby Fleetham Hall* [13/20]

Kirkby Fleetham, DL7 0SU
NORTHALLERTON (0609) 748226
1m N of village **Real Food** £11–£16

How refreshing to find a cook who has absorbed Elizabeth David, received the wisdom of the French chefs of the 1970s, but doesn't try to compete with the Roux brothers: typical dishes are spiced apple soup, fish roulade, chicken breast with Pernod, praline ice-cream with apricot sauce. The meat may occasionally be overcooked, but roast lamb is pink, and vegetables are varied and nicely done. The Grants have developed first-class supply lines and also have their own walled garden for herbs and difficult-to-get vegetables and now do their own smoking. The remote Georgian hall with its rose-coloured hallways, antique furniture, and log fire in winter, is run as a country house with a comforting rather than polished air about it; service is mostly efficient and friendly. The 38-page wine list comes complete with selection matrix, maps, a little lecture, and regional notes. Clarets are extensive, with good value throughout; burgundy shippers are varied, although Duboeuf sweeps the board with village Beaujolais. Justice is done to English and German wines, and particularly to drinkers of half-bottles; major Alsace wines are represented by Gisselbrecht, Muré and Trimbach. Credit cards are not accepted for weekend breaks.

CHEF: Chris Grant PROPRIETORS: David and Chris Grant
OPEN: all week D only, and Sun L MEALS: 12.30 to 1.30, 7 to 9
PRICES: Set Sun L £7 (£11), Set D £12·50 (£16). Service inc CARDS: Amex, Visa
SEATS: 45. Private parties: 20 private room. Car-park, 30 places. Children's helpings. Music
ACCOMMODATION: 15 rooms, all with bath/shower. B&B £38 to £55. Garden. Helicopter pad. TV. Phone. Doors close at 11 [GHG]

KIRKBY LONSDALE Cumbria map 7

▲ *Eaveslea* [new entry, zero rated]

New Road, Kirkby Lonsdale LA6 2AB
KIRKBY LONSDALE (0468) 71209 £9–£16

A detached building set in its own, well-kept grounds. The dining-room is spacious and there is a set menu that uses local meats and plenty of herbs from the garden. The ten-herb salad is served with a vinaigrette; celery and chervil soup comes with granary bread; a fine dill sauce is offered with the salmon en croûte. The gooseberry, rhubarb and pear flan is a fine finish. Thirty wines, starting with house Loire at £4·50. More reports, please.

CHEF: Sandra Boyer PROPRIETORS: David and Sandra Boyer
OPEN: Tue to Sat D, Sun L (plus Sun and Mon D for residents) CLOSED: Jan
MEALS: 12 to 2.30, 7 to 9
PRICES: Set Sun L from £5·50 (£9), Set D from £12·50 (£16)
SEATS: 24. Private parties: 30 main room. Car-park, 20 places. No children under 10. Smart dress preferred. No smoking in dining-room. Wheelchair access (also WC). Classical music. Air-conditioned
ACCOMMODATION: 5 rooms, all with bath/shower. Rooms for disabled. D, B&B £35 to £60. No children under 10. No pets. Garden. Croquet. Lift. TV. Scenic

KNARESBOROUGH North Yorkshire map 5

Schwallers [12/20]

6–8 Bond End, Knaresborough HG5 9AO
HARROGATE (0423) 863899 **Real Food** £10–£18

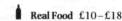

'We are a Swiss restaurant that lets our ingredients dictate the style of dishes,' explains Martin Schwaller in an apt summary of the best of modern cooking. Fish comes from Scotland on Fridays and translates into excellent monkfish with fennel sauce, or salmon cooked en papillote with a herb infusion, or hot crab pie. There are some classy touches that give a lift to the comfortable, lived-in upstairs dining-room – brown rolls baked for each meal, a bottle of mineral water on each table, the use of free-range eggs – though the intermediate sorbet is an unnecessary flamboyance. Good dishes have been lamb, either with a sauce of mustard and kidneys or provençale; beef Wellington; the rösti potatoes. Wild mushrooms are served with the venison, and Yorkshire goats' cheeses appear on a board of a dozen specimens. As you might expect, sweets are a strong point. The timing of meals has posed problems, but there is compensation in a fine wine list. The quintet of Alsace wines comes from the co-operative at Ribeauvillé, founded in 1895 and the oldest in France, and includes a Tokay '81 at £6·75, a gold medal winner. Interesting propositions include sherry by the half-bottle, and the list of experimental wines which are sold cheaply provided that Mr Schwaller can taste a glass to judge if it should go on the main list. CELLARMAN'S CHOICE: Rioja Contino '78 at £7·85.

CHEF: Martin Schwaller PROPRIETORS: Caroline and Martin Schwaller
OPEN: Wed to Sun, also Mon D MEALS: 12 (12.30 Sun) to 2, 7 to 10.30
PRICES: £13 (£18), Set L from £6·25 (£10), Set D from £10·25 (£15) CARDS: Access, Visa
SEATS: 35. Private parties: 48 main room. Vegetarian meals. Children's helpings. No smoking in dining-room. Jazz and classical music

Restaurants are graded on a scale of 1–20. In the region of 8–9 expect to find places that may not be restaurants but cafes, pubs, bistros and small hotels. In the category of 10–11 you can expect to find the best food in the locality. Ratings of 12 or more are given to restaurants we regard as serving the best food in the region.

KNUTSFORD Cheshire map 5

▲ *La Belle Epoque* [11/20]

60 King Street, Knutsford WA16 2DT
KNUTSFORD (0565) 3060 and 2661 £19

The sense of being in a museum has spread to the dining-room of this art nouveau shrine where John Galsworthy reputedly drank. It has the first art nouveau fireplace in Britain, Chinese Chippendale chairs and Venetian glass floors in the comfortable bar, and a bronze statue in the centre of the dining-room. Yvonne Holt's menu is cast in the mould of home-made walnut bread rolls; veal and pork sausage with apple and calvados sauce; excellent cream of cauliflower soup. The breast of duck with a sauce of Grand Marnier and kumquats has been good. Vegetables are sparse but fresh, and herbs are from the garden. The five bedrooms are good value. The wine list has some works of art of its own, including Ch. Mouton-Rothschild '71 at £75, half a dozen Alsace at a tenth of the price and some other regional French around the £5·50 mark.

CHEF: Yvonne Holt PROPRIETORS: Keith and Nerys Mooney
OPEN: all week, D only CLOSED: 1st week Jan MEALS: 7.30 to 10
PRICES: £12 (£19). Service 10% CARDS: Access, Amex, Diners, Visa
SEATS: 70. Private parties: 90 main room, 20 and 100 private rooms. Vegetarian meals. No pipes in dining-room. Children's helpings. No children under 10. Wheelchair access. Music
ACCOMMODATION: 5 rooms, all with bath/shower. B&B £25 to £35. Garden. No children under 10. No pets. TV. Scenic. Doors close at 12. Confirm by 2 [GHG]

LACOCK Wiltshire map 2

▲ *At the Sign of the Angel* [11/20]

Church Street, Lacock SN15 2LA
LACOCK (024 973) 230
2–3m outside Chippenham on A350 **Real Food** £17–£21

The Levis family have run this quiet, pretty inn for 30 years, and the tradition of good English cooking using high-quality local ingredients does not change. The best of the fruit and vegetables are from the back garden, eggs are free-range and milk and cream come from their own Jersey herd. Meals are based around well-hung roasted meats, but there is no choice. Dover sole has also been good. For pudding there might be treacle lick or more often sorbets including, unusually, plum. Coffee is taken upstairs in a TV room. Low doors, sloping floors, ancient beams and antique furniture bring home the fact that this is a fifteenth-century wool-merchant's house. Excellent apple and blackcurrant purée and herb sausages for breakfast. The esteemed Viña Ardanza '76 from La Rioja Alta is £7·50.

CHEF: J.S.Levis PROPRIETOR: L.M.Levis
OPEN: all week, exc Sat L and Sun D CLOSED: 22 Dec to 4 Jan MEALS: 1 to 1.30, 7.30 to 8
PRICES: Set L £12 (£17), Set D £15·50 (£21)
SEATS: 40. Private parties: 20 main room, 20 private room. Smart dress preferred. No children under 12. One sitting
ACCOMMODATION: 6 rooms, all with bath/shower. B&B £48 (double; no single rooms). Pets welcome. Garden. No children under 12. Phone. Scenic. Confirm by 5.30 [GHG]

▲ *Red Lion* [9/20]

High Street, Lacock SN15 2LQ
LACOCK (024 973) 456 — £6–£12

Good pub food is served here, opposite the Fox Talbot photographic museum – home-made sausages with Urchfont mustard, beef pie, grilled salmon. The bread is excellent and the Wadworth's beer is well kept too.

CHEFS: Monica Travers and Sylvia Lockey PROPRIETOR: John Levis
OPEN: all week CLOSED: Christmas Day MEALS: 12 to 2, 7 to 10
PRICES: £8 (£12). Minimum £4·50. Bar meals about £4·50 (£6)
SEATS: 50. 15 tables outside. Private parties: 40 main room. Vegetarian meals. Children's helpings (L only)
ACCOMMODATION: 3 rooms, 1 with bath/shower. B&B £20 to £32. No children under 7. Pets welcome. Afternoon teas. Scenic. Doors close at 11

LANCASTER Lancashire — map 7

BACKGROUND BRIEFING: *Good pub lunches are to be had at the Stonewell Tavern in Lower Church Street. The Upper Crust, where smoking is not allowed, also has good snack lunches. The market, lately in a tent since the original building burned down, has a good Lancashire cheese stall with choice of mild, crumbly, tasty or strong. Stanley's is the best of the three fruit stalls; oddly there do not appear to be any greengrocers outside the market. The shrimp stall does not open until after the boats have come in (usually after 10am), but it is worth queuing for fresh shrimps, rough or peeled. Atkinsons coffee-shop in China Street has 24 varieties.*

LANGLEY MARSH Somerset — map 1

▲ *Langley House* [11/20]

Langley Marsh TA4 2VF
WIVELISCOMBE (0984) 23318
off A361, 1m N of Wiveliscombe — £16–£21

A tranquil country-house hotel with food and service to match the surroundings. All main courses are served with vegetables from the McCullochs' walled garden. There is no choice in the four-course menus before the pudding. Meals seem to start French and end English, moving from prawn and avocado pot pourri and Bresse chicken with mushroom, to blackberry and apple pie and wine and lemon syllabub. The farmhouse Stilton is served with home-made biscuits. Breakfasts, too, are in the farmhouse style. The wine list is short but varied. House Mouflon d'Or is £5·75, or try the CELLARMAN'S CHOICE: red Sancerre '82, from Natter, at £7·90.

'I have had a long flirtation with cuisine nouvelle, *but have found that the public is becoming increasingly disenchanted with small if beautifully prepared dishes that become more and more like a production from Kew Gardens.'* (West Country restaurateur)

CHEF: Rosalind McCulloch PROPRIETORS: Francis and Rosalind McCulloch
OPEN: all week, D only CLOSED: Nov to Feb MEALS: 7.30 (8.30 Fri and Sat)
PRICES: Set D from £12 to £17 (£16 to £21). Service inc
SEATS: 18. Private parties: 35 main room, 18 private room. Car-park, 10 places. Vegetarian meals by arrangement. Children's helpings by arrangement. No children under 7. No smoking in dining-room. Wheelchair access. One sitting
ACCOMMODATION: 6 rooms, all with bath/shower. B&B £24. Deposit: £10. No children under 7. Dogs welcome. Garden. TV. Phone. Scenic. Doors close at 12.30 [GHG]

LEDBURY Hereford & Worcester — map 2

▲ *Hope End Country House Hotel* [12/20]

Hope End, Ledbury HR8 1VQ
LEDBURY (0531) 3613
2m N of Ledbury just beyond Wellington Heath — **Real Food** £18

More aptly called a country-house home than a hotel, this minareted and arched farmhouse set in 40 acres of parkland, nature reserve and bluebell wood is tended by the Hegartys with the reverence of someone treasuring a vintage bottle of claret (and Mr Hegarty knows his wines). It is secluded and hard to find: from Ledbury follow the road to Bromyard, go under the railway bridge and take first right following the signpost to Wellington Heath. Follow this winding road for about a mile, turn right at the T-junction and continue to bear right for a quarter of a mile and you come to a large farm on the right called Hope Farm. Hope End is on the left, just after the farm. . . . The set five-course menu changes nightly, taking in ham wrapped in sea kale with a Dijon mustard sauce, pike fillet with lemon butter sauce, breast of wood pigeon in perry sauce. Before that there is always an unusual vegetable soup and afterwards a piquant salad. Vegetables are fresh from the walled garden, and home-made oat biscuits accompany the single Gloucester or blue Wensleydale. Help yourself to coffee after dinner in the upstairs lounge. Bedrooms are like a suite, with enormous beds, a sofa, rugs and books. Healthy goats'-milk yoghourt and muesli at breakfast. The atmosphere is individual and peaceful, and the Hegartys frown on denims. The wine list has matured, with magnificent vintages of the '70s showing strongly, plenty of half-bottles including five from Alsace, and generous mark-ups on pedigree bottles.

CHEF: Patricia Hegarty PROPRIETORS: John and Patricia Hegarty
OPEN: all week, D only CLOSED: Dec to Feb MEALS: 7.30 to 9
PRICES: Set D £16 (£18). Service inc CARDS: Access, Amex, Diners, Visa
SEATS: 24. Private parties: 6 main room. Car-park, 10 places. Smart dress preferred. No smoking. No children under 14. Wheelchair access
ACCOMMODATION: 7 rooms, all with bath/shower. Rooms for disabled. B&B from £31. Deposit: £30. Garden. No children under 14. Phone. Scenic. Doors close at 11. Confirm by 6 [GHG]

LEEDS West Yorkshire — map 5

BACKGROUND BRIEFING: *Wing Lee Hong stores, 6 Edward Street, has a large selection of Chinese goods. Mullaco Asian Foods and Spices, 35 Oxford Street, Batley provides a similar service for Indian groceries, and sells its own home-made pickles (take a container). Groocock & Sons, 31 Otley Road is a traditional grocer where white-coated assistants serve excellent bacon, bread and coffee. Pollards, 28 Lands Lane has a large range of teas and coffees to take away or drink on the premises with snacks. Schofield's department store has a decent food-hall, and Ainsley's is a good chain of bakers. The excursion out to Farnley is well worth it for Alan Porter's Farnley Shop with its splendid range of English and European cheeses along with salamis, butters, hams, fresh herbs, wine, coffee, and home-made ice-cream. Nash's Tudor Fish Restaurant at 17 Merrion Street does good cheap meals.*

Bryan's [9/20]

9 Weetwood Lane, Headingley, Leeds LS16 5LT
LEEDS (0532) 785679 £5

Bryan's remains, after 51 years, probably the finest fish and chip shop in the country. Its beige, box-like, no-frills institutional dining-room on the road out of Leeds has waitresses that are friendly in the way that only Yorkshire people are. The fish is magnificent because it is fresh and correctly fried, using beef dripping. (It comes out of Aberdeen, which has the best fish available at present.) There are fat-cut chips to go with it, tea, and mushy peas, and there is a £2.10 menu for pensioners in the afternoon. Always busy, and rightly so.

CHEF: Alan Jackson PROPRIETOR: Jan Saxton
OPEN: Mon to Sat MEALS: 11.30am to 11.30pm
PRICES: £4 (£5). Minimum £1·98
SEATS: 140. Private parties: 100 main room. Car-park, 50 places. Children's helpings. Wheelchair access (also WC). Music. Air-conditioned

La Grillade [10/20]

Wellington Street, Leeds LS1 4HJ
LEEDS (0532) 459707 and 459952 £10–£13

A plain, labyrinthine cellar with bare brick walls, low ceilings and ageing French posters. There are three choices of menu – a *carte*, a set menu and specials on the blackboard. Main courses come on huge wooden platters; chips come in a glass bowl. The Toulouse sausage is excellent, and the champignons bordelaise and the salad of lardons are good. Profiteroles are a bit heavy. The waiters are so French you might find yourself talking to them in French. An unpretentious wine list with a dozen bottles. There is a sister wine bar, The Waterhole (see entry below).

CHEF: Orenzo Tadolino PROPRIETORS: Meritlight Ltd
OPEN: Mon to Sat, exc Sat L CLOSED: 1 week at Christmas MEALS: 12 to 2.30, 7.30 to 11
PRICES: £9 (£13), Set L and D £6·20 (£10) CARDS: Access, Visa
SEATS: 62. Private parties: 20 main room. Children's helpings. Air-conditioned

Jumbo Chinese Restaurant [10/20]

120 Vicar Lane, Leeds LS2 7NL
LEEDS (0532) 458324 £10

By Cantonese standards the menu is a mere stripling, with 70-odd items plus dim-sum snacks. After 12 years a lick of paint would not hurt the decor, but the food is both good value and of a standard, and the service has improved. Good dishes we have eaten are crab with ginger; Hong Kong roast duck; chicken in a paper bag; bean curd hot-pot; capital spare ribs. The dim-sum are good, and some hold that the cheung-fun is better than at the Sang Sang around the corner. They are helpfully described in English, too. Licensed.

CHEF: Yat Sun Lo PROPRIETORS: Lin Dai Lai, Tony Kwan and Yat Sun Lo
OPEN: all week CLOSED: 25 Dec MEALS: noon to 11.45
PRICES: £6 (£10) CARDS: Access, Amex
SEATS: 120. Private parties: 180 main room. Children welcome. Music. Air-conditioned

Mandalay [10/20]

8 Harrison Street, Leeds LS1 6PA
LEEDS (0532) 446453 £7–£14

An elegant Indian restaurant reminiscent of the days of the Raj, with roof fans, cane chairs, a comfortable reception/bar area and a grand piano, which is played at weekends. They also have a cinema room. The kitchen is scrupulously clean, and the tandoori chef works behind a glass screen in full view of the restaurant. Pity some of the tandoori chicken quarters and lamb are reheated, which may account for their dryness, but nan are cooked fresh to order. Sauces are thick, with varied spicing: mild with jumbo prawns in jhinga masala, strong with lamb in biriani and kalahi josh. Dhal is smooth and full-bodied. Fresh coriander is used everywhere. Good service.

CHEF: Mohammed Bacar PROPRIETORS: T.Sheish and S.M.Sharma
OPEN: Mon to Sat, exc Sat L MEALS: 12 to 2.30, 6 to 11.30
PRICES: £7 (£14), Set L £3·50 (£7). Service 10% CARDS: Access, Amex, Diners, Visa
SEATS: 125. Private parties: 160 main room, 30 private room. Vegetarian meals. Children welcome. No jeans. Wheelchair access (also WC). Live music Fri and Sat. Air-conditioned

Salvo's [9/20]

115 Otley Road, Headingley, Leeds L56 3PQ
LEEDS (0532) 755017 £13

There are no tables for two here; the pizza chef bakes in the centre of the dining-room and is known to burst into Italian love songs; and the waitresses appear to have been picked for their good looks. It is popular and the atmosphere buzzes. The pizzas are excellent and other portions generous. House Italian is £4·95.

CHEF: Graham Spink PROPRIETORS: Salvo Dammone and Geppino Dammone
OPEN: Mon to Sat CLOSED: 25 and 26 Dec MEALS: 12 to 2, 6 to 11.30
PRICES: £9 (£13)
SEATS: 52. Private parties: 20 main room. Vegetarian meals. Children's helpings. Wheelchair access. Music. Air-conditioned

Restaurants are checked every year and their entries rewritten. The restaurant scene changes very rapidly so don't be caught with an out-of-date Guide.

'We were assailed at every opportunity by the unspeakable phenomenon, the non-comprehending, Malvern-water-pouring French waiter, but getting service when required was impossible.' (On eating in Bedfordshire)

Sang Sang [12/20]

7 The Headrow, Leeds LS1 6PN
LEEDS (0532) 468664 and 435160 £10–£14

In the centre of town, opposite the Orient, up from the Shabab and round from the Jumbo. The dining-room is clean and friendly with, at one end, a big circular sign in Chinese characters denoting Double Happiness (a wedding blessing). The waiters jolly everyone along as they pick up the dishes from the serving hatch. It is a long Chinese dragon of a menu with mainly Cantonese but some Peking dishes too, and not much monosodium glutamate. Alpha dishes have been the subtle squid with salt and pepper, the duck with plum sauce, prawns in rice-paper, and chicken with mange-tout. Steamed scallops are a must as is the roast belly-pork. Rice and Chinese vegetables are treated respectfully. Licensed.

CHEFS: F.C.Cheung and K.S.Liu
PROPRIETORS: Thomas Y.Ma, F.C.Cheung, K.M.La and P.S.Chow
OPEN: all week MEALS: noon to 11.45
PRICES: £8 (£14), Set L and D from £6·50 (£10), Snacks from 85p (95p) CARDS: Access, Amex, Diners, Visa
SEATS: 120. Private parties: 90 main room, 30 private room. Vegetarian meals. Children welcome. Wheelchair access. Chinese music. Air-conditioned

Shabab [10/20]

2 Eastgate, Leeds LS2 7JL
LEEDS (0532) 468988 £6–£12

Mohammed Tanvir's Eastgate operation (one of three he runs in Yorkshire) is good value for money. £3 per head at lunch-time brings two large chunks of lamb tikka with raita; murgh korma, a delicately spiced, smooth creamy sauce with coriander and lots of chicken; an aubergine and potato side-dish; and mutli-coloured Basmati rice. Furnishing is comfortable; service polite rather than friendly. Licensed.

CHEF: Muhabat Ali PROPRIETOR: Mohammed Tanvir
OPEN: all week CLOSED: 25 Dec MEALS: 11.30 to 2.30, 6 to 11.30
PRICES: £7 (£12), Set L £2·95 (£6). Service 10% CARDS: Access, Amex, Carte Blanche, Diners, Visa
SEATS: 80. Private parties: 70 main room. Vegetarian meals. Children welcome. Indian music

The Waterhole [8/20]

43 Great George Street, Leeds LS1 3BB
LEEDS (0532) 458856 £9

The only authentic wine bar in the city and boasting 100 wines in all, including eight of the nine *cru* Beaujolais from the excellent '83 vintage. The menu changes regularly and has included large plates of salami; casseroles; and fresh salmon. Crêpes are done to order and fondue bourguignonne is a speciality.

PROPRIETORS: Meritlight Ltd
OPEN: Mon to Fri MEALS: 12 to 2.30, 5.30 to 9.30 (10 Fri)
PRICES: £6 (£9)
SEATS: 100. Private parties: 80 main room. Vegetarian meals. Children welcome in restaurant. Air-conditioned

LEICESTER Leicestershire map 5

Water Margin [9/20]

76–78 High Street, Leicester LE1 5YP
LEICESTER (0533) 56422 and 24937 £7–£14

The best things to have in this Cantonese restaurant are the dim-sum, particularly prawn dumplings, meatballs with Chinese mushrooms, and char siu in a dough. Good reports also of the satay beef. The service can be disorganised. Tea is inclusive, but house French at £4·85 isn't.

CHEF: Tony Au PROPRIETOR: Mr Chan
OPEN: all week MEALS: noon to 11.15
PRICES: £8 (£14), Set L and D from £4 (£7). Service 10% CARDS: Access, Amex, Diners, Visa
SEATS: 200. Private parties: 100 main room. Vegetarian meals. Children welcome. Jacket and tie preferred. Music. Air-conditioned

LEIGHTON BUZZARD Bedfordshire map 3

▲ *Swan Hotel* [new entry, zero rated]

High Street, Leighton Buzzard LU7 7EA
LEIGHTON BUZZARD (0525) 372148 £11–£17

Quite *the* place in Leighton Buzzard at the moment. Formerly a pub, now a 39-bedroom hotel. There is a long menu that wanders from hearty spare ribs to monkfish with ginger and includes a complete vegetarian section. Predictably some dishes are better than others, with the kitchen working on this scale, but the traditional dishes are done well – Molly's broth of white beans and smoked sausage; Posting-house beef; Burnt Cambridge cream; and bread-and-butter pudding. The nut croquettes are excellent, too. A basic wine list. More reports, please.

CHEF: Gregor Nicholl PROPRIETORS: Eric and Felicity Stephens
OPEN: all week MEALS: 12 to 2, 7 to 9.30 (7.30 to 10 Fri and Sat, 7 to 10.30 Sun)
PRICES: £12 (£17), Set L from £7·50 (£11), Set D from £10·50 (£14) CARDS: Access, Amex, Diners, Visa
SEATS: 55. 3 tables outside. Private parties: 65 main room, 30 private room. Car-park, 10 places. Vegetarian meals. Children's helpings. Smart dress preferred. Wheelchair access
ACCOMMODATION: 39 rooms, all with bath/shower. B&B £40 to £50. Children welcome. Baby facilities. Pets welcome. Afternoon teas. TV. Phone. Doors close at 12. Confirm by 6 day before arrival

Entries are compiled from the unsolicited reports from readers and are checked by inspectors; each restaurant is asked to supply details of its operation. Report forms can be found at the back of the Guide.

LEWES East Sussex map 3

La Cucina [10/20]

13 Station Street, Lewes BN7 2DA
LEWES (0273) 476707 £12

A cheery, good-value, pine-clad restaurant offering decent portions of well-cooked Italian food. Almost everything on the menu is raw when ordered. There is classic home-made cannelloni and plenty of seafood, including good mussels and occasionally such fish as brill. Among the well-chosen Italian wines from good producers are a few unusual bottles, for example, Bianco di Custoza.

CHEFS: S.Marrone, P.Hicks and Jose Vilas PROPRIETOR: Jose Vilas
OPEN: Mon to Sat CLOSED: last week Aug, 1st week Sept, 24 Dec to 7 Jan MEALS: 12 to 2, 6.30 to 11
PRICES: £8 (£12). Service 10% for parties over 5 CARDS: Access, Amex, Visa
SEATS: 47. Private parties: 30 main room, 20 private room. Vegetarian meals. Children welcome. Italian music

Kenwards [14/20]

Pipe Passage, 151A High Street, Lewes BN7 1XU
LEWES (0273) 472343 Real Food £16

The restaurant is hard to find: Pipe Passage is just a chink in the High Street, hardly wide enough to get a pram down. John Kenward is now in sole charge of the kitchen again, which gives full rein to the individuality of his cooking. The loyalty of the menu is to simplicity and Real Food, and the flavours Mr Kenward manages to invoke are strikingly vivid. A common device is to cook different parts of an animal in different ways and serve them together – breast and thigh of guinea-fowl; pheasant breast fried lightly and the pan de-glazed with stock, cider and apple while the casseroled limbs are warmed through in the oven; the tail of a loin of lamb roasted, the eye pan-fried, the bones making a stock with Malaga for the sauce, served with a warm mushroom salad tossed in butter and more Malaga. Other interesting combinations are leeks and artichokes with ginger; oysters and fennel; and duck with cider and turnips. Vegetables are immaculate and unadulterated. To finish, try the chocolate hazel-nut cake. The dining-room lacks a little pezazz because essentially this is a cook's restaurant. But the wine list is a pleasure, with a powerful Alsace section that includes quartets of all the four leading grapes, plus equally fine showings of *cru* Beaujolais, Rioja and *cru* burgundies at nearly affordable prices. CELLARMAN'S CHOICE: Imperial Gran Reserva '73 at £8·30.

CHEF: John Kenward PROPRIETORS: John and Caroline Kenward
OPEN: Tue to Sat, D only MEALS: 7.30 to 9.30
PRICES: £12 (£16). Service inc
SEATS: 25. Private parties: 10 main room. Vegetarian meals. Children welcome. Music

'We were welcomed as though we were a rescue party – possibly the *rescue party. The lady behind the bar had stored up several months of conversation, and was keen to relieve the pressure on her overcrowded memory.'* (On eating in a remote part of Cumbria)

The Sussex Kitchen [8/20]

The Pelham Arms, High Street, Lewes BN7 1XL
LEWES (0273) 476149 £8–£11

A popular seventeenth-century inn with a comfortable dining-room, limited menu, but good-quality English food ranging from crab cocktail to steak and kidney pie, with large meringues to finish.

CHEFS: Pat Bolton and Nina Bloomfield PROPRIETOR: Harry Gilmore
OPEN: Tue to Sat MEALS: 12.30 to 1.30, 7 to 9.30
PRICES: £8 (£11), Set L £4.25 (£8). Minimum £3.85 CARDS: Access, Visa
SEATS: 48. Private parties: 36 main room. Car-park, 20 places. Vegetarian meals. Children's helpings. Wheelchair access (1 step). Air-conditioned

LIFTON Devon map 1

▲ *Arundell Arms* [11/20]

Lifton PL16 0AA
LIFTON (0566) 84666
on A30, 4m E of Launceston **Real Food** £11–£21

An old country house famous for its fishing and shooting facilities. The south Devon beef is hung for three weeks, salmon comes out of the hotel's own stretch of the Tamar, and in season there can be partridge and snipe. Menus are sensibly limited and mix the traditional, such as steak, kidney and Guinness pudding, with the less so, like chicken pot-roasted with mussels. Chef Philip Burgess's training at L'Ecu de France in London shows in the quenelles of salmon. Sweets are served with clotted cream from a local herd of Friesians. Sixty wines with something for everyone and something from just about everywhere. House French, German or Spanish from £5 to £5·35.

CHEF: Philip Burgess PROPRIETOR: Anne Voss-Bark
OPEN: all week CLOSED: 5 days at Christmas MEALS: 12.30 to 2, 7.30 to 9
PRICES: £14 (£21), Set L from £7 (£11), Set D from £12 (£16), Snacks from £1 (£1·10), Bar meals from £4 (£4·40) CARDS: Access, Amex, Diners, Visa
SEATS: 70. Private parties: 80 main room, 30 private room. Car-park, 80 places. Vegetarian meals. Children's helpings. Smart dress preferred
ACCOMMODATION: 28 rooms, 26 with bath/shower. B&B £24·50 to £47. Children welcome. Baby facilities. Pets welcome. Afternoon teas. Garden. Fishing. Shooting. Golf. TV. Phone. Scenic. Doors close at 11.30 [GHG]

LIMPSFIELD Surrey map 3

Old Lodge [12/20]

High Street, Limpsfield RH8 0DR
OXTED (088 33) 2996 £6–£25

The oak-beamed dining-room has large panels and could be a set from a costume drama about the Civil War; the tables are Cromwellian and the chairs big. Waiters wear a uniform of black trousers and white shirt. Cheap it is not, which is one reason why we are reluctant to raise the rating to 13, although some of John Mann's cooking has been very good. Meals build up to a crescendo, with sweets such as strawberry cheesecake and strawberry sauce, or iced Tia Maria soufflé in a biscuit basket on a plate of vanilla sauce and angel hair. Elsewhere there is a lot of raspberry vinegar about the menu. Main-course portions of such protein-rich dishes as salmon stuffed with smoked trout pâté, or sweetbread casserole with fennel sauce, are not small. The saucing is improving. There is an English theme as well, which has produced immaculate roast beef and Yorkshire pudding for lunch on Sunday. The wine list is not generously priced but has some good vintages in claret and also English wines of interest. House wine is £7·50.

CHEF: John Mann PROPRIETORS: The Clivaz family
OPEN: Tue to Sun, exc Sat L and Sun D CLOSED: 1st 2weeks Jan MEALS: 12 to 2.15, 7 to 9
PRICES: Set L £2·50 to £15 (£6 to £19), Set D £13·75 to £21·75 (£17 to £25), Snacks from £1·75. Service inc. Licensed, plus bring your own: no corkage CARDS: Access, Amex, Diners, Visa
SEATS: 60. 5 tables outside. Private parties: 51 main room. Car-park, 30 places. Vegetarian meals. Children's helpings. Smart dress preferred. No cigars/pipes in dining-room. Wheelchair access (also WC). Classical music

LINCOLN **Lincolnshire** map 6

BACKGROUND BRIEFING: *The Wig and Mitre, 29 Steep Hill is an informal eating-place serving some good food. Mushroom pâté, steaks, and sole cooked in a Chinese style with ginger, spring onion and soy, have been successful dishes. Jane Howard, 83 Bailgate is a delicatessen with a very good range of cheeses, oils, salamis, pâtés, salads, quiches and chocolates. A. W. Curtis & Son is the city's best known pork butchers, with good stuffed chine, pies and sausages.*

Harvey's Cathedral Restaurant [10/20]

1 Exchequergate, Castle Square, Lincoln LN2 1LU
LINCOLN (0522) 21886 £16–£18

This is a minute's walk from the cathedral, at the top of Steep Hill, and decorated in lush colours. The Harveys' special evenings bring in dishes from Andalucia, Tuscany, the Caribbean and Mediterranean, some of which find their way on to the eclectic five-course dinner menu. Flavours tend to be big and portions filling: tarte alsacienne is filled with juicy onions and a knock of Pernod in a cream and egg base; beans and sausage come in a soup. Main courses – sesame lamb kofte kebab; turbot in lobster sauce; venison with port, cranberries and chestnuts – are less successful than the puddings, such as Bournvillea, a rich dark chocolate pot; or Captain Ginger, a creamy home-made ice-cream. Take their advice and drink one of the excellent clarets with simple dishes such as pink roast lamb. Sadly, Alsace wines are to be dropped, but there are good burgundies, red Loires to be served cool, and a good selection from South Africa. A flexible pricing policy makes expensive bottles relatively good value. CELLARMAN'S CHOICE: Pouilly Fumé, les Chantalouettes '83, from Gitton, at £10·50 (which may be superseded by '84 at £11·50).

CHEFS/PROPRIETORS: Adrianne and Bob Harvey
OPEN: all week, exc Sun L CLOSED: 1st 5 days Jan MEALS: 11.45 to 2, 7 to 9.30
PRICES: L £9 (£16), Set D from £12·50 (£18) CARDS: Access, Visa
SEATS: 55. Private parties: 24 main room, 36 private room. Vegetarian meals. Children's helpings

▲ *White's* [14/20]

Jews House, 15 The Strait, Lincoln LN2 1UD
LINCOLN (0522) 24851 — **Real Food** £22

Reputedly the oldest dwelling-house in Europe and found at the foot of an almost vertical cobbled hill leading up to the magnificent cathedral. Colin and Gwen White run an honest, happy kitchen. They describe it as an extension of family eating, which is not very wide of the mark. Their ingredients are first-class: organically grown vegetables, free-range eggs, geese from a friend, guinea-fowl and other game from South Scarle, and both locally ground and also French flours for breadmaking. They have started making their own ricotta and yoghourt, which binds the timbale of aubergines and tomatoes for the roast loin of kid. The cooking – a mix of regional dishes from Italy, France and England – has a depth to it: pea, pear and watercress soup with croûtons; chicken livers sauté with bacon, garlic, ginger, sherry and water-chestnuts; shellfish ragout; and pheasant with a sauce of chestnuts, orange and port. The craft is as evident in the roasting of a lean crown of lamb as in the lightness of the quenelles or one of the two English mutton dishes (a rare treat now) – in a pie or boiled with caper sauce. Vegetables are now plated in the modern style and the set menu has given way to a short *carte* and a good-value menu for light lunches. It is not cheap by Lincolnshire standards, but Lincolnshire is one of the least expensive counties in Britain. They have a cottage up the road if you want to stay over. The wines, like the food, have been assembled with precision, with an eye on half-bottles, fine vintages, including '70s clarets and '78 Rhônes, and a seductive spread from £7 to £25. There are cognacs, marcs and calvados too. As we went to press the restaurant had just been put up for sale, so check first.

CHEF: Colin White PROPRIETORS: Colin and Gwen White
OPEN: Mon to Sat, exc Tue L CLOSED: Christmas to New Year MEALS: 12 to 2.30, 7.30 to 10.30
PRICES: £17·50 (£22), Snacks £2.50 (£2·75). Licensed, plus bring your own: corkage £1
CARDS: Access, Amex, Diners, Visa
SEATS: 30. Private parties: 32 main room. Vegetarian meals. No cigars/pipes in dining-room. Children's helpings. Wheelchair access
ACCOMMODATION: 2 rooms. B&B £24 to £36

LIPHOOK Hampshire — map 2

Lal Quilla [9/20]

15 The Square, Liphook GU30 7AB
LIPHOOK (0428) 722095 and 722704 — £14

Varied spicing characterises the cooking on a menu of regular dishes here, going from mild lamb pasanda and king prawn in coconut, to rich chicken tikka and hot samosas. Tandoori dishes include a mixed grill at £6·75. Karahi chicken or lamb is pot-roasted with coriander and garlic; chicken jal frezi is cooked with green pepper and onion. As well as an enormous 'special' menu for two, and a

All inspections are carried out anonymously as we accept no handouts.

vegetarian thali, there is kulfi, rasmalai or rasgulla to finish. House French is £5·95.

CHEF: Abdul Munim PROPRIETOR: H.Zaman
OPEN: all week MEALS: 12 to 2.30, 6 to 11.30
PRICES: £7 (£14) CARDS: Access, Amex, Diners, Visa
SEATS: 50. Private parties: 50 main room. Vegetarian meals. Children welcome. Classical music. Take-away service

LITTLEWICK GREEN Berkshire map 2

Warrener Restaurant [11/20]

Warren Row, Littlewick Green RG10 8QS
LITTLEWICK GREEN (062 882) 2803
between Knowl Hill on A4 and
Remenham Hill on A423 £14–£20

This is a restaurant that could be brilliant if it understood that making dishes look good is only part of the battle. On the one hand there are some very interesting things to eat, such as excellent smoked wood-pigeon served with dark plum sauce, and yet on the other the gravlax is laid out on top of a sweet glaze. Simpler things work well, like courgette and cauliflower soup; salmon, despite its tomato skin garnish; vegetables, although served with parsimony; and the Double Gloucester. Who needs a sorbet between courses? And nice as it is to have eight kinds of very good petits fours this underlines the point about over-elaboration – it just does not happen in the very best restaurants. There are some fine clarets and burgundies, at a price.

CHEF: Keith Walker PROPRIETORS: Mr and Mrs M.A.O'Shea
OPEN: Tue to Sat, exc Sat L CLOSED: 1st week Apr MEALS: 12.30 to 2.30, 7.30 to 9.30
PRICES: £15 (£20), Set L from £9·50 (£14) CARDS: Access, Amex, Diners, Visa
SEATS: 40. Private parties: 40 main room. Car-park, 20 places. Vegetarian meals by arrangement. Children's helpings. No children under 8. Jacket and tie. Wheelchair access. Classical music

LIVERPOOL Merseyside map 5

BACKGROUND BRIEFING: *Chinese and Indian restaurants survive by staying open late – in some cases until three or four in the morning. But the Chinese scene is a pale shadow of its former self. Kam Po in Nelson Street has snacks and cheap meals; Yuet Ben has a short basic Pekingese menu; and ABC Takeout in Rathbone Road is reported to be a good chippie and Peking take-away (the chef used to cook at Lao's, Rankin Hall, 44 Ullet Road, Sefton Park). A pub called The Nook has a high percentage of Chinese customers and occasionally serves Chinese snacks. Shun On Supermarket (below the Far East, see entry) has a good range of fresh vegetables and fruit, semi-prepared food, and dried and tinned ingredients. Mandarin, 40 Victoria Street serves good crab with ginger and spring onion, and bok choi with oyster sauce. A smattering of Greek places includes Reno's in Henry Street. Burger and pizza joints are taking over in popularity*

Prices quoted are for an average three-course meal including service and VAT and half a bottle of house wine (or the equivalent in an ethnic restaurant).

from the old-style corner cafes, whose demise means it gets harder to find a decent breakfast, although Franks on Dock Road still does an early-morning fry-up. Busy eateries which serve up atmosphere with inexpensive food include Villa Italia, 40 Stanley Street and Everyman Bistro, Hope Street.

The Armadillo [11/20]

20–22 Mathew Street, L2 6RE
051-236 4123 £15

The old fruit-market area has had a lot of money spent on it lately and it is hardly the dive it was when the Cavern was in its heyday. Martin Cooper's honest restaurant smacks of the Habitat generation, both in the decor – wood chairs and tables, and polished wood floor – and the short menu – belly pork and celeriac salad, trout ceviche, and chicken dijonnaise. The cheaper daytime buffet is upgraded at night. Vegetable soups are excellent, as is the fish from the city market, for example carp fillets, which come with a lemon and butter sauce. Also good have been the steaks, and veal with cider. Welsh lamb steaks are baked in vine leaves with Gruyère, garlic and herbs; vegetables are lined up in a single, oval earthenware dish. Ice-creams are the best bet to finish; other desserts have not always been as fresh as they might. Coffee is strong and service matter of fact. The wine list has been rethought and expanded to 60 bottles. House Cordier is £6. CELLARMAN'S CHOICE: Domaine de Gaillat '78 at £6·95.

CHEF/PROPRIETOR: Martin Cooper
OPEN: Mon to Sat, exc Mon D CLOSED: 1 week after Christmas MEALS: 10.30 to 6, 7.30 to 10.30
PRICES: £10 (£15), Bar L from £1 (£1·10). Minimum £1 at L CARDS: Access, Visa
SEATS: 65. Private parties: 50 main room. Vegetarian meals. Children's helpings (L only). Jazz. Self-service at L

Beaujolais [9/20]

50 Seel Street, L1 4AZ
051-709 1327 £14

More of a new Beaujolais than a *cru*, but the effort goes into the cooking rather than the decor and the food tastes good enough. The menu is scrawled on the board – good grilled mushrooms, authentic onion soup, steak au poivre with plenty of garlic bread, pork with cider, and apple charlotte to finish. Service is willing, and there are some corny jokes on the menu like Blue Max for the Stilton and port sauce served with steak. House Yugoslav is £5.

PROPRIETORS: Onymange Ltd
OPEN: Mon to Sat, D only CLOSED: bank hols MEALS: 7.30 to 11.30 (12 Fri and Sat)
PRICES: £9 (£14). Service 10% CARDS: Access, Amex, Diners
SEATS: 60. Private parties: 35 main room. Vegetarian meals. Children's helpings. Wheelchair access. Music. Air-conditioned

'It is difficult to ruin smoked salmon, but the smoked mountain ham popped over a chunk of fresh pineapple was certainly not inspired by the Roux brothers.' (On eating in Liverpool)

Carrageen Cafe [9/20]

9 Myrtle Parade, L7 NEL
051-733 3641 £3

The decor may be rudimentary but some very good vegetarian cooking is done here. Serve yourself from the counter and share a wooden table. Salad portions are big – plates only hold a maximum of three of the ten on offer. Bread is baked each morning; vegetable soups are healthy purées; the spring onion roulade would not be out of place in a top French restaurant; and a frequent sub-theme to the blackboard menu is curry. Good dishes have been tomato, spinach and cream cheese pancakes; garlic and red-cabbage salad; curried bulgar-wheat mix; enormous carob orange cake; and maple and raspberry cake. There are exotic teas, or take your own wine for 50p corkage.

CHEFS/PROPRIETORS: Carolyn Berkson and William Craig
OPEN: Mon to Sat, daytime only MEALS: 12 to 6.30
PRICES: £2 (£3). Unlicensed, but bring your own: corkage 50p
SEATS: 50. Private parties: 50 main room. Vegetarian meals. Children's helpings. Classical music. Air-conditioned. Self-service

Casa Italia [8/20]

Temple Court, 40 Stanley Street, L2 6SS
051-227 5774 £12

The cheapest of the trio of Italian restaurants in the court. It serves pizzas and pasta in a large, quasi-rustic room broken up by columns. The sweets are the same as in the more expensive restaurants. A jolly place. The waiter asked our female inspector for a date.

CHEF: Paul Butler
OPEN: Mon to Sat MEALS: noon to 10
PRICES: £7 (£12)
SEATS: 100. Vegetarian meals. Children welcome. Jacket and tie preferred. Wheelchair access (3 steps)

Elham [11/20]

95 Renshaw Street, L1 2SP
051-709 1589 £15

It is on the quality of the meats – usually char-grilled – that this Middle Eastern restaurant prides itself. Lamb cutlets and kebabs are consistently good as is the squid, which is also char-grilled. The meze is good value and incorporates starters from different countries, such as bastarma (deep-fried sausages from Armenia), baba ghanoush (grilled aubergine and sesame from the Lebanon), and falafel (deep-fried broad bean and chickpea rissoles). Pitta bread, rice, and salads are their equal. Look also for ispanak ala-dajaj – boneless chicken with spinach.

The Guide is always anxious to recruit new inspectors. If you would like to apply, write to the editor enclosing a) a detailed report on a restaurant where you have eaten and b) a comparative study of restaurants known to you.

The restaurant fills up quickly after the pubs close, but the service copes well. Licensed, but Metaxa seven-star brandy at £1·50 a go is the pinnacle of the list.

CHEF/PROPRIETOR: H.M.Safar
OPEN: all week, D only MEALS: 7 to 2.30am (3.30 Fri and Sat)
PRICES: £10 (£15). Service inc CARDS: Access, Amex, Diners, Visa
SEATS: 65. Private parties: 70 main room, 30 private room. Vegetarian meals by arrangement. Children's helpings. Wheelchair access. Music

Far East Restaurant [11/20]

27–35 Berry Street, L1 9DF
051-709 3141 and 6072 £7–£15

This is over the best Chinese supermarket in the city. The decor is typically lurid Chinese, with blown-up views of Sydney, Paris, Hong Kong and Peking, and there is seating for 250 people. The long Cantonese menu features interesting casseroles and hot-pots, such as aromatic fish's head and sea cucumber, and also a wide range of noodle soups and fried noodle dishes. To eat cheaply there are plenty of one-dish meals and also good dim-sum in the shape of spare ribs in black bean sauce, prawn toasts, beef cheung-fun, and steamed chicken with mushrooms. Good dishes from the main menu have been the soups, deep-fried crispy chicken, and deep-fried bean curd with minced prawn stuffing. Rice comes in enormous bowls and orange segments arrive with the bill. Tea, though, has been fey and the service stretched. Licensed.

CHEFS: Kai-Wah Chan and C.L.Tse PROPRIETOR: Tsun-Loi Cheung
OPEN: all week MEALS: noon to 11.30 (11.45 Fri and Sat)
PRICES: £8 (£15), Set L £2·80 (£7), Set D from £7·50 (£12). Service 10% CARDS: Access, Amex, Diners, Visa
SEATS: 250. Private parties: 300 main room. Car-park, 45 places. Vegetarian meals. Children welcome. Wheelchair access (also WC). Music

La Grande Bouffe [10/20]

48A Castle Street, L2 7LJ
051-236 3375 £10–£15

The decor is not going to win an award (hard chairs, padded former church pews, wobbly tables, paper napkins, and heavy, thick wine glasses) but the cooking is more than competent and draws on a variety of sources – chicken satay, ragout of lamb, spicy lentil soup. Nuts are used a lot – ground almonds and apricots go with a chicken suprême, and there has been a sweet carrot and almond cake as a dessert. Vegetables are fresh and the coffee strong and plentiful. A wide-ranging wine list with seven Loires starting at £4·15 and a good sprinkling of halves. CELLARMAN'S CHOICE: Chablis, Côte de Léchet '83 from Defaix at £9·95.

CHEFS: Jean Kassim, Juliet Shield, Sheila Benson, Terry Lewis and James Price
PROPRIETOR: Juliet Shield
OPEN: Mon to Sat, exc Mon D and Sat L MEALS: 12 to 2.15, 6 to 10
PRICES: £11 (£15), Set L £5·95 (£10), Set Sat D from £8·25 (£12). Also cut-price menu pre- and post-theatre. Minimum £1·50 at L. Service 10% CARDS: Access, Amex, Visa
SEATS: 90. Private parties: 12 main room, 20 private room. Vegetarian meals. Children's helpings. Jazz. Air-conditioned

LODDISWELL Devon map 1

Lavinia's [10/20]

Loddiswell TQ7 4ED
KINGSBRIDGE (0548) 550306 £21

Lavinia Davies has lived here since she was three and has cooked here for some ten years. One feature of the menu is the seafood hors d'oeuvre, which can include as many as 12 kinds of fish including oysters and smoked prawns. Lobster, when available, is served cold, thermidor or Newburg. Meat dishes are hearty, such as veal kidneys wrapped in smoked bacon and cooked in butter with a madeira sauce. Vegetables come from the garden when possible, and bread is always home made. There are some very good names on the wine list – not always of the best vintages, but not over-priced, either. House French is £6·50.

CHEF: Lavinia Davies PROPRIETORS: Jeremy and Lavinia Davies
OPEN: Tue to Sat, D only CLOSED: Nov to Easter MEALS: 7.30 to 9.30
PRICES: Set D from £18 (£21). Service inc CARDS: Access, Visa
SEATS: 30. Private parties: 36 main room. Car-park, 15 places. Children's helpings. Smart dress preferred. No pipes in dining-room. Classical music

LONG MELFORD Suffolk map 3

Countrymen [9/20]

Hall Street, Long Melford CO10 9JA
SUDBURY (0787) 79951 £8–£20

Inexpensive meals are served in this family-run, beamed dining-room with a large fireplace and hunting scenes. Fish dishes are the best: grilled sardines, or turbot meunière. There are plenty of mentions for the Italian trifle from the large selection of sweets in the cold cabinet. House Italian is £4.50, and there are interesting ciders and apple juices.

CHEF: Stephen Errington PROPRIETORS: Stephen and Janet Errington
OPEN: Tue to Sun, exc Sun D CLOSED: 1 week Feb and Oct MEALS: 12 to 1.30, 7 to 9
PRICES: Set L from £5 (£8), Set D from £7 to £15.50 (£10 to £20) CARDS: Access, Visa
SEATS: 32. Private parties: 40 main room, 12 private room. Children's helpings by arrangement. No children under 10 at D. Smart dress preferred. No cigars/pipes in dining-room. Wheelchair access (also WC). Music

LOSTWITHIEL Cornwall map 1

Trewithen [10/20]

3 Fore Street, Lostwithiel PL22 0AD
BODMIN (0208) 872373 £14

A stone and pine dining-room run with a sense of humour – 'Copacabanana???' is among the sweets. Lobsters are from Mevagissey, venison sausages are made locally, and the inspiration for prawns with coconut and pineapple is from

The Guide *does not accept free meals.*

Polynesia. The menu is sensibly short, as is the wine list. House wine is £4·95.
CELLARMAN'S CHOICE: Rock's elderflower wine at £3·30, or Campo Viejo Rioja, Reserva '76 at £6·80.

CHEFS/PROPRIETORS: Mr and Mrs Brian Rolls
OPEN: Tue to Sat, D only (also Mon D in summer) MEALS: 7 to 9.30
PRICES: £10 (£14) CARDS: Access, Diners, Visa
SEATS: 30. Private parties: 20 main room, 20 and 14 private rooms. Vegetarian meals. Children's helpings. Wheelchair access (also WC). Air-conditioned

LOUGHBOROUGH Leicestershire map 5

Restaurant Roger Burdell [new entry, zero rated]

11–12 Sparrow Hill, Loughborough LE11 1BT
LOUGHBOROUGH (0509) 231813 £12–£20

This manor house in the middle of Loughborough offers good food and value amid pink and grey elegance. Roger Burdell, who was at Hambleton Hall, grows his own herbs and salad ingredients, collects wild mushrooms, and occasionally shoots his own game. The cooking is ambitious – salad of pigeon breasts sliced with red cabbage, or mushrooms, ceps and truffles in puff pastry to start, before sliced teal with al dente vegetables, or chicken hearts stuffed with watercress and walnuts. Sauté sirloin fillets in madeira sauce and medallions of lamb with basil are both good-quality meats served pink. Finish with a brandy-snap basket filled with three sorbets in raspberry sauce. The cafetière of coffee is left on the table. There is a welcome glass of Kir to begin with, helpings are well-judged, and service is attentive. The menu changes monthly. The list of 100 wines is strong on claret; although there is no house wine Ch. Moulin de Landry '78 and Mâcon-Blanc Villages '84 are both around £7·50. More reports, please.

CHEF/PROPRIETOR: Roger Burdell
OPEN: Tue to Sun, exc Sun D MEALS: 12.30 to 2, 7.15 to 9.15
PRICES: Set L from £7·50 (£12), Set D £16·50 (£20). Minimum £7·50. Service inc
CARDS: Access, Amex, Diners, Visa
SEATS: 60. Private parties: 40 main room, 20 private room. Vegetarian meals by arrangement. Children's helpings (Sun L only). No cigars/pipes in dining-room. Wheelchair access

LOUTH Lincolnshire map 6

Mr Chips [8/20]

17–21 Aswell Street, Louth LN11 9BA
LOUTH (0507) 603756 £2+

The fish does not come out of Grimsby any more – but all the way from Fraserburgh, where the quality catch is to be found. This chippie has been in the Hagan family since 1921, and before that they worked the boats. It is bright, efficient and big, with both a take-away counter and a sit-down cafeteria. The

'Had I come direct from London, instead of from Corse Lawn, the dinner would have seemed better.' (On eating in Lincolnshire)

fish is freshly fried and there is a huge turnover – most of Louth gets in here once a week. Pots of tea 30p. Children and pensioners get preferential treatment.

PROPRIETORS: J.P.Hagan & Co. Ltd
OPEN: Mon to Sat CLOSED: 25, 26 Dec, 1 Jan MEALS: 11 to 11
PRICES: £2+. Service inc
SEATS: 200. Private parties: 200 main room. No-smoking area. Children's helpings. Wheelchair access. Self-service. Air-conditioned

LOWER BRAILES Warwickshire map 2

▲ *Feldon House* [11/20]

Lower Brailes OX15 5HW
BRAILES (060 885) 580
on B4035, 4m E of Shipston on Stour **Real Food** £10–£13

'The menu is set because ours is a small operation – it would not be viable to offer a choice of dishes unless we used convenience foods. We decide on menus when we shop, choosing whatever is best and most fresh.' Well said, Mr Witherick. The end results are some deceptively simple meals that are both English and elegant. The rating would be higher if it were not for the fact that this is an unusual set-up, in which the dining-room is booked rather than a table. The restaurant is unlicensed, but complimentary sherries come before dinner and no corkage is charged. Typically good have been the potted veal with chives and cranberry jelly held in an upturned mushroom, before main courses of salmon or lamb cutlets. Strawberries are served with cream and shortbread. Breakfasts are good, too. 'We try to fit in with whatever people want.'

CHEF: Allan Witherick PROPRIETORS: Allan and Maggie Witherick
OPEN: all week MEALS: 12.30 to 2, 7.30 to 9
PRICES: Set L £9 (£10), Set D £12 (£13). Unlicensed, but bring your own: no corkage
SEATS: 16. Private parties: 12 main room, 4 private room. Car-park, 9 places. Vegetarian meals by arrangement. Children's helpings (L only). Wheelchair access
ACCOMMODATION: 4 rooms. B&B £10·50 to £21. Children welcome. Baby facilities. Pets welcome. Garden. Confirm by 4

LUDLOW Shropshire map 5

Dinham Weir Restaurant [10/20]

Dinham Bridge, Ludlow SY8 1EH
LUDLOW (0584) 4431 £11–£14

Underneath the castle, on the banks of the river Teme. Klaus and Joan Hirsch have introduced a full-scale vegetarian menu by popular demand, built around main courses of stuffed aubergines or Russian vegetable pie, which is a cabbage, cream-cheese and egg filling inside pastry. Elsewhere the more conventional menu holds its own with warm granary rolls; good mushroom and tarragon

'Service was friendly and discreet and presumably run on ball bearings.' (On eating in Herefordshire)

ramekins; plenty of vegetables; and typically stodgy treacle tart with whipped cream. A short list of wines, not all of which have vintages.

CHEF: Karin Dawson PROPRIETORS: Klaus and Jean Hirsch
OPEN: Tue to Sat MEALS: 12 to 1.30, 7 to 9.15
PRICES: £10 (£14), Set D £8·25 (£11), Cut-price L menu. Service inc CARDS: Access, Visa
SEATS: 36. Private parties: 36 main room. Vegetarian meals. Children's helpings. No children under 10 at D. Wheelchair access. Piano music

▲ *Feathers Inn* [new entry, zero rated]

Bull Ring, Ludlow SY8 1AA
LUDLOW (0584) 5261 £9–£20

Regulars are divided over whether the old bar was cramped or cosy, and whether the refurbished one is spacious and comfortable or large and impersonal. Either way, this masterpiece of half-timbering deserves a chef of talent to do it justice. Vincent Jeffers, in his mid-twenties, came here via Hintlesham Hall. His ambition is for people to eat as well in Ludlow as they can in London. That seems possible with dishes such as quail breast salad with basil; scallops in lime sauce; medallions of lamb with water-chestnuts and ginger; and strawberries in green peppercorn sauce. Early reports indicated that fresh ingredients were well used, and there was praise for scallops, braised lamb kidneys, the vegetables, and the new ungimmicky style. At inspection Mr Jeffers was away, and we quibble with soggy toast, clammy skin on the quail, and poor courgettes. The ideas are good, though, and the beginnings promising. Classic French wines are inviting, but there are inexpensive bottles too. House wine is £5·50. CELLARMAN'S CHOICE: Crozes-Hermitage, Domaine de Thalabert '82, from Jaboulet, at £9·90. More reports, please.

CHEF: Vincent Jeffers PROPRIETORS: Feathers Hotel Ltd
OPEN: all week MEALS: 12.15 to 2, 7.30 to 9
PRICES: £15 (£20), Set L from £5·25 (£9), Set D from £12·50 (£17), Snacks from 85p (£1). Minimum alc £7.50 CARDS: Access, Amex, Carte Blanche, Diners, Visa
SEATS: 80. Private parties: 25 main room, 80 and 40 private rooms. Car-park, 38 places. Vegetarian meals. Children's helpings. No pipes in dining-room. Wheelchair access (also WC). Air-conditioned
ACCOMMODATION: 37 rooms, all with bath/shower. B&B £39 to £54. Deposit: £10. Children welcome. Baby facilities. No pets. Afternoon teas. Air-conditioning. Lift. TV. Phone. Confirm by 6 [GHG]

Penny Anthony [10/20]

5 Church Street, Ludlow SY8 1AP
LUDLOW (0584) 3282 £9–£15

This is usually a controversial choice for inclusion, with as many votes in favour as against, but Penny Anthony has seen off all competition since 1977 and even if standards go up and down in every department, from the service to the crème brûlée – one reporter went on two occasions and once it was excellent and once it was not – all round it still rates a 10. Starters of quiche niçoise and fish soup have

If you cannot honour a restaurant booking, always phone to cancel.

been good before seafood kebabs with hollandaise. Vegetables are steamed. The wine list includes some very good bottles, especially from the Rhône, as well as 23 house wines from £4·20 to £5·80.

CHEF/PROPRIETOR: Penny Anthony
OPEN: Mon to Sat CLOSED: Dec and Jan MEALS: 12 to 2, 7 to 10
PRICES: £10 (£14), Set L and D from £5·50 to £11·50 (£9 to £15). Special L dish daily
CARDS: Amex, Diners, Visa
SEATS: 50. Private parties: 15 main room. Vegetarian meals. Children welcome. Wheelchair access

LYME REGIS Dorset map 2

Toni [9/20]

14–15 Monmouth Street, Lyme Regis DT7 3PX
LYME REGIS (029 74) 2079 £13

An Italian/Austrian terrazza 200 yards from the sea front. The pasta is freshly made, as are the soups, and the menu is sensibly short and to the point. Twenty wines, including a pair of Barolos. House Cadillac is £4·75.

CHEF: Ingrid Taylor PROPRIETORS: Ingrid and Peter Taylor
OPEN: Tue to Sat, D only CLOSED: Oct to Easter MEALS: 7 to 10
PRICES: £9 (£13). Minimum £4·30 CARDS: Amex, Diners, Visa
SEATS: 30. Private parties: 8 main room. Children's helpings. No children under 5. Music

LYMINGTON Hampshire map 2

▲ *Railings Restaurant, Stanwell House Hotel* [10/20]

High Street, Lymington SO4 9AA
LYMINGTON (0590) 77124 £10–£16

A more appropriate name might be Château Barton. In the cellar are rows of Ch. Langoa-Barton going back to '37 and Ch. Léoville-Barton going back to '45 – the two vineyards are only 20 yards apart and the wines are virtually the same price, but they taste intriguingly different. There are other good wines from across the world to go with the not over-expensive, old-style French meals that feature medallions of beef with mushrooms, as well as tournedos Rossini and Florida cocktail.

CHEF: Kenneth Bull PROPRIETORS: Jeremy and Jane Willcock
OPEN: all week CLOSED: 3 days at Christmas MEALS: 12.30 to 2, 7 to 9.30 (10.30 Sat)
PRICES: Set L from £6·50 (£10), Set D £9·50 to £12·50 (£13 to £16). Service inc
CARDS: Access, Amex, Diners, Visa
SEATS: 60. Private parties: 12 main room, 20 private room. Children's helpings. No cigars/pipes in dining-room. Air-conditioned
ACCOMMODATION: 30 rooms, all with bath/shower. B&B £28·35 to £44·50. Children welcome. No dogs. Afternoon teas. TV. Phone. Doors close at 11.30. Confirm by 6

Many of the better restaurants offer bargain lunches for half the price of a meal in the evening. Details are given in the text.

LYMPSTONE Devon map 1

River House [11/20]

The Strand, Lympstone EX8 5EY
EXMOUTH (0395) 265147 £13–£19

The first-floor dining-room faces west across the River Exe, so in the evening the view is of the sun setting on the water, where boats and yachts are anchored, before it goes down behind the wooded hills, the church and the railway line on the far bank. The view is best at high tide. The menu is eclectic, basically English (with dishes such as coddled chicken) and built around old stalwarts; the experimentation seems to be kept for special tastings out of season. The starter of plaice fillet rolled around a scallop and garnished with prawns in an intense wine and cream sauce is the single version of the Three Little Fish main course. Rack of lamb is baked whole with fresh oregano in a sticky madeira sauce. Vegetables are generous but erratic. Sweets are less sophisticated and not the strongest department. The wine list has at least a couple of bottles from most regions. There are inexpensive snacks in the downstairs bar at lunchtime.

CHEF: Shirley Wilkes PROPRIETORS: Mr and Mrs J. Wilkes
OPEN: Tue to Sun, exc Sun D MEALS: 12 to 1.45, 7 to 9.30
PRICES: £13 (£19), Set Sun L from £8·50 (£13), Snacks at L from £1·25 (£1·40). Also cut-price L menu CARDS: Access, Amex, Visa
SEATS: 35. Private parties: 25 main room, 14 private room. Vegetarian meals. Children's helpings. No children under 5. Smart dress preferred. No cigars/pipes in dining-room. Can accommodate disabled in lounge by arrangement

LYTHAM ST ANNE'S Lancashire map 5

Bennett's Bistro [10/20]

15 Park Street, Lytham, Lytham St Anne's FY8 5LU
LYTHAM (0253) 739265 £13

There are no linen tablecloths but nor is there any frozen fish at this relaxed bistro. Lytham shrimps are potted in spiced butter, and there are some careful touches to the cooking: a lime-flavoured vinaigrette for the chicory, prawn and orange salad, and fresh damsons in the port sauce for the roast duck. French table wine is £3·95.

CHEF/PROPRIETOR: J. E. Thompson
OPEN: Tue to Sat MEALS: 12 to 2.30, 7 to 10.30
PRICES: £9 (£13), Snacks from £1.35 (£1.50)
SEATS: 50. Private parties: 12 main room. Vegetarian meals. Children's helpings by arrangement. Smart dress preferred. Music

▲ *C'est la Vie, Dalmeny Hotel* [12/20]

South Promenade, St Anne's, Lytham St Anne's FY8 1LX
LYTHAM (0253) 725871 £17

A friendly family hotel complex with a kitchen that knows what it is about. The one-course lunch is a bargain at £3·50 for roast turkey with carrots, peas and new potatoes, served with wholemeal bread and plenty of butter. The evening menu includes contemporary favourites, such as tomato and tarragon soup and avocado and bacon salad, but there are also strong Lancashire overtones with fresh Lytham shrimps, or black pudding with a Dijon cream sauce. The roast rack of lamb with fresh herbs is carved off the trolley in the dining-room otherwise there is fresh cold salmon. Good sweets in the shape of banoffi pie, tortes and flans. Solid wine list with a Côtes du Rhône from Ponnelle at £5 as the house wine and, from the same *négociant*, Chassagne-Montrachet '80 at £9·85.

CHEFS: Keith Davies and Paul Caddy PROPRIETORS: The Webb family
OPEN: all week, exc Sun D MEALS: 12.15 to 2 (3 Sun), 7.30 to 9.30
PRICES: £12 (£17)
SEATS: 48. 6 tables outside. Private parties: 48 main room. Vegetarian meals by arrangement Car-park, 30 places. Smart dress preferred. Children's helpings at L. Wheelchair access (also WC). Classical music. Air-conditioned
ACCOMMODATION: 86 rooms, 82 with bath/shower. Rooms for disabled. B&B £23·50 to £33. Deposit: £10. Baby facilities. No pets. Afternoon teas. Swimming-pool. Sauna. Solarium Games room. Squash court. Lift. TV. Phone. Scenic

MACCLESFIELD Cheshire map 5

Harlequin's [9/20]

68A Chestergate, Macclesfield SK11 6DY
MACCLESFIELD (0625) 32657 £12

This wine bar has a big cellar strong in all the traditional French wine regions and also in Rioja. The food is prepared on the premises and ranges from moussaka to dressed crab and steaks; there's a set fondue dinner.
CELLARMAN'S CHOICE: Sauvignon de St Bris '83 from Remon at £5.

CHEF: Chris Bates PROPRIETORS: Stuart Wilson and Alan Jones
OPEN: Mon to Sat CLOSED: 25 and 26 Dec, bank hols MEALS: 12 to 2.30, 5.30 (7.30 Sat) to 10 (10.30 Fri and Sat)
PRICES: £8 (£12), Snacks from 48p CARDS: Access, Visa
SEATS: 125. 13 tables outside. Private parties: 54 main room. Vegetarian meals. Children's helpings. Wheelchair access (also WC). Music

MALDON Essex map 3

Francine's [10/20]

1A High Street, Maldon CM9 7PB
MALDON (0621) 56605 £16

Barry Davies cooks in what might be the smallest restaurant kitchen in the country – it measures eight feet by ten. He produces large portions of such modern bistro dishes as scallops wrapped in bacon, grilled and served with a saffron sauce; and smoked turkey and avocado salad dressed with walnut oil. House French is £4·75.

CHEF: Barry Davies PROPRIETORS: Mr and Mrs Davies
OPEN: Tue to Sat, D only MEALS: 7.30 to 9.30
PRICES: £12 (£16). Minimum £7 CARDS: Access, Visa
SEATS: 26. Private parties: 26 main room. Car-park, 8 places. Children welcome. Wheelchair access

Wheelers [8/20]

13 High Street, Maldon CM9 8TB
MALDON (0621) 53647 £8

At the far end of town is this fish and chip shop with an Olde Tea Shoppe feel – it has a multitude of black beams, white walls, and dark-stained tables. The menu warns that there will be a quarter of an hour's wait before the plaice, dogfish, haddock or skate arrives, but it is the real thing with crisp batter and not greasy. The chips are short and in short supply. Fish soups are home-made and first-class. The fish has come from the same Grimsby merchant for the last 25 years, and this business has been in the Wheeler family since 1895. House German comes in one-and-a-half litre bottles at £6·20.

CHEF: R.H. Wheeler PROPRIETORS: The Wheeler family
OPEN: Tue to Sat MEALS: 11.30 to 1.45, 6 to 9.30
PRICES: £5 (£8)
SEATS: 52. Private parties: 52 main room. Children's helpings

MALVERN WELLS Hereford & Worcester map 2

Croque-en-Bouche [15/20]

221 Wells Road, Malvern Wells WR14 4HF
MALVERN (068 45) 65612 Real Food £22

It is important to understand that, for all its reputation, this is a husband-and-wife operation. Marion Jones cooks, Robin serves. No one else is employed, and that is why for £20 or so it is possible to eat regional French food as well as anywhere in Britain. On the minus side this means you are expected to be punctual; Mr Jones sometimes gets hassled; and you serve yourself from the tureens and bowls left on the table. There is none of that superstar chi-chi of the chef coming out of the kitchen for a chat, either. The six-course set dinners start with a soup, offer four choices of main dish, and include a salad course dressed variously in walnut or extra vergine olive oil. There is a Normandy-style generosity in the use of cream, cheese and butter amid the bourrides, confits, ceviches, pistou and paloise. In the space of six months no fewer than 57 different dishes have been eaten and endorsed by different people. Typical are a simple asparagus and egg vinaigrette; the smoked haddock soup; the terrine of crab; a casserole of wild rabbit; lamb stuffed with sweetbreads; partridges in madeira sauce; and turbot with leeks and a beurre blanc sauce. It is cooking that talks through the quality of its ingredients. Rosemary, sage and all the other herbs are from the greenhouse at the foot of the steep garden and are used judiciously. An Englishness arrives with the cheeseboard. Besides half a dozen French specimens come single Glouceseter, Blue Wensleydale, Belvoir Blue, and sheep's milk cheese. To finish there is strawberry tart, ginger meringue, or hazel-nut praline ice-cream. The same care in the food is seen in the alcohol department – a choice of 14 suggested aperitifs includes the house concoction of raspberry liqueur (home-made) with sparkling white burgundy. The wine list is a wonder, now expanded with more red Rhônes and white Australian wines, the gentlest of mark-ups and a fascinating, comprehensive showing of all the French regions. The Alsace section is impressive, with a generous showing of special cuvées and réserve personnelles from top producers, and there are four Vendange Tardive wines.

After Robin Jones's attack on local producers in last year's *Guide* there was a concerted protest from traders who banded together as the Vale of Evesham Co-operative for publicity purposes and showed at Harrods. But the reality is that asparagus production – once the pride of Evesham – is only a fraction of what it was 20 years ago, and is still decreasing. Evesham is not even listed as a major asparagus area now. Yet there has been some improvement in supplies, with more unusual lettuces available from Birmingham market and good-quality local leeks.

CHEF: Marion Jones PROPRIETORS: Robin and Marion Jones
OPEN: Wed to Sat, D only CLOSED: Christmas MEALS: 7.30 to 9.15
PRICES: Set D £17·70 (£22). Service inc
SEATS: 22. Private parties: 10 private room. Children welcome. No cigars/pipes in dining-room. Wheelchair access

MANACCAN Cornwall map 1

New Inn [8/20]

Manaccan TR12 6HA
MANACCAN (032 623) 323
off B3293, 1m S of Helford £10

A hard-to-find, old-fashioned pub with a big garden, much used by the yachting set. The locally smoked salmon is first-class and so are the Cornish pasties. Real Cornish ales.

CHEFS/PROPRIETORS: Mr and Mrs P. Cullinan
OPEN: all week, exc Tue D MEALS: 11.30 to 2, 6.30 to 9.30 (Sun 12 to 1.30, 7 to 10)
PRICES: £7 (£10), Snacks from 85p. Service inc
SEATS: 30. 10 tables outside. Private parties: 12 main room. Car-park, 7 places. Vegetarian meals. Children's helpings. Smart dress preferred. Wheelchair access (also men's wc)

MANCHESTER Greater Manchester map 5

BACKGROUND BRIEFING: *As we go to press Yang Sing – the Chinese restaurant that in the past has been most highly rated by this Guide – is planning to open at its new address: 34 Princess Street. Recent reports on the old premises have been divided between praise for some skilful and imaginative cooking, and worries that a degree of laxity had crept into the operation, with many of the authentic and difficult Cantonese dishes being withdrawn in favour of dishes more popular with Western taste. Casba, 489 Wilmslow Road, Withington, has Middle Eastern dishes as well as dishes like sole bonne femme, and there are good reports of the kibbeh, braised lamb and grills. Paradise, 123 Wilmslow Road, Rusholme, is a good, cheap, unlicensed Indian restaurant, and Sam's Chop House is a lunch-time only institution, formerly for men only, and originally for the now extinct bowler-hat brigade. It serves straightforward meat dishes. Koreana, 40 King Street, is the first Korean restaurant in this country to open outside London.*

If you cannot honour a restaurant booking, always phone to cancel.

Armenian Taverna [11/20]

3–5 Princess Street, M2 4DN
061-834 9025 £12

Sound, authentic, Middle Eastern cooking using fresh ingredients is served in this restaurant, which was first established in 1969. The menu never changes, but is long enough not to be dull. The 15 starters can accumulate into a meze – there is a vegetarian meze too – and include excellent tabouleh and falafel. Couscous is a feature, as are the charcoal-grilled kebabs of which the khash khash (spicy lamb on a bed of grilled tomatoes) is popular. To finish, the baklava has been consistently good. House French is £5, and there is an interesting choice of Russian and Polish vodkas.

CHEF: Kevork Kizir PROPRIETORS: Armenian Restaurants Co. Ltd
OPEN: all week, exc Sat L and Sun L MEALS: 12 to 3, 5.30 to 11.30 (12 Fri and Sat)
PRICES: £7 (£12). Service 10% CARDS: Access, Amex, Diners, Visa
SEATS: 75. Private parties: 100 main room. Vegetarian meals. Children's helpings. Middle Eastern music. Air-conditioned

Assam Gourmet [new entry, zero rated]

17A Bloom Street, M1 3HZ
061-236 6836 £5–£17

One of the newer Indian restaurants in Manchester, opposite the bus station. Inside is luxurious and European, however, and the menu ostentatiously advertises crab, lobster and venison. Dishes seem to be freshly cooked despite the long menu, and the spicing tends to be bland which some people, if not purists, prefer. After a dozen visits one old hand confirms the prawn puri, onion bhajia, chicken tikka, and the generous curries as good cornerstones of meals. The Assam specialities include roast duck with coconut milk and ginger; another variation is half the bird pot-roasted with cardamom and cinnamon. There are good reports on the thali, too. Main courses are followed by the hottest towels in town and a curious mixture of typically English sweets, like gateaux, and Indian ones, like gulab jamun. Licensed.

CHEFS: B.B.Deb, B.P.Deb and K.Bhatta PROPRIETORS: Assam Gourmet Ltd
OPEN: all week CLOSED: Christmas and Good Friday MEALS: 12 to 2.15, 6 to 11.15 (12 Fri and Sat, 10.30 Sun)
PRICES: £8 (£14), Set L £2·50 (£5), Set D from £13·50 (£17). Service 10% CARDS: Access, Amex, Diners
SEATS: 80. Private parties: 50 main room, 30 private room. Vegetarian meals. Children's helpings. Jacket and tie. Indian music. Air-conditioned

Café Istanbul [9/20]

79 Bridge Street, M3 2RH
061-833 9942 £7–£13

Friendly, unpretentious Turkish eating-house with a good range of cold starters in the meze and main courses built largely around lamb, mostly char-grilled to good effect to give it a smoky flavour. Tables are crowded together. Sauces are distinct – fiery tomato and yoghourt for the mixed kebabs; cooling yoghourt, cucumber, mint and garlic. Lunch is good value and in the evening you can eat late. Turkish wines includes Villa Doluca at £6·50; alternatively an unvintaged Gewürztraminer at £7·90 might cover the variety of flavours.

CHEF: Hasan Bicer PROPRIETOR: Sacit Onur
OPEN: Mon to Sat MEALS: 12 to 3, 6 to 11.30
PRICES: £9 (£13), Set L £3·75 (£7), Set D £7 (£10), Snacks from £2 (£2·20)
CARDS: Access, Visa
SEATS: 40. Private parties: 40 main room. Vegetarian meals. Children's helpings Wheelchair access (also ladies wc). Music

Connaught [11/20]

58–60 George Street, M1 4HF
061-236 0191 £8–£19

The dim-sum, notably the spare ribs and the custard tarts, are excellent in this Cantonese restaurant. On the main menu the starters and the fish dishes are most reliable, though the lemon chicken gets mentions from readers. Standards fluctuate but the food can be excellent. Service does not seem to be improving. House wine is now an exorbitant £8·50 a litre.

PROPRIETORS: Connaught Properties (N.W.) Ltd
OPEN: all week CLOSED: 25 and 26 Dec MEALS: noon to 11.40
PRICES: £9 (£19), Set L from £2·40 (£8), Set D from £7 (£13). Service 10% CARDS: Access, Amex, Diners, Visa
SEATS: 150. Private parties: 250 main room, 80 and 60 private rooms. Vegetarian meals. Children's helpings (exc Sat D). Wheelchair access (also wc). Chinese music. Air-conditioned

Gaylord [new entry, zero rated]

Amethyst House, Spring Gardens M2 1EA
061-832 6037 and 4866 £7–£14

A smart Indian restaurant doing serious cooking with good ingredients. The small shop-front entrance belies the large upstairs restaurant with its filigree lights and hanging stringed instruments. The food is a cut above the usual tandoori fare, with a good tandoori mix for £7·45, including sweet and coffee. Chutneys, pickles and raita are first-rate, as are onion-flavoured nan, dhal with lentils, and whole beans. Good sweets, excellent knowledgeable service, and a comprehensive wine list with house French at £4·25.

CHEFS: W. Ram and K. Kumar PROPRIETORS: Tandoori Catering Consultants Ltd
OPEN: all week MEALS: 12 to 3, 6 to 11.30 (11 Sun)
PRICES: £8 (£14), Set L from £3·95 (£7), Set D from £5·95 (£9). Cover 25p. Service 12·5%
CARDS: Access, Amex, Diners, Visa
SEATS: 90. Private parties: 90 main room. Vegetarian meals. Children welcome. No-smoking area. Indian music

Reports on good shops, small hotels and cafes in your area are welcome.

All restaurants listed in the Guide *have been independently nominated by a number of readers and have been checked by inspectors.*

Happy Gathering [12/20]

33 George Street, M1 4HQ
061-236 1149 £7–£18

Emporium-style Cantonese restaurant that is more traditional in its cooking than the equally excellent Hong Kong. The kitchen is divided into several departments – dim-sum; roasting and wind-drying; main dishes and so on. All the dim-sum are made in-house and a billboard in Chinese on the wall proclaims the restaurant's specialities, such as suckling pig and edible jelly-fish with pork shank (the only restaurant in the UK to feature this). There are more than 30 dim-sum snacks, all of very high standard except occasionally the very tricky jellied soup *inside* a dumpling of wheat-flour dough. In London the Chinatown restaurants rely heavily on passing trade, but in Manchester it is the regulars who keep them going, hence waiters wear badges with their name and rank so that they get to know customers ('Captain' is a new addition to restaurant vocabulary). This traditional allegiance to a particular restaurant also explains the popularity of Woo Sang – established ten years ago – against which both this and the Hong Kong are competing. For the moment the new ones have a distinct edge, and have not Westernised standards as the Yang Sing appeared to be doing at the end of its reign in George Street.

CHEF: Mr Yung PROPRIETOR: Michael Man
OPEN: all week MEALS: noon to 11.45 (2am Fri and Sat)
PRICES: £9 (£18), Set L £2·25 (£7), Set D from £7 (£11). Service 10% CARDS: Access, Amex, Diners, Visa
SEATS: 300. Private parties: 420 main room. Vegetarian meals. Children welcome. Music. Air-conditioned

Hong Kong [12/20]

47 Faulkner Street, M1 4EE
061-236 0565 £5–£14

Up a steep flight of stairs, this Cantonese restaurant in an old warehouse is given an illusion of space by its mirrors and of warmth by the orange lamp shades and red tablecloths. It has been shaping up as perhaps the best of all the Cantonese restaurants in Manchester. The dim-sum are very fine – excellent pork cheung-fun, prawns in wrapping paper, steamed ribs, sui mai and also cold pork dishes. The waiters help balance meals and it pays to be adventurous in choosing. Some of the soups, and dishes like beef with cashew, have not been of the class of the Peking duck, or fillet steak with ginger, beef in OK sauce, chicken casserole with spring onions and ginger, or duck with fresh orange sauce. The sweet-and-sour sauce is blood red and more sweet than sour, and even the Yang Sing speciality of sizzling fillet steak is well done here. The set lunch is £2·40. Rudimentary wines, but Chinese liqueurs such as Mou Tai and Kuei Lu Chiew for the brave.

CHEF: Chan Ling Kung PROPRIETOR: Dai Lee
OPEN: all week CLOSED: 24 and 25 Dec MEALS: 12 to 12
PRICES: £9 (£14), Set L £2·40 (£5), Set D £7·50 (£11). Service 10% CARDS: Access, Amex, Diners, Visa
SEATS: 350. Private parties: 200 main room. Children welcome. Music. Air-conditioned

Hung Chun [12/20]

56 Faulkner Street, M1 4FH
061-236 6120 £5–£11

This opened on the fifth day of the first month of the year of the Ox (25 Feb, 1985) and a very auspicious date it must be. It is a terrific family-style (rather than formal) Cantonese restaurant specialising in casserole dishes – unpretentious and not expensive. The walls have red flock on them and the table-cloths are peach-coloured and covered by the inevitable white paper cloths. There is a flair and invention about the cooking we have not found before. Although pork-rind beef brisket is the norm for all Manchester Chinese restaurants, this is the only one we have eaten at where the beef is braised with pre-deep-fried pork-rind, which gives a contrasting bouncy texture to the beef sitting in a rich and delicious sauce. Sauté scallops are cut across and stuffed with prawn paste at £1 a piece. Dover sole is pan-fried with mange-tout and sold according to weight. Also alpha is the most famous of all cantonese soups – fish maw. The wun-tun is made every day and is highly regarded locally. The high rating reflects that while many Chinese restaurants are allowing themselves to become Westernised (to our concern), this is the real thing. Licensed.

CHEF: Mr So PROPRIETOR: Mr Pang
OPEN: all week MEALS: noon to midnight
PRICES: £6 (£11), Set L £2 (£5), Set D £6 (£9). Service 10%. Licensed, plus bring your own: corkage £1·50 CARDS: Access, Amex
SEATS: 100. Private parties: 80 main room. Vegetarian meals. Children welcome. Classical music. Air-conditioned

Kai's [10/20]

16 Nicholas Street, M1 4EJ
061-236 2041 £6–£8

Essentially a restaurant for the Chinese community. It is Cantonese, unpretentious and scores for authenticity. A new addition to the repertoire is a Buddhist vegetarian menu, but it is the roast meats that impress, although the cold roast crispy belly-pork may be too fatty for Western taste. The one-plate meals, such as fine beef with seasonal vegetables, are excellent value. The waitresses are more courteous than the waiters. Open until 4.45am.

CHEF: Mr Lam PROPRIETORS: Charles Chan and Kai Le
OPEN: all week, D only MEALS: 5pm to 4.45am
PRICES: £6 (£8), Set D £5 (£6). Service 10%. Unlicensed, but bring your own: no corkage
CARDS: Access, Amex, Diners, Visa
SEATS: 100. Private parties: 100 main room. Vegetarian meals. Children welcome. Oriental music. Air-conditioned

The 1987 Guide *will appear before Christmas 1986, so reports are particularly important in the spring. Report forms are at the back of this book, but just write a letter if you prefer. Address them to* The Good Food Guide, *Freepost, 14 Buckingham Street, London WC2N 6BR. No stamp is necessary if you post in the UK.*

Kathmandu Tandoori [10/20]

42–44 Sackville Street, M1 3WE
061-236 4684 and 2436 £6–£13

An out-of-the-way Nepalese restaurant run for the past six years by Gopal Mohan. There is a general air of plushness, and service is smooth. The tikka dishes, especially the fish, have been good, and the mixed tandoori grill has a charcoal flavour. Accompaniments – nan, poppadums, Basmati rice and kulfi – are all of a good standard. Also notable is the lamb dopiaza and the chicken moghlai. 'All spices are freshly ground, and no tinned paste, tinned food, or curry powder is used.' Well said. Licensed.

CHEF/PROPRIETOR: Gopal Mohan Dangol
OPEN: all week CLOSED: 25 Dec, L on bank hols MEALS: 12 to 2.30, 6 to 12
PRICES: £5 (£11), Set L from £3 (£6), Set D £4·50 to £9·50 (£8 to £13). Snacks from 95p
Service 10%. Licensed, plus bring your own: corkage 50p CARDS: Access, Amex, Diners, Visa
SEATS: 250. Private parties: 120 main room, 80 and 30 private rooms. Vegetarian meals. Children's helpings. Wheelchair access. Oriental music. Air-conditioned

Kosmos Taverna [12/20]

248 Wilmslow Road, M14 6LD
061-225 9106 £10–£13

The waiters may wear name badges and have a line in bad jokes but this narrow, boisterous Greek restaurant offers excellent value. Last year, amazingly, it scored as much as any other Greek restaurant in the *Guide*; this year the White Tower (see London) takes over, but the food here is still well above average. The 15-item meze comes in three stages and includes beef and onions stewed in wine, and haricot beans with celery and garlic. More unusual dishes have been scrambled egg with garlic and onions and barbecued quail with cumin and coriander. Vegetarians can make a good meal from grilled goats' cheese followed by chickpeas with spinach. The Italian house red goes well, or there is Courtakis retsina at £4·95.

CHEF: Loulla Astin PROPRIETORS: Stewart and Loulla Astin
OPEN: all week, D only CLOSED: 25 and 26 Dec MEALS: 6.30 to 11.30 (12.30 Fri and Sat)
PRICES: £9 (£13), Set D £6·50 (£10) CARDS: Access, Visa
SEATS: 70. Private parties: 40 main room. Vegetarian meals. Children's helpings. Wheelchair access. Greek music

Market Restaurant [12/20]

30 Edge Street, M4 1HN
061-834 3743 £13

Clothing warehouses surround this small restaurant with 1930s food adverts, flowers on each table and a set three-by-three menu – three courses, three choices in each – that changes weekly. Olives and brown bread are left on the table. The menu plunders the northern hemisphere seemingly at random for its dishes – pork souvlakia, halibut baked with yoghourt, lime and ginger, or chicken Marsala. There is always a vegetarian choice and these are especially good – Stilton pâté, aubergine cheesecake, cheese and onion pie. Salmon en croûte has also been outstanding. Service is friendly and knowledgeable. The blue Cheshire farmhouse cheese goes well with the vin du patron served in old milk bottle carafes. CELLARMAN'S CHOICE: Hugh Rock's sparkling gooseberry wine, made by the champagne method, at £7·90.

CHEF: Lin Scrannage PROPRIETORS: Peter and Anne O'Grady and Lin Scrannage
OPEN: Tue to Sat, D only CLOSED: 1 week in spring, all Aug, 1 week at Christmas
MEALS: 6.30 to 10.30
PRICES: £8 (£13) CARDS: Access, Amex
SEATS: 30. Private parties: 30 main room. Vegetarian meals. Children welcome. Music

Mina Japan [new entry, zero rated]

63 George Street, M1 4NS
061-228 2598 £13–£16

In the heart of Manchester's Chinatown, this is now the most northerly of the English Japanese restaurants (though there is the spectacular Aye in Scotland – see Edinburgh). Recipe books with illustrations are presented to diners unfamiliar with the food, but the menu stays with the mainstream of the cookery – sushi, sukiyaki and tempura. They claim to do more variations on norimaki sushi than any other restaurant in Britain – 85. It is easy enough to spend serious money here, but with good advice from the owners and a little judicious practice with the menus it is possible to eat reasonably. For instance, a small portion of selected sushi is an ample starter for two. The sukiyaki is brought to the table for cooking – a plate of wafer-thin slices of raw beef, Chinese cabbage, leeks, carrots, noodles, bean sprouts, bean curd, onions, all of which are cooked on a hot griddle with soy and then put into bowls containing a raw beaten egg. Green tea comes free. Chef Yasuto Kawano has a certificate for cooking, awarded by examination by the Japanese government – such certificates are highly respected in Japan. Licensed. More reports, please.

CHEF: Yasuto Kawano PROPRIETOR: Nori Shibahara
OPEN: Mon to Sat MEALS: 12.15 to 3, 7 to 11.30 (1 Sat)
PRICES: £9 (£16), Set D from £8 (£13) CARDS: Access, Amex, Diners, Visa
SEATS: 65. Private parties: 40 main room, 4 private room. Vegetarian meals. No children under 5. Japanese music. Air-conditioned

Moss Nook [12/20]

Ringway Road, M22 5NA
061-437 4778
on B5166, 1m from Manchester
Airport and M56 £22–£24

Manchester's most ambitious European restaurant – although before we award an extra rating mark the technical excellence of the cooking needs to be married with better-quality supplies, and the menu needs to recognise the fact that seasons change. It is plush and rather in the grip of expense-account eating, which means the well-drilled waiters stand ceremonially to attention before they whisk off the silver salvers from the main dishes. Robert Thornton cooks in the modern French style. Fresh granary rolls are served at the start of the meal. Meat dishes have been very fine – lamb en croûte or with kidneys and bacon, and boned poussin stuffed with a herb forcemeat. Pancakes stuffed with either shellfish or chicken have been wafer-thin. Oddities include fried Maryland baby crab with garlic butter. Sweets tend to look prettier than they taste, and some sticky petits fours arrive with the good coffee. A long French wine list has some noticeable gaps, for instance in the Beaujolais and northern Rhône, that if filled would help bring the prices down. The red wines are pretentiously decanted over a candle-flame, but then when you're charging £30 for the Echézeaux '81 you have to do something – Peter Dominic sells it for around £10.

CHEFS: Robert Thornton and Pauline Harrison PROPRIETORS: Pauline and Derek Harrison
OPEN: Mon to Sat, exc Sat L and Mon CLOSED: 2 weeks from 24 Dec MEALS: 12 to 1.30, 7 to 9.30 (10 Sat)
PRICES: £15·50 (£22), Set L and D £18 (£24). Service 10% CARDS: Access, Amex, Diners, Visa
SEATS: 50. 8 tables outside. Private parties: 10 main room. Car-park, 30 places. Vegetarian meals. No children under 12. Smart dress preferred. Music. Air conditioned

Mr Kuks [12/20]

55A Mosley Street, M2 3HY
061-236 0659 and 3539 £12–£17

The decor in this basement is plain and simple but it is by far the most authentic Peking restaurant in the country. The owner and chef come from Shantung which – Peking duck apart – supplies the basis of the cuisine. It is a long menu with a section in Chinese detailing the noodles and pasta which are typical – boiled Peking dumplings with a vinegar and ginger dip are the kind the Chinese tend to eat at their New Year, and the spring onion cakes are among the best we have eaten in Britain. The special Peking noodles are the home-made dancing noodles that Peking chefs show off in restaurants, though their meat sauce does not dance quite so much. Lamb dishes have been excellent – the barbecued breast of lamb is crisp, a little fatty, served with a dip of garlic, vinegar and soy, and typical of the Shantung area, where chefs reputedly chew raw garlic as they cook. Also good has been the lamb with spring onion, centrepieces of thin sliced cod in wine sauces, and grilled prawn specials. The creamed Chinese cabbage is one of those fascinating dishes that Peking chefs claim as their own but which is obviously not too different from European versions. To finish, the red bean pancakes are masterful. Our only nervousness in raising the rating is the price of the Peking duck – £22, which seems disproportionately expensive – and the fact that the menu still has some curry and chop suey dishes which should be avoided. House French is £4·75.

CHEF: Mr Lau PROPRIETORS: Stephen Kuk and Geoffrey Cohen
OPEN: Tue to Sun, exc Sun L MEALS: 12 to 2.30, 6 to 11.30
PRICES: £9 (£17), Set L and D from £7 (£12), Cheaper Set L available. Service 10%
CARDS: Access, Amex, Diners, Visa
SEATS: 95. Private parties: 95 main room. Vegetarian meals. Children's helpings. Chinese music. Air-conditioned

If you suspect that a restaurant is using processed food, always ask. It would be a contravention of the Trade Descriptions Act for the restaurant to lie.

Mulberry's [12/20]

400 Wilmslow Road, Withington, M20 9BN
061-434 4624 £18

Inevitable long waits testify to the local opinion that this is among the best in the city. It is especially popular with Manchester's beau monde, and not just because the live music features the North's answer to Billie Holliday. Fish potage is a robust mix of potatoes, white fish, garlic and tomatoes flavoured with fresh coriander; baked mussels arrive on top of mushrooms covered with breadcrumbs; and spicy beef has chilli, garlic and Worcester sauce for devilment. Capability Brown's name is invoked for lamb cutlets, pear with Stilton, and for chicken with watercress, grapefruit and cream. The kitchen entertains with combinations such as fishcakes with a light curry sauce, and kidneys with a sweet-and-sour sauce of lemon, orange, port and cranberries. Portions are such that pudding may be unnecessary, but if it is, brown bread ice-cream comes with granary crumbs and a strong madeira flavour, cheesecake is given a butterscotch sauce, and there is ginger sponge and treacle tart. Service combines correctness with informality. The wine list veers awkwardly between £6 generics and expense-account claret and burgundy. House French is £5·50.

CHEF: Malcolm Wallace PROPRIETORS: Armenian Restaurant Co. Ltd
OPEN: all week, D only CLOSED: bank hols MEALS: 7 to 12
PRICES: £13 (£18). Post-theatre menu. Minimum £4·50 CARDS: Access, Amex, Diners, Visa
SEATS: 56. Private parties: 150 main room. Car-park, 40 places. Vegetarian meals. Children's helpings by arrangement. Wheelchair access (also WC). Music. Air-conditioned

On the Eighth Day [8/20]

109 Oxford Road, M1 7DU
061-273 1850 £4

Free-range eggs, organic grains and cereals, and sugar-free baking are the staples of this main-road cafe between the city and the university. It's run as a co-operative, and the system works well, with both chef and menu changing daily. The music ranges from classical to pop. Unlicensed and no corkage.

OPEN: Mon to Sat, exc Mon and Sat D MEALS: 11.30 to 3, 5 to 7
PRICES: £3 (£4). Unlicensed but bring your own: no corkage
SEATS: 42. Vegetarian meals. Children's helpings. No smoking in dining-room. Wheelchair access (also WC). Music. Self-service

Rajdoot [10/20]

St James House, South King Street, M2 6DW
061-834 2176 and 7092 £8–£16

A long-established north Indian restaurant in office-block Manchester, with a dark but plush interior, close tables, and efficient, if uncommunicative, waiters in bright cotton tunics. There are moist and delicately spiced lamb and chicken tandoori dishes, and lamb's kidneys are good, too. Chicken moghlai and bhuna

All inspections are carried out anonymously as we accept no handouts.

josh are reliable; pheasant is well complemented by its masala sauce. Nan may be doughy and soggy; sweets are sticky or tinned. House wine is £5·25.

CHEF: Mr Salik PROPRIETOR: D.R.Sarda
OPEN: all week, exc Sun L CLOSED: Christmas and bank hols MEALS: 12 to 2.30, 6.30 to 1
PRICES: £8 (£16), Set L £4 (£8), Set D from £8·50 (£13). Cover 50p. Minimum £4·50. Service 12.5% CARDS: Access, Amex, Diners, Visa
SEATS: 96. Private parties: 125 main room. Vegetarian meals. Children's helpings. Indian music. Air-conditioned

Tandoor [10/20]

34 Charlotte Street, M1 4FD
061-236 1085 £6–£12

In a basement off Portland Street, between Chinatown and the commercial centre, is this relaxed and low-lit north Indian restaurant. The service starts slowly but speeds up. The lamb dishes are highly praised – lamb pasanda has plenty of lean, tender lamb in a rich, buttery, creamy sauce. Nargis kofte is red tandoori lamb minced and wrapped around a hard-boiled egg and served in a similar-looking sauce, which in fact tastes quite different. The chicken jal frezi is also good. Traffic-light-coloured rice and freshly baked nan bread have been a little erratic. The two Alsace wines, from Meyer, at £6·10, match the spices.

CHEFS: Laxman Khadka and Purna Bahadur Shrestha PROPRIETORS: Tandoor Ltd
OPEN: Mon to Sat MEALS: 12 to 2.30, 6.30 to 11.30
PRICES: £6 (£12), Set L from £2·75 (£6), Set D from £8 (£12). Cover 30p. Minimum £3. Service 10%, D only CARDS: Access, Amex, Diners, Visa
SEATS: 70. Private parties: 25 main room. Vegetarian meals. Children's helpings. No-smoking area. Indian music

Terrazza [10/20]

14 Nicholas Street, M1 4FE
061-236 4033 and 0250 £17

A clean and airy Italian restaurant with ceramic tile floors. The bean and pasta soup is a proud starter, most of the pasta is freshly made, and other good dishes include rack of lamb or an unusual breast of chicken with lemon, honey and ginger – some cross-fertilisation going on here with the local Chinese community, surely. Salads are good and the sweets trolley impresses. They do vegetarian dishes but these have exposed the limitations of the kitchen. Espresso coffee. House Valpolicella is £5·10.

CHEF: Mr Dasilda PROPRIETORS: L. & P. Restaurants Ltd
OPEN: Mon to Sat, exc Sat L MEALS: 12 to 2.30, 7 to 11.30
PRICES: £11 (£17), Cover 50p CARDS: Access, Amex, Diners, Visa
SEATS: 110. Private parties: 60 main room. Vegetarian meals. Children welcome. Jacket and tie preferred. Music

'We were assailed at every opportunity by the unspeakable phenomenon, the non-comprehending, Malvern-water-pouring French waiter, but getting service when required was impossible.' (On eating in Bedfordshire)

That Café [10/20]

1031 Stockport Road, Levenshulme, M19 2TB
061-432 4672 £13

The feel is 1930s, with songs to match the decor. The reasonably priced menu is bistro in style: a generous pot of smooth liver pâté; Hawaiian cocktail of prawns, mayonnaise and pineapple; pork fillet with sage, onion and apple stuffing covered in cream and sherry sauce. Broccoli and Brie crêpes are available as a change from meat. The Real Food award has been withdrawn because we have not been totally convinced by the prawns, ice-cream or Canadian smoked salmon. Service is informal, cheerful and helpful. A basic wine list with house French at £4·25. CELLARMAN'S CHOICE: Côte de Beaune-Villages '81, from Morey, at £7·95.

CHEF/PROPRIETOR: Joe Quinn
OPEN: Tue to Sun D; Sun L MEALS: 12 to 3, 7.30 to 11
PRICES: £9 (£13) CARDS: Access, Amex, Visa
SEATS: 45. Private parties: 50 main room. Vegetarian meals, Children's helpings. Music

Truffles [new entry, zero rated]

63 Bridge Street, M3 3BQ
061-832 9393 £10–£21

Truffles calls itself a gourmet restaurant – not a sentiment necessarily in line with the principles of the *Guide*. If it is necessary to be discerning to appreciate something, then its merits cannot be that obvious. The word, from the French, was originally used to describe a sensitive palate for the professional tasting of wines rather than for the enjoyment of food. Epicurean, with its controversial overtones of sensuality, hedonism and even luxury, might be more appropriate to this Victorian-style dining-room, and even encompass the distant strains of Johnny Mathis. The menu is French, with translations, and could change with the seasons. The kitchen's specialities have been good – celery, apple and cream soup; charcoal-grilled pigeon breast with mango; veal with orange sauce. Sweets fade. The short wine list has wines from all over. The gourmet recommendation would be for the '78 minor clarets and the'83 Alsace wines from Ritzenthaler, but the CELLARMAN'S CHOICE is Muscadet, Château Gautronnières '83 at £5·75. More reports, please.

CHEF: John Steel PROPRIETORS: Ann and John Steel
OPEN: Tue to Sat, exc Sat L CLOSED: 2 weeks Aug, bank hols MEALS: 12.15 to 2.30, 7 to 11
PRICES: £15 (£21), Set L from £5·25 (£10) CARDS: Access, Amex, Diners, Visa
SEATS: 30. Private parties: 45 main room. Vegetarian meals. Children welcome. Wheelchair access. Music. Air-conditioned

Woo Sang [11/20]

19–21 George Street, M1 4AG
061-236 3697 £5–£15

Hot, busy, entertaining and excellent value, especially at lunchtime when two dishes, fried rice and tea costs £2·40, or there are 30-plus dim-sum snacks mostly at 85p each and helpfully described in English. Despite the crush, the waiters manage to advise, and the Cantonese kitchen keeps up the overall standards even if some dishes misfire. Good are the beef with OK sauce, the sizzling steaks, huge lobsters (seasonal price) and bird's nest dishes. It is worth exploring the more unusual avenues of the long menu – fresh scallops, crabs and scampi are steamed with ginger and spring onions. There is plenty of tripe. Some wines, a quartet of Chinese liqueurs including Mou Tai at £1·25 a glass and also Tsing Tao Chinese beer at 85p.

CHEF: Chun Chong Kwan PROPRIETOR: Woo Sang Co. Ltd
OPEN: all week MEALS: 12 to 11.45
PRICES: £8 (£14), Set L £2·40 (£5), Set D £12 (£15). Service 10% CARDS: Access, Amex, Diners, Visa
SEATS: 210. Private parties: 110 main room, 100 private room. Vegetarian meals. Children's helpings. Music. Air-conditioned

MARCH Cambridgeshire map 6

Acre [new entry, zero rated]

March PE15 9JD
MARCH (0354) 57116 £5

A pub that has been refurbished with care. Mrs Charnock cooks good, simple dishes – roast pork with veal crackling, apple sauce and fresh vegetables; bread-and-butter pudding. The cheeses are ripe and service, by local women, is excellent. House French is £3·10. More reports, please.

CHEF: Mrs Charnock PROPRIETOR: Mr Charnock
OPEN: Mon to Sat, L only MEALS: 12.30 to 2.30
PRICES: £3 (£5). Service inc
SEATS: 50. 5 tables outside. Children's helpings. Wheelchair access. Music

MATLOCK Derbyshire map 5

▲ *Riber Hall* [12/20]

Matlock DE4 5JU
MATLOCK (0629) 2795
1m off A615 at Tansley £13–£22

This Elizabethan manor with a walled garden and hillside views stands next to the Victorian folly, Riber Castle. Rooms are in converted out-houses, and the dining-room is intimate. Alex Biggin has a memory for faces, and enjoys serving good food from a modern French menu. Good starters are the fish soup, the smoked quail salad before thick medallions of lamb laid on croûtons. Game casserole combines hare, pheasant, venison and partridge in rich gravy. The Duke of Cambridge tart is a magnificent and enormous finish, so it might be wise to choose the rest of your dishes accordingly. Meals can be disappointing on chef Howard Mosley's day off. There are some fine Bordeaux, including five vintages of Ch. La Lagune; a good collection of burgundies, particularly from Raoul

▲ *This restaurant has rooms.*

Clerget, whose '66 Nuits St Georges at £26·75 is CELLARMAN'S CHOICE; plentiful champagnes, along with the unusual still Coteaux Champenois from Château de Saran; good Rhônes and Loires; Domaine Ott wines from Provence; and Hill Smith Estate wines from Australia.

CHEF: Howard Mosley PROPRIETOR: Alex Biggin
OPEN: all week MEALS: 12 to 1.30, 7 to 8.30
PRICES: £16 (£22), Set L £7·20 (£13) CARDS: Access, Amex, Diners, Visa
SEATS: 50. Private parties: 34 main room, 14 private room. Car-park, 50 places. Vegetarian meals. Children's helpings. No children under 10. Jacket and tie
ACCOMMODATION: 11 rooms, all with bath/shower. B&B £42 to £55. Deposit: £20. No children under 10. No pets. Afternoon teas. Garden. TV. Phone. Scenic. Doors close at 12 [GHG]

MAWGAN Cornwall — map 1

Yard Bistro [9/20]

Trelowarren, Mawgan TR12 6AF
MAWGAN (032 622) 224
off B3293, 1st L after village (coming from Helston) — £14

A converted coach-house in the stable yard of a private estate. Locally caught fish, good soups, steaks, light lunches, and over a dozen wines.

CHEF: Trevor Bayfield PROPRIETOR: Sir John Vyvyan
OPEN: Tue to Sun, exc Sun D CLOSED: 16 Dec to 1 Mar MEALS: 12 to 2, 7 to 9
PRICES: £10 (£14), Bar L from £1 (£1.10)
SEATS: 50. 7 tables outside. Private parties: 50 main room. Car-park, 40 places. Children's helpings (in summer). Wheelchair access (also WC). Music

MAYFIELD East Sussex — map 3

Old Brew House [10/20]

High Street, Mayfield TN20 6AG
MAYFIELD (0435) 872342 — £10–£16

The fish comes straight from the boats at Hastings to Jon and Sue Barnes's small restaurant in a sixteenth-century timbered building. The style is French, at its best with classic dishes such as veal vallée d'Auge. Other dishes may be rather elaborate: avocado surprise is filled with smoked salmon, water-chestnuts and curried mayonnaise topped with crispy bacon. House French is £5·50.

CHEF: Sue Barnes PROPRIETORS: Jon and Sue Barnes
OPEN: Tue to Sat, D only, and Sat L; closed Tue after bank hols CLOSED: 2 weeks autumn, 24 Dec to 2 Jan MEALS: 12.30 to 1.30, 7.30 to 9 (9.30 Sat)
PRICES: Set L £6·25 (£10), Set D £11·50 (£16) CARDS: Amex, Diners, Visa
SEATS: 22. Private parties: 22 main room. Vegetarian meals. No children under 12. Music

Entries are compiled from the unsolicited reports from readers and are checked by inspectors; each restaurant is asked to supply details of its operation. Report forms can be found at the back of the Guide.

MELBOURN Cambridgeshire map 3

Pink Geranium [12/20]

Melbourn SG8 6DX
ROYSTON (0763) 60215
just off A10, 10m SW of Cambridge £11–£15

Indian and Chinese restaurants have virtually taken over catering in this part of Cambridgeshire, but Ellen Shepperson's old thatched cottage still flies a flag for Anglo-French cooking. Every nook and cranny is given a table of its own and the name is not the Pink Geranium for nothing. There are some precious touches, such as 'smoked salmon curls (£5·50)', and salmon mousse 'made to a secret recipe', but the main-course roast ducks and the chateaubriand (£18·50 for two) are reliable and some of the saucing quick-witted – saffron and cream for scallops; cream, Stilton and cider for entrecôte. The set lunch is good value. Take with a pinch of salt the local newspaper's assurance that, 'the wine list will satisfy every palate'. Of the 35-odd wines there are a few of interest, but the strength is in the expensive red burgundies, which can be financially painful.

CHEF: Nicholas Barrett PROPRIETOR: Ellen Shepperson
OPEN: Tue to Sat, exc Sat L CLOSED: last 2 weeks Aug MEALS: 12 to 2.30, 7 to 9.30
PRICES: £9 (£15), Set L £6·75 (£11). Cover 50p. Service 10% CARDS: Access, Amex, Diners, Visa
SEATS: 50. Private parties: 20 main room, 18 private room. Car-park, 25 places. Vegetarian meals by arrangement. Children's helpings. Wheelchair access

MELMERBY Cumbria map 7

Village Bakery [11/20]

Melmerby CA10 1HE
LANGWATHBY (076 881) 515 **Real Food** £9

Ecologically speaking, this 200-year-old barn could take an award – the cast-iron doors on the traditional oven were taken from a demolished oven in Edinburgh; the only cooking fuel is wood, with pizzas baked on the brick, sole, steaks and trout cooked over the embers, and 180 loaves in each batch. Bread, rolls and pies are baked first and cakes and biscuits later as the oven cools. Flour is stone-ground organic wheat from the watermill at Little Salkeld. The heat from the oven also fuels a greenhouse built on top. Naturally the vegetables are organic, from the Whitleys' five-acre smallholding. The doors open at 8.30 for breakfasts of Loch Fyne kippers or grills, including free-range eggs and Cumberland sausage. Lunch is roast sirloin of beef, hamburgers or baked potatoes. Jersey cream is poured liberally over the sweets. The house wine is £3·25 and there is Theakston's bitter or Aspall's organic cider.

CHEF: Diane Beeching PROPRIETORS: Andrew and Liz Whitley
OPEN: Tue, Thur to Sun CLOSED: Christmas to Easter MEALS: 8.30 to 5
PRICES: £6 (£9)
SEATS: 40. 2 tables outside. Private parties: 25 main room. Vegetarian meals. Car-park, 8 places. No smoking. Children's helpings. Wheelchair access

This restaurant has an exceptional wine cellar.

MERSHAM Kent map 3

▲ *Stone Green Hall* [12/20]

Mersham TN25 7HE
ALDINGTON (023 372) 418
off A20, 3m S of Ashford **Real Food** £16–£18

The Kempstons hide themselves away in their family hall (it's badly signposted because 'we don't like passing trade'). It is a building of contrasts: an almost shambolic collection of rooms for drinks, one smart, modern dining-room with huge interesting paintings, a magical conservatory filled with camellias and gardenias, and a formal garden that is beginning to fulfil its potential magnificence. The cooking relies heavily on the best of the local produce – cod's roe fried and served with bacon and a parsley sauce to start, or celeriac and sweetcorn soup with coriander. There are some interesting eastern touches to conventional dishes, such as an Indian-style ratatouille or Chinese king prawns with salt and chilli. The Romney Marsh lamb takes pride of place: it comes from Coopers at Aldington and is cut slightly ragged but is tender and flavoursome and served perhaps with a mung bean casserole or a blackcurrant relish, stir-fried vegetables and roast potatoes. To finish, the cheese stew is a fondue for dipping into, and the ginger pudding is first-class. There is no hesitation in raising the score by one point from last year, and a rating of 13 is not far away. Book early in the week or they may not be open. It is a small, changing, enthusiast's wine list with a tendency to dry whites and gutsy reds. The house wines are typical – a white Loire and a Bulgarian red at £5·50.

CHEFS: James Kempston and Phillip Colthup PROPRIETORS: A.E.Kempston Ltd
OPEN: D Mon to Sat, and L Sun CLOSED: Feb MEALS: 12.30 to 1.45, 7.30 to 9
PRICES: Set L £10·50 (£16), Set D £12·50 (£18). Cover £1 CARDS: Access, Amex, Visa
SEATS: 35. 3 tables outside. Private parties: 20 main room, 15 private room. Vegetarian meals. Car-park, 25 places. Children's helpings. No children under 8. Wheelchair access (also WC). Air-conditioned
ACCOMMODATION: 3 rooms, all with bath/shower. B&B from £30. Deposit: £10. Air-conditioned. No children under 8. No pets. TV. Scenic. Garden. Tennis. Croquet. Doors close at 12 [GHG]

MIDDLE WALLOP Hampshire map 2

▲ *Fifehead Manor* [12/20]

Middle Wallop SO20 8EG
ANDOVER (0264) 781565
on A343, 7m SW of Andover £11–£21

This old, red-brick Hampshire house is set back from the main road. Tall trees shadow the croquet lawn and the motel-style rooms which are cheaper than, but not as elegant as, the rooms in the main house. The dining-room is bare-floored with wine racks stacked in the fireplace; old Hampshire scenes are depicted on the place-mats. Nicholas Ruthven-Stuart cooks a very good mid-Channel menu – for starters there have been excellent soups, from vivid-coloured crab to watercress, both with generous measures of cream; great wedges of Roquefort tart; or else his pâté, a traditional version of pork and livers baked in pastry. Main courses have included roast quails with a port and lime sauce, garnished with peaches, prunes and nectarines; home-cured ham on a salad of diverse leaves from the garden, with a sweet vinaigrette; lamb en croûte with a tarragon cream sauce. Service is willing, if unpolished, and the home-made treacle bread is excellent. In August there are mirabelles from their own tree. It is an undiscovered address for excellent bar meals, though afternoon teas have been let down by commercial jam. Forty wines, starting with a vin de pays at £5·30.

CHEF: Nicholas Ruthven-Stuart PROPRIETOR: Margaret Leigh Taylor
OPEN: all week CLOSED: 1 week at Christmas MEALS: 12 to 2.30, 7.30 to 9.30
PRICES: £17 (£21), Set L £8 (£11), Set D £14·50 (£17), Snacks from £1·50. Service inc
CARDS: Access, Amex, Diners, Visa
SEATS: 40. 6 tables outside. Private parties: 40 main room, 12 private room. Car-park, 50 places. Children's helpings. Wheelchair access (also wc)
ACCOMMODATION: 16 rooms, all with bath/shower. Rooms for disabled. B&B £36 to £52. Children welcome. Baby facilities. No pets in public rooms. Afternoon teas. Garden. Croquet. TV. Phone. Doors close at 12. Confirm by 6

MIDHURST West Sussex — map 3

Maxine's [10/20]

Red Lion Street, Midhurst GU29 9PB
MIDHURST (073 081) 6271 — £10–£17

An old, wood, tea-shop-style building on the pretty village square, run by a husband-and-wife team. He cooks, she serves. The bean soup is a magnificent meal in itself, filled with garlic, onions, cumin, smoked sausage and bacon. Other good dishes have been the roast chicken, the brill, and the fresh orange quark cake. The peripherals are very good, from warm brown bread to superb vegetables, but some of the saucing can be odd. An interesting list of 70 wines is well spread, both in regions and price.

CHEF: Robert de Jager PROPRIETORS: Robert and Marti de Jager
OPEN: Wed to Sun, Mon D MEALS: 12 to 2, 7 to 10
PRICES: £14 (£17), Set L and D £7·95 (£11), Set Sun L £6·95 (£10). Daily bargain L dish. Service inc CARDS: Access, Amex, Diners, Visa
SEATS: 24. Private parties: 30 main room. Children's helpings. Classical music

MORPETH Northumberland — map 7

The Gourmet [10/20]

59 Bridge Street, Morpeth NE61 1PQ
MORPETH (0670) 56200 and 56205 — £9–£18

Pasta is made daily at this friendly Italian restaurant with an over-long menu. Cafetière coffee. CELLARMAN'S CHOICE: Corvo, Duca di Salaparuta at £6·75.

CHEF: R.H. Wilkinson PROPRIETORS: P. Paesano and R.H. Wilkinson
OPEN: Mon to Sat, exc Mon L MEALS: 11.30 to 2, 6.30 to 11
PRICES: £13 (£18), Set L £3·95 (£9), Set D £8·95 (£14). Also cut-price L menu
CARDS: Access, Amex, Diners, Visa
SEATS: 50. Private parties: 30 main room, 50 private room. Car-park, 6 places. Vegetarian meals. Children's helpings. Take-away service

MOULTON North Yorkshire map 7

Black Bull [11/20]

Moulton DL10 6QJ
BARTON (032 577) 289
2m SE of Scotch Corner £11–£18

The Bull is the local pub, a seafood restaurant (no booking) and also an à la carte restaurant sited in a first-class carriage of the *Brighton Belle* and a conservatory. The kitchen for all three prides itself on its fish – salmon smoked at Craster; scallops from Wearside; classic sole dishes; live Dublin Bay prawns; paella; or lobster at a pricey £11 a pound. The crayfish and lobster are kept in an out-house by the car-park. The rest of the menu concentrates on game – very good partridge plus wild duck and grouse – but there are also variations on Aberdeen Angus steaks, from sandwiches in the bar with more meat than bread, to chateaubriand. The Pagendams have encouraged local produce since 1963, and there is an interesting Swaledale cheese soufflé as well as black pudding with apple sauce. The beers are well kept and the Pagendams run their own wine business. CELLARMAN'S CHOICE: Gewürztraminer '83, from Louis Gisselbrecht, at £7.

CHEF: Charles Somerville PROPRIETORS: Mr and Mrs G.H.Pagendam
OPEN: Mon to Sat, exc Sat L MEALS: 12 to 1.30, 7 to 10.15
PRICES: £13 (£18), Set L £6·50 (£11), Snacks from £1 (£1·10)
SEATS: 130. Private parties: 30 main room, 30 and 10 private rooms. Car-park, 80 places. No children under 7

MULLION Cornwall map 1

▲ *Old Inn* [9/20]

Mullion TR12 7HN
MULLION (0326) 240240 £15

A part-thatched, whitewashed village pub decorated with relics from an eighteenth-century Dutch ship, *Hollandia*, which sank off the coast of Cornwall on her maiden voyage. Lobsters in the tank come from local pots, and good value extends from crab salad or avocado with raspberries and cottage cheese, to grilled lemon sole or veal Benedictine from an unchanging menu, to the accommodation. Devenish and Cornish bitter.

CHEF: Penny Gayton PROPRIETORS: Jack and Penny Gayton
OPEN: all week, exc Sun and Mon D CLOSED: Rest Oct to Easter. Bar and accommodation open all year MEALS: 12 to 2 (1.30 Sun), 7 to 9
PRICES: £11 (£15), Bar snacks from 80p CARD: Visa
SEATS: 14. 7 tables outside. Private parties: 14 main room. Car-park, 12 places. Children welcome. Music
ACCOMMODATION: 5 rooms, 3 with bath/shower. B&B £10 to £13 per room. Deposit: £10. No children under 14. No pets. TV. Scenic. Doors close at 12

Restaurant tricks (3): The bad practice of making a cover charge is dying out, but please report to us on any restaurant still doing so.

NANTWICH Cheshire map 5

Cellars Bistro [10/20]

1–3 Pillory Street, Nantwich CW5 5BZ
NANTWICH (0270) 627566 £7–£13

Good, honest bistro cooking with a vegetarian bent is served here. It's not all French – there is Turkish lamb casserole or spicy Malay chicken, too. Bread is wholemeal, vegetables plentiful, and there is a wide choice of sweets. House French is £5·50.

CHEF: Angela Simpson PROPRIETORS: Angela and Frank Simpson
OPEN: Tue to Sat L, Thur to Sat D MEALS: 12 to 2, 6.30 to 10
PRICES: £9 (£13), Set L from £2·75 (£7). Cheaper Set L and D available CARDS: Access, Amex, Diners, Visa
SEATS: 30. Private parties: 30 main room. Vegetarian meals. Children's helpings. No smoking in dining-room. Classical music

Jade House [10/20]

12A Love Lane, Nantwich CW5 5BH
NANTWICH (0270) 626456 £6–£13

A useful little Cantonese restaurant. Mr Po Cheong Chiu is an accomplished chef and the service is friendly. Lunch on Thursday, Friday and Saturday is a remarkable £2·30. House Nicolas is £4·90.

CHEF/PROPRIETOR: Po Cheong Chiu
OPEN: all week D, Thur to Sat L MEALS: 12 to 2, 6 to 11.30 (12 Fri and Sat)
PRICES: £7 (£13), Set L £2·30 (£6), Set D from £6·50 (£10). Service 10%
CARDS: Access, Visa
SEATS: 50. Private parties: 50 main room. Vegetarian meals. Children welcome. Chinese music. Air-conditioned

▲ *Rookery Hall* [10/20]

Nantwich CW5 6DQ
NANTWICH (0270) 626866
In Worleston, 1½m off A51 on B5074 £23–£34

Good-quality, competent cooking albeit at an exorbitant price. The ingredients are Real, there are views across the Cheshire countryside, and the dining-room has mahogany panelling, polished tables, crystal glasses, a wooden floor and an open fire. The staff are still serious, but more benign than a couple of years ago under the previous regime. The English-style dishes draw the most consistent praise – mulligatawny soup; onion tart; roast saddle of lamb; bubble and squeak; bread-and-butter pudding. But the menu also has a fancy for modern French dishes, which are more erratic and often over-rich. The rooms are beautiful, and breakfast at a phenomenal £7·95 has free-range eggs and crystallised honey. The wines are so expensive that it is cheaper to drink the house wine at £2 a glass than to buy a bottle at £12·50. The marks-ups are night-time robbery. The

Reports on good shops, small hotels and cafes in your area are welcome.

whole operation would be more successful if the prices were brought into line with abilities rather than pretensions. Hence the rating of 10 – we find it hard to take such prices seriously.

CHEF: Brian Hamilton PROPRIETORS: Audrey and Peter Marks
OPEN: all week MEALS: 12.15 to 1.45, 7 to 9.15 (9.45 Sat)
PRICES: Set L £12·95 (£23), Set D £22·50 (£34) CARDS: Access, Amex, Diners, Visa
SEATS: 55. Private parties: 40 main room, 20 private room. Car-park, 30 places. No children under 10. Jacket and tie at D. No smoking in dining-room. Wheelchair access (also WC)
ACCOMMODATION: 11 rooms, all with bath/shower. B&B £52·50 to £80. Deposit: 50%. No children under 10. No pets. Afternoon teas. Garden. Tennis. Fishing. Croquet. Helicopter pad. TV. Phone. Scenic. Doors close at 12 [GHG]

NAYLAND Suffolk — map 3

▲ *The Bear* [12/20]

Bear Street, Nayland CO6 4HY
COLCHESTER (0206) 262204
6m N of Colchester on A134 — £14–£17

Pots of tea are produced on arrival; the rooms are large; the beds are comfortable. The Naismiths are good hosts and their geniality spreads to an elegant country menu typified by the use of free-range eggs, Stilton from Colston Basset and herbs from the garden. Among the avocado and pâté dishes are also to be found goujons of salmon with apricot sauce; noisettes of lamb or its kidneys served Turbigo. Vegetables are organically grown and sweets are endorsed, from apple sorbet to summer pudding. Good breakfasts of eggs, bacon and mushrooms and fresh bread. There is a sensible show of 60-odd wines with some bargains for the quick-witted, such as Hermitage, La Chapelle '79, from Jaboulet, at £10·50. You couldn't buy the '83s in France for that price and they won't be drinkable for years. Solid Beaujolais too, and Abbot ales.

CHEF: John Naismith PROPRIETORS: John and Katy Naismith
OPEN: Tue to Sat D, Sun L MEALS: 12.30 to 1.45, 7.30 to 9.30
PRICES: £12 (£17), Set L and D (Tue to Fri) from £8·50 (£14) CARDS: Access, Visa
SEATS: 50. 6 tables outside. Private parties: 50 main room. Car-park, 30 places. Vegetarian meals by arrangement. Children's helpings by arrangement. Wheelchair access (also WC). Classical music
ACCOMMODATION: 5 rooms, 4 with bath/shower. B&B £25 to £35. Children welcome. Baby facilities. Dogs welcome. Swimming-pool. Garden. Tennis. Croquet. TV [GHG]

NEASHAM Durham — map 7

▲ *Newbus Arms Hotel* [10/20]

Neasham Road, Neasham DL2 1PE
DARLINGTON (0325) 721071 — £7–£24

A comfortable, friendly luxury hotel that makes a fine stop-over on a north–south drive. The restaurant menu is ambitious, ranging from home-pickled trout with iced vodka to a very large beef, Guinness and oyster pie. Good dishes have been the salmon mousse; the citrus water-ice with a slug of champagne; lambs' kidneys with a sauce of green peppercorns and shallots; and most of the handsome sweets. Vegetables are home-grown. There are some interesting '70s clarets and good Beaujolais on the well-thought-out wine list. The Willmotts have opened a cheaper, popular bistro in the hotel, with dishes on the lines of deep-fried mushrooms with garlic mayonnaise, and main courses around £5. There's even been grilled swordfish steak with parsley butter.

CHEF: Paul Bensley PROPRIETORS: Amanda and John Willmott
OPEN: all week, exc Sat L CLOSED: 25 Dec MEALS: 12.30 to 2, 7 to 10 (10.30 Sat)
PRICES: Set L and D £10·75 to £19·75 (£14 to £24), Set Sun L £5·75 (£7).
Service inc CARDS: Access, Amex, Diners, Visa
SEATS: 35. Private parties: 12 main room, 15, 25 and 90 private rooms. Car-park, 100 places. Vegetarian meals. Children's helpings. Wheelchair access (also WC). Classical music and jazz
ACCOMMODATION: 23 rooms, all with bath/shower. Room for disabled. B&B £31 to £39 Children welcome. Baby facilities. Pets welcome. Garden. Sauna. Fishing. TV. Phone. Scenic. Confirm by 6

NEWARK Nottinghamshire — map 5

Gannets [8/20]

35 Castlegate, Newark NG24 1AZ
NEWARK (0636) 702066
opposite castle — £7

A terraced property with a dusty awning on a busy, dirty main road. Inside, the pine tables are tightly packed and the room given a lighter feeling by spotlights in the ceiling, but it is the display of salads and sweets at the counter that reassures most about this all-day cafe. Good home-made soups, such as beef and tomato or cream of pumpkin, are served with granary bread, while the babotie – a mildly curried beef stew bound with an egg custard – stands out among the hot main courses. Sweets are also well up to standard – fruit crumbles made with wholemeal flour, or equally good mocha cake. House French is £4·50 a litre.

CHEF/PROPRIETOR: Hilary Bower
OPEN: Mon to Sat MEALS: 10 to 4.30
PRICES: £4 (£7)
SEATS: 38. 5 tables outside. Vegetarian meals. Children's helpings. Music. Self-service

NEWBRIDGE see PENZANCE

NEWCASTLE UPON TYNE Tyne & Wear — map 7

BACKGROUND BRIEFING: *Mario's, near the station, offers food to suit all pockets in its inexpensive pizzeria and adjoining restaurant. The expanding Chinatown did boast a very good restaurant in the Ming Dynasty but there has been a change of chef. For German food there is the Blackgate Restaurant, The Side (off Dean Street). Visit the old market to see traditional sights, such as complete sets of offal hanging at the specialist stalls, but also for the cheese stall, where there is hard local goats' from Alston. Wholemeal stotty sandwiches and flapjacks can be had from Country Fare, while in butchery the firm of W.G. Lough & Son, 1, 2 and 5 Holly Avenue, West Jesmond, is the best.*

Fisherman's Lodge [new entry, zero rated]

7 Jesmond Dene, Jesmond, Newcastle NE7 7BQ
TYNESIDE (091) 2813281 £13–£26

This well-established, expensive fish restaurant in Jesmond Dene has, for no apparent reason, drawn a lot of recommendations this year. The fish comes out of North Shields and Whitley bay and is cooked with some panache – a trio of thin batter parcels are filled with king prawns and avocado purée; crab comes with green ginger; and turbot with leek. Other good dishes have been the salmon Victoria (poached with a lobster sauce), sole normande, and trout with a chive sauce. Puddings are mainly fruits and sorbets plus a couple of high calorie ones. Service is worth a tip, but the canapés and petits fours are still of the standard that kept this place out of the *Guide* in the past. The wine list is for clairvoyants – no details on it. House Italian is £6·70. More reports, please.

CHEF: Terence Laybourne PROPRIETORS: Franco and Pamela Cetoloni
OPEN: Mon to Sat, exc Sat L CLOSED: 25 Dec to 2 Jan MEALS: 12 to 2, 7 to 11
PRICES: £18 (£26), Set L from £8·90 (£13) CARDS: Access, Amex, Diners, Visa
SEATS: 70. 3 tables outside. Private parties: 14 main room, 40 and 14 private rooms. Car-park, 45 places. Children's helpings. No children under 6. Smart dress preferred. Wheelchair access

Jade Garden [10/20]

53 Stowell Street, Newcastle NE1 4YB
NEWCASTLE (0632) 615889 £6–£16

There has been a lot of to-ing and fro-ing among chefs in the city's Chinatown over the last year, but the Garden remains solid – packed and noisy at night for the Cantonese dishes, such as lemon chicken, spare ribs with chilli, deep-fried wun-tun, and hot-and-sour soup. Orange slices come with the bill. House French is £5, but ask for the Chinese alcoholic drinks like Mou Tai and Mei-Kwei-Lu.

CHEF: Kwok Wah Chiu PROPRIETORS: Alex Chung and Chuen Fai Liu
OPEN: all week MEALS: noon to 11.15 (12 Fri and Sat)
PRICES: £10 (£16), Set L £2·50 (£6), Set D £8 (£12) CARDS: Access, Amex, Diners, Visa
SEATS: 120. Private parties: 120 main room. Vegetarian meals. Children welcome. Wheelchair access (also WC). Music. Air-conditioned

Pizzeria Francesca [8/20]

136 Manor House Road, Jesmond, Newcastle NE2 2NA
NEWCASTLE (0632) 2816586 £5

An unpretentious, popular, dependable and cheap pizza house – the Francesca pizza has everything on it, minestrone gets a heap of Parmesan ladled on top by the waiter, bread is home made and the pasta dishes, notably the cannelloni, are

All inspections are carried out anonymously as we accept no handouts.

The Guide *accepts no advertising and does not allow restaurants to use their inclusion for publicity.*

consistently well reported. Sweets are not quite so good. There can be long queues; lunch prices are even cheaper than the evening ones. House Italian is £4·20.

CHEF/PROPRIETOR: Antonio Sardone
OPEN: Mon to Sat MEALS: 12 to 2.30, 5 to 8.45
PRICES: £1·75 (£5)
SEATS: 35. Children welcome. Music

Le Roussillon [new entry, zero rated]

52–54 St Andrews Street, Newcastle NE1 5SF
NEWCASTLE (0632) 611341 £7–£11

Jean-Pierre Embarck cooks in the style of the Languedoc, Roussillon and Provence in this bright, plush pension of a restaurant. A lot of cream and herbs are used. Good dishes have been the paper-thin pancakes filled with crab, monkfish, scallops and prawns; cassolette of snails and hazel-nuts in a cream sauce; carré d'agneau; and plaited salmon and halibut with a mild ginger sauce. Salads are dressed with good olive oil. Sweets are less good, and a chef of his calibre ought not to be using tinned asparagus. The wines could be improved. More reports, please.

CHEF/PROPRIETOR: Jean-Pierre Embarck
OPEN: Mon to Sat, exc Sat L CLOSED: 1st 2 weeks Aug MEALS: 12 to 2, 7 to 10
PRICES: £11 (£16), Set L from £3·25 (£7) CARDS: Access, Amex, Visa
SEATS: 55. Private parties: 60 main room. Vegetarian meals by arrangement. Children welcome. Jacket and tie. French music

Rupali [10/20]

6 Bigg Market, Newcastle NE1 1UU
NEWCASTLE (0632) 328629 £6–£14

Looks not unlike any other run-of-the-mill curry house from the outside, but the welcome is big and the cooking distinct. The tandoori dishes are consistently good, as is the dhal josh, which is not on the menu but that is not a problem. The eight set meals are priced around £5 but it has been possible to lunch for under £2. A chauvinistic note on the menu says, 'Gentlemen: prices are not shown on the Ladies' Menu'. Probably better that the lady does not find out how cheap the wines are . . .

CHEF: Abdul Khalick PROPRIETOR: Abdul Latif
OPEN: all week, exc Sun L MEALS: 12 to 2.30, 6 to 11.30
PRICES: £8 (£14). Set D Thur £5 (£6) CARDS: Access, Amex, Diners, Visa
SEATS: 54. Private parties: 50 main room. Vegetarian meals. Jacket and tie. Children's helpings. Oriental music

Sachins [11/20]

Old Hawthorn Inn, Forth Banks, Newcastle NE1 3SG
NEWCASTLE (0632) 619035 £10–£16

A former pub, now smartened up with bright-green canopies. Punjabi cooking dishes up plenty of tandooris, including a starter 'cocktail' of chicken tikka and drumsticks, mutton tikka and mince, and king prawn tails. Spicing is varied, a lot of cream and butter is used, and there is a fondness for nuts and eggs. Some sauces are decorated with edible silver. Bhindi bhaji is fresh and firm, and grated marrow in a cream and spice sauce would make a good vegetable main course. Nan are enormous but light as a feather. Service is prompt, relaxed, and able to advise; rock makes a change from sitar music. Avoid the upstairs overflow dining-room. Prices are above par. Try Theakston's best bitter.

CHEF: Abdur Rehmann PROPRIETOR: L.G.Cunningham
OPEN: Mon to Sat MEALS: 12 to 2.30, 6 to 11.30
PRICES: £10 (£16), Set L from £7·95 (£10) CARDS: Access, Amex, Diners, Visa
SEATS: 100. 6 tables outside. Private parties: 70 main room, 30 private room. Car-park, 6 places. Vegetarian meals. Children's helpings. Wheelchair access. Rock music

Wan Ton House [new entry, zero rated]

7 Cross Street, Newcastle NE1 4XE
NEWCASTLE (0632) 323692 £7–£26

Formerly the Town House cafe, but now perhaps the best of the Newcastle Chinese restaurants, especially if you want to take the eastern route through the Cantonese menu, via ox tripe, chicken fat and fish heads, rather than the western way of sweet-and-sour pork and so on. Sunday is the big day for specials and also dim-sum. Notably good have been the wun-tun soup, Peking spare ribs, and sizzling steaks. The casserole dishes are worth exploring, especially for people eating alone. Excellent is the stewed bean curd with assorted meats served in a single pot – the curd is fried and then mixed with pork, prawns, ox tripe, squid, crab dumplings, wood ear fungus, Chinese mushrooms, shredded ginger and Chinese leaves. In fact it is enough for two people. Licensed. More reports, please.

CHEF: T.C.Yau PROPRIETORS: Jimmy Chan and Timmy Ho
OPEN: all week MEALS: noon to 11
PRICES: £17 (£26), Set L £2·50 (£7), Set D from £5 (£9). Service 10% CARDS: Access, Visa
SEATS: 80. Private parties: 50 main room, 40 private rooms. Vegetarian meals. Children welcome. Music

NEWENT Gloucestershire map 2

Soutters [10/20]

1 Culver Street, Newent GL18 1DB
NEWENT (0531) 820896 £19

A husband-and-wife-run dark restaurant with some rather coy touches like the posters in the ladies' of men with their private parts covered by pinned-on bows and feathers. The menu is sensibly short and bistro in essence, though *nouvelle cuisine* in presentation. The less ambitious dishes are the best, hence the drop in the rating – lamb with Stilton as the sauce, plenty of vegetables. The wine list is a bit of a jumble. House French is £5.95.

CHEF: C.Soutter PROPRIETORS: Mr and Mrs C.Soutter
OPEN: Tue to Sat, D only MEALS: 7.30 to 9.30
PRICES: £14 (£19) CARDS: Amex, Diners
SEATS: 20. Private parties: 20 main room Vegetarian meals. Children's helpings. Music

NEW MILTON **Hampshire** map 2

▲ *Marryat Room, Chewton Glen Hotel* [12/20]

Christchurch Road, New Milton BH23 6QS
HIGHCLIFFE (042 52) 5341
on A337, between New Milton and Highcliffe £13–£46

The newly opened road takes you through beautiful grounds up to this sprawling, deceptive modern house. As drop-off points on the international circuit go, Chewton Glen might have been the blue-print – the trimmings, from the large plates, the hot rolls and the cafetière coffee to the single chocolate truffle brought on a large silver salver, are all first-class. The menu, too, feels as if it has been picked for the brochure rather than from the market – plenty of salades tièdes, smoked trout with horseradish, and so on. The execution varies from the excellent, such as the port sauce with a mushroom mousse and the crème brûlée with blackcurrant, to the less so. At one inspection meal the calf's liver with raspberry vinegar sauce was pretty sad, a result apart from anything else of trying to serve raspberries in May; there was even summer pudding on the same menu. Vegetables were overcooked. A new restaurant manager will have taken over by autumn 1985 and perhaps he will instil more joie de vivre – and a little more English – into the waiters. There is also some new family technology to keep the wines (Beaujolais at 12°C, claret at 18°C) and cheeses under optimum conditions. The choice of the former is extensive and expensive, but there is a house wine at lunchtime only – a ridiculous practice – at £5·75.
CELLARMAN'S CHOICE: Chablis '83, from Moreau, at £9·75.

CHEF: Pierre Chevillard PROPRIETOR: Martin Skan
OPEN: all week MEALS: 12.30 to 2, 7.30 to 9.30
PRICES: £29 (£37), Set L from £8·25 (£13), Set D from £25 to £40 (£31 to £46). Service inc CARDS: Access, Amex, Diners, Visa
SEATS: 120. 6 tables outside at L. Private parties: 20 main room, 80 and 6 private rooms. Car-park, 100 places. Children's helpings. No children under 7. Jacket and tie. No cigars/pipes in dining-room
ACCOMMODATION: 44 rooms, all with bath/shower. B&B £50 to £75. No children under 7. No pets. Garden. Outdoor swimming-pool. Tennis. Snooker. Helicopter pad. TV. Phone. Confirm by 3 [GHG]

NEWTON **Warwickshire** map 5

Tabuteau's [10/20]

Newton Grange, Newton CV23 0DR
RUGBY (0788) 860348
on B5414, 3m NE of Rugby £18

Vegetables are mostly local; the farmer's wife brings free-range eggs; trout come from Draycote Water; and the Tabuteau-Harrisons grow their own herbs to add to homely soup. Dinner is served at 8.15 and 9.15 in two different dining-rooms, with a choice of half a dozen traditional items per course, such as crab au gratin, or a tartlet of prawns, onion and cream cheese. Main courses consume a lot of alcohol: venison is casseroled with port; beef is braised in brandy and red wine. Richness continues into puddings, such as a truffle made with coffee, chocolate, almonds and cognac. The atmosphere benefits from an informal approach: 'We avoid hiring professional waiters or waitresses because they bustle and hurry too much.' A helpfully annotated, not overpriced list of 170 wines features late '70s clarets and some well-known burgundies.

CHEFS/PROPRIETORS: David and Stephanie Tabuteau-Harrison
OPEN: Tue to Sat, D only MEALS: 7.30 and 8.30
PRICES: Set D £13·85 (£18) CARDS: Access, Amex, Visa
SEATS: 38. Private parties: 27 main room, 16 private room. Car-park, 18 places. Vegetarian meals. No children under 10. Smart dress preferred. No smoking during meals. Wheelchair access (1 step)

NEWTOWN IN ST MARTIN Cornwall map 1

Anthea's [11/20]

MANACCAN (032 623) 352
8m SE of Helston £10–£13

Honest, down-to-earth food without any nonsense served for half the week during the summer. There is room to park the car in the car-park at the back unless the washing is out. The dining-room is small and candle-lit, and the menu is surprisingly stylish. Mussels come in a cream and curry sauce, and the beef in sour cream sauce is exceptional. Touches such as the brown bread, excellent unsalted butter and free-range eggs belie the relaxed, easy-going atmosphere. Finish with sticky toffee pudding. It is unlicensed but there's a pub next door.

CHEF/PROPRIETOR: Anthea France
OPEN: Wed to Sat, D only CLOSED: Nov to Easter MEALS: 7.30 to 10
PRICES: Set D from £9 to £12 (£10 to £13). Unlicensed, but bring your own: no corkage
SEATS: 26. 1 table outside. Private parties: 26 main room. Car-park, 8 places. Vegetarian meals. Children's helpings. Wheelchair access (also WC). Music

NORTHALLERTON North Yorkshire map 7

Bettys [8/20]

188 High Street, Northallerton DL7 8LF
NORTHALLERTON (0609) 5154 £9

One of the smaller of the quartet of famous tea-rooms established in 1919 (see Harrogate, Ilkley and York). Like its sisters it mixes a Swiss-inspired menu of patisseries and specialist teas with healthy Yorkshire traditions, such as curd tart, fat rascals and Ripon spiced bread. Welsh rarebit comes with chutney, and the salads are fresh. There are five breakfasts, from a fry-up to a Swiss health breakfast. All but one of the 16 wines are from the '83 Alsace vintage from Jean-Jacques Müller, and they are all £6-plus. There is a single Gewürztraminer, Cuvée Exceptionelle '76 at £11·40.

PROPRIETORS: Bettys Ltd
OPEN: all week, daytime only MEALS: 9 to 5.30 (2 to 5.30 Sun)
PRICES: £5 (£9). Snacks from 80p (90p)
SEATS: 58. Vegetarian meals. Children's helpings. No-smoking area. Wheelchair access. Baby facilities

NORTHAMAM Devon map 1

▲ *Grays* [11/20]

4 Fore Street, Northam EX39 1AW
BIDEFORD (023 72) 76371 £16

Diners over five feet ten inches should beware the kneecapping threat as they sit down, but there is lots of room for elbows and dishes among the flower vases on the tables. The set menu offers good choice and value. Good dishes have been avocado soup; dark and moist mushroom and walnut pâté; chicken breast stuffed with apricots and almonds in a wine and cream sauce; and pork fillet in a red wine and plum sauce. Vegetables come in generous quantities and often as purée – creamed sprouts and creamed parsnips – but there are also potatoes baked with onions, and unusual cabbage with orange. Finish with magnificent sticky toffee pudding, a rival for the Sharrow Bay version (see Ullswater), then coffee and Bendicks chocolates. A good spread of 40 wines with house Choix du Roy £5·43 a litre.

CHEF: Colin Gray PROPRIETORS: Colin and Paula Gray
OPEN: Tue to Sat, D only MEALS: 7.30 to 9.30
PRICES: Set D £11·95 (£16) CARDS: Access, Visa
SEATS: 26. Private parties: 18 main room. Vegetarian meals by arrangement. No children under 8. Wheelchair access (also WC). Music
ACCOMMODATION: 3 rooms. B&B £12·50 to £25. No children under 8. Garden. TV. Scenic

NORTHAMPTON Northamptonshire map 3

BACKGROUND BRIEFING: *The covered market has good fish on Wednesday, Friday and Saturday, or try Tom Love in the Grosvenor Centre. The Daily Bread Co-operative near the Bedford roundabout sells a wide range of pulses, rice, dried fruits, muesli ingredients, burghul and inexpensive spices. Back's, opposite the Guildhall, is a cramped and well-stocked delicatessen. Many places sell Bates's local Brixworth pâté, but for cheese there is David Lloyd's stall on Kettering market on Thursday and Friday.*

Royal Bengal [10/20]

39–41 Bridge Street, Northampton NN1 1NF
NORTHAMPTON (0604) 38617 and 36100 £6–£14

There are moist, well-spiced tandoori dishes and chicken and lamb tikka masala on a big menu that goes from mild lamb pasanda to hot, flavoursome dhansak. Good tarka dhal, bhajia and nan. The atmosphere is quiet. House wine is £4·50, or there is draught lager.

CHEF/PROPRIETOR: Abdul Rohim
OPEN: all week CLOSED: 25 Dec MEALS: 12 to 2.30, 6 to 12 (1 Fri and Sat)
PRICES: £7 (£14), Set L from £2·95 (£6), Set D from £3·30 (£7) CARDS: Access, Amex, Diners, Visa
SEATS: 100. Private parties: 100 main room, 30 private room. Vegetarian meals. Children's helpings. No-smoking area. Wheelchair access (also WC). Indian music. Air-conditioned

Restaurants rating 12 or more serve the best food in the region.

NORTHLEACH Gloucestershire — map 2

Old Woolhouse [12/20]

The Square, Northleach GL54 3EE
NORTHLEACH (045 16) 366 — £20

Mr Astic is one of the better chefs in this *Guide* but he runs his restaurant to suit himself. Dinner is at 8.15, the menu is classical French, and it is difficult to get a table. His execution is masterly. The wine list matches the seriousness of the cooking.

CHEF: Mr Astic PROPRIETOR: Mrs Astic
OPEN: Tue to Sat, D only CLOSED: Christmas MEALS: 8.15
PRICES: Set D £16·50 (£20). Service inc
SEATS: 18. Vegetarian meals by arrangement. Children welcome. One sitting

NORTH WEALD BASSET Essex — map 3

Wo Ping [10/20]

60 High Street, North Weald Basset CM16 6BY
NORTH WEALD (037 882) 3815 — £12–£19

Alan Man's smart Chinese restaurant offers Cantonese, Pekinese and Szechuan dishes. The food is good value. Among notable dishes eaten have been Peking-style steamed fish and the fillet steak with ginger and spring onions. Old favourites like wun-tun soup, sesame prawn toasts, and deep-fried seaweed are deftly done. Singapore noodles make a change from rice. House Wan Fu is a pricey £6·50. It's a good place to take all the family.

CHEF/PROPRIETOR: Alan Man
OPEN: all week D, Thur to Sun L MEALS: 12 to 1.45, 5 to 11 (11.45 Thur, Fri, Sat)
PRICES: £8 (£14), Set L and D from £7·50 to £14·50 (£12 to £19).
Service 10% CARDS: Access, Amex, Diners, Visa
SEATS: 60. Private parties: 40 main room. Car-park, 20 places. Vegetarian meals. Children welcome. Music. Air-conditioned

NORWICH Norfolk — map 6

BACKGROUND BRIEFING: *This year readers gave as many votes against as for Winners, 14–16 Lower Goat Lane. Those in favour of the restaurant being listed mentioned good steaks, those against could not take the place seriously. Other casualties are the two Bombays at 9 Magdalen Street and 43 Timber Hill. The former is more spacious but they are both open late and still reliable dishes include the chicken jal frezi and brinjal bhaji. The Mousetrap, 2 St Gregory's Alley (there is a shop of the same name in Bury St Edmunds), has a good selection of cheeses in prime condition. The Mecca delicatessen, Orford Hill, is on four floors, and Rainbow, 16 Dove Street, makes its own bread and has a selection of nuts, dried fruit and pulses. There is a very good market (every day except Sunday) with fish stalls, good, cheap and exotic fruit and vegetables, a herb and spice stall, and places for nuts, pulses and dried fruit.*

Restaurants rating 12 or more serve the best food in the region.

Brasted's [new entry, zero rated]

8–10 St Andrews Hill, Norwich NR2 1AD
NORWICH (0603) 625949 £12

This scrubbed pine bistro with a coffee-shop gets its fish daily off the boats. There is a small menu and Mr Brasted (who also deals in pianos) is an ebullient host. Sardines and mussels are very good starters before main courses of rack of lamb with rosemary or pork à la crème. Home-made ice-creams. More reports, please.

CHEFS: J. Brasted and P. Morgan PROPRIETOR: J. Brasted
OPEN: all week, exc Mon D, Sun L MEALS: 12 to 2.30, 7 to 10
PRICES: £10 (£12), Snacks from 95p. Service inc
SEATS: 28. Private parties: 20 main room. Vegetarian meals. Children's helpings. Wheelchair access. Classical music

Green's Seafood Restaurant [10/20]

82 Upper St Giles Street, Norwich NR3 1AQ
NORWICH (0603) 623733 £17

This is the best fish in town: it's fresh. There is a heavy dependence on cream sauces – fillet of plaice with whisky, turbot with prawns and garlic, and monkfish all come with cream. Other dishes include squid with red wine, turbot with prawns and herb butter, and a seafood platter. Rarities appear from time to time, such as porbeagle shark, which is pink and tastes like veal, and samphire grass, although it's a mite expensive by the time it has come from the salt marshes to the table. Vegetables are good, there is live piano music, and most people seem too full to sample the puddings. House Minervois is £5·20. George, the pet lobster, has apparently met his demise.

CHEF/PROPRIETOR: Dennis Crompton
OPEN: Mon to Sat, exc Sat L CLOSED: 1 week at Christmas, bank hols
MEALS: 12.15 to 2.15, 7 to 10.45
PRICES: £12 (£17). Service 10% CARDS: Access, Visa
SEATS: 54. Private parties: 30 main room. Vegetarian meals. No children under 7 at D. No cigars in dining-room. Music. Air-conditioned

Marco's [11/20]

17 Pottergate, Norwich NR2 1DS
NORWICH (0603) 624044 £12–£20

Above-average Italian cooking, from the cured beef served with olive oil and fresh figs, to the partridge marinated in wine, roasted, carved into three and served with a sauce of garlic, prunes and cream. Marco Vessalio has been here for 16 years. He has his own two-acre salad garden and grows his own herbs. He also has a certificate in herbal medicine. The menu changes with the markets. Pasta, from gnocchi to tagliatelle, is freshly made, and the Dutch veal dish with Marsala sauce draws good reports. Fish is strong, too. To finish there are ice-creams and sorbets. The wine list covers nearly all the Italian regions, from Frascati at £5·50 to Barolo '78 at £10 and so on. Vintages and producers don't always appear because small purchases mean they vary, but advice is on hand.

CHEF/PROPRIETOR: Marco Vessalio
OPEN: Tue to Sat CLOSED: Aug MEALS: 12.30 to 2, 7.30 to 10
PRICES: £16 (£20), Set L £8·50 (£12). Service inc CARDS: Access, Amex, Diners, Visa
SEATS: 40. Private parties: 20 main room, 20 private room. Vegetarian meals. Children's helpings. Wheelchair access

Tatlers [10/20]

21 Tombland, Norwich NR3 1RF
NORWICH (0603) 621822 £9–£15

Wholesome English meals that go down well with a bottle of red wine are served in this informal, sometimes chaotic restaurant. Typical and good have been pheasant pâté; pigeon, duck and orange pie; wild duck with elderberry sauce served with carrots, cauliflower and potatoes; Grand Marnier syllabub and apricot tart. Some decorative *nouvelle* touches have crept in, such as the octagonal plates, but the garnishing on the excellent smoked salmon mousse seems to have died down and all the Stilton and apple mousse gets is a fan of apple slices. The wine list is carefully put together. The minor '78 clarets should be coming through this year, or there are vins de pays from Bouches-du-Rhône and Vaucluse at £4·50. CELLARMAN'S CHOICE: Syrah de l'Ardèche '83 at £6·10.

CHEFS: Simon Evans and Mark Corbluth PROPRIETORS: Michael and Peter Killingbeck
OPEN: Mon to Sat, exc Sat L MEALS: 12.30 to 2, 6.30 to 11
PRICES: £10 (£15), Set L from £5·50 (£9) CARDS: Access, Amex, Diners, Visa
SEATS: 88. Private parties: 30 main room; 30 and 20 private rooms. Vegetarian meals. Children's helpings. Wheelchair access. Classical music

NOTTINGHAM Nottinghamshire map 5

Les Artistes Gourmands [11/20]

61 Wollaton Road, Beeston, Nottingham NG9 2NG
NOTTINGHAM (0602) 228288 £9–£11

At last! A decent French restaurant in the orbit of Nottingham, which was beginning to look like a culinary black hole. There are queues on Saturdays but in the week there is a three-course bon marché menu for £7·50. It feels very French, with lace curtains, creaky old wooden chairs, white-painted brick walls hung with dried flowers and posters of French wine country, fresh carnations on the tables and taped classical guitar music – only in France there would probably be no tablecloths. Good dishes that have followed the cheese puff pastries with a glass of the Loire Kir have been pork and bacon terrine; steak in mushroom sauce, and salmon with a white wine sauce. Burgundy beef has been excellent. There is an attempt to get away from the usual bistro-clichés and into dishes such as pheasant and cabbage and also, more ambitiously, monkfish with crayfish sauce. Vegetables are modern, in the sense of being al dente and often purées. Sweets are all made in-house. The bread is good and the cheeseboard has included Brie, Camembert, goats' and Port-Salut. The short list of good drinking wines from the lesser regions is strongest in the Rhône. House red is £5·70. CELLARMAN'S CHOICE: Crozes-Hermitage, Domaine de Thalabert '80, from Jaboulet, at £9·30.

CHEFS: J.L.David and Philippe Keon **PROPRIETOR:** Philippe Keon
OPEN: Mon to Sat, exc Mon D and Sat L **CLOSED:** 3 weeks Jan, 1 week Aug
MEALS: 12 to 1.30, 7 to 10.30 **PRICES:** Set L from £5·80 (£9), Set D from £7·50 (£11). Service inc **CARDS:** Access, Visa
SEATS: 40. 5 tables outside. Private parties: 30 main room. Vegetarian meals. Children's helpings. Wheelchair access. French popular music

Chand [10/20]

26 Mansfield Road, Nottingham NG1 3GX
NOTTINGHAM (0602) 474103 £6–£12

This unpretentious Indian restaurant, on a busy main street close to the Victoria shopping-centre, is a good place for family eating. The seats and lights are red, the tablecloths and curtains blue. Flock is restricted to panels on tan walls and there are fresh flowers and Indian needle-point pictures. Curries are often a better choice than the tandoori range, and there are some interesting hot and sweet Parsee dishes. Onion bhajias are light and crisp; meat bhuna is well-trimmed beef cooked fairly dry with onion, green pepper and fresh coriander; and the mixed vegetables have been a fine serving of broccoli, onion, pepper, peas and carrots. Poppadums – plain and spiced – are freshly cooked and not greasy.

CHEF: M.Ayub **PROPRIETORS:** M.Khizer and M.Ayub
OPEN: all week **MEALS:** 12 to 2.30, 5.30 to 12.30
PRICES: £7 (£12), Set L £2·95 (£6), Set D £3·90 (£7). Minimum £4·50 **CARDS:** Access, Amex, Diners, Visa
SEATS: 75. Private parties: 50 main room, 50 private room. Vegetarian meals. Children's helpings. Wheelchair access. Indian music

Pagoda [10/20]

31–33 Greyfriar Gate, Nottingham NG1 7EF
NOTTINGHAM (0602) 501105 £4–£14

A chintzy, plastic-flowered Cantonese restaurant with a good, if pricey, range of dim-sum served until half-past four in the afternoon. A combination of pork dumplings (sui mai); pork ribs in black bean sauce; prawn in rice-flour roll (cheung-fun); and glutinous rice and chicken would feed two people for under £5, tea included. Noodles in soup also provide inexpensive, one-plate meals during the day. Otherwise it is is one of those Chinese menus that rambles on like the Great Wall, with strengths in fish and duck, notably roast duck with prawn-meat stuffing. Many dishes give off a pungent smell that seductively pervades the

'The portion control was appalling – the half a duck could have been a pigeon on a starvation diet.' (On eating in the Midlands)

The 1987 Guide will appear before Christmas 1986, so reports are particularly important in the spring. Report forms are at the back of this book, but just write a letter if you prefer. Address them to The Good Food Guide, *Freepost, 14 Buckingham Street, London WC2N 6BR. No stamp is necessary if you post in the UK.*

restaurant. Service is helpful and, wonder of wonders, here is a wine list in a Chinese restaurant assembled with some understanding – two '83 Alsace wines, a Pinot Blanc and a Gewürztraminer, are about £6 and suit well.

CHEFS: Kwok-Fai Law and Cheung-Sing Tang
PROPRIETORS: Patrick M.K.Liu, Kwok-Fai Law and Cheung-Sing Tang
OPEN: all week CLOSED: 25 Dec MEALS: noon to 11.30
PRICES: £8 (£14), Set L from £1 (£4). Minimum £5 at D. Service 10% CARDS: Access, Amex, Diners, Visa
SEATS: 90. Private parties: 90 main room. Vegetarian meals. Children's helpings. Jacket and tie preferred. No smoking in dining-room. Wheelchair access. Chinese music

Staropolska [10/20]

King John's Arcade, 13–15 Bridlesmith Gate, Nottingham NG1 2GR
NOTTINGHAM (0602) 502672 £7–£12

This inexpensive lunchtime vegetarian cafe turns into a basement Polish restaurant at night, when a glass of iced vodka is presented to get everyone in the mood. The pierogi (pastry filled with potatoes, onions and curd and served with sour cream) and the kotlety (mushroom patties with a piquant cream sauce) are good, before copious main courses of good steaks or chicken with cream and paprika and onions. The Polish cheesecake is indulgent. To drink there are flavoured vodkas or eastern European wines.

CHEF: Jan Laskowski PROPRIETORS: Jan and Sheila Laskowski
OPEN: Mon to Sat, exc Mon D MEALS: 11 to 3.15, 7 to 10
PRICES: L £3 (£7), Set D from £7·75 (£12) CARDS: Access, Diners
SEATS: 65. 6 tables outside. Private parties: 24 main room. Vegetarian meals at L, by arrangement at D. Children welcome. Music. Self-service at L

Le Têtard [10/20]

10 Pilcher Gate, Nottingham NG1 1QE
NOTTINGHAM (0602) 598253 £9–£15

A crêperie in the lace-market area serving a dozen filling fillings: leeks wrapped in ham with Mornay sauce; porc dijonnaise; mixed seafood; and sweet ones with maple syrup, brandy and mincemeat, or apricot and almond. Starters include charcuterie and garlic mushrooms; bowlfuls of salad come heavily dressed; and specials run to fillet steak done as mock wild boar. The French wine list offers a red Gaillac; '83 Gewürztraminer, from the Ribeauvillé Co-operative, at £6·95; and CELLARMAN'S CHOICE: Chablis '83, Domaine de Vauroux at £8·10 (£4·10 for a half-bottle).

CHEFS/PROPRIETORS: Alain Duval and Gérard Morange
OPEN: Mon to Sat, exc Sat L MEALS: 12 to 2.30, 6 to 10.30
PRICES: £12 (£15), Set L £6·50 (£9), Set D £8·50 (£11). Service inc CARDS: Access, Amex, Diners, Visa
SEATS: 84. Private parties: 60 main room, 40 private room. Children's helpings. Wheelchair access. Music

Reports on good shops, small hotels and cafes in your area are welcome.

OADBY Leicestershire map 5

La Maison [10/20]

Glen Rise, Oadby LE2 4RG
GREAT GLEN (053 759) 2308
A6, 4m S of Leicester £15

The good value and friendly service continue to impress at this small, family-run restaurant. An accordionist makes conversation difficult on Wednesdays. The menu is strictly bistro, with starters of snails, pâtés, ham and artichoke hearts in cream sauce, trout with watercress and caper mayonnaise, and tomato and vegetable soup (misleadingly called pot-au-feu). Main courses have included lamb daube with yoghourt, beef stew with a puff-pastry crust, saddle of rabbit with vegetables and mustard, and a well-reported chicken milanese. The short and eccentric wine list ranges from carafe French at £2·50 for half a litre to Ch. Latour '73 at £23·50.

CHEF: Rosemary Wilkes PROPRIETORS: Rosemary and Trevor Wilkes
OPEN: Tue to Sat, D only MEALS: 7 to 9.45
PRICES: Set D £11 (£15) CARDS: Access, Amex, Visa
SEATS: 54. Private parties: 20 main room. Car-park, 30 places. Children welcome. Smart dress preferred. Wheelchair access (also WC). Live music

OLNEY Buckinghamshire map 3

Olney Wine Bar [8/20]

9 High Street South, Olney MK46 4EB
BEDFORD (0234) 711112
on A509, 5m N of Newport Pagnell £9

The bow-window shop-front with its Dixon of Dock Green lamp gives straight on to big tables, a fireplace and a solid wooden counter; the back room, with its old bread oven, is darker and busier. Service is from the bar: Mediterranean fish salad with squid, prawn pil-pil, lasagne, moussaka, steak and chips, and cold meats to go with bowls of salad. Good puds. Three dozen wines, many around a fiver, mostly '80s vintages. House French is £3·95. CELLARMAN'S CHOICE: KWV Roodeburg '80 at £4·85.

CHEF: D. Vernon PROPRIETORS: A.R., R.C. and R.A. Plumbridge
OPEN: all week, exc Sun D CLOSED: 1 week at Christmas MEALS: 12 to 2.15, 7 to 10
PRICES: £6 (£9), Snacks from 90p (£1) CARD: Visa
SEATS: 92. Private parties: 50 main room. Vegetarian meals by arrangement. Children welcome. Smart dress preferred. Wheelchair access (also WC). Music

ONCHAN see ISLE OF MAN

'A request for a vegetarian meal was met with tomato soup, a terrine with tomato sauce, and a mushroom and tomato ragout for main course – in short, not a good balance.' (On eating in the Lake District)

ORFORD Suffolk

map 3

Butley-Orford Oysterage [9/20]

Market Hill, Orford IP12 2LQ
ORFORD (039 45) 277

Real Food £9

The Pinneys have their own fishing boats in the Orford River, their own oyster concession and an oak-smokehouse for salmon, trout, sprats, cod's roe and eels. There's not much cooking, but all the fish is wild and the atmosphere informal. A dozen oysters and a bottle of Muscadet (or the English house wine – Finn Valley from Otley) leaves change from £10.

CHEF: Mathilde Pinney PROPRIETORS: Richard, William and Mathilde Pinney
OPEN: all week CLOSED: Jan and 1st 2 weeks Feb MEALS: 12 to 2.15, 6 to 8.30
PRICES: £6 (£9)
SEATS: 50. Private parties: 25 main room. Wheelchair access

ORTON Cumbria

map 7

▲ *Gilded Apple* [9/20]

Orton CA10 3RQ
ORTON (058 74) 345
2m N of M6 exit 38

£10–£16

The rooms here are cheap and in the stone-walled, emerald-green dining-room there is good-value home cooking of the likes of rabbit casserole or enormous portions of roast duck with abundant vegetables. Some of the less conventional combinations are not so effective. 'A' for effort. Meals are cheaper mid-week out of season. The house wine, a Sardinian, is £5·25, and a few other interesting bottles are listed.

CHEF/PROPRIETOR: Silas Rains
OPEN: Tue to Sun D, and Sun L MEALS: 12 to 2, 6.30 to 10
PRICES: £11 (£16), Set L £5·50 (£10). Service 10% L CARDS: Access, Visa
SEATS: 40. Private parties: 30 main room, 30 and 15 private rooms. Vegetarian meals by arrangement. Children welcome. Music
ACCOMMODATION: 3 rooms. B&B £8·50 to £17. Dogs welcome

OSWESTRY Shropshire

map 5

Good Companion Wine Bar [8/20]

10 Beatrice Street, Oswestry SY11 1QG
OSWESTRY (0691) 655768

£11

A wine bar not only with character but also an unusually good selection of wines. Mostly local produce goes into dishes such as taramosalata, kebabs and

Places rating 8 or 9 may not be restaurants at all but still serve very good food. In this category expect to find pubs, cafes, small hotels and wine bars.

All Guide *inspectors are anonymous. Anyone purporting to represent the* Guide *is an impostor.*

goulash. Vegetarians do well, as do people with a sweet tooth – there are Pavlovas and cheesecakes. Good house claret at 95p a glass.

CHEF: Denise Hickman PROPRIETORS: C.J. and D.Hickman
OPEN: Tue to Sat MEALS: 12 to 2.45, 7.30 to 11
PRICES: £6 (£11). Also cut-price L menu CARD: Visa
SEATS: 90. Private parties: 12 main room, 50 private room. Vegetarian meals. No children under 8 at D. Wheelchair access. Jazz

OTTERY ST MARY Devon map 1

The Lodge [12/20]

17 Silver Street, Ottery St Mary EX11 1DB
OTTERY ST MARY (040 481) 2356 £21

A small, relaxed restaurant, near the thirteenth-century church, decorated with antique clocks. Laver-bread is sent twice a week from Swansea market and is used to fill mushrooms along with bacon and served as a starter. The same kind of care goes into all the menu. It is inspired by its ingredients and turns out pigeon salad dressed in walnut oil; sweetbreads en brioche with a light curry sauce; duck with kumquats; and the classic quails Rossini. The quality of the meat is high. To finish there is the politely named négresse en chemise, or a hot Stilton pâté by way of a savoury. The wine list takes a broad sweep across Europe and is not greedily priced. House French from Duboeuf is £5·50.
CELLARMAN'S CHOICE: Ch. Cissac '71 at £15·75.

CHEF/PROPRIETOR: Diane Shenton
OPEN: Tue to Sun, exc Sun D MEALS: 12 to 2, 7 to 9.30
PRICES: Set L and D £16·50 (£21) CARDS: Amex, Diners, Visa
SEATS: 25. Private parties: 28 main room. Vegetarian meals. Children's helpings. Wheelchair access (3 steps; also WC). Classical music

Oswalds [new entry, zero rated]

25 Silver Street, Ottery St Mary EX11 1DB
OTTERY ST MARY (040 481) 2262 £15

We prefer cooking simply with first-class ingredients rather than thinking up complicated dishes, explains Mrs Oswald. Hear! Hear! She and her husband have been evolving their bistro into more of a restaurant, supplementing the main-course charcoal grills of steak, lamb or Bratwurst with daily specials that sometimes betray Mr Oswald's German ancestry, such as the sirloin of beef marinated in red wine and served with a sour cream sauce with raisins. Their butcher dresses his own meat, fish is out of Brixham and the local greengrocer keeps the supply of fresh vegetables coming throughout the year. The wine list is

The 1987 Guide will appear before Christmas 1986, so reports are particularly important in the spring. Report forms are at the back of this book, but just write a letter if you prefer. Address them to The Good Food Guide, *Freepost, 14 Buckingham Street, London WC2N 6BR. No stamp is necessary if you post in the UK.*

an interesting mix of German and French. CELLARMAN'S CHOICE: Gewürztraminer '83 from Louis Gisselbrecht at £6·90. More reports welcome.

CHEFS/PROPRIETORS: Mr and Mrs P. Oswald
OPEN: Mon to Sat, exc Mon L MEALS: 12 to 2, 7.30 to 9.30
PRICES: £10 (£15)
SEATS: 29. Private parties: 12 main room. Children's helpings. Wheelchair access. Music

OUNDLE Northamptonshire map 6

Tyrrells [12/20]

6–8 New Street, Oundle PE8 4EA
OUNDLE (0832) 72347 **Real Food** £13–£18

An old dining-room rather like a snug, with tiled floors and wooden tables. The ingredients are first-class and Kevin Boon keeps a sure hand on the cooking range. The menu moves with the markets and seasons, but portions are uniformly large, from the chicken livers on rice to the protein-rich avocado with cheese. Fish is handled in the old ways – mussels and bacon are put on kebabs, the fish bake leans heavily on shellfish – while lamb is done in the Basque way and pigeon is pot-roasted with mushrooms. To finish there is rhubarb and almond pudding and good profiteroles. Service is welcoming. The functional wine list is strongest in burgundy, and there are a few collector's items, such as Sylvaner '79, from Gisselbrecht, at £6·90.

CHEF: Kevin Boon PROPRIETORS: Mike and Hilary Tyrrell
OPEN: all week, exc Mon L, Sun D CLOSED: bank hols MEALS: 12 to 2, 7 to 10 (10.30 Sat)
PRICES: £11 (£18), Set Sun L £7·95 (£13), Snacks £4·95 (£5·50). Cheaper set L available. Service 10% Sat CARDS: Access, Visa
SEATS: 48. 4 tables outside. Private parties: 20 main room. Children's helpings (Sun L only) No children under 5. No cigars in dining-room. Smart dress preferred. Wheelchair access. Music

OXFORD Oxfordshire map 2

BACKGROUND BRIEFING: *In winter the rafters of the covered market in the city centre are hung with game. John Lindsey is the best butcher and has spawned a high-quality specialist shop opposite (M. Seller). The cheese stall has an interesting range. Oxford's best lunch for around £1 is a filled continental roll from Palm's delicatessen, followed by a fruit tart from the Blanc bakery stall (the main shop is next to Brown's in Woodstock Road). Down the High Street, Frank Cooper – now part of a multi-national – has taken over a former bookshop to sell its classic marmalades. Further east, in the Cowley Road, the Indian grocers have been joined by a small shop selling take-away savoury dishes and the Royal range of Asian sweet-meats (see Southall background briefing). The Oxford Beer Shops, 105 Bullingdon Road; 3 Ostler Road, Headington; and 12 Western Road, have British and imported beers. There is a pasta bar war in Little Clarendon Street where Pasta Pasta (it has another branch in the covered market) has a small eating-area and Fasta Pasta does good lunchtime sandwiches. Restaurant Elizabeth on St Aldate's has a remarkable wine list, and La Sorbonne in the High Street has a cut-price room – the Casse-Croûte – where onion tart, grilled salmon and apple sorbet have been good. China House on Queen Street has dim-sum at lunch-time. There is an eccentric eating-area at the back of the Hi Lo Jamaican store in the*

Cowley Road, and the Nag's Head in Hythe Bridge Street is still the place for doorstep-sized sandwiches.

Browns [11/20]

5–9 Woodstock Road, Oxford OX2 6AH
OXFORD (0865) 511995 £5–£10

One thousand meals a day are served in this elegant, jumping brasserie where queues for tables are frequent. The place underlines the argument that what people want is good, plain food at prices they can afford: here it takes the guise of steak, Guinness and mushroom pie; char-grilled lamb steaks with rosemary; spaghettis; and hot sandwiches. Browns also has that elusive quality of all good restaurants in that it fizzes – in no small part because of the vivacious waitresses dressed to match the 23 cocktails. There is a string quartet in the afternoons and a jazz duo late at night. House wine from Dolamore, who must have introduced more Oxford undergraduates to the grape than anyone else, is £3·95.

CHEF: Eamonn Hunter PROPRIETORS: J.L.Mogford and J.P.Mayhew
OPEN: all week CLOSED: 24 to 28 Dec MEALS: 11 (12 Sun and bank hols) to 11.30
PRICES: £3 (£5) to £7 (£10)
SEATS: 220. 4 tables outside. Vegetarian meals. Children's helpings. No-smoking area. Wheelchair access (also wc). Music. Air-conditioned

Cherwell Boathouse [10/20]

Bardwell Road, Oxford OX2 6SR
OXFORD (0865) 52746
off Banbury Road, alongside Dragon
School Playing Field £10–£12

Formerly an Edwardian boathouse on the Cherwell, with eight tables on the paved roof in summer. The atmosphere is relaxed and easy going, and chef Patrick Glennie Smith sometimes comes out to pour the wine. The menu changes weekly and is essentially English and strong on game in winter – roast pheasant with oatmeal stuffing, or partridge casserole. The puddings can be the main attraction along with an excellent wine list – apple pie; prune/plum suet balls with fresh orange sauce; Stilton with apples and oranges; other dishes have been more ragged but taste okay. The wine list is bolstered by their own shipping firm and has spectacular, not overpriced, clarets through the '70s, powerful Rhônes and white burgundies. CELLARMAN'S CHOICE: Côtes du Ventoux, La Vieille Ferme, '81 from Perrin at £4·50.

CHEF: Patrick Glennie Smith PROPRIETOR: Anthony Verdin
OPEN: D all week, Sun L CLOSED: Christmas to New Year MEALS: 12.30 to 2.30, 8 to 10.30
PRICES: Set L £8·25 (£10), Set D £9·50 (£12). Snacks from £1 (£3). Service inc
CARDS: Access, Amex, Diners, Visa
SEATS: 35. 8 tables outside. Private parties: 50 main room. Car-park, 12 places. Children's helpings. Wheelchair access (also wc). Music

We keep files on every restaurant, so reports of poor meals are just as valuable as reports of good meals because they save unnecessary inspections.

Gee's [10/20]

61 Banbury Road, Oxford OX2 6PE
OXFORD (0865) 511472 £10–£19

The conservatory, built *circa* 1896 and until quite recently a nurseryman's sales outlet, is elegantly furnished, with a swish little menu too – vegetarian dishes are given asterisks, and there is adventure in the spaghetti with wild mushrooms and in the fillet of turbot with crab ravioli. Fish is consistently good. Starters tend towards the Italian, and the main courses to the anglo-international of filet en croûte – very big – or chicken Kiev. It is a mystery how asparagus soup can sell for the same price as mushroom soup in March. Although it is not cheap compared with its sister, Browns, on the Woodstock Road, it is usually crowded and you may have to queue. Sunday brunch is fun. Twenty not badly picked wines include a Gewürztraminer '83 from Kuentz-Bas at £8·50; house Beaujolais is £4·95.

CHEF: Nicholas Steiger PROPRIETORS: J.M.Partnership
OPEN: all week CLOSED: Christmas week MEALS: 12 to 2, 7 (7.30 Sun) to 11.30
PRICES: £14 (£19), Set L £6·75 (£10) CARDS: Access, Visa
SEATS: 85. Private parties: 85 main room. Vegetarian meals. Children welcome. Wheelchair access (also WC). Air-conditioned

Munchy Munchy [12/20]

6 Park End Street, Oxford OX1 1HH
OXFORD (0865) 245710 £11

Ethel Ow's small Indonesian cafe still offers the best value in Oxford. The menu changes daily with now excellent fish tending to appear on Wednesdays and Thursdays. As you go in, debate with Mrs Ow at the counter the merits of king prawns on spinach; scallop and aubergine; or charcoal-grilled beef satay. She has a spicer's armoury of mace, cloves, turmeric, tamarind, coriander, honey and coconut. Some dishes can be quite hot, and the papaya and the passion creams can make a welcome finish. The door is locked when it's full and queues form. This cafe earns its high rating for the splendour and spontaneity of the cooking. There is a range of teas or take your own wine for 30p extra a head. Alsace wines go well.

CHEF: Ethel Ow PROPRIETORS: Tony and Ethel Ow
OPEN: Tue to Sat MEALS: 12 to 2.10, 5.30 to 9.40
PRICES: £5 (£11). Licensed, plus bring your own: no corkage
SEATS: 41. Private parties: 7 main room. Vegetarian meals. No children under 6 Fri and Sat D

Le Petit Blanc [15/20]

272 Banbury Road, Summertown, Oxford OX2 7DY
OXFORD (0865) 53540 **Real Food** £14·50–£23

Do not be fooled by talk that this is only the bistro to Raymond Blanc's Manoir aux Quat' Saisons or by the red checked cloths and the posters and cartoons. John and Christine Burton-Race have achieved almost as much in the old Quat' Saisons dining-room as their mentor has done at Great Milton. This is a tremendous little restaurant, not expensive for what it is, based firmly on the one hand on regional French cooking and on the other on inspiration and respect for ingredients that characterises the finest modern cooking. Far from plundering the French markets they, along with Blanc, have set out to cultivate local supplies – chickens are reared at Abingdon, crayfish too are English; periodically they advertise in the local paper for fish, fruit, vegetables . . . All these ingredients are translated into dishes with real poise. To start: terrine of brill with tarragon sauce; warm pigeon or else duck magret salad; quail galantine; marinade of salmon and monkfish with coriander. Of many alpha fish dishes halibut with vermouth, chives and a tomato sauce, and red mullet with a butter, tomato and anchovy sauce stand out. Equal to these are the pheasant in port sauce; sweetbreads with red cabbage, courgettes and tomatoes; roast saddle of lamb. The host of recommended sweets is as long: cassis mousse; chocolate marquise; orange soufflé with Grand Marnier. The set lunch at £13 is a snip. The house Rhône at £5·40 does not match cooking of this calibre, and it is worth looking for something better, such as the Fleurie '83 or the Mâcon Chaintré '83, or taking your own (corkage £2·50). As we went to press there were plans to move lock, stock and barrel up the road: check when booking.

CHEF: J.W.Burton-Race PROPRIETOR: Raymond Blanc
OPEN: L Tue to Sat, D all week MEALS: 12.15 to 2.15, 7.15 to 10.15
PRICES: Set L £13 (£14·50), Set D £18·50 (£23). Licensed, plus bring your own: corkage £2·50 CARDS: Access, Visa
SEATS: 50. Vegetarian meals. Children welcome. Wheelchair access (also WC). Air-conditioned

PADIHAM Lancashire map 5

▲ *Le Jardin Bistro* [9/20]

35 Burnley Road, Padiham BB12 8BY
PADIHAM (0282) 71358 £12

A family-run, fun little bistro that is short on wines but offers imaginative Elizabeth David-style cooking in an area noticeable otherwise for its gastronomic dullness or pomposity. Especially worthwhile have been dishes as varied as a genuine salade niçoise and excellent Christmas pudding. Soups range from herb, to onion and Stilton; there may be cassoulet; and there are crumbles to finish. House Loire is £4·60. Theakston's beers.

CHEF: Alan Farmer PROPRIETORS: Alan and Angela Farmer
OPEN: Wed to Sat, D only MEALS: 7 to 11
PRICES: £8 (£12)
SEATS: 32. Private parties: 32 main room. Vegetarian meals. Children's helpings. Classical music
ACCOMMODATION: 2 rooms. B&B £10 to £16. No pets. Doors close at 11

If you suspect that a restaurant is using processed food, always ask. It would be a contravention of the Trade Descriptions Act for the restaurant to lie.

Restaurant tricks (1): Charging each person for every serving of vegetables even when the diners have shared portions between them.

PADSTOW Cornwall map 1

Seafood Restaurant [14/20]

Riverside, Padstow PL28 8BY
PADSTOW (0841) 532485 Real Food £16–£26

An uncomplicated, now very popular fish restaurant. The enormous seafood platter arrives loaded with mussels, prawns, king prawns, whole crab and so on, all virtually untampered with by the kitchen. The supply lines are Real Food in the best sense – lobsters, crabs and crawfish from local fishermen; mussels, cockles and winkles from the Camel estuary; oysters and clams from Porth Navas in Cornwall; langoustines from the Irish Sea via Newlyn in summer or overnight train from Loch Fyne in Argyll in winter. The occasional meat item on the menu comes from the excellent Russel Hume of Exeter, and a local farmer supplies clotted cream and vegetables grown to specification. Richard Stein also cold-smokes his ham, cured in red wine, over tamarisk wood. The airy, ground-floor dining-room with many pictures and mirrors is a place to eat lobster – plainly grilled with butter, or as a salad with tomato and basil, or as part of a grillade of fish and shellfish with fennel. This plain cooking approach is typical. 'I dislike dishes such as lobster thermidor because they smother the flavour of the fresh lobsters,' says Mr Stein. Thermidor is hence employed only with lesser fish. But even so the kitchen can cook elegant dishes – salmon steak in puff pastry with a Muscadet and herb sauce recalls the great days of the Horn of Plenty at Gulworthy.

To merit a rating of 14 the front-of-house operation should have a firmer hand than the young girls manage at the moment, but on the other hand the guiding principles and the quality of the food compensate, and you can go in your yellow wellies if you like. It has taken 11 years for the people around Padstow to discover the restaurant – now it is difficult to get a table and there are plans to expand. The wine list is strong and long on expensive white burgundies, but there is a good range of lesser white areas, including some interesting Alsace wines, such as Gewürztraminer, Cuvée Tradition '79, from Hugel, at £9·90, or a good-value '83 from the Pfaffenheim co-operative at £5·95. Mr Stein recommends them as an aperitif. CELLARMAN'S CHOICE: Chablis premier *cru* Fourchaume from Moreau at £9·85.

CHEF: Richard Stein PROPRIETORS: Richard and Jill Stein
OPEN: Mon to Sat, exc Sat L CLOSED: Jan and Feb; check opening times Nov and Dec
MEALS: 12 to 1.45, 7.30 to 9.30 (10 Sat)
PRICES: £18 (£26), Set L and D £10·50 (£16) CARDS: Access, Amex, Diners, Visa
SEATS: 75. 2 tables outside. Private parties: 24 main room. Children's helpings. Air-conditioned

PAINSWICK Gloucestershire map 2

▲ *Painswick Hotel* [new entry, zero rated]

Kemps Lane, Painswick GL6 6YB
PAINSWICK (0452) 812160 £8–£16

This Georgian house was built as a vicarage, and the private chapel with its ornate ceiling is now the hall. The restaurant is in the former Parish Room where

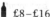

Sunday School was held; it later became the billiard room. Gillian and Michael Hill run the establishment themselves with Gregory Wyatt in the kitchen cooking a set dinner in the style of gravlax, carrot and orange soup, and chicken breast with Pernod and a watercress sauce. There is a vegetarian dinner available and vegetables have been well handled. Good dishes eaten have been the exotic Szechuan-style beef, the Polynesian chicken, pork with Pommery mustard, and also the gateaux to finish. Lunches are good value. It is a serious wine list, with good minor clarets from Cordier, and not overpriced: a helpful selection at the beginning can be used to simplify the choice. Gewürztraminer '81, from Fleith, is £7·50; Ch. le Gardéra '81 is £6·75. More reports, please.

CHEF: Gregory Wyatt PROPRIETORS: Gillian and Michael Hill
OPEN: all week, exc Sun D (residents only) CLOSED: 1 week after Christmas
MEALS: 12.30 to 2, 7.30 to 9.30
PRICES: L £5 (£8), Set Sun L £7·25 (£10), Set D £13 (£16). Service inc CARDS: Access, Amex, Diners, Visa
SEATS: 60. 6 tables outside. Private parties: 60 main room, 25 private room. Car park, 25 places. Vegetarian meals by arrangement. Children's helpings (L only). No cigars/pipes in dining-room. Music
ACCOMMODATION: 15 rooms, 14 with bath/shower. B&B £30 to £40. Children welcome. Baby facilities. Afternoon teas. Garden. TV. Phone. Scenic. Doors close at 11.30

PANGBOURNE Berkshire map 2

▲ *Copper Inn* [new chef, zero rated]

Church Road, Pangbourne RG8 7AR
PANGBOURNE (073 57) 2244 £14–£23

There are fine jars of bottled fruits and chutneys in the square, pine, quarry-tiled dining-room of this smart eighteenth-century hotel, but we are not sure if they ever get eaten. An element of catering may have taken over, which is out of keeping with a restaurant featuring gourmet evenings – there has been stale bread; a few out-of-condition specimens on an otherwise fabulous English cheeseboard from James's of Beckenham; and an odd sauté pasta dish. Nevertheless, there have been good main courses of fried fillet of plaice, duck with a sweet blood orange sauce and roast sirloin. Vegetables are treated with conviction – and usually quite a lot of butter and salt. Meals in the bar are good value, as is an extensive wine list strong in burgundy, wines from Provence and also Alsace: two Vendange Tardive '76s appear – Riesling, from Dopff & Irion, at £13·75 and Gewürztraminer, from Robert Faller, at £13·50. House Chardonnay or Gamay is £5·40.

CHEF: Paul Gilmore PROPRIETOR: Michel Rosso
OPEN: all week MEALS: 12.30 to 2.15, 7.30 to 9.30 (10 Fri and Sat, 9 Sun)
PRICES: £15 (£23), Set L £8·75 (£14), Snacks from 95p (£1·05) CARDS: Access, Amex, Diners, Visa
SEATS: 50. 6 tables outside. Private parties: 12 main room, 10 private room. Car-park, 30 places. Vegetarian meals. Children's helpings. Wheelchair access
ACCOMMODATION: 21 rooms, all with bath/shower. Rooms for disabled. B&B £40·75 to £52·50. Baby facilities. Afternoon teas. Garden. TV. Phone

All letters to the Guide *are acknowledged with a list of changes since we went to press.*

PEASMARSH **East Sussex** map 3

▲ *Flackley Ash* [new entry, zero rated]

Peasmarsh TN31 6YH
PEASMARSH (079 721) 381
on A268, 3m NW of Rye £12

We only have a couple of reports on this hotel, but do know that the Bennetts run a trawler from Rye harbour and that the catch ends up on the dining-room table. They also smoke their own whiting. Otherwise there are steaks. More reports, please.

CHEF: Clive Bennett PROPRIETORS: Clive and Jeanie Bennett
OPEN: all week MEALS: 12.30 to 1.45, 7 to 10
PRICES: Set D from £7·50 (£12), Bar meals from £1·40 (£1·55). Service 10% on parties over 5 CARDS: Access, Amex, Diners, Visa
SEATS: 70. 2 tables outside. Private parties: 100 main room. Car-park, 50 places. Children's helpings. Music
ACCOMMODATION: 20 rooms, all with bath/shower. B&B £26 to £42. Deposit: £20. Children welcome. Baby facilities. Pets welcome. Garden. Croquet. Fishing. Golf. TV. Doors close at 12. Confirm by 6

PENRITH **Cumbria** map 7

Passepartout [12/20]

51 Castlegate, Penrith CA11 7HY
PENRITH (0768) 65852 **Real Food** £19

The Taylors have a kitchen the size of a pocket handkerchief, change the menu every 10 days and serve largely peasant food with strong Far Eastern influences. The menu is original and imaginative, varying from fine gravlax served with an optional glass of caraway-flavoured akvavit, to the Thai dish of chicken and coconut-milk soup. But it also takes in more familiar French dishes, like turbot in champagne sauce or veal sweetbreads normande. The courtyard has been planted with herbs, which are used liberally, and the seasoning is vivid. Sweets concentrate on alcoholic mixes of fruit – pineapple with mint and Kentucky bourbon, and figs soaked in raspberry liqueur. There's an interesting wine list with a powerful Alsace section that includes an unusual red Pinot Noir, Réserve Personnelle '81, from Hugel, at £11·75. The house wines, at £4·95, are well chosen, or try the CELLARMAN'S CHOICE: Zaca Mesa '79, a California Chardonnay, at £10·50.

CHEF: David Taylor PROPRIETORS: David and June Taylor
OPEN: Mon to Sat, D only; Sun D July and Aug and before bank hols
CLOSED: Jan to mid-Feb MEALS: 7.30 to 10
PRICES: £14 (£19) CARDS: Access, Visa
SEATS: 26. Private parties: 30 main room. Vegetarian meals by arrangement. Children welcome. Wheelchair access. Music

CELLARMAN'S CHOICE: This is a wine that is more expensive than the house wine but is good value and fitting for the kind of food served.

PENZANCE Cornwall map 1

▲ *The Abbey* [9/20]

Abbey Street, Penzance TR18 4AR
PENZANCE (0736) 66906 £14

This is a private house run as a hotel with a short menu of honest cooking and which requires booking in advance. Take your own alarm clock: Mrs Cox (formerly Jean Shrimpton) is very possessive about hers and even accused the editor of stealing one. (It's in the drawer in the dresser, where the chambermaid put it.) It is also a mark of the *Guide*'s anonymity at inspections that she told a newspaper that she was inspected by 'a scruffy hitch-hiker'. Can't think who that could be – our man was the one in the Gucci suit.

CHEFS/PROPRIETORS: Mr and Mrs M.D.Cox
OPEN: all week, D only MEALS: 7.30 to 8.30
PRICES: Set D from £10·50 (£14). Service inc
SEATS: 24. Private parties: 24 main room. Car-park, 4 places. Vegetarian meals. Children's helpings. No children under 5. Wheelchair access
ACCOMMODATION: 6 rooms, all with bath/shower. B&B £35 to £40. Deposit: £40. No children under 5. No pets in public rooms. TV. Scenic. Doors close at 10. Confirm by 6

Enzo [11/20]

Penzance TR20 8QM
PENZANCE (0736) 63777
in Newbridge, 3m W of Penzance £14

This family-run Italian fish restaurant now has a conservatory dining-room replete with tiled floors, terracotta tubs holding orange, lemon and grapefruit trees and vines running up the trellised walls. Choose your fish or steaks from a refrigerated cabinet – grey mullet, bream, trout, lemon sole, monkfish. Sea-bass is grilled over charcoal and finished in a pan with mint. More ambitious are the scallops in a cream sauce with apples, artichokes and mushrooms on home-made spaghetti. There is a trolley with starters – good antipasti – and another with puddings. 'Tira mi su' is Italian cream cheese and chocolate on a sponge base. Bread is home-made, and so is most of the pasta. The wine list stays in Italy, except for one champagne. There are two Frascati including the dry di Monteporzio Catone at £5·90. CELLARMAN'S CHOICE: Spanna del Piemonte '74 at £9·10.

CHEF/PROPRIETOR: V. Mauro
OPEN: all week, D only CLOSED: Sun Oct to Whitsun MEALS: 7 to 9.30 (10.30 Sat in summer)
PRICES: £8 (£14) CARDS: Access, Amex, Diners
SEATS: 70. Private parties: 50 main room, 30 private room. Vegetarian meals. Car-park, 30 places. Children's helpings. Wheelchair access

All letters to the Guide *are acknowledged with a list of changes since we went to press.*

'They do a mixed grill which contains 30 ounces of meat, and if you manage to eat it all you are given a signed certificate by the waitress.' (On eating in Greater Manchester)

Harris's [10/20]

46 New Street, Penzance TR18 2LZ
PENZANCE (0736) 64408 £17

Simple, straightforward dishes are served promptly with a smile in this upstairs restaurant. The fish is local and the vegetables fresh. House wine, from Georges Duboeuf, is £4·75.

CHEF: Roger Harris PROPRIETORS: Anne and Roger Harris
OPEN: Mon to Sat MEALS: 12 to 2, 7 to 10
PRICES: £11 (£17). Service 10% CARDS: Amex, Diners, Visa
SEATS: 30. Private parties: 20 main room. Children welcome

Rosie's [new entry, zero rated]

12–13 Chapel Street, Penzance TR18 4AW
PENZANCE (0736) 63540 £16

The great thing about Rosie's is the Today's Fresh Fish menu. Like the meat menu, it changes daily, in the case of fish according to what is available at the nearby Newlyn fish market. Prices are for the most part almost up to London levels, but when Rosie (in real life Mary Rose Gale) says 'prawn cocktail' what she means is fresh prawns with orange and lemon mayonnaise. Crabs are potted and served with grapefruit, a good combination, though it can make the mayonnaise taste funny. Interesting main dishes are the fish stew served in the French way with a strong rouille and a salad; and John Dory fillets with potato, onion, saffron and thyme. A little more cohesion between sauces and the main events would help. The jelly hasn't impressed, but oatmeal meringue with strawberries has. A good choice of 20 wines under £10. More reports, please.

CHEF: Mary Rose Gale PROPRIETORS: Terence and Mary Rose Gale
OPEN: Mon to Sat, D only; D all week July and Aug CLOSED: check Nov to Mar
MEALS: 7 to 10
PRICES: £12 (£16) CARDS: Access, Visa
SEATS: 45. Private parties: 12 main room. Vegetarian meals by arrangement. Children's helpings by arrangement. Wheelchair access. Classical music

PICKERING North Yorkshire map 6A

▲ *Forest and Vale Hotel* [10/20]

Malton Road, Pickering YO18 7DL
PICKERING (0751) 72722 and 73775 £10–£15

A busy, Georgian hotel, well used by locals and useful for touring the Yorkshire Dales and Moors. The food is conventional catering-school-style, but artistically arranged and served with a big smile. The deep-fried Whitby haddock is excellent, and main courses come with lots of vegetables. The menu is far too long to be Real Food, but it is not expensive and portions are large. There are some good bottles on the list of around 50 wines, with some mark-ups in the

The Guide *does not accept free meals.*

region of 100 per cent – Gewürztraminer '83 from Hugel is £5·40 for a half. House Provence is £5·30. CELLARMAN'S CHOICE: Sancerre '83 Domaine Dezat at £10.

CHEF: Tony Spittlehouse PROPRIETORS: Paul Merritt and Donald C.W. Careswell
OPEN: all week MEALS: 12 to 2, 7 to 9.30
PRICES: £11 (£15), Set L £5·25 (£10), Set D £8·50 (£13), Snacks from 70p (80p)
CARDS: Access, Amex, Diners, Visa
SEATS: 60. 5 tables outside. Private parties: 140 main room, 40 private room. Car-park, 70 places. Vegetarian meals by arrangement. Children's helpings. Smart dress preferred. Wheelchair access. Music
ACCOMMODATION: 23 rooms, 18 with bath/shower. Rooms for disabled. B&B £19 to £38. Children welcome. Baby facilities. No pets in public rooms. Afternoon teas. Garden. TV. Doors close at 12. Confirm by 6

PICKWORTH Leicestershire map 6

▲ *Manor House* [13/20]

Pickworth PE9 4DT
CASTLE BYTHAM (078 081) 525
off A1, 6m NW of Stamford **Real Food** £17

Go up a single-track road, over two cattle-grids and through a field of sheep to get to this large, stone, mid-Victorian house. It looks much like a rectory and has been tastefully restored in William Morris/Laura Ashley style with Victorian and Edwardian furniture and original fireplaces. Roy and Veronica Richards run it as both their home and the office for his wine business, and sadly they will only open for dinner on Fridays and Saturdays in 1986, except by arrangement. The five-course dinners are good value; the food is Real and the cooking accomplished, from pea or spinach and coconut soup with yeasty bread through fine fish dishes of hake in prawn sauce; salmon with sorrel; and brill deauvillaise. Main courses, too, show a dexterity of technique and ideas – lamb with an hollandaise served plated with four new potatoes, four spears of asparagus and a separate bowl of red and green lettuces with a lemon vinaigrette; casserole of pork with Gewürztraminer; chicken breast with a sharp reduction of sherry vinegar. All the quartet of cheeses – especially the goats' – are well maintained, and sweets carry through the sense of adventure – poached pear with strawberry sorbet and cardamom sauce. The rating would be higher if the dining-room, which Veronica Richards runs with an assured smile, were open more often. But Mr Richards' wine business seduces him; the only consolation is a fantastic cellar that contains some of the best-value wines in this book, especially for burgundy, claret and Rhônes.

CHEF: Roy Richards PROPRIETORS: Roy and Veronica Richards
OPEN: Fri and Sat D CLOSED: 22 Dec to 2 Jan MEALS: 7.30 to 9.30
PRICES: Set D £14·50 (£17). Service inc
SEATS: 20. Private parties: 20 main room. Car-park, 30 places. Children welcome. No smoking in dining-room
ACCOMMODATION: 2 rooms, both with bath/shower. B&B £15 to £25. Children welcome. Baby facilities. No pets

An index of restaurants by name appears at the back of the Guide.

PINNER Greater London map 3

La Giralda [10/20]

66 Pinner Green, Pinner HA5 2AB
01-868 3429 £7–£12

There's a cheap lunch for £3·50 in this bustling Spanish restaurant with four dining-rooms and one of the best cellars of Riojas in Britain. The menu is mostly tourist Spanish – gazpacho, chicken fried in garlic oil, chateaubriand. Fish is fresh and 'nothing is frozen or processed in any way'. The wines offer remarkable value.

CHEFS: David Brown and Derek Knight PROPRIETOR: David Brown
OPEN: Tue to Sat CLOSED: Aug MEALS: 12 to 2.30, 6.30 to 10.30
PRICES: Set L from £3·50 (£7), Set D from £8·50 (£12). £1·50 discount to diners vacating by 8 CARDS: Access, Amex, Diners, Visa
SEATS: 120. Private parties: 50 main room, 35 and 16 private rooms. Vegetarian meals. Children's helpings. Wheelchair access (also WC). Air-conditioned

PLUMTREE Nottinghamshire map 5

Perkins Bar Bistro [11/20]

Old Railway Station, Plumtree NG12 5NA
PLUMTREE (060 77) 3695 £12

Without much doubt the best railway station food in England – and it's not run by British Rail. Tony and Wendy Perkins have converted this 1880 former Midland Railway Company station, with views over the countryside, into an informal bistro making good use of inexpensive ingredients, such as salted topsides and ox-tongue. Fish comes direct from the boats at Filey; fresh herbs are by post from Kent. Smoked dishes, such as chicken, salmon, excellent haddock with a cream sauce, are one theme and classical dishes, like crème Crécy (one of many good soups) or blanquette d'agneau à l'ancienne, another. Herb butter garnishes the calf's liver but there is marchand de vin butter for the steaks. Vegetables are fresh and varied; the sweets are calorific and industriously presented. Lunch is cheaper than dinner. The supplementary wine list that changes every two months is more interesting than the 25 standard bottles on the main list. House French is £3·90.

CHEF: Tony Perkins PROPRIETORS: Tony and Wendy Perkins
OPEN: Tue to Sat MEALS: 12 to 2, 7 to 10 (11 Fri and Sat)
PRICES: £8 (£12), Snacks from £1 (£1·10) CARDS: Access, Amex
SEATS: 65. 6 tables outside. Private parties: 12 main room, 30 private room. Car-park, 40 places. Vegetarian meals. Children's helpings. Wheelchair access. Music

Restaurant tricks (2): By law, prices on the menu displayed in the window must include VAT. But no such obligation applies to the menu inside.

Entries are compiled from the unsolicited reports from readers and are checked by inspectors; each restaurant is asked to supply details of its operation. Report forms can be found at the back of the Guide.

PLYMOUTH Devon map 1

Clouds [new entry, zero rated]

102 Tavistock Place, Plymouth PL4 8AY
PLYMOUTH (0752) 262567 £13–£17

Behind the library and down some steps. Clouds is a bar with an open fire and serves dishes such as crispy-skinned duck Montmorency and rack of lamb with minted onion sauce. More reports, please.

CHEF: K.P.Belt PROPRIETORS: G.B.White and K.P.Belt
OPEN: Tue to Sat, exc Sat L MEALS: 12 to 2, 7.30 to 11
PRICES: L £8 (£13), D £11 (£17), Set D £9·75 (£15) CARDS: Access, Amex, Diners, Visa
SEATS: 35. 3 tables outside. Private parties: 35 main room. Vegetarian meals by arrangement. Children's helpings. Music

Hosteria Romana [new entry, zero rated]

58 Southside Street, The Barbican, Plymouth PL1 2LA
PLYMOUTH (0752) 668827 and 669707 £15–£17

We have good reports on this Italian restaurant which gets its fish from the local boats and has the traditional ten variations on veal. The pasta, from lasagne to spaghetti carbonara, has been good, and the guitarist serenades. The chef, Marco Colombo, assures us that everything is fresh and 'the restaurant is unique'. Classy and expensive collection of Italian wines. More reports, please.

CHEF: Marco Colombo PROPRIETORS: Enrico Moreschi, Sabato Cinque and Marco Colombo
OPEN: all week MEALS: 12 to 2, 7 to 11
PRICES: £11 (£17), Set D £10 (£15) CARDS: Access, Amex, Diners, Visa
SEATS: 120. 10 tables outside. Private parties: 90 main room, 50 private room. Vegetarian meals. No children under 8 at D. Smart dress preferred. Wheelchair access. Organ and guitar music

Mister Barrett's [new entry, zero rated]

36 Admiralty Street, Stonehouse, Plymouth PL1 3RU
PLYMOUTH (0752) 21177 £15

Stephen Barrett was in the *Guide* for two years at The Piermasters and re-opened here in the summer of 1984 as chef and proprietor. Fish and shellfish are well bought, well cooked, and well priced, and you get what the fleet's brought in: red mullet, monkfish, squid and mussels. Sometimes there are simple dishes, but the more varied and interesting ones seem more popular, such as Staverton pork fry, with smoked gammon, liver, sausage and mushrooms. Thomas Sellick's sweetbreads are poached in Sauternes and served with chestnut paste; fillet of Devon steer is cooked with bacon and Beaujolais. Short wine list with house French at £4·95. CELLARMAN'S CHOICE: Clyst '83, from Exeter, at £6·95.

CHEF/PROPRIETOR: Stephen Barrett
OPEN: Mon to Sat, exc Sat L MEALS: 12 to 2.30, 7 to 11
PRICES: £11 (£15) CARDS: Access, Visa
SEATS: 28. Private parties: 32 main room. Vegetarian meals. Children's helpings. Classical music and jazz

POLPERRO Cornwall map 1

The Kitchen [12/20]

Fish Na Bridge, Polperro PL13 2RQ
POLPERRO (0503) 72780 **Real Food** £11

A small, uncluttered restaurant with a big fire in winter. Fine local crabs are dressed or made into fritters, and the steaks are of good quality, whether plain or au poivre. Other good dishes are potted Stilton with port; tomato and mint soup; lobster; and the sea-trout with fresh herbs. To finish, the banana toffee pie gets many votes. The nearest parking is 200 yards up the hill. The Porters are considerate hosts. There are 30 well chosen wines from all over the globe. CELLARMAN'S CHOICE: Bulgarian Sauvignon blanc at £5·95.

CHEF: Judith Porter PROPRIETORS: David and Judith Porter
OPEN: Tue to Sun D only, June to Oct; Tue to Sat D Mar to May and Oct; Fri and Sat Nov to Mar MEALS: 6.30 to 9.30
PRICES: Set D from £6·95 (£11) CARDS: Access, Amex, Diners, Visa
SEATS: 22. Vegetarian meals. Children's helpings (at 6.30). Classical music

POOLE Dorset map 2

Gulliver's [new entry, zero rated]

292 Sandbanks Road, Lilliput, Poole BH14 8HX
CANFORD CLIFFS (0202) 708810 £15

An intimate French restaurant whose hospitality is due mainly to Josephine Pearce's charm in the dining-room. For the last five years she and husband Richard have been fighting hard against the pervading mediocrity of food standards that blight seaside towns caught between a retired population of locals on fixed incomes and an influx of holidaymakers when the sun chooses to shine. As a result, the menu is fashioned around such conservative favourites (no criticism) as seafood pancakes and five variations of steak. But other dishes have poise too – lamb with tarragon; skewers of king prawns and fillet steak grilled with garlic butter and served with braised rice; beef Wellington with a classy madeira sauce; and salmon en papillote have all been good. To finish, there is lemon soufflé or flambé chocolate meringue with Sambuca. If you order when booking, Mr Pearce is happy to prepare bouillabaisse or lobster dishes. Vegetarians are always catered for. Some better wines would suit the food. More reports, please.

CHEF: Richard Pearce PROPRIETORS: Richard and Josephine Pearce
OPEN: Tue to Sat, D only, plus Mon during summer CLOSED: first 3 weeks Jan
MEALS: 7 to 10.30
PRICES: £11 (£15) CARDS: Access, Visa
SEATS: 32. 2 tables outside. Private parties: 36 main room. Vegetarian meals. Children's helpings. Wheelchair access. Music

The Guide is always anxious to recruit new inspectors. If you would like to apply, write to the editor enclosing a) a detailed report on a restaurant where you have eaten and b) a comparative study of restaurants known to you.

▲ *The Mansion House* [12/20]

Thames Street, Poole BH15 1JN
POOLE (0202) 685666 £12–£18

It used to be necessary to be a member here to eat – £20 a year if you lived within a 30-mile radius, £12 for members from further afield – and there's not much else about. We understand, however, that by 1986 membership rules will be lifted. The residential, late-Georgian house contrasts with much of modernised Poole. Fish is good, from halibut with crab and courgette mousse, to large local crab salads. Conventional dishes, such as smoked salmon, and venison in red wine, are balanced by less usual items: Kenya beans and limes in the prawn salad, peach and saffron sauce with the salmon crêpe, and nut butter and avocado with the calf's liver. Rooms are comfortable. Respectable wines with CELLARMAN'S CHOICE: Ch. Grivière '82, from the Médoc, at £8·35.

CHEF: Pierre Magnin PROPRIETORS: Robert and Valerie Leonard
OPEN: all week, exc Sun L CLOSED: 2 weeks at Christmas MEALS: 12 to 2.15, 7.30 to 10
PRICES: £11 (£18), Set L from £7·95 (£12), Set D £12·50 (£17), Snacks from 90p (£1). Service 10% CARDS: Access, Amex, Diners, Visa
SEATS: 65. Private parties: 100 main room, 31 and 12 private rooms. Car-park, 40 places. Children's helpings. Jacket and tie. No jeans. Music. Air-conditioned
ACCOMMODATION: 19 rooms, all with bath/shower. B&B £38 to £56. No children under 8. Dogs welcome. Afternoon teas. TV. Phone

POOL IN WHARFEDALE West Yorkshire map 5

▲ *Pool Court* [13/20]

Poole Bank,
Pool in Wharfedale LS21 1EH
ARTHINGTON (0532) 842288/9
and 842414 Real Food £16–£24

This has the feel of a very fine restaurant indeed, smart without being dull or stuffy. The hallway desk sends you to the bar on the right or to the dining-room on the left, which buzzes as the crew of young waiters whip their way around the tables. The menu is grand opera – avocado and langoustines salad, liver with citrus fruit, duck with limes, and always a vegetarian dish of the day. Close attention is paid to the small details – the savoury cheese sweetmeats; the choice of fresh rolls; the intensity of the Jerusalem artichoke soup; the brilliant Turkish delights with coffee, and a handsome wine list that does not ignore the fact that some people want to drink at the £5 level. It has Real Food too, as witness the breakfast of free-range eggs with a platter of sausage, kidneys, bacon, and tomatoes. . . . The four new rooms are sheer runaway luxury (albeit at a price) and in a class of their own: your own combination to unlock the door, a safe (behind the picture on the wall), a nude sculpture, alarm clock, the 200-strong wine list left in the room alongside Hugh Johnson's *World Atlas of Wine*, slippers, TV, *Radio* and *TV Times*, dried fruit, *Harpers & Queen*, flowers, a drinks wardrobe including bottles of champagne and glasses, pot-pourri, a leather jewellery box, heat thermostat, writing-paper, huge mirrors, neat auburn lamps, zig-zag pink and green wallpaper, and inlaid lights. And then there's the bathroom – robes, fancy taps, a shower cap, a clockwork frog in the bath, lavender room fragrance, talcum powder, hand lotion, camomile soap, four spotlights over the basin mirror like a Hollywood dressing-room, a plant, and even a candle. A worthy award-winner.

CHEF: Melvin Jordan PROPRIETOR: Michael Gill
OPEN: Tue to Sat, D only CLOSED: 2 weeks July to Aug, 2 weeks at Christmas
MEALS: 6.30 to 9.30
PRICES: Set D £10 to £18 (£16 to £24) CARDS: Access, Amex, Diners, Visa
SEATS: 65. Private parties: 32 main room, 24 private room. Vegetarian meals. Car-park, 65 places. Smart dress preferred. Children's helpings. Wheelchair access. Air-conditioned
ACCOMMODATION: 4 rooms, all with bath/shower. B&B £42 to £67. No pets. Garden. Air-conditioning. TV. Phone. Confirm by 6 [GHG]

POUGHILL Cornwall map 1

▲ *Reeds* [11/20]

Poughill EX23 9EL
BUDE (0288) 2841
1m NE of Bude £18

It is necessary to stay overnight to eat at Margaret Jackson's peaceful turn-of-the-century house set in four acres of beautifully restored gardens with lily-ponds, an orchard and many rare shrubs. In spring there are wild daffodils, snowdrops and violets. The menu is built up around the best produce that Cornwall can provide. Fish is from Bideford, free-range eggs from Mrs Jackson's daughter's birds. Meat comes down from the excellent Mr Russel Hume of Exeter. Vegetables are from the garden. The style ranges from Elizabeth David's pork en terrine to Michel Guérard's guinea-fowl with smoked bacon to the Turkish imam bayeldi. Notably good have been lemon sole with a prawn and wine sauce, smoked salmon pâté (the fish flown in from Limerick), and veal with buttered noodles. There is no stinting on the cream, which comes in a separate jug, served with the very good sweets such as almond meringue. There is a useful supply of half-bottles on the short well-chosen list that concentrates on the £5 to £7 range. The rating is low because of the restrictions on the eating.

CHEF/PROPRIETOR: Margaret Jackson
OPEN: Fri to Mon, D only CLOSED: Christmas MEALS: 8
PRICES: Set D £15 (£18). Service inc
SEATS: 10. Private parties: 10 main room. Car-park, 10 places. No children under 16. Smart dress preferred. One sitting
ACCOMMODATION: 3 rooms, all with bath/shower. B&B £35 to £60. Deposit: £10. No children under 16. Garden. Scenic. Doors close at 12. Confirm by 1 [GHG]

POULTON-LE-FYLDE Lancashire map 5

The Stocks [10/20]

2 Queens Square, Poulton-le-Fylde FY6 7BS
BLACKPOOL (0253) 882294 £10–£17

This German restaurant in a 400-year-old cottage takes its name from the original stocks that stand opposite. 'When we call something home-made, it really is,' promises Charles Ruppert. The Black Forest ham is served with a glass of kirsch, and for main courses there are clever variations on steak, or Councillor's Bowl – beef fillet, pork and veal steak served on sauté potatoes and vegetables. Lunch is inexpensive. Fifteen German wines plus some unvintaged French. CELLARMAN'S CHOICE: Lauffener Jungfer '81, a red wine made from Schwarzriesling, at £6·40.

CHEFS/PROPRIETORS: Charles and Sheila Ruppert
OPEN: Thur and Fri L, Tue to Sat D CLOSED: last 2 weeks Aug MEALS: 11.30 to 2, 7 to 10
PRICES: L £7 (£10), D £13 (£17) CARD: Access
SEATS: 60. Private parties: 36 main room, 24 private room. Vegetarian meals by arrangement. Children's helpings. Smart dress preferred. Music

POWBURN Northumberland map 7

▲ *Breamish House Hotel* [11/20]

Powburn NE66 4LL
POWBURN (066 578) 266
on A697, 1m N of Glanton £12–£17

A former shooting-lodge in five acres of woodland on the edge of a National Park. Over the last four years Graham Taylor has built it up slowly into a comfortable hotel where the set, four-course menus are less conservative than they appear at first glance. There has been good, rough-textured pork and liver pâté, flavoursome dark mushroom soup, and chicken breast with a tarragon sauce. The meat is of a high quality. Vegetables come in quartets, such as broccoli, carrots, braised celery and potatoes. Stilton has been in good condition, and the sweets are creamy. The 70 wines are exceptionally good value – Châteauneuf-du-Pape, Domaine de Mont-Redon '81, is £7·25; Muscat '81, from Riegenbach-Moser, is £5·75.

CHEF: Patricia Portus PROPRIETOR: Graham Taylor
OPEN: all week, D only, and Sun L CLOSED: Jan MEALS: 1, 8 to 9
PRICES: Set L £8 (£12), Set D £13 (£17). Cheaper L by arrangement
SEATS: 30. Private parties: 8 main room. Car-park, 30 places. Vegetarian meals by arrangement. Children's helpings (Sun L only). No children under 12. Jacket and tie preferred. No smoking. Wheelchair access (also WC). One sitting
ACCOMMODATION: 10 rooms, all with bath/shower. B&B £27 to £45. Deposit: £10 per person. No children under 12. Pets by arrangement. Afternoon teas. Garden. TV. Phone. Scenic. Doors close at 12. Confirm by 6 [GHG]

PRESTBURY Cheshire map 5

The Galley [10/20]

New Road, Prestbury SK10 4HP
PRESTBURY (0625) 829466 £10–£12

Mr Forster was a fishmonger before opening this good-value restaurant in a row of terraced houses. The decor is basic but the atmosphere is relaxed and the menu

If you cannot honour a restaurant booking, always phone to cancel.

to the point – good fish dishes, such as mussels with celery and onion soup, and baked haddock florentine, backed up with steaks and good beef casserole. To finish there have been smooth chocolate pots and chewy meringues. Service is not that polished, but the bill is not that big. Blanc de Blancs is £4·95.

CHEFS/PROPRIETORS: The Forster family
OPEN: Tue to Sat, D only CLOSED: Aug MEALS: 7.15 to 10.15 (10.30 Fri and Sat)
PRICES: £7 (£12), Set D from £5·70 (£10) CARD: Access
SEATS: 60. Private parties: 24 main room. Vegetarian meals by arrangement. Children's helpings (D only)

PRESTON Lancashire map 5

Tiggis [8/20]

38–42 Guildhall Street, Preston PR1 3NU
PRESTON (0772) 58527 £10

Hidden away behind the high street and not very well lit (parking is difficult), this is an Italian answer to the Hard Rock Café (see London), only the queues are inside, warm and usually drinking: at weekends the wait for a table may be an hour. Beef dishes, such as Stroganoff and medallions braised in Barolo, have been good. The pasta is reliable and the garlic bread pungent. Coffee is weak but the atmosphere is lively. House Trebbiano is £4·60.

CHEF: Flaviano Donè PROPRIETOR: Lino Della Pesca
OPEN: Mon to Sat MEALS: 12 to 2, 6.30 to 11.30
PRICES: £7 (£10). Service inc CARDS: Access, Visa
SEATS: 180. Vegetarian meals. Children's helpings. Wheelchair access. Italian music

PRIORS HARDWICK Warwickshire map 2

Butchers Arms [10/20]

Priors Hardwick CV28 8FM
BYFIELD (0327) 60504
5m SE of Southam £14–£17

Historically, inns were often built to feed and house the men building the church, but the Butchers Arms predates its church and claims to date from the fourteenth century. It is tucked away on the edge of the village (take the Boddington Road off the A361), surrounded by four-and-a-half acres of gardens. Lino Pires' red, plush, heavily Edwardian dining-room has built up a local reputation as the place to go for Sunday lunch or for a big occasion. The menu is big, and big on Stroganoff and grilled sole and even beluga caviare (£16). It is aptly named because there are plenty of steaks, which well match the impressive

'Nouvelle cuisine *is all very well for summer, with its fresh young stuff daintily boiled and steamed. But in winter I can do without subtlety. When I eat out in winter I like things to taste of the fire – I want something zingy and palate-boggling, real belly-timber with a touch of the Hallelujah Chorus (not a modern solo Japanese instrument).'* (On eating in Yorkshire)

showing of vintage clarets, burgundies and, a rarity, good Portuguese.
CELLARMAN'S CHOICE: Dão Reserva '73 at £9.

CHEF/PROPRIETOR: Lino Pires
OPEN: all week, exc Sat L and Sun D MEALS: 12 to 2, 7.15 to 10
PRICES: £10 (£17), Set L £7·50 (£14), Set D £7·50 (£14), Bar snacks from £1·25 (£2). Service inc
SEATS: 100. 6 tables outside. Private parties: 35 main room. Car-park, 120 places. Smart dress preferred. Children welcome. Wheelchair access (also wc). Air-conditioned

PULBOROUGH West Sussex map 3

Stane Street Hollow [12/20]

Codmore Hill, Pulborough RH20 1BG
PULBOROUGH (079 82) 2819
on A29, at N end of village **Real Food** £17

René Kaiser might earn an entry in a *Good Gardening Guide* – his restaurant is self-sufficient in vegetables for 10 months of the year and the eggs are from his own free-range chickens. He also smokes fish out of Newhaven and Brighton as well as meats for dishes such as pork with madeira sauce garnished with pears and cranberries. After 10 years he has not lost his sense of excitement for food – croquettes of mixed sweetbreads and brains are fried and served with a blackcurrant vinegar dressing; pheasant, venison and rabbit have contributed to a fine casserole; and his own cockerels have been made into fruitful curries. Yet he also offers some classical dishes that are protected species these days, such as veal Marengo. To finish there has been quark cheesecake with redcurrant purée, and blackberries served warm with cream and ice-cream. Even the wine list looks like an allotment, with short, orderly rows of Bordeaux, hocks, burgundies and Clicquot champagnes. Trimbach's magnificent Tokay '81 at £7·25 figures from Alsace, and from Switzerland's Valais there is the CELLARMAN'S CHOICE: Rhonetaler '83, Pinot Noir, at £7·95.

CHEF: René Kaiser PROPRIETORS: René and Ann Kaiser
OPEN: Tue to Sat, exc Tue and Sat L CLOSED: 2 weeks May, 3 weeks Oct
MEALS: 12.30 to 1.15, 7.30 to 9.15
PRICES: £12 (£17), Cheaper set L available
SEATS: 35. Private parties: 24 main room, 16 private room. Car-park, 14 places. Children's helpings

RAVENSTONEDALE Cumbria map 7

▲ *Black Swan* [new entry, zero rated]

Ravenstonedale CA17 4NG
NEWBIGGIN-ON-LUNE (058 73) 204
4m SW of Kirkby Stephen £9–£14

A refurbished hotel seven minutes off the M6, now run by a husband and wife. Christopher Davy cooks in the modern style, putting plenty of emphasis on local ingredients including seasonal game, beef and lamb, and Eden salmon and sea-trout, as well as offering Cotherstone cheese and goats' cheese from Tynedale Dairy. Dishes range from trout en papillote and lemon sole poached in vermouth, to ragout of beef with walnuts and oranges, or lamb and rosemary pie, all served with colourful, attractively presented vegetables. Alison takes care of the sweets and makes hearty, old-fashioned puddings as well as light, healthy confections. No TV or telephone disturbs the peace in the pastel bedrooms, and there are superb full English breakfasts to start the day. A modest, but varied wine list organised by 'character' – aromatic, full bodied and dry, fresh and light. More reports, please.

CHEFS/PROPRIETORS: Christopher and Alison Davy
OPEN: Mon to Sat, D only, Sun L (Bar L all week, exc Mon Oct to Apr)
CLOSED: 1st week Nov, and Jan, Feb MEALS: 12.30 to 1.45 (1.15 Sun), 7.30 to 8.45
PRICES: Set L £6·50 (£9), Set D from £11·25 (£14), Bar meals from £2·20. Service inc
CARDS: Access, Amex, Visa
SEATS: 24. Private parties: 30 main room. Car-park, 20 places. Children's helpings. Smart dress preferred. Wheelchair access (2 steps; also wc)
ACCOMMODATION: 6 rooms, 3 with bath/shower. B&B £20 to £32. Children welcome. Baby facilities. No pets in public rooms. Garden. Fishing. Golf. Doors close at 11.30. Confirm by 6 [GHG]

REDLYNCH Wiltshire — map 2

▲ *Langley Wood* [10/20]

Hamptworth Road, Redlynch SP5 2PB
ROMSEY (0794) 390348
off B3080, 7m SE of Salisbury, between
Downton and Landford — £12–£15

A small country house on the edge of the New Forest, run mainly as a restaurant. Meats, such as devilled kidneys, are better than the sauces they come with – there is not much evidence of apricot and Cointreau in the veal terrine, for example. Spinach and mushroom pancake is covered in Mornay sauce. Vegetables are plentiful; puddings are chocolaty. Bread and cakes are made in-house. More reports, please.

CHEF: Sylvia Rosen PROPRIETORS: David and Sylvia Rosen
OPEN: Mon to Sat D, Sun L MEALS: 12.45 to 2, 7.30 to 11
PRICES: £11 (£15), Set Sun L £8·50 (£12) CARDS: Access, Amex, Diners, Visa
SEATS: 30. Private parties: 65 main room. Car-park, 25 places. Vegetarian meals. Children's helpings (Sun L only). Smart dress preferred. No cigars/pipes in dining-room. Wheelchair access (also wc). Classical music
ACCOMMODATION: 3 rooms. B&B £11 to £22. Children welcome. Baby facilities. Dogs welcome. Afternoon teas. Garden

REETH North Yorkshire — map 7

▲ *Burgoyne Hotel* [10/20]

Reeth DL11 6SN
RICHMOND (0748) 84292 — £9–£12

From any direction it is a handsome drive to this hotel. Its views and the surrounding countryside invite exploration. The Cordingleys have been here since 1969 and still run the place with friendliness, so that it feels like home only on a bigger scale. The use of local foodstuffs,such as Cumberland sausages, local cheeses, and Jersey cream, underlines the strength of the short, middle-of-the-road set menus. Apart from the melon garnished with glacé cherry there is fine roast beef and Yorkshire pudding with plenty of fresh vegetables for Sunday lunch; other main courses, such as roast duck with cherry sauce, and steak and kidney pie, are continually endorsed. A good place for a weekend break. The rating is dropped one point because standards elsewhere in the region have risen. The wine list has 40 inexpensive wines.

CHEFS: P.A.Cordingley and K.Vitty PROPRIETORS: C.S.P.andP.A.Cordingley
OPEN: all week, D only, and Sun L CLOSED: Nov to Easter MEALS: 1 to 1.45, 7.30 to 8.15
PRICES: Set L £5·25 (£9), Set D £8·30 (£12), Snacks from £1·90 (£2·10)
SEATS: 40. 6 tables outside. Private parties: 40 main room. Car-park, 8 places. Vegetarian meals by arrangement. Children's helpings
ACCOMMODATION: 10 rooms. B&B £12·50, D, B&B £20·50. Children welcome. Pets welcome. Scenic. Confirm by 5 [GHG]

RICHMOND Surrey — map 3

BACKGROUND BRIEFING: *Richmond bursts with restaurants. There are a number of cheap places of interest, notably the two branches of Pasta House on Richmond Hill and Kew Road, and Mrs Beaton's, co-operatively run with a different cook every day. Of the burger bars, try the Village in Friars Stile Road. There are few recommendations for the plentiful Italian restaurants. Of the many Chinese, nearly all are too Westernised to be considered for inclusion.*

Lichfield's [14/20]

Lichfield Terrace, Sheen Road, Richmond TW9 1AS
01-940 5236 — Real Food £17–£29

Redecorated in yellow with new narrow, high-backed chairs. The style is that of a chic restaurant attached to a grand hotel: crisp and neat with good, unhurried service and efficient air-conditioning. The menus continue to excite. Novel combinations are artfully achieved, for example the artichoke and hazel-nut salad starter; scallops sauté in ginger butter with a mousse of their corals; or an autumnal dessert of apple in three forms on the same plate – tart with ginger, ice-cream with raisins, and a charlotte. Other recommended dishes are the duck foie gras and orange salad, noisettes of lamb, and even the steaks. Fish, though, is Stephen Bull's best subject. Excellent small vegetables come on a separate plate. Odd flaws appear every so often, notably in the pastry department, but sauces are generally fine enough to save the day. Old favourites, such as the St Emilion au chocolat, still please more than the brown bread ice-cream. The menu goes a bit over the top saying how good everything is – 'dishes suggested by today's market', or 'an interesting selection of cheese' – but the quest for cottage-industry supplies brings wild mushrooms from Berkshire and Oxford, herbs from Somerset, and dandelion, nettle and nasturtium leaves from a local gardener,

'In my experience, the quality of Chinese food is in inverse ratio to the pattern of the wallpaper.' (On eating in Surrey)

and these underwrite the quality of the meals. The wine list runs to well over 100 particularly well-chosen bottles, of which about 10 fall under the £10 mark, including '82 Alsace Rieslings from Hugel and Gisselbrecht and the sparkling Cristal de Pinot Gris '82 from Dopff & Irion. House bottles are Sauvignon de Bordeaux (white) and Torres Coronas (red), each £6·50.

CHEF: Stephen Bull PROPRIETORS: Stephen and Lindsay Bull
OPEN: Tue to Sat, exc Sat L CLOSED: 1 week Christmas, 1 week May, 2 weeks Sept
MEALS: 12.15 to 2, 7 to 10.30
PRICES: £21 (£29), Set L from £14 (£17). Service inc set only CARDS: Access, Amex
SEATS: 38. Private parties: 36 main room. Children's helpings. Wheelchair access. Air-conditioned

Red Lion [10/20]

18 Red Lion Street, Richmond TW9 1RW
01-940 2371 and 948 1961 £13–£18

The waiters are helpful in suggesting interesting dishes in this Peking/Szechuan restaurant, the least ostentatious of all the Richmond/Kew orientals but over the years the most reliable. Garlic and ginger figure heavily on the menu. The aromatic crispy duck could be improved, but other dishes are well up to the standard of westernised Chinese restaurants – the cold meats and fish with pickles to start; abalone with Chinese mushrooms and bamboo shoots; king prawns in hot sea-spiced garlic sauce; and pan-fried noodles. The set meals are good value. House wine is £2·90 for half a carafe.

CHEFS: Luc Cuong Thai and C.K.Howe PROPRIETORS: Cantatia Ltd
OPEN: all week MEALS: 12 to 2.30, 6 to 11.30
PRICES: £10 (£18), Set L from £8 (£13), Set D from £10 (£15). Service 10% CARDS: Access, Amex, Diners, Visa
SEATS: 88. Private parties: 44 main room, 44 private room. Vegetarian meals. Children welcome. Wheelchair access. Music. Air-conditioned

Restaurant Madeleine [new entry, zero rated]

122 Sheen Road, Richmond TW9 1UR
01-948 4445 £16

In case you might miss the point the menu assures diners that the vegetable terrine with mayonnaise is, 'very special,' and the chicken stuffed with crab, 'very unusual.' But this is a small, classically inclined little French restaurant run with good humour and offering 30 or so dishes a night. There have been good reports on the lamb marseillaise, minced duck and grapefruit, and pork with bananas and chilli. There are simpler dishes, such as Dutch calf's liver. To finish there are alcoholic ice-creams and sorbets, or rhubarb pancake. The short wine list has some good Rhônes and medal-winning '82 Alsace wines. House Bordeaux is £5·20. More reports, please.

CHEF: J.Grebot PROPRIETOR: Mrs Rouillard
OPEN: Tue to Sat, D only CLOSED: 2 weeks Sept MEALS: 7.30 to 10.45
PRICES: £10 (£16) CARDS: Amex, Visa
SEATS: 28. Vegetarian meals by arrangement. No children under 12. Wheelchair access. Music

RIPON North Yorkshire map 7

Old Deanery [11/20]

Minster Road, Ripon HG4 1QS
RIPON (0765) 3518 £15

In a former ecclesiastical building in the shade of the cathedral Jurg and Jane Bleiker (he trained in Switzerland, she trained as a customer) take a relaxed attitude to everything. This extends from no dress rules and no bookings to casual service and laissez-faire sauces: there has been too much cream with the Swiss veal special and an unworthy sauce with the Delice Helvetia (spaghetti mixed with cream, cheese, peppers and mushrooms, made into a rissole and deep-fried). Minuscule vegetables. Cream also trickles through the hot smokies with cheese and whisky, and salmon with strawberries, but there are crispy mussels in beery batter served with a prawn sauce, home-made spicy sausages with onion sauce, and Nidderdale trout in green ginger wine with almonds. Wines include house Italian at £2·60 for half a litre.
CELLARMAN'S CHOICE: Crozes-Hermitage, Caves St Pierre '81 at £7·95.

CHEF: Jurg Bleiker PROPRIETORS: Jurg and Jane Bleiker
OPEN: Mon to Sat, exc Sat L CLOSED: 25 and 26 Dec MEALS: 12 to 2, 7 to 10
PRICES: £10 (£15), Bar meals from £1·95. Service inc
SEATS: 70. 6 tables outside. Private parties: 30 main room. Car-park, 30 places. Vegetarian meals. Children's helpings. Wheelchair access (1 step; public WC for disabled 25 yds). Music

RIPPONDEN West Yorkshire map 5

Over the Bridge [12/20]

Millfold, Ripponden HX6 4DJ
HALIFAX (0422) 823722 £19

The river Ryburn runs under the bridge. There is no sign outside, but the pub can offer directions. A good-value, four-course menu at £13·50 offers half a dozen starters and mains, separated by a soup or sorbet. Vegetarians are looked after with eggs florentine and mushroom flan. Good meat dishes – ballotine of duck, pork with crackling – may be followed by tangerine sorbet, superb but messy rhubarb meringues, or English cheeses. Service is local. In place of house wine a Muscadet '82 is served by the glass.

CHEF/PROPRIETOR: Ian H. Beaumont
OPEN: Mon to Sat, D only CLOSED: bank hols MEALS: 7.30 to 9.30
PRICES: Set D £13·50 (£19) CARD: Amex
SEATS: 48. Private parties: 14 main room. Car-park, 50 places. No children under 12. Smart dress preferred. Wheelchair access

The 1987 Guide will appear before Christmas 1986, so reports are particularly important in the spring. Report forms are at the back of this book, but just write a letter if you prefer. Address them to The Good Food Guide, *Freepost, 14 Buckingham Street, London WC2N 6BR. No stamp is necessary if you post in the UK.*

ROADE Northamptonshire — map 3

▲ *Roadhouse Restaurant* [11/20]

16 High Street, Roade NN7 2NW
ROADE (0604) 863372 — £11–£15

Susan and Christopher Kewley charm their guests in their unpretentious and relaxed little restaurant. The walls are terracotta-coloured, which doesn't distract much from the food, and there is a big fire left over from the pub that was here before. The Kewleys use local produce and run a modern-style menu from which the leeks in pastry cases, guinea-fowl en croûte, venison with a sauce sharpened with chocolate, and the vegetables have all been good. Meals end on an up with lemon syllabub and meringues with cream and more chocolate. Everything is made on the premises. House Côtes du Rhône '83 is £4·50.

CHEF: Christopher Kewley PROPRIETORS: Christopher and Susan Kewley
OPEN: Tue to Sat, exc Sat L MEALS: 12 to 2, 7 to 10
PRICES: £11 (£15), Set L £7 (£11), Set D £21 (£25) for two. Service 10%
CARDS: Access, Amex, Visa
SEATS: 32. Private parties: 40 main room. Car-park, 15 places. Children welcome. Wheelchair access (also wc)
ACCOMMODATION: 3 rooms. B&B £12 to £20

ROCHDALE Lancashire — map 5

One Eleven [new entry, zero rated]

111 Yorkshire Street, Rochdale OL16 1YJ
ROCHDALE (0706) 344901 — £15

By the time you reach the third flight of thick-carpeted stairs leading up to the restaurant the smells from the kitchen are evident. There is a small reception/bar with cane chairs, plates and sepia photographs of old Rochdale. The dining-room is plain but smart. Good dishes have been a vegetable and lentil soup, superb lamb with honey and rosemary, and fillet 111 (one eleven). Vegetables are left in their dishes on the table and have included that rarity – fresh peas. The waitress recites the sweets, which include fine Pavlovas and fresh fruit, and there is, of course, excellent Lancashire cheese. Filter coffee. House French is £5·50. More reports, please.

CHEF/PROPRIETOR: Catherine Adamson
OPEN: Thur to Sat D CLOSED: last week June, 1st week July, 1st week Sept
MEALS: 7.30 to 9.30
PRICES: Set D £10·95 (£15). Service 10% CARDS: Access, Amex, Diners, Visa
SEATS: 30. Private parties: 30 main room. No children under 14. Smart dress preferred. Music. Air-conditioned

The 1987 Guide will appear before Christmas 1986, so reports are particularly important in the spring. Report forms are at the back of this book, but just write a letter if you prefer. Address them to The Good Food Guide, *Freepost, 14 Buckingham Street, London WC2N 6BR. No stamp is necessary if you post in the UK.*

ROCKFORD Essex map 3

Renoufs [12/20]

1 South Street, Rochford
SOUTHEND (0702) 544393 £11–£20

Derek Renouf operates on a grand scale, with hotel plans on their way to fruition, his son to follow in the business, and a menu of the length normally found in a Cantonese restaurant. Shellfish come all ways: scallops with bacon, crab claws with lobster sauce, plus half a dozen variations on the cocktail theme. Fish is smoked on the premises. The speciality, though, is duckling, and this is the only place for pressed duck done in the style of Paris's Tour d'Argent: the breast meat carved thinly, sauté with diced liver, shallots, herbs, red wine, cognac, and juice from the carcase, the legs barbecued separately. There are Loire and Rhône wines for under £10, burgundies owe a lot to Reine-Pédauque, and clarets are safe.

CHEF/PROPRIETOR: Derek Renouf
OPEN: Tue to Sat, exc Sat L CLOSED: 3 weeks Jan, 2 weeks June MEALS: 12.15 to 2, 7.15 to 9.45 (10.15 Sat)
PRICES: £14 (£20), Set L and D £8·50 (£11). Service inc set only CARDS: Access, Amex, Diners, Visa
SEATS: 65. Private parties: 12 main room. Vegetarian meals. Children welcome. Wheelchair access (also wc). Music. Air-conditioned

ROCKLEY Wiltshire map 2

Loaves and Fishes [11/20]

Rockley Chapel, Rockley SN8 1RT
MARLBOROUGH (0672) 53737 £12–£14

A Victorian church of grey stone on the edge of the Marlborough Downs, converted to a small country restaurant with tables in the nave, transept and vestries, separated by curtains. Prawn and tomato mayonnaise comes with warm, brown wholemeal bread made with locally ground flour. There is no choice of main course, but roast beef is likely on Sundays. To finish, fruity apricot mousse and hot Queen of puddings with crumbly meringue. English cheeses include a local goats'. Friendly service.

CHEF: Angela Rawson PROPRIETORS: Angela Rawson and Nikki Kedge
OPEN: Wed to Sat D, Sun L MEALS: 12.30 to 1, 7.30 to 8.30
PRICES: Set L £11·75 (£12) Set D £13 (£14). Service inc. Unlicensed, but bring your own: corkage 5%
SEATS: 28. Private parties: 28 main room. Car-park, 10 places. Vegetarian meals. Children's helpings. Wheelchair access (also wc). Classical music

Restaurant tricks (5): Pricing wine to include VAT and then adding another 15 per cent on the total at the end of the meal.

All Guide *inspectors are anonymous. Anyone purporting to represent the* Guide *is an impostor.*

ROMSEY Hampshire map 2

Old Manor House [12/20]

21 Palmerston Street, Romsey SO5 8GF
ROMSEY (0794) 517353 **Real Food** £11–£22

This is a place to eat game in season: woodcock, partridge, hare, rabbit and sometimes more appear on the same menu. Mauro Bregoli lays out his hunting spoils for display, including fresh mushrooms, duck and even grouse. Superb trout comes from the Test. The kitchen will then produce a salad of dandelion leaves, confit of duck and warm pigeon breast; or else partridge, either jugged or plainly roasted and served with its own juice. The menu is varied and imaginative and features an Italian's penchant for pasta – home-made noodles are served with a piquant sauce of ham that has been smoked in-house – and good fish dishes, such as mussels provençale and the seafood platter. The set lunch at £6·95 is good value, as are the bar snacks. A little more generosity in the restaurateuring (such as correctly adding up the bill) plus a consistency of standards would be appreciated. The wine list has some wonderful clarets and burgundies, at a price, and the Alsace is good value in the context: Pinot Gris, Les Maquisards '82, from Dopff & Irion, is £4·50 for a half.
CELLARMAN'S CHOICE: Maître d'Estournel at £8·50.

CHEF/PROPRIETOR: Mauro Bregoli
OPEN: Tue to Sun, exc Sun D CLOSED: 25 to 30 Dec MEALS: 12 to 2, 7 to 10
PRICES: £16 (£22), Set L £6·95 (£11), Bar meals from 95p. Service inc CARDS: Access, Amex, Diners, Visa
SEATS: 55. 5 tables outside. Private parties: 14 main room, 25 private room. Car-park, 12 places. Children welcome. Smart dress preferred. No cigars/pipes in dining-room. Wheelchair access

ROSS-ON-WYE Hereford & Worcester map 2

▲ *Pengethley Hotel* [11/20]

Harewood End, Ross-on-Wye HR9 6LL
HAREWOOD END (098 987) 211
on A49, 4m N of Ross **Real Food** £14–£19

This whiter-than-white Georgian country house is on the Welsh–English border. The Ryeland sheep that graze in the grounds find themselves on a menu that is at its best with Anglo-Welsh dishes, such as chilled cucumber and fennel soup; marinated sea-bass; or noisettes of lamb. Salmon, out of the Wye, is poached in white wine and fish stock and served with a dill and cream sauce. Vegetables are side-plated, the honey ice-cream is home-made, and the bread freshly baked. The

The Guide *does not accept free meals.*

All restaurants listed in the Guide *have been independently nominated by a number of readers and have been checked by inspectors.*

Restaurant tricks (1): Charging each person for every serving of vegetables even when the diners have shared portions between them.

wine list is encyclopaedic – better on quality than value for money; very strong in Rhônes and Loires and minor clarets.

CHEF: Ian Mann PROPRIETOR: Andrew Sime
OPEN: all week MEALS: 12.30 to 1.45, 6.30 to 9.15
PRICES: Set L £9·50 (£14), Set D from £15·50 (£19). Service inc CARDS: Access, Amex, Diners, Visa
SEATS: 140. 5 tables outside. Private parties: 90 main room. Car-park, 70 places. Vegetarian meals. Children's helpings. Jacket and tie. Wheelchair access (also wc). Piano and guitar music
ACCOMMODATION: 20 rooms, all with bath/shower. Rooms for disabled. B&B £49 to £84. Deposit: £10 per night. Children welcome. Baby facilities. No pets in public rooms. Afternoon teas. Garden. Outdoor swimming-pool. Fishing. Snooker. Helicopter pad. TV. Phone. Scenic. Doors close at 12. Confirm by 6

ROTHLEY Leicestershire map 5

▲ *Rothley Court* [new entry, zero rated]

Westfield Lane, Rothley LE7 7LG
LEICESTER (0533) 374141
on B5328, ½m off A6, between
Leicester and Loughborough £15–£25

The Nubian slave figures in the coffee-lounge and on the half-landing are part of a fireplace sent from Egypt by Lord Kitchener. The manor has a recorded history dating from Roman times, and its latest role is as an hotel with an ambitious restaurant. The menu straddles Ogen melon and grilled Dover sole with parsley butter, as well as more complex and ornate dishes, such as a fricassee of Dutch veal with an asparagus and mushroom sauce with saffron rice. There are good reports of the wild mushrooms with pastry, and the fillet of beef with two sauces. Cheeses are from good suppliers, herbs are from the garden, and the service is obliging. The wine list does not seem to have the same poise. Is Brouilly '83 really the same price as '84? The split vintages seem to take no account of the quality of the harvest – the '83 Alsace wines, for example, will be better than those from '82. More reports, please.

CHEF: Bruce Sangster PROPRIETORS: B.J. and N.H.Purcell
OPEN: all week, exc Sat L and Sun D CLOSED: 25 and 26 Dec MEALS: 12 to 2, 7 to 9.30 (10 Sat)
PRICES: £16 (£25), Set L from £9 (£15), Set D from £15 (£21), Snacks from £1·50 (£1·65). Also cut-price L menu in summer. Service 10% CARDS: Access, Amex, Diners, Visa
SEATS: 50. 8 tables outside. Private parties: 95 main room, 60 and 16 private rooms. Car-park, 100 places. Children welcome. Jacket and tie. No pipes in dining-room. Wheelchair access. Classical music
ACCOMMODATION: 34 rooms, 31 with bath/shower. B&B £46 to £56. Children welcome. Baby facilities. No pets in public rooms. Afternoon teas. Garden. Helicopter pad. TV. Phone. Scenic

Restaurants are graded on a scale of 1–20. In the region of 8–9 expect to find places that may not be restaurants but cafes, pubs, bistros and small hotels. In the category of 10–11 you can expect to find the best food in the locality. Ratings of 12 or more are given to restaurants we regard as serving the best food in the region.

ROXWELL Essex map 3

Farmhouse Feast [11/20]

The Street, Roxwell CM1 4PB
ROXWELL (0245 48) 583
4m W of Chelmsford **Real Food** £13–£14

Good home cooking with a strong vegetarian vein is served in this early sixteenth-century building. There are fresh vegetable crudités with mayonnaise dips on the table, and the main courses of the week are recited verbally – boiled salt beef cooked with horseradish; skate with black butter; roast lamb with brandy and apricot sauce; lentil loaf with cider sauce; and so on. Help yourself to salad starters, after which a tureen of soup arrives. Back to self-service for trifle gateau soufflé-style desserts. Rocks Country Elderflower is on the short, basic wine list, as is house French at £6 a litre.

CHEFS: Juliet Upson, Allan Green and Peter Spence
PROPRIETORS: Rosemary and Juliet Upson
OPEN: Tue to Sat, exc Tue and Sat L CLOSED: 2 weeks June, 1 week Jan MEALS: 12 to 1.30, 7 to 9.30
PRICES: Set L from £9 (£13), Set D from £10 (£14) CARDS: Access, Visa
SEATS: 60. Private parties: 24 main room, 24, 16 and 12 private rooms. Vegetarian meals. Children's helpings. Wheelchair access. Classical music. Partly self-service

RYE East Sussex map 3

Simmons [13/20]

68 The Mint, Rye TN01 7EN
RYE (0797) 222026 **Real Food** £13–£19

This beamed, 500-year-old building down the cobbled High Street has handsomely set tables with three glasses in a row for each place setting and pink napkins. Sunday lunch is the real bargain, when the leftovers from the sensible, varied menu have to be finished. During the rest of the week there have been dishes of poise in the shape of salmon and cream soup; duck liver pâté; duck breast fanned out in the *nouvelle cuisine* style with a little apple and green pepper sauce; grilled sea-bass with fennel mayonnaise and copious vegetables. In season there is Romney Marsh lamb, roasted and served with a tarragon and cream sauce. The cheeseboard is left on the table and provides a good show of English tradition, with a blue Red Leicester and fine Cheddar, as well as French specimens. Of the sweets the caramel meringues stand out – whipped egg-whites poached in milk with vanilla and then topped with a caramel mixture that includes nuts. Plenty of cafetière coffee. Kenneth Simmons is quite an alchemist with the alcohol. He imports, and then uses a massive fireplace for storing a very fine list indeed (although there is little reason to stray from the excellent Doudet-

Restaurant tricks (2): By law, prices on the menu displayed in the window must include VAT. But no such obligation applies to the menu inside.

Restaurant tricks (3): The bad practice of making a cover charge is dying out, but please report to us on any restaurant still doing so.

Naudin house burgundy). He enjoys making up Martinis as well as discussing his little armoury of calvados, armagnac and marc de champagne.

CHEF: Susan Simmons PROPRIETORS: Kenneth and Susan Simmons
OPEN: Tue to Sat, D only, and Sun L CLOSED: first 2 days Oct, 3 weeks Feb MEALS: 12 to 2, 7 to 10
PRICES: £11 (£19), Set L from £6·95 (£13), Set D £9·50 (£15). Minimum £6·95 at L, £9·50 at D. Service 10% CARDS: Access, Amex, Diners, Visa
SEATS: 24. Private parties: 28 main room. Smart dress preferred

SAFFRON WALDEN Essex map 3

Old Hoops [new entry, zero rated]

15 King Street, Saffron Walden CB10 1HE
SAFFRON WALDEN (0799) 22813 £15

The Irwin and Morrison husbands cook, the wives are front of house, and between them they achieve a good mix of old-style courtesy and small-town bonhomie. The decor, like some of the combinations of foods, is a bit frantic – constellations of silver balls hang from the ceiling and there are children's crayoned drawings on the walls. There is lots of choice on an adventurous menu: Billy Bye soup is as good a plate of fresh mussels in creamy sauce as anyone's; gamey wild duck with sour cherry and port is impressive, too. The vegetables have the same honesty of taste. Puddings include excellent crème brûlée and an eclair filled with tropical fruit and cream and served with a tart apricot sauce. Other dishes are more clumsy – the simpler combinations work best. House wine is £3·95. CELLARMAN'S CHOICE: Viña Esmerelda '83, from Torres, at £6.

CHEFS: Don Irwin and Ray Morrison PROPRIETORS: Chris and Don Irwin, Sue and Ray Morrison
OPEN: all week, exc Sun D MEALS: 12.30 to 3.30, 7 to 11
PRICES: £10 (£15). Also cut-price menu CARDS: Access, Amex, Diners, Visa
SEATS: 45. Private parties: 44 main room. Vegetarian meals. Children's helpings. Classical music and jazz. Air-conditioned

▲ *Saffron Hotel* [11/20]

10–18 High Street, Saffron Walden CB10 1AZ
SAFFRON WALDEN (0799) 22676 £12–£23

An old timber building near the church. From outside it looks like a pub, but inside there is a small courtyard with a goldfish pool, a grey parrot in a cage and a comfortable, green, velvet-upholstered dining-room. The menu is extensive and international. Of many good dishes highlights are the well-hung venison with juniper, gin and cream sauce; and excellent salmon with fresh prawns and mussels. Other courses show the care of the kitchen – minestrone, fresh, undressed salads, seven vegetables. As well as a predictable sweets trolley there is

CELLARMAN'S CHOICE: This is a wine that is more expensive than the house wine but is good value and fitting for the kind of food served.

Restaurants rating 10 and 11 serve the best food in the locality.

admirable bread-and-butter pudding, and coffee comes with yellow single cream. Around 50 wines, helpfully described, and plenty of halves.
CELLARMAN'S CHOICE: Sauvignon de St-Bris '82 at £6·55.

CHEFS: R.H. Craddock and D. Berriel PROPRIETORS: R.H. and J.E. Craddock, K. Widdowson
OPEN: Mon to Sat, exc Sat L MEALS: 12 to 2, 7 to 9.30
PRICES: £15 (£20), Set L and D from £8·95 (£12). Snacks from £1. Minimum £6·50. Service inc CARDS: Access, Visa
SEATS: 28. 7 tables outside. Private parties: 35 main room, 85 private room. Car-park, 10 places. Children's helpings. Wheelchair access. Music
ACCOMMODATION: 18 rooms, 12 with bath/shower. B&B £14·50 to £38. Children welcome. TV. Phone. Doors close at 11.30

ST ALBANS Hertfordshire map 3

Diomides [8/20]

97 St Peter's Street, St Albans AL1 3AA
ST ALBANS (0727) 33330 and 34155 £11–£14

Good-value meze at £8 per head (for two or more) includes prawns in dressing, taramosalata, hummus and salad. Main-course portions of stifado and kebabs are less generous; sausages are spicy; and galatoboureko and coffee are good to finish. Service may be slow. House wine is £4·20.

CHEFS/PROPRIETORS: Mr and Mrs Diomides Machlouzarides
OPEN: all week, exc Sun L MEALS: 12 to 2, 6 to 11.15
PRICES: £9 (£14), Set L and D from £7·60 (£11). Cover 50p. Service 10% CARDS: Access, Amex, Diners, Visa
SEATS: 54. Private parties: 40 main room, 20 private room. Vegetarian meals. Children's helpings. Wheelchair access (1 step). Music

ST AUSTELL Cornwall map 1

▲ *Boscundle Manor* [11/20]

Tregrehan, St Austell PL25 3RL
PAR (072 681) 3557
off A390, 2m E of St Austell **Real Food** £18

'I have been cooking a daily menu for the past six months and find it less restrictive and more interesting than a *carte*,' says Mary Flint. Therein lies a sentiment that could change the catering industry in this country. As Girardet has said in Switzerland, cooking should be spontaneous according to what is available at market. Of course, Andrew and Mary Flint's eighteenth-century manor with its own secluded gardens is not quite in the same league as Girardet's Crissier restaurant, but the menu takes the best of the local catch of brill, turbot, sole, lobster and crab, and the Flints are creating their own soft fruit garden. The set dinners contain many conservative choices, such as avocado vinaigrette and good charcoal-grilled steaks, but there has also been excellent sea-trout baked with rosemary, pan-fried veal with a cream sauce with grain mustard, capers and sherry, and home-made Marsala and raisin ice-cream. The hotel is more of a home than a business. Interesting wines in the cellar include a rare pair of '76s from Alsace – Dopff & Irion's Pinot Gris, Les Maquisards at £14, and

Gewürztraminer, Les Sorcières at £15 – and vintage Rioja for less than £10. CELLARMAN'S CHOICE: Rioja, Marqués de Murrieta '79 at £10·50.

CHEF: Mary Flint PROPRIETORS: Andrew and Mary Flint
OPEN: Mon to Sat, D only CLOSED: 23 Dec to 4 Feb MEALS: 7.30 to 9
PRICES: Set D £15 (£18). Service inc CARDS: Access, Amex, Visa
SEATS: 20. Private parties: 20 main room, 8 and 15 private rooms. Car-park, 12 places. Vegetarian meals. Children's helpings. Wheelchair access (also wc)
ACCOMMODATION: 9 rooms, all with bath/shower. B&B £33 to £50. Deposit: 25%. Children welcome. Dogs welcome. Garden. Outdoor swimming-pool. Croquet. TV. Phone. Doors close at 12 [GHG]

ST MARGARET'S AT CLIFFE Kent — map 3

▲ *Wallett's Court* [12/20]

West Cliffe, St Margaret's at Cliffe CT15 6EW
DOVER (0304) 852424
on B2058 — £18–£30

William Pitt rented this seventeenth-century cliff-top manor (once the palace of Eleanor of Castile, wife of Edward I) to get away from the damp rooms of Walmer Castle. Chris and Lea Oakley run what is almost a museum now as a bed-and-breakfast hotel during the week, but on Saturday nights the spectacular dining-room becomes a serious restaurant serving some of the best meals in Kent. Mr Oakley trained at Le Gavroche and was head chef at Le Poulbot. He is a *saucier* of high skills. The dining-room has white plastered walls, the honey-coloured ceiling has beams supported by intricately carved posts, and there is a vast fireplace and carved antique furniture. The menu runs to four courses with a choice of two starters, two main dishes and three sweets. Superb dishes have been the pastry cases filled with asparagus and an intense butter sauce flavoured with thyme, and also the strawberry shortcake – two round, buttery wafers with a layer of thick cream and the fruit inside sitting on a strawberry sauce that has been given a greater vibrancy by the addition of blackcurrants. Some of the sauces do not sound encouraging – sole cooked with a green chartreuse, root vegetables with a lobster sauce, Martini-flavoured mint sauce for salmon – but the execution is masterly, in the latter case the Martini added judiciously to a wine, butter and fish stock liaison to give added edge. The vegetables can be overcooked and the coffee a bit thin, but the petits fours compensate. The wine list is still basic but adequate. House claret is £5. The Oakleys may open for special evenings on Fridays this year and say that they are happy to cater for private parties of eight or more.

CHEF: Chris Oakley PROPRIETORS: Chris and Lea Oakley
OPEN: Sat D only MEALS: 8 to 11.30
PRICES: Set D from £14 to £25 (£18 to £30). Cut-price menu for residents
SEATS: 30. Private parties: 30 main room. Car-park, 16 places. Vegetarian meals. Children's helpings. One sitting
ACCOMMODATION: 7 rooms, 5 with bath/shower. Rooms for disabled. B&B £14 to £22. Children welcome. Baby facilities. No pets. Garden. Scenic. Doors close at 12. Confirm by 4 [GHG]

This restaurant has an exceptional wine cellar.

SALISBURY Wiltshire map 2

Crane's [13/20]

90–92 Crane Street, Salisbury SP1 2QD
SALISBURY (0722) 333471 **Real Food** £14–£18

Back to the *ancien régime*! Tom Geary has officially filed for divorce from *nouvelle cuisine*. 'Is a tomato rose really a substitute for a classically prepared meal? I think not.' His bonhomie spills over from the kitchen into the dining-room, conservatory and even the garden. He runs a happy restaurant. Back to the limelight have come dishes like braised tongue with madeira and mustard sauce; breast of corn-fed chicken served with a fricassee of its leg meat, langoustines, mushrooms, sherry, whisky and cream. Simpler but excellent have been the onion soup; the lamb cutlets with mint chutney; and also the intriguing New Orleans chowder bouchées filled with diced potato, fish, garlic sausage, tomato, chilli and coriander in a cream-wine sauce. There are black olives to nibble at the start, fresh home-made rolls in the middle and a huge pot of coffee at the end. Dinner may be better than lunch. There's something for everyone on the wine list, with house claret at £4·60. CELLARMAN'S CHOICE: Pommard, Les Bertins '80 at £16·50.

CHEF: Tom Geary PROPRIETORS: Tom and Joan Geary
OPEN: Mon to Sat CLOSED: bank hols exc 25 Dec MEALS: 12 to 1.45, 7 to 9.30
PRICES: L £10 (£14), D £14 (£18). Minimum £3·50 L, £7·50 D. Service 10%
CARDS: Access, Amex, Diners, Visa
SEATS: 34. 3 tables outside. Private parties: 20 main room. Smart dress preferred. No children under 12. Wheelchair access. Music

SCARBOROUGH North Yorkshire map 6A

Lanterna [10/20]

33 Queen Street, Scarborough YO11 1HQ
SCARBOROUGH (0723) 363616 £15

The Arecco family have run this popular Italian restaurant in the old town for 16 years. They do not use frozen vegetables and the fish can be excellent, from lobster thermidor to grilled sole. The music is loud and the house Barbera is £5 a litre. CELLARMAN'S CHOICE: Barbaresco '78 at £6·50.

CHEF: G. Arecco PROPRIETORS: The Arecco family
OPEN: Tue to Sat, D only MEALS: 7 to 9.30
PRICES: £10 (£15) CARD: Visa
SEATS: 36. 12 tables outside. Private parties: 36 main room. Vegetarian meals. Children welcome (no babies). Wheelchair access. Music

'The only light relief of the evening was provided by the sight of the two young chefs who occasionally poked their heads out of the kitchen to see whether it was all clear for them to take the two women, who had been previously waiting for them, upstairs for some more satisfying entertainment. Fortunately, their patience was rewarded around 11 o'clock.' (On eating in Warwickshire)

SCOTSDIKE Cumbria map 7

▲ *March Bank Country House Hotel* [12/20]

Scotsdike CA6 5XP
LONGTOWN (0228) 791325
on A7, 3m N of Longtown, 2m S of
Canonbie £9–£15

Set in three acres, a hundred yards back from the A7, overlooking the Esk river. The Grant family have run this unpretentious hotel for nine years, relying heavily on the best local produce – free-range eggs, Cumberland sausages traditionally made without extenders – and baking a range of their own breads with organically grown and stone-ground flours. Patricia Grant's three-course menus are heroically English. As well as roast beef and Yorkshire pudding there has been carrot and coriander soup, orange braised pork, Cumberland ham baked in pastry, bread and butter pudding, old-fashioned sherry trifle, and Cumberland cheeses. Occasional foreigners are goulash or the cheesecakes – even the lemonade is home-made. Twenty wines mostly under £7 a bottle. CELLARMAN'S CHOICE: Ch. Cambin la Pelouse '79 Haut-Médoc, £7·90.

CHEFS: Patricia and Louise Grant PROPRIETORS: Albert and Patricia Grant
OPEN: all week CLOSED: 27 Jan to 10 Mar MEALS: 12.15 to 1.30, 7.30 to 8.30
PRICES: £8 (£11·50), Set L £6 (£9), Set D £11·50 (£15). Minimum £4. Service 10%
SEATS: 26. 4 tables outside. Private parties: 32 main room. Vegetarian meals. Car-park, 30 places. Smart dress preferred. No smoking. Children's helpings. Wheelchair access (also WC). Light classical music
ACCOMMODATION: 7 rooms, 4 with bath/shower. 1 room for disabled. B&B £26 to £38. Pets welcome. Garden. Fishing: rods supplied. Helicopter space. Baby facilities. Scenic. Confirm by 10 [GHG]

SEATOLLER Cumbria map 7

Yew Tree [11/20]

Seatoller CA12 5XN
BORROWDALE (059 684) 634
at foot of Honister Pass £12

Jugged hare is the thing to eat at this stone cottage at the foot of Honister Pass. It comes in a large, oval, earthenware dish with at least two large pieces of gamey meat in a thick sauce, slightly sweetened by orange, with root vegetables. Otherwise there are potted shrimps, steaks and rustic soups. During the day the dining-room runs a sort of gift shop and offers hikers a shorter menu. There is always a vegetarian dish. Ham and eggs is £3·50, while 'More ham and two eggs' is £4·50. House Rhine is £4·30. CELLARMAN'S CHOICE: Ch. La Gurgue '79, £9·50.

CHEF: Ian Charlton PROPRIETORS: Ian and Lynn Charlton
OPEN: Tue to Sun, exc Sat L MEALS: 12 to 5, 5 to 8 (6 to 9.30 Sat)
PRICES: £7 (£12), Snacks from £1·10 (£1·25). Daily bargain dish
SEATS: 50. 5 tables outside. Private parties: 40 main room. Car-park, 6 places. Vegetarian meals. Children's helpings. Wheelchair access (also WC). Music

SHARDLOW Derbyshire map 5

La Marina [10/20]

London Road, Shardlow DE7 2XX
DERBY (0332) 792553
on A6, 6m SE of Derby £13

A former transport cafe, light and spacious, with Italian music and food. Set lunches include minestrone, goujons of plaice or lamb chops, and home-made Italian cake. Lasagne is very good, vegetables al dente, trout variable, puddings unsurprising, and wines basic. House Italian is £4·50 a litre.

CHEF: Salvatore Cacace PROPRIETOR: Salvatore Pitzettu
OPEN: Tue to Sun MEALS: 12 to 2.30, 7 to 10.30 (10 Sun)
PRICES: £8 (£13). Cover 30p
SEATS: 60. Private parties: 60 main room. Car-park, 50 places. Vegetarian meals by arrangement. Children's helpings by arrangement. Wheelchair access (also wc). Italian music. Air-conditioned

SHARPTHORNE West Sussex map 3

▲ *Gravetye Manor* [13/20]

Vowels Lane, Sharpthorne RH19 4LJ
SHARPTHORNE (0342) 810567
West Hoathly turning off B2110
between East Grinstead and Turners Hill Real Food £33

The most English of the southerly country-house hotels, complete with a fabulous garden. There are stone floors under the carpets, log fires, pictures, antiques, fresh flowers; no music, no bustle, low voices in the background. The service at its best glides. Among some very good dishes made from first-class local produce, including free-range eggs, have been: lobster bisque; salad of foie gras; oeufs en cocotte before halibut with dill; venison, neatly fanned out on the plate, with asparagus. Vegetables, many from the garden, are served on side plates. The white chocolate mousse is a fitting finale. Some of the cooking lacks the passion we demand for 14 – there is too much reliance on luxury items for their own sake – and the bread policy needs to be improved, but even so the hotel ranks high on any list of 'civilised luxuries' this country can offer! And then there are the wines . . . clarets going back to '61, albeit at a price, but also half a dozen *cru* Beaujolais from the excellent '83s, and even better-value wines from Alsace, from Trimbach, around the £8 mark. The house white is Mâcon-Lugny, Les Genièvres '83, from Latour, at £5·60 for a half, which sets the tone.

▲ *This restaurant has rooms.*

Restaurant tricks (4): Charging for service but leaving the total on the credit card slip blank, thus inviting an extra tip.

Restaurant tricks (5): Pricing wine to include VAT and then adding another 15 per cent on the total at the end of the meal.

CHEF: Allan Garth PROPRIETOR: Peter Herbert
OPEN: all week CLOSED: 25 Dec evening to non-residents MEALS: 12.30 to 2, 7.30 to 9.30 (10 Sat)
PRICES: £21 (£33). Service inc
SEATS: 60. Private parties: 10 main room, 18 and 14 private rooms. Car-park, 30 places. Children's helpings. No children under 7. Smart dress preferred. No smoking in dining-room
ACCOMMODATION: 14 rooms, all with bath/shower. B&B £53 to £93. No children under 7. Baby facilities. No pets. Garden. Fishing. Croquet. Clock golf. TV. Phone. Scenic. Doors close at 12

SHEFFIELD South Yorkshire map 5

Deakins [10/20]

376 Fulwood Road, Ranmoor, Sheffield S10 3GD
SHEFFIELD (0742) 301772 £13

The menu changes on the first Thursday of each month at this small dining-room, with most innovation among the starters. Service is helpful and the portions are of traditional Yorkshire proportions. Good dishes have been lamb with caper sauce; pork stuffed with apples and raisins; salmon with parsley butter; and the generous quantities of fresh vegetables. The sweets don't vary much but are consistently good, and have included pithiviers, marquise, meringues and trifles. A brusque wine list, but it does have Gewürztraminer '83, from Hugel, at £8·55. Vin de table is £4·45.

CHEF: Susan Crosbie PROPRIETORS: George Slater and Susan Crosbie
OPEN: Thur to Sat D (other times by arrangement) MEALS: 7.30 to 9.45
PRICES: Set D £9·95 (£13) CARD: Access
SEATS: 30. Private parties: 30 main room. Car-park, 3 places. Vegetarian meals by arrangement. Children's helpings. Classical music

Nirmal's Tandoori [11/20]

193 Glossop Road, Sheffield S10 2GN
SHEFFIELD (0742) 24054 £13

The best Indian food in town is served in this cramped but smartly decorated restaurant with partitions for privacy. Sour yoghourt and almond soup with cumin and coriander, king prawn dopiaza, home-made chutneys, and kulfi are all good. Service is prompt, and blackboard specials are explained by the waiter.

CHEF: Mrs Dupta PROPRIETOR: Mr P.L. Dupta
OPEN: all week, exc Sun L MEALS: 12 to 2.30, 6 to 12 (1 Fri and Sat)
PRICES: £6 (£13), Set D from £9 (£13). Service 10% CARDS: Access, Amex, Visa
SEATS: 54. Private parties: 26 private room. Vegetarian meals. Children welcome. Wheelchair access (also WC). Indian music. Take-away service

---

The Guide *is always anxious to recruit new inspectors. If you would like to apply, write to the editor enclosing a) a detailed report on a restaurant where you have eaten and b) a comparative study of restaurants known to you.*

Toffs [11/20]

23 Matilda Street, The Moor, Sheffield S1 4QB
SHEFFIELD (0742) 20783 **Real Food** £7–£14

At last, some Real Food in Sheffield. Wedged between a betting shop and an amusement arcade is this smart lunchtime cafe that is evolving as a restaurant on Thursday, Friday and Saturday nights. There is a vegetarian bias, and pride is taken in the fact that the food is unprocessed, not an easy achievement in this part of Yorkshire. It is a family business: Tessa Bramley cooks, husband Peter runs the front of house, son Andrew specialises in the wines, and grandfather grows the flowers and herbs, including borage flowers that decorate some of the desserts. Of many endorsed dishes typical are hare terrine with cranberry and orange relish; grayling in pastry with hollandaise; hazel-nut roulade as a starter; and chicken breast with a coating of sesame seeds and a cream and lime sauce. Vegetables are cooked al dente and are plentiful. To finish there is fine plum tart or calvados apple pie. In the daytime there are variations on these, plus quiches and coleslaw and teacakes. There is a short list of carefully chosen wines, not greedily marked-up, which include Gewürztraminer, Domaine des Comtes de Lupfen, special reserve '83, from Paul Blanck, at £6·55 or CELLARMAN'S CHOICE: Beaune, Clos du Roi '80, from Chanson, at £9·45. Good eaux-de-vie and cognacs, too.

CHEF: Tessa Bramley PROPRIETORS: The Bramley family
OPEN: Mon to Sat L, and Thur to Sat D MEALS: 10 to 3 (4.30 Sat), 7.15 to 8.15
PRICES: L £3 (£7), Set D from £9·75 (£14). Minimum £2 at L. Service inc alc only
SEATS: 50. Private parties: 40 main room. Vegetarian meals. Children welcome. Wheelchair access (also WC). Classical music. Self-service at L

Zing Vaa [8/20]

55 The Moor, Sheffield S1 4PG
SHEFFIELD (0742) 22432 and 29213 £6–£14

Precipitous steps lead down from the modern pedestrian shopping mall to this big basement Cantonese restaurant with stir-fried everything. As well as sizzling dishes, dim-sum, and a dish of three kinds of quick-fried seafood, there is fish from Hull and Anglesey, steamed whole. Licensed.

CHEF: K.Y.Kong PROPRIETORS: Roger Cheung and K.Tse
OPEN: all week MEALS: noon to midnight
PRICES: £8 (£14), Set L from £3 (£6), Set D from £7 (£11) CARDS: Access, Amex, Diners, Visa
SEATS: 130. Private parties: 45 main room, 35 private room. Car-park at night. Vegetarian meals. Children welcome. Wheelchair access (at rear). Music. Air-conditioned

The 1987 Guide will appear before Christmas 1986, so reports are particularly important in the spring. Report forms are at the back of this book, but just write a letter if you prefer. Address them to The Good Food Guide, *Freepost, 14 Buckingham Street, London WC2N 6BR. No stamp is necessary if you post in the UK.*

SHEPSHED Leicestershire — map 5

Turtles [new entry, zero rated]

42 Brook Street, Shepshed LE12 9RG
SHEPSHED (0509) 502843
off A512, 4m W of Loughborough — £16

One of those rare places where the turtle soup does not come out of a tin. It may have to be frozen, due to the nature of the trade, though a tank in the bar is filled with the creatures. Otherwise only the prawns, scampi, snails and frogs' legs are likely to have seen the inside of a freezer. It is a long menu, built up around traditional stocks. There are interesting, rare dishes, such as smoked goose breast and Parma ham with cranberry and ginger relish, and crab with tarragon and Dijon mustard. The main course of loin of lamb with a crème de menthe and cream sauce is mentioned by nearly all reporters. Vegetables are seasonal and the bread rolls plentiful. Sweets, from crème brûlée with raspberries to mango fool, have been approved. The atmosphere is relaxed and the service swift and smartly dressed. Two dozen wines, and more than a hundred spirits. More reports, please.

CHEFS/PROPRIETORS: Valerie Thompson and Steven Hickling
OPEN: Tue to Sat, D only MEALS: 7 to 10.30
PRICES: £11 (£16) CARDS: Access, Amex, Diners, Visa
SEATS: 46. Private parties: 50 main room. Car-park, 8 places. Vegetarian meals. Children's helpings. No children under 8. Wheelchair access. Music

SHEPTON MALLET Somerset — map 2

Blostin's [9/20]

29 Waterloo Road, Shepton Mallet BA4 5HH
SHEPTON MALLET (0749) 3648 — £8–£15

The Reeds took over in February 1985 and are still feeling their way. The menu is not so much à la carte as à la blackboard. Good raw materials are used, particularly beef – served in a pastry case – and vegetables. Both cooking and service are well intentioned but don't yet match the sound of quenelles of chicken with raspberry vinegar or chocolate marquise. The wine list is short on halves, but house red and white are £4·85.

CHEF: Nick Reed PROPRIETORS: Nick and Lynne Reed
OPEN: all week, exc Sat L and Sun D MEALS: 12 to 2, 7 to 9.30 (10 Sat)
PRICES: £11 (£15), Set L £4·95 (£8), Set D from £7·95 to £8·95 (£11 to £12). Service inc
CARDS: Access, Diners, Visa
SEATS: 32. Private parties: 30 main room. Vegetarian meals. Children's helpings. Smart dress preferred. Wheelchair access. Music

▲ *Bowlish House* [11/20]

Wells Road, Shepton Mallet BA4 5JD
SHEPTON MALLET (0749) 2022 — 🍷 £13

This spacious Georgian house with a fish-tank in the hall has assorted clocks and old pictures that give it an impressive, albeit unpretentious, air. Eat at your own pace – celery and Stilton soup; fish terrine; red mullet fillets with provençale sauce; pork casserole with apricots and dates; half a dozen vegetables; brown bread ice-cream, and chocolate marquise. Some of the cooking lacks polish, but the serious business of this house is in the cellar – the wine list runs longer than *Dallas* but is not overpriced. There are six Alsace wines from Louis Gisselbrecht in the £7 range, burgundies from the early '70s, and clarets from the '60s at three times that price and mercifully, unless you have got the whole afternoon free, 13 house wines at £3·50. There are marcs, single malts, scrumpy . . . an alcoholic's heaven.

CHEF: Tony Lund PROPRIETORS: Brian and Julia Jordan
OPEN: all week, D only CLOSED: 4 days at Christmas MEALS: 7 to 10
PRICES: Set D from £11 (£13). Service inc
SEATS: 26. 3 tables outside. Private parties: 36 main room, 12 private room. Car-park, 20 places. Vegetarian meals. Children's helpings. Smart dress preferred. Separate smoking area. Wheelchair access (also WC). Cellar tours and wine discussion groups
ACCOMMODATION: 4 rooms, all with bath/shower. Rooms for disabled. B&B £25 to £29. Children welcome. Baby facilities. Pets welcome. Afternoon teas. Garden. Croquet. Helicopter pad. TV. Doors close at 1 [GHG]

SHERE Surrey — map 3

La Chaumière [10/20]

Gomshall Lane, Shere GU5 9HE
SHERE (048 641) 2168 — £11–£18

A backwater near the dreadful A25. The feeling in the low beamed dining-room is one of domesticity with a touch of formality. Fish is good – scallops with gin and cream, prawns wrapped in bacon with orange and yoghourt, and grilled turbot. Bread is fresh and vegetables are inclined to be close to rawness. Sunday lunch is good value, otherwise the menu tends to the gastronomically ambitious. Sixty mainly French wines, with house Cuvée de la Reine at £5·50.
CELLARMAN'S CHOICE: Ch. Lestage '82 at £8·95.

CHEF: Andrew Keen PROPRIETOR: John Gater
OPEN: all week MEALS: 12 to 1.45, 7 to 10.30
PRICES: £12 (£18), Set L £7·50 (£11) CARDS: Access, Amex, Diners, Visa
SEATS: 48. 6 tables outside. Private parties: 26 main room, 26 private room. Car-park, 20 places. Vegetarian meals. Children's helpings (L only). No children under 5. Wheelchair access (also WC). Music

SHILDON Durham — map 7

Rajah Tandoori [10/20]

100 Main Street, Shildon DL4 1AQ
BISHOP AUCKLAND (0388) 772451 and 773563 — £15

A spacious dining-room with a long menu. Five main ingredients – chicken, lamb, beef, prawn and king prawn – are given varying curry treatments including 'very hot' and 'extremely hot', as well as figuring as tandooris. Dishes

This restaurant has an exceptional wine cellar.

claim a variety of origins, from Kashmir (with nuts and sultanas), to Malaya (mild, with bananas, pineapple and cream), to Singapore (very hot with bhindi). A nine-item thali is £8. Licensed.

CHEF: Moyna Miah PROPRIETOR: Abdus Subhan
OPEN: all week, exc Sun L MEALS: 12 to 2.15, 6 to 11.30
PRICES: £8 (£15). Service 10% CARDS: Access, Amex, Diners, Visa
SEATS: 60. Private parties: 40 main room. Car-park, 30 places. Vegetarian meals. Children's helpings. Indian music

SHINFIELD Berkshire map 2

Nico Ladenis, whose previous restaurant in Battersea, Chez Nico, rated 16/20 in the 1985 *Guide*, is opening at The Old Vicarage, Church Lane, shortly after we go to press. Initially a restaurant, from spring 1986 it may have rooms.

SHIPDHAM Norfolk map 6

▲ *Shipdham Place* [11/20]

Church Close, Shipdham IP25 7LX
DEREHAM (0362) 820303
between Dereham and Watton,
16 m N of Thetford **Real Food** £23

The de Blanks run their hotel on the lines of a family business in France. It is comfortable, personal and very relaxed, though they have moved out now and the operation is going on to more professional lines. The food is some of the best for many miles, owing to Justin de Blank's husbanding of the best ingredients and Melanie's guiding verve in the kitchen. The emphasis is on prime ingredients and quantity, with the leaning towards fish ever stronger: excellent poached fillets of halibut, monkfish with peas and chives, turbot with hollandaise. Also good have been the duck with cassis sauce, pressed chicken breast terrine, lamb with red wine and tarragon sauce, the salads, the unpasteurised French cheeses, and the triumphant summer pudding. There is no choice of food, but the wine list is a challenge in itself, with plenty of half-bottles and also magnums of old clarets and burgundies.

CHEFS: Melanie de Blank and Jenny Pickering PROPRIETORS: Justin and Melanie de Blank
OPEN: L Sat and Sun by arrangement (large parties only), D Wed to Mon
CLOSED: Christmas and weekdays Jan to Feb MEALS: 7.45 to 9
PRICES: Set D £16·50 (£23). Service 10%
SEATS: 30. Private parties: 24 main room, 8 private room. Vegetarian meals by arrangement. Car-park, 18 places. Smart dress preferred. No smoking. Children's helpings. Terrace for summer evenings
ACCOMMODATION: 9 rooms, all with bath/shower. B&B £35 to £55. Deposit: £20. Pets welcome. Afternoon teas. Garden. Baby facilities. Confirm by 12

Entries are compiled from the unsolicited reports from readers and are checked by inspectors; each restaurant is asked to supply details of its operation. Report forms can be found at the back of the Guide.

SHIPLEY West Yorkshire map 5

Aagrah [11/20]

27 Westgate, Shipley BD18 3QX
BRADFORD (0274) 594660 £10

This basement, north Indian restaurant serves some of the best food in the area. Pendant shades with gold tassels are fitted, casino-like, over the tables. A wicker and brass fan spins on the ceiling. The colours are reds, maroons and indigo. Brass plates and a couple of paintings of rural India share the walls with some crazy paving. The meat dhansak served with Basmati rice has been excellent, and with spinach and cauliflower bhajia and raita constituted one impressive inspection meal. Specialities include chicken and lamb dishes cooked in a karahi (metal bowl), and vegetarian thalis. As in other Bradford restaurants a separate plate of garnishing is given: this one was dressed with mint and yoghourt. Licensed.

CHEFS: M.Sabir and M.Aslam PROPRIETORS: Mr and Mrs Sabir, Mr and Mrs Aslam
OPEN: all week, D only MEALS: 6 to 12.45 (2 Thur to Sat)
PRICES: £5 (£10) CARDS: Access, Diners, Visa
SEATS: 40. Private parties: 40 main room. Vegetarian meals. Children's helpings. Oriental music

SHIPSTON ON STOUR Warwickshire map 2

▲ *White Bear* [9/20]

High Street, Shipston on Stour CV36 4AJ
SHIPSTON ON STOUR (0608) 61558 £16

Straightforward cooking is found in this often crowded pub. It always seems to be a quarter past six, according to the clock that hangs on the dining-room wall alongside the painted plates and French natural history pictures. 'We are not evangelical about our cooking', explain Hugh and Suzanne Roberts, who have been here since 1977. There have been some kitchen changes since last year but, with a few exceptions, the reports on dishes are positive, especially those in the bar. Start with a pâté of duck liver; mushrooms and herb cheese; or crevettes with a garlic mayonnaise. Good main dishes have been rack of lamb, which comes as four linked chops with garlic and rosemary, and game pie – chunks of pheasant, partridge, hare and beef-steak in gravy with juniper berries, with a light pastry lid. Vegetables have been fresh, even in the freezing weather last March: purée of parsnips and parsley; carrot fingers; cauliflower au gratin with roast split almonds. Dauphinois potatoes come in a separate bowl. The bread-and-butter pudding is first-class. The wine list will expand in '86 when the

Real Food *denotes that the restaurant does not use processed food.*

Prices quoted are for an average three-course meal including service and VAT *and half a bottle of house wine (or the equivalent in an ethnic restaurant).*

All restaurants listed in the Guide *have been independently nominated by a number of readers and have been checked by inspectors.*

Roberts are released from their brewery ties. Pints of draught Bass or try the CELLARMAN'S CHOICE: Côtes du Ventoux '82, from Jaboulet, at £6.

CHEFS/PROPRIETORS: Hugh and Suzanne Roberts
OPEN: all week, exc Sun D MEALS: 12 to 1.45, 7.30 to 9.30
PRICES: £10 (£16), Snacks from £1 (£1.10). Licensed, plus bring your own: no corkage
CARDS: Access, Amex, Diners, Visa
SEATS: 35. 4 tables outside. Private parties: 50 main room. Car-park, 20 places. Vegetarian meals. Children's helpings. Smart dress preferred. Wheelchair access (also WC)
ACCOMMODATION: 10 rooms, all with bath/shower. B&B £18 to £35. Children welcome. Baby facilities. Pets welcome. TV. Confirm by 6

SHIPTON GORGE Dorset — map 2

▲ *Innsacre Farmhouse Hotel* [12/20]

Shipton Gorge BT6 4LJ
BRIDPORT (0308) 56137
off A35, 2m SE of Bridport — £11–£14

The dining-room is a long, low, stone building where the Smiths bred rare pigs before opening as a restaurant with rooms 18 months ago. As you go up the drive the remaining five pigs may be eating last night's slops of lobster shells and ox-tail bones. The menu is short, well put together and good value (lobster only £2 extra). All good have been the ox-tail soup; pigeon salad with pine kernels; oriental beef with water-chestnuts, bamboo shoots and oyster sauce; and the Sunday lunch of mixed hors d'oeuvre and roast beef. The ingredients, including excellent fish, are in their prime, and vegetables are varied without being ostentatious. Cheese and sweets tend to the conservative but show the same care in handling. Service is jovial and afternoon tea includes home-made biscuits. Rooms are more boarding-house than hotel. A functional wine list.

CHEFS: H.M.Smith, C.Cooke and T.Windsor PROPRIETORS: J.H. and H.M.Smith
OPEN: all week MEALS: 12 to 2, 7.15 to 10.30
PRICES: Set L £7·25 (£11), Set D £10·25 (£14), Snacks from £2 (£2·20) CARDS: Access, Amex, Diners, Visa
SEATS: 42. 4 tables outside. Private parties: 60 main room. Car-park, 40 places. Vegetarian meals. Children's helpings. No cigars/pipes in dining-room. Wheelchair access (also WC). Classical music
ACCOMMODATION: 5 rooms, 1 with bath/shower. B&B £14 to £28. Deposit: 10%. Children welcome. Baby facilities. Pets welcome. Afternoon teas. Garden. Scenic. Confirm by 7

SHIPTON-UNDER-WYCHWOOD Oxfordshire — map 2

▲ *Lamb Inn* [10/20]

Shipton-under-Wychwood OX7 6DQ
SHIPTON-UNDER-WYCHWOOD (0993) 830465 — £9–£13

A comfortable old Cotswold stone inn with a strong local following for honest straightforward cooking, served either in the bar or in the dark dining-room. Vegetarians do well and Sunday lunch is good value. Good dishes have been the main courses of honey-roast lamb in its own juices; roast beef and Yorkshire pudding; the show of fresh vegetables. English traditional sweets include trifle, rhubarb pie and treacle tart. The Pavlovas are good, too. Hook Norton beers and a better than average pub wine list that includes a pair of Kuentz-Bas Alsace wines.

CHEF: George Benham PROPRIETORS: Hugh and Lynne Wainwright
OPEN: Mon to Sat, D only, and Sun L MEALS: 12.30 to 1.45, 7.30 to 9.15
PRICES: Set L from £6·50 (£9), Set D from £10 (£13). Service inc CARDS: Access, Amex, Diners, Visa
SEATS: 26. Private parties: 26 main room. Car-park, 30 places. No children under 14. Wheelchair access
ACCOMMODATION: 5 rooms, all with bath/shower. B&B £20 to £30. Deposit: £10. No children under 14. No pets. Garden. Confirm by 6

SHREWSBURY Shropshire map 5

Delany's [9/20]

St Julians Craft Centre, St Alkmonds Square,
Shrewsbury SY1 1UH
SHREWSBURY (0743) 60602 **Real Food** £7

The PVC green cloths are pretty vivid in this vegetarian restaurant. It is a funky small room in what used to be the vestry of the church and is now a craft centre. The ingredients are Real Food – free-range eggs, fresh bread baked daily, organic vegetables – and they underwrite the cooking, the blackboard menu reflecting the seasons and a range of flavours and textures. Good dishes have been the carrot soup, courgette and mushroom bake, and the inventive salads like kidney beans with celery, tomato and onion. More use of fresh rather than dried herbs would improve matters even more. A speciality is cauliflower in a rich paprika and yoghourt sauce topped with poppy seeds. House French is £2·95 for 25cl.

CHEFS/PROPRIETORS: Peter Gwynne and Gary Kirkman
OPEN: Mon to Sat, L only, and Sat D MEALS: 10.30 to 2.30, 8 to 8.30
PRICES: £4 (£7). Service inc
SEATS: 32. Private parties: 32 main room. Vegetarian meals. Children welcome. No smoking. Jazz. Self-service

Old Police House [11/20]

Castle Court, Castle Street, Shrewsbury SY1 2BG
SHREWSBURY (0743) 60668 £8–£15

This county jail and police station now has vines and creepers in the garden and all kinds of Victoriana inside. Order in the bar-lounge before moving into the candle-lit dining-room. Ham cornets are filled with asparagus; duck and liver pâté comes en croûte with a creamy pepper sauce; Wye salmon is served with fennel sauce; and roast beef is with savoury dumplings. Vegetables are a good assortment, but come in *nouvelle* portions. Second helpings of apple tart or lemon Swiss roll with chocolate sauce are offered freely, though. Interesting wines, well chosen at the cheap end: Bulgarian Cabernet Sauvignon is £5·20, and Château

▲ *This restaurant has rooms.*

du Grand Moulas '83 is £5·35. CELLARMAN'S CHOICE: Châteauneuf-du-Pape, Domaine du Vieux Télégraphe '81 at £9·45.

CHEF: David Campbell PROPRIETOR: Simon Rudd-Clarke
OPEN: Mon to Sat, exc Sat L MEALS: 12 to 1.45, 7 to 9.45
PRICES: Set L from £4·50 (£8), Set D £10·95 (£15) CARDS: Access, Amex, Diners, Visa
SEATS: 36. Private parties: 20 main room, 10 private room. Car-park, 2 places. Vegetarian meals. Children's helpings. No-smoking area. Classical music

SHURDINGTON Gloucestershire map 2

▲ *The Greenway* [11/20]

Shurdington GL51 5UG
CHELTENHAM (0242) 862352
on A46 2½m S of Cheltenham £9–£20

A plush, sixteenth-century manor approached up a long drive. The small dining-room overlooks a stone patio and lily pond, with parkland and a pair of splendid oaks beyond. The set menu is swanky, featuring ravioli stuffed with lobster and served with a cheese and mustard sauce, and boned quails served with their eggs and a madeira sauce. Main courses of poached salmon with a cream and chive sauce, and the spring lamb with onion sauce to the side – both served with excellent vegetables – have been good, which is a positive sign, though as yet other dishes have not been sufficently well-balanced to justify a rating of 12. The pastry department is being expanded, and fresh bread and more varied puddings are on the way. 'Our maximum mark-up on any wine is £10,' explains Tony Elliott, which means that the best value is in the expensive clarets, though Beaujolais and Rhônes are not overpriced. From Alsace there is Muscat, Réserve '83, from Trimbach, at £10·70. On the other hand Montagny '82 at £16·30 must earn nearly the whole tenner. A new injection of 22 half-bottles should help.

CHEF: William Bennett PROPRIETORS: Tony and Maryan Elliott
OPEN: all week, exc Sat L and Sun D CLOSED: L bank hol Mons MEALS: 12.30 to 2, 7.30 to 9
PRICES: Set L £6 and £12 (£9 and £15), Set D £17·50 (£20). Service inc CARDS: Access, Amex, Diners, Visa
SEATS: 35. 4 tables outside. Private parties: 10 main room, 22 and 12 private rooms. Car-park, 30 places. Vegetarian meals. No children under 7. Jacket and tie preferred. No cigars/pipes in dining-room. Wheelchair access (also WC)
ACCOMMODATION: 12 rooms, all with bath/shower. B&B £50 to £65. No children under 7. No pets. Garden. Croquet. Helicopter pad. TV. Phone. Scenic. Doors close at 12

SILEBY Leicestershire map 5

Old School Restaurant [11/20]

7 Barrow Road, Sileby LE12 7LW
SILEBY (050 981) 3941 £9–£13

Good honest English cooking is served in this granite and slate school house, which still has the old school desks, dunce's hat, cane and gowns. Steak and Guinness pie; ox-tail casserole; rabbit in mustard and cider are popular. Help yourself from a tureen of soup. Proprietor Jackie Baum (formerly Jackie Fleet) tells us that her mother still prepares all the sweets and her father looks after the wine. House red is £4·95.

CHEF/PROPRIETOR: Jackie Baum
OPEN: L Tue to Fri and Sun, D Mon to Sat CLOSED: 1 to 15 July and 26 Dec to 1 Jan
MEALS: 12 to 2, 7 to 9.30 (6.30 to 10 Sat)
PRICES: £8·50 (£13), Set Sun L £5·75 (£9) CARDS: Access, Amex, Visa
SEATS: 60. Private parties: 75 main room, 50 private room. Vegetarian meals. Car-park, 35 places. Smart dress preferred. Children's helpings. Wheelchair access (also WC). Music

SKIPTON North Yorkshire map 5

▲ *Oats* [new entry, zero rated]

Chapel Hill, Skipton BD23 1NL
SKIPTON (0756) 68118/9 £10–£20

A square-set, double-fronted stone building with floral sofas, lace curtains, a carved Victorian sideboard, and dark glass tables with chrome legs. After it was dropped from the *Guide* last year (following a senior inspector's report), readers wrote in to recommend its reinstatement. The *Guide* is nothing if not democratic, so here it is. A wide range of dishes has been enjoyed, from spicy tomato soup, to thinly sliced pink calf's liver with a light, piquant sauce, to salmon set in aspic and looking like Battenberg cake. Duck has come out well, too: sauté livers in puff pastry; pink breast served with duck pâté. Sauces made from pan juices and alcohol, not flour; a bargain lunch for £5; and crisp canapés and crudités have all pleased customers. So we despatched another senior inspector, who this time reported fresh scallops, pink calf's liver, and home-made pineapple sorbet, but all this off-set by poor pastry; thick sauces everywhere, some covered with skin; insipid, rubbery vegetables; and dishes not appearing as described – mangoes supposedly poached in red wine, for instance, came unpoached. Service is willing, efficient and helpful. The strength of the *Guide* is that users should say which restaurants ought to be included. Most of the time we agree, but in the case of Oats cuisine we have our differences. House wine is £5·75.
CELLARMAN'S CHOICE: Côtes du Rhône, Les Grands Bois '84 from François Peyret, at £6·95 (£3·80 for a half-bottle). More reports, please.

CHEF: Roger M. Grime PROPRIETOR: Martin Duce
OPEN: Tue to Sat MEALS: 12 to 2, 7 to 9.45
PRICES: £14 (£20), Set L £5 (£10), Set D £10 (£15) CARDS: Access, Amex, Diners, Visa
SEATS: 50. Private parties: 45 main room, 40 and 20 private rooms. Car-park, 40 places. Children's helpings. Jacket and tie preferred. No cigars/pipes in dining-room. Wheelchair access (also WC). Music. Air-conditioned
ACCOMMODATION: 5 rooms, all with bath/shower. Rooms for disabled. B&B £42 to £68. Children welcome. Air-conditioning. TV. Phone. Doors close at 12. Confirm by 2

The 1987 Guide will appear before Christmas 1986, so reports are particularly important in the spring. Report forms are at the back of this book, but just write a letter if you prefer. Address them to The Good Food Guide, *Freepost, 14 Buckingham Street, London WC2N 6BR. No stamp is necessary if you post in the UK.*

SLAIDBURN Lancashire map 5

▲ *Parrock Head Farm* [10/20]

Slaidburn BB7 3AH
SLAIDBURN (020 06) 614
1m NW of Slaidburn £11

Good plain cooking is to be found in this remote seventeenth-century working farm. The atmosphere is homely and comfortable. The linen is crisp and white, and there are fresh flowers everywhere. The soups are good, or there are Morecambe Bay shrimps on toast or a Norwegian cocktail of apple, prawn and celery to start. Fillet steak comes with herb butter, or there may be Bowland venison. Vegetables are cooked firm and there is no stinting. To finish there are fruit pies, cherries marinated in brandy, or meringue with cream. The drive from Clitheroe is scenic and the upstairs lounge is comfortable. Breakfasts are spectacularly good. Some inexpensive wines.

CHEF/PROPRIETOR: Patricia Holt
OPEN: all week, exc Sun L CLOSED: Dec and Jan MEALS: 12.15 to 2, 6.30 to 8
PRICES: £9 (£11). Snacks from £2. Service inc CARD: Amex
SEATS: 25. Private parties: 16 main room. Car-park, 20 places. Children's helpings. Wheelchair access (also WC)
ACCOMMODATION: 7 rooms, all with bath/shower. Rooms for disabled. B&B £16 (double). Pets welcome. Afternoon teas. Garden. TV. Scenic. Doors close at 12 [GHG]

SMARDEN Kent map 3

▲ *The Bell* [9/20]

Bell Lane, Smarden TN27 8PW
SMARDEN (023 377) 283 £2+

Smarden prides itself on being one of the best-kept villages in Kent, and the local is pretty well kept too: a fifteenth-century pub with stone floors, open fireplaces, a large garden, good-value snacks – sandwiches, salads, pizzas and basket meals with chips. The steak and kidney pie is generous. Real ales: Fremlins, Young's, Fuller's, Theakston's, and local Biddenden cider.

CHEF: Lesley Banks PROPRIETOR: Ian Turner
OPEN: all week CLOSED: 25 Dec MEALS: 12 to 2, 6.30 to 10 (10.30 Fri and Sat)
PRICES: Bar meals from £1·95, Snacks from 70p. Service inc CARDS: Access, Visa
SEATS: 60. 15 tables outside. Private parties: 20 main room. Car-park, 18 places. Vegetarian meals. Children's helpings. Wheelchair access
ACCOMMODATION: 4 rooms. B&B £10 to £18. Deposit: £10. Children welcome. Pets welcome. Garden. TV. Confirm by 12

Restaurant tricks (3): The bad practice of making a cover charge is dying out, but please report to us on any restaurant still doing so.

CELLARMAN'S CHOICE: This is a wine that is more expensive than the house wine but is good value and fitting for the kind of food served.

SOLIHULL West Midlands map 5

Liaison [12/20]

761 Old Lode Lane, Solihull BG2 8JE
021-743 3993 £17–£22

This white and green, modern restaurant does many interesting dishes, for instance salmon marinated with herbs, lime juices and passion fruit; shellfish minestrone; and chicken with a sorrel and peach sauce. The accent is put strongly on presentation, but without losing sight of the principal purpose. Especially good have been the duck and wild mushroom salad dressed with the juice of wild strawberries; lamb fillet with rosemary; and plaice with a cream sauce. Vegetables are served on a side-plate; French cheeses come with walnut bread. To finish, pancakes are filled with chocolate and hazel-nuts and served with a mint sauce. Coffee is kept warm on little heaters. House Chardonnay is £5·95. CELLARMAN'S CHOICE: Quincy '83 at £7·25. A range of marcs and eaux-de-vie.

CHEF: Patricia Plunkett PROPRIETORS: Patricia Plunkett and Ank Van Der Tuin
OPEN: Tue to Sat, D only CLOSED: 2 weeks at Christmas, all of Aug MEALS: 7 to 10
PRICES: £16 (£22), Set D Tue £12·50 (£17) CARDS: Access, Amex, Diners, Visa
SEATS: 34. Private parties: 40 main room. Children welcome. No pipes in dining-room. Wheelchair access. Music

SOUTHALL Greater London map 3

BACKGROUND BRIEFING: *Little India. Even the smallest fast-food kiosk has a name such as Shahi Nan Kebab, and signs that elsewhere might read, 'Baptist Church,' here say, 'Guru Granth Gurdwana.' Getting off the train at Southall, turn either left towards old Southall, where there is the Roxy (real name – Sagoo & Takhar), 114 The Green, which is constantly nominated for its cheapness, and The Brilliant (see entry), or right towards the Broadway. This is a continuation of the Uxbridge Road and has some interesting eating. Moti Mahal at number 94 is a Bombay version of McDonalds, with a young crowd having a good time and, on the walls, back-lit photos of tikkas and kebabs. The Babu is a Pakistani place with excellent spinach curry, while the Maharaja at 171–175 is the establishment most recommended to Westerners in this part of town. General stores for all kinds of Indian consumables include Sira and Dokal. Royal Sweet & Bombay Halwa Ltd has the best sweet-meats. The cooks at most high street tandooris could learn something even from the tiny kiosk on the railway bridge, where for £1·35 a kebab roll and a can of coconut soda provide a riot of fresh, vivid flavours.*

Brilliant [11/20]

72–74 Western Road, Southall UB2 5DZ
01-574 1928 £10–£12

Not just a restaurant but a great place to eat and a focus for the local Asian community: grannies and children pile in and are still eating at midnight. Formica-topped tables are set up in rows like in a canteen, and the menu brings no surprises. Fried eggs have a hot chilli injection and are deep-fried in pakora batter, and vegetable samosa is big on spices, but most people start with buttered or jeera chicken. Half a masaladar chicken at £10 seems expensive, but it serves two to three people. Big potatoes come with chunks of gummy aubergine in a rich sauce; keema peas are unbeatable. Perfectly friendly and informative service. Drink lassi, or Kenyan or Kingfisher beer.

CHEF: D.K. Anand PROPRIETORS: K.K. and D.K. Anand
OPEN: Tue to Sun, exc Sat and Sun L CLOSED: Aug MEALS: 12 to 3, 6 to 11.30 (12 Fri and Sat)
PRICES: £9 (£16), Set L from £6 (£10), Set D from £8 (£12). Service 10% CARDS: Access, Amex, Diners, Visa
SEATS: 120. Private parties: 80 main room, 40 private room. Vegetarian meals. Children's helpings. Wheelchair access (also wc). Indian music. Air-conditioned

SOUTHAMPTON Hampshire map 2

Pearl Harbour [9/20]

86A–88A Above Bar Street,
Southampton SO1 0DT
SOUTHAMPTON (0703) 225248 £6–£14

The English cooking is unimpressive but the Chinese is another story – good hot-and-sour soup, lemon chicken, crispy beef with black bean sauce, and paper-wrapped prawns are served in this first-floor restaurant. House French is £4·50.

CHEF: K.H. Li PROPRIETOR: Tony Y.M. Chan
OPEN: all week MEALS: noon to 11.30 (12 Fri and Sat)
PRICES: £7 (£14), Set L from £2·50 (£6), Set D from £6·50 (£10). Service 10%
CARDS: Access, Amex, Diners, Visa
SEATS: 120. Private parties: 150 main room. Vegetarian meals. Children's helpings. Music. Air-conditioned

SOUTHEND-ON-SEA Essex map 3

Alvaro's [10/20]

32–34 St Helens Road, Westcliffe-on-Sea,
Southend SS0 7LB
SOUTHEND-ON-SEA (0702) 335840 £10–£19

A family-run Portuguese restaurant that serves good fish dishes, such as fish casserole, grilled sardines, and scallops with pork and bacon. To finish there is apple, sultana and cinnamon pie. There is a range of ports and madeiras, as well as good-value Portuguese wines.

CHEF: Jose Rodrigues PROPRIETORS: Alvaro and Joyce Rodrigues and Jose Rodrigues
OPEN: Tue to Sun, exc Sat L MEALS: 12 to 2 (2.30 Sun), 7 to 10.30 (11 Fri and Sat, 10 Sun)
PRICES: £12 (£19), Set Sun L £6·75 (£10). Service 10% CARDS: Access, Visa
SEATS: 60. Vegetarian meals by arrangement. Children's helpings. Smart dress preferred. Wheelchair access. Music

Places rating 8 or 9 may not be restaurants at all but still serve very good food. In this category expect to find pubs, cafes, small hotels and wine bars.

Pipe of Port Wine Bar [9/20]

84 High Street, Southend-on-Sea SS1 1HS
SOUTHEND-ON-SEA (0702) 614606
entrance in Tylers Avenue £11

A basement wine bar serving some home-made items, particularly pies – steak and kidney with mushroom; game; and vegetarian – plus Scotch salmon in season. Ports are a speciality, with half a dozen normally available by the glass. Champagne is available by the tankard, and a short list of wines includes CELLARMAN'S CHOICE: Gisselbrecht's '83 Pinot d'Alsace, at £5·40.

CHEFS/PROPRIETORS: S.A.Jones, S.E.Jones, J.Cliff and I.W.McCormack
OPEN: Mon to Sat MEALS: 11 to 2.15, 6.30 to 10.45
PRICES: £7 (£11), Snacks from £1·10 (£1·20) CARDS: Access, Diners, Visa
SEATS: 130. Private parties: 40 main room, 40 and 20 private rooms. Vegetarian meals. No children under 16. Smart dress preferred. Music

Slassor's [10/20]

145 Eastern Esplanade, Southend-on-Sea SS1 2YD
SOUTHEND-ON-SEA (0702) 614880 £11

The Coke and Vimto cans on display belie the quality of the menu. Leslie Slassor works behind a glass partition at the back of the brightly lit dining-room, while his wife Margaret waits on the seven red-and-white-clothed tables. Fish is the main business, with thermidors of prawns (fairly rich) or monkfish; hearty bourrides; baked dishes of eggs and smoked haddock; salmon with prawns. Veal is also stuffed with prawns and is deep-fried. The chicken with calvados has also been good; vegetables less so. To finish there is a pretty conceit of a large meringue swan filled with good, buttery vanilla ice-cream and cream, with an identical cygnet in its wake. The cheesecake is first-class and the trifle alcoholic. Coffee and other trimmings could sharpen up a little and would raise the rating happily. Unlicensed, but there's an off-licence next door which keeps white wine in the fridge.

CHEF: Leslie Slassor PROPRIETORS: Margaret and Leslie Slassor
OPEN: Mon to Sat, exc Mon L MEALS: 12 to 2, 7 to 9.30
PRICES: £9 (£11). Unlicensed, but bring your own: corkage 75p CARDS: Access, Visa
SEATS: 22. Private parties: 30 main room. Children's helpings. Music

SOUTH GODSTONE Surrey map 3

La Bonne Auberge [12/20]

Tilburstow Hill, South Godstone RH9 8JY
SOUTH GODSTONE (0342) 893184 £17

The standard of presentation and the aspirations at this neat French restaurant are high. The menu is gastronomic chic – dishes include bone-marrow en brioche with beurre rouge; guinea-fowl cooked in Vacqueyras; and a pre-dessert sweet. The service is excellent and there are endorsements on file for 52 different dishes, ranging from the show of breads to scallops with basil in a vol-au-vent, to brill with beurre rouge (a popular sauce which is a beurre blanc using red wine), to pepper steaks, to lemon tart. If some of the inconsistencies could be ruled out of meals a higher rating would be possible. Choosing a better table butter would be a good start. Coffee is served in the lounge. The wine list underwrites the restaurant's ambition with fine spreads in all the major regions and mark-ups to the tune of 100 per cent. The house Merlot is sensibly pegged at £5·35 but the Alsace is good for £2 to £3 more. Their German wines and Rhônes are a bit young yet, but there are fine bottles from everywhere else.

CHEF: Jean-Pierre Bonnet PROPRIETOR: Antoine L.S.Jalley
OPEN: Tue to Sun, exc Sun D MEALS: 12.15 to 2, 7 to 10
PRICES: Set L and D from £13 (£17). Service inc CARDS: Access, Amex, Diners, Visa
SEATS: 48. 4 tables outside. Private parties: 80 main room, 20 private room. Car-park, 70 places. Vegetarian meals by arrangement. Children's helpings. Smart dress preferred. Wheelchair access (also WC). Classical music

SOUTH MOLTON Devon map 1

▲ *Stumbles* [11/20]

131–134 East Street, South Molton EX36 3BU
SOUTH MOLTON (076 95) 3683 £11–£16

There are some interesting things to eat in this wine bar-cum-restaurant, which was originally two late-sixteenth-century cottages. A soup of fresh oysters, for instance, or Swedish roast lamb with a sauce made from black coffee, cream and brown sugar. The pork butchery is by Heal Farm at King's Nympton, which raises traditional breeds and cures in the old-fashioned way – on the menu may be grilled loin with Stilton sauce, home-baked hams, and bacon sausages. There is a new, Chinese dimension, producing crab with black bean and soy sauce and sherry, and Cantonese duck, both rare enough in these parts where the ethnic revolution has yet to percolate. The wine list is not quite the peer of that at Highbullen Hotel, run by Colette Potter's parents (see Chittlehamholt), but nevertheless has some very fine bottles indeed – Brouilly, Ch. des Tours '83 is £7·90; Lebanese Château Musar '78 is £9.50; and the Australian Sémillon '83 from Rothbury Estate is £9·80. House French is £5·50.

CHEF: Colette Potter PROPRIETORS: Mr and Mrs M.J. Potter
OPEN: all week, exc Sun D MEALS: 12.30 to 2.30, 7.30 to 10
PRICES: £11 (£16), Set Sun L £7·50 (£11), L snacks from £1·50 (£1·65) CARDS: Access, Amex, Diners, Visa
SEATS: 50. 10 tables outside. Private parties: 50 main room. Car-park, 30 places. Vegetarian meals. Children's helpings. Classical music
ACCOMMODATION: 7 rooms, all with bath/shower. Rooms for disabled. B&B £15 to £25. Children welcome. No pets in public rooms. Afternoon teas. TV

SOUTHSEA Hampshire map 2

BACKGROUND BRIEFING: *Many cheap eating places have appeared in the last couple of years, notably Fatty Arbuckle's, and Barnaby's on Osborne Road. For wholefoods try Country Kitchen in Marmion Road; in the same street Brewers sells an interesting range of teas and coffees. Akram Stores in Palmerston Road is good for Indian spices and groceries, while Jays in Castle Road has good cheeses and will cook hams to order.*

Bistro Montparnasse [10/20]

103 Palmerston Road, Southsea PO5 3PS
PORTSMOUTH (0705) 816754 £15

A smart bistro in the Southsea shopping-centre, done out in terracotta with framed posters and hanging plants. The straightforward Anglo-French menu changes monthly and might be more adventurous, but local seafood is used, and lobster is simply and effectively grilled with tarragon butter. Large, meaty mushrooms come with garlic butter; carrot and coriander soup is subtly flavoured; and guinea-fowl is casseroled in a boozy wine sauce. Chocolate tipsy trifle is like mother used to make. Service, enthusiastic and charming, is by shirt-sleeved young men and a French waitress. The 40 mostly French wines owe a lot to Harveys and CELLARMAN'S CHOICE is Les Forts de Latour '74 at £12·40.

CHEF: Diana Grosvenor PROPRIETORS: Colin Herbert and Diana Grosvenor
OPEN: Mon to Sat, D only CLOSED: 25 to 27 Dec and 1st week Jan MEALS: 7 to 11 (12 Sat)
PRICES: £9 (£15) CARDS: Access, Amex, Diners, Visa
SEATS: 40. Private parties: 18 main room. Vegetarian meals by arrangement. Children's helpings. Wheelchair access. Music. Air-conditioned

---

SOUTHWELL Nottinghamshire map 5

Leo's [new entry, zero rated]

12 King Street, Southwell NG24 0EN
SOUTHWELL (0636) 812119 £17

A half-timbered Grade II listed Georgian building that fronts the main road, with a side entrance and pre-war Hollywood decor. Ambitions are high: 'lamb poached with vegetables in the style of Mosimann' is a trimmed fillet with greens; and conger eel, rock salmon, monkfish and hake rendezvous in a tomato and fennel sauce. But in practice the master's touch is often conspicuous by its absence; the fish terrine has been soft-textured and lemon cake disappointing. But it is still good for Nottingham, offering home-cured salmon with mango; parsnip timbale with spicy vinaigrette; and strips of rare beef with paprika, anchovy and cream. Service needs to catch up with the kitchen. Wines go from racy Lamborghini at £6·40, through Faustino Gran Reserva Rioja '76 at £7·90, to Ch. Cos-d'Estournel '70 at £65.

CHEF: Heather Hodgkinson PROPRIETORS: Heather and Tony Hodgkinson
OPEN: Wed to Sat D, Sun L (L other days by arrangement) MEALS: 12 to 2, 7 to 10
PRICES: Set L and D £12·50 (£17) CARDS: Amex, Diners, Visa
SEATS: 26. Private parties: 30 main room. Children's helpings. Music. Air-conditioned

---

SOUTHWOLD Suffolk map 6

▲ *The Crown* [new entry, zero rated]

90 High Street, Southwold IP18 6DP
SOUTHWOLD (0502) 722275 £12–£14

An eighteenth-century inn restored by Adnams the wine merchants serving bar food and real ales as well as restaurant meals. There is spotlit dining-room set up by Sue Miles (ex-Escargot and Soho Brasserie in London). The three-course menus include a couple of choices at each stage. Fish is from the local boats – look for the steamed cod with soy, ginger and spring onion, and the Southwold fish soup. The wine list is a corker, offering the whole of Adnams' cellar (with notice), and there is a cruover machine for tasting by the glass. More reports, please.

CHEF: Sue Miles PROPRIETORS: Adnams plc
OPEN: all week, exc Mon D and Tue D MEALS: 12 to 2, 7.30 to 10
PRICES: £11 (£14), Set L £9 (£12), Set D £10 (£13). Service inc CARDS: Access, Amex, Visa
SEATS: 24. 4 tables outside. Private parties: 40 private room. Car-park, 10 places. Children's helpings
ACCOMMODATION: 10 rooms, all with bath/shower. B&B £20 to £32. Children welcome. Baby facilities. Pets by arrangement. Afternoon teas. TV. Phone

SPARK BRIDGE Cumbria — map 7

▲ *Bridgefield House* [12/20]

Spark Bridge LA12 8DA
LOWICK BRIDGE (022 985) 239
4m N of Ulverston, off A5084 on back road from Spark Bridge to Coniston

Real Food £16

A stone and slate Victorian building set in three acres of farmland overlooking the River Crake. The scenery is flatter and more peaceful than other parts of the Lakes but no less beautiful. Rosemary and David Glister have been restoring the carved ceilings, cast-iron fireplaces and tiled hearths. The six-course menu changes from day to day. It always includes a savoury and is Real Food down to the oatmeal biscuits with leek and potato soup and the free-range eggs from their chickens. Main dishes come with four vegetables – turkey breast with herb breadcrumbs and sauté potatoes, Jerusalem artichokes with cream, pan-fried celery and peppers, buttered broccoli. They are 85 per cent self-sufficient in vegetables. Also good, and unusual, has been potted goose with sage jelly. The sweets course is a high spot, with blueberry and Bramley apples with cream, Jamaican bananas with Tia Maria and toasted almonds, or kiwi and Grand Marnier meringue. Last, but not least, the choice is between a pear with Stilton and walnuts or poached quails' eggs on toast. Good breakfast grills. The welcome is always warm. Plenty of half-bottles run throughout the good wine list; look for the '78 white burgundies. House Premières Côtes de Bordeaux is £5·40.

CHEF: Rosemary Glister PROPRIETORS: David and Rosemary Glister
OPEN: all week, D only MEALS: 7.30 for 8
PRICES: Set D £12·50 (£16) CARDS: Access, Amex, Diners
SEATS: 24. Private parties: 24 main room. Car-park, 10 places. No smoking in dining-room. Vegetarian meals. Children's helpings. Wheelchair access (also WC). One sitting
ACCOMMODATION: 6 rooms, 4 with bath/shower. Rooms for disabled. B&B £13·50 to £40. Children welcome. Baby facilities. Pets welcome. Garden. Fishing. Scenic. Confirm by 5 [GHG]

Restaurant tricks (4): Charging for service but leaving the total on the credit card slip blank, thus inviting an extra tip.

SPILSBY Lincolnshire map 6

Buttercross [9/20]

18 Lower Market, Spilsby PE23 5JT
SPILSBY (0790) 53147 £8–£9

Morning coffee, moderate lunches and full-scale dinners are served in this husband-and-wife-run English bistro. It is comfortable and rural, with pine furniture, and toilets across the yard. The evening meals can come up trumps with roast guinea-fowl one night, or else lamb cutlets cooked Lincolnshire style – no pink at all. Sweets are home made, and the bananas fried in butter are the pick. 'We cater for people arriving by Rolls-Royce or by bus.' House French is £4·75.

CHEF: Tim Boskett PROPRIETORS: Tim and Janette Boskett
OPEN: Daytime Mon to Sat, plus Fri and Sat D MEALS: 10 to 4.30 (2 Tues), 7.30 to 9.30
PRICES: L £4 (£8), Set D from £6 (£9), Snacks from 90p (£1)
SEATS: 40. 2 tables outside. Private parties: 20 main room. Vegetarian meals. Children welcome. Wheelchair access. Classical music

SPURSTOW Cheshire map 5

Rembrandt [10/20]

Whitchurch Road, Spurstow CW6 9TD
BUNBURY (0829) 260281
on A49, 4m S of Tarporley £13–£20

Well-run pink French restaurant with a classically inclined menu that encompasses Parma ham with melon, chicken chasseur and big steaks 'cooked not more than medium'. Fish, including oysters and lobster, is the main force – witness the avocado filled with prawns, and sea-bass and shrimps with a lightly curried cheese sauce. The wild duck has also been good and there is a vast array of sweets. Clarets go back to the '60s, albeit at a price, and there is a strong Alsace section to the list with half-bottles of Tokay '78, and also Muscat '83, both from Hugel, and both at £5·20. CELLARMAN'S CHOICE: Pinot Blanc '83, from Hugel, at £8·15.

CHEF: A.J.Phillips PROPRIETOR: R.I.Roberts
OPEN: Tue to Sun, exc Sun L CLOSED: bank hols, exc 25 Dec MEALS: 12 to 3, 7 to 10
PRICES: £16 (£20), Set L and D £9·70 (£13), Bar meals from £2·25. Service inc
CARDS: Access, Diners, Visa
SEATS: 80. Private parties: 80 main room, 20 and 24 private rooms. Car-park, 100 places. Vegetarian meals. Children welcome. Jacket and tie. No pipes in dining-room. Wheelchair access. Music. Air-conditioned

Places rating 8 or 9 may not be restaurants at all but still serve very good food. In this category expect to find pubs, cafes, small hotels and wine bars.

If you suspect that a restaurant is using processed food, always ask. It would be a contravention of the Trade Descriptions Act for the restaurant to lie.

STADDLEBRIDGE North Yorkshire map 7

▲ *McCoy's* [13/20]

The Tontine, Staddlebridge DL6 3JB
EAST HARLSEY (060 982) 671
junction of A19 and A172 £27

This was the mail stop between York and Newcastle in the days of coach and horses. Now it is one of the more distinctive restaurants in the north. Hoagy Carmichael croons every night, the stuffing still comes out of the sofas, bare wires still hang out of the walls. The cutlery is pretty grotty, and the starched, deep-pink cloths are darned in matching pink cotton. There is no pomp, pressure or pretensions, but the food varies from the good to the sublime – witness the kidneys in the middle of a white plate, surrounded by a copper-brown meat demi-glaze and on top of them a yellow cream and mustard sauce; or a whole, square wafer of thin, buttery pastry built in layers and sandwiched with a delicate crème pâtissière and finely sliced fresh peaches, the top caramelised with a salamander to give a criss-cross effect. Other fine dishes from the jet-black shiny covered menus are the mousse of scallops embedded with coral garnished with beluga caviare and served with a lemon vinaigrette; the raw marinated beef that tastes rather better than it looks; wild mushrooms in puff pastry; or a whole Whitby lobster with a tomato purée. The bread has improved, and the local unsalted butter is excellent – served in a child's nursery saucer with a duck, teddy bear and Larry the Lamb on it. It is a radical place, although the wine list is less so, concentrating on expensive claret and burgundy. A new addition of half-bottles is a shrewd move, however, and includes Ch. Cissac '70 at £15, and others around £4.

CHEFS/PROPRIETORS: The McCoy family
OPEN: all week, D only CLOSED: 25 Dec, 1 Jan MEALS: 7 to 10.30
PRICES: £20 (£27) CARDS: Access, Amex, Diners, Visa
SEATS: 60. 15 tables outside. Private parties: 40 main room, 40 private room. Car-park, 100 places. Vegetarian meals. Children's helpings. Music. Air-conditioned
ACCOMMODATION: 8 rooms, all with bath/shower. B&B £37·50 to £47·50. Children welcome. Baby facilities. Pets welcome. Afternoon teas. Garden. Helicopter pad. Air-conditioning. TV. Phone. Scenic

McCoy's Bistro [11/20]

The Tontine, Staddlebridge DL6 3JB
EAST HARLSEY (060 982) 671
junction of A19 and A172 £8–£17

The basement bistro, in what used to be the servants' quarters to the above entry, is one of the most popular eating places in the area. This is good food. The short menu is strong on fish, and prices are substantially lower than at McCoy's. The black pudding is French, rather than Yorkshire, otherwise look to the tours de

'The weekly visit to market by one of the chefs has proved a good change. Better, far far better, selection of fresh produce . . . and it has given the kitchen more pride in their product.' (Lakeland restaurateur)

force of salmon Wellington or huge Dover soles. There's Camerons real ale, or house burgundy at £6·55.

CHEFS/PROPRIETORS: The McCoy family
OPEN: all week CLOSED: 25 Dec, 1 Jan MEALS: 12 to 2.30, 7 to 10.30
PRICES: £11 (£17), Set L from £3·50 (£8), Set D from £6 (£11) CARDS: Access, Amex, Diners, Visa
SEATS: 60. Private parties: 70 main room. Car-park, 100 places. Vegetarian meals. Children's helpings. Music. Air-conditioned

STAMFORD Lincolnshire map 6

▲ *The George* [11/20]

71 St Martin's, Stamford PE9 2LB
STAMFORD (0780) 55171 £21

A justifiably famous old coaching-inn. The cold buffet is first-class, with cuts of beef, game pie and salads of many colours. Hot dishes are equally good, notably the boiled silverside with dumplings and baked potatoes, and the roasts. It is a large place and the service fluctuates according to the pressure of private parties, which on a big wedding Saturday may be considerable. Steaks are char-grilled in the historic open courtyard. Meals in the spacious dining-room have lost poise as they have become more French. Breakfasts are traditional fry-ups and are cooked to order. There are interesting Italian wines on the buffet/bar menu and it is possible to drink well and cheaply, if you have read your Hugh Johnson carefully, especially of the '83 Germans – Rüdesheimer Berg Rottland Riesling, Kabinett, '83, is £11·35. CELLARMAN'S CHOICE: Muscadet, Cuvée Laurent Sauvion '84, a gold medal winner that is £9·55.

CHEF: Chris Pitman PROPRIETORS: Poste Hotels Ltd
OPEN: all week MEALS: 12.30 to 2.30, 7.30 to 10.30
PRICES: £15 (£21), Bar meals and snacks from £2. Cover 60p. Service inc CARDS: Access, Amex, Diners, Visa
SEATS: 85. 20 tables outside. Private parties: 30, 22, 20 and 10 private rooms. Car-park, 150 places. Vegetarian meals. Children's helpings. Smart dress preferred. Wheelchair access (also WC)
ACCOMMODATION: 44 rooms, all with bath/shower. B&B £42·50 to £58·72. Children welcome. Baby facilities. Small dogs welcome. Afternoon teas. Garden. Croquet. TV. Phone [GHG]

STAPLETON North Yorkshire map 7

Bridge Inn [11/20]

Stapleton DL2 2QQ
DARLINGTON (0325) 50106
2m SW of Darlington £5–£16

Nicholas Young's kitchen serves a large, friendly bar with steak sandwiches and ploughman's lunches as well as serving the comfortable Victorian dining-room. The smoked salmon from Craster is superb, served with home-made rolls made from flour from Carrs at Silloth (not Muncaster, as we said last year). The care to ensure good ingredients extends to bringing fresh fish from Hartlepool, and finding a local gamekeeper who breeds quails, which are roasted stuffed with garlic, thyme and sage and served with a fine bread sauce. There is a strong emphasis on presentation: lamb cutlets, for instance, are fanned out on the plate and garnished with a leaf of mint, and the poached peach with a strawberry purée is decorated with a spider's web of cream. Fifty wines, among them house French at £4·20.

CHEF: Nicholas Young PROPRIETORS: Nicholas and Catherine Young
OPEN: Tue to Sat D, Sun L MEALS: 12 to 2, 7 to 9.30 (10 Sat)
PRICES: £12 (£16), Bar meals from £3 (£5) CARDS: Access, Amex, Diners, Visa
SEATS: 30. 4 tables outside. Private parties: 30 main room. Car-park. Vegetarian meals. Children's helpings. Wheelchair access (also WC)

STAVELEY North Yorkshire map 7

Royal Oak [9/20]

Main Street, Staveley HG5 9LD
COPGROVE (090 14) 267 £13

Good old-fashioned pub with real ales and real home cooking. Game pies are sold for home consumption and it is taken on trust you will return the dish ('Never lost one yet, though one did take 12 months to come back'). Soups are thick, vegetables steamed and generous, and the pastry on the apple pie carefully made. Scotch bitter. House French is £4·50. CELLARMAN'S CHOICE: Gewürztraminer '83 from Willm at £8·90.

CHEF: Elisabeth Gallagher PROPRIETORS: Peter and Elisabeth Gallagher
OPEN: all week, exc Tue and Sun D MEALS: 12 to 2.30, 7 to 11
PRICES: £9 (£13)
SEATS: 50 at L, 22 at D. 9 tables outside. Private parties: 25 main room. Car-park, 25 places. Children's helpings. Jacket and tie. Wheelchair access (also WC)

STEEPLE ASTON Oxfordshire map 2

Red Lion [10/20]

South Street, Steeple Aston OX5 3RY
STEEPLE ASTON (0869) 40225 £15–£21

Ramekins of gratiné smoked haddock in a béchamel sauce are served in the low beamed dining-room, followed by pink saddle of lamb with onion sauce and firm marrow and crisp runner beans. Good salmon mayonnaise in summer, and a winter hot-pot dish, such as veal with lemon, or lamb with mustard, with proper bread. Summer pudding is made with mulberries, raspberries and blackcurrants

We keep files on every restaurant, so reports of poor meals are just as valuable as reports of good meals because they save unnecessary inspections.

Entries are compiled from the unsolicited reports from readers and are checked by inspectors; each restaurant is asked to supply details of its operation. Report forms can be found at the back of the Guide.

from the village. Colin Mead's bar serves a range of eight Islay malts as well as house wine at £4·40 and Wadworth and Hook Norton ales.

CHEF: Margaret Mead PROPRIETORS: Colin and Margaret Mead
OPEN: Tue to Sat, D only CLOSED: 2 weeks Oct MEALS: 7.30 to 9.30
PRICES: Set D from £11 to £17 (£15 to £21) CARDS: Access, Visa
SEATS: 20. 4 tables outside. Private parties: 12 main room, 20 private room. Car-park, 16 places. Vegetarian meals by arrangement. Children's helpings. No children under 3

STOCKBRIDGE Hampshire — map 2

Game Larder [new owners, zero rated]

New Street, Stockbridge SO20 6HG
ANDOVER (0264) 810414 — £9–£19

Once a malt-house and brewery and at one time a below-average restaurant, but now in the capable hands of the Donovans, who have been in the *Guide* before with the Milk House at Montacute. They have brought with them the superb guinea-fowl recipe, in which the bird is marinated in red wine then roasted with garlic, tarragon, onion, carrots and the sauce made from the marinade. Also still on the menu are their Stilton, sage and potato puffs with a gribiche sauce. Other good dishes have been the rack of lamb with a garlic, rosemary and redcurrant sauce; haddock in cream; and duck dishes. Vegetables are fresh and the lyonnaise potatoes especially good. Sweets have been less successful. An extensive wine list, with house French from Berry Bros at £5·80. More reports, please.

CHEF: Charles Donovan PROPRIETORS: Charles and Joan Donovan
OPEN: Tue to Sat MEALS: 12 to 2, 7 to 10
PRICES: £15 (£19), Set L from £6 (£9), Snacks from £1·50. Also cut-price L menu. Service inc CARDS: Access, Amex, Diners, Visa
SEATS: 60. 2 tables outside. Private parties: 70 main room, 20 private room. Car-park, 6 places. Children's helpings. Wheelchair access (3 steps; also wc). Classical music

STOKE BRUERNE Northamptonshire — map 2

The Butty [11/20]

5 Canalside, Stoke Bruerne NN1 4ER
ROADE (0604) 863654
off A508 — £11–£16

A serious little Italian restaurant on the bank of the Grand Union Canal, by a lock and next door to the waterways museum. Carlo Bertozzi chats across the room and likes guests to stay for the whole evening. Pasta is home made and can include cappelletti – squares filled with ricotta and mince poached in chicken consommé. Also good are the tortellini and the minestrone. The cooking is more authentic than the average trattoria – toasted seeds on top of the celery soup ('we eat a lot of seeds in Italy'), sweet-and-sour sauce with either duck breast or huge pork chops. Liver comes either in the Venetian style with onions or else with sage; fillet steaks with Dolcelatte. Sweets are varied and excellent – Strega ice-cream topped with chocolate; chocolate mousse with mandarin liqueur; half a peach caramelised under the grill with cream and brown sugar. Good Tokay on a strongly Italian list of wines plus a few rarities – Brunello '75, Barbaresco '74, and some older still Barolo including a '52 at £18·50.

CHEF: Carol Bertozzi PROPRIETORS: Carlo and Carol Bertozzi
OPEN: Mon to Sat, exc Sat L MEALS: 12.30 to 1.30, 7.30 to 9.45
PRICES: Set L from £7·50 (£11), Set D £13 (£16). Service inc CARDS: Access, Visa
SEATS: 32. 5 tables outside. Private parties: 34 main room. Vegetarian meals. Car-park. Smart dress preferred. No children under 8

STON EASTON Somerset map 2

▲ *Ston Easton Park* [12/20]

Ston Easton BA3 4DF
CHEWTON MENDIP (076 121) 631
on A37, 11m S of Bristol £20–£29

The Union Jack flies above this Grade II listed Palladian mansion set in its own parklands. At night the building is floodlit and the staff greet you at the door. Inside is equally impressive. It was saved from a demolition order in 1958 and restored originally to be a private house. The old parlour has been turned into the dining-room. It is a place for proposals. The short menu is at its best with the English dishes – best end of lamb with an onion sauce; beef with a celeriac purée; even bread-and-butter pudding, though the Ston Easton tulip filled with fruit sorbets impresses as a sweet and is typical of Robert Jones's eye for presentation. The staff are friendly, the atmosphere that of a house party and the wines are as aristocratic as the house. The mark-ups are more than 100 per cent but the range is magnificent in claret and burgundy. There are halves of '76 Vendange Tardive from Hugel under £15, and the house wines are £6.

CHEF: Robert Jones PROPRIETORS: Peter and Christine Smedley
OPEN: all week MEALS: 12.30 to 2, 7.30 to 9.30 (10 Fri and Sat)
PRICES: £21 (£29), Set L £13·50 (£20), Snacks from £4 CARDS: Access, Amex, Diners, Visa
SEATS: 40. 8 tables outside. Private parties: 40 main room, 22 private room. Vegetarian meals. Car-park, 40 places. Jacket and tie. No cigars/pipes in dining-room. Children's helpings. No children under 12. Wheelchair access
ACCOMMODATION: 20 rooms, all with bath/shower. B&B £50 to £140. Afternoon teas. Snooker. Helicopter pad. Pets restricted to kennels. No children under 12. TV. Phone. Garden. Croquet. Scenic. Doors close at 12. Confirm by 6 [GHG]

STONHAM Suffolk map 3

▲ *Mr Underhill's* [13/20]

Stonham IP14 5DW
STOWMARKET (0449) 711206
on A140, 300yds S of junction with A1120 Real Food £21

This small, private house has only 30 seats and when they are all taken it feels pretty crowded. There is no choice on the four-course menu, except for desserts, but you can discuss what you like when you book. Christopher Bradley cooks in the modern French idiom – among many good dishes have been soufflé suissesse, inverted and grilled with more cheese and onion; carrot tourte; duck with apple and ginger butter; and loin of lamb, either with sorrel and mint or madeira and rosemary. The Bradleys grow their own herbs and salad vegetables; they also butcher and hang their own meat. Fish is hard to find and features less frequently – courtesy of Marks & Spencer when it does. To finish there is good lemon tart or chocolate marquise before petits fours with coffee. Regulars now get a newsletter, and there are food and wine workshops. A good selection of wines. CELLARMAN'S CHOICE: Campo Viejo, Gran Reserva '73 at £7·45.

CHEF: Christopher Bradley PROPRIETORS: Christopher and Judy Bradley
OPEN: Tue to Sat, D only MEALS: 7.30 to 8.45
PRICES: Set D £15·95 (£21) CARDS: Amex, Visa
SEATS: 30. Private parties: 30 main room, 16 private room. Car-park, 12 places. Vegetarian meals. Children's helpings by arrangement. No smoking during meals. Wheelchair access (also WC)
ACCOMMODATION: 1 room, with bath/shower. B&B £27·50 to £30. Deposit: £10. Children welcome. No pets. TV

STONOR Oxfordshire — map 2

Five Horseshoes [9/20]

Maidensgrove RG9 6EX
NETTLEBED (0491) 641282 — £3–£9

A small, old, isolated, cheerful, beamed, well-appreciated pub with a blackboard menu of home-made dishes from which a good meal can be built up at a reasonable price. Smoked trout pâté, pheasant pie, 'nutty pork' with rice, big steaks, treacle and walnut tart. Brakspear's ordinary and special bitters.

CHEF: Hazel Funnell PROPRIETORS: Brakspear's Brewery
OPEN: all week, exc Sun D CLOSED: 25 Dec (D) MEALS: 12 TO 2, 7.30 TO 10
PRICES: Bar meals £2·80 to £8 (£3 to £9), Snacks from £1 (£1·10)
SEATS: 50. 30 tables outside. Private parties: 12 main room. Car-park. Vegetarian meals. No children under 14 inside. Wheelchair access (also WC)

STONY STRATFORD Buckinghamshire — map 3

Bekash Tandoori [9/20]

50 High Street, Stony Stratford MK11 1AQ
MILTON KEYNES (0908) 562249 and 568521 — £10–£12

A smart Indian restaurant with a strong local following; some very hot chicken, meat and prawn sylhet dishes; mild kormas; and sweet-sour Persian dhansaks. Good nan; polite service. Kingfisher beer is 85p.

CHEF: Chunu Miah PROPRIETORS: M.A.Rahman, M.A.Miah
OPEN: all week MEALS: 12 to 2.15, 6 to 11.45
PRICES: £7 (£12), Set L and D from £7·25 (£10) CARDS: Access, Amex, Diners, Visa
SEATS: 110. Private parties: 40 main room. Car-park, 40 places. Vegetarian meals. Children's helpings. No children under 3. Wheelchair access (also WC). Indian music. Air-conditioned

Restaurants rating 12 or more serve the best food in the region.

Stratfords [11/20]

7 St Paul's Court, 118 High Street, Stony Stratford MK1 1IA
MILTON KEYNES (0908) 566577 £12–£18

The acoustics are pretty sensitive in this former Victorian chapel with well-spaced tables and an indoor garden where the altar used to be. It was obviously designed for a vicar with a low voice. Michael Roberts' cooking has got noticeably better since he simplified the menu, but his eye for display remains, with the crudités artistically arranged on white octagonal plates. The sauces can be slightly heavy and repetitive, but the sweetbreads with saffron sauce have been excellent; also the lamb, either en croûte or served with a perfectly judged sauce of green peppercorns. Duck is home smoked and served with an apple and orange mousse on a salad with a walnut oil dressing. Sweets seem to be on the up. Service is unobtrusive and competent. The wine list is maturing nicely, strong on burgundy in particular and with a good range of cheaper wines. CELLARMAN'S CHOICE: Chablis, *premier cru*, Fourchaume '81 from Albert Pic at £13.

CHEF: Michael Roberts PROPRIETOR: Judith Wells
OPEN: Tue to Sat, exc Sat L CLOSED: 3 weeks at Christmas, 2 weeks in Aug MEALS: 12 to 2, 7.30 to 9.30 (10 Sat)
PRICES: Set L from £8·50 (£12), Set D from £13·95 (£18)
SEATS: 75. Private parties: 75 main room, 20 private room. Car-park, 20 places. No children under 6. Wheelchair access

STORRINGTON West Sussex map 3

Manleys [14/20]

Manleys Hill, Storrington RH20 4BT
STORRINGTON (090 66) 2331 £22–£26

The credentials of Karl Löderer's timbered restaurant are lobster, saffron, and asparagus – and if asparagus is out of season, he gets it flown in from California. The tables are set with pink cloths and well-cared-for silver, and are run by professionals with a pride in what they do. The shock of what all this costs is initially softened by the fact that VAT is not included in the prices on the menu. That comes later. Nevertheless, restaurants of this calibre are rare enough. The quality of the butter with the hot rolls; the home-smoked chicken; the gravlax served as three generous slices with a salad of radicchio and endive, these are all things we have come to expect of Mr Löderer. Yet his cooking has such exactitude that he creates flavours where others would lose them – in the mousseline of scallops with saffron sauce; in a parfait of chocolate. His loyalty is to tradition, and there is no quibbling with a typically Austrian main course of veal with with spinach spätzli. Lobster is a feature. Vegetables are cooked in butter and not steamed, and the selection of friandises with coffee is worthy of a *chocolatier/pâtissier*. So, inevitably, the rating is raised. The wine list is rather short-tempered with anyone who cannot afford the excellent burgundies,

All letters to the Guide *are acknowledged with a list of changes since we went to press.*

although the house wines at around £8 are good examples and there is an interesting rosé in Château de Selle, Domaines Ott '82 at £12·42.

CHEF/PROPRIETOR: Karl Löderer
OPEN: Tue to Sun, exc Sun D CLOSED: first week Jan, last 2 weeks Aug, first week Sept
MEALS: 12 to 2, 7 to 9.15
PRICES: £17 (£26), Set Sun L £14 (£22). Service inc CARDS: Access, Amex, Diners, Visa
SEATS: 36. Private parties: 10 and 12 private rooms. Car-park, 15 places. Vegetarian meals. Children's helpings. Jacket and tie preferred. No cigars/pipes in dining-room. Wheelchair access. Air-conditioned

STOURPORT-ON-SEVERN Hereford & Worcester map 5

Severn Tandoori [10/20]

11 Bridge Street, Stourport-on-Severn DY13 8UX
STOURPORT (029 93) 3090 £7–£14

A smart, comfortable, candle-lit tandoori restaurant in a Georgian listed building where the staff are happy to explain dishes in the not over-long menu. Spices and herbs are ground daily. Notable have been the lamb tikka, the curries, the biriani dishes, and well-separated rice. Good reports on the sweets, too. Lassi to drink. Licensed.

CHEF: A.Audud PROPRIETORS: S.A.Quayum, M.Miah, A.Audud, Z.Ali and M.Meah
OPEN: all week MEALS: 12 to 2.30, 6 to 11.30
PRICES: £7 (£12), Set L from, £3·50 (£7), Set D from £10 (£14) CARDS: Access, Amex, Diners, Visa
SEATS: 70. Private parties: 70 main room. Vegetarian meals. Children's helpings (weekdays only). No children under 4. Smart dress preferred. Wheelchair access (2 steps; also WC). Indian music

STRATFORD-UPON-AVON Warwickshire map 2

BACKGROUND BRIEFING: *Stratford has become synonymous with cynical catering, and of the 20 to 30 eating-places in the town, excluding pubs, only a couple stand out: Hills (see entry) and the Slug and Lettuce, Union Street, a pub/bistro serving a varied menu with fresh ingredients. It offers good value in the £3 to £6 range. The Dirty Duck (Black Swan) in Southern Lane is the place to spot stars. When we said, in some editions of last year's* Guide, *that the Dover sole at the Theatre Restaurant was £15·60, we should have added that the price included two other courses as well. If you want to stay over for the theatre the two big country-house hotels nearby, Ettington Park (see Alderminster) and Billesley Manor at Billesley, give value for rather a lot of money.*

Hill's [14/20]

3 Greenhill Street, Stratford-upon-Avon CV37 6LF
STRATFORD-UPON-AVON (0789) 293563 £17

The tables on the upstairs balcony look down into the pit of Shaun Hill's smart pink restaurant like a miniature version of the Royal Shakespeare Theatre on the other side of town. Post-theatre dinners ramble on into the small hours. His script is varied, witty and imaginative – fresh pasta with chicken livers, garlic and lemon; fish soup with croûtons; venison with marc. Meats have been of very high quality, notably well-hung steaks and the rack of lamb. Vegetables come in fours, and portions all through are substantial. To finish,there is outstanding rhubarb pie with orange custard, or raspberry and hazel-nut meringue or prune and armagnac tart. The touches are of the quality we expect for a score of 14 – the bread is home made, the good cheeses are from Major Patrick Rance, the coffee-pot is left on the table, and the house wines, from Provence, are good, not expensive (£6) and chosen by Roger Vergé. The list of 50 wines is varied, and each is selected with an eye to quality – Ch. Latour St Bonnet '75 £12; Ch. Cissac '79 £13·50; Venegazzù, Conte di Loredan '79 £7.

CHEF/PROPRIETOR: Shaun Hill
OPEN: Tue to Sat MEALS: 12.30 to 2, 5.30 to 11.30
PRICES: £13 (£17). Service inc CARDS: Access, Amex, Diners, Visa
SEATS: 35. Children's helpings. Wheelchair access (also WC)

Rumours [new entry, zero rated]

10 Henley Street, Stratford-upon-Avon CV37 6PT
STRATFORD-UPON-AVON (0789) 204297 £9–£18

Some good-humoured descriptions run through the menu of this former greengrocer's. Moneybagger Beef is, 'garnished with £9 notes,' or the Walnut Thing is in fact nut ice-cream with a chocolate and coffee sauce garnished with cherries. It is professionally run and the ingredients are good – chanterelle salad, for example, is dressed with good quality oil. There have been good reports of the Mae West Duck, steaks, and salmon. Cheeses come from Paxton & Whitfield in London, which is a recommendation. Lunches are inexpensive. There are a dozen vins de table around £5 and another dozen of interest around £10. More reports, please.

PROPRIETORS: Vinos Ltd
OPEN: all week MEALS: 12 to 2.30, 6 to 10.30 (12 to 3, 7 to 10 Sun)
PRICES: £13 (£18), Set L from £4·50 (£9), Set D £9·95 (£11) CARDS: Access, Amex, Diners, Visa
SEATS: 34. Private parties: 20 main room, 20 private room. Vegetarian meals. No children under 8. Wheelchair access. Classical music

STREATLEY Berkshire map 2

▲ *Swan Hotel* [new entry, zero rated]

Streatley RG8 9HR
GORING (0491) 873737
4m NW of Pangbourne £16–£26

One of the brightest new stars to emerge last year. John Robson was secretary of Brooks's, the St James's Street club, for eight years and has taken Richard Sparrow from the Connaught to run the kitchens of this seventeenth-century inn on one of the more eye-pleasing stretches of the Thames. Opposite is Withy Eyot island, floodlit at night, where they have planted their herb garden. Inside, the furnishings appear to be designed for the executive, and the big windows from the dining-room look out on to the river. It is a large-scale operation – seating for 70, 25 bedrooms, and an Oxford college barge (used for informal suppers) moored alongside the 30-acre grounds – but the menu is sensibly restrained in the modern classical style, as preached by Michel Bourdin at the Connaught. The quality of the meats is high – long, thick bullet-shaped pieces of beef arrive in a caramel-coloured sauce flavoured with capsicums, and best end of fillet of lamb is served with girolle and oyster mushrooms sitting on a pastry tart to one side and a little pool of meat reduction on the other. Equally good have been the tart of scallops and mussels, and the panaché of scallops and lobster in a light mustard sauce. The touches are elegant – sevruga caviare garnishes the smoked salmon rolls filled with crab meat; there are different vegetables for different main-course dishes; and a wonderful choice of English and French cheeses arrives with walnut and sultana bread and a helpful, annotated menu. Sparrow's skill as a *pâtissier* is seen especially in the sweets such as chocolate and strawberry shortcake. Grapes dipped in brittle toffee and white chocolate truffle come with the coffee.

We could quibble with the canapés, and our fingers are crossed that the menu will move with the seasons and not get stuck in international clichés, but for the moment the set meals – especially the lunch at £11·50 – are good value, and there are cheaper bar snacks too. On top of all this there is the wine list, admirable in its scope, though less so in some of its pricing – even allowing for the care that has been taken to find 60 clarets, including '49s, '59s and '61s; there are similar treasures among burgundies and German wines, as well as the very finest champagnes, among them that rarity, Bollinger Vieilles Vignes '79, blanc de noir, from pre-phylloxera vines. The wines under £10, including the house Mâcon-Lugny at £7·95, nonetheless represent good value.

CELLARMAN'S CHOICE: Sancerre, Domaine Saget '83, at £7·95.

CHEF: Richard Sparrow PROPRIETORS: Gulliver Hotels Ltd

OPEN: all week MEALS: 12.30 to 2, 7.30 to 9.30

PRICES: £22 (£26), Set L £11·50 (£16), Set D £19·50 (£24), Bar meals from £3, Snacks from £1·25. Minimum £16. Service inc CARDS: Access, Amex, Diners, Visa

SEATS: 70. Private parties: 8 main room, 24 and 12 private rooms. Car-park, 120 places. Children's helpings by arrangement. Jacket and tie preferred. No cigars/pipes in dining-room. Wheelchair access (1 step)

ACCOMMODATION: 25 rooms, all with bath/shower. Rooms for disabled. B&B £45 to £67·50. Baby facilities. No pets. Afternoon teas. Garden. Helicopter pad. TV. Phone. Scenic. Confirm by 6

STRETE Devon map 1

Laughing Monk [new entry, zero rated]

Strete TQ6 0RN
STOKE FLEMING (0803) 770639
on A379, 4m SW of Dartmouth £13

Despite the aggravating alliteration of daily dishes, naff names on the monastic menu – Brother Philip's Folly, Deacon's Duckling, Reverend's Roast and Sister Sheila's Seduction – and the daft descriptions – 'tickled' with spices, 'seethed' in tomatoes and wine – the food is serious enough. Sole comes from Brixham market to be poached and served with an hollandaise; venison pie is cooked with beer and vegetables; and a brace of boned quail is wrapped in puff pastry. Waitresses dress up in ecclesiastical garb. The short wine list includes house

French at £4·95. CELLARMAN'S CHOICE: Côtes de Brouilly '83, from Dépagneux, at £7·80.

CHEFS: Dale Bell and Isobel Tancock PROPRIETORS: Dale and David Bell
OPEN: Mon to Sat, D only MEALS: 7 to 10
PRICES: Set D from £8·50 (£13). Service 10% CARDS: Access, Amex, Diners, Visa
SEATS: 74. Private parties: 74 main room. Car-park, 20 places. Vegetarian meals. Children's helpings. No children under 7. Smart dress preferred. Classical music

STUCKTON Hampshire — map 2

Three Lions Inn [11/20]

Stuckton Road, Stuckton SP6 2HF
FORDINGBRIDGE (0425) 52489
¾m off A338 at Fordingbridge — £20

After eight years here, the Wadsacks expect to have taken over the freehold and be moving up a gear in the coming months. It is already a serious restaurant drawing people from across the county. The cooking is classically inclined and betrays their northern European background in sweet-cured Swedish herring fillets or venison Baden-Baden or calves' kidneys Café de Paris. Everything served in the former farmhouse is cooked to order, often using herbs from the kitchen garden. Lunches are more easy-going and cheaper. To finish there are coupes, marquises and roulades. The wine list may well improve when the tied tenancy ends, and look particularly for the Rhônes. CELLARMAN'S CHOICE: Crozes-Hermitage '78 from Bessac at £8·50.

CHEF: Karl-Hermann Wadsack PROPRIETORS: Eldridge, Pope & Co.
OPEN: Tue to Sun, exc Tue L and Sun D CLOSED: Feb, Easter, 2 weeks July to Aug, 1 week Oct, Christmas to New Year MEALS: 11 to 2.30, 7 to 10.30
PRICES: £14 (£20), Bar snacks from £1·60. Service 10%
SEATS: 34. Car-park, 30 places. No children under 14. Wheelchair access (also WC). Music. Air-conditioned

STURMINSTER NEWTON Dorset — map 2

▲ *Plumber Manor* [12/20]

Sturminster Newton DT10 2AF
STURMINSTER NEWTON (0258) 72507
2m SW of Sturminster Newton on
Hazelbury Bryan road — £18

The Prideaux-Brune family run their Jacobean manor more as a restaurant with rooms than a hotel. The tables in the dining-room are set with flowers, crisp linen and gleaming cutlery. The menu strikes a balance between plain, traditional dishes, such as best end of lamb Shrewsbury or chateaubriand, and stylish modern dishes, such as gravlax or pigeon breasts with orange and red peppers. Fish is reliably good, from hot crab to lobster thermidor to scallop kebabs. The calorific sweets made by Mrs Baker are generally praised, especially the

The Guide *does not accept free meals.*

cheesecake with apricot brandy sauce, but not the almond meringues with grapes. House French is £5·50.

CHEF: Brian Prideaux-Brune PROPRIETORS: The Prideaux-Brune family
OPEN: Tue to Sun, D only CLOSED: 2 weeks Nov, Feb MEALS: 7.30 to 9.30
PRICES: Set D from £14 (£18)
SEATS: 60. Private parties: 40 main room, 22 and 12 private rooms. Car-park, 20 places. Vegetarian meals by arrangement. No children under 12. Jacket and tie preferred. No cigars/pipes in dining-room. Wheelchair access (also WC)
ACCOMMODATION: 12 rooms, all with bath/shower. Rooms for disabled. B&B £32 to £55. No children under 12. No pets. Garden. Tennis. Croquet. TV. Scenic [GHG]

SUDBURY Suffolk map 3

Fords Bistro [new entry, zero rated]

47 Gainsborough Street, Sudbury CO10 6ET
SUDBURY (0787) 74298 £10

A moderately priced, cheerful new bistro which serves several vegetarian dishes. Screens separate the tables. There have been good reports of dishes as diverse as whole crabs with mayonnaise and wholemeal walnut bread; minestrone; vegetable moussaka; lamb steaks with garlic butter; and charcoal-grilled trout. House French is £3·75. More reports, please.

CHEFS/PROPRIETORS: G. and J. Ford
OPEN: Mon to Sat MEALS: 12 to 2, 7 to 10
PRICES: £6 (£10). Special bargain dishes at L CARD: Visa
SEATS: 36. Private parties; 12 main room. Vegetarian meals. Children's helpings. Wheelchair access. Air-conditioned

SURBITON Surrey map 3

Chez Max [13/20]

85 Maple Road, Surbiton KT6 4AW
01-399 2365 £17–£22

A modern French restaurant in an increasingly trendy part of Surbiton – ten minutes from the shopping centre and five from the station. The atmosphere is pleasant if a little impersonal, but Max Markarian's cooking contrasts textures and flavours well and his saucing is adept. The egg and cheese mousse on a bed of spinach survives all changes on the menu. Other good dishes have been chicken with lobster; the duck breast in a sauce of orange, lemon, lime and port, with its legs crisped up arriving afterwards as a second course; medallions of lamb around a purée of spinach with a light garlic sauce. The food can look picturesque – veal kidneys in a madeira sauce surrounding spring onions resemble a stained-glass window. The bread rolls are warm. Fish dishes tend to be elaborate, such as brill stuffed with salmon mousse and served with a blackcurrant sauce. To finish there is fine chocolate mousse or hazel-nut meringues filled with the fruits of the season. Good range of wines. House

Real Food *denotes that the restaurant does not use processed food.*

Muscadet is £6·30 or CELLARMAN'S CHOICE: Ch. les Moines '76 from Reynier at £12.

CHEF: Max Markarian PROPRIETORS: Mr and Mrs Max Markarian
OPEN: Tue to Sat, exc Sat and Sun L MEALS: 12.30 to 2, 7.30 to 10.30
PRICES: £15 (£22), Set L £12 (£17). Service 12·5% CARDS: Access, Amex, Diners, Visa
SEATS: 32. Private parties: 23 main room. No pipes in dining-room. No children under 7. Wheelchair access (also wc)

SUTTON Surrey map 3

Partners 23 [14/20]

23 Stonecot Hill, Sutton SM3 9HB
01-644 7743 £13–£19

This small restaurant in a parade of shops and with a brown awning has been revamped, and now has a very well-dressed dining-room with pink walls, cane and chrome furniture, admirable friendly service, and some very fine food indeed. It is modern in style but with good cutlery, white and pink floral plates and a fashionable menu to match – flowering courgettes with hollandaise, maize-fed chicken breast with its own mousse and a sorrel and cream sauce. The feel is more that of dining in the country than the suburbs. The kitchen prides itself on its fish terrines, such as an excellent salmon and almond with beurre blanc. It also keeps its saucing in check to good effect, as when eight slices of duck breast – roasted as a whole so that the skin remains crisp – rest on top of a tart lime and lemon sauce. The high quality of the butchery shows in the Scotch beef with a red wine sauce, and the saddle of lamb with a madeira sauce on which whole cloves of garlic float. The quest for the unusual produces smoked tuna with fresh limes as a starter, and also a perfect rhubarb sorbet – the taste of the year in the south – but at the same time the care taken over the salad dressings and in the making of the meringues indicates that here is a kitchen of talent. The incidentals point that way, too – hot poppy-seed rolls, expert Melba toast, fine butter and generous quantities of good coffee. A well-balanced wine list has Wantz's Pinot Blanc '81 from Alsace as one of a quartet of house wines at £5·95, plus a fine range of half-bottles including Ch. Cissac '70 at £11·90, and a *premier cru* Sauternes, Ch. Guiraud '76, at £11·60 per half. To finish there are six eaux-de-vie d'Alsace.

CHEFS: Tim McEntire, Rebecca Jones and Andrew Males
PROPRIETORS: Andrew Thomason and Tim McEntire
OPEN: Tue to Sat, exc Sat L CLOSED: 1 week Dec, 2 weeks Aug MEALS: 12.30 to 2, 7.30 to 9.30
PRICES: Set L from £8·75 (£13), Set D £14·50 (£19) CARDS: Access, Amex, Diners, Visa
SEATS: 34. Private parties: 36 main room. Vegetarian meals by arrangement. Wheelchair access. Air-conditioned

Many of the better restaurants offer bargain lunches for half the price of a meal in the evening. Details are given in the text.

Restaurants are checked every year and their entries rewritten. The restaurant scene changes very rapidly so don't be caught with an out-of-date Guide.

SWAY Hampshire map 2

▲ *Pine Trees* [11/20]

Mead End Road, Sway SO4 OEE
LYMINGTON (0590) 682288
off B3055, NW of station £11–£16

A comfortable old hotel with comfortable armchairs, Alice in Wonderland pictures on plates on the wall, and a large, Victorian dining-room lit by a bottomless parrot cage overhanging the central light; the feeling is almost sepulchral. There is no choice on the menu. The cooking is elegant in its simplicity – salmon and trout are poached, the former with a mild curry sauce and the latter with a wedge of lemon and buttered brown bread. Fine fillet steaks are grilled and served with fresh vegetables. You help yourself from 15 cheeses on an oval platter, and good sweets arrive in the shape of chocolate and rum mousse and orange Boodles fool. Bread is home-baked and the croissants first-class. Rooms are spotless. The rating is raised one point by popular demand, which is a victory for common sense. House French is £5.

CHEFS/PROPRIETORS: Betty and John David
OPEN: all week, D only, and Sun L MEALS: 12.45 to 1.15, 8 to 8.45
PRICES: Set L £8 (£11), Set D £13·50 (£16). Service inc CARDS: Access, Amex, Diners, Visa
SEATS: 18. Private parties: 24 main room, 6 private room. Car-park, 12 places. Children's helpings. Wheelchair access (also WC)
ACCOMMODATION: 6 rooms, 5 with bath/shower. B&B £22 to £37. No children under 12. No pets. Afternoon teas. Garden. Doors close at 11. Confirm by 6 [GHG]

SWINDON Wiltshire map 2

BACKGROUND BRIEFING: *Swindon Rendezvous, 12–12A Theatre Square, just by the Wyvern Theatre, is the best bet for eating out. It is a cavernous space with extraordinary chandeliers, but dishes such as lamb and cucumber soup, fresh Chinese vegetables, and deep-fried beef in chilli sauce have been excellent. Outside the town the School House Restaurant, Hook, Wootton Bassett, is a pretty Victorian building with hearty dinner-party-style cooking, useful in the area, and sometimes serving a splendid pudding of banana, sticky butterscotch and cream. Mamma's Kitchen, 122 Victoria Road prepares good-value pizzas and pasta dishes. The Carrefour hypermarket has to be seen to be believed, but food shopping does not seem to be a high priority in town. C.H. Palmer & Son, 1 Market Street is a good butcher, and J. & T. Cumming, 7 Market Street has good fish. There is a* WI *stall in the Wyvern Theatre on Friday mornings.*

TAMWORTH Staffordshire map 5

Kealeys [10/20]

36 Market Street, Tamworth B79 7LR
TAMWORTH (0827) 55444 £16

The service is good, though the pace is leisurely because the kitchen cooks to order. The menu is fashionably *nouvelle* and there are good dishes to be had, for instance, starters of prawn and scallop feuilleté, and smoked salmon mousseline, before grilled halibut with lobster sauce. Vegetables are cooked al dente. To finish there are fresh raspberries in brandy-snaps. Fifty wines, but the prices do not seem to reflect the different qualities of different vintages. House French is £4·95.

CHEFS/PROPRIETORS: E. and S. Kealey
OPEN: Tue to Sat D MEALS: 7.30 to 10
PRICES: Set D £10·95 (£16) CARDS: Access, Visa
SEATS: 32. Private parties: 38 main room. Vegetarian meals. Children's helpings (D only). Smart dress preferred. Music. Air-conditioned

TARRANT MONKTON Dorset — map 2

▲ *Langtons* [10/20]

Tarrant Monkton DT11 8RX
TARRANT HINTON (025 889) 225
off A354, 1m from Tarrant Hinton — £9–£13

The post office at Bryanston roasts the coffee for this restaurant, which is in converted stables adjoining a seventeenth-century pub. Herbs are home grown, and fruit jellies – quince, sloe and redcurrant – home made and served with the roasts and terrines. Interesting dishes have been smoked eel salad, sole and sorrel terrine, and a main course of pigeon braised with red cabbage. There is a healthy emphasis on game in season. House Bass to drink, or house French at £4·75 a litre.

CHEF/PROPRIETOR: Christopher Goodinge
OPEN: all week D, Sun L MEALS: 12 to 2, 7 to 9.30
PRICES: £9 (£13), Set L £5·50 (£9) CARDS: Access, Amex, Diners, Visa
SEATS: 36. Private parties: 24 main room. Car-park, 50 places. Vegetarian meals. Children's helpings. Wheelchair access (also wc). Music
ACCOMMODATION: 1 room. B&B £7.50 to £15. Children welcome. No pets. Garden. Scenic

TAUNTON Somerset — map 2

▲ *Castle Hotel* [12/20]

Castle Green, Taunton TA1 1NF
TAUNTON (0823) 72671 — **Real Food** £11–£31

The prices are high but then so are the aspirations at this luxury hotel (with twelfth-century garden attached) in the town centre. The ingredients are good and the suppliers credited at the front of the menu, which is a positive idea – meat comes from the excellent Russell Hume at Exeter or, in the case of pork, from Heal Farm at King's Nympton, which specialises in traditional breeds and cures. The saucing has lacked resilience at times, but chef Chris Oakes cooks some clever dishes, such as artichoke and scallop soup and chilled crab soup with black pepper and cucumber, served with fingers of crab rarebit. His soufflés are very good – especially the white and dark chocolate – as are the lamb and beef dishes. Vegetables are varied and, as with other dishes, come in portions that owe more to *nouvelle cuisine* than to Somerset. The brown and white chocolate mousse is excellent. The wine list has plenty of historical interest in vintage clarets, burgundies and Rhenish wines, balanced in a financial sense by two dozen house wines at around £6 each. CELLARMAN'S CHOICE: Ch. de Montdespic '78 at £6·90.

CHEF: Christopher Oakes PROPRIETOR: The Chapman family
OPEN: all week MEALS: 12.30 to 2, 7.30 to 9 (9.30 Fri and Sat)
PRICES: £25 (£30), Set L from £7·50 (£11), Set D from £15·50 to £26 (£20 to £31)
CARDS: Access, Amex, Diners, Visa
SEATS: 65. Private parties: 110 main room, 50 private room. Car-park, 30 places. Vegetarian meals. Children's helpings. Smart dress preferred. Wheelchair access
ACCOMMODATION: 35 rooms, all with bath/shower. Rooms for disabled. B&B £43·25 to £73·50. Children welcome. Baby facilities. Pets welcome. Afternoon teas. Garden. Lift. TV. Phone. Confirm by 6 [GHG]

TEMPLE SOWERBY Cumbria map 7

▲ *Temple Sowerby House* [new entry, zero rated]

Temple Sowerby CA10 1RZ
KIRKBY THORE (0930) 61578
on A66, 6m E of Penrith £13

The Hartleys took over this Georgian-fronted house in the Eden Valley, with its comfortable, antique-filled rooms and panelled dining-room at the end of '83. They offer a four-course menu for around £10 with a limited choice: smoked chicken salad, or crab and cucumber quiche, before creamy fish pie with scallops and prawns, or rolled shoulder of lamb with orange and coriander stuffing. Coq au vin has plenty of vin, and vegetables are seasonal. There is praise for walnut and caramel pie, hazel-nut meringue cake, and coffee and mint fudge served in front of the fire. Some of the bedrooms have a four-poster, and there is a good spread of preserves, including local honey, for breakfast. House wine is £4·50, and among the other 50, CELLARMAN'S CHOICE is Gevrey-Chambertin '79, from Louis Latour, at £14·50.

CHEFS: Geraldine Keenan and Eva Hartley PROPRIETORS: The Hartley family
OPEN: all week, D only CLOSED: Christmas and New Year MEALS: 7.30 to 9
PRICES: Set D £9·50 (£13) CARDS: Access, Amex, Visa
SEATS: 26. Private parties: 14 main room. Car-park, 20 places. Children's helpings. No children under 11 at D (but high teas). Smart dress preferred. No smoking in dining-room. Wheelchair access (also WC)
ACCOMMODATION: 12 rooms, all with bath/shower. Rooms for disabled. B&B £26 to £38. Children welcome. Baby facilities. No pets. Afternoon teas. Garden. TV. Phone. Scenic. Doors close at 11 [GHG]

TETBURY Gloucestershire map 2

▲ *Gentle Gardener* [10/20]

Long Street, Tetbury GL8 8AA
TETBURY (0666) 52884 £9–£16

A big black and red building on the main street, well used by locals in this town which is now almost as much a fixture on the Royal Britain tour-map as Windsor. It operates as a pub, hotel, wine bar and restaurant, though the latter is on the spartan side with bare wooden floors, glass-topped tables and gardening paraphernalia stacked on top of the wine-rack. Wholesome pies – usually based on turkey – are a feature, and there are good pork dishes with Gloucester cheese sauces, plus a few more sophisticated touches like a chicken liver pâté engrained with spinach and peppercorns. The rating is reduced because the operation is too stretched to merit a 12 rating, or it may be that some meals, notably Sunday lunch, are just not of the calibre of others. There is excellent local cider from Sherston to drink, otherwise some interesting Italian wines feature as wines of the week. CELLARMAN'S CHOICE: Sylvaner, Réserve '82, from Heim, at £6·75.

CHEF: Judy Knock PROPRIETORS: Judy and Warren Knock
OPEN: Wed to Sat, Sun L MEALS: 12.15 to 1.45, 7.30 to 10
PRICES: Set Sun L £5·50 (£9), Set D £12·50 (£16), Bar meals from £3 (£3·30), Snacks from £1 (£1·10) CARDS: Diners, Visa
SEATS: 28. 10 tables outside. Private parties: 30 main room, 65 private room. Vegetarian meals by arrangement. Children's helpings. Smart dress preferred. Wheelchair access (also WC). Classical music. Partly self-service
ACCOMMODATION: 5 rooms, 1 with bath/shower. B&B £15·50 to £26·50. Deposit: £10. Children welcome. Afternoon teas. Garden. Doors close at 12. Confirm by 6

THAXTED Essex map 3

Recorder's House [new entry, zero rated]

17 Town Street, Thaxted CM6 2LD
THAXTED (0371) 830438 £13–£20

This historic house used to do a lot of grills but it now has a fashionable menu with some interesting dishes, such as snails with Dijon mustard and almonds and smoked eggs. The execution does not always match up to the promise, judging by the standards of a restaurant rating 12 or 13, but a shorter menu would give the kitchen more time. There are good dishes, such as smoked chicken roulade, trout stuffed with cucumber and topped with almonds. When fresh the sweets are very good; choux pastry is fashioned into a swan. There is a short wine list and the waiter will probably tell you that your choice is, 'absolutely marvellous.' House Muscadet is £5·25. More reports, please.

CHEF: Roy Hawkins PROPRIETORS: Roy Hawkins and Michael Rubal
OPEN: Tue to Sat D, Sun L CLOSED: 3 weeks Jan MEALS: 12.15 to 2.30, 7 to 10
PRICES: £14 (£20), Set L £8·50 (£13). Service 10% CARDS: Access, Amex, Diners, Visa
SEATS: 50. 4 tables outside. Private parties: 100 main room, 12 private room. Vegetarian meals by arrangement. No children under 5 at L, or under 10 at D. Smart dress preferred. Classical music

THEALE Berkshire map 2

Red Peppers [9/20]

21 High Street, Theale RG7 5AH
READING (0734) 303408 £10–£16

A relaxed and friendly restaurant with a range of starters, from mushrooms stuffed with home-made pâté and deep-fried, to Cleethorpes avocado, which is mixed with pineapple and chicken in a fruity mayonnaise. Individual beef Wellington or an escalope of veal cooked with wine and cream to follow. House wine is paid for according to the quantity consumed, and a whole bottle comes to £4·25.

CHEFS: Lynne Symons and Ian Lewis PROPRIETORS: Mr and Mrs G.Symons
OPEN: Tue to Sat, exc Sat L MEALS: 12 to 2, 7 to 10
PRICES: £11 (£16), Set L from £6·95 (£10) CARDS: Access, Visa
SEATS: 36. Private parties: 20 main room. Vegetarian meals by arrangement. No children after 8. Smart dress preferred. Wheelchair access. Music

THORNAGE Norfolk map 6

▲ *The Black Boys* [14/20]

Thornage NR25 7QG
MELTON CONSTABLE (0263) 861218
on B1110, 2½m SW of Holt **Real Food** £19

A small, old, beamed former pub in a tiny village surrounded by beautiful country. It is a restaurant with two twin-bedded rooms. Ann Carr and Martin MacKeown run the restaurant professionally and at an easy pace. Persian prayer rugs hang on the wall and a collection of Victorian jugs adorn the shelves. In winter brick-built, wood-burning stoves give out a homely smell. The style of Ann Carr's cooking is modern – smoked pork served with slices of avocado and pear; marinated halibut with chicory – but there are some interesting influences, as seen in the poppy-seed pancakes stuffed with home-smoked salmon, and also the lamb with aubergine and a side dish of burghul (cracked wheat), which complements well. Chicken breast is served on a separate plate from which you help yourself, with a jug of pungent reduced brown sauce and some wild mushrooms. Best of all, though, has been a classic execution of sweetbreads in a madeira sauce. The eight cheeses come from the excellent Holt cheese shop and are usually at a peak of ripeness and served with home-made wholemeal biscuits. To finish, the hazel-nut galette with hazel-nut cream would not disgrace a three-star restaurant in France, and the peppermint parfait is nearly in the same class. There is plenty of coffee, which comes with excellent chocolate truffles. Breakfasts are extensive, uncooked but very good – brioches, conserves, smoked ham. The French wine list has been put together from a number of suppliers. It includes two Alsace wines from Pierre Sparr – a Gerwürztraminer, Cuvée Centenaire '81 at £10·35, and an intriguing Muscat '75 at £6·35. It is rare to find such an old vintage – '75 was a good year – on a restaurant list and it may not have passed its best. The rest of the list, with the better value at the more expensive end where the mark-ups are lower, is similarly tempting.

CHEF: Ann Carr PROPRIETORS: Ann Carr and Martin MacKeown
OPEN: Tue to Sat, D only CLOSED: Nov to Mar MEALS: 7 to 9.30
PRICES: £14 (£19) CARDS: Access, Amex, Diners, Visa
SETS: 28. Private parties: 20 main room. Car-park, 14 places. Vegetarian meals by arrangement. No children under 12. No smoking in dining-room
ACCOMMODATION: 2 rooms, both with bath/shower. B&B £40 (double). Deposit: £7. No children under 12. No pets. Garden. Scenic [GHG]

THORNBURY Avon map 2

▲ *Thornbury Castle* [13/20]

Castle Street, Thornbury BS12 1HH
THORNBURY (0454) 418511 Real Food £20–£25

A regal calm has settled on Kenneth Bell's baronial castle. The family portraits look down from the wood-panelled walls of the church-like dining-room. The only modern chink in the sense of history is the menu, put together with a master's eye for variety. Fish is the main suit – excellent salmon either marinated in white wine, orange and lemon or baked in pastry (for two) or with a saffron sauce; sea-bass grilled with a fennel and Pernod sauce; Cornish crab mousse; scallops with a lemon and tarragon sauce; turbot baked in hock with two mustards. But there is also pasta, salad, and even a leek and potato soup, as well as superb veal – two thick slices of loin with wild mushrooms and a montilla sauce – or roast duck with kumquats. Vegetables come in small portions on neat side plates. To finish, the lemon tart is outstanding. Leisurely drinks before dinner are served in the library overlooking the smart gardens sandwiched between the church and castle, which gives time to study what is a wonderful assembly of wines – long on Californias and old vintages. It is a very handsome place to stay overnight . . . at a price.

CHEF/ PROPRIETOR: Kenneth Bell
OPEN: all week CLOSED: 5 days at Christmas MEALS: 12.30 to 1.30, 7 to 9
PRICES: £20 (£25), Set L £15·50 (£20). Service inc
SEATS: 50. Private parties: 25 main room. Car-park, 30 places. No children. Wheelchair access. Piano player
ACCOMMODATION: 12 rooms, all with bath/shower. B&B £44 to £145. Garden. Helicopter pad. No children 'unless known'. TV. Phone. Doors close at 12 [GHG]

THORNTON HEATH Surrey map 3

Bunga Raya [9/20]

785 London Road, Thornton Heath CR4 6AW
01-689 4612 £12

Interesting dishes in this plain Malay cafe include satay, crab with ginger, and chicken curry with coconut milk. Finish with tropical fruit ice-cream. Licensed.

CHEF/PROPRIETOR: F.T. Lim
OPEN: all week, D only MEALS: 6 to 10
PRICES: £7 (£12), Set D from £8·50 (£12) CARD: Visa
SEATS: 45. Private parties: 45 main room. Vegetarian meals. Children welcome. Wheelchair access. Music

Ming Garden [new entry, zero rated]

850 London Road, Thornton Heath CR4 7PA
01-648 0991 £5–£12

This used to be a good take-away, near the now defunct Thornton Heath Pond, but it has been refurbished with bamboo and marble and fitted with a 130-item Cantonese and Peking menu. Good dishes are the spare ribs, hot-and-sour soup, prawn satay, and chicken in yellow bean sauce. The set menus start at £7 a head. Wan Fu or Lai Ying Chinese-style wines are £5·50. More reports, please.

CHEF: For Tai To PROPRIETOR: Sau Chuen To
OPEN: all week CLOSED: 25 and 26 Dec MEALS: 12 to 2.30, 5.30 to 12
PRICES: £7 (£12), Set L from £2·50 (£5), Set D from £5 (£8). Minimum £4·50 at D. Service inc CARDS: Access, Amex, Diners, Visa
SEATS: 46. Private parties: 40 main room. Children's helpings. Wheelchair access. Chinese music. Air-conditioned

THORNTON-LE-FYLDE Lancashire — map 5

▲ *River House* [11/20]

Skippool Creek, Thornton-le-Fylde FY5 5LF
POULTON-LE-FYLDE (0253) 883497
4m N of Blackpool — £10–£20

A small, family establishment in a gentleman farmer's residence with antique furniture, bric-à-brac and a wonderful view of the river Wyre. The staff wear magician-style white gloves. The menu is strong on game and poultry – for specialities like duckling the Scotts prefer people to order in advance. Good dishes eaten have been avocado and Brie; venison; grouse; beef Wellington. Vegetables are excellent, but sweets can fade. One of the rooms has a Victorian hooded bath. A selection of Louis Latour burgundies holds up the wine list. House Cordier is £4·50.

CHEFS/PROPRIETORS: Bill and Carole Scott
OPEN: all week MEALS: 12 to 2, 7.30 to 9.30
PRICES: £15 (£20), Set L and D £7 (£10) CARDS: Access, Amex
SEATS: 45. Private parties: 45 main room. Car-park, 20 places. Vegetarian meals. Children's helpings. Wheelchair access (also WC). Classical music. Air-conditioned
ACCOMMODATION: 4 rooms, 1 with bath/shower. B&B £22 to £32. Children welcome. Baby facilities. Pets welcome. Garden. TV. Air-conditioning. Scenic. Confirm by 6

THORPE-LE-SOKEN Essex — map 3

▲ *Thorpe Lodge* [new entry, zero rated]

Landermere Road, Thorpe-le-Soken CO16 0NG
CLACTON-ON-SEA (0255) 861 509
on B1414, ¾m from village — £11–£18

A converted farmhouse with four bedrooms, on the outskirts of the village. The dining-room is staffed by trainees in tartan or ties and the napery gleams. There's a lot of garlic butter in use – starters include avocado Kiev – and a partiality for making dishes en croûte. Favourable reports have been filed on the smoked prawns in curried mayonnaise, and the home-made soups. Last year's Christmas

Restaurants are graded on a scale of 1–20. In the region of 8–9 expect to find places that may not be restaurants but cafes, pubs, bistros and small hotels. In the category of 10–11 you can expect to find the best food in the locality. Ratings of 12 or more are given to restaurants we regard as serving the best food in the region.

Day lunch was said to be excellent. Wines are from Lay & Wheeler. More reports, please.

CHEF: Simon Dicks PROPRIETORS: Rhoda and Ron Dicks
OPEN: all week MEALS: 12 to 2, 7 to 9.30
PRICES: £13 (£18), Set L from £7·50 (£11), Set D from £8·50 (£12), Snacks from £1·50 (£1·65). Set meals by arrangement only, exc Sun L CARDS: Access, Diners, Visa
SEATS: 52. 3 tables outside. Private parties: 40 main room, 40 and 26 private rooms. Car-park, 20 places. Vegetarian meals. Children's helpings. Smart dress preferred. No pipes in dining-room. Wheelchair access
ACCOMMODATION: 4 rooms, all with bath/shower. B&B £20 to £35. Deposit: £10. No pets. Afternoon teas. Garden. TV. Doors close at 12

THORPE MANDEVILLE Northamptonshire map 2

Three Conies [new entry, zero rated]

Thorpe Mandeville OX17 2EX
BANBURY (0295) 711025
on B4525, 6m NE of Banbury £16

A Hook Norton pub with a restaurant. The menu appears conservative, but is cooked with some skill and respect for fresh raw materials. Tagliatelle gets a slug of vodka and some garlic in its cream sauce; cold salmon is served with a watercress mayonnaise. Other dishes are not over-complicated and there have been good cream and butter sauces. Sixty wines. Coteaux du Tricastin '83 is £6. More reports, please.

CHEF: Mary Ann Gilchrist PROPRIETORS: A.J. and M.A. Gilchrist
OPEN: all week, exc Mon D and Sun D MEALS: 12 to 2, 7.30 to 9.30
PRICES: £12 (£16), Bar meals from £1·50 (£1·65), Snacks from 70p (80p). Service 10%
CARDS: Access, Visa
SEATS: 28. Private parties: 30 main room. Car-park, 25 places. Vegetarian meals. Children's helpings (Sun L only). No cigars/pipes in dining-room. Wheelchair access

---

THREE LEGGED CROSS East Sussex map 3

The Bull [9/20]

Three Legged Cross TN5 7HH
TICEHURST (0580) 200586
off B2087, ½m N of Ticehurst £11

A text book country pub with oak furniture, rough brick walls and two bars, one for drinking and one for drinking and eating. The cooking is honest, generous and without gimmicks. Taramosalata comes in a huge pot with no fewer than a dozen triangles of toast; soft roes come straight from the pan laid on crisp fried bread and sprinkled with fiery paprika. Main dishes tend to be stuffed or else barbecued in summer. Fish is fresh. The sorbets are first-class. Shepherd Neame beers or house French at £4.

CHEFS/PROPRIETORS: E. Moir and M. Francis
OPEN: all week, exc Sun D and Mon D MEALS: 11.30 to 2, 7 to 9
PRICES: £8 (£11), Bar meals from £3·50, Snacks from 75p. Service 10% in rest
SEATS: 25. 6 tables outside. Private parties: 18 main room, 18 private room. Car-park, 12 places. Children's helpings (L only). Wheelchair access (also WC). Self-service at L

TICKTON Humberside map 6

▲ *Tickton Grange Hotel* [new entry, zero rated]

Tickton HU17 9SH
LEVEN (0401) 43666
off A1035, 2½m NE of Beverley £13–£22

The five-course dinner at this country-house hotel, with three and a half acres of lawns and trees, offers a good choice of local and fresh ingredients combined with smooth sauces and good service. Fish is from Ramus Seafoods in Harrogate, which is a recommendation in itself; the fish finds itself served as excellent tomato and crayfish mousse, or the unusual sea-bass poached with coconut milk and saffron. Also successful is the breast of guinea-fowl in a cream and sesame oil sauce. The wine list is thinly spread, but not rapaciously priced.
CELLARMAN'S CHOICE: house claret from Henri Rodier at £7·55. More reports, please.

CHEF: David Leaf PROPRIETORS: The Whymant family
OPEN: all week MEALS: 12 to 2, 7.30 to 9.30 (7 to 9 Sun)
PRICES: £8 (£13), Set D £16·50 (£22). Cheaper set L and D available for residents
CARDS: Access, Amex, Diners, Visa
SEATS: 45. Private parties: 60 main room, 80 and 16 private rooms. Car-park, 65 places. Children's helpings by arrangement. Smart dress preferred. Wheelchair access (also WC). Music
ACCOMMODATION: 15 rooms, all with bath/shower. B&B £40·50 to £55. Children welcome. Baby facilities. No pets in public rooms. Afternoon teas. Garden. TV. Phone. Scenic. Confirm by 12

TISBURY Wiltshire map 2

The Garden Room [new entry, zero rated]

2 High Street, Tisbury SP3 6PS
TISBURY (0747) 870907 £13

Jennie Robertson built a local reputation as an outside caterer before turning this converted old shop into a restaurant dressed in cool greens and murals. The menu has *nouvelle* inclinations. Good dishes have been crab mousse with two sauces; deep-fried aubergines with pots of yoghourt and fresh tomato; pork fillet in a juniper and orange sauce, served with a side dish of sliced carrot, celeriac, and a single swirl of duchesse potato. To finish there is hot crêpe normande, stuffed with apples and topped with a crust of crisp sugar, or crème brûlée, said to be as good as any served in the Connaught in London. Six reds and six whites make up the reasonably priced wine list. Service is by local girls who don't take the operation as seriously as everyone else. More reports, please.

CHEF: P. Firmin PROPRIETOR: Jennie Robertson
OPEN: Tue to Sat, exc Sat L MEALS: 12.30 to 1.30, 7.30 to 9.45
PRICES: Set L and D from £9 (£13) CARDS: Access, Visa
SEATS: 30. Private parties: 20 main room, 10 private room. Car-park, 12 places. Vegetarian meals. Children welcome. Wheelchair access (also WC). Classical music

TIVERTON Devon map 1

Hendersons [11/20]

18 Newport Street, Tiverton EX16 6NL
TIVERTON (0884) 254256 £14

The principles here are straightforward and as good as any: go out and buy what is fresh in the market, build the menu around the ingredients, and cook them simply. That's how cooking is done for lunch, though dinner menus are more formal. Elizabeth Ambler has worked with Joyce Molyneux at the Carved Angel (see Dartmouth) and cooks to recipes from Elizabeth David – rillettes, tagliatelle, lamb à la bretonne and so on. She does a fine daube de boeuf, too. The local lamb and the cheeses are the best Devon has. The wine list is organised under such headings as Fruitier Red Wines, but there are very good bottles to be found, all with fulsome descriptions. In all it is strong in depth and not overpriced. CELLARMAN'S CHOICE: Riesling '83, from Louis Gisselbrecht, at £7·10.

CHEF: Elizabeth Ambler PROPRIETORS: Nevill and Elizabeth Ambler
OPEN: Tue to Sat CLOSED: 4 days at Christmas MEALS: 12.15 to 2, 7.15 to 9.45
PRICES: £11 (£14), Set D £10·50 (£14). Service inc CARDS: Access, Amex, Visa
SEATS: 50. 2 tables outside. Private parties: 50 main room. Vegetarian meals. Children's helpings

TORQUAY Devon map 1

Green Mantle [10/20]

135 Babbacombe Road, Torquay TQ1 3SR
TORQUAY (0803) 34292
1½m from town centre £13

Gavin Dalgleish serves while his wife Andrée cooks. There are only six well-spaced tables, and everything is done to order. As well as the usual range of bistro dishes there has been good fresh fish – salmon with lobster sauce, grilled Dover sole, and turbot with mustard sauce. House vin de table is £4·60. CELLARMAN'S CHOICE: Gewürztraminer '82, from Baron de Hoen, at £8·35.

CHEF: Andrée Dalgleish PROPRIETORS: Gavin and Andrée Dalgleish
OPEN: Tue to Sat, D only CLOSED: 1st 2 weeks Nov MEALS: 7 to 10 (later by arrangement)
PRICES: Set D from £8·75 (£13) CARDS: Amex, Diners, Visa
SEATS: 20. Private parties: 24 main room. Vegetarian meals. Children's helpings. Smart dress preferred. Wheelchair access. Music

Remy's [new entry, zero rated]

3 Croft Road, Torquay TQ2 5VN
TORQUAY (0803) 22359 £13

Remy Bopp has moved here lock, stock and barrel from Belper. He is originally from Alsace, though his menus are now fairly Anglicised. His ingredients are mostly fresh – which could make him a unique figure in the town. More attention is paid to the taste of dishes than to garnishing. Standards fluctuate, though that may be because the restaurant is a new operation. Typical of the good dishes have been snails in pastry cases; lamb's kidneys in a Meaux mustard sauce; pork with kirsch; and soufflé glacé au Grand Marnier. Coffee is strong. When Mr Bopp gets his supply network going the food may well move up a gear. Some good wines, especially in the Beaujolais and from the south west of France. More reports, please.

CHEF/PROPRIETOR: Remy Bopp
OPEN: Mon to Sat, D only CLOSED: 2 weeks at Christmas MEALS: 7.15 to 9.30
PRICES: Set D £9·85 (£13). Service inc CARDS: Amex, Visa
SEATS: 40. Private parties: 20 main room, 20 private room. Children's helpings by arrangement. Smart dress preferred. Music

TORRINGTON Devon map 1

Rebecca's [10/20]

8 Potacre Street, Torrington EX38 8BH
TORRINGTON (0805) 22113 £9–£15

This is open all day, and the rather twee, tea-shop atmosphere is distracting. Paul Lilly does most of the cooking with more than a little flair and produces some interesting regional dishes, such as a Welsh parsley pancake, and Devon-style pasties made with salmon. We have eaten excellent Cumberland sausage; roast partridge; and genuine Yorkshire pudding with gravy. Sweets fade. Standards tend to suffer from the pressure of the place being open all day – dried herbs in the quince sauce for veal, stewed Cona coffee – but even so there is no hesitation in raising the rating from cafe status to restaurant, though it is probably more appropriate as a lunch venue. House white is £5·50 a litre.

CHEFS/PROPRIETORS: Paul and Gill Lilly
OPEN: Mon to Sat CLOSED: 3 weeks Jan MEALS: 9am to 10pm
PRICES: £9 (£15), Set D from £5 (£9), snacks from 99p (£1·10) CARDS: Access, Amex, Visa
SEATS: 42. Private parties: 42 main room. Vegetarian meals. Children's helpings. Wheelchair access (also WC). Music

TOTNES Devon map 1

Elbow Room [10/20]

6 North Street, Totnes TQ9 5NZ
TOTNES (0803) 863480 £18

Rosemary Sellick cooks everything to order in this 400-year-old converted cider press with an Elizabethan open fireplace, stone walls and beamed ceiling. It is a conservative French menu – donkey pie excepted, which is a pork and beef pie in a light pastry. Other bakes, such as the seafood pot, are good. Elsewhere the repertory stays firmly with the old school: potatoes duchesse; boeuf smitane; truite Cleopatra – the last executed with more than usual finesse. Vegetables and sweets, such as almond sponge or plums stewed in red wine, are good too. Despite the high mark-ups there is a good choice of wine to be found on the well-spread, 100-strong list, though the older Alsace will be worn out by now. CELLARMAN'S CHOICE: Côtes de Ventoux, from Thevenin, at £5·80.

CHEF: Rosemary Sellick PROPRIETORS: Mr and Mrs B. J. Sellick
OPEN: Wed to Sat, D only MEALS: 7.30 to 9 (9.30 Sat)
PRICES: Set D from £13 (£18). Minimum £8 CARDS: Amex, Visa
SEATS: 34. 6 tables outside. Private parties: 40 main room. Vegetarian meals by arrangement. No children under 8. Jacket and tie preferred. No smoking during meals. Music

TREBARWITH Cornwall map 1

▲ *Trebarwith Strand Hotel* [10/20]

Trebarwith PL34 0HB
CAMELFORD (0840) 770326 £19

Trebarwith Strand consists of half a dozen houses, a couple of pubs and a shop. This hotel was founded by two couples seven years ago, and the pine bar has wall-to-wall windows overlooking the Atlantic ('no point in cleaning them') and a thousand paperbacks for rainy days. The relaxed downstairs dining-room is eclectic, with hard-wood benches, and a top hat hanging on the coat stand but Suzy Bowler's menu, drawn from many sources, changes daily and the food is cooked with flair – excellent little crab pasties to start, before chicken baked with lime and coconut, or tasty, if not very subtle, duck breast with port and orange sauce. To finish, there is excellent goats' cheese and hazel-nut ice-cream. The connected House on the Strand bistro is cheap and popular. An emerging wine list. CELLARMAN'S CHOICE: Brouilly, Château des Tours '84 at £7·96.

CHEF: Suzy Bowler PROPRIETORS: Ray and Suzy Bowler, Tom and Margaret Rolfe
OPEN: all week, D only CLOSED: Oct to Mar MEALS: 7 to 9
PRICES: £15 (£19)
SEATS: 30. Private parties: 30 main room. Vegetarian meals. No smoking. Children's helpings
ACCOMMODATION: 10 rooms, 7 with bath/shower. B&B £18 to £36·50. Deposit: 10%. Children welcome. Baby facilities. Pets welcome. Scenic [GHG]

TREGONY Cornwall map 1

▲ *Tregony House* [9/20]

Tregony, Truro TR2 5RN
TREGONY (087 253) 671 £10

This small country house gives remarkable value for money. The dining-room seats only 12, so book well ahead. Mary Lock is a generous cook. Herbs from the garden go to make carrot and lovage soup and to decorate the salad of cracked wheat, mushrooms, tomatoes and green peppers. The vegetables that accompany such main courses as braised topside in red wine, or baked trout with a watercress stuffing, are a feature in themselves – carrots and saffron rice, flageolets in garlic sauce. The low rating reflects the nature of the operation rather than its quality. House wine is £3·95 or try the CELLARMAN'S CHOICE: Rioja Marqués de Cáceres at £4·95.

If you cannot honour a restaurant booking, always phone to cancel.

CHEF: Mary Lock PROPRIETORS: Mr and Mrs T.E.Lock
OPEN: all week, D only CLOSED: 31 Oct to 1 Mar MEALS: 7 to 7.15
PRICES: Set D £8 (£10)
SEATS: 12. Car-park, 6 places. Vegetarian meals by arrangement. Children's helpings (residents only). No children under 5. Jacket and tie. Wheelchair access. Music. One sitting
ACCOMMODATION: 6 rooms, 1 with bath/shower. B&B £17 to £34. Deposit: £20. No children under 5. Pets by arrangement. Afternoon teas. Doors close at 11. Confirm by 6 [GHG]

TUNBRIDGE WELLS Kent map 3

BACKGROUND BRIEFING: *The good food shops are some distance apart and parking is a nightmare so the advice is to park and then walk. Close to the Pantiles is Rishi Dayanand's Store, 4B London Road, where the range of foreign foodstuffs might save you a trip to Soho. Pilgrims, 37 Mount Ephraim, is a wholefood restaurant that has a section selling healthfoods, fruit and vegetables, home-made cakes and a range of dishes prepared to high standards by locals. W.J.Hill & Sons, 119 Mount Pleasant, has excellent pies, sausages and home-cooked meats. Round the corner in Camden Road is a shop selling beans, pulses and dried fruits from hessian sacks and nearby, at 11 Monson Road, A Piece of Cake makes its goods in full view. About ten miles east, just north of Cranbrook on the A229, there is a good farm shop called Bumbles, selling fruit, vegetables, plants, herbs, jams, and so on. Perfect Partners, 7 Stone Street, Cranbrook, has a range of cheese, wines, pâtés, yoghourt, and fresh pasta. Iden Croft Herbs, Frittenden Road, Staplehurst, supplies culinary as well as medicinal and aromatic herbs. Unpasteurised Jersey cream can be bought from several farms in the district – that from White House Farm, Three Chimneys, Biddenden (just along from the Three Chimneys pub, see Biddenden) being especially recommended. Tenterden has a good general market on Fridays, and Gourmet Pantry, a delicatessen with good fish. Wines from the local vineyards – Lamberhurst, Tenterden, Biddenden and Westfield – are appearing more and more on restaurant menus across the whole country. And there is the excellent Biddenden cider.*

▲ *La Galoche, Mount Edgecombe Hotel* [9/20]

The Common, Tunbridge Wells TN4 8BX
TUNBRIDGE WELLS (0892) 26823 £11

A strange place – formerly a wine bar with good-value food and a mediocre wine list, but now two restaurant rooms have been opened and it is more difficult to classify. The simpler dishes have been good: whitebait, plateau de fruits de mer, grilled Dover sole, grilled lamb cutlets. Limited desserts. Jolly and good value.

CHEF/PROPRIETOR: David Barnard
OPEN: Mon to Sat MEALS: 12 to 2, 7 to 11
PRICES: £8 (£11). Bar meals from £2 (£2·20), Snacks from 80p (90p)
SEATS: 40. 6 tables outside. Private parties: 30 main room, 24, 16 and 12 private rooms. Car-park, 25 places. No children under 12. No pipes in dining-room. Wheelchair access (also wc)
ACCOMMODATION: 6 rooms, 3 with bath/shower. B&B £13 to £26. No children under 12. Garden. Doors close at 12. Confirm by 6

Reports on good shops, small hotels and cafes in your area are welcome.

Thackeray's House [12/20]

85 London Road, Tunbridge Wells TN1 1EA
TUNBRIDGE WELLS (0892) 37558 £14–£20

Bruce Wass, formerly chef at Odins in London, has opened up the second oldest house in Tunbridge Wells as a serious modern restaurant. It is a Grade I listed building where novelist William Makepeace Thackeray lived. The set-price menus are fashionable and built on the best local produce, including fish from Rye and cheeses from James's in Beckenham. Good dishes have been the hot sole and salmon trout pâté; exotic salads, including marigolds and nasturtium leaves; brill with Dijon mustard and chives; and navarin of lamb with turnips and tarragon. Most dishes are 'with' a wine or alcohol, 'and' a herb or fruit. To finish there is chestnut ice-cream with an apricot compote, or chocolate armagnac loaf. The wine list of some 60 bottles has been chosen with care and has a good spread of price and vineyards. There are a pair of '83 Alsace wines, from Louis Gisselbrecht, for £8·45. CELLARMAN'S CHOICE: St-Véran '83 at £8·45.

CHEF/PROPRIETOR: Bruce Wass
OPEN: Tue to Sat CLOSED: 1 week Easter, 1 week Christmas, 2 weeks summer
MEALS: 12.30 to 2.30, 7 to 10
PRICES: Set L from £8·90 (£14), Set D from £14·85 (£20). Service 10% CARDS: Access, Amex, Visa
SEATS: 35. 8 tables outside. Private parties: 16 main room, 16 private room. Children's helpings

TWICKENHAM Greater London map 3

Cézanne [12/20]

68 Richmond Road, Twickenham TW1 3BE
01-892 3526 £15

This used to be a Spanish ceramic/pottery shop. The high, stucco and mock timber ceiling and frontage remain and contrast oddly with the metal and wicker seats, the German crockery and the papered walls. Some of the cooking has been excellent – a fricassee of fish with tropical fruits; lamb paloise; duck with lemon, lime and orange sauce. The sweets are a feature, from an amazing mandarin tart with sabayon, to hazel-nut ice-cream with real chocolate sauce, to a pear glazed with a strawberry sauce in a vanilla sauce. The kitchen seems to be better at *nouvelle* than *ancienne*. The pace is leisurely and tables are not double booked. Coffee has been a bit shy. An intriguing choice of about 30 wines includes a few bargains, such as Hermitage '76, from Sichel, at £11·50.

CHEFS: Steven Hardman, Moira Muluey and Tim Jefferson
PROPRIETORS: Tim and Philippa Jefferson
OPEN: Mon to Sat, exc Sat L CLOSED: 1 week at Christmas, bank hols MEALS: 12.30 to 2, 7 to 10.30 (11 Fri and Sat)
PRICES: £11 (£15), Set L and D by arrangement CARDS: Access, Amex, Visa
SEATS: 38. Private parties: 40 main room. Children's helpings. Wheelchair access. Classical music

All inspections are carried out anonymously as we accept no handouts.

ULLSWATER Cumbria map 7

▲ *Sharrow Bay* [14/20]

Howtown Road, Ullswater CA10 2LZ
POOLEY BRIDGE (085 36) 301 and 483
2m from Pooley Bridge on E side of lake, signposted Howtown and Martindale

Real Food £18–£29

The grand opera of Sharrow Bay has been going for as long as the *Guide* itself. Again last year, in the space of only four months, more than 120 dishes and wines from the long menu were endorsed by readers and inspectors, which is testimony enough. It is not a place to go to worry about cholesterol. Meals are the culinary equivalent of the Oscar awards ceremony. The finest ingredients from suppliers fostered over 36 years arrive bathed in cream and butter sauces. The crescendo of the meal reaches its natural climax with the sweets – sticky toffee pudding; hazel-nut parfait with cherry sauce; fresh fruit terrine with strawberry sauce . . . A strong sub-theme of English cookery runs right through, alongside the French inspirations – beef consommé; roast grouse; Cumberland pork roasted with rosemary, stuffed with onions, served with crackling and its own gravy; Queen of Puddings. Portions are sometimes described as avalanches. Lilies are rather more than gilded – come coffee a stupefied silence seems to fall in the whole dining-room. The view is out on to Ullswater. Even afternoon tea is an occasion for which you should book and arrive early to secure a good table from which to eat the array of toast, sandwiches, biscuits, scones and cakes. Breakfasts, too, are first-class. The wine list is heavily stocked with Louis Latour's clarets and burgundies. In the Alsace section is the Tokay, Sélection de Grains Nobles '76, from Hugel, at £31 – a once-in-a-lifetime experience. More accessible financially are the Mâcon-Lugny, Les Genièvres '83 at £8·75, and the Beaujolais-Villages '83, from Bouchard, at £6·60.

CHEFS: Juan Martin, Colin Akrigg, Philip Wilson and Alison Kennedy
PROPRIETORS: Francis Coulson and Brian Sack
OPEN: all week CLOSED: Dec to Feb MEALS: 1 to 1.45, 8 to 8.45
PRICES: £14 (£18), Set L £17·50 (£21), Set D £25 (£29). Service inc
SEATS: 65. Private parties: 10 main room. Car-park, 30 places. Vegetarian meals. No children under 13. No smoking. Wheelchair access. One sitting
ACCOMMODATION: 29 rooms, 24 with bath/shower. Rooms for disabled. D, B&B £54 to £150. No children under 13. No pets. Afternoon teas. Garden. Fishing. TV. Phone. Scenic. Doors close at 12. Confirm by 10 [GHG]

UNDERBARROW Cumbria map 7

▲ *Greenriggs Country House* [new entry, zero rated]

Underbarrow LA8 8HF
CROSTHWAITE (044 88) 387
3m W of Kendal

£15

A homespun enterprise run by the Smithsons since 1984 in an eighteenth-century farmhouse: from the dining-room – a Victorian addition – there are fine views across the Lyth Valley. Sarah cooks an orderly four-course dinner for

English tastes: pear with Stilton cream, carrot and orange soup, salmon with cucumber cream, and blackcurrant cheese mousse. Portions are hearty and flavours also speak out in more elaborate combinations: sweet-and-sour pork with lychees; kabanos sausage with fruit sauce; and lamb stuffed with ham, served with a fruity soured cream. Nuts feature regularly in stuffings – hazel-nuts for trout, chestnuts for pork – and vegetables preserve their texture. Sound, careful cooking is helped by a slightly formal service to produce a sense of occasion. Wines are European, include half-bottles, and are reasonably marked-up. House red or white is £3·90. CELLARMAN'S CHOICE: Rioja Gran Reserva '75, Paternina, at £7·90.

CHEF: Sarah Smithson PROPRIETORS: Doug and Sarah Smithson
OPEN: all week, D only CLOSED: Jan and Feb MEALS: 7.30 to 8
PRICES: Set D £10·50 (£15)
SEATS: 30. Private parties: 36 main room, 10 private room. Car-park, 25 places. Vegetarian meals by arrangement. Children welcome (high teas). Smart dress preferred. No smoking in dining-room. One sitting
ACCOMMODATION: 14 rooms, 10 with bath/shower. B&B £17 to £34. Deposit: £10. Children welcome. Baby facilities. No pets in public rooms. Afternoon teas. Garden. Scenic. Doors close at 12

UPPINGHAM Leicestershire — map 6

▲ *Lake Isle* [new entry, zero rated]

16 High Street East, Uppingham LE15 9PZ
UPPINGHAM (0572) 822951 — £9–£14

There is a French farmhouse atmosphere to this restaurant behind an old shop-front, with its log fire and pine. Lunches are light on the pocket and flexible – there are inclusive prices for one, two, or three courses, including a glass of house wine. Food is fresh and cooked to a high standard, and ranges from fish soup, goujons of seafood and sardines in puff pastry, to Roquefort and pear salad, and calf's liver lyonnais. Combinations are more effective for being simple: madeira sauce for chicken breast; and apple and gooseberry sauce with roast loin of pork on Sunday. But, as in the days of Roy and Veronica Richards (now at Manor House, Pickworth), the reason for simplicity may well be that wine is the focal point around which food revolves. The well-chosen selection for under £11, which includes Durup Chablis, Alsace from Sipp as well as Dopff & Irion, Torres Gran Coronas, Savigny-lès-Beaune '82 from Simon Bize (£10·50), and a generous spattering of half-bottles, is a model of ungreedy mark-ups. The list of fine wines follows the same principles but moves into classed-growth clarets spanning '53 to '79, including Ch. Beychevelle '66 at £35, and a range of good burgundies.

CHEF: D. Whitfield PROPRIETORS: D. and C.L. Whitfield
OPEN: Tue to Sun, exc Sun D MEALS: 12 to 2, 7 to 10
PRICES: Set L from £5·75 (£9), Set D from £10·50 (£14) CARDS: Access, Amex, Diners, Visa
SEATS: 35. Private parties: 40 main room. Vegetarian meals. Children's helpings. Wheelchair access
ACCOMMODATION: 5 rooms, all with bath/shower. B&B £22 to £30. Children welcome. TV. Phone. Doors close at 12

VERYAN Cornwall map 1

▲ *Treverbyn House* [10/20]

Pendower Road, Veryan TR2 5QL
TRURO (0872) 501201 **Real Food** £12

The simple, French, set dinners served in this Edwardian house in the town centre say quite a lot about the state of food supplies in Cornwall. For the most part they are rearrangements on familiar themes – egg with shrimps; sole bonne femme; chicken provençale. The fish is either local or out of Newlyn, and both the scallops – sometimes served with a tartare sauce, sometimes as fruits de mer, sometimes provençale – and the brill have been first-class. Beef is bought well hung. The provençale sauces are made with the Gardners' own tomatoes; main courses come with three vegetables gleaned from local growers. Help yourself to 'sweets various: clotted cream' from the fine trolley and cafetière coffee; alternatively, the Cheddars and Stilton have been in good condition. The wine list is remarkably good value around the £5 mark with two Alsace wines at that price – a Tokay and a Riesling, both '83s from the Turkheim Co-operative. There are also good Rhônes and Loires.

CHEF: John Gardner PROPRIETOR: Josephine Gardner
OPEN: all week, D only MEALS: 7.30 to 8.30
PRICES: Set D from £9 (£12)
SEATS: 18. Private parties: 14 main room. Car-park, 10 places. Vegetarian meals by arrangement. Children's helpings. No children under 7. Smart dress preferred. Wheelchair access
ACCOMMODATION: 4 rooms. B&B £14 to £28. Deposit: £10. No children under 7. No pets. Afternoon teas. Fishing. Scenic

WADHURST East Sussex map 3

▲ *Spindlewood Hotel* [11/20]

Wallcrouch TN5 7JG
TICEHURST (0580) 200430
on B2099, 2½m SE of Wadhurst £16–£17

Before the Fitzsimmons came here in 1979 this Victorian country house, built in 1882 and now with a gravel drive, had been a set of old people's flatlets. The renovation continues: some of the rooms are now complete and the rest, plus the hall, library and part of the restaurant, will follow. The son Robert saws down trees as well as waiting at tables and making up enormous log fires. There is no sense of rush. The kitchen has an enterprising network of suppliers: a Ticehurst farmer/butcher, a local producer of vegetables and fruit, including asparagus, and fish comes from Hastings and Rye. Successful dishes on a hotel-style menu have been duck liver in cognac and cream sauce; veal sweetbreads in a brioche with mushroom and grain mustard sauce; boned legs of hare stuffed with chestnuts, bacon and mushrooms. An interesting main course is the lamb chop with redcurrant sauce, lamb's kidney with mustard sauce and lamb's liver with madeira sauce, all separate but on the same plate. Sweets are catering college staples – rum and pineapple choux buns; baked apple with hot golden pudding;

hot apple and raspberry tartlet; Bakewell tart; chocolate and raspberry roulades. There are reputedly 40,000 daffodils in the garden and some of them end up crystallised with kiwi and melon fruit sorbet. The varied wine list, with reasonable mark-ups, includes two wines from Alsace – Gewürztraminer, from Hugel, at £8·80, and Riesling, Médaille d'Or, both '82 and '83 (ask for '83) at £6·80 – and nine dessert wines, among them the luscious Bingen Osterberg Scheurebe Beerenauslese '76 at £12·95 for a half bottle. The house wine is French at £4·90.

CHEF: Harvey Aram PROPRIETORS: The Fitzsimmons family
OPEN: all week CLOSED: 4 days at Christmas MEALS: 12.15 to 1.30, 7.15 to 9
PRICES: L £12 (£16), Set L and D from £13 (£17). Cut-price menu for residents
CARDS: Access, Amex, Visa
SEATS: 40. Private parties: 50 main room, 10 private room. Car-park, 60 places. Vegetarian meals. Children's helpings. Classical music
ACCOMMODATION: 9 rooms, all with bath/shower. B&B £28 to £60. Deposit: 10%. Children welcome. Baby facilities. Garden. Tennis. TV. Phone. Doors close at 12. Confirm by 6 [GHG]

WALBERSWICK Suffolk map 6

▲ *Mary's* [9/20]

Manor House, Walberswick IP18 6UT
SOUTHWOLD (0502) 723243 £8–£10

For the last 16 years Mary Allen has run this homely little restaurant on the principle that you can call in at any time of the day and eat exactly what you want. There's a smokehouse in the garden, where they cure fish and sausages, and other choices on the menu range from excellent chicken vol-au-vents and fisherman's pot with salad, to grilled local slip soles. Fish is a strong point. Afternoon teas are served in a separate room. House French is £3·60.

CHEF: Ruth Boyce PROPRIETOR: Mary Allen
OPEN: all week, L only, also Fri and Sat D CLOSED: Mon to Thur, Nov to Apr
MEALS: 12 to 2.15, 7.15 to 9 (later by arrangement)
PRICES: £5 (£8), Set D £7·50 (£10), Snacks from 60p (70p)
SEATS: 54. 10 tables outside. Private parties: 54 main room. Car-park, 20 places. Children's helpings. Wheelchair access (also WC). Music
ACCOMMODATION: 2 rooms. B&B £9·50 to £19. Children welcome. Afternoon teas. Garden

Potter's Wheel Restaurant [9/20]

Village Green, Walberswick IP18 6TT
SOUTHWOLD (0502) 724468 £3–£9

It is necessary to book at least a day ahead for a table on Friday and Saturday nights. Dinner at £7·50 is excellent value, especially for the puddings. There is a choice of three dishes per course, ranging from roast partridge to courgette and mushroom bake. The fifty pence corkage includes glasses and the use of the fridge for white wine. Service is very friendly and considerate. The rest of the week Lesley Scott operates this as an inexpensive lunch-time only cafe with a strong

▲ *This restaurant has rooms.*

vegetarian bent, and may feature locally smoked mackerel, mushroom fritters with blue cheese sauce, or lasagne.

CHEF/PROPRIETOR: Lesley Scott
OPEN: all week for L, exc Tue; Fri and Sat D CLOSED: Christmas to Easter MEALS: 12 to 2, 7.30 to 9
PRICES: Set L from £2·50 (£3), Set D £7·50 (£9). Unlicensed, but bring your own: corkage 50p CARD: Access
SEATS: 24. Private parties: 24 main room. Vegetarian meals. Children's helpings (by arrangement at D). Wheelchair access. Classical music

WALFORD Hereford & Worcester map 4

▲ *Walford House* [new entry, zero rated]

Walford HR9 5RY
ROSS-ON-WYE (0989) 63829
on B4228 3m SW of Ross-on-Wye £10–£18

An historic house near the Forest of Dean. The five-course set menu is built round the best of local produce – free-range eggs, home-produced lamb or sometimes kid, pike and salmon from the Wye, with herbs and most of the vegetables coming from the garden. With notice, Raymond Zarb will cook specialities. Good dishes have been brill with sorrel sauce; veal zürichoise with rösti potatoes; and guinea-fowl with fresh peas. The handsome rooms look out on countryside. There is a fine wine cellar stocked with '66 Fixin and Grands Echézeaux, and old cognacs and armagnacs. House French is £5·80. More reports, please.

CHEF: Raymond Zarb PROPRIETORS: Joyce and Raymond Zarb
OPEN: all week MEALS: 12 to 1.45, 7.30 to 9.30
PRICES: £13 (£18), Set L from £7·50 (£10), Set D from £11 (£14). Service inc
CARDS: Access, Amex, Diners, Visa
SEATS: 50. 5 tables outside. Car-park, 100 places. Children's helpings. Jacket and tie. No smoking in dining-room. Wheelchair access (also WC)
ACCOMMODATION: 10 rooms, all with bath/shower. B&B £36. Deposit required: 10%. Children welcome. Baby facilities. Pets by arrangement. Afternoon teas. Garden. TV. Scenic. Doors close at 12. Confirm by 6

WALLINGFORD Oxfordshire map 2

Brown & Boswell [11/20]

28 High Street, Wallingford OX10 0BU
WALLINGFORD (0491) 34078 £6–£16

The main dishes here have been first class, which is the mark of a good restaurant: pigeon breasts with Cabernet glaze; noisettes of pork in bacon with sage and apple jelly; venison, well-hung and superb quality meat, lightly pan-fried so it is coloured outside and rare inside. Vegetables are indeed interesting, witness purée of potatoes and horseradish, and vegetarians have fared excellently, notably with an aubergine parmigiano. The rating is reduced one point because this consistency has not spread to other courses and they lack polish and pezzaz. Music is Bing Crosby and baroque. Fascinating young wine list arranged by style rather than region, not overpriced and backed up by some big guns listed under 'bin-ends'. The house wine is Bulgarian, or try the CELLARMAN'S CHOICE: Ch. Charron '82 at £6·90.

CHEFS: Robert Boswell and Paul Bridgewood
PROPRIETORS: Bryan and Buzz Brown, and Robert and Patricia Boswell
OPEN: Tue to Sun, exc Tue L CLOSED: last 2 weeks Mar, second week Oct
MEALS: 12 to 2.30, 7 to 10
PRICES: £9 (£15), Set L from £3 (£6), Set D from £12 (£16) CARDS: Access, Amex, Diners, Visa
SEATS: 35. Private parties: 24 main room, 24 and 12 private rooms. Vegetarian meals. Children's helpings. Wheelchair access. Classical music and jazz

Lamb Wine Vault [8/20]

Castle Street, Wallingford OX10 0BS
WALLINGFORD (0491) 39606 £9

A useful wine bar offering at least half a dozen wines by the glass for tasting, and home-cooked food that depends on what has been cooked in whose home. Good cheeses, otherwise it is pâtés, pies and hot-pots. CELLARMAN'S CHOICE: Gewürztraminer '83, from Heim, at £5·95.

PROPRIETORS: Nick and Carole Treadaway
OPEN: Tue to Sat MEALS: 12 to 2.30, 6 to 9
PRICES: £6 (£9) CARDS: Access, Diners, Visa
SEATS: 30. Private parties: 20 main room. Vegetarian meals. Children's helpings. Smart dress preferred. No-smoking area. Classical music

WALTON-ON-THE-HILL Surrey map 3

Ebenezer Cottage [12/20]

36 Walton Street, Walton-on-the-Hill KT20 7RT
TADWORTH (073 781) 3166 Real Food £15–£25

Lettuce and herbs are imported from Paris and any extras are sold to a local greengrocer, who in turn supplies other restaurants and customers – Real Food working at its best. The only pity is that no one in Surrey can offer the same standard of produce, which would cut the cost and probably give somebody a job too. An irony is that this is essentially an English restaurant, sited in a seventeenth-century farmhouse still with the original wattle, daub and timber. The set menu is good value, though the *carte* can be more expensive, and there are some intriguing combinations of ingredients – crab and prawn soup, veal with ginger and lime, saffron chicken, and lamb with crab and curry sauce. The kitchen belongs to the English school of Patum Peperium thinking. There are plainer dishes as well, and interesting sweets in the crème brûlée, apple tart and summer pudding vein. The atmosphere is relaxed and the waiters are courteous

Entries are compiled from the unsolicited reports from readers and are checked by inspectors; each restaurant is asked to supply details of its operation. Report forms can be found at the back of the Guide.

without fawning. It's a good place to find a slice of old England. The wine list is higgledy piggledy but there are usually some interesting bin-ends.

CHEF: Richard Brown PROPRIETORS: E.and A.J.Hamilton
OPEN: Tue to Sun, exc Sun D CLOSED: 1 week from 26 Dec MEALS: 12.30 to 1.45 (12.30 for 1 Sun L), 7.30 to 9.30 (10 Sat)
PRICES: £18 (£25), Set L from £10·50 (£15) CARDS: Access, Amex, Diners, Visa
SEATS: 68. Private parties: 20 main room, 8 and 16 private rooms. Car-park, 30 places. Vegetarian meals. Children's helpings (L only). No smoking. Wheelchair access. Classical music

WARMINSTER Wiltshire map 2

Agra [new entry, zero rated]

32 East Street, Warminster BA12 9BN
WARMINSTER (0985) 212713 and 215530 £12–£14

A useful Indian restaurant in the area and now under new ownership, although the striking naïve panels of Moghul emperors toying with their mistresses remain. Good dishes have included king prawn butterfly, tarka dhal, chicken korma, and lamb pasanda dishes cooked with red wine. There is a tandoori section too. If you fancy wine there is a Gewürztraminer, and among the liqueurs lurks a prunelle de Bourgogne.

CHEF: M.Ali PROPRIETOR: M.Rahman
OPEN: Tue to Sun MEALS: 12 to 1.45, 6.15 to 11.15
PRICES: £8 (£14), Set D from £7·95 (£12). Minimum £5·50. Service 10% CARDS: Access, Amex, Visa
SEATS: 44. Private parties: 50 main room. Vegetarian meals. Children welcome. Smart dress preferred. Indian music. Take-away service

Cooper's [new entry, zero rated]

28 High Street, Warminster BA12 9AF
WARMINSTER (0985) 216911 £7–£14

Omitted from last year's *Guide* because of a change of ownership, but the Brownings have continued the tradition of honest food at a reasonable price in this eighteenth-century house. There are good vegetable soups, omelettes, seafood pancakes, and casseroles in the daytime. In the evening there is a more formal menu with fine arrays of vegetables around centrepieces such as good veal with green peppers or pork fillet with prunes. To finish there are pies, pots and syllabubs. Thirty-six wines from Averys' La Bonne Vie at £3·95. CELLARMAN'S CHOICE: Fleurie, Château des Deduits '84 at £7·90.

CHEF: M.Browning PROPRIETORS: R. and M.Browning
OPEN: Tue to Sat MEALS: 12 to 2, 7.30 to 10
PRICES: £10 (£14), Set L £3·45 (£7), Set D £7·75 (£11) CARDS: Access, Amex, Diners, Visa
SEATS: 30. 2 tables outside. Private parties: 14 main room, 12 private room. Vegetarian meals. Children's helpings. Wheelchair access. Music

'We find that farm shops offer nothing special and we rely on Waitrose for the bulk of our foodstuffs.' (Hampshire restaurateur)

WARWICK Warwickshire map 2

Randolph's [12/20]

19–21 Coten End, Warwick CV34 4NT
WARWICK (0926) 491292 **Real Food** £22

In a block of refurbished sixteenth-century cottages with candlelight and an open log fire, David Randolph cooks for up to 30 customers, while Mrs Randolph serves. Supplies are taken seriously. Fish comes from Birmingham wholesale market and from Newquay in Cornwall – scallops for a spring salad with walnut oil dressing; live lobsters for mousses and sauces; red mullet, and seaweed for steaming it; John Dory to go with Scotch salmon. There is also grated salt cod in a raw fish starter with lime juice. Stock-pots keep the sauces robust, and the Randolphs' garden provides up to 20 different varieties of herb. Sometimes the kaleidoscope of flavours is head-spinning. Consider, for example, a starter of a short pastry case containing a ring of leek wrapped round mussels, served cold on a watercress sauce and accompanied by a pastry case containing calves' kidneys sauté with truffles and wild mushrooms, served hot with a beetroot sauce. There is also, however, good aiguillette of wild duck en brioche, and calves' kidneys on home-made tagliatelle with madeira sauce. Stoneground wholewheat flour is used for daily bread-making, and appetisers and petits fours are made in-house. Stylish presentation extends to the octet of vegetables. Cheeses include Reblochon, the powerful Boulette d'Avesnes, and Pont-l'Eveque. Puddings include the definitive chocaholic confection: a sandwich of three chocolates – coffee-flavoured, orange-flavoured white, and rich dark – in a light, creamy almond sauce. The wine list sensibly avoids high-priced white burgundy, although it edges into triple figures for a Ch. Margaux '66 among other good Bordeaux. The Loire and Rhône provide more affordable bottles.
CELLARMAN'S CHOICE: Mâcon-Clessé '83, from Thevenin, at £8·75.

CHEF: D.L.Randolph PROPRIETORS: D.L. and D.A.Randolph
OPEN: Mon to Sat, D only CLOSED: 1 week at Christmas MEALS: 7.45 to 9
PRICES: £16 (£22) CARDS: Access, Visa
SEATS: 30. Private parties: 30 main room. Children's helpings by arrangement. Smart dress preferred. No pipes in dining-room. Wheelchair access

WASHINGTON West Sussex map 3

George's Carvery [10/20]

Old London Road, Washington RH20 4AL
WASHINGTON (0903) 892947
on A24, 5m N of Worthing £10–£16

A good-value carvery. To start there has been the unusual banana and prawns in cold creamy curry sauce, or gazpacho, before beef, lamb or veal. Vegetables are good, and to finish there is yoghourt with caramel and meringue, or plum

The Guide is always anxious to recruit new inspectors. If you would like to apply, write to the editor enclosing a) a detailed report on a restaurant where you have eaten and b) a comparative study of restaurants known to you.

mousse with fruit salad. Coffee tastes better on the flower-hung open terrace. A good family place. Vin de pays de l'Hérault at £4·75.

CHEF: Justin Wheeler PROPRIETOR: David Leaker
OPEN: Tue to Sun L, Fri and Sat D MEALS: 12 to 2.30, 7 to 10
PRICES: £12 (£16), Set L from £7·70 (£10), Set D from £8·70 (£11). Service 10% at D
CARDS: Access, Amex, Diners, Visa
SEATS: 44. 6 tables outside. Private parties: 40 main room. Car-park, 40 places. Children's helpings. Wheelchair access (also WC)

WATERHOUSES Staffordshire — map 5

The Old Beams [new entry, zero rated]

Waterhouses ST10 3HW
WATERHOUSES (053 86) 254
on A523, 7m SE of Leek — £13–£21

Run by a husband-and-wife team who put an accent on set business lunches but cook a more flexible, pricier menu at night. Convincing dishes have been the warm pigeon breast salad; shrimp bisque with armagnac; calves' kidneys in mustard sauce; and chicken with Stilton. Vegetables are unadulterated and a strong point, and there is fine walnut and sultana bread with cheeses. Finally, the house speciality is a chestnut-filled meringue with chocolate sauce. A hundred wines, ranging from a Rhône vin de table at £6·35, to CELLARMAN'S CHOICE: Bourgogne rouge '78 from Jadot at £7·50, and beyond. More reports, please.

CHEF: Nigel J. Wallis PROPRIETORS: Nigel and Ann Wallis
OPEN: Tue to Sat MEALS: 12 to 2 (1.45 Sat), 7 to 10
PRICES: £15 (£21), Set L £7·50 (£13) CARDS: Amex, Diners, Visa
SEATS: 36. 3 tables outside. Car-park, 18 places. Children's helpings by arrangement. No children under 4. Wheelchair access. Classical music

WATERMILLOCK Cumbria — map 7

▲ *Leeming Country House* [12/20]

Watermillock CA11 0JJ
POOLEY BRIDGE (085 36) 622 — £11–£26

The setting is magnificent: acres of well-tended lawns, trimmed hedges, gravel paths and an extraordinary variety of enormous trees. Walk to the shores of Ullswater where cows graze in the shadow of the fells. The brochure says the Georgian house with Regency-style ironwork balcony and pillars was converted into a 'small' country-house hotel in 1969. It is hard to imagine its ever being small. The rooms are on a grand scale, with floor-to-ceiling doors and windows and elaborate ceilings. The dining-room dwarfs its tables, which are set with a lot of napery. The five-course dinner is about the same price as the set lunch at Le Gavroche (see London). There is plenty of choice. Dishes arrive lavishly bedecked with all manner of garnishes, as if they could not speak for themselves. But they can – avocado terrine contrasts well with its broccoli and walnut salad; crab profiteroles have been freshly made; venison in game sauce with glazed peaches has been excellent. At a rough count the salad has contained 19 ingredients which are not on garnishing duty. Sweets continue the elaborate theme – passion fruit and mango soufflé comes with raspberry sauce. Service is not affected by the grandeur of the house. The wine list is enormous, with many *cru* '50s and '60s clarets, but magnums of the house burgundy are £7·20, or try the CELLARMAN'S CHOICE: Ch. Plagnac '75 at £10·60.

CHEF: Jon Reed PROPRIETORS: Mr and Mrs M.J.Fitzpatrick
OPEN: all week CLOSED: Jan and Feb MEALS: 12.30 to 1.45, 7.30 to 8.45
PRICES: Set L from £6 (£11), Set D £19·50 (£26). Service 15% CARDS: Access, Amex, Diners, Visa
SEATS: 80. 5 tables outside. Private parties: 80 main room, 20 private room. Car-park, 35 places. No children under 6. Jacket and tie preferred. Wheelchair access (also WC)
ACCOMMODATION: 25 rooms, all with bath/shower. Rooms for disabled. B&B £35 to £64. Deposit: £15. No children under 10. No pets. Afternoon teas. Garden. Fishing. Helicopter pad. Phone. Scenic. Doors close at 12. Confirm by 6

WATH-IN-NIDDERDALE North Yorkshire map 7

▲ *Sportsman's Arms* [12/20]

Wath-in-Nidderdale HG3 5PP
HARROGATE (0423) 711306
2m NW of Pateley Bridge **Real Food** £8–£22

The quality of the raw materials is high at this restaurant with rooms in Upper Nidderdale. The local lamb and beef and Westmorland venison are excellent. Fish comes directly from Whitby. The menu is short, and has one foot in Yorkshire – black pudding with apple and onion – and the other in the Mediterranean – langoustines with a chive and lemon sauce. Notably good are the crabs and lobster; the chicken breast with a blue-cheese sauce; the salmon en papillote; and roast beef and Yorkshire pudding for the excellent-value Sunday lunch. To finish, as well as brandy-snaps and local cheeses, there are fruit sablés with cream. It is a sweeping wine list with clarets, burgundies and Rhônes going back more than a decade; mark-ups are about 100 per cent. Look for the '83 Alsace and Australian wines. House burgundy is £5·80. Theakston's beers.

CHEFS: J.R.Carter and J.J.Topham PROPRIETOR: J.R.Carter
OPEN: all week, exc Sun D MEALS: 12 to 1.45, 7 to 10
PRICES: £16 (£22), Set L from £5·75 (£10), Set D from £6·95 (£8) CARDS: Access, Amex, Diners, Visa
SEATS: 45. 6 tables outside. Private parties: 60 main room. Car-park, 50 places. Vegetarian meals. Children's helpings. Wheelchair access (also WC)
ACCOMMODATION: 6 rooms, 2 with bath/shower. B&B £20 to £35. Children welcome. Pets welcome. Afternoon teas. Garden. Fishing

WEMBLEY Greater London map 3

Moghul Brasserie [new entry, zero rated]

525 High Road, Wembley HA0 4AG
01-903 6967 and 902 8665 £11–£14

The first days of the Moghul, which opened in May 1985, seem to promise as much as the other jewels in Amin Ali's crown, Lal Qila and the Red Fort (see

London), bringing similar style in a sort of Passage to Wembley. From glass-fronted cocktail bar to brightly lit cream walls and tablecloths, to Habitat-style cane chairs and rainbow cushions, the decor is westernised Indian chic. Moghul cuisine is billed as open-fire cooking meeting delicate herbs and spices. The menu is big on lamb (including brains) and chicken, but vegetables get a fair crack of the whip too: fragrant, cumin-flavoured Bombay aloo cocktail; muttar paneer; chana masala; spinach with green peppers, onion, celery and cardamon; and there is a boiled egg in tomato gravy. Tandoori quails arrive sizzling noisily, with necks bent under; steamed haddock-like fish with courgettes and a tomatoey yoghourt sauce comes with plenty of saffron. Spices are used without overkill, as in karahi josh. Peshawari nan is excellent, and poppadums (called papar here), pickles, and raita all pass muster. Service is not hurried. Drink spiced tea, lassi, or Kingfisher beer (80p). More reports, please.

CHEF: Ador Miah PROPRIETOR: Amin Ali
OPEN: all week MEALS: 12 to 2.30, 6 to 11.30
PRICES: £8 (£14), Set Sat and Sun L £6·95 (£11). Minimum £7. Service 12.5%
CARDS: Access, Amex, Diners, Visa
SEATS: 60. Private parties: 70 main room, 20 private room. Car-park, 12 places. Vegetarian meals. Children's helpings. Jacket and tie preferred. Wheelchair access. Indian music. Air-conditioned

Peking Castle [9/20]

379 High Road, Wembley HA9 8AA
01-902 3605 £9–£11

There are a few Anglicised and Cantonese dishes as well as Peking specialities in this neighbourhood restaurant; at the end of the menu is a long, tantalising section written in Chinese script. Chopsticks are available on request. Grilled dumplings, deep-fried beef in chilli sauce, chicken with cashew-nuts, and good steamed rice are favourites. Courvoisier or Rémy Martin is £1 and £1·30 a glass.

CHEF/PROPRIETOR: W.C.Hsu
OPEN: Mon to Sat MEALS: 12 to 2, 6 to 11 (11.30 Fri and Sat)
PRICES: £6 (£11), Set L and D from £5·80 (£9). Minimum £5. Service 10% CARDS: Access, Amex, Visa
SEATS: 50. Private parties: 50 main room. Children welcome. Air-conditioned

WENTBRIDGE West Yorkshire map 5

▲ *Wentbridge House* [new entry, zero rated]

Wentbridge WE8 3JJ
PONTEFRACT (0977) 620444
½m off A1, 4m SE of Pontefract £14–£22

A formal, red-flock wallpapered restaurant overseen by the extremely competent Master Sommelier Otto Hinderer and offering a good choice of fresh produce. Its strengths are quality meats and excellent sauces and its weakness is the length of the menu, which can lead to some ordinary starters. Notably good main courses have been noisettes of lamb with a sauce of onion purée, wine and cream, and lemon sole stuffed with mushrooms in a vermouth sauce. Sweets are always a feature – there are wonderful cheesecakes and Dutch apple tart. The wine list is

immodestly priced but it is an extraordinarily complete collection of some of the best bottles of the last fifteen years and only the level of the mark-ups stops us giving a bottle denotation. House French is £3·75 for half a litre.
CELLARMAN'S CHOICE: House Champagne at £15, or Verdicchio Classico, Castelli di Jesi '83 at £7. More reports, please.

CHEF: Charles Carter PROPRIETORS: M.M. and K.C.Dupuy
OPEN: all week CLOSED: 25 Dec D MEALS: 12.30 to 2, 7.30 to 9.30
PRICES: £16 (£22), Set L from £9 (£14), Snacks from £1·25. Service inc CARDS: Access, Amex, Diners, Visa
SEATS: 55. Private parties: 140 main room, 18 private room. Car-park, 70 places. Children's helpings. Smart dress preferred. Wheelchair access (also WC)
ACCOMMODATION: 20 rooms, 17 with bath/shower. B&B £22 to £38. Garden. TV. Phone. Doors close at 12.30

WEST BEXINGTON Dorset map 2

▲ *Manor House Hotel* [9/20]

Beach Road, West Bexington DT2 9DF
BURTON BRADSTOCK (0308) 897616
on the coast, 3m NW of Abbotsbury £13–£14

It is worth knowing about this hostelry overlooking Chesil Bank. Although the restaurant is unpolished, the cooking is honest and generous, the bar does good snacks and real ales, and the rooms are clean. Fish has been good, especially the moules marinière, the grilled sardines, and the smoked haddock for breakfast. So, too, the roast pheasant served with plenty of hot, fresh vegetables. A speciality is guinea-fowl fried in butter, with a cream sauce flavoured with brandy and pineapple. Butter is the main cooking medium. Sweets are less good, and the wine list is minimal, but a cafetière is left on the table with some oddly psychedelic petits fours. If the Bishop's Tipple is still on, don't touch it if you are driving.

CHEF: Clive Jobson PROPRIETORS: Richard and Jayne Childs
OPEN: all week MEALS: 12 to 2, 7 to 10 (10.30 Sat)
PRICES: Set L £8·45 (£13), set D £9·65 (£14). Snacks from £1·25 (£1·40) CARDS: Access, Amex, Visa
SEATS: 65. 18 tables outside. Private parties: 65 main room, 20 private room. Car park, 50 places. Vegetarian meals. Children's helpings. Music
ACCOMMODATION: 11 rooms, 2 with bath/shower. B&B £16·50 to £29. Deposit: £10. Baby facilities. No pets. TV. Garden. Scenic. Confirm by 6 [GHG]

WEST BYFLEET Surrey map 3

Chu-Chin-Chow [10/20]

63 Old Woking Road, West Byfleet KT16 0JX
BYFLEET (093 23) 49581/2 £15–£24

An attractive, airy, Peking/Szechuan restaurant with immaculate linen. Service is good but slow. Dishes are neatly arranged. Notably good have been sesame prawns; steamed sea-bass with shredded ginger, spring onions and soya sauce;

Kung Po chicken with a lethal amount of garlic and chilli sauce; and crispy duck. Good and plentiful tea; strong coffee; scented towels.

CHEF: Mr Wan PROPRIETOR: Robert To
OPEN: all week MEALS: 12 to 2, 6 to 11
PRICES: £16 (£24), Set L and D from £10 (£15). Minimum £8. Service 10% CARDS: Access, Amex, Diners, Visa
SEATS: 110. Private parties: 120 main room. Children welcome. Wheelchair access. Music. Air-conditioned

WEST CLANDON Surrey — map 3

Onslow Arms [new entry, zero rated]

The Street, West Clandon GU4 7TE
GUILDFORD (0483) 222447 — £15–£26

There's a lot of saucing and garnishing to the food in this up-market, olde worlde restaurant, but what is underneath is pretty good. At first glance the menu also feels pretentious, but then there are items not usually found in these parts of Surrey, such as oyster mushrooms, and tresses of salmon and turbot with ginger. Especially worthwhile are the artichoke hearts with giant prawns; salmon with a superb beurre blanc flavoured with sorrel; and very fine tournedos with rather a lot of good madeira sauce. There are plenty of different vegetables and the wild strawberry sorbet was one of the best eaten at inspections last year. The crème brûlée is exemplary, too. The wine list reflects the fact that this is expense-account territory – it is dull and expensive, with no regard for the quality of different vintages. A pity. More reports, please.

CHEF: Ewart Morgan PROPRIETOR: Alan John Peck
OPEN: Tue to Sun, exc Sun D MEALS: 12.30 to 2.15, 7.30 to 10.30
PRICES: £16 (£26), Set L £8·50 (£15), Bar snacks from 60p. Service 15%, exc on snacks
CARDS: Access, Amex, Diners, Visa
SEATS: 80. 12 tables outside. Private parties: 160 main room, 60 private room. Car-park, 200 places. Vegetarian meals. Children's helpings. Smart dress preferred. No pipes in dining-room. Wheelchair access (also WC). Music

WESTERHAM Kent — map 3

Shapla Tandoori [10/20]

20 London Road, Westerham TN16 1BD
WESTERHAM (0959) 63397 and 62163 — £9–£10

An Indian restaurant that's busy but restful – except when the chef sings – and serving satisfying chicken tikka, mildly spiced, and masala dishes from a standard menu. Tandoori king prawns, sag josh and chicken are all good, as are the rice and poppadums. Efficient service.

CHEFS: O.S.Singh and A.K.Hazra PROPRIETOR: A.K.S.Choudhury
OPEN: all week CLOSED: 25 and 26 Dec MEALS: 12 to 2.15, 6 to 11.15
PRICES: £5 (£10), Set L and D from £5·30 (£9) CARDS: Access, Amex, Diners, Visa
SEATS: 66. Private parties: 50 main room. Vegetarian meals. Children's helpings. Wheelchair access (also WC). Music

WEST MERSEA Essex map 3

▲ *Le Champenois, Blackwater Hotel* [12/20]

20–22 Church Street, West Mersea CO5 8QH
COLCHESTER (0206) 383338 and 383038 £9–£18

A French family restaurant, set in a late-Victorian coaching-inn, where the local tide-table hangs in the bar. Madame Chapleo greets. The food is serious, making use of local ingredients, including West Mersea oysters prepared in the French manner. The mushrooms champenois are sliced, cooked in garlic butter and cream; guinea-fowl is roasted and served with madeira sauce; the ratatouille made with good oil. The attention to detail, without recourse to smothering sauces, lifts the cooking. Calves' kidneys dijonnaise are flambé in marc de Bourgogne. English dishes, such as pigeon pie, have also been highly rated. The cheeseboard is French, and usually the sweets are a tour de force; chocolate bavarois and crème caramel. There is fresh French bread and strong coffee, and croissants for breakfast. Redoubtable, well-chosen French wine list concentrates on the better value wines. CELLARMAN'S CHOICE: Morgon, Charmes 'Princesse Lieven' '83, from Duboeuf at £7·85.

CHEF: R.Roudesli PROPRIETOR: Mrs M.Chapleo
OPEN: all week, exc Tue L and Sun D CLOSED: 2 weeks Jan MEALS: 12 to 2, 7 to 10
PRICES: £13 (£18), Set L from £5·50 (£9), Snacks from £1·50 (£1·65) CARDS: Access, Amex
SEATS: 46. 3 tables outside. Private parties: 55 main room, 25 private room. Car-park, 20 places. Children's helpings. Smart dress preferred. Wheelchair access (also WC). French popular music
ACCOMMODATION: 7 rooms, 4 with bath/shower. B&B £16 to £27. Deposit: 10%. Children welcome. Baby facilities. Pets by arrangement. Afternoon teas. Garden. TV. Scenic. Doors close at 1. Confirm by 9

WETHERAL Cumbria map 7

Fantails [10/20]

The Green, Wetheral CA4 8ET
WETHERAL (0228) 60239 £14

A friendly, family-run à la carte restaurant in a seventeenth-century hay-loft. Game is shot locally and salmon netted in the Solway. Steaks – hung for three weeks – are of high quality, as are fish. There are some typically Scottish touches, such as mussel brose, and pork flamed in whisky and served with a cream and tomato sauce, but there has also been an unusual Burmese dish of mushrooms sauté in butter with a cream sauce flavoured with coconut and almonds, and served on rice. The Latin motto over the bar translates as, 'May your worries yield to this place'. House French is £5·25 or there is the surprising, and different, Rock's elderflower wine from Berkshire.

CHEFS: G.S.Ferguson and D.Todhunter PROPRIETORS: Mrs P. and G.S.Ferguson and L.A.Norman
OPEN: Tue to Sat CLOSED: Feb MEALS: 12 to 2, 6 to 9.30
PRICES: £9 (£14) CARDS: Access, Amex, Diners, Visa
SEATS: 75. Private parties: 50 main room, 25 private room. Car-park, 16 places. Vegetarian meals. Children's helpings. No-smoking area.

WETHERBY West Yorkshire map 5

L'Escale [new entry, zero rated]

16 Bank Street, Wetherby LS22 4NQ
WETHERBY (0937) 63613 and 62751 £14–£22

A single-storey, stone-faced, purpose-built building in the centre of town. The dining-room is formal but comfortable, and there is no shortage of waistcoated waiters. The *carte* changes quarterly and is essentially of French persuasion. Good dishes have been the hot sole mousseline with watercress sauce; rich and creamy tomato and basil soup; and a fine passion fruit sauce with virtually caramelised juices from the pan to go with half a roast duck. To finish there is a good apple tart or soufflé glacé aux marrons, and plentiful coffee. The wine list has helpful descriptions and is strong in most of the major French regions. More reports, please.

CHEF: Simon Partridge PROPRIETORS: Paul and Karin Bidgood
OPEN: Tue to Sat D, Sun L MEALS: 12 to 2.30, 7 to 11
PRICES: £16 (£22), Set L £7·95 (£14) CARDS: Access, Amex, Diners, Visa
SEATS: 70. Private parties: 35 main room, 35 private room. Car-park, 8 places. Children's helpings (Sun L only). Smart dress preferred. No pipes in dining-room. Wheelchair access (also men's wc). Music

WETHERSFIELD Essex map 3

Rudi's [11/20]

Village Green, Wethersfield CM7 4BS
GREAT DUNMOW (0371) 850723 £9–£16

The Black Forest gateau served in this white, converted bakery is a genuine version. Rudi and Dilys Haindl's Austrian-French restaurant seems to specialise in dishes that in other places might be boil-in-the-bag – chicken Kiev, venison marchand de vin, and so on. But the kitchen does not cut corners, except perhaps on the vegetables, and there have been very good mushrooms stuffed with sausagemeat; game casserole made of venison, pigeon and hare braised in brown ale with carrots, onions and leeks; and seafood pancakes. The Apfelstrudel takes 40 minutes to arrive but is quite something. Sunday lunch is more traditionally English, with roast sirloin with fine horseradish sauce. It is friendly and the atmosphere genial. Monthly Austrian evenings. Unexciting wines except for the CELLARMAN'S CHOICE: Stift Klosterdawn '83 from Klosterneuburg at £7·20.

CHEF: John Jones PROPRIETORS: Rudi and Dilys Haindl
OPEN: Tue to Sun, exc Sun D MEALS: 12 to 2, 7 to 9.30 (10 Sat)
PRICES: £13 (£16), Set L £6·50 (£9). Service inc
SEATS: 56. Private parties: 38 main room, 20 private room. Car-park, 10 places. Children's helpings. Wheelchair access (also wc). Music

Restaurants are graded on a scale of 1–20. In the region of 8–9 expect to find places that may not be restaurants but cafes, pubs, bistros and small hotels. In the category of 10–11 you can expect to find the best food in the locality. Ratings of 12 or more are given to restaurants we regard as serving the best food in the region.

WEYBOURNE Norfolk map 6

Gasché's [10/20]

The Street, Weybourne NR25 7SY
WEYBOURNE (026 370) 220
on A149, 3m NE of Holt £10–£22

For more than 30 years the *Guide* has noted this Swiss restaurant's competence at feeding the north Norfolk coast on fried whitebait, wiener Schnitzel and cream meringues. There have been many ups and downs in our relationship, and this year marks another lurch. Portion-size cannot be argued with – aubergine with lamb, pheasant with red cabbage, chicken chasseur, sole meunière, and the selection of vegetables are more than generous. But over-cooking and slow-moving swamps of floury sauces make the prospect less attractive. Mussels have come to a particularly sticky end. Other reasons for the substantial drop in score from last year's 12/20 include the relatively high prices and the use of commercial products, such as proprietary liver sausage on an hors d'oeuvre plate of cold meats. But if there is little else to do in Weybourne – nothing on at the church, the road to Sheringham is blocked, the beach frozen, and the nearby bird sanctuaries closed – there is a big welcome in Mr Gasché's pine tables, home-made crisps and roaring log fire. House wine is French from Cordier at £3·40 the half-litre.

CHEFS: Nigel Massingham and Mark Sayers PROPRIETOR: E.R.Steiner-Gasché
OPEN: Tue to Sun, exc Sun D MEALS: 12.30 to 2, 7 to 9
PRICES: £15 (£22), Set L from £4·95 (£10), Set D from £10·95 (£17) CARDS: Access, Amex, Diners, Visa
SEATS: 70. Private parties: 35 main room, 12 private room. Car-park, 35 places. Vegetarian meals. Children's helpings. Wheelchair access (also WC)

WEYBRIDGE Surrey map 3

The Colony [11/20]

3 Balfour Road, Weybridge KT13 8HE
WEYBRIDGE (0932) 42766 and 55544 £11–£19

This used to be an Italian restaurant called Russo, but is now run by Michael Tse who managed the Kew Rendezvous. It is a smart, expensive, second-generation Chinese restaurant: the tables are well spaced and set with crisp linen, silver chopsticks and silver spoon rest. The menu roams idly across the different regions of China, stopping longest in Peking for duck, smoked fish, grilled prawns and so on. The presentation of dishes is attractive – whole steamed sea-bass, for example, is brought to the table decorated with spring onion and ginger. The sizzling dishes, like lamb with more ginger and spring onion, announce themselves noisily hissing and spitting on the black, cast-iron griddle. The new fashionable dish in Chinese restaurants of iceberg lettuce leaves served with a mince of pork, chicken, mushroom and shrimp, to make up into sandwiches à la Peking duck, has been excellent, but also well reported have been the old, old favourites like sweet-and-sour pork, toasted sesame prawns, and spare ribs. Look for the deep-fried shredded beef in chilli sauce – it is also worth asking about other dishes not on the menu, because Szechuan tripe and mashed bean cake have been known to be offered. House white is £5·50.

CHEF: Kam Yau Pang PROPRIETOR: Michael Tse
OPEN: all week MEALS: 12 to 2.30, 6 to 11 (11.30 Fri and Sat)
PRICES: £10 (£19), Set L from £6 (£11), Set D from £10 (£15). Minimum £10. Service 12.5% CARDS: Access, Amex, Diners, Visa
SEATS: 80. Private parties: 70 main room, 20 private room. Children welcome. Chinese music

Gaylord [8/20]

73 Queens Road, Weybridge KT13 9UQ
WEYBRIDGE (0932) 42895 and 55325 £10–£15

A smart Indian restaurant with flock wallpaper and a lot of plant life, where the quality of cooking seems to fluctuate from the wonderful to the less so. However, for the past year it has been in a good phase, producing light samosas, crispy bhajias, good tandooris and well-marinated and tender lamb tikkas. Peshwari nan has a full complement of sultanas, almonds and coconut. Drink Dortmund lager.

CHEF: Mosraf Ali PROPRIETOR: M.S.Rahman
OPEN: all week MEALS: 12 to 2.30, 6 to 11.30 (12 Fri and Sat)
PRICES: £9 (£15), Set D from £5·95 (£10). Service 12.5% CARDS: Access, Amex, Diners, Visa
SEATS: 43. Private parties: 53 main room. Vegetarian meals. Children's helpings. Wheelchair access (also WC). Indian music

The Gourmet [10/20]

27 Thames Street, Weybridge KT13 8AY
WEYBRIDGE (0932) 46666 £15

The atmosphere here is casual and relaxed. Reasonably priced Cantonese and Peking dishes are cooked to a high standard and include strips of duck on shredded lettuce and bean sprouts; scallops with a peppery soy sauce; beef in green peppers in black bean sauce; stuffed prawns in batter; and special fried rice. Some pork and beef dishes, however, have had a low meat content. Licensed. The owner has also opened a provision shop on the main street.

CHEF: Mr Ma PROPRIETOR: Mr Yeung
OPEN: Mon to Sat, exc Mon L CLOSED: 3 weeks Jan MEALS: 12.30 to 2.30, 6.30 to 10.30
PRICES: £8 (£15) CARDS: Access, Visa
SEATS: 50. Private parties: 20 private room. Vegetarian meals. Children welcome. Wheelchair access (1 step). Music

WHITBY North Yorkshire map 6A

Magpie Café [9/20]

14 Pier Road, Whitby YO21 3JN
WHITBY (0947) 602058 £4–£9

A bright, chintzy and clean cafe in a Georgian building opposite the fish quay and now in the third generation of the McKenzie family. There are views of the boats in Whitby harbour from both upstairs and down. The large menu is almost all fish and it is always the day's catch that is served, whether cod or local salmon. Lobster comes off the boats in the morning and is served with a generous salad and thinly sliced brown bread. Choose between ice-cream and home-made sweets, including good apple pie, or try the more unusual simnel cake and cheese to finish. Charming and easy-mannered service. Afternoon tea is £2; pots of tea come with all the set lunches.

CHEFS/PROPRIETORS: Sheila and Ian McKenzie
OPEN: all week, exc Fri CLOSED: Oct to Mar MEALS: 11.30 to 2.30, 3.30 to 6.30
PRICES: £8 (£9), Set L from £4 (£4·40). Unlicensed, but bring your own: no corkage
SEATS: 95. Private parties: 47 main room. Vegetarian meals. Children's helpings

WHITEHAVEN Cumbria — map 7

Bruno's [new entry, zero rated]

9–10 Church Street, Whitehaven CA28 7AY
WHITEHAVEN (0946) 65270 — £6–£12

A bustling little Italian restaurant with huge paintings on the wall and a wine bar downstairs serving good pizzas. Rolls are home-made and the cannelloni, tortellini and spaghetti all draw recommendations. Fish is a speciality – not just lobster, but also sole cooked in a paper bag. Good cheesecake to finish. The set lunch is inexpensive. House wine is £4·95 a litre. More reports, please.

CHEF/PROPRIETOR: Bruno Camigiani
OPEN: all week, exc Sun D MEALS: 12 to 2.30, 6 to 10.30
PRICES: £9 (£12), Set L from £3·25 (£6). Service inc CARDS: Access, Visa
SEATS: 50. Private parties: 32 main room, 18 and 10 private rooms. Vegetarian meals. Children's helpings. Italian music

WHITNEY-ON-WYE Hereford & Worcester — map 2

▲ *Rhydspence Inn* [11/20]

Whitney-on-Wye HR3 6EU
CLIFFORD (049 73) 262
1¼m W of Whitney-on-Wye — **Real Food** £11–£13

Readers rightly admonished the *Guide* office for the low rating last year. It was given mainly on the basis of the bar meals, which continue, rather than on those served in the beamed dining-room – such good dishes as jugged hare, Breton fish soup, pike quenelles with shrimp and lobster sauce, and oxtail casserole. The ribs of beef arrive whole at the table to be carved into thick slices, rare in the centre, crisp on the outside. David Wallington says: 'We have strayed into *nouvelle cuisine* and out again.' There is a very fine show of cheese, including Double and Single Gloucesters, Devon Garland and Stilton from Colston Basset. Sweets range from profiteroles to chocolate rum crunch. The wines, like the menu, have an

Prices quoted are for an average three-course meal including service and VAT and half a bottle of house wine (or the equivalent in an ethnic restaurant).

accent on value, with some good Italian reds around £5. Hook Norton ale. CELLARMAN'S CHOICE: Chianti Classico, Castello d'Uzzano '78 at £6·75.

CHEF: David Wallington PROPRIETORS: David and Florence Wallington
OPEN: Wed to Sat, and Sun L, plus Tue L and D Easter to Oct CLOSED: 2 weeks Mar
MEALS: 12 to 1.45, 7 to 9.30
PRICES: £10 (£13), Set L and D £8 (£11), Bar snacks from £1·25. Minimum £8 in rest
CARDS: Amex, Visa
SEATS: 50. 12 tables outside. Private parties: 20 main room. Car-park, 60 places. Vegetarian meals. Children's helpings. Wheelchair access (also WC)
ACCOMMODATION: 3 rooms, 2 with bath/shower. B&B £16 to £32. Deposit: £5. No children under 10. No pets. Garden. Fishing. TV. Scenic. Doors close at 11. Confirm by 7.30

WICKHAM Hampshire — map 2

▲ *The Old House* [12/20]

The Square, Wickham PO17 5JG
WICKHAM (0329) 833049 — £16

Not cheap, but the modern bourgeois cooking served in the unhurried and relaxed dining-rom of the Skipwiths' Georgian house provides real value. Pheasants, mallards, partridges, and so on are local, but maize-fed chickens come from Brittany, wild mushrooms and saffron from Bordeaux. Chef Colin Wood changes the menu weekly. Fish specialities include monkfish in red wine sauce on noodles, sole mousseline with beurre blanc, and salmon with rosemary. More typical are the roast chicken with tarragon, or chicken rillettes. Sauces are a strong point. Vegetarians have been well looked after. The *crêpe sans rival* is, in fact, filled with a cream custard, marzipan, and ground hazel-nuts flavoured with Pernod, and topped with kiwi, baked with a meringue coating and served with a raspberry sauce! A short, interesting list of wines. The house white is a Muscadet, the red a Côtes du Rhône. CELLARMAN'S CHOICE: Gewürztraminer, Fleur d'Alsace '81 from Hugel at £9·10.

CHEF: Colin Wood PROPRIETORS: Richard and Annie Skipwith
OPEN: L Tue to Fri, D Mon to Sat CLOSED: 2 weeks Jul/Aug, 1 week Christmas, 2 weeks Easter MEALS: 12 to 1.45, 7 to 9.30
PRICES: £11·30 (£16). Service inc. Licensed, plus bring your own: corkage £2
CARDS: Access, Amex, Diners, Visa
SEATS: 45. Private parties: 34 main room, 14 private room. Car-park, 12 places. No pipes in dining-room. Children's helpings. Wheelchair access (also WC)
ACCOMMODATION: 10 rooms, all with bath/shower. B&B from £39. Garden. Children welcome. Baby facilities. TV. Phone. Scenic [GHG]

WILLERBY Humberside — map 6

▲ *Le Restaurant Français, Willerby Manor Hotel* [10/20]

Well Lane, Willerby HU10 6ER
HULL (0482) 652616
4½m from Hull centre — £9–£18

Everyone, including the chef, seems to want to be absolutely sure everything is absolutely OK during meals in this French restaurant.
'Is everything all right?'

'Well, seeing as you're asking, the brown and beige colour scheme doesn't add much, but you've got an elegant dining-room, I will say that. What I don't quite understand is why you write out the menu in French and then translate it into English underneath. Do you get a lot of French people in? And to be absolutely frank, I wonder . . . no the leek and celery soup's fine, thanks . . . I wonder whether the terrine of sole, pistachio nuts, rock lobster, queenies, and tomato coulis should all be on the same plate at the same time? I mean, I wouldn't have minded the pistachios to nibble before the meal and the queenies as a main course. But the lamb was lovely. What was the "de patûrage au petit bouquet d'asperges" – was that the sauce? And you're right, not many places would give you 10 different slivers of cheese on one plate. No, I didn't realise your chef trained at the Dorchester and that then he was a senior lecturer in catering. Yes, the house wine was lovely, thanks, and very good value. Perhaps next time I'll try your CELLARMAN'S CHOICE: Morgon '82, Domaine des Vieux Cèdres, from Loron at £9.'

CHEF: Derek Baugh PROPRIETORS: J. Townend and Sons Ltd
OPEN: all week, exc Sat L and Sun D MEALS: 12.30 to 1.45, 7 to 7.45
PRICES: £14 (£18), Set L £6 (£9), Set D £7·50 (£11) CARDS: Access, Amex, Diners, Visa
SEATS: 75. Private parties: 70 main room, 350 and 40 private rooms. Car-park, 200 places. Children's helpings. Smart dress preferred. Music
ACCOMMODATION: 42 rooms, all with bath/shower. B&B from £36·75. Children welcome. No pets. Garden. Helicopter pad. TV. Phone. Confirm by 6

WILLITON Somerset map 1

▲ *White House Hotel* [13/20]

Williton TA4 4QW
WILLITON (0984) 32306 and 32777 **Real Food** £18

The inspirations in this white house where Kay and Dick Smith have been since 1967 are Elizabeth David and Jane Grigson. The hotel has evolved slowly in that time into a restaurant with rooms, and the menu has recently been expanded. Most things that grow are cooked – soups of pumpkin or sorrel and lentil – and loganberries are popped on the crème brûlée. Main dishes tend to the classics of country cooking – pheasant normande; sole Dugléré; beef fillet with sauce béarnaise; and confit of duck. The inclusive menu offers at least four choices in each of the three courses, and there are fine cheeses – hard, unpasteurised British specimens that go well with the magnificent wines in the cellar. House Côtes du Rhône is £5 but there is also Bandol '74 at £8·80; non-vintage Ch. Bahans-Haut-Brion at £10; and a white Auxey-Duresses '82 at £10. Fine brandies and malts too.

CHEFS/PROPRIETORS: Dick and Kay Smith
OPEN: all week, D only CLOSED: Nov to 17 May MEALS: 7.30 to 8.30
PRICES: Set D £13·50 (£18)
SEATS: 30. Private parties: 21 main room. Car-park, 20 places. Children's helpings (D only). Wheelchair access. One sitting
ACCOMMODATION: 13 rooms, 7 with bath/shower. Rooms for disabled. B&B £19 to £32. Deposit: £20. Children welcome. Dogs welcome. TV

WINCHCOMBE **Gloucestershire** map 2

Corner Cupboard Inn [12/20]

Gloucester Street, Winchcombe GL54 5LX
WINCHCOMBE (0242) 602303 £15

An old, honey-coloured Cotswold building with mullioned windows and steps leading up to the front door. The dining-room is at the back of the pub and there is strictly no smoking allowed. Christopher Wickens runs a virtually one-man operation (there are snacks only at lunch-time), so the menu is short. His style is country cooking with a vegetarian bias, as in hazel-nut and mushroom roulade with watercress mayonnaise. The quality of the meat is excellent, from ribs of roast beef to pot-roast ham in cider, to rack of lamb with Cumberland sauce. Not all the innovations are as successful as others, which can make standards uneven – hence the relatively low rating. But Mr Wickens' strawberry cheesecake is one of the best in Gloucestershire. Sensibly, he offers a single cheese, perhaps a Sharpham from Totnes. It is probably the best-value 14-bottle wine list in the country, with only Châteauneuf-du-Pape, Domaine Font de Michelle '81, at £9·75, out of the £5 bracket.

CHEF/PROPRIETOR: Christopher Wickens
OPEN: Tue to Sat MEALS: 12.30 to 2.30, 7.15 to 9
PRICES: Set D £11·50 (£15)
SEATS: 16. Private parties: 16 main room. Car-park. Vegetarian meals by arrangement. No smoking in dining-room. Wheelchair access. Jazz

WINDERMERE **Cumbria** map 7

▲ *Miller Howe* [15/20]

Rayrigg Road, Windermere LA23 1EY
WINDERMERE (096 62) 2536
on A592 between Windermere
and Bowness **Real Food** £24·50

John Tovey's theatre of food plays to packed houses: the view over the lake, the lights dimmed, everyone sitting down together, and the dishes arriving in unison like a chorus . . . Best to go out of season and not on Saturday when there are two sittings – Miller Howe is now an institution on the international circuit, a boarding house *par excellence*. Despite there being no choice, the cooking is varied, light, inventive, and not *nouvelle* or even modern but individual. A new soup in the repertory is Nip and Nip (turnip and parsnip with cream and croûtons). Other evenings have started with asparagus, pea and lettuce or a minestrone of ham, honey, beer, stock and vegetables, followed by chicken livers with herbs and Marsala dressed with walnut oil. For the main course, the duck breast is marinated for 11 days before arriving at the table with a gooseberry and elderflower purée with green peppercorn sauce and the usual dazzling array of vegetables – glazed carrots with herbs, baked red cabbage with apple and spices, French beans, grated zucchini with lime, deep-fried curried celeriac, purée of sprouts with hazel-nuts, and baked jacket potato with cheese and herb pâté arranged at the points of a clock around the plate. Tovey has spent much of the year writing a new book on vegetable cookery. To finish in summer, the farmhouse berry pies take a lot of beating. Six to eight cases of oranges are used each week to make up the fresh orange juice for breakfast, which is magnificent. The picnic lunches include avocado, pâté, rare beef salad with dressing, grapes, sweet biscuits and chocolate. The opening of the sister project at Uplands (see under Cartmel) does not appear to have adversely affected operations. There are 51 South African wines around £8 that merit exploration, though not everyone is as convinced by them as Mr Tovey, and also a quintet of good Alsace wines from Hugel plus a well-chosen small spread from everywhere else, none ridiculously priced.

CHEF: Robert Lyons PROPRIETOR: John J. Tovey
OPEN: all week, D only CLOSED: Dec to Mar MEALS: 8.30 (7 and 9.30 Sat)
PRICES: Set D £18·50 (£24·50). Service 12.5% CARDS: Access, Amex, Diners
SEATS: 70. Private parties: 30 main room. Car-park, 60 places. Smart dress preferred. No smoking. No children under 12. Wheelchair access. Music. Air-conditioned. 1 sitting: 2 Sat
ACCOMMODATION: 13 rooms, all with bath/shower. D, B&B £48 to £75 per person. No children under 12. Pets welcome. Afternoon teas. Garden. Scenic [GHG]

Roger's [13/20]

4 High Street, Windermere LA23 1AF
WINDERMERE (096 62) 4954 £17

This restaurant goes from strength to strength. Roger and Alena Pergl-Wilson change the menu daily in their unfussy, relaxed little French restaurant. Meals have been good in every department. The quality of the meats is excellent, especially steaks, ribs and the grouse; fish is too, whether plain, as with the smoked salmon, marinated, as with the Danish herrings with dill, or sauced, as with the scallops with grapefruit or else with monkfish in pastry and with a prawn sauce. Salads are brought in from Paris, but most other ingredients are local, including sometimes Windermere char. The sweets sparkle – crème brûlée; St Emilion chocolate pudding with a raspberry sauce; hazel-nut meringue with coffee cream. Out of season there are regular evenings of French provincial cooking. To suit the Alsace wines the menu offered onion tart, sauerkraut with pork, smoked fish, goose, salami served with butter beans and new potatoes, and yeastcake with a rum syrup and apricot sauce. To drink there was a Gewürztraminer '79 at £7·85 off the short but carefully put together list.
CELLARMAN'S CHOICE: Vouvray '78 from Marc Brédif £8·50.

CHEF: Roger Pergl-Wilson PROPRIETORS: Roger and Alena Pergl-Wilson
OPEN: L Tue to Fri, D Mon to Sat CLOSED: Sun and Mon Jan to Mar MEALS: 12.30 to 1.30, 7 to 10
PRICES: £10 (£17). Special regional French nights Dec to Apr, £9·50 (£16) CARDS: Access, Amex, Diners, Visa
SEATS: 24. Private parties: 28 main room. Children's helpings. Wheelchair access. Music

'The minted egg pie tasted like Aquafresh – OK in the morning when brushing the teeth, not so good at lunch.' (On eating in Birmingham)

All Guide *inspectors are anonymous. Anyone purporting to represent the* Guide *is an impostor.*

WINDSOR Berkshire map 3

▲ *Oakley Court* [10/20]

Windsor Road, Water Oakley, Windsor SL4 5UR
MAIDENHEAD (0628) 74141
M4 exit 8/9, then A308 to Maidenhead £16–£34

Five million pounds was spent renovating this Gothic folly, which has been used as a backdrop for Dracula films, the St Trinians series, Rocky Horror Show, and Murder by Death starring Peter Sellers. Judging by the prices on the *carte* – £5 for a bowl of consommé, £10 for a slice of scallop and sole pâté, and £15 for scampi and noodles with wild mushrooms, herbs, Pernod and cream – they must be well on the way to recouping the outlay. Some of Murdo MacSween's combinations on the set menu are intriguing: hot quiche of brie and prawns; salad of broccoli and mango in a sherry vinaigrette, but there are also pleasurable, straightforward dishes, such as terrine of duck with orange salad, and escalope of pork with mustard and spinach cream sauce. There is a choice of seven house carafes at £7·35, otherwise it's a list appealing to those on expense accounts.

CHEF: Murdo MacSween PROPRIETORS: Celebrated Country Hotels
OPEN: all week MEALS: 12.30 to 2, 7.30 to 10
PRICES: £25 (£34), Set L from £12 (£16), Set D from £18 (£22), Snacks £2. Cheaper set L available summer. Service inc CARDS: Access, Amex, Diners, Visa
SEATS: 120. 10 tables outside. Private parties: 40 main room, 180 private room. Car-park, 120 places. Vegetarian meals. Children's helpings. No children under 5 at D. Jacket and tie at D. No jeans at D. No cigars/pipes in dining-room. Wheelchair access. Pianist
ACCOMMODATION: 91 rooms, all with bath/shower. B&B £58 to £74. Children welcome. Baby facilities. No pets. Afternoon teas. Garden. Croquet. Fishing. Golf. Snooker. Helicopter pad. TV. Phone. Scenic. Confirm by 6 [GHG]

WINKLEIGH Devon map 1

▲ *Kings Arms* [12/20]

The Square, Winkleigh WX19 8HQ
WINKLEIGH (083 783) 384 £19

The small dining-room of this thatched pub sees six-course dinners of no little poise served each night. Melvyn Popham has cooked here since 1975 and owes one or two debts to other chefs, such as John Tovey at Miller Howe (see Windermere) for peach filled with herb pâté and the Sharrow Bay team (see Ullswater) for sticky toffee pudding. But his execution is good and there are seductive dishes, such as crab in pastry with an armagnac sauce, and breast of local farm chicken with lime, bacon and hollandaise. Coffee has been left to stew, which is a pity. Bar snacks are useful. It's a bit of a pub wine list, but the Beaujolais are interesting and there is a selection of eaux-de-vie.

CHEF: Melvyn John Popham PROPRIETORS: Roy Falkner and Dennis Hawkes
OPEN: Tue to Sat, D only CLOSED: 2 weeks Feb, 3 weeks Nov MEALS: 7.45 to 8.15
PRICES: Set D £16·50 (£19). Service inc CARDS: Access, Amex, Diners, Visa
SEATS: 14. Private parties: 18 main room. Vegetarian meals by arrangement. Children welcome. Smart dress preferred. No smoking until sweets. Wheelchair access. Piano music. Air-conditioned. One sitting
ACCOMMODATION: Self-contained flat, 2 bedrooms, sleeps 4. £25 per night, £105 per week

WITHERSLACK Cumbria map 7

▲ *Old Vicarage* [13/20]

Witherslack LA11 6RS
WITHERSLACK (044 852) 381
off A590, follow signs to Witherslack church

Real Food £19

There are views of Morecambe Bay from some of the bedrooms at this individual Georgian hotel, set in a remote and lakeless part of the county where the hills are gentle enough for the most feeble hiker. Furnishings are a mixture of *bona fide* antiques, up-market second-hand, and Habitat, with wallpapers in the public rooms owing something to William Morris; the effect could be called *nouveau rural*. A house-party feel is strengthened by the no-choice menu and a firm eight o'clock dinner. Half the dining-room was once a kitchen, and the hearth and its original pot-bracket are now given over to wine racks; a huge wood-framed mirror gives a sense of space. The quality of ingredients continues to be the strong point. Since last year the herb garden has been extended to add savour to an expanding repertoire of dishes, from wun-tuns and vegetarian gougères, to lovage soup and the seasonal sauces for mousseline of locally smoked wild trout. The kitchen has kept up with the growing range of meat products from Mr Woodall of Waberthwaite in Cumbria, and now offers his parma-style, air-cured Cumberland ham (served with melon) as well as the sausage, lamb and pork on which he established his reputation. Menus are carefully and successfully planned. One typical evening a fine wedge of tart, filled with fresh tomatoes, cream-cheese, basil and chives, preceded a lettuce, watercress, lemon and mint soup. The main course of un-pink lamb with a smooth, concentrated rosemary sauce was served with well-treated vegetables – shredded runner beans, rich carrot purée, courgettes with egg, butter and cheese, and boiled new potatoes. Although the cheeseboard – including good Lancashire, blue Brie, single and double Gloucester, Stilton, Gruyère and Jarlsberg – is set to come after the puddings, the arrangement is flexible if you want it to accompany the dregs of your main-course wine. There is a sweet tooth in the kitchen that could be tempered in the Queen of Puddings. The wine list, with around a hundred mostly French wines, has some for about the prices as on a merchant's shelves: Ch. Talbot '61 at £45·35 is not expensive. There is no house wine, but several bottles figure at around £5·50. Some of the clarets are too young, or from undistinguished years, but the wines of the month are well chosen. Theakston's beer and a good selection of malts.

CHEFS/PROPRIETORS: Roger and Jill Burrington-Brown, Irene and Stanley Reeve
OPEN: all week, D only CLOSED: 1 week at Christmas MEALS: 7.30 to 8
PRICES: Set D £14·50 (£19) CARDS: Access, Amex, Diners, Visa
SEATS: 35. Private parties: 18 main room, 10 private room. Car-park, 18 places. Vegetarian meals by arrangement. Children's helpings. No children under 10. Smart dress preferred. No smoking during meals. Classical music. One sitting
ACCOMMODATION: 7 rooms, all with bath/shower. B&B £31·50 to £50. Children welcome. Pets by arrangement. Garden. TV. Phone. Scenic. Confirm by 5 [GHG]

All inspections are carried out anonymously as we accept no handouts.

WOBURN Bedfordshire map 3

Crispins [new entry, zero rated]

22–23 Market Place, Woburn MK17 9PZ
WOBURN (052 525) 516 £4–£14

This used to be a butcher's shop, but now the old tiled floor is covered with rugs and the beamed dining-rooms are lit by candles and open fires. The menu is one step on from bistro – chicken breast stuffed with Somerset Brie, and duck with calvados sauce. Bread is wholemeal, and there is a vegetarian menu from which the mushroom Stroganoff and the leek croustade have been good. The service from Gina Mann, while her husband David cooks, is thoughtful. A creative sweets trolley, and 20 wines. More reports, please.

CHEFS: David Mann and Paul Birley PROPRIETORS: David and Gina Mann
OPEN: Mon to Sat MEALS: 12.15 to 2, 7. to 9.30 (10 Fri and Sat, up to 10.30 after theatre)
PRICES: £11 (£14), Set L £6·95 (£10), L snacks from £1·50, Buffet L from £3·95. Service inc CARDS: Access, Amex, Diners, Visa
SEATS: 56. 4 tables outside. Private parties: 28 main room, 14 private room. Vegetarian meals. Children's helpings. Wheelchair access. Classical music

Paris House [13/20]

Woburn MK17 9QP
WOBURN (052 525) 692
off B528, 1½m E of Woburn in Abbey grounds £15–£28

This small black and white folly surrounded by a little fenced garden is becalmed in the middle of the deer park. Quite how Peter Chandler makes ends meet here, when the ratio of Père David deer to humans is approximately 30 to 1, is a mystery. It is an exclusive restaurant almost by default, and could be a lot better if it was full more of the time. More business might also brush up the service a bit – its quality accounts for the drop in the rating. Nevertheless the holly wallpaper and tartan chairs give the dining-room a serious aspect and Mr Chandler's apprenticeship at Le Gavroche has been well learned – asparagus pastry cases with a beurre blanc sauce that has in fact become rouge from using red wine; turbot with a crayfish sauce; gratin of fresh seafood in a tomato sauce; breast of duck with a sharp cassis sauce. Other trimmings are the product of the Roux' 20 years' restaurateuring – large canapés over good champagne cocktails; fresh bread; excellent petits fours; cheeses from Philippe Olivier in Boulogne. Of course, all this comes at a price, to which a thorough French wine list, that is not cheap, adds quickly.

CHEF/PROPRIETOR: Peter Chandler
OPEN: Tue to Sun, exc Sun D CLOSED: Feb MEALS: 12.30 to 2.30 (12 to 2 Sun), 7 to 10
PRICES: £21 (£28), Set L from £12·50 (£15), Set D from £15 (£18). Service inc
CARDS: Access, Amex, Diners, Visa
SEATS: 52. 5 tables outside. Private parties: 35 main room, 14 private room. Car-park, 20 places. Vegetarian meals. Children's helpings. No children at D. Smart dress preferred

Restaurant tricks (1): Charging each person for every serving of vegetables even when the diners have shared portions between them.

WOODBRIDGE Suffolk — map 3

Royal Bengal [11/20]

6 Quay Street, Woodbridge IP12 1BX
WOODBRIDGE (039 43) 7983 — £9–£15

There is continuing support for this well-appointed tandoori near the theatre. There are five set, four-course menus; a compendium of British Indian restaurant curries, from scampi korma to meat phal; vegetable accompaniments including a Madras dhal sambar, as well as the more usual pulse dish tarka dhal; and a range of items cooked in the tandoor. Prices are in the middle range for this type of place. Lager is £1·10 a pint.

CHEF: Mr Malek PROPRIETOR: A.M.Khan
OPEN: all week MEALS: 12 to 2.30, 6 to 10.30
PRICES: £7 (£12), Set L and D £5·65 to £11·60 (£9 to £15). Minimum £4. Service 10%
CARDS: Access, Amex, Diners, Visa
SEATS: 52. Private parties: 28 main room, 12 private room. Car-park, 8 places. Vegetarian meals. Children's helpings. No children under 6. Smart dress preferred. Wheelchair access (also WC). Classical music

Wine Bar [10/20]

17 Thoro'fare, Woodbridge IP12 1AA
WOODBRIDGE (039 43) 2557 — £9

Sally O'Gorman's cooking leaves most other wine bars standing. She is a natural cook who creates imaginative dishes with a sure touch for fresh herbs, sauces and flavourings, and does clever things with crêpes, stuffing them with minced chicken and spinach, or prawns and avocado in a beurre blanc. Everything is top-hole: spinach and mushroom roulade with garlic is the size of a large sausage roll but light, and the wine cuts clean through the oil in the accompanying wine mayonnaise. Salads include briefly steamed peppers soaked in a provençale sauce of tomato and garlic; crisp lettuce; raw mushrooms; roasted buckwheat and chickpeas. Tarts are made with crumbly pastry that just melts. Ice-creams are ambrosial – rum, banana and nut – and lime cheesecake on oatmeal is stunning: the zest and juice sing and linger. Service is charming. Wines are around £4 and £5.

CHEF: Sally O'Gorman PROPRIETORS: Sally O'Gorman and Richard Lane
OPEN: Tue to Sat CLOSED: 25 and 26 Dec MEALS: 12 to 2.30, 7 to 11
PRICES: £6 (£9)
SEATS: 50. Vegetarian meals. Music

WOODSTOCK Oxfordshire — map 2

▲ *Feathers Hotel* [12/20]

Market Street, Woodstock OX7 1SX
WOODSTOCK (0993) 812291 — £13–£23

Unhurried hotel with a bar that is painted green throughout, down to the radiators. The menu changes daily, rolling from poached haddock for breakfast to trout with sorrel sauce for lunch, to partridge for dinner. It is modern in style. The set lunch is good value and has included an ornate terrine of pheasant studded with pistachios, inset with a streak of duck mousse, and served with a Cumberland sauce. Simpler dishes are good, too, like pea and pear soup, the loin of pork with tarragon, and the steaks. Great efforts are made for effect – a hazelnut parfait has had a chocolate sauce worked with cream into a feather pattern. Dinners end with coffee and toasted marshmallows, taken by the fire in the lounge. The bedrooms are not as grand as the public area but in all the place is extremely popular with many readers. The cellar has almost a hundred wines, well chosen, strong in claret and burgundy and with good choices from other regions.

CHEF: Stanley Mathews PROPRIETOR: Gordon Campbell-Gray
OPEN: all week MEALS: 12.15 to 2.15, 7.15 to 9.45 (10.15 Sat)
PRICES: £18 (£23), Set L from £9·50 (£13), Set D from £14·50 (£18). Service inc
CARDS: Access, Amex, Diners, Visa
SEATS: 35. 6 tables outside. Private parties: 10 main room, 40 private room. Vegetarian meals. Children's helpings. Wheelchair access
ACCOMMODATION: 15 rooms, all with bath/shower. B&B £38 to £64. Children welcome. Pets by arrangement. Afternoon teas. TV. Phone. Doors close at 12. Confirm by 4 [GHG]

WOOLACOMBE Devon map 1

▲ *Little Beach Hotel* [10/20]

The Esplanade, Woolacombe EX34 7DJ
WOOLACOMBE (0271) 870398 £13

A good-value bed and breakfast hotel overlooking the Atlantic. Breakfasts are first-class and the dinner menu varies from the plain, as in pork chops, to the elaborate, as in the poached pear stuffed with cream cheese and served with an elderflower mayonnaise. Soups are a strong point, as are sweets like lemon meringue pie. There are no TVs in the rooms because guests are encouraged to mingle – nor are there any tea-making facilities 'because we believe in service'. Would it be possible to acquire a few bottles of better wine?

CHEF: Alan Bradley PROPRIETORS: Alan Bradley and Nic Lowes
OPEN: all week, D only CLOSED: Oct to Feb MEALS: 7.15 to 8
PRICES: Set D £9·75 (£13), Bar snacks at L for residents only from 85p. Service inc at D for residents only CARDS: Access, Visa
SEATS: 30. Car-park, 6 places. Children's helpings. Classical music
ACCOMMODATION: 10 rooms, 8 with bath/shower. B&B £15·50 to £27. Deposit: £20. Children welcome. Baby facilities. Pets welcome. Sauna. Scenic. Doors close at 11.30. Confirm by 5 [GHG]

WOOLER Northumberland map 7

▲ *Ryecroft Hotel* [new entry, zero rated]

Wooler NE71 6AB
WOOLER (0668) 81459 £7–£12

A family-run hotel serving real ales and a traditional menu that changes every day. Vegetable soups are home-made, there are casseroles and good quality roasts for main courses, and the sweets trolley is all crumbles, trifles and tarts. It is the only bar south of the river Tweed to serve Lorimer and Clark's 80/- beer. House Riesling is £4·25. More reports, please.

CHEFS: Pat McKechnie and Michael Ord PROPRIETORS: Pat and David McKechnie
OPEN: Wed to Sat D, and Sun L (Bar L Mon to Sat, June to Aug) CLOSED: 1st 2 weeks Nov, and 24 Dec to 1 Jan MEALS: 12.30 to 1.30, 7 to 8.30 (Bar 12 to 2)
PRICES: Set Sun L £4·50 (£7), Set D £9 (£12), Bar meals from £1·50 (£1·65) CARDS: Access, Visa
SEATS: 26. Private parties: 30 main room, 20 private room. Car-park, 20 places. Vegetarian meals by arrangement. Children's helpings. No smoking in dining-room
ACCOMMODATION: 11 rooms. B&B £14 to £27. Deposit: £5. Children welcome. Baby facilities. No pets in public rooms. Afternoon teas. Garden. Scenic. Doors close at 12

WOOLHOPE Hereford & Worcester — map 2

▲ *Butchers Arms* [8/20]

Woolhope HR1 4RF
FOWNHOPE (043 277) 281
off B4224, 7m SE of Hereford — £5–£14

A pretty, black and white cottage by a stream, with antique tables and a chance to play quoits and darts. The bar and restaurant menus overlap slightly and produce farmer's and ploughman's lunches, steak dishes, good lasagne, and combinations of lamb with almonds, yoghourt and spices, or chicken with lemon and cinnamon. Vegetables are first-class, prices are reasonable. Hook Norton Best Bitter and Old Hookey, and Marston's Pedigree.

CHEF: Mary Bailey PROPRIETORS: Mary Bailey and Bill Griffiths
OPEN: Wed to Sat D, Bar meals all week MEALS: 7 to 9 (Bar 12 to 2.15, 7 to 10)
PRICES: £10 (£14), Snacks from £1·25 (£1·40), Bar meals from £4·15 (£5)
SEATS: 70. 7 tables outside. Private parties: 26 main room. Car-park, 80 places. Vegetarian meals. No children under 14 in bar at D. No cigars/pipes in dining-room. Folk music
ACCOMMODATION: 3 rooms. B&B £12·50 to £27. TV. Scenic. Doors close at 11.30

WORCESTER Hereford & Worcester — map 2

BACKGROUND BRIEFING: *Bottles in Friar Street is still the outstanding wine bar. The Food for Thought delicatessen, 20 Mealcheapen Street, run by Russell Jones and Guy Davis, has a wide range of European foodstuffs. It also has a restaurant and patio open seven days a week serving good morning coffee, lunch and afternoon tea. Hodsons, close to the cathedral at the top of the High Street, has a range of patisserie and snacks. The Slug and Lettuce in the Cornmarket is a popular pub-cum-wine bar. Terry Thompson's stall in the city centre's market hall sells a wide range of fresh fish.*

Brown's [11/20]

24 Quay Street, Worcester WR1 2JN
WORCESTER (0905) 26263 — £18–£21

It is a hard push for anything to match the dining-room in this 1790 grain-mill, converted six years ago. But the kitchen team has been the same since the restaurant opened and works in the modern vein. Fish – 12 stone a week brought from the excellent Birmingham market – has been good, especially the turbot and the salmon with chive sauce. Other good dishes have been the salad starters, such as bacon with chicken livers; the steaks; poached chicken with a herb cheese stuffing; the cheeseboard. There is plenty of choice for sweet, and the service is young and friendly. The wine list hasn't many bargains but sports some good quality names, though not always of the best years. CELLARMAN'S CHOICE: Les Coères '83, from Michel, at £9·95.

CHEF: W.R.Tansley and S.Meredith PROPRIETORS: W.R. and P.M.Tansley
OPEN: Mon to Sat, exc Sat L CLOSED: 1 week at Christmas, bank hols MEALS: 12.30 to 1.45, 7.30 to 9.30
PRICES: Set L £12·95 (£18), Set D £15·95 (£21). Service 10% CARDS: Access, Amex, Visa
SEATS: 80. Private parties: 80 main room. Vegetarian meals by arrangement. No children under 5. Wheelchair access (also wc)

Cornucopia [new entry, zero rated]

Tolladine Road, Warndon, Worcester WR4 9UP
WORCESTER (0905) 58615 £11–£20

This barn conversion is half a mile from exit 6 on the M5 and potentially a star among motorway cafes. There is a long and ambitious modern menu backed up by five flambé dishes. Broccoli soup, prawn cocktail, steak with green peppers, and duck with orange have all been of a standard. Coffee is strong. The 80 wines are stored in a wine loft above the heads of diners. House French is £4·75. More reports, please.

CHEF: Peter Walters PROPRIETORS: John Narbett and Keith Partridge
OPEN: all week, exc Sat L and Sun D MEALS: 12.30 to 2, 7.30 to 10
PRICES: £15 (£20), Set L £7·50 (£11) CARDS: Access, Amex, Diners, Visa
SEATS: 70. Private parties: 40 main room, 100 private room. Car-park, 80 places. Vegetarian meals. Children's helpings (Sun L only). Wheelchair access (also wc). Music

WORKSOP Nottinghamshire map 5

Royal Rib [10/20]

114 Bridge Street, Worksop S80 1HT
WORKSOP (0909) 477520 £9–£14

Something of a gentlemen's club, run efficiently and in down-to-earth fashion. The kitchen is visible through a glass partition. The food is not over-cooked and much is home made, from soups to charcoal-grilled lamb steak, and splendid Bakewell tart. Good value and popular in the area.

CHEF/PROPRIETOR: Malcolm Hickman
OPEN: Tue to Sun, exc Sat L and Sun D MEALS: 12 to 1.45, 7 to 10 (10.30 Fri)
PRICES: £10 (£14), Set L £5·75 (£9), Set D £7 (£10) CARDS: Access, Visa
SEATS: 34. Private parties: 45 main room. Car-park, 30 places. Vegetarian meals by arrangement. Children's helpings. Smart dress preferred. Wheelchair access. Music. Air-conditioned

'The proprietor claims – not without some justification – to be the Muhammad Ali of at least the Plymouth area restaurateurs.' (A Plymouth restaurant)

WORLESTON see NANTWICH

WORTHING West Sussex map 3

Frooms [10/20]

7 Brunswick Road, Worthing BN11 3NG
WORTHING (0903) 38960 £10–£18

In a run-down dimly lit street is this old fashioned Regency-style restaurant that has an extraordinary museum of a wine list and serves good fish – turbot and lobster with brandy sauce, and salmon with hollandaise. All the sauces are made on the premises. The wine glasses are large enough to hold nearly a whole bottle of one of the 200-odd clarets that go back all the way to Ch. Margaux '25 at £165·10. There's a good showing particularly of the '50s and '60s, mostly in the £20 to £30 range.

CHEF: D.Lazarus PROPRIETOR: Marcus Martinez
OPEN: Mon to Sat, exc Sat L MEALS: 12 to 2, 7 to 10 (10.30 Sat)
PRICES: £12 (£18), Set L £6·45 (£10), Set D £9·45 (£13·50) CARDS: Access, Amex, Diners, Visa
SEATS: 40. Private parties: 40 main room. Smart dress preferred. Children's helpings. Wheelchair access (also wc). Classical music. Cocktail bar

Paragon Restaurant [new entry, zero rated]

10 Brunswick Road, Worthing BN11 3NG
WORTHING (0903) 33367 £10–£18

Comfortable surroundings, good value, and a nod towards France for the menu. There is good onion soup and grilled Dover sole; chicken breasts are stuffed with Camembert, or cooked with walnuts and white wine; calves' kidneys come with mustard sauce. Pasta appears – gnocchi with a provençale sauce and Gruyère – and other items, such as asparagus or duck, turn up occasionally. Service is deft and the wines, starting with house French at £5, are reasonably priced. More reports, please.

CHEFS: Paul Harding and M.Douglas PROPRIETORS: J.G.Puddick and E.Lucani
OPEN: Mon to Sat CLOSED: bank hols MEALS: 12 to 2.15, 7 to 10.15 (10.30 Sat)
PRICES: £14 (£18), Set L £7·25 (£10), Set D £9·85 (£13). Service inc CARDS: Access, Amex, Diners, Visa
SEATS: 47. Private parties: 40 main room, 40 private room. Vegetarian meals by arrangement. Children welcome. Smart dress preferred. Wheelchair access (1 step; also men's wc). Music

All restaurants listed in the Guide have been independently nominated by a number of readers and have been checked by inspectors.

The Guide is always anxious to recruit new inspectors. If you would like to apply, write to the editor enclosing a) a detailed report on a restaurant where you have eaten and b) a comparative study of restaurants known to you.

If you cannot honour a restaurant booking, always phone to cancel.

WOTTON UNDER EDGE Gloucestershire map 2

Ellerncroft [new entry, zero rated]

Ellerncroft Road, Wotton under Edge GL12 7AY
DURSLEY (0453) 844556
on B4060, to NW of village £12–£19

A refurbished Victorian mansion with a sweeping drive and gardens, where a full-time gardener is employed to bring the five acres of vegetable garden back to life and there are hens for eggs. The set-price menu makes use of the best of local produce. Typical of good dishes eaten have been terrine of smoked fish; leek and Stilton mousse with tomato vinaigrette; ragout of guinea-fowl, venison and rabbit under a pastry lid; and noisettes of lamb wrapped in smoked salmon. Gravlax is unusually served with a gin-and-tonic sorbet. To finish there are more ices or strawberry profiteroles. The wine is chosen with immense care, especially in the £5 to £10 range, which includes an Alsace Riesling '79, from Heim, at £7·10: Vacqueyras '80, from Combe, at £6·95 but also, a bargain, CELLARMAN'S CHOICE: Condrieu '83, from Vernay, at £13·50.

CHEFS: Shirley Anne Bell and Anne Logan
PROPRIETORS: John Payne and Shirley Anne Bell
OPEN: Wed to Sat D, Sun L MEALS: 12.30 to 2.30, 7.30 to 10
PRICES: Set L £8·50 (£12), Set D £14·50 (£19) CARDS: Access, Amex, Visa
SEATS: 30. 3 tables outside. Private parties: 40 main room. Car-park, 40 places. Vegetarian meals. Children welcome. No-smoking area. Wheelchair access (also WC)

WRELTON North Yorkshire map 6A

Huntsman [new entry, zero rated]

Wrelton YO18 8PG
PICKERING (0751) 72530
2m W of Pickering, off A170 £10–£14

Three cheers for Yorkshire pudding being served in its proper place – as a starter at Sunday lunch before the roast beef, with three courses costing under £6. The *carte* ranges much wider, cooking chicken from dhansak to Maryland. Roast duckling is treated to an apple pancake and gravy, or a marinade of orange juice, dry sherry, spices, garlic and soy sauce. Some combinations are less restrained: chicken filled with Cambazola cheese, wrapped in bacon, baked and served with a red wine sauce; pork fillet with lobster meat and asparagus spears. Puddings run to ice-cream with butterscotch sauce, chocolate roulade with a mint centre, or a peach with caramel sauce. A modest wine list has been put together with some care, with house white and red for under £6. CELLARMAN'S CHOICE: Ch. Carteau Côtes Daugay '82, from St Emilion, at £7·95.

CHEF: David Bell PROPRIETORS: David and Annette Bell
OPEN: Tue to Sun, exc Sun D CLOSED: 1 week Nov, 2 weeks Jan MEALS: 12 to 1.45, 7 to 9.30
PRICES: Set Sun L £5·45 (£10), Set D from £9 (£14), Bar meals at L from £1·45 (£1·60)
SEATS: 45. Private parties: 55 main room. Car-park, 30 places. Children's helpings. No smoking in dining-room. Wheelchair access (also WC). Music

WRIGHTINGTON Lancashire map 5

The High Moor [13/20]

Highmoor Lane, Wrightington WN6 9PS
APPLEY BRIDGE (025 75) 2364
N off A5209, 6m NW of Wigan **Real Food** £20

Lancashire lad Jim Sines worked abroad before coming here in the spring of 1984. He takes food seriously, using local supplies for much of the time, buying plentiful Fylde vegetables from market gardeners and smallholders. The pubby atmosphere of the seventeenth-century inn with its wheel-back chairs and sporting prints belies what he does with the ingredients. Flavoursome beef consommé comes with bonemarrow, croûtons, an asparagus spear, mange-tout and a carrot or two; fillet of beef is a generous hunk served with woodland mushrooms in a sauce with cream and port. Sauces can be rich and dishes elaborate, from beurre blanc with chives to accompany hot asparagus profiteroles, to a puddle of champagne, fish stock and cream underneath sole soufflé with smoked salmon and leeks. Sometimes simplicity can be more successful, as with the vegetables or a prettily presented exotic fruit salad with ice-cream. Canapés and petits fours round out the meal, but the coffee could be improved. Service is efficient, friendly and knowledgeable. The wine list has something for most pockets; house wine is £6, and CELLARMAN'S CHOICE is Ch. Cissac '79 at £16.

CHEF: James Sines PROPRIETOR: John Nelson
OPEN: Tue to Sun, exc Sat L and Sun D CLOSED: 1st week Jan, 3 weeks Aug MEALS: 12 to 2, 7 to 10
PRICES: £14 (£20). Service 10% CARDS: Access, Amex, Diners, Visa
SEATS: 65. Private parties: 52 main room. Car-park, 45 places. Vegetarian meals by arrangement. Children welcome. Wheelchair access. Music. Air-conditioned

WYE Kent map 3

Wife of Bath [10/20]

4 Upper Bridge Street, Wye TN25 5AW
WYE (0233) 812540 £17

The good Wife approaches middle age with aplomb and her gratiné of fennel with blue cheese, and duck roasted with apples and served with a brandy sauce remain intact. The menu is sensibly short (less sensibly written in French) and the dining-room comfortable. The list of three-dozen wines includes three of Hugel's Alsace wines – Muscat, Cuvée Traditionelle '81, is £8·45. House burgundy is £5·05.

CHEF: R. Johnson PROPRIETORS: R. Johnson and B.H. Boots
OPEN: Tue to Sat CLOSED: 1 week at Christmas MEALS: 12 to 2, 7 to 10
PRICES: £11·45 (£17). Cover 80p CARDS: Access, Amex
SEATS: 50. Private parties: 18 private room. Car-park, 15 places. Children's helpings. Wheelchair access

An index of restaurants by name appears at the back of the Guide.

WYMONDHAM Norfolk map 6

Adlard's [13/20]

16 Damgate Street, Wymondham NR18 0BQ
WYMONDHAM (0953) 603533 **Real Food** £16

There is a feeling that the Adlards have pitched camp in this small, seventeenth-century cottage and that all the family's belongings are on show because there is nowhere else to put them. Plates, rugs and paintings hang on the walls, plants pack the windowsill facing on to the street. The wooden tables don't quite stand steady on the uneven flagstone floor, and are covered with floral cloths and strips of lace, wicker mats, and two elegant wine glasses per setting. But make no mistake, this is a very good restaurant, and the only surprise is that it is not in some elegant and spacious historic building and staffed by waiters in black suits. David Adlard trained at the Carved Angel (see Dartmouth) and the Connaught (see London) and cooks a short, three-course menu with a choice of three dishes in each. Mary runs the front of house with a Massachusetts accent and the kind of *brio* you would expect in a top-class New York or French restaurant. Meals are easily paced and there are masterful dishes – especially main courses. Magnificent noisettes of lamb – hung for a week – with a mousse of peas and a red wine sauce; chicken breast of wonderful flavour cooked with red wine and shallots and some noodles; wild duck with elderberry vinegar garnished with caramelised apples; roast rack of lamb with rosemary and Meaux mustard. Before these come smoked salmon quenelles or white fish terrine with a Cromer crab tart, and with them superb vegetables; and afterwards choose between a simple salad or the ripe, varied cheeseboard. To finish there is excellent lemon tart; brandy snaps filled with lemon syllabub; caramelised pears with a pear sabayon. Bread rolls come hot from the oven. The wines are mainly from Adnams. CELLARMAN'S CHOICE: Château du Grand Moulas '83 at £6, or Quincy '84 from Mardon at £6·45.

CHEF: David Adlard PROPRIETORS: David and Mary Adlard
OPEN: Tue to Sat, D only MEALS: 7.30 to 9.30
PRICES: Set D from £11·50 (£16) CARDS: Access, Visa
SEATS: 25. Private parties: 22 main room. Children welcome. Air-conditioned

YALDING Kent map3

▲ *Walnut Tree* [8/20]

Yalding Hill, Yalding ME18 6JB
MAIDSTONE (0622) 814266 £11–£17

This is not called the Walnut Tree for nothing: home-grown walnuts find themselves pickled or dried, and served with veal, along with onion, mushroom, white wine, calvados and cream. Paillards of raw beef come with a sauce containing a store-cupboardful of ingredients: oil, capers, black and green olives, Dijon mustard, dill pickle, green peppercorns, garlic, vinegar and parsley. Vegetables, except for peas, are grown locally and organically. Fremlins ales and two wine lists; ask for the better one.

CHEF: Mrs L.V.Russell **PROPRIETORS:** Mr and Mrs R.W.Russell
OPEN: Tue to Sun, exc Sun D **CLOSED:** 2 weeks Oct **MEALS:** 12 to 2, 7 to 10
PRICES: £12 (£17), Set L and D £6·45 (£11). Snacks from 70p. Service 12.5% **CARDS:** Access, Amex, Diners, Visa
SEATS: 55. 6 tables outside. Private parties: 55 main room, 55 and 12 private rooms. Car-park, 14 places. Vegetarian meals. Children's helpings. Wheelchair access (also WC). Jazz
ACCOMMODATION: 2 rooms, B&B £11 to £22. Baby facilities. Pets welcome. Afternoon teas. TV. Scenic. Confirm by 12

YORK North Yorkshire — map 5

BACKGROUND BRIEFING: *Rich English cities with the visible history that attracts tourists seem to have kept up the tradition of the elegant tea-room (see entries for Bettys and Taylors). York's good retail bakeries include Yates, Low Petergate (with another branch in New Street), where there is parkin, Pontefract cakes and fat rascals. Gillygate Wholefood Bakery, Miller's Yard, Gillygate, has good breads. Oriental Food Supplies, 5 Gillygate, just outside the city walls, has a fine range of spices and some exotic vegetables, but the best selection of fruit and vegetables – all labelled with variety and source – is at G. B. Hannon, Stonegate. Choosa Cheese, Silver Street boasts some 180 varieties, and the city market at Newgate has stalls selling fish, such as fluke and sole, from Scarborough. The pork butcher, Scott's, 81 Lower Petergate has black puddings, sausages, raised pies, haslet, and roast chaps. From July to December – with the emphasis on Christmas – they also supply the famous but now rare York hams. There is a bistro downstairs at Middlethorpe Hall (see entry) serving English country cooking for about £10 a head.*

Bettys [8/20]

6 St Helen's Square, York YO1 2QP
YORK (0904) 59142 — £9

First opened in 1936, and not much has changed. The central bakery produces 200 types of cakes a day, and the queues show that this is one of the most popular places to eat in the city. It is also deceptively unassuming: although the Welsh rarebit, the omelettes, the hearty soups, and the cakes are recommended there is also – as at the other three branches in the north (see Harrogate, Ilkley and Northallerton) – a superb selection of '83 Alsace wines, not overpriced, and also rare coffees, such as Jamaican Blue Mountain Peaberry or Peruvian Chanchamayo.

PROPRIETORS: Bettys Ltd
OPEN: all week, daytime only **MEALS:** 9 (9.30 Sun) to 5.30
PRICES: £5 (£9), Snacks from 80p (90p)
SEATS: 177. Vegetarian meals. Children's helpings. No-smoking area. Pianist. Air-conditioned. Baby facilities

This restaurant has an exceptional wine cellar.

The Guide *accepts no advertising and does not allow restaurants to use their inclusion for publicity.*

▲ *Middlethorpe Hall* [13/20]

Bishopthorpe Road, York YO2 1QP
YORK (0904) 641241
1½m outside city, by racecourse £10–£24

The feeling that here is a stately home that has been carefully and expensively restored – witness the stylish furniture, antiques, paintings and prints – is reinforced by the footman in livery who opens the door to the fine, wood-panelled dining-room which in winter has a big open fire. What else would one expect but English food, such as pâté of pheasant, grouse, rabbit and hare; pink roast beef with Yorkshire pudding; Bakewell tart; strawberry flummery. The flavour is not, however, entirely traditional. More modern are terrine of sweetbread and pear served with walnut salad; pieces of North Sea fish in a saffron sauce; scallops steamed with ginger and butter sauce; smoked leg of mutton; and hot pineapple served with white pepper. Plain sprouts and crisp green beans may be combined with more elaborate broccoli with almonds; fondant potatoes; or tomatoes stuffed with mushrooms. Service is 'Certainly, Sir', and back to the kitchen to find out what's in the dishes. Lunch at £10, including VAT, service and half a bottle of sound white burgundy, is a bargain. House wine is £7 per bottle, and CELLARMAN'S CHOICE is house champagne Bouzy Brut from Barancourt at £14·50.

CHEF: Aidan McCormack PROPRIETORS: Historic House Hotels Ltd
OPEN: all week MEALS: 12.30 to 1.45, 7.30 to 9.45
PRICES: £17 (£24), Set L from £10 (£10), Set D £15·50 (£19). Service inc CARDS: Acces, Amex, Diners, Visa
SEATS: 60. Private parties: 40 main room, 40, 20 and 14 private rooms. Car-park, 70 places. Vegetarian meals. No children under 8. Jacket and tie
ACCOMMODATION: 31 rooms, all with bath/shower. B&B £50 to £90. No children under 8. No pets. Afternoon teas. Garden. Fishing. Golf. Helicopter pad. Air-conditioning. Lift. TV. Scenic [GHG]

St Williams [9/20]

3 College Street, York YO1 2JF
YORK (0904) 34830 £7

If it were not for the round tables it would be possible to imagine that you were eating in a luxurious monastery. Lunches here are perhaps the best value in the city, and in summer long trestle tables are set out in the outside courtyard of the fifteenth-century building where the Convocation of York meets. Eating is a case of pot luck, because the food, which is hot, fresh and good when it leaves the kitchen, is then placed on cold tiles under hot lamps. By one o'clock the baked potatoes can be as hard as bullets. But then there are huge portions of cottage pie or Coronation chicken, and fine honey and raisin tart. House French is £3·95, or there is Rock's elderflower wine or Theakston's bitter.

CHEF: Michael Room PROPRIETORS: Milburns Restaurants Ltd
OPEN: all week, daytime only MEALS: 10 (12 Sun) to 5 (L 12 to 2.30)
PRICES: £3 (£7). Snacks from 40p (45p)
SEATS: 140. 6 tables outside. Private parties: 80 main room, 200, 80 and 30 private rooms. Vegetarian meals. Children's helpings (L only). No-smoking area

Taylors Tea Rooms [8/20]

46 Stonegate, York YO1 2AS
YORK (0904) 22865 £5

A sister of the Bettys Café group, Taylors' upstairs, nineteenth-century rooms serve toast and teacakes, cream teas, sandwiches, salads, Earl Grey fruitcake, and Yorkshire rarebit made with Theakston's ale and roast ham. Over a dozen teas, hot or iced coffee, and a museum of a shop downstairs.

PROPRIETORS: Taylors Tea and Coffee Ltd
OPEN: all week, daytime only MEALS: 9 (12 Sun) to 5.30
PRICES: £4 (£5), Snacks from 80p (90p). Unlicensed
SEATS: 65. Vegetarian meals. Children's helpings. No-smoking area

Scotland

ACHILTIBUIE Highland — map 8

▲ *Summer Isles Hotel* [new chef, zero rated]

Achiltibuie IV26 2YG
ACHILTIBUIE (085 482) 282
26m N of Ullapool — **Real Food £9–£22**

It's like *Dynasty* up here. Sarah Irvine has had a baby. Eric Hanson is now doing most of the cooking. Mark Irvine and his friend Geraldine are taking over more to let Robert (his father) get on with his hydroponicum (see below) and food-smoking. All this coming and going has not gone unnoticed in the dining-room, where standards have yo-yoed, but the principles remain the same – brown bread baked fresh every day, healthy salads, minimum use of salt and white sugar, and all the vegetables grown organically or in the hydroponicum, an advanced greenhouse which can now produce strawberries by 24 April. At dinner there is a set menu of Real Food served to guests only, although the attached Kitchen Garden restaurant does more simple meals at lunchtime. There are good wines in the cellar and Robert Irvine likes to discuss them and advise a choice depending on the menu – there's no wine list. More reports on the next episode, please.

CHEFS: Sarah Irvine and Eric Hanson PROPRIETOR: Robert Irvine
OPEN: all week CLOSED: mid-Oct to Easter MEALS: 12 to 2, 7.30
PRICES: L £5 (£9), Set D £18 (£22). Service inc
SEATS: 28. Private parties: 8 main room. Car-park, 24 places. Vegetarian meals by arrangement. No children under 8 at D. No smoking in dining-room. One sitting at D
ACCOMMODATION: 14 rooms, 8 with bath/shower. B&B £16 to £32. No children under 8. No pets in public rooms. Afternoon teas. Garden. Fishing. Scenic. Doors close at 10.30. Confirm by 6 [GHG]

ALTNAHARRIE see ULLAPOOL

Entries are compiled from the unsolicited reports from readers and are checked by inspectors; each restaurant is asked to supply details of its operation. Report forms can be found at the back of the Guide.

We keep files on every restaurant, so reports of poor meals are just as valuable as reports of good meals because they save unnecessary inspections.

ANSTRUTHER Fife map 8

The Cellar [13/20]

24 East Green, Anstruther KY10 3AA
ANSTRUTHER (0333) 310378 **Real Food** £12–£21

The fish here comes direct from the Pittenweem boats and is served as fresh as possible and without masking the flavour with heavy sauces. Peter Jukes cooks it just so and no more, and Vivien serves. The flagged-floor dining-room is long and narrow, with a coal fire at each end and framed tapestry prints above them. The menu is of four courses with four choices at each. Outstanding have been shrimp and mussel bisque served in giant bowls; gravlax; halibut with fresh limes; turbot with a vermouth and cream sauce; and lobster thermidor. Game dishes are not necessarily as good, but both steaks and lamb are. Lunches are more simple and have included crab and smoked salmon quiche. The good list of wines is very strong in Chablis, of which there are eight, and includes a Riesling and a Gewürztraminer Cuvée Tradition from Hugel, both '81. House Muscadet is £6·95. CELLARMAN'S CHOICE: Puligny-Montrachet '81, from Moreau, at £13·95.

CHEF: Peter Jukes PROPRIETORS: Peter and Vivien Jukes
OPEN: all week, exc Sun L CLOSED: 2 weeks Nov, 1 week Apr, bank hols MEALS: 12.30 to 2, 7.30 to 9.30
PRICES: £15 (£21), Set Sun L £6·95 (£12), Set D from £13 (£18), Bar lunches from 90p (£1) CARDS: Access, Visa
SEATS: 32. Private parties: 32 main room. Vegetarian meals by arrangement. Children's helpings by arrangement. No cigars/pipes in dining-room. Wheelchair access (also WC). Classical music

ARDEONAIG Central map 8

▲ *Ardeonaig Hotel* [new entry, zero rated]

Ardeonaig FK21 8SU
KILLIN (056 72) 400
on S bank of Loch Tay, 6m NE of Killin £9–£18

A family-run hotel (formerly a drovers' inn) with a simple three-course menu. Typical is melon, roast haunch of venison, and marshmallow surprise. Good cheeses. The Russells are tireless hosts, rooms are comfortable, and bar snacks are equally good. Vin de table is £4·25. More reports, please.

CHEF: Mrs Ellis Jones PROPRIETORS: Mr and The Hon Mrs John Russell
OPEN: all week D, Sun L (Bar L all week) CLOSED: Nov to Easter MEALS: 12.30 to 2, 8 to 8.45
PRICES: £15 (£18), Set Sun L £7 (£9), Set D from £10·50 (£13), Bar meals from 65p. Service inc
SEATS: 30. Private parties: 45 main room. Car-park, 40 places. Vegetarian meals by arrangement. Children's helpings. No children under 7 in dining-room. Jacket and tie. Wheelchair access
ACCOMMODATION: 14 rooms, all with bath/shower. B&B £18·50 to £37. Deposit: £10. Children welcome. Baby facilities. No pets in public rooms. Afternoon teas. Garden. Salmon fishing. Helicopter pad. Scenic. Doors close at 11.30. Confirm by 6

This restaurant has an exceptional wine cellar.

ARISAIG Highland map 8

▲ *Arisaig House* [11/20]

Beasdale, Arisaig PM39 4NR
ARISAIG (068 75) 622 £21

The roads up to this 1864 mansion are single-track. You could take the overnight sleeper from Euston and be picked up at Beasdale station by the Smithers. The house is stylish and tranquil, with the feeling that dust would not dare settle. David Wilkinson's set five-course menus are built around the best local produce: free-range eggs, fresh prawns, honey from their own bees, although butter and cheese tend to be French. There is no choice and the structure of the meals is the same: fish, soup, meat and vegetables, sweet or ice, cheese. Especially good have been the fish mousses; monkfish with ginger; Cullen skink; saddle of lamb with redcurrant sauce; and beef olives rolled around haggis. The crème brûlée has a crust. Afternoon teas are well reported and the packed lunches are enormous. The 40 wines give a good range, especially at the cheaper end. There are also eaux-de-vie and, naturally, malts.

CHEF: David Wilkinson PROPRIETORS: John and Ruth Smither
OPEN: all week, D only CLOSED: Nov to Mar MEALS: 7.30 to 8.30
PRICES: Set D £19 (£21). Service inc CARD: Visa
SEATS: 30. 5 tables outside. Private parties: 8 main room. Car-park, 16 places. No children under 10. No smoking in dining-room
ACCOMMODATION: 16 rooms, all with bath/shower. B&B £26·50 to £90. No children under 10. No pets. Garden. Snooker. Croquet. Jetty. Helicopter pad. TV. Phone. Scenic [GHG]

AUCHTERHOUSE Tayside map 8

▲ *Old Mansion House Hotel* [10/20]

Auchterhouse DD3 0QN
AUCHTERHOUSE (082 626) 366/7/8 £12–£20

A converted sixteenth-century Scottish manor house, with a well-kept garden and a wood for walks. The dining-room has a Jacobean plaster ceiling and fireplace, and the occasional clashes in furniture are mirrored in the food: a wonderful restaurant dish of sole stuffed with mousseline of turbot in a white wine sauce beats a rather ordinary bar lunch of potato and celery soup, chicken liver pâté, and not so good raspberry sorbet. Puddings, such as plum pie with ice-cream, crème brûlée, and passion fruit sorbet, are all good. Main courses on the long menu cost around £9. The list of over 100 wines has a good spread of prices and includes some from Italy, Austria, South Africa, California, and Australia.

An index of restaurants by name appears at the back of the Guide.

The 1987 Guide *will appear before Christmas 1986, so reports are particularly important in the spring. Report forms are at the back of this book, but just write a letter if you prefer. Address them to* The Good Food Guide, *Freepost, 14 Buckingham Street, London WC2N 6BR. No stamp is necessary if you post in the UK.*

House wine is £5·50. CELLARMAN'S CHOICE: Crozes-Hermitage '80, from Revol, at £8·35.

CHEF: Campbell Bruce PROPRIETORS: Nigel and Eva Bell
OPEN: all week CLOSED: 1 to 8 Jan MEALS: 12.30 to 1.45, 7.15 to 9.30 (8 Sun)
PRICES: £14 (£20), Set L from £8 (£12), Bar meals from £2·95 (£3·25) CARDS: Access, Amex, Diners, Visa
SEATS: 50. 5 tables outside. Private parties: 12 main room, 20 private room. Car-park, 50 places. Vegetarian meals. Children's helpings. No children under 10 at D. No pipes/cigars in dining-room. Wheelchair access
ACCOMMODATION: 6 rooms, all with bath/shower. B&B £38·50 to £55. Children welcome. Baby facilities. No pets in public rooms. Garden. Swimming-pool. Tennis. Squash. TV. Phone. Scenic. Doors close at 12

AUCHTERMUCHTY Fife map 8

The Hollies [new entry, zero rated]

2 Low Road, Auchtermuchty KY14 7AU
AUCHTERMUCHTY (033 72) 279
on A91 £16

This pub, run by a young husband-and-wife team, is in a 250-year-old listed building. Malcolm Smith was the chef at Balcraig House (see Scone). There is a short, fresh menu that has included fine pork and cider casserole, pigeon breast salad, and vegetable terrine. Service is enthusiastic. There are some good wines and digestifs which indicate ambition. More reports, please.

CHEF/PROPRIETOR: Malcolm Smith
OPEN: Mon to Sat D (L by arrangement), Bar L all week MEALS: 7 to 10 (Bar 12 to 2)
PRICES: £12 (£16), Bar meals from £2 (£2·20), Snacks from 95p (£1·05)
CARDS: Access, Visa
SEATS: 28. Private parties: 32 main room. Children's helpings. Wheelchair access. Air-conditioned

BALLATER Grampian map 8

▲ *The Green Inn* [11/20]

9 Victoria Road, Ballater AB3 5QQ
BALLATER (0338) 55701 £14

A relaxed, well-run bistro in a granite building in the centre of town. The Hamiltons' attention to small details, such as providing sharp knives for steaks, runs through to raising hens for eggs. The short menu is mainly built around local produce. Venison comes with port and redcurrant jelly sauce, salmon with cream and chives. The potted smoked salmon is good, as are the steaks. Sweets are sweet and can end meals on a high note – plenty of profiteroles and very good

Restaurants are graded on a scale of 1–20. In the region of 8–9 expect to find places that may not be restaurants but cafes, pubs, bistros and small hotels. In the category of 10–11 you can expect to find the best food in the locality. Ratings of 12 or more are given to restaurants we regard as serving the best food in the region.

iced raspberry soufflé. A short list of wines. The Fitou '83 at £4·95 is probably better value than the house wine at £3·50 for half a litre.

CHEFS: A.C.S. Hamilton and Zoe Brown PROPRIETORS: Mr & Mrs A.C.S. Hamilton
OPEN: all week CLOSED: Jan and Feb, weekdays Nov and Dec MEALS: 12 to 2, 7 to 9.30
PRICES: £9 (£14), Snacks at L from 75p (85p)
SEATS: 30. 2 tables outside. Private parties: 28 main room. Vegetarian meals. Children's helpings. Wheelchair access (also wc). Classical music. Air-conditioned
ACCOMMODATION: 3 rooms, all with bath/shower. B&B £12·50 to £25. Deposit: £10. Children welcome. Dogs welcome. Air-conditioning. Scenic. Doors close at 11.30

▲ *Tullich Lodge* [11/20]

Ballater AB3 5SB
BALLATER (0338) 55406
1½m E of Ballater on A93 £17

There is an elegant simplicity about the four-course menus at this hotel, which is really Neil Bannister's and Hector MacDonald's private house. The roast ribs of beef that usually make up the centrepieces have been under threat from more fish lately – notably lobster, or baked sea-trout with parsley butter. The produce is the best the region can provide, which means on the one hand that the Stilton and Cheddar have to come up from London, but on the other that there may be nettle flan or pipérade with free-range eggs. Bread is wholemeal and baked in-house, and the salmon is smoked by the kitchen, too. A solid selection of 50 or so wines.

CHEF: Neil Bannister PROPRIETORS: Hector MacDonald and Neil Bannister
OPEN: all week CLOSED: Dec to Mar MEALS: 1, 7.30 to 9
PRICES: Set L and D £14 (£17), Bar L from £4. Service inc CARD: Amex
SEATS: 26. Private parties: 20 main room. Car-park. Children's helpings at L, and high teas. Jacket and tie. No smoking in dining-room. Wheelchair access (2 steps; also wc). One sitting
ACCOMMODATION: 10 rooms, all with bath/shower. B&B £43 to £76. Children welcome. Baby facilities. No pets in public rooms. Garden. TV. Phone. Scenic. Confirm by 5 [GHG]

BELLOCHANTUY Strathclyde map 8

▲ *Putechan Lodge Hotel* [new entry, zero rated]

Bellochantuy PA28 6Q
GLENBARR (058 32) 266
on A38, 10m NW of Cambeltown £17

Reputedly the best place to eat in Kintyre. It was a shooting-lodge but has been elegantly extended. There are fine grilled herrings in oatmeal and the smoked trout is good. House wine is £6. More reports, please.

CHEFS/PROPRIETORS: Peter and Terry Moll
OPEN: all week CLOSED: 6 Jan to 1 Mar MEALS: 12.30 to 1.45, 7 to 9
PRICES: £12 (£17) CARDS: Access, Diners, Visa
SEATS: 45. 3 tables outside. Private parties: 25 main room, 120 private room. Car-park, 40 places. Children's helpings. Wheelchair access (also wc). Classical music
ACCOMMODATION: 12 rooms, 8 with bath/shower. Rooms for disabled. B&B £18 to £32. Children welcome. Baby facilities. Pets welcome. Afternoon teas. Garden. Fishing. Golf. Beach. Snooker. Scenic. Doors close at 12

BLAIR DRUMMOND Central map 8

Broughton's [11/20]

Blair Drummond FK9 4XE
DOUNE (0786) 841897
on A873 ¾m W of Blair Drummond **Real Food** £17

An old farmhouse set in seven acres of parkland, and where the waitresses carry the blackboard menus round the dining-room. The menu changes according to the produce, which is mostly local, and Tony Broughton skins and dresses his own game. Helen cooks. The set-price menu has a choice of half a dozen or so dishes at each stage. There have been good soups to start, such as onion, or celery and Stilton, or else trout and mushroom pâté. Steaks are consistently well reported, and there are dressed crabs. Some of the game can be tough and might profitably be cooked in other ways; the vegetables might also be better. Good sweets, though, in the tradition of almond cakes, coffee gateau, meringues, and greengage pie. There are carefully chosen wines from the less expensive regions and a good burgundy section, too. The mark-ups are reasonably gentle. House Bordeaux is £5·90 a litre. CELLARMAN'S CHOICE: Ch. Bel-Air '79 at £6·95.

CHEF: Helen Broughton PROPRIETORS: Tony and Helen Broughton
OPEN: Tue to Sat, D only CLOSED: 3 weeks early spring MEALS: 7.30 to 10
PRICES: Set D £12·50 (£17) CARD: Access
SEATS: 40. Private parties: 24 main room. Car-park, 16 places. Vegetarian meals by arrangement. Children welcome. Wheelchair access (also WC). Air-conditioned

BUNESSAN see MULL

BUSTA see SHETLAND

CALLANDER Central map 8

▲ *Roman Camp Hotel* [11/20]

Main Street, East End, Callander FK17 8BG
CALLANDER (0877) 30003 £12–£19

The sizeable River Teith provides the only noticeable sound in the landscaped gardens around the Denzlers' country-house hotel. The dining-room is a long, narrow room with rows of tables on each side. The cooking has lacked consistency, hence the rating demotion of one point – good steaks have had less good sauces. But the game, especially pheasant with grapes, the venison with cranberries in half a pear, and the lamb and chicken dishes, have all been of a

▲ *This restaurant has rooms.*

'I drink it when I'm happy and when I'm sad. Sometimes I drink it when I'm alone. When I have company I consider it obligatory. I trifle with it if I'm not hungry and drink it when I am. Otherwise I never touch it – unless I'm thirsty.' (Mme Lily Bollinger on champagne)

standard, likewise the sweets. Some interesting middle-European wines. House French is £6·20.

CHEFS: Sami Denzler and Keith Mitchell PROPRIETORS: Mr and Mrs Denzler
OPEN: all week CLOSED: end Nov to mid-Feb MEALS: 12.30 to 1.55, 7 to 8.55 (8.30 Oct to Apr)
PRICES: Set L from £8·40 (£12), Set D from £15 (£19). Service inc
SEATS: 40. Private parties: 20 main room. Car-park, 30 places. Children's helpings by arrangement. Smart dress preferred. No smoking. Wheelchair access
ACCOMMODATION: 11 rooms, all with bath/shower. Room for disabled. B&B £32 to £57. Deposit: £15. Children welcome. Baby facilities. Dogs welcome. Garden. Fishing. TV. Scenic. Doors close at 11. Confirm by 5 [GHG]

CANONBIE Dumfries & Galloway — map 8

▲ *Riverside Inn* [12/20]

Canonbie DG14 0UX
CANONBIE (054 15) 295 and 512 — £16

A comfortable, traditionally furnished inn on the banks of the Esk which goes in for such solid fare as haunch of roe-deer, marinated and roasted, with cream and juniper berries in the sauce; Angus beef sirloin steak; and salmon with a watercress hollandaise. Ingenuity with starters puts mushrooms into strudel pastry with a cream sauce, and turns smoked salmon into ice-cream. Good Scottish produce also extends to Loch Fyne oysters, kippers, herrings and mussels and, from over the border but closer to home, Mr Woodall's dry-cured Cumbrian ham, which is served with pear slices. Tagliatelle is home made, fillet of lamb is wrapped in bacon and given an onion sauce, and vegetables run to cabbage with caraway, and carrots with gin. Puddings are not for dieters: baked butterscotch bread-pudding comes with cream; sherry trifle with strawberries and cream is served in a breakfast cup. A mainly French wine list has two Alsace wines from Hugel, and a CELLARMAN'S CHOICE to go with game: Gigondas '80, Domaine Les Gallières, from Hilarion Roux, at £9·90.

CHEFS/PROPRIETORS: Robert and Susan Phillips
OPEN: Mon to Sat CLOSED: 2 weeks Feb MEALS: 12 to 2, 7.30 to 8.30 (7 to 9 Sun)
PRICES: Set D £12 (£16), Bar L from £1·75 (£2) CARDS: Access, Visa
SEATS: 28. 4 tables outside. Private parties: 28 main room. Car-park, 25 places. Children's helpings by arrangement. No smoking in dining-room. Wheelchair access
ACCOMMODATION: 6 rooms, all with bath/shower. B&B £28 to £38. Deposit: £10. Fishing. Scenic. Doors close at 11.30. Confirm by 1 [GHG]

COLONSAY Strathclyde — map 8

▲ *Isle of Colonsay Hotel* [10/20]

Colonsay PA61 7YP
COLONSAY (095 12) 316
ferry from Oban Mon, Wed and Fri — Real Food £12

To say this hotel is out of the way is an understatement, but it is the focal-point of the island. The food is Real because the hotel virtually has no option. There are free-range eggs; the boats bring in clams and prawns; and the garden provides much of the fruit and vegetables. Meals are straightforward with no choice, offering perhaps green beans with walnut and cottage-cheese salad; boeuf en daube; garlic prawns; pigeon pie; or roast leg of pork. There are Islay cheeses cooked in ramekins. Sweets are sympathetically light after the big portions that go before. Big breakfasts include fresh orange juice. And there are no chips. House French is £3·15.

CHEF: Christa Byrne PROPRIETORS: Kevin and Christa Byrne
OPEN: all week D, plus Bar L MEALS: 12 to 1.30, 7.30 (8 Fri in summer)
PRICES: Set D £10 (£12), Bar meals from £1. Service inc CARDS: Access, Amex, Diners, Visa
SEATS: 30. 3 tables outside. Private parties: 30 main room. Car-park, 30 places. Vegetarian meals. Children's helpings (plus high teas at 6). No cigars/pipes in dining-room. Wheelchair access (also wc). One sitting
ACCOMMODATION: 11 rooms, 8 with bath/shower. Rooms for disabled. B&B £12 to £24. Deposit: £15. Children welcome. Baby facilities. Afternoon teas. Garden. Fishing. Golf. Snooker. Sailing. Helicopter pad. TV. Phone. Scenic

---

CROMARTY Highland map 8

Le Chardon [new entry, zero rated]

Church Street, Cromarty IV11 8XA
CROMARTY (038 17) 471 £9–£15

In this lovely village at the tip of the Black Isle it seems incongruous to find an eighteenth-century listed pub done up, on a tight budget, in tasteful pink and green and with a French name. The owner/chef is Robyn, so it narrowly escaped being called Robyn's Nest; Le Chardon is probably better, but the food isn't as French as all that. It does, however, tackle some unusual combinations that pay off handsomely – smoked haddock mousse with a green mayonnaise; sweet-and-sour marinated herring with grapefruit and a dab of sour cream sauce; cauliflower with grated nuts and coconut; and mid-course sorbets from bramble-leaf to rosehip to China tea. There are still plenty of less adventurous but nonetheless satisfying dishes – venison with cherry sauce; goujons of sole with tartare sauce; beef and wine stew. Six-course dinners are good value at £11·50, and always include a vegetarian main course. Sweet-tasting bread is made in the village and deserves better than pats of Anchor butter. Service is efficient and the wine list good, despite its brevity. CELLARMAN'S CHOICE: Pomerol, Ch. de Sales '78 at £14·85.

CHEF: Robyn Aitchison PROPRIETORS: Robyn and Mena Aitchison
OPEN: Tue to Sun D, and Sun L (weekday L in summer) CLOSED: Jan MEALS: 12.30 to 2, 7.30 to 9.30
PRICES: £6 (£9), Set Sun L £6·50 (£10), Set D £11·50 (£15) CARDS: Access, Amex, Visa
SEATS: 25. Private parties: 30 main room. Vegetarian meals. Children's helpings (L only). No children under 8 at D. No smoking in dining-room. Wheelchair access. Classical music

---

The Guide is always anxious to recruit new inspectors. If you would like to apply, write to the editor enclosing a) a detailed report on a restaurant where you have eaten and b) a comparative study of restaurants known to you.

If you cannot honour a restaurant booking, always phone to cancel.

CULLIPOOL Strathclyde map 8

Longhouse Buttery [11/20]

Isle of Luing, Cullipool PA34 4TX
LUING (085 24) 209
ferry from Cuan £10–£16

Cullipool is a friendly and untidy sprawl of a village on the windy Atlantic coast with stunning views of Mull and the tiny islands. 'It would help our trading position,' writes Audrey Stone, 'if the Buttery became the place to lunch.' That is not unreasonable, considering it is open for dinner on only three evenings a week in July and August, and that the island's other amenity is a shop. To say the Buttery is useful in the area is rather an understatement. Partner Edna Whyte's etchings line the walls, and it is she who greets customers. The food, what there is of it either in sandwiches or salads, is impeccable – squat lobster tails; fresh prawn salads; egg mayonnaise made with free-range eggs; wild salmon; triple meringue and cream. For £6·50 the Cullipool mixed platter contains a slice of everything on the menu. Vegetables and salads usually come from the garden. The elusive five-course dinners are £13·50. Portions seem to have got smaller. Wines are harder to get around here than fish . . . .

CHEF: Audrey Stone PROPRIETORS: Audrey Stone and Edna Whyte
OPEN: Mon to Sat L; also Thur, Fri and Sat D July and Aug CLOSED: Oct to mid-May
MEALS: 11 to 4.30, 7.30 to 11
PRICES: L £7 (£10), Set D £13·50 (£16). Service inc
SEATS: 24. Private parties: 12 main room. Car-park, 10 places. Vegetarian meals. Children's helpings. Wheelchair access (also WC)

CUPAR Fife map 8

Ostlers Close [12/20]

25 Bonnygate, Cupar KY15 4BU
CUPAR (0334) 55574 £18

An ostler is someone who looks after horses, and horses used to be kept up this narrow lane off the Cupar Bonnygate. The Grahams run a small, simple, good-value place with a limited but carefully compiled menu. Game is caught locally, which shows in the fan of succulent pigeon breast, and so is salmon, which goes into an excellent mousse in pastry for a starter. Particularly good are the vegetables, which in summer come straight out of the garden. Strips of root vegetables poached in chicken stock and saffron have gone well with pan-fried venison collops. James Graham's Swiss training comes in handy for the

▲ *This restaurant has rooms.*

The 1987 Guide *will appear before Christmas 1986, so reports are particularly important in the spring. Report forms are at the back of this book, but just write a letter if you prefer. Address them to* The Good Food Guide, *Freepost, 14 Buckingham Street, London WC2N 6BR. No stamp is necessary if you post in the UK.*

Apfelstrudel. Fifty wines, with house Sauvignon at £5·15 and Mercurey, Clos des Corvées '81 at £9·40.

CHEF: James Graham PROPRIETORS: Amanda and James Graham
OPEN: Mon to Sat, exc Mon L MEALS: 12.15 to 2, 7 to 9.30
PRICES: £12 (£18). Minimum £10 CARDS: Access, Visa
SEATS: 30. Private parties: 22 main room. Vegetarian meals by arrangement. Children's helpings. No children under 6 at D. No smoking during meals. Wheelchair access (also wc)

DIRLETON Lothian map 8

▲ *Open Arms Hotel* [9/20]

Dirleton EH39 5EG
DIRLETON (062 085) 241 £11–£19

This hotel has been under the same management for 30 years. Menus are good value, with roast beef, haunch of venison, fresh salmon, and ham cooked in brown sugar and cloves. There are light lunches and a set-price dinner with half a dozen choices per course and more than a little patriotism about many of the dishes. Sweets are a forte – flummery, gateaux and crumbles. Seventy wines, with house burgundy at £6.

CHEF: A.Douglas PROPRIETOR: A.Neil
OPEN: all week MEALS: 12.30 to 2.30, 7 to 9.30
PRICES: L £6 (£11), Set Sun L £7 (£12), Set D £13·75 (£19), Bar meals from £2·50 (£2·75). Service 10% CARDS: Access, Amex, Diners, Visa
SEATS: 65. Private parties: 35 main room. Car-park, 40 places. Vegetarian meals. Children's helpings. No pipes in dining-room. Wheelchair access (also wc)
ACCOMMODATION: 7 rooms, all with bath/shower. B&B £42·50 to £60. Children welcome. Baby facilities. Pets welcome. Afternoon teas. Garden. Fishing. Golf. Helicopter pad. TV. Phone. Scenic. Doors close at 12. Confirm by 6.30

DRUMNADROCHIT Highland map 8

▲ *Polmaily House Hotel* [13/20]

Drumnadrochit IV3 6XT
DRUMNADROCHIT (045 62) 343
on A831, 2m W of Drumnadrochit **Real Food** £15

The guiding principles at this small country-house hotel are Real Food and value for money. Alison Parsons does not use farmed venison or salmon, and her recipes owe a lot to the Highlands. Ham and haddie is a version of a traditional Finnan haddock and ham dish; collops of venison come with blackcurrants and cassis; young grouse is roasted. There are plentiful supplies of fish, from oysters to langoustines, out of Loch Fyne. Halibut has bravely been done au poivre. To finish there are Highland cheeses or chocolate marquise, or home-made ice-creams. Nick Parsons gives constructive advice on the wines from his judiciously assembled cellar, strongest in claret and burgundy, but there are also good

'Comparatively it's a really poor place, OK if you are desperate and rather drunk.'
(On eating in Edinburgh)

bottles from minor areas, such as the CELLARMAN'S CHOICE: Sancerre '83, from Vacheron, both red and white at £8·80.

CHEF: Alison Parsons PROPRIETORS: Alison and Nick Parsons
OPEN: all week, D only CLOSED: mid-Oct to Apr MEALS: 7.30 to 9.30
PRICES: £10 (£15) CARDS: Access, Amex, Diners, Visa
SEATS: 30. Private parties: 12 main room. Car-park, 20 places. Children's helpings. No cigars/pipes in dining-room. Wheelchair access. Classical music
ACCOMMODATION: 9 rooms, 7 with bath/shower. B&B £20 to £45. Deposit: £25. Children welcome. Baby facilities. No pets. Garden. Swimming-pool. Tennis. Scenic. Doors close at 12. Confirm by 5 [GHG]

DRYBRIDGE Grampian map 8

The Old Monastery [12/20]

Drybridge AB5 2JB
BUCKIE (0542) 32660
2½m S of Buckie (not in village) **Real Food** £15

The Craigs' new bar overlooking the Moray Firth has brought two advantages – inexpensive, relaxed bar lunches, and the chance to buy wines from a first-class list. Local supplies of goats' cheese, free-range chickens and guinea-fowl have also been established, and the local Aberdeen Angus beef is of very high quality. Recent meals have been particularly good – notably a dish of scallops with a dry vermouth, garlic and cream sauce, served with five vegetables. Quantities are not small. As always, the half-dozen sweets are a focal-point. The cellar has a handsome range of French and German wines at competitive prices – those marked with an asterisk are not for retail sale but are good for drinking in the restaurant. CELLARMAN'S CHOICE: Jean Baumard's Savennières, Clos du Papillon '83 at £6·80, and Beaune du Château at £10·90.

CHEF: Douglas Craig PROPRIETORS: Anthea and Douglas Craig
OPEN: Tue to Sat MEALS: 12 to 1.45, 7 to 9 (9.30 Sat)
PRICES: £11 (£15), Bar meals at L from £2·90 (£3·20), Snacks from £1·50 (£1·65)
SEATS: 40. Private parties: 35 main room. Car-park, 28 places. Children's helpings. No children under 8 at D. No cigars/pipes in dining-room. Wheelchair access. Classical music

DULNAIN BRIDGE Highland map 8

▲ *Muckrach Lodge Hotel* [9/20]

Dulnain Bridge PH26 3LY
DULNAIN BRIDGE (047 985) 257
on A398, ½m W of village £17

A former shooting-lodge, now a small, family-run hotel set in 10 acres of the Dulnain Valley with views of the Cairngorms. Bar lunches are the best bet: home-made broth; sandwiches generously filled with locally caught salmon; and friendly and unobtrusive service. Dinners are more variable although puddings, such as chocolate pot, mocha cheesecake, and local cheeses, are more reliable. A

Reports on good shops, small hotels and cafes in your area are welcome.

sensible list of predominantly French wines has house red and white at £6·10, and CELLARMAN'S CHOICE: Ch. Smith-Haut-Lafitte '76 at £14·05, while stocks last.

CHEFS: Mrs Ogilvie, Mrs Fone and John Sinclair
PROPRIETORS: The Ogilvie and Fone families
OPEN: all week MEALS: 12 (12.30 Sun) to 2, 7.30 to 8.30
PRICES: Set D from £12·80 (£17), Bar L from £3·50 (£4)
SEATS: 40. Private parties: 40 main room. Car-park, 50 places. Vegetarian meals by arrangement. Children's helpings. No cigars/pipes in dining-room. Wheelchair access. Piano music
ACCOMMODATION: 9 rooms, all with bath/shower. B&B £19 to £36. Children welcome. Baby facilities. Garden. Fishing. Scenic. Doors close at 11.30

DUNBLANE Central map 8

▲ *Cromlix House* [14/20]

Dunblane FK15 9JT
DUNBLANE (0786) 822125
off B8033, 4m N of Dunblane **Real Food £8–£27**

There is no heavy advertising for this amazing house in the middle of a 5,000-acre estate. The sign could not be smaller, and nowhere is there any indication that this is a hotel. Once on the drive, avoiding the picnicking rabbits, you know that, whatever else, this is going to be an experience. The house is imposing, the gardens are well kept, and the rabbits like it all, too. A roaring fire is laid specially; tables are set with beautiful silver, including two decorative silver pheasants, a low, stunning flower arrangement, silver wine-holders and a tiny dish solely for the cork from the wine bottle. The place exudes quiet elegance, and the drawing-room is filled with such diverse books as *Practical Horsemanship* and *Searchlight on Spain* by the Duchess of Atholl. Of course there are Wedgwood plates – and extremely good Wedgwood, too. Glasses are crystal and cutlery is silver, or at least most of it is. The manager serves at critical points, and otherwise there are young girls who call women 'ma'am'.

The menu is discussed with you on the lines of 'The chef thought you might like . . .'. Game is the thing: wild duck with wild rice and port sauce; loin of hare with baby vegetables; venison with roasted baby onions. Superb have been the designer plate of smoked fish, interleaving mussels, scallops, halibut and brilliant gravlax, with the dill adding to the salmon flavour rather than distracting; Angus beef – both sirloin and fillet of stunning flavour overshadowing their sauce; and lobster mousse wrapped in a leaf of spinach with an hollandaise sauce. Vegetables are cooked al dente, and there are other good little touches, such as immaculate home-made rolls, high-class unsalted butter, sharp home-made horseradish sauce and so on, before sweets that are of an equal calibre, whether old-fashioned steamed toffee pudding or calorific strawberry torte. The coffee, though, stews. There were a few ups and downs early last year between the manager Stephen Coupe leaving and Grant Howlett (ex-Maison Talbooth at Dedham in Essex) taking over, but inspectors since have been impressed. The breakfast kedgeree is spicy and the orange juice freshly squeezed. The wine list is sound in claret and not bad on anything else; your bank manager will be glad the

Ch. Margaux '73 is £25 because that will probably stop you ordering it. House Rhône is £7·25.

CHEF: Stephen Frost PROPRIETOR: Ronald Eden
OPEN: all week CLOSED: Feb MEALS: 12 to 2.30, 7 to 9.30
PRICES: Set L £4 to £13 (£8 to £17), Set D from £23 (£27). Service inc CARDS: Access, Amex, Diners, Visa
SEATS: 40. 3 tables outside. Private parties: 24 main room, 24, 16 and 8 private rooms. Car-park, 24 places. Vegetarian meals. Children's helpings (high teas). Jacket and tie. No-smoking area. Wheelchair access. Music
ACCOMMODATION: 14 rooms, all with bath/shower. B&B £47·50 to £87·50. Deposit: 50%. Children welcome. No pets in public rooms. Afternoon teas. Garden. Tennis. Shooting. Fishing. Croquet. Helicopter pad. Air-conditioning. TV. Phone [GHG]

DUNDEE Tayside — map 8

Raffles [new entry, zero rated]

18 Perth Road, Dundee DD1 4LN
DUNDEE (0382) 26344 — £11

Everything is made on the premises, including the bread, at this good-value, informal restaurant. The decor is all plants, dark stained woodwork, and Victorian-style tables and chairs. The menu has interesting touches, like Polish ogorki (potato, cucumber and dill), as well as jugged hare and Aberdeen Angus rib eye steaks. Lunches draw the most reports – smoked salmon mousselines, flans, beef carbonade, salads, and vegetable curry are all recommended. The blackboard wine list has a good choice at around £5. More reports, please.

CHEFS: Mrs J. McCabe and Anna Cipars PROPRIETORS: Mr and Mrs James McCabe and Anna Cipars
OPEN: L Tue to Sat, D Fri and Sat CLOSED: 2 weeks at Christmas MEALS: 11 to 7.30 (10.30 Fri and Sat)
PRICES: £8 (£11), Snacks 60p to £1·75. Minimum £8·50 D
SEATS: 50. Private parties: 50 main room. Vegetarian meals. Children's helpings. Wheelchair access (also wc)

DUNOON Strathclyde — map 8

▲ *Ardenslate Hotel* [10/20]

James Street, Hunter's Quay, Dunoon PA23 8JS
DUNOON (0369) 2068 — £8–£12

Mary Hunter's hotel has little to distinguish it from the other large Victorian houses that characterise this area. Furniture and decor are a mix of antique and almost-modern. The majority of diners are resident, many elderly, enjoying the abundant peace and quiet and the magnificent views over the Firth of Clyde. It is, however, the reliably good food that sets Ardenslate apart from its neighbours. Menus are short and unambitious with some good dishes standing out from the fruit juice, egg mayonnaise and citrus fruit cocktail staples of small Scottish hotels. For example, smoked haddock pancakes and roast, stuffed loin of pork with prune and apple have been excellent. Other main course specialities are salmon pie with cucumber sauce; apricot-stuffed shoulder of lamb; and pot-roast chicken breast with orange mushroom sauce. All come with hot, fresh vegetables – some home grown. Miss Hunter is a self-confessed dessert specialist and cites as the best examples of her skill her chiffon pies, apple tarts that are 'almost as good as my grandmother used to make', rich Seville chocolate mousse, hazel-nut meringues, Pavlovas and choux pastries. The cold gooseberry and elderflower soufflé is particularly good. Pre-dinner drinks are served in the lounge as there is no bar. The short and unpretentious wine list includes house wines at £5 a litre.

CHEF: Mary Hunter PROPRIETORS: M.Hunter and Mary Hunter
OPEN: all week, exc Sun D CLOSED: Oct to Dec, and Mon to Thur Dec to May
MEALS: 12 to 2, 6.30 to 8 (9 Fri and Sat)
PRICES: D £8 (£12), Set L from £4·50 (£8), Set D from £6 (£9), Snacks at L from £1·25 (£1·40) CARDS: Access, Visa
SEATS: 35. 3 tables outside. Private parties: 40 main room. Car-park, 6 places. Children's helpings to 7pm. No children under 6 after 7pm. No smoking in dining-room. Wheelchair access (2 steps)
ACCOMMODATION: 8 rooms, 5 with bath/shower. Rooms for disabled. B&B £12 to £34. Deposit: £10. Children welcome. Baby facilities. No pets in public rooms. Garden. Scenic. Doors close at 12. Confirm by 5.30

DUNVEGAN see SKYE

EDDLESTON see PEEBLES

EDINBURGH Lothian map 8

BACKGROUND BRIEFING: *Tinelli's, 139 Easter Road, has a two-course lunch for £6·50. They have a range of Italian wines and cheeses, and sometimes attempt to marry the Italian with the Scottish – salmon and pasta, veal and Drambuie. Skippers Bistro, 1A Dock Place, Leith, is good with young children and has served fine dishes along the lines of mushroom and cauliflower soup, haddock florentine, and crab claws with mayonnaise. The bar meals at the Cramond Inn, Cramond Village (Cramond Glebe Road), are worth a mention, as is the individual but enjoyable experience of the Armenian Aghtamar Lake-Van-Monastery-in-Exile, 55 Abbeyhill, Canongate, which is a bizarre, good-value place too eccentric for a main listing. The splendour of the original Victorian decor at the Café Royal Oyster Bar, West Register Street, deserves better food.*

Alp-Horn [12/20]

167 Rose Street, EH2 4LS
031-229 4787 £5–£13

This is one of the best Swiss restaurants in Britain. It is run with the precision of a cuckoo clock and is good value – a main dish, including garnishes and excellent rösti or spätzli, can be had for under £6. The starters and desserts are mainly uncooked, so the kitchen can cook main courses to order and produce them rapidly. Notably good have been the wind-dried beef; all the venison dishes; liver with a madeira sauce; and veal with orange and mushroom sauce. Naturally the sweets, which are all coupes and vacherins, are of a standard. House Mosel is £6·40 a litre.

CHEF/PROPRIETOR: Miggi Meier
OPEN: Tue to Sat CLOSED: 2 weeks from 25 Dec, 3 weeks June MEALS: 12 to 2, 6.30 to 10
PRICES: £8 (£13), Set L from £3·50 (£5). Service 10% CARD: Access
SEATS: 44. Private parties: 16 main room. Vegetarian meals by arrangement. Children's helpings. Wheelchair access. Music

Aye [14/20]

SCOTTISH NEWCOMER OF THE YEAR

80 Queen Street, EH2 4NF
031-226 5467 £12–£42

Aye is, in this case, not the Scottish for 'yes' but the Japanese for 'love'. And a love affair it is. We are head over heels. It is not simply the cooking that impresses, but the complete experience that is offered from the moment you walk in and are given a seat and a complimentary glass of Japanese plum wine. A menu arrives with some startling prices. The restaurant has four aspects, representing the seasons. There is a Japanese tea ceremony room for Cha-Kaiseki food at a mere £38; the sushi room, decorated with tiles showing Japanese cherry trees; and the tempura room, with a cypress wood bar, a single flower, and including the tempura kitchen with the chef carving and frying. The service is embarrassingly good. A lady in a kimono shuffles her way to and fro, bowing a lot. The only problem is that no one speaks recognisable English, which can make finding out what you are eating an art.

The set menus cover all the main avenues of Japanese cooking, and start at £18. Make no mistake, in any language this is the very finest food, from the sushi onwards. The tempura set meal opens with the arrival of a lacquered tray with beautifully arranged appetisers of duck marinated in soy and saké; noodles set in jelly; and a peeled tomato filled with custard. (*Nouvelle cuisine* just cannot compete in terms of presentation.) Soup, a fish-stock with four pieces of different fish and sea-flowers, comes in a crimson and black lacquered bowl. The tempura follows in stages and at each stage the dip of hot soy is replenished – two king prawns, green pepper, and stunning salmon and asparagus, then an aubergine, sliced fourteen times into a fan, then a tree of noodles which is a feat of cooking not seen in a Scottish kitchen before. And then the meal moves on with a seaweed salad dressed in sesame oil, then rice, pickles and finally Japanese tea and strawberries, or ice-cream with green syrup. That meal might take three hours to eat. It is expensive, but consider what you get for it (and there is an affordable lunch menu). There are wines but saké is the correct drink. This is the start of a beautiful relationship.

CHEF: Mrs H. Yokkaichi PROPRIETORS: Old Parr Co.
OPEN: Tue to Sun, exc Sun L CLOSED: Sun, Oct to Mar MEALS: 12 to 2, 7 to 11.30
PRICES: Set L from £8 (£12), Set D from £18 to £35 (£24 to £42). Service 10%
CARDS: Access, Amex, Diners, Visa
SEATS: 110. Private parties: 30 main room, 30 private room. Vegetarian meals. Children's helpings. Wheelchair access. Japanese music. Air-conditioned

Many of the better restaurants offer bargain lunches for half the price of a meal in the evening. Details are given in the text.

Champany Inn Town [13/20]

2 Bridge Road, Colinton, EH13 0LF
031-441 2587 **Real Food** £23

This used to be Clive and Anne Davidson's retail butcher's shop before they went into the restaurant business with the Champany Inn at Linlithgow (see entry). Their Edinburgh off-shoot has a shorter menu and wine list, but the quality of the meats and the cooking is just as high. Steaks – the best in Britain – are char-grilled as blue as you like and served with seasonal vegetables and a selection of mustards, including Champany's own, mixed with honey. Also outstanding are the veal chops. To start and finish come home-marinated herrings in sour cream; thinly sliced Black Forest ham fried in butter; apple pie with excellent pastry; vanilla meringue. The restaurant is somewhat cramped, with low, stripped-beam ceilings, two handsome dressers, polished mahogany tables and antique chairs on a tiled floor. After Eights come with cafetière coffee. Prices are lower than at Linlithgow because cuts are served on the bone. The wine list maintains the variety of the older establishment but has less to make the bank manager's eyes water. The strength is in the Loire and the Beaujolais – Fleurie '83, from Duboeuf, is £9. House wines, KWV Roodeberg and Chenin Blanc, are £6·50.

CHEF: Nigel Best PROPRIETORS: Clive and Anne Davidson
OPEN: Mon to Sat CLOSED: 24 Dec to 13 Jan MEALS: 12.30 to 2, 7 to 10
PRICES: £16 (£23). Cheaper set L and D available. Service 10% CARDS: Access, Amex, Diners, Visa
SEATS: 36. Private parties: 36 main room. Children welcome

Cosmo's [11/20]

58A North Castle Street, EH2 3LU
031-226 6743 £17

An honest, welcoming trattoria. The pasta is home made and the fish fresh. Good dishes have been the crab à la Russe, cold seafood platter, crayfish bisque, and saltimbocca. Sweets may not be so good. The waiters are attentive. House Merlot is £6 a litre.

CHEF/PROPRIETOR: Cosmo Tamburro
OPEN: Tue to Sat, exc Sat L MEALS: 12.30 to 2.15, 6.30 to 10.15
PRICES: £11 (£17). Minimum £5·50. Service 10% CARDS: Access, Visa
SEATS: 62. Private parties: 25 main room. Children welcome. No pipes in dining-room. Wheelchair access. Music

▲ *Donmaree Hotel* [10/20]

21 Mayfield Gardens, EH9 2BX
031-667 3641 £10–£24

This has a grand dining-room, and there are some fine wines that are not overpriced – for example, halves of Ch. Cissac '78 for £5·70. The menu is far too

The Guide accepts no advertising and does not allow restaurants to use their inclusion for publicity.

long and conservative, but the shellfish is kept in tanks in-house, and the steaks in various guises are consistently well reported and come with hosts of vegetables.

CHEFS: S.Prandstatter and David McFarlane PROPRIETORS: Mr and Mrs Kirkwood White
OPEN: Mon to Sat, exc Sat L MEALS: 12.30 to 2, 6.30 to 10
PRICES: £16 (£24), Set L £5·95 (£10), Set D (residents only) £9·95 (£14). Service 10%
CARDS: Access, Amex, Visa
SEATS: 42. Private parties: 42 main room. Car-park, 8 places. Children welcome. Classical music
ACCOMMODATION: 17 rooms, 14 with bath/shower. B&B £34·50 to £52. Garden [GHG]

Kalpna [9/20]

2–3 St Patrick Street, EH8 9ES
031-667 9890 £8–£9

Gujerati and southern Indian vegetarian/wholefood cooking, with a reputation extending beyond Edinburgh. The decor is simple, bright and clean, and there are separate smoking and no-smoking rooms. Thalis are particularly good; pakoras are delicate; and there is praise for spinach, lentils, stuffed tomatoes, and spiced mushrooms. Navratan korma mixes vegetables in a cream sauce with fresh herbs; palak paneer combines spinach with curd cheese, spices and herbs. There is lassi to drink, and service is good without being fussy.

CHEF: Ajay Bharatdwaj PROPRIETORS: Mr Jogee and Mrs Mehta
OPEN: Mon to Sat MEALS: 12 to 2, 5.30 to 11
PRICES: £5 (£9), Set D from £4·50 (£8). Service 12.5% CARDS: Access, Visa
SEATS: 60. Private parties: 40 main room, 30 private room. Vegetarian meals. Children's helpings. No-smoking area. Wheelchair access. Indian music

Mackintosh's [11/20]

24A Stafford Street, EH3 7BD
031-226 7530 £10–£16

Terrific decor ('restrained art nouveau'); a good menu ('*nouvelle* Scottish'); a super starter ('onion tarte paysanne'); perfect vegetables; a slightly gauche main course ('kidney rolled up inside an escalope of veal'); better to have fish and the Chablis; good cheeses; rich puddings; sober service; not cheap.

CHEF: Pierre Levicky PROPRIETOR: Eve Mackintosh
OPEN: Mon to Sat, exc Sat L MEALS: 12 to 2, 6.30 to 10.15 (11 during Festival)
PRICES: Set L from £6·80 (£10), Set D from £12 (£16) CARDS: Access, Amex, Diners, Visa
SEATS: 26. Private parties: 26 main room. Vegetarian meals by arrangement. Children's helpings. Air-conditioned

Martins [11/20]

70 Rose Street, North Lane, EH2 3DX
031-225 3106
between Frederick Street and Castle Street £11–£19

A modern-looking brasserie found up a back lane among warehouses. The welcome is direct and enthusiastic. The menu has homely, provincial-style items reminiscent of the 1970s (the decor is more up to date), but the kitchen seems to be stretched by the menu choice and there is some poor technique. However, local opinion maintains that here is some of the best restaurant food in the city. There are special mentions for the broccoli and caraway soup, the mild-cured smoked salmon, beef Stroganoff, and pheasant with calvados sauce. Good reports of the sweets, too, including an unusual and surprising crème brûlée mousse, Marsala trifle with fresh brambles, and port and prune mousse. A short list of wines with house vin de pays du Gard at £6.

CHEFS: Michael Wildman, William Trayner and Coleman Maguire
PROPRIETORS: Martin and Gay Irons
OPEN: Tue to Sat, exc Sat L CLOSED: 2 weeks from 25 Dec, 2 weeks June MEALS: 12 to 2, 7 to 10 (10.30 Fri and Sat)
PRICES: Set L from £6·75 (£11), Set D from £14·50 (£19). Service 10% on parties over 5
CARDS: Access, Amex, Diners, Visa
SEATS: 28. Private parties: 34 main room, 10 private room. Vegetarian meals. Children's helpings. Wheelchair access (2 steps)

Maxies Bistro [8/20]

32 West Nicolson Street, EH8 9DD
031-667 0845 £12

A crowded, noisy, lively and cosmopolitan bistro for all age-groups. Tables are shared and service is happy-go-lucky and rather hit-or-miss. Fillet steak and venison are both good, but served in the same sauce; chicken is tasty. House wine is brought to the table uncorked and you are charged for what you drink. Chess, backgammon and scrabble sets are available on loan from the bar.

CHEFS: Ian Macdonald and Norman McLeod PROPRIETOR: Ian Macdonald
OPEN: all week, exc Sun L MEALS: 12 to 2.30, 5 to 12
PRICES: £8 (£12). Also cut-price L menu CARDS: Access, Visa
SEATS: 84. Private parties: 30 main room. Vegetarian meals. Children welcome. Classical music

New Edinburgh Rendezvous [new entry, zero rated]

10A Queensferry Street, EH2 4PG
031-225 2023 and 3777 £7–£23

Once called the Bamboo Hut but now under a new regime. The waiters understand English, and the Peking banquet for £8·80 a head impresses. It runs to ten courses and includes fine hot-and-sour soup; crispy aromatic duck, de-boned expertly by the waiter who gives a demonstration on how to make the traditional pancake with plum sauce, spring onion, cucumber and duck; beef with chilli and garlic; and lemon chicken. Noodles are hand made, which is the

The 1987 Guide *will appear before Christmas 1986, so reports are particularly important in the spring. Report forms are at the back of this book, but just write a letter if you prefer. Address them to* The Good Food Guide, *Freepost, 14 Buckingham Street, London WC2N 6BR. No stamp is necessary if you post in the UK.*

mark of a good Peking restaurant. Look also for the grilled dumplings. House white is £5·80 a litre. More reports, please.

CHEF: Jimmy T.W.Wong PROPRIETORS: Peter S.Y.Ng, Jimmy T.W.Wong and Jimmy S.C.Wong
OPEN: all week MEALS: 12 to 2, 5.30 to 11.30 (1 to 11.30pm Sun)
PRICES: £15 (£23), Set L £3·20 (£7), Set D from £7·30 (£11). Service 10% CARDS: Access, Amex, Diners, Visa
SEATS: 135. Private parties: 135 main room, 60 private room. Vegetarian meals. Children's helpings. Wheelchair access. Classical music. Air-conditioned

▲ *Pompadour Room, Caledonian Hotel* [12/20]

Princes Street, Edinburgh EH1 2AB
031-225 2433 £31

Alan Hill has managed to get the Cinderella of Edinburgh's restaurant society to the ball and dancing at last. Madame Pompadour might have approved of the decor: the grey wall panels with silk panels of flowers and birds, the oval-backed chairs, the pianist hidden behind his carnations, the waiters who flurry and fuss around each table. The menu rambles on into nonsensical romantic descriptions of food and deceives when it could flatter, because the kitchen has many classy touches – the poppyseed rolls; claggy brown bread; the scallop mousse with scraps of basil and lime and its roe for effect; the duck breast with two sauces, one a demi-glaze with cinnamon and the other a cream version flavoured with pear and with clumps of undercooked and buttery spinach. At lunchtime there is a heroic and laudable menu drawn from all over Scotland using traditional recipes. In the evening the *nouvelle cuisine* appears dressed with some E.F.Benson sillinesses: venison and breast of quail 'with two little secrets'; 'delicious' chicken liver terrine and truffles. Fish has been excellent, and smoking is done in-house. The sweets trolley is typical of our reservations – the white chocolate gateau is more face-powder than charm, but the passion fruit sorbet is first-class. At these prices – gravlax £9·50 at night, £3·50 at lunchtime – we expect a *tour de force* not a dinner-dance (Fridays and Saturdays) so the rating is kept down. The wine list has a lot of showy expensive bottles, but the Alsace section includes five of the main grape varieties, each of which would suit the evening menu. House red is £7·50.

CHEF: Alan Hill PROPRIETORS: Gleneagles Hotels plc
OPEN: all week, exc Sat and Sun L MEALS: 12.30 to 2, 7.30 to 10.30
PRICES: £23 (£31) CARDS: Access, Amex, Diners, Visa
SEATS: 64. 22 tables outside. Private parties: 80 main room. Car-park, 185 places. Jacket and tie. Children's helpings. Wheelchair access (also WC). No-smoking area. Piano player. Dinner and dancing Fri and Sat evenings
ACCOMMODATION: 254 rooms, all with bath/shower. Rooms for disabled. B&B £61·50 to £93. Deposit: price of 1 night. Afternoon teas. Children welcome. No pets. Lift. Phone

Entries are compiled from the unsolicited reports from readers and are checked by inspectors; each restaurant is asked to supply details of its operation. Report forms can be found at the back of the Guide.

Restaurant tricks (1): Charging each person for every serving of vegetables even when the diners have shared portions between them.

Raffaelli [10/20]

10 Randolph Place, EH3 7TA
031-225 6060 £17

A smart Italian restaurant, open throughout the day. Lasagne is better than average; calamari are fresh; and herbs such as rosemary and sage come through strongly. It is good to find osso buco served here alla Toscana with white beans, and there is a nutmeg-flavoured spinach cake with white sauce. Service comes at breakneck speed. The adjacent wine bar serves snacks. There is Barolo of the '71 and '74 vintages from a decent Italian selection. CELLARMAN'S CHOICE: Vernaccia di San Gimignano '83 at £5·90.

CHEFS: Gerry Puffy and Aldo Scanferia PROPRIETOR: Bruno Peter Raffaelli
OPEN: Mon to Fri MEALS: 12.15 to 9.30 (10 Fri)
PRICES: £12 (£17). Service 10% CARDS: Access, Amex, Diners, Visa
SEATS: 60. Private parties: 60 main room, 35 private room. Vegetarian meals by arrangement. Children's helpings. Wheelchair access

Ravello [10/20]

86 Morningside Road, EH10 4BY
031-447 9724 £13

The pasta is freshly made in this small, family trattoria and there can be good fish, too. House Italian is £4·85.

CHEF/PROPRIETOR: Giovanni Palumbo
OPEN: Tue to Sat, D only MEALS: 5.30 to 11.30
PRICES: £8 (£13)
SEATS: 60. Private parties: 50 main room, 16 private room. Children's helpings. Air-conditioned

Shamiana [11/20]

14 Brougham Street, EH3 9JH
031-228 2265 and 229 5578 £13

Soothing ambience with cane and chrome chairs, pink tablecloths and fresh flowers. The short list of north Indian dishes avoids interminable lists of birianis and the like. There are good tandooris, tikkas and kebabs – seekh and shashlik – but it is the careful spicing of dishes that sets the restaurant apart from the competition: there is fenugreek in the methi chaman josh; delicate badami josh with fresh coriander, lots of nuts, and good meat in a turmeric sauce. The tandoori oven turns out impeccable nan, light as a feather. Diners with children appear to get the best service.

CHEFS: M.Rafique and Mr Yaseen PROPRIETOR: M.E.Jogee
OPEN: Mon to Sat, D only CLOSED: 25 Dec and 1 Jan MEALS: 6 to 11
PRICES: £6 (£13). Service 12.5% CARDS: Access, Amex, Diners, Visa
SEATS: 42. Vegetarian meals. Children's helpings. Wheelchair access. Classical music

'If Sharrow Bay is Wagner, Miller Howe is Tchaikovsky, then Pool Court is Brahms, less obviously brilliant, less self-confident, but a delight.' (On eating in the north)

Vito's [10/20]

55A Frederick Street, EH2 1LH
031-225 5052 £10–£15

A rustic, Mediterranean-style basement with low ceilings, white walls and heavy wood and rush seats. The food is robustly Italian, with a few continental dishes for good measure: outstanding pasta – including linguine al pesto – and excellent fresh seafood, as well as specialities like veal parmigiano and tournedos buongustaio (with ham, mushrooms and Marsala sauce). Short, familiar wine list and good-value house wine by the carafe (£5·40 a litre) . . . to drink out of stoneware goblets.

CHEF: F.Fusco PROPRIETORS: Glen Rea Ltd
OPEN: Mon to Sat MEALS: 12 to 2.30, 6.30 to 11
PRICES: £9 (£15), Set L and D £6 (£10). Service 10% CARDS: Access, Amex, Diners, Visa
SEATS: 70. Private parties: 45 main room, 30 private room. Vegetarian meals. Children's helpings. Music

Waterfront Wine Bar [9/20]

1C Dock Place, Leith, EH6 6LU
031-554 7427 £10

A small bar with not enough chairs, unless the sun shines and tables are put out by the lock. There is a bistro-type blackboard menu that has included good fish dishes, like hake with pepper sauce, barbecued codling, and marinated anchovies. From May to September the barbecue is in action. Wines are from Corney and Barrow, whiskies are from the Scottish Malt Whiskies Society, and there is scrumpy, too.

CHEF: Robin Bowie PROPRIETORS: Helen and Ian Ruthven, Sarah Reid and Robin Bowie
OPEN: Mon to Sat (and Sun D May to Sept) MEALS: 11am to midnight (1am Fri and in summer)
PRICES: £6 (£10)
SEATS: 70. 20 tables outside. Vegetarian meals. Children's helpings. Wheelchair access (also wc, 2 steps). Music

ERISKA Strathclyde map 8

▲ *Isle of Eriska Hotel* [12/20]

Eriska PA37 1SD
LEDAIG (063 172) 371
off A828, 12m N of Oban **Real Food** £16–£29

The Buchanan-Smiths' baronial country house, set on its own 280-acre island, aims to re-create the house-party atmosphere of Eriska's heyday, which was quite a few years ago – pre-1914 at least. The dining-room's reputation rests on its beef – Aberdeen Angus bought on the hoof at Forfar. The sirloin is hung for between 12 and 17 days at a temperature of 36°F and carved off the trolley as the centrepiece of six-course meals. The kitchen brigade has been beefed up with the arrival of chef Simon Burns now that the hotel is open from March to November. There is little to no choice on a menu that builds up through onion soup and

Loch Linnhe langoustines with garlic butter to savouries of Welsh rarebit, but the new materials include milk from the Buchanan-Smiths' own Jersey cows and eggs from their free-range chickens, while the whole-wheat bread is good enough for it to be listed as a speciality. There are some good Rhônes on the wine list, as well as clarets, but as yet they are too young to drink. The Alsace wines from Trimbach embrace the excellent '83s which can only get better. CELLARMAN'S CHOICE: Ch. du Trentin '79 at £7·20.

CHEFS: Simon Burns, Simon Bentley and Philip Harvey
PROPRIETORS: Robin and Sheena Buchanan-Smith
OPEN: all week CLOSED: Dec to Mar MEALS: 12.45 to 1.45, 7.30 to 8.30
PRICES: Set L from £10 (£16), Set D from £20 (£29), Light lunches £5 (£6) CARD: Access
SEATS: 40. Private parties: 10 main room, 12 private room. Car-park, 50 places. Children's helpings. No children under 10 at D. Jacket and tie at D. Wheelchair access (also WC). Special menus by prior arrangement
ACCOMMODATION: 21 rooms, all with bath/shower. Rooms for disabled. D, B&B £55 to £110. Deposit: price of 1 night. Children welcome. Baby facilities. Garden. Tennis. Fishing. Croquet. Water-skiing. Wind-surfing. Yachting. TV. Phone. Scenic. Doors close at 11. Confirm by 4 [GHG]

FORT WILLIAM Highland map 8

▲ *Inverlochy Castle* [13/20]

Fort William PH33 6SN
FORT WILLIAM (0397) 2177/8
off A82, 3m N of Fort William **Real Food** £15–£32

Inverlochy Castle walks a thin line between Disneyland and *haute cuisine*. We have dropped the rating one point because we fear the former is taking over. The waiters seem to say 'The wine is a good choice' as if by remote control. At these prices we feel entitled to be critical of such platitudes, which can also creep into the otherwise excellent cooking. The location is indeed glorious. All those Bens, including Nevis, as well as the loch, and the hills covered in rhododendrons in June are quite conversation-stoppers. Inside, the amazing drawing-room is overshadowed by a magnificent ceiling with two whoppers of chandeliers. The atmosphere hits you, although if you have a mind to notice such things then so will the imitation antique chairs in the dining-room and the plastic blue garden chairs. It is a short, set menu whose parents are old school French and Scottish. The latter is most evident in the cheap butter used for the brandy-snap batter for the dessert tuiles, and the cheapskating on the fumet in which the salmon is poached – even though its beurre blanc is aristocratic. These are criticisms at a high level, but that is where the chef, François Huguet, is operating. Testimony of that are his deep and satisfying prawn bisque, his quenelles of pike, his orange soufflé (made with free-range eggs), and his strawberry sorbet. Petits fours do not come with coffee, and the service is considerably more obsequious if talked to in an American accent. The wine list is impressive, but academic unless you can

'The bill was a stratospheric £129, of which about £33 was for aperitifs and wine. At such prices (I estimate my main dish cost me 50p for each lukewarm forkful) a cover charge of £1.50 seems superfluous.' (On eating in Bedfordshire)

afford to buy labels irrespective of price. Who knows what a Montrachet '71 will be like today? Find out for £80·50.

CHEF: François Huguet PROPRIETOR: Grete Hobbs
OPEN: all week CLOSED: mid-Nov to mid-Mar MEALS: 12.30 to 1.45, 7.30 to 9
PRICES: Set L from £9 (£15), Set D £23 (£32) CARDS: Access, Visa
SEATS: 10. Private parties: 8 main room. Car-park, 10 places. No children under 10. Jacket and tie. No smoking in dining-room
ACCOMMODATION: 16 rooms, all with bath/shower. B&B £70 to £95. Children welcome. Baby facilities. No pets. Garden. Tennis. Fishing. Golf. Snooker. Helicopter pad. TV. Phone. Scenic [GHG]

GATTONSIDE Borders — map 8

Hoebridge Inn [10/20]

Gattonside TD6 9LZ
MELROSE (089 682) 3082
off B6360, 3m SE of Galashiels — £14

Honest Italian dishes are served in this family-run restaurant in a converted bobbin mill. Specials include the fettucine with smoked salmon, tarragon, tomatoes and cream, and the haunch of venison with a game sauce. House Merlot is £2·90 for half a litre.

CHEF: Carlo Campari PROPRIETORS: Mr and Mrs Campari
OPEN: Tue to Sun, D only, (D all week June to Sept) CLOSED: 2 weeks in Apr and Oct, 25 Dec and 1 Jan MEALS: 6.30 to 10
PRICES: £9 (£14) CARD: Visa
SEATS: 46. Private parties: 10 main room. Car-park, 15 places. Vegetarian meals. Children's helpings. No pipes in dining-room. Wheelchair access (2 steps). Music

GLASGOW Strathclyde — map 8

BACKGROUND BRIEFING: *Even before the 'Glasgow's miles better' campaign, food supplies in the city had radically improved. For Chinese provisions try Cheung Ying, 63 Cambridge Street; for Indian and Pakistani, the plethora of small shops around the Woodlands and Byres Road complex. Bedi's on Byres Road is a good cheap place for nuts and spices. Lasagne, salads and coffee beans are good from both branches of the Italian store, Fazzi's (232 Clyde Street and 67 Cambridge Street); and the delicatessen at 111 Great Western Road has a good range of Greek foods, including home-prepared dishes. The best chain stores for food are Asda at Maryhill and the Clydebank Safeway. A good wholefood shop is Grassroots on Great Western Road (near Kelvinbridge underground station), and the nearby Fruit and Roots has a range of exotic fruit and vegetables at the most reasonable prices in the West End. For butchery in the various areas of the city try A. Gillespie on Great Western Road; Sloane's, 351 Byres Road; J. W. Lewis, 130 Drymen Road, Bearsden, and 14 Clober Crescent, Milngavie. Good game from G. Stewart, 10 Allison Street. For wet fish recommendations include Corrigan's, 186 Howard Street; Peter's, 1 Houston Place; Macgregor, 311 Crow Road. Beveridge's, a fishmonger in Byres Road, now regularly has oysters and crayfish while keeping up good standards on other produce, and also sells free-range eggs. Of the delicatessens Peckhams, 43 Clarence Drive, is known for its cheeses; Ramekins, Mews Arcade, off Byres Road, for its chicken liver pâté and cheesecakes; Epicures, 46 West*

Nile Street, for its cheeses; and Guys in Byres Road for its wide range of items. Despite the Scottish genius for bakery, Glasgow fares remarkably badly for bread and cakes. Allans of Station Street, Milngavie, is a good supplier, though. The Pâtisserie Françoise delivers good French bread and croissants across the city and has a tiny tea-room in Byres Road. The Danish Food Centre has closed. For cheap lunches there is La Parmigiana, 447 Great Western Road; Peppino's, 11 – 13 Hyndland Street; and also Pythagoras, 410 Sauchiehall Street. For fish and chips there is Lena's at Dumbarton Road, and the best hamburgers are at Tom Sawyer's, 242 Woodlands Road. The Peking Inn, 191 Hope Street, has some of the best Peking and Cantonese cooking in the city, including beautifully presented scallops with Chinese leaves and ginger and onion; and chicken with black bean sauce. Also Chinese, with a good atmosphere and some fine food, is Lafitte's, 46 – 50 Kirkston Park, East Main, East Kilbride. Pizzaville on Byres Road has some good, cheap pizzas, and there are votes for the wine bar/brasserie Lautrec's, 14 Woodlands Terrace; and De Quincys wine bar, 71 Renfield Street. The Willow Room, 217 Sauchiehall Street, is notable for its Mackintosh decor as much as its toastie lunches and scone teas. An Indian worth checking out is the Koh-i-noor in Gibson Street.

Amritsar Tandoori [9/20]

9 Kirk Road, Bearsden Cross, G61 3RG
041-942 7710 £7–£14

One of the most agreeable Indian restaurants in the city. The quality of the meat is good, and there is unusual use of veal, venison and pheasant. There is also white fish pakora to start, and halva to finish. Biriani has almonds and raisins. Spicing is varied. There are portions for children, otherwise they are big. Drink lassi, or Tennent's lager at 95p a pint.

CHEF: Naranjan Singh PROPRIETOR: Bhopinder Purewal
OPEN: all week, exc Sun L MEALS: noon to midnight
PRICES: £9 (£14), Set L £2·95 (£7) CARDS: Access, Amex, Diners, Visa
SEATS: 80. Private parties: 80 main room. Car-park, 10 places. Vegetarian meals. Children's helpings. Music. Air-conditioned. Take-away service

Asha [8/20]

415 Sauchiehall Street, G2 3LG
041-332 4996 £9

Glasgow's answer to Edinburgh's Kalpna, serving vegetarian dishes in an upstairs room. The decor may be a bit dull, but the food is well above average and has included, for example, delicate curried lotus leaf; poppadums with black pepper; and courgettes, cauliflower, peas and mushrooms in a nutty sauce with brown rice. Samosas are crisp, thalis are copious, and there is halva for pudding.

The 1987 Guide will appear before Christmas 1986, so reports are particularly important in the spring. Report forms are at the back of this book, but just write a letter if you prefer. Address them to The Good Food Guide, *Freepost, 14 Buckingham Street, London WC2N 6BR. No stamp is necessary if you post in the UK.*

Waiters might be more communicative. The exotic fruit juices are more interesting than the wine.

CHEF: Mr Swamy PROPRIETOR: M.D.Saeed
OPEN: all week MEALS: 12 to 2.30, 5.30 to 11.30
PRICES: £5 (£9). Service inc CARDS: Access, Amex, Diners, Visa
SEATS: 60. Private parties: 30 main room. Vegetarian meals. Children's helpings. Indian music

La Bavarde [11/20]

9 New Kirk Road, Bearsden, G61 3SJ
041-942 2202 £7–£14

A noisy, well-liked eating house where sometimes there may be wild boar or kid on the short menu. Fish usually come unsauced with butter and rosemary, and there are some unusual dishes, like crab en croûte and deer and tangerine pie. Offal is good, notably sweetbreads, and to finish there are fresh fruits with liqueurs and cream. The rating is dropped one point to put it more properly into context, but the set lunch is still the best value in Glasgow. There are some vintage clarets and burgundies but otherwise it is a drinking list longest in Italian wines.

CHEF: Peter Bannister PROPRIETOR: Armenio Trevisan
OPEN: Tue to Sat CLOSED: 2 weeks at Christmas, last 3 weeks July MEALS: 12 to 1.30, 6.30 to 9.30
PRICES: £10 (£14), Set L from £3·40 (£7) CARDS: Access, Amex, Diners, Visa
SEATS: 52. Vegetarian meals. Children's helpings. Wheelchair access

The Buttery [12/20]

654 Argyle Street, G3 8UF
041-221 8188 £22

An old-fashioned, black-painted house with gold lettering outside, looked down on three sides by tenements, the Holiday Inn and the motorway flyover. Inside is how restaurants used to be – a large Edwardian bar with lounge sofas, Spy magazine cartoons, waitresses in long, frilly aprons over black, and a panelled and sectioned dining-room. By contrast, the menu is fashionably modern and strongest with the native ingredients, like salmon fillet with a cream and orange sauce garnished with seaweed, or the undercut of fillet of venison roasted and served with a port and orange jelly. Some of the good work that deserves a score of 13 is undone because the kitchen appears overstretched – especially since the opening of the sister operation, Rogano's (see entry) – and the standards are inconsistent, especially in the pastry department, which veers from excellent to drab. A shorter menu would help. Nevertheless there is plenty of imaginative brio and visual acrobatics – the butter is even etched with squiggles. The wine list is a solid choice of respectable vineyards and négociants, but not that kindly priced –

'Service at the table was by young ladies who were willing and attentive enough but who seemed more at home in the stables. A sort of ham-fisted gentility.' (On eating in Cambridgeshire)

Pinot Gris, Les Maquisards '82, from Dopff & Irion, is £10·75. House Chenin Blanc is £5·95. CELLARMAN'S CHOICE: Ch. Haut-Marbuzet '79 at £14·95.

CHEF: Ferrier Richardson PROPRIETORS: Dukes of Argyle Street
OPEN: Mon to Sat, exc Sat L MEALS: 12 to 2.30, 7 to 10.30 (pre- or post-theatre by arrangement)
PRICES: £15 (£22), Bar meals from £1·50 (£1·65). Service 10% CARDS: Access, Amex, Diners, Visa
SEATS: 50. Private parties: 8 main room, 8 private room. Car-park, 30 places. Children welcome. Wheelchair access (also WC). Classical music. Air-conditioned

Café Gandolfi [9/20]

64 Albion Street, G1 1NY
041-552 6813 £8

A useful, smart cafe open from 9.30 in the morning to 11.30 at night for coffee or a full meal. There are hot soups; smoked salmon quiche; pizzas; and good sandwiches. House Chianti is £5 a litre.

CHEFS: Maggie Clarence and Andrew Bickerstaff PROPRIETOR: Iain Mackenzie
OPEN: Mon to Sat CLOSED: bank hols MEALS: 9.30am to 11.30pm
PRICES: £5 (£8). Service 10% on parties over 5 and bookings
SEATS: 60. Private parties: 60 main room. Vegetarian meals. Children's helpings. Wheelchair access (also WC). Music

Loon Fung [10/20]

417 Sauchiehall Street, G2 3LG
041-332 1240 and 332 1477 £12–£16

Originally a cinema, now a Cantonese restaurant with a typically huge menu of some 150 dishes. The dim-sum, hard to find in west Scotland, are exotic – water-chestnut and turnip cake; steamed duck's feet; lotus seed paste dumplings. Otherwise the lemon chicken is popular; fresh scampi are steamed and served with a garlic sauce; and the fried bean curd with pork is good. Other authentic specials include eel, tripe, suckling pig. Service is almost over-zealous. Licensed.

CHEF: Sau Lun Lee PROPRIETOR: Dominic Woo
OPEN: all week CLOSED: 3 days Jan MEALS: 12.30 to 11.30
PRICES: £9 (£16), Set D from £8·50 (£12) CARDS: Access, Amex, Visa
SEATS: 120. Private parties: 200 main room. Vegetarian meals. Children welcome. Wheelchair access (also WC). Music. Air-conditioned

Pavarotti Trattoria [new entry, zero rated]

91 Cambridge Street, G3 6RU
041-332 9713 £20

The kind of place you might find tucked away in a back street in Florence. It is unfussy, homely and friendly and the food is honest. There is good minestrone and pasta but the fish is the thing to go for. The soup containing mussels,

An index of restaurants by name appears at the back of the Guide.

langoustines, salmon and monkfish in a white wine, tomato and parsley reduction is superb. House Chianti is £5·30. More reports, please.

CHEF: Tony Sorento PROPRIETOR: Mimmo Sorento
OPEN: Mon to Sat MEALS: 12.30 to 2.30, 5.30 to 11
PRICES: £14 (£20). Also cut-price L menu
SEATS: 35. Private parties: 35 main room. Vegetarian meals. Children's helpings. Wheelchair access (also WC)

Poachers [11/20]

Ruthven Lane, off Byres Road, G12 9BG
041-339 0932 £21

The service is now exclusively female in this low-ceilinged private house down a mews. The tablecloths are plastic, but the food is serious enough, especially the fish such as halibut fillets in a white wine, shallot and mushroom sauce, or gigantic grilled plaice with parsley butter. The menu is longer than it ought to be, which has led to some sillinesses such as boned and stuffed guinea-fowl with a tinned chestnut stuffing, but sweetbreads have come in a very good wine sauce and the vegetables are provided in large quantities. The conservative choices tend to be the best. The rating is dropped two points because of the new competition in the city and because of bad inconsistencies in standards. Lunches seem to be less good than dinners. Some serious wines on the exclusively French list; house Bulgarian Cabernet Sauvignon is £5·60.

CHEF: William Orral PROPRIETORS: Mr and Mrs F. Bergius, Mr and Mrs P. Scott
OPEN: Mon to Sat MEALS: 12 to 2.30, 6.30 to 11
PRICES: £14 (£21). Licensed, plus bring your own: no corkage CARDS: Access, Amex, Diners, Visa
SEATS: 45. 5 tables outside. Private parties: 22 main room. Car-park, 10 places. Vegetarian meals. Children's helpings. Wheelchair access

Preet Palace Tandoori [10/20]

Bearsden Shopping Centre, Milngavie Road, Bearsden, G61 2TX
041-942 9067 £6–£13

Special dishes include karahis, tandooris, pakoras of mushroom, chicken and fish, and nargisi kebab, which is a boiled egg covered with minced meat, herbs and spices. Chicken comes buttered, or with chick-peas or banana. Good ice-creams. Licensed

OPEN: all week, exc Sun L MEALS: noon to 11.30 (5 to 11.30 Sun)
PRICES: £8 (£13), Set L £3 (£6) CARDS: Access, Amex, Diners, Visa
SEATS: 50. Car-park, 200 places. Vegetarian meals. Children's helpings. Wheelchair access (also WC). Indian music

The 1987 Guide *will appear before Christmas 1986, so reports are particularly important in the spring. Report forms are at the back of this book, but just write a letter if you prefer. Address them to* The Good Food Guide, *Freepost, 14 Buckingham Street, London WC2N 6BR. No stamp is necessary if you post in the UK.*

Rogano's [new entry, zero rated]

11 Exchange Place, G1 3AN
041-248 4055 £20

This was a famous restaurant from the 1930s to the early 1950s, when the bar stretched the length of the room and oysters and beer flowed upstairs while couples courted downstairs. It is now the sister restaurant to The Buttery (see entry) but is more modern and fashionable, with a sleek menu of fish, and waiters who don't fuss. It has been decorated stylishly with huge mirrors, alcoves and a bar with booths (where it is possible to eat a cheap snack). The pasta in the seafood lasagne has been freshly made; brill is served with chicory in a subtle wine and cream sauce; and meat dishes, such as venison soup, or kidneys in a deep demi-glace, have also been well handled. The desserts are ingenious, a very bland bavarois lifted by a powerful sauce of Kalhua, or warm pancakes stuffed with a purée of apples. Espresso coffee, good white wines and a few malts, including Laphroaig.

CHEF: Ferrier Richardson PROPRIETORS: Dukes of Exchange Place
OPEN: Mon to Sat MEALS: 12 to 2.30, 7 to 10.30
PRICES: £14 (£20). Service 10% CARDS: Access, Amex, Diners, Visa
SEATS: 50. Private parties: 20 main room, 14 private room. Children welcome. Music. Air-conditioned

Shish Mahal [9/20]

45 Gibson Street, G12 0HI
041-339 8256 and 334 7899 £11

Well-prepared, good-value Indian food is courteously served in a spotless dining-room. Dishes are explained on the menu where necessary and, apart from seafood and tandoori specialities, most are under £3. There is a further encouragement of a 20 per cent discount at lunchtime, and the menu also has a children's section. There is no licence, but no corkage charge either; glasses are provided free of charge. Otherwise drink fresh orange juice, or try hot or cold gulab jamun with ice-cream.

CHEFS/PROPRIETORS: Ali A. Aslam and Nasim Ahmed
OPEN: all week CLOSED: 25 Dec, 1 Jan MEALS: 11.45 to 11.30 (11.45 Fri and Sat)
PRICES: £7 (£11). Minimum £4·50. Unlicensed, but bring your own: no corkage
CARDS: Access, Amex, Diners, Visa
SEATS: 110. Private parties: 50 main room, 50 private room. Vegetarian meals. Children's helpings. Wheelchair access. Music. Air-conditioned

Ubiquitous Chip [11/20]

12 Ashton Lane, G12 8SJ
041-334 5007 £15

The old Chip, with its entrance via a cobbled courtyard, has a patriotic feel to its menus – there are oak-smoked Loch Tay eels; creel-caught langoustines; Highland teal served with port and orange sauce; pheasant with beer and cream; Oban-landed brill; and spectacular Hebridean carrageen snow-eggs – a chilled jelly made out of purplish-red north Atlantic seaweed with a splash of Grand

Marnier and the eggs spun in brown sugar – to finish. The strength of the produce gives the cooking a solid base. Corners are not cut in the cooking. Stocks, for example, are made in-house whereas most Glasgow restaurants use cubes, and this is reflected in good reports on the soups, notably the shellfish bisque. All fish dishes draw praise, as do the imaginative vegetables, such as creamed parsnips with almonds, and braised red cabbage in the German style. Some of the sauces, though, can be a bit fey. It is a splendid wine list, one of the best in Britain, and includes a '28 Anjou which is still drinkable.

CHEF/PROPRIETOR: R.Clydesdale
OPEN: Mon to Sat MEALS: 12.30 to 2.30, 5.30 to 11
PRICES: £12 (£15). Service inc CARDS: Access, Amex, Diners, Visa
SEATS: 100. Vegetarian meals. Children's helpings. Wheelchair access (1 step; also wc)

GULLANE Lothian map 8

La Potinière [14/20]

Main Street, Gullane EH31 2AA
GULLANE (0620) 843214 **Real Food £14–£19**

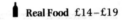

Lunch is the major meal of the day, as in France, supported with evening meals on Saturdays only – usually booked months in advance. Hilary Brown cooks a no-choice set menu while husband David serves all 20-odd diners single-handed in the small hall of a dining-room. Simple decorations run to a few pictures, some wooden wine cask labels and a dresser at the far end stacked with bottles of digestifs and plates from great French restaurants. The tables are solid and simply set, reinforcing the message that the Browns serve good food and wines with a minimum of fuss and bother. The kitchen's allegiance is to the dairy – within that format the menus barely change. To start there is usually a vegetable soup – broad bean and lovage, cauliflower, courgette – or occasionally a thick, hearty haddock. Then comes the mousse – calf's liver with red pepper sauce; or turkey liver; sole and smoked salmon – or maybe a courgette soufflé. Both courses are served with fresh French bread for mopping up the sauces. Poultry is the usual centrepiece, often with pommes dauphinoise: duck breast with a port sauce, chicken with leeks and more cream, or stuffed with walnuts. The rigid discipline of only slight variations repays in the power of the flavours. Brie is the favoured cheese. The lemon tart is a classic, or there is an iced orange tart. Two and a half hours after starting the meal comes the coffee. The wine list is a rare collection of bottles – an enthusiast's choice – with many items that cost three times as much, and more, elsewhere; the choice of Chablis and vintage claret is copious. The list really merits *two* bottle symbols.

CHEF: Hilary Brown PROPRIETORS: David and Hilary Brown
OPEN: Mon, Tue, Thur, Fri and Sun L, Sat D CLOSED: 1 week June, Oct MEALS: 1, 8
PRICES: Set L £10 (£14), Set D £14·75 (£19)
SEATS: 32. Private parties: 30 main room. Car-park, 10 places. Children welcome. No smoking in dining-room. Wheelchair access. One sitting

Prices quoted are for an average three-course meal including service and VAT and half a bottle of house wine (or the equivalent in an ethnic restaurant).

HADDINGTON Lothian map 8

▲ *Browns Hotel* [new entry, zero rated]

1 West Road, Haddington EH41 3RD
HADDINGTON (062 082) 2254 £18

A detached Georgian house with a set French menu. We have eaten fine smoked fish omelette, mushroom soup with almonds, and chateaubriand, but the avocado soup is less convincing. To finish, the syllabub is sharp, then take coffee in the lounge. Twenty interesting wines. More reports, please.

CHEF: Colin Brown PROPRIETORS: Margaret and Colin Brown
OPEN: Mon to Sat, D only CLOSED: 2 weeks Oct MEALS: 7.30 to 9
PRICES: Set D £13·50 (£18)
SEATS: 30. Private parties: 30 main room. Car-park, 10 places. Vegetarian meals by arrangement. Children's helpings. Wheelchair access (also WC)
ACCOMMODATION: 6 rooms, 4 with bath/shower. B&B £22 to £30. Deposit: £5. Children welcome. Baby facilities. No pets. Garden. TV. Scenic. Doors close at 12. Confirm by 8

HARRIS Western Isles map 8

▲ *Scarista House* [13/20]

Scarista PA85 3HX
SCARISTA (085 985) 238
on A859, 15m SW of Tarbert **Real Food** £17

Scarista has the remoteness of a crofter's cottage and this encourages guests to muck in and chat in the lounge of this Church of Scotland manse-style house before and after dinner. Alison Johnson's cooking of a four-course set dinner is typical of the new morality that is emerging in many menus. Affected by the cruelty of factory farming, she and her husband Andrew have fostered supplies that allow ducks at least to 'quack before they croak'. She is an inventive cook practising a style of cuisine that is in many ways more advanced than Anton Mosimann's first steps into *cuisine naturelle* at the Dorchester in London. Mussels are cooked with fennel, sole with pine kernels, squid is casseroled with peppers, and soups are made of potato and yoghourt. Main courses still frequently contain meat, such as fillet of beef with aubergines, or gigot of mutton with haricots. The cheeses and the breakfast bacon are brought from England, but otherwise ingredients are local and some, including the eggs, indigenous. The new wine list has grown into a well-balanced maturity with excellent bottles from less famous vineyards, strong in red Rhônes and '70s clarets. CELLARMAN'S CHOICE: Coteaux

Restaurants rating 10 and 11 serve the best food in the locality.

Restaurants rating 12 or more serve the best food in the region.

Places rating 8 or 9 may not be restaurants at all but still serve very good food. In this category expect to find pubs, cafes, small hotels and wine bars.

New restaurants that we have not been able to assess completely are given a zero rating for this year. We are particularly keen to have reports on these places.

des Baux-en-Provence, Domaine de Trévallon '80 at £5·50. Malt whiskies, of course, including Macallan '64 at £1·50 a glass.

CHEF: Alison Johnson PROPRIETORS: Andrew and Alison Johnson
OPEN: Mon to Sat, D only CLOSED: Nov to Mar MEALS: 8 to 10
PRICES: Set D £13·50 (£17)
SEATS: 20. Private parties: 8 main room. Car-park, 10 places. Children's helpings. No children under 8. No smoking in dining-room. Wheelchair access
ACCOMMODATION: 7 rooms, all with bath/shower. B&B £35 to £48. Deposit: £10. No children under 8. Pets welcome. Garden. Scenic [GHG]

INVERNESS Highland map 8

▲ *Dunain Park* [10/20]

Inverness IV3 6JN
INVERNESS (0463) 230512
on A82, 3m SW of Inverness £24

A converted Victorian country house surrounded by farmland and woods, and comfortably furnished – indeed, some of the bedrooms look like a furniture store with armchairs and tables lined up in rows. The cooking has been inconsistent, which leads to a drop in the rating, but the raw materials are first-class: eggs are free-range, and in the butchery department the lamb and beef are excellent. The understanding of fish seems less astute. Breakfasts are impressive – chunky porridge, home-made sausages, Stornoway black pudding. The wine list has seen rather too many visitors from America to be good value, but the Alsace section, mostly provided by Hugel, is very strong. If you can afford it the Tokay, Vendange Tardive '76, is £26·50. If not, halves of Riesling '81 are £4·60.

CHEF: Judith Bulger PROPRIETORS: Judith and Michael Bulger
OPEN: all week CLOSED: Nov to mid-Mar MEALS: 12.30 to 2, 7.30 to 9 (8 Sun)
PRICES: Set D £19 (£24), Bar meals from £5 (£5·50)
SEATS: 25. 3 tables outside. Car-park, 30 places. Vegetarian meals by arrangement. Smart dress preferred. No smoking in dining-room. Wheelchair access
ACCOMMODATION: 9 rooms, all with bath/shower. B&B £44 to £72. Deposit: £44. Baby facilities. No pets in dining-room. Afternoon teas. Garden. Croquet. Helicopter pad. Scenic. Doors close at 11.30

KELSO Borders map 8

▲ *Sunlaws House* [10/20]

Heiton, Kelso TD5 8JZ
ROXBURGH (057 35) 331
on A698, 3m S of Kelso £19

A country-house hotel serving good breakfasts; ordinary bar lunches of tomato soup with a hint of Stilton, and rollmops with stupendously good oatcakes; salmon and steak dishes that scarcely do justice to the ingredients; good vegetables; and ritzier dishes with prices to match the Rolls and Mercs that turn

▲ *This restaurant has rooms.*

up. Wines include fine claret; house wine at £5·95; and CELLARMAN'S CHOICE: Ch. Cissac '78 at £12·25 (£6·50 per half, £24·50 per magnum). More reports, please.

CHEF: Robert Grindle PROPRIETORS: Duke and Duchess of Roxburghe
OPEN: all week MEALS: 12.30 to 2, 7.30 to 9.30
PRICES: £12 (£19). Bar meals from £3·50 (£3·85). Snacks from £2 (£2·20) CARDS: Access, Amex, Diners, Visa
SEATS: 40. 5 tables outside. Private parties: 45 main room, 20 private room. Car-park, 30 places. Children's helpings. No pipes in dining-room. Wheelchair access (also WC)
ACCOMMODATION: 15 rooms, all with bath/shower. Rooms for disabled. B&B £33 to £53. Children welcome. Baby facilities. No pets in public rooms. Afternoon teas. Garden. Tennis. Fishing. Croquet. Clay pigeon shooting. Helicopter pad. TV. Phone. Confirm by 7.30 [GHG]

KENTALLEN Highland map 8

▲ *The Holly Tree* [10/20]

Kentallen PA38 4BY
DUROR (063 174) 292
on A828, 3m S of Ballachulish **Real Food** £17

Prawns come from the loch next to this converted railway station which has one of those great west Highlands views from the dining-room. Alasdair Robertson encourages small regional suppliers, grows some of his own herbs and salads, and has mushrooms picked locally. Soups range from a hearty lentil broth with egg yolk and port, to mussel and onion stew, to a classic consommé. There is plenty of fish and game on a menu that is both Scottish and classic French – potted, spiced crab; halibut with vermouth sauce; salmon in its cooking juices; roast grouse; and hare with red wine, have all been good. Trout is smoked as a salad, or baked with either rosemary and cream or, more traditionally, almonds. Berries are the source of much innovation – raspberries come with venison, and the old Robert Carrier dish of strawberries and pineapple served with green peppercorns is one of many fine sweets. Service is informal. The hotel seems to close in the day like a bed and breakfast place. The rating is reduced because either something has gone seriously wrong and standards have slipped or we substantially over-rated it last year. The short, eclectic wine list is backed by some fine bin-ends, or there is CELLARMAN'S CHOICE: Ch. Haut-Marbuzet '78 at £12·05. House Gamay is £5·05.

CHEF: Alasdair Robertson PROPRIETORS: Alasdair and Jane Robertson
OPEN: all week June to Oct; Thur to Tue Easter to May; Thur to Sun D only, and Sun L, winter CLOSED: 4 Jan to 1 Feb MEALS: 12.30 to 2.30, 6.30 to 9.30
PRICES: £13 (£17). Service inc CARDS: Access, Diners, Visa
SEATS: 60. Private parties: 16 main room. Car-park, 20 places. Children's helpings. No smoking in dining-room. Wheelchair access (also WC). Classical music
ACCOMMODATION: 2 rooms, both with bath/shower. Rooms for disabled. B&B £10 to £18. Deposit: £10. Children welcome. Pets welcome. Afternoon teas. Garden. TV. Scenic

---

Entries are compiled from the unsolicited reports from readers and are checked by inspectors; each restaurant is asked to supply details of its operation. Report forms can be found at the back of the Guide.

KILCHRENAN Strathclyde map 8

▲ *Ardanaiseig Hotel* [10/20]

Kilchrenan PA35 1HE
KILCHRENAN (086 63) 333
off B845, 9m S of Taynuilt £14–£25

The house and gardens are compensation enough for any lapses in the food or service. Main course fish dishes such as salmon hollandaise are consistently well reported. The beef is, of course, Aberdeen Angus. David Merriman spends the winter in the kitchens of well-known chefs. Last year he was at Le Manoir aux Quat' Saisons (see Great Milton). There are good clarets and burgundies in the cellar from the '70s. House wines from £6·25.

CHEF: David Merriman PROPRIETORS: Ardanaiseig Hotel Ltd
OPEN: all week CLOSED: mid-Oct to Easter MEALS: 12.30 to 2, 7.30 to 9
PRICES: £10 (£14), Set D £21·50 (£25). Minimum £6. Service inc CARDS: Access, Amex, Diners, Visa
SEATS: 40. Private parties: 30 main room. Car-park, 20 places. No children under 8. Jacket and tie. No cigars/pipes in dining-room
ACCOMMODATION: 14 rooms, all with bath/shower. B&B £60 to £130. Deposit: £40. No children under 8. Pets by arrangement. Afternoon teas. Garden. Tennis. Fishing. Snooker. Helicopter pad. TV. Phone. Scenic [GHG]

▲ *Taychreggan Hotel* [12/20]

Kilchrenan PA35 1HQ
KILCHRENAN (086 63) 211 £12–£17

The Taylors have been installed in their remote but comfortable small hotel by Loch Awe for 12 years. The fish is their main asset – fresh prawns out of Loch Etive; smoked salmon from the smokery at Taynuilt, or else from Oban. The simple four-course, unadulterated dinners are built around prime ingredients and cooked with skill. There are no fireworks, but when the local cheeses are served at their peak there is no need for any. Fine sweets to finish. The cold table lunch either in the bar or outside is consistently good value. Unfortunately the Ch. Latour '70 has doubled its price in two years, but you are unlikely to find it cheaper than £55. The strength of the clarets and burgundies makes the list expensive, but it is balanced with some cheaper regional wines. The Rhônes are excellent. The Gewürztraminer, Vendange Tardive '76, from Hugel, at £16·40 is a rare, brilliant wine, though the CELLARMAN'S CHOICE is Ch. Lynch-Bages '73 at £14·50. House claret is £5·95.

CHEFS: Gail Struthers, Dorothy Laurie, Joyce MacDougall and Nan MacIntyre
PROPRIETORS: John and Tove Taylor
OPEN: all week CLOSED: mid-Oct to Easter MEALS: 12 to 2.15, 7.30 to 9
PRICES: Set L £7·50 (£12), Set D £12·50 (£17), Snacks from £1 (£1·10) CARDS: Access, Amex, Diners, Visa
SEATS: 40. 10 tables outside. Private parties: 16 main room. Car-park, 30 places. Children's helpings. Wheelchair access
ACCOMMODATION: 17 rooms, 14 with bath/shower. B&B £27 to £54. Baby facilities. Dogs welcome. Afternoon teas. Garden. Fishing. Boats. Wind surfing. Doors close at 12. Confirm by 6 [GHG]

KILFINAN Strathclyde map 8

▲ *Kilfinan Hotel* [10/20]

Kilfinan PA21 2AP
KILFINAN (070 082) 201
on B8000, 4m NW of Tighnabruaich £17–£18

An out-of-the-way country hotel in what was once a very ordinary roadside pub with fine views. Snacks and lunch dishes are substantial and good value: a double decker club sandwich is £2·20, smoked mackerel pâté with hot toast is £1·30. On the *carte* there is beef and ham terrine with soured cream; salmon wrapped in lettuce with saffron sauce; profiteroles with whisky, cream and butterscotch sauce. Service is friendly and helpful. The wines are adequate, with house French at £3·50. CELLARMAN'S CHOICE: Ch. Léoville-Las-Cases '77 at £10·50.

CHEF: Mrs R. Mallinson PROPRIETOR: N.K.S.Wills
OPEN: all week MEALS: 12 to 2, 7.30 to 9.30
PRICES: D £13 (£18), Set D from £14 (£17), Bar lunches from £1·80 (£2) CARDS: Access, Amex, Diners, Visa
SEATS: 24. 2 tables outside. Private parties: 50 main room. Car-park, 20 places. Children's helpings. Smart dress preferred. Wheelchair access (also WC). Classical music
ACCOMMODATION: 11 rooms, 9 with bath/shower. B&B £23 to £35. Children welcome. Baby facilities. No pets. Afternoon teas. Garden. Fishing. Golf. Helicopter pad. TV. Phone. Scenic. Doors close at 11

KILLIECRANKIE Tayside map 8

▲ *Killiecrankie Hotel* [10/20]

Killiecrankie PH16 5LG
PITLOCHRY (0796) 3220 £3–£14

The throng of people in this secluded, white and slate, family-run hotel is testimony to its good value. Order at the bar from a menu that is commendably patriotic – partan bree (crab soup), fried haddock, game casserole. Good dishes eaten have been sole with a Drambuie sauce, chicken with a gravy enriched with whisky, and fillet steak with béarnaise sauce. Vegetables are cooked more firmly now, and on occasion there will be mutton. Inexpensive, varied wines include the CELLARMAN'S CHOICE: Gewürztraminer '82, from Hugel, at £5·80.

CHEFS: Paul Booth and James Harding PROPRIETORS: The Hattersley Smith family
OPEN: all week CLOSED: mid-Oct to late March MEALS: 12.30 to 2, 7 to 10 (opens earlier for Pitlochry theatre-goers)
PRICES: Set D from £10 (£14), Bar lunches from £2·50 (£3)
SEATS: 70. Private parties: 20 main room. Car-park, 30 places. Vegetarian meals. Children's helpings (D only). Cheaper set D available. No smoking in dining-room. Wheelchair access (also WC)
ACCOMMODATION: 12 rooms, 10 with bath/shower. B&B £17·25 to £34·50. Children welcome. Baby facilities. Dogs welcome. Afternoon teas. Garden. Croquet. Putting. Scenic. Doors close at 12. Confirm by 6 [GHG]

This restaurant has an exceptional wine cellar.

KINGUSSIE Highland map 8

▲ *The Cross* [12/20]

High Street, Kingussie PH21 1HX
KINGUSSIE (054 02) 762 **Real Food** £14–£16

Mr Hadley takes his special occasions seriously. At Christmas there was mulled wine, Rudolph's soup and smoked salmon before traditional main course and pudding, finishing up with Christmas cake in front of the fire. Saturday evenings are given over to seven-course dinners, which might begin with ceviche, Hramsa mushrooms, or west coast prawns aïoli. Sorbets in the middle are given names like Medicinal or (thankfully) Flealess, which may or may not give a clue as to what's in them. Local venison and Angus beef are dished up as main courses, haggis is combined with Drambuie, and variations on a theme include coq au gin. There are Scottish cheeses, too. Seven courses with wine, drinks before and after, coffee, and bed and breakfast come to £25 a head. Vegetarians have had dishes prepared on request, but there is always something for them on the monthly changing *carte*. Mr Hadley is an attentive host who gives good advice on his wines. They are overwhelmingly French, with a particularly good showing of clarets, but there are four English wines, and house red and white are under £4. CELLARMAN'S CHOICE: Ch. La Cardonne '78 at £9·95.

CHEF: Ruth Hadley PROPRIETORS: Tony and Ruth Hadley
OPEN: Tue to Sun, D only CLOSED: 2 weeks May and Oct MEALS: 6.30 to 10
PRICES: £10 (£14), Set Sat D £12·50 (£16)
SEATS: 24. Private parties: 18 main room. Vegetarian meals. No children under 8. No smoking in dining-room. Wheelchair access
ACCOMMODATION: 3 rooms, all with bath/shower. Rooms for disabled. B&B £12·50 to £25. Deposit: £10. No pets

▲ *Osprey Hotel* [11/20]

KINGUSSIE (054 02) 510 **Real Food** £14

Securicor bring the cheeseboard from London to this small, family-run hotel in the Spey valley. Not all supplies travel so far – peat-smoked salmon comes from Uist, venison from Inverness, oatcakes from Orkney. Over half a dozen choices of starter and dessert prop up a no-choice main course which may be a traditional lamb navarin, venison casserole, or noisettes of Scottish lamb with a mushroom and rosemary sauce. Unusually, for these parts, the vegetables are fresh and well treated. The range of puddings has included lemon crunch, strawberry shortcake, chocolate meringue gateau and treacle tart. Coffee comes with chocolate and truffles. The weighty wine list has house French at £5·10 a litre; a page and a half of inexpensive French country wines; a fine spread of clarets and white Bordeaux; sparkling wines that include Cuvée d'Alsace, brut, from Dopff,

Restaurants are graded on a scale of 1–20. In the region of 8–9 expect to find places that may not be restaurants but cafes, pubs, bistros and small hotels. In the category of 10–11 you can expect to find the best food in the locality. Ratings of 12 or more are given to restaurants we regard as serving the best food in the region.

at £9; and ten still Alsace wines, including Gewürztraminer Vendange Tardive '76, from Hugel, at £22.

CHEF: Pauline Reeves PROPRIETORS: Duncan and Pauline Reeves
OPEN: all week, D only CLOSED: Nov and Dec MEALS: 7.30 to 8.30
PRICES: Set D from £10 (£14) CARDS: Access, Amex, Diners, Visa
SEATS: 24. Private parties: 10 main room. Car-park, 10 places. Vegetarian meals. Children's helpings. No children under 3 at D. No smoking during meals. One sitting
ACCOMMODATION: 8 rooms, 2 with bath/shower. B&B £12 to £40. Deposit: £10 per person. Children welcome. No pets in public rooms. Afternoon teas. Confirm by 6 [GHG]

KIRKMICHAEL Tayside map 8

▲ *Log Cabin Hotel* [10/20]

Kirkmichael PH10 7NB
STRATHARDLE (025 081) 288
on A924, 9m E of Pitlochry £15

A Norwegian-log hotel with a turf roof and a straightforward menu that makes the best of local produce. The sea-trout and wild salmon apparently arrive in the kitchen with sea-lice still on them. Venison is blast frozen, but by way of compensation they are fat stags that have been properly hung. Aberdeen Angus ribs are carved to order. It is a noisy place with a feel of the outdoors; the dining-room has no *carte* and is not aiming for expense account diners. Breakfasts are good – proper porridge, home-made muesli, local kippers, ham, Ayrshire bacon and so on. The wine list has been expanded with some New World wines. House French is £5. CELLARMAN'S CHOICE: South African white Uitkyk Carlsheim '83 at £8·45.

CHEF: Elizabeth Sandell PROPRIETORS: Brian and Elizabeth Sandell
OPEN: all week CLOSED: mid-Nov to mid-Dec MEALS: 7.30 to 9 (Bar L 12 to 2)
PRICES: Set D from £12 (£15), Bar meals from £1·75. Service inc CARDS: Access, Amex, Diners, Visa
SEATS: 85. Private parties: 85 main room. Car-park, 60 places. Vegetarian meals. Children's helpings. Wheelchair access (also WC)
ACCOMMODATION: 13 rooms, all with bath/shower. Rooms for disabled. B&B £30 to £50. Deposit: £20. Children welcome. Baby facilities. Pets welcome. Afternoon teas. Golf. Snooker. Scenic. Doors close at 11. Confirm by 6 [GHG]

KIRKWALL see ORKNEY

LINLITHGOW Lothian map 8

Champany Inn [14/20]

Champany Corner, Linlithgow EH49 7LU
PHILPSTOUN (050 683) 4532
2m NE of Linlithgow at junction of
A904 and A803 Real Food £27

The best steaks in Britain are served by waitresses in gingham under this six-sided converted horse-mill with a peaked roof. The velveteen chairs are surrounded by hunting prints, candle-light, polished wood, and gleaming silver;

at the back there is a floodlit garden. What makes these steaks so special? Clive Davidson gives six reasons:

1. The breed. 'I don't like Aberdeen Angus pure-bred so I try to use Scots blue-grey, the ugliest beast you ever saw. Never get near Charolais or a Charolais cross because it is too fibrous. Hereford has too much marbling. What you want is a piece of beef that glistens, with creamy-coloured fat that flakes off when you scrape it with your nail. It must never be at all rubbery.'

2. The feed. 'You want a steer that has had to work for his meals, so the meat is best when they have been battling to find the short grass in June and July. When the grass is too young and tender, they gorge themselves and swell up. Very bad.'

3. Hanging. 'We hang the meat for at least four weeks and we have had some very good results hanging it for eight. It goes into a chilled room – 39°, one degree above the EEC limit – where ionisers help to retard the fungus growth and weight loss. Still, by the time we finish, we have lost about a quarter of the original weight – 10 per cent from ageing, 15 per cent from trimming. An ordinary supermarket steak has not been aged at all.'

4. The cut. 'My absolute favourite is pope's eye, which is cut against the grain from the point where the hind leg connects with the body. It is never flabby and always full of flavour.'

5. Thickness. 'You can't cook a thin steak well. Ours are a minimum of one and a quarter inches thick, and they should be thicker.'

6. Cooking. 'I paint the steaks with olive oil, which has a low flash-point: that means that the meat cannot burn before it cooks. I use a lava-rock grill, heated with gas, that has to be lit an hour before cooking. I turn the steak as few times as possible, seldom more than three times because that toughens it. And I never salt the meat before cooking, because if you do that the juices escape.'

By way of a choice there are also lobsters, crayfish, oysters and scallops kept in the pool at the back, or there is spit-roasted Norfolk duckling. Elsewhere on the menu pâté is rolled in nuts and served with oatcakes; vegetable soup is home made. Chips are freshly cooked and there is plenty of cream to go with the apple pie. The Davidsons run a Chophouse as well, next door to the dining-room, which has cheaper cuts and is good for families.

It was here, two miles away from her birthplace at Linlithgow Palace, that Mary Queen of Scots used to picnic with her court. She probably never drank wines like these – nor was served by a wine waiter called Andrew Backus! Reds get a particularly strong showing, with the emphasis on burgundy rather than Bordeaux: seven burgundy pages include one of Beaujolais from, appropriately, Duboeuf and six for everything else, from two Côtes Chalonnaises at £9·50, to La Tâche, Domaine de la Romanée-Conti '78, at £103·50. Alsace wines have a fair representation with two Rieslings, including Trimbach's Cuvée Frédéric Emile, Vendange Tardive '76 at £19·85, and four Gewürztraminers from £8·15. Italy provides Barolo Riserva from four old vintages and the fashionable Brunello di Montalcino Riserva, Tenuta Argiano '75, at £18·20. South Africa, also well represented, supplies the house wine – KWV Roodeberg and Chenin Blanc at £6·50 a bottle.

CHEFS: David Gibson and Clive Davidson PROPRIETORS: Clive and Anne Davidson
OPEN: Mon to Sat, exc Sat L CLOSED: 24 Dec to 13 Jan MEALS: 12 to 2, 7.30 to 10
PRICES: £19 (£27). Minimum £7·50. Service 10% CARDS: Access, Amex, Diners, Visa
SEATS: 50. 5 tables outside. Private parties: 50 main room. Car-park, 100 places. No children under 12. Smart dress preferred. Wheelchair access

LYBSTER Highland map 8

▲ *Bayview Hotel* [12/20]

Russell Street, Lybster KW3 6AG
LYBSTER (059 32) 346
off A9 £4–£15

The Huttons decided that they didn't want to bring up their children in the depths of Surrey and moved to the cheapest place they could find. Eleven years later they are enjoying doing a wonderful job in a part of the world that needs them. There are three bedrooms with endless hot water, all the rooms are spotless, and the welcome is big. Four tables can seat 16 people, but then not much breathing can go on. Food, like the atmosphere, is homely: thick vegetable soup, goujons of sole with tartare sauce, Lybster lobster salad, home-baked ham with spinach, fillet of beef with madeira sauce, and home-made bread to mop it up. Mousses, and pastry for tarts, are good; fruit salad is excellent. Breakfast is whole-wheat toast and a choice of six teas, and there is a coffee-shop and grill-room. Thirty wines include CELLARMAN'S CHOICE: Ch. Moncets '79, Lalande-de-Pomerol at £6·45.

CHEF: Norma Hutton PROPRIETOR: Ranald Hutton
OPEN: all week, exc Sun D MEALS: 12 to 2.30, 7.30 to 10
PRICES: £8 (£12), Set L £6 (£9), Set D £11·75 (£15), Bar meals from £2 (£4) CARDS: Access, Amex, Carte Blanche, Diners, Visa
SEATS: 20. Private parties: 20 main room. Car-park, 20 places. Vegetarian meals by arrangement. Children's helpings. Wheelchair access
ACCOMMODATION: 3 rooms. B&B £12·50 to £23. Children welcome. Baby facilities. Pets welcome. Afternoon teas. TV. Fishing. Golf. Doors close at 1.30

MOFFAT Dumfries & Galloway map 8

▲ *Beechwood Country House Hotel* [12/20]

Moffat DC10 9RS
MOFFAT (0683) 20210
turn off A701 up Harthope Place, then left Real Food £11–£16

New dishes on the set, four-course dinner menu at the McIlwrick's comfortable 100-year-old grey stone hotel have included saddle of lamb with horseradish and cream, and the restaurant now also has supplies of quail. The choice of dishes is conservative, but the ingredients are good, from free-range eggs onwards, and give a lift to dishes such as shellfish chowder; shellfish cocktail with prawns, shrimps and crab; roast mallard with a cassis sauce. Vegetables are excellent, as is the choice of Scottish and English cheeses. Desserts tend to be sticky – blackcurrant flan with Jersey cream – although there have been experiments with an ice-cream maker. There are neat touches in the bedrooms – flowers, tea-making equipment, bubble bath, shoe cleaners, sewing kit, paper handkerchiefs, cottonwool balls and even an aerosol air freshener in the bathroom! There is no bar and you are introduced to other guests over drinks in the lounge. The snack lunch is rather more than a snack and afternoon teas are a feature, as are breakfasts. The excellent wine list has prompted the McIlwricks to open their own wine shop in Moffat (15 Well Street), though the Alsace section, unusually, does not offer the same value as the Rhônes or minor clarets. There are interesting Italian wines. CELLARMAN'S CHOICE: Ch. Cissac '78 at £9·95.

CHEF: Sheila McIlwrick PROPRIETORS: Keith and Sheila McIlwrick
OPEN: all week CLOSED: Jan MEALS: 12.30 to 1.30, 7.30 to 9.30
PRICES: Set L £7 (£11), Set D £11·50 (£16), Bar meals from £4·15 (£4·60) CARDS: Access, Amex, Diners, Visa
SEATS: 30. 2 tables outside. Private parties: 30 main room. Car-park, 20 places. Vegetarian meals. Children's helpings. No children under 8 at D. Jacket and tie. No smoking in dining-room. Wheelchair access
ACCOMMODATION: 8 rooms, all with bath/shower. B&B £19 to £45. Children welcome. Baby facilities. No pets. Afternoon teas. Garden. Mini croquet. Phone. Scenic. Doors close at 11. Confirm by 5 [GHG]

MULL Strathclyde map 8

▲ *Ardfenaig House* [11/20]

Bunessan, Mull PA67 6DX
FIONNPHORT (068 17) 210 **Real Food** £14

This small country house has five bedrooms. There are sixteen acres of grounds which slope down to a sea loch. Guests are introduced to each other in the bar before no-choice dinners along the lines of Dutch pea soup, chicken à la crème, and strawberries; or local smoked salmon, jugged lamb chops, and coffee cream parfait. Cheese and coffee are always there. The food is Real because it has to be. All bread and marmalade is home made. House wine is Paul Masson at £3 a pint. The short wine list has Ch. Haut-Beychevelle-Gloria '76 at £7·10, and Corvo, Duca di Salaparuta '80 at £5·40. CELLARMAN'S CHOICE: Rioja Imperial from C.V.N.E. '75 at £6·80.

CHEFS/PROPRIETORS: Ian C. A. Bowles and Robin Drummond-Hay
OPEN: Mon to Sat, D only CLOSED: Oct to Apr MEALS: 7.30
PRICES: Set D £12·50 (£14). Service inc
SEATS: 12. Car-park, 8 places. Vegetarian meals. No children under 12. Jacket and tie. No smoking in dining-room. One sitting
ACCOMMODATION: 5 rooms. D, B&B £40 to £80. No children under 12. No pets in public rooms. Garden. Fishing. Scenic. Doors close at 12. Confirm by noon [GHG]

▲ *Tiroran House* [12/20]

Tiroran, Mull PA69 6ES
TIRORAN (068 15) 232 £8–£19

A converted shooting-lodge run as a country-house hotel; it overlooks Loch Scridain and the hills of Mull, and there's plenty of peace and quiet: only the birds break the rules. Dinner is among the antiques in the dining-room or under the vines in the sun porch. There is a choice of three simple starters and puddings, and just one main course. Local suppliers come up with fish and shellfish for a flavoursome crab and sweetcorn soup, smoked salmon, or poached haddock wrapped around scallops with a creamy sauce. The Blockeys have their own chickens and ducks for eggs, make gravlax, bake bread, and employ a gardener to grow vegetables: fennel in white sauce, and creamed spinach, have been praised, as have been olives and steamed lemon pudding. The Wing Commander acts as if he owns the place, which of course he does, and everybody is treated as a personal friend, so it's just like being at a private dinner party until the bill arrives. Forty-odd sound wines include two English ones from Tenterden, and sherry and madeira. CELLARMAN'S CHOICE: Ch. de Montdespic '78, from Côtes de Castillon, which has gone up only 30p since last year and is now £6·50.

CHEF: Sue Blockey PROPRIETORS: Wing Commander and Mrs Blockey
OPEN: all week, D only (L residents only) CLOSED: mid-Oct to 1 May MEALS: 7 for 7.45
PRICES: Set L £6 (£8), Set D £16·50 (£19). Service inc
SEATS: 20. Private parties: 8 main room. Car-park, 20 places. No children under 10. Jacket and tie. No smoking. One sitting
ACCOMMODATION: 9 rooms, all with bath/shower. Rooms for disabled. B&B £30 to £76. Deposit: £25. No children under 10. Pets by arrangement. Garden. Fishing. Scenic [GHG]

NAIRN Highland — map 8

▲ *Clifton Hotel* [12/20]

Viewfield Street, Nairn IV12 4HW
NAIRN (0667) 53119 — **Real Food** £16

The back of this eccentrically theatrical hotel has 'uninterrupted views of mountains and sea for a hundred miles', says Gordon Macintyre, who has been here for 54 years and on whose presence the atmosphere and service depend. Lunch is served in the small Green Room (no smoking) where the proprietor's own eighteenth-century and early nineteenth-century silver is used. Local fish is prominent: salmon with red butter sauce, scallops with white wine, halibut with beurre blanc, fine fish soup. Starters of tabouleh, smoked shrimps, and salmon mousse are well reported, as are main meat courses of calf's liver, and venison. Bread is home made and eggs free-range. The dessert trolley has been dispensed with, and there is now a sweet menu in English. But if it includes 'chocolate mousse' then why also 'mousse de fromage'? The extensive wine list has 30 clarets, some 20 champagnes, interesting Rhône and Loire selections and a sprinkling from other European regions. From Austria there is a splendid Eiswein Rheinriesling Auslese, Lenz Moser '78, at £23·50. House claret is £6·70.

CHEFS: Forbes Scott and J. Gordon Macintyre PROPRIETOR: J. Gordon Macintyre
OPEN: all week CLOSED: Dec to Mar MEALS: 12 to 1.30, 7 to 9.30
PRICES: £11 (£16), Snacks from £1 (£1·10) CARDS: Access, Amex, Diners, Visa
SEATS: 55. Private parties: 100 main room, 12 private room. Car-park, 20 places. Vegetarian meals. Children's helpings. Smart dress preferred. No-smoking area. Music
ACCOMMODATION: 16 rooms, all with bath/shower. Rooms for disabled. B&B £30 to £62. Children welcome. Afternoon teas. Scenic. Doors close at 12 [GHG]

NEWTON STEWART Dumfries & Galloway — map 8

▲ *Kirroughtree Hotel* [12/20]

Newton Stewart DG8 6AN
NEWTON STEWART (0671) 2141 — £16–£21

This fine Georgian mansion has been given a new lease of life as a country-house hotel, and with Ken MacPhee (ex-Inverlochy Castle) at the helm the cooking is serious and impressive. There are two awesome and elegant dining-rooms – one in blue for non-smokers, the other in red – where local girls in tartan skirts serve in friendly fashion and know the ways of the kitchen. Set dinners run to four courses, with fish as the high point. Turbot wrapped around a salmon mousseline has been better than cassoulet of chicken livers with mushrooms; the beautifully arranged plate of mixed seafood (local salmon, trout, sole, scampi and turbot) more memorable than roast duckling with blackcurrant sauce. The quality of the raw materials can't be faulted, but sauces and pastry tend to let the side down. There's a fine array of vegetables, but the cheeses could be more carefully chosen, even though there are some good local varieties on offer. Strong coffee with a chocolate mint crisp to finish. The wine list is extensive, classy and not especially cheap, with two pages devoted to half-bottles, and detailed showings of claret going back to '61.

CHEF: Ken MacPhee PROPRIETORS: Mr and Mrs H. Velt
OPEN: all week CLOSED: mid-Nov to 1 Mar MEALS: 12.30 to 1, 7 to 9.30
PRICES: L £12 (£16), Set D £17 (£21). Service inc
SEATS: 60. 8 tables outside. Private parties: 30 main room, 30 private room. Car-park, 40 places. No children under 10. Jacket and tie. No-smoking area. Wheelchair access (9 steps; also WC)
ACCOMMODATION: 23 rooms, all with bath/shower. Rooms for disabled. B&B £28 to £52. Deposit: 10%. No children under 10. Pets welcome. Afternoon teas. Garden. Tennis. Fishing. Golf. Croquet. Bowls. Helicopter pad. TV. Phone. Scenic. Doors close at 11 [GHG]

OLD MELDRUM Grampian — map 8

▲ *Meldrum House* [11/20]

Old Meldrum AB5 0AE
OLD MELDRUM (065 12) 2294
½m N of village — £21

Robin Duff of Meldrum runs this house, which has been in his family since 1236. Happy 750th birthday! Several hundred acres of gardens and parks plus antique furniture, tapestry screens, original paintings and log fires make a suitably lairdly setting for a few Scottish flourishes: whisky in the chicken, Arbroath smokies and smoked fish soup, and salmon steaks. Chicken also comes stuffed with local seafood, hare comes jugged, and the Auld Alliance may account for sweetbreads in burgundy. There is watercress soup to start, and lemon and honey crunch pie to finish. Service is attentive enough to provide toothpicks and iced water and to ask if everything is up to standard, now and again. And again and again. There is port for the Stilton, cognac for the coffee, and house wine at £7.
CELLARMAN'S CHOICE: Bourgogne, Irancy '82 at £12.

CHEF: Robert Aiken PROPRIETOR: Robin Duff
OPEN: all week CLOSED: mid-Dec to mid-Mar MEALS: 12 to 1.30, 7 to 9.30
PRICES: Set D £13 (£21), L snacks from £1·50 (£2). Service 10% CARDS: Amex, Diners
SEATS: 60. Private parties: 40 main room, 60, 30 and 25 private rooms. Car-park. Vegetarian meals by arrangement. Children's helpings (high teas). Smart dress preferred at D. No pipes in dining-room. Wheelchair access (also WC)
ACCOMMODATION: 11 rooms, 9 with bath/shower. Rooms for disabled. B&B £30 to £45. Children welcome. No pets in public rooms. Garden. Helicopter pad. TV. Phone. Scenic

ORKNEY map 8

▲ *Foveran* [9/20]

St Ola, Kirkwall, Mainland KW15 1SF
KIRKWALL (0856) 2389
on A964, 2½m W of Kirkwall £19

This remote but comfortable hotel does not use any pre-prepared dishes or frozen ingredients. Lobsters are held in a tank until needed, and Orkney beef is stuffed with oysters or with haggis. Orkney farmhouse cheeses are liberally used for saucing. A rudimentary wine list with a couple of Moniack Castle Scottish country wines – silver birch and elderflower, both at £5·95. Two Orkney malts.

CHEF: Norma Hasham PROPRIETORS: Norma and Bashir Hasham
OPEN: Mon to Sat CLOSED: mid-Oct to end Nov MEALS: 7 (6.30 Sun for residents) to 9
PRICES: £14 (£19) CARDS: Access, Visa
SEATS: 45. Private parties: 45 main room. Car-park, 12 places. Children's helpings. Wheelchair access (also WC). Classical music
ACCOMMODATION: 8 rooms, all with bath/shower. B&B £17·50 to £29. Deposit: 10%. Children welcome. Baby facilities. Pets by arrangement. Afternoon teas. Scenic. Doors close at 11. Confirm by 5

Hamnavoe [new entry, zero rated]

35 Graham Place, Stromness KW16 3BY
STROMNESS (0856) 850606 £17

Hamnavoe is the local word for 'the sheltered harbour'. Sewing machines still with their wheels and treadles have been converted into tables for the pale green dining-room, which has an open fire at one end. The menu is French, using local produce and particularly good fish and lamb. Excellent dark-brown bread starts meals before crab with whisky, scallops with garlic, and lamb cutlets with pears and redcurrant jelly. Silver-wrapped butter and inferior chocolate have been a let-down, but these are early days for the restaurant. The wine list is notable for its elegant handwriting and its down-to-earth choices. House vin de pays du Tarn is £5. More reports, please.

CHEF: Vanessa Leslie PROPRIETORS: Catriona Cussen and Denis Moylan
OPEN: all week, exc Tue D MEALS: 12 to 2.30, 7 to 10
PRICES: £12 (£17) CARDS: Access, Visa
SEATS: 36. Private parties: 38 main room. Vegetarian meals by arrangement. Children's helpings. Wheelchair access

'I visited this restaurant from Swindon with my girlfriend (visiting from London). We were joined by her parents from Cardiff, who knew the restaurant well. We all four shared a plat de fruits de mer. We all four experienced gastro-enteritis during the following week. This may have been caused by flu, wine, or coincidence.'
(On eating in Wales)

'The information which you provide in the Guide *does not mention the £1.50 cover charge nor the 15 per cent service charge. You do suggest that dinner may cost an arm and a leg. The arrival of the bill nearly resulted in paraplegia.'* (On eating in London)

PEAT INN Fife map 8

Peat Inn [15/20]

SCOTTISH RESTAURANT OF THE YEAR

Peat Inn KY15 5LH
PEAT INN (033 484) 206
at junction of B940 and B941, 6m SW
of St Andrews **Real Food** £13–£23

From the outside there is no clue as to the qualities of David Wilson's extraordinary little restaurant at the crossroads named after the pub. The dining-areas take their character from heavy dark chairs, ornately carved sideboards, tapestry wall-hangings and silver plates. The waitresses in print dresses move swiftly. It is informal first, and elegant second.

The ingredients are impeccable. Pigeons shot by a local farmer become a charlotte to start; alternatively the breasts may be served in a brandy and juniper sauce with noodles. The wild mushrooms in September and October are not flown over from Paris but gathered locally. There are chanterelles and boletus to be found here, too. So are very good lobsters out of Anstruther, served whole with a crayfish sauce. Of many first-class dishes eaten again last year game stands out – roast wild duck with a sharp blueberry sauce; young partridge served with its own juices; saddle of venison in red wine. Of course the fish is also good, from the speciality of scallops in a spiced sauce with Barsac, to the day's catch steamed and served with a leek sauce. The sweets, fittingly for one of the finest restaurants in Scotland, are also highlights, from Pavlovas to fruit tarts to little pots of chocolate with rosemary cream.

To go with all this there is a fabulous cellar of wines, comprehensive and up to date in its ideas about price and quality. It also shows a collector's enthusiasm for subtle differences – four Gewürztraminers, from three different producers, go back to '76, while 13 different Puligny-Montrachets start at £12·50. The Pinot Gris, Les Maquisards '81, from Dopff & Irion, might make an interesting alternative at £9.

CHEF: David Wilson PROPRIETORS: David and Patricia Wilson
OPEN: Tue to Sat CLOSED: 1 week Jan, 1 week Apr, 1 week Oct MEALS: 12.30 for 1, 7 to 9.30
PRICES: Set L £9·50 (£13), Set D £19·50 (£23). Service inc CARDS: Amex, Diners, Visa
SEATS: 48. Private parties: 24 main room, 12 private room. Car-park, 24 places. Children's helpings. No smoking during meals. Wheelchair access (also WC). One sitting

PEEBLES Borders map 8

▲ *Cringletie House Hotel* [13/20]

Eddleston, Peebles EH45 8PL
EDDLESTON (072 13) 233
on A703, 2m N of Peebles **Real Food** £12–£18

The fish dishes in Aileen and Stanley Maguire's brown-stone, turreted mansion are reliably good – scallops with fennel and Pernod, deep-fried monkfish with sauce rémoulade, prawn cheesecake. The four-course set dinners are well balanced, starting with variations on mousses and avocado before soups, such as a good almond, and usually a trio of sauced main dishes. Spicy Moroccan lamb is good. Vegetables will usually come from their own two-acre walled garden, and sweets arrive on a laden trolley. The house itself is both relaxed and of a past era. Pre-dinner drinks are served in the bar by the fire, and the cellar is well stocked with claret.

CHEFS: Aileen Maguire and Sheila McKellar PROPRIETORS: Mr and Mrs Stanley Maguire
OPEN: all week CLOSED: Jan and Feb MEALS: 1 to 1.45, 7.30 to 8.30
PRICES: L £7 (£12), Set Sun L £8·50 (£13), Set D £13 (£18). Minimum £4
SEATS: 56. Private parties: 30 main room. Car-park, 40 places. Vegetarian meals by arrangement. Children's helpings. No smoking in dining-room. One sitting
ACCOMMODATION: 16 rooms, 11 with bath/shower. B&B £19 to £44. Children welcome. Dogs welcome. Afternoon teas. Garden. Tennis. Croquet. Putting. Helicopter pad. Lift. Scenic. Doors close at 11. Confirm by 5 [GHG]

PERTH Tayside map 8

Coach House [12/20]

8 North Port, Perth PH1 5LU
PERTH (0738) 27950 £10–£19

Looking like a tea-shop, with tables close together and little decoration, the Coach House is a former antique shop with a wrought-iron spiral staircase going up to a gallery. Tony and Betty Heath get first-class supplies of scallops, langoustines and sea-trout from George Campbell and Sons, and smokies from Spinks of Arbroath – hot scallop mousse in a Sauternes and cream sauce, and a soft mousse of flavoursome smoked trout on chunky slices of smoked salmon are both knockouts. Pea, lettuce and watercress soup is good enough to be a meal in itself. Breast of pigeon is served with avocado and a lemon and Meaux mustard dressing, or with a port and juniper sauce. A sauce of cream, mustard and calvados may be better than the kidneys it comes with, but vegetables are perfectly cooked and flavoursome. Meringues for the Pavlova are soft inside, and quark is used to lighten the Van der Hum cheesecake. Service is friendly, and the value warrants a detour if you are in the area. Over 50 wines on a sensible list, with house French at £4·85 and CELLARMAN'S CHOICE: Bordeaux, Château Montlau '82 at £7·40.

CHEF: Tony Heath PROPRIETORS: Tony and Betty Heath
OPEN: Tue to Sat MEALS: 12.30 to 2, 7.15 to 10
PRICES: Set L from £6·50 (£10), Set D from £14·50 (£19) CARDS: Access, Visa
SEATS: 36. Private parties: 24 main room. Children's helpings. No children under 8 at D. No pipes in dining-room. Wheelchair access

Timothy's [10/20]

24 St John Street, Perth PH1 5SP
PERTH (0738) 26641 £11

Scandinavian appetisers make much use of Danish salami and caviare, smoked mackerel, mussels and herring but there are also soups of nettle and dandelion.

Restaurants rating 10 and 11 serve the best food in the locality.

Smørrebrød items are fancifully titled – Norseman's Choice is a prawn cocktail, Roaming Dane is ham cooked with a 'curried banana concoction'. Portions seem to be getting skimpier for the price. Italian house wine is £5·95 for a jugful (8 glasses); iced akvavit is 85p.

CHEF: C.Laing PROPRIETORS: C.and A.Laing
OPEN: Tue to Sat MEALS: 12 to 2.30, 7 to 10.15
PRICES: £6 (£11) CARD: Access
SEATS: 45. Vegetarian meals. Children's helpings. Wheelchair access. Classical music. Air-conditioned

PORT APPIN Strathclyde — map 8

▲ *The Airds Hotel* [14/20]

SCOTTISH HOTEL OF THE YEAR GFG '86

Port Appin PA38 4DF
APPIN (063 173) 236 — Real Food £21

There comes a point, writing about Scotland, when to go on about the scenery sounds monotonous, but if one is going to munch away in front of a spectacular view the front dining-room here is the place to do it. Ingredients, particularly fish, are first-class: salmon comes with an hollandaise, halibut with vermouth and cream, and scallops are turned into mousseline. Sometimes the parts are better than the whole – delicately flavoured poached scallops, whoppers, have been overpowered by a strong tomato coulis – but there is good beef en croûte, and lamb with redcurrant and mint jelly. Visitors enjoy Scottish specialities, and sweets sometimes oblige with Atholl brose, or a slug of Drambuie in the raspberry ice-cream. Date and walnut pudding comes with butterscotch sauce, hazel-nut meringue is sandwiched with cream and raspberries, and crème brûlée is excellent. Service is kilted, sincere and friendly, breakfast is a knockout, and the wines are worth a detour: comprehensive and authoritative in Bordeaux and Burgundy, up to the mark in Rhône and Loire, with plenty of choice from Germany and a dabble in other countries, too. Half-bottles are wonderful.

CHEF: Betty Allen PROPRIETORS: Eric and Betty Allen
OPEN: all week, D only CLOSED: Nov to Mar MEALS: 8
PRICES: Set D £15·50 (£21)
SEATS: 50. Private parties: 40 main room. Car-park, 30 places. Children's helpings at 6pm. No smoking in dining-room. Wheelchair access (also WC). One sitting
ACCOMMODATION: 15 rooms, 11 with bath/shower. Rooms for disabled. D, B&B £45 to £90. Deposit: £30. Children welcome. Pets by arrangement. Afternoon teas. Garden. Scenic. Doors close at 11.30. Confirm by 4 [GHG]

PORTSONACHAN Strathclyde — map 8

▲ *Portsonachan Hotel* [12/20]

Portsonachan PA33 1BL
KILCHRENAN (086 63) 224
on B840, 8m SW of Dalmally, off A819 — Real Food £12

Christopher Trotter bakes his own bread fresh for each meal and cooks the best of what the local countryside can provide, without swamping it in over-elaborate sauces. 'I use Scottish ingredients and recipes, with beliefs from France and

England,' he says. The four-course menu can contain such touches as scallops with turmeric; Cullen skink; roast beef; and excellent raspberry and cinnamon tart to finish. It can help to have a knowledge of local lore to translate Mrs Young's Barbary lamb or Mrs Crichton's cloutie dumpling. Lady Macdonald's cake (see Kinloch Lodge, Skye) is carrot. Service is cheerful. Cream is served with the porridge in the morning. House French is £4·10 and there is a patriotic Kir made of Scottish wine with Scottish raspberry liqueur.

CHEF: Christopher Trotter PROPRIETORS: Christopher and Caroline Trotter
OPEN: all week CLOSED: mid-Nov to 23 Dec, 3 Jan to end Feb MEALS: 12 to 2, 8 to 9
PRICES: Set D from £9 (£12), Bar meals from 75p (85p)
SEATS: 50. 6 tables outside. Private parties: 50 main room, 15 private room. Vegetarian meals by arrangement. Children's helpings. Smart dress preferred. No smoking in dining-room. Wheelchair access (also WC). One sitting
ACCOMMODATION: 17 rooms, 3 with bath/shower. B&B £15 to £30. Deposit: £20. Children welcome. Baby facilities. No pets in public rooms. Afternoon teas. Garden. Fishing. Scenic. Doors close at 11.30. Confirm by 6 [GHG]

ST ANDREWS Fife map 8

▲ *Grange Inn* [new chef, zero rated]

Grange Road, St Andrews KY16 8LJ
ST ANDREWS (0334) 72670
1m S of St Andrews £10–£23

A new chef took over here as we went to press, but owner David Grahame is not likely to let things get out of hand. He has built up an enviable local reputation for excellent regional cooking – lentil soup; ravioli stuffed with crab; roast quail or roast beef. The arrival of Joseph O'Brien, who has worked at Chewton Glen and Greywalls, could add dimensions to the operation. First reports indicate that standards are very much on the up. Cigarette smoke can be an annoyance from some people, despite the fact that there's supposed to be no smoking in the dining-room. More reports, please.

CHEF: Joseph O'Brien PROPRIETORS: Anne Krzyzanouska and David Grahame
OPEN: all week MEALS: 12.15 (12.30 Sun) to 2, 7 to 9.30
PRICES: £16 (£23), Set L from £4·75 (£10), Snacks from 75p (85p)
SEATS: 40. Private parties: 40 main room. Car-park, 30 places. Vegetarian meals. Children's helpings. No children under 8 at D. No smoking in dining-room. Wheelchair access (2 steps)
ACCOMMODATION: 2 rooms, both with bath/shower. B&B £15 to £30. Children welcome. No pets. Phone. Scenic. Doors close at 1. Confirm by 6

SCARISTA see HARRIS

SCONE Tayside map 8

▲ *Balcraig House* [10/20]

SCONE (0738) 51123/4/5
off A94, 1½m NE of Perth Real Food £21

This is an extraordinary proposition. The wine cellar is one of the most comprehensive in Britain and not overpriced. The dining-room is formal and elegant. Attached to the restaurant is a farm and a market garden growing more than a hundred vegetables. The menu, though, needs slashing in half because the kitchen struggles to produce nearly as many different dishes as there are customers, and meals are erratic, especially with fish. Good points are the home-made rolls, cold sorrel and lettuce soup, venison with crème de cassis sauce, roast wild mallard, and always the vegetables. Sweets are also consistently of a high calibre. There are 10 '70s Alsace wines from Dopff & Irion alone, with most well under £10. The clarets are heroic, though the CELLARMAN'S CHOICE is Fleurie, La Madone '83, from Duboeuf, at £7·50. The 120 different malt whiskies go back to 1938.

CHEF: Eamonn Webster PROPRIETORS: Michael and Kitty Pearl
OPEN: all week, D only MEALS: 7 to 10.45 (10 Sun)
PRICES: Set D from £18·50 (£21). Service inc CARDS: Access, Amex, Diners, Visa
SEATS: 36. Private parties: 40 main room. Car-park, 20 places. Children's helpings. Wheelchair access (also WC). Air-conditioned
ACCOMMODATION: 10 rooms, all with bath/shower. B&B £38·50 to £65. Children welcome. Pets welcome. Afternoon teas. Garden. Tennis. Fishing. Golf. Riding. Helicopter pad. TV. Phone. Scenic. Doors close at 1. Confirm by 6 [GHG]

SELKIRK Borders map 8

▲ *Philipburn House Hotel* [10/20]

Selkirk TD7 5LS
SELKIRK (0750) 20747 £12–£20

The local opinion is emphatic that this is one of the best restaurants in Scotland, the more so since simple menus have evolved to include elaborate and novel dishes. Other reports are less favourable. It is Real Food in the sense that breakfast kippers are not dyed, but then why serve packet sweetcorn with the pastry egg hollandaise? One chap claims the gazpacho is 'perfectly seasoned', but one inspector points out that it has no oil, garlic or flavour. As a hotel it is fine – surrounded by rhododendrons in May and self-catering cottages all year; as a restaurant it is up and down. Yet the Sachertorte that figures among the traditional sweets is said to be a variation on the one served at Sachers in Vienna. One explanation for the conflicting reports could be the excellent wine list, which cuts a fine dash through all the major regions, not just Bordeaux and Burgundy, but Vouvray, Italy, and Spain, though the Alsace section could be fading.

CHEFS: Jim Hill and Brian Hogg PROPRIETORS: Jim and Anne Hill
OPEN: all week CLOSED: Jan MEALS: 12.15 to 2.15, 8 to 9.30
PRICES: £13 (£20), Set L from £7 (£12), Set D from £13 (£19). Cheaper set meals available
CARDS: Access, Amex, Carte Blanche, Diners, Visa
SEATS: 70. 12 tables outside. Private parties: 30 main room. Car-park. Vegetarian meals. Children's helpings. No children under 12 at D. Wheelchair access (also WC). Music
ACCOMMODATION: 16 rooms, 12 with bath/shower. Rooms for disabled. B&B £22. Deposit: 10%. Children welcome. Baby facilities. Pets by arrangement. Afternoon teas. Garden. Fishing. Snooker. Badminton. TV. Phone. Scenic. Doors close at 1. Confirm by 6

Restaurant tricks (3): The bad practice of making a cover charge is dying out, but please report to us on any restaurant still doing so.

SHETLAND map 8

▲ *Burrastow House* [10/20]

Walls, Shetland ZE2 9PD
WALLS (059 571) 307
3m W of Walls **Real Food** £15

The welcome is as warm as the log fires in the dining-room and the lounge of this remote listed house built in 1759. The food is Real Food of necessity – the lamb has grazed on heather, and some people hold it as the finest in the UK. Three-pound legs are cooked in honey and cider or else boned and stuffed with apricots. You have to order the main course when booking, which must be at least a day ahead. Scallops, roast pheasant with bread sauce and gravy have also been good, accompanied by roast potatoes, cauliflower, sprouts and carrots. Bread is home made, and of course there is smoked salmon. Cheeses are local, and coffee is brewed at the table. Breakfast is freshly squeezed orange juice, herring fillet in oatmeal, and coffee. Vegetarians are well catered for; wine drinkers less so, but there's not much wrong with Johnson Reserve claret at £5·25.

CHEF: Stella Tuckey PROPRIETORS: Harry and Stella Tuckey
OPEN: all week, D only (L residents only) CLOSED: 23 Dec to 10 Jan MEALS: 7 to 9.30
PRICES: Set D from £12·50 (£15). Service inc
SEATS: 10. Private parties: 12 main room. Vegetarian meals. Car-park, 8 places. No smoking. Children's helpings. Classical music
ACCOMMODATION: 3 rooms, all with bath/shower. B&B from £22·50. Pets welcome. Garden. Fishing. Golf. TV. Baby facilities. Scenic [GHG]

▲ *Busta House* [8/20]

Busta, Mainland ZE2 9QN
BRAE (080 622) 506
25m N of Lerwick, signposted in Brae village £10–£15

Edwin and Rachel Cope's comfortable hotel overlooks its own harbour. The menu changes daily, and usually offers traditional home cooking, such as mutton soup, herrings in oatmeal, and trifle. The dishes are attractively presented. Rooms have plenty of trimmings, like hair-dryers and trouser presses. House burgundy is £4·90.

CHEF: Rachel Cope PROPRIETOR: Edwin Cope
OPEN: all week CLOSED: mid-Dec to mid-Jan MEALS: 12.30 to 1.30, 7 to 9.30
PRICES: Set L £7·50 (£10), Set D £13 (£15), Bar L from £2·75. Service inc
SEATS: 56. Private parties: 20 main room. Car-park, 30 places. Vegetarian meals by arrangement. Children's helpings. Smart dress preferred. No smoking in dining-room
ACCOMMODATION: 21 rooms, all with bath/shower. B&B £20 to £60. Children welcome. Baby facilities. No pets in public rooms. Afternoon teas. Garden. Fishing. Golf. TV. Phone. Scenic. Confirm by 6 [GHG]

SKEABOST BRIDGE see SKYE

Restaurants rating 12 or more serve the best food in the region.

SKYE Highland map 8

▲ *Harlosh Hotel* [new entry, zero rated]

Dunvegan IV51 5AB
DUNVEGAN (047 022) 367 £11–£15

Peter Bates has his own boat equipped with lobster and prawn creels. The fish is the thing – Bracadale is a garlic shellfish ragout, and the crab claws are excellent. There are also steaks and haggis. House wine is Scottish Moniack at £4·50. More reports, please.

CHEF: Peter Bates PROPRIETORS: Peter and Rosalyn Bates
OPEN: all week (L for residents only) CLOSED: mid-Nov to Easter MEALS: 12 to 2, 6.30 to 9
PRICES: £11 (£15), Set L £7·50 (£11), Set D from £10·50 (£14)
SEATS: 20. Private parties: 30 main room. Car-park, 30 places. Vegetarian meals. Children's helpings. Wheelchair access (also WC). Music
ACCOMMODATION: 7 rooms, 1 with bath/shower. B&B £12 to £24. Deposit: 20%. Children welcome. Baby facilities. Afternoon teas. Garden. Fishing. Golf. Snooker. Scenic. Confirm by 6

▲ *Kinloch Lodge* [13/20]

Isle Ornsay, Sleat IV43 8QY
ISLE ORNSAY (047 13) 214 and 333
1m off A851 between Broadford and Armadale £20

'Two-star decor and five-star food' describes the priorities. The lodge is decorated – and feels – like a house rather than a hotel. Lady Macdonald's weakness for puddings (her book is on sale) is shared by most visitors; the range includes rich chocolate and almond cake; ginger ice-cream with hot chocolate sauce; iced whisky and honey creams; meringues; and fruit mousses. The four-course menu, with a choice of two items for each, shows the French vogue for using curry flavouring everywhere – in soups and mayonnaise and with scallops with onion, coconut, lemon juice and tomato purée. Granary bread is baked fresh every day. Venison (sika deer) is hung for about 14 days, depending on the weather, cooked on a bed of vegetables, smeared with dripping and basted with milk; the vegetables are liquidised with port, redcurrant jelly and stock to make the sauce. Salmon fillets, and after all they should know how to cook them up here, are simply popped into a hot oven for five minutes. Efforts are being made to find further supplies of organically grown vegetables. These are all the signs of a restaurant deserving 13 points, and for the most part it all works well, but occasionally the execution may just miss the mark, as in tepid, bland, devilled seafood, or unsatisfactory pastry under a mushroom quiche. Breakfasts

'Grapefruit sorbet with crème de menthe – I do not need to describe this. All you have to do is go to the chemist, buy a bottle of Listerine mouthwash, roll a little around and you will have duplicated the flavour exactly.' (On eating in Perth)

'French waiters . . . have an extra dimension of being nearly as rude as possible without actually being it.' (On eating in London)

including white Stornoway pudding are very fine. There are 60 mostly European wines, with a few additional bin-end clarets.

CHEF: Lady Macdonald and Peter Macpherson PROPRIETORS: Lord and Lady Macdonald
OPEN: all week, D only CLOSED: 4 days at Christmas, 11 Jan to 28 Feb MEALS: 8 to 10
PRICES: Set D £16·50 (£20)
SEATS: 25. Private parties: 8 main room. Car-park, 25 places. Vegetarian meals by arrangement. Children's helpings. No children under 10. Wheelchair access (also WC)
ACCOMMODATION: 10 rooms, 9 with bath/shower. Rooms for disabled. B&B £34 to £68. Deposit: 10%. Baby facilities. No pets in public rooms. Afternoon teas. Garden. Fishing. Scenic. Confirm by 6 [GHG]

▲ *Skeabost House Hotel* [9/20]

Skeabost Bridge IV51 9NP
SKEABOST BRIDGE (047 032) 202 £7–£14

Salmon for lunch comes out of the river at the back of this shooting-lodge, converted into a hotel in the early 1950s. Beef and lamb are always fresh, and the cooking is wholesome and unpretentious. Wines from Irvine Robertson of Edinburgh.

CHEF: Mrs McNab PROPRIETORS: Major and Mrs Stuart, Mr and Mrs McNab and J. Stuart
OPEN: all week CLOSED: mid-Oct to Easter MEALS: 12 to 1.30, 7 to 8
PRICES: Set L from £3·40 (£7), Set D £9·80 (£14), Snacks from 80p (90p)
SEATS: 75. Private parties: 20 main room. Car-park, 30 places. Children's helpings (high teas). Jacket and tie
ACCOMMODATION: 27 rooms, 17 with bath/shower. Rooms for disabled. B&B £18 to £33. Deposit: £10. Children welcome. Baby facilities. No pets in public rooms. Afternoon teas. Garden. Fishing. Golf. Snooker. Helicopter pad. Scenic. Doors close at 12. Confirm by 3

Three Chimneys [12/20]

Colbost, Dunvegan IV51 9SY
GLENDALE (047 081) 258
on B884, 4m W of Dunvegan £13

An old crofter's cottage on the loch looking over to the Outer Hebrides. Much of the produce is local, and the bread and cake for the cheeseboard are baked daily in-house. Good dishes have been the Scotch broth; the salmon; chicken with apricots or else sauté with honey, lemon and thyme; and inexpensive salad lunches. Crab tarts are baked daily, or else there's the stock-pot, which usually contains lamb. To finish there has been good rhubarb crumble or else cloutie dumplings. House French £4·65, or there is elderflower wine from Moniack Castle.

CHEF: Shirley Spear PROPRIETORS: Eddie and Shirley Spear
OPEN: all week, exc Sun L CLOSED: Oct to Apr MEALS: 12 to 2, 7 to 9
PRICES: £9 (£13). Minimum £5
SEATS: 35. 3 tables outside. Private parties: 24 main room. Car-park, 40 places. Vegetarian meals. Children's helpings. Music

Restaurant tricks (4): Charging for service but leaving the total on the credit card slip blank, thus inviting an extra tip.

SLEAT see SKYE

STEWARTON Strathclyde map 8

▲ *Chapeltoun House* [10/20]

Stewarton KA3 3ED
STEWARTON (0560) 82696
on B769, 2m SW of Stewarton £13–£23

This is one of the very few places in the region that doesn't serve processed foods. Breads are baked specially by a local baker, and jam for the hearty breakfasts is home made. Many of the dishes on the menu are unnecessarily elaborate, but there is also traditional cock-a-leekie soup and steaks. Service is friendly and the building baronial. There are some excellent wines in the cellar, including a full house of *cru* Beaujolais, classed growth clarets through the '70s (although little at the bottom end of the price range), and good bottles from other regions, among them Crozes-Hermitage, Les Meysonniers '83, from Chapoutier, at £7·90. Burgundies are mostly négociant wines, including CELLARMAN'S CHOICE: Pernand-Vergelesses '73, from Chanson, at £12.

CHEFS: Alan Russell and Tom O'Donnell PROPRIETORS: Alan and Elizabeth Russell
OPEN: all week, exc Sat L CLOSED: 25 and 26 Dec, 1 to 15 Jan MEALS: 12 to 2, 7 to 9.30
PRICES: £16 (£22), Set L £8·50 (£13), Set D £17·50 (£23) CARDS: Access, Amex, Diners, Visa
SEATS: 48. Private parties: 12 main room, 48 and 12 private rooms. Car-park, 50 places. Vegetarian meals by arrangement. Children's helpings (Sun L only). Smart dress preferred. No cigars/pipes in dining-room
ACCOMMODATION: 6 rooms, all with bath/shower. B&B £40 to £60. Deposit: £25 per room. No children under 12. Garden. Golf. TV. Phone. Scenic

STROMNESS see ORKNEY

TARBERT Strathclyde map 8

▲ *West Loch Hotel* [10/20]

Tarbert PA29 6YF
TARBERT (088 02) 283
on A83, 1m S of Tarbert £18

A welcoming, clean hotel facing Loch Tarbert, simply but adequately furnished, with good-value three-course meals of generally consistent quality. The Thom family produces excellent tomato soup; oysters wrapped in bacon on toast; light salmon quiche with crisp pastry; home-made game pie; and lemon meringue pie. Scallops and goats' cheese come from Islay; herrings from Loch Fyne; lamb from

CELLARMAN'S CHOICE: This is a wine that is more expensive than the house wine but is good value and fitting for the kind of food served.

The Guide *accepts no advertising and does not allow restaurants to use their inclusion for publicity.*

Kintyre; and oysters are caught locally. Service is good, and there is a short list of unvintaged wines. CELLARMAN'S CHOICE: Ch. Léoville-Las-Cases '79 at £12·60.

CHEFS: Janet and Janine Thom PROPRIETORS: The Thom family
OPEN: all week CLOSED: Nov MEALS: 12 to 2, 7 to 8.30
PRICES: Set D £13·50 (£18), Bar meals at L from 85p (£1) CARD: Access
SEATS: 30. Private parties: 30 main room. Car-park, 20 places. Children's helpings. No smoking in dining-room. Wheelchair access (also wc). Classical music
ACCOMMODATION: 6 rooms. B&B £19 to £29. Children welcome. Baby facilities. No pets in public rooms. Afternoon teas. Scenic

TIRORAN see MULL

TWEEDSMUIR Borders — map 8

▲ *Crook Inn* [12/20]

Tweedsmuir ML12 6QN
TWEEDSMUIR (089 97) 272
on A701, 1m N of Tweedsmuir — **Real Food** £17

'Our food has become more Real and less *nouvelle*,' explain the Masraffs. That can only mean less cant and more cooking, which must be for the good. There is now a smaller set menu changing with the seasons at their remote inn where, say locals, Robbie Burns would pop in to write his poems. Typically good are the orange and avocado salad dressed with walnut oil, the gravlax, and the duck salad. The second course is the fish of the day, which could be poached sole or hot scallop mousse with saffron sauce. The quality of the beef, both as fillets or as medallions, shows how Scotland earned its reputation for beef, Scottish cheeses come with oatmeal biscuits, and sweets are a forte – especially the Easter cheesecake and the chocolate mousse in layered whirls of white and dark in a wine glass. Service is warm. The wine list keeps an eye on your pocket with good sections of claret and burgundies for under £10. House French is £6·25. CELLARMAN'S CHOICE: Ch. Latour St-Bonnet '79 at £7.

CHEFS/PROPRIETORS: Mr and Mrs Masraff
OPEN: all week CLOSED: mid-Jan to mid-Feb MEALS: rest 7.30 to 8.45; bar 11 to 2.30, 5 to 11
PRICES: Set D £12·50 (£17), Bar meals from £2 (£2·20)
SEATS: 30. Private parties: 30 main room. Car-park, 60 places. Vegetarian meals by arrangement. Children's helpings at bar. No children under 10 at D. Smart dress preferred. No cigars/pipes in dining-room
ACCOMMODATION: 8 rooms, 6 with bath/shower. B&B £22 to £36. Deposit: £10. Children welcome. No pets in public rooms. Garden. Fishing. Scenic. Doors close at 11.30. Confirm by 6 [GHG]

'Evidently, the restaurant itself has some doubts, since the head waiter, the table waiter and the wine waiter all asked if we were enjoying the meal several times each and the chef himself made the same enquiry once.' (On eating in Humberside)

'The biscuits for the cheese arrived in their tin with the price still on – we were charged exactly double.' (On eating in Kent)

TYNDRUM Central map 8

Clifton Coffee House [8/20]

Tyndrum FK20 8RY
TYNDRUM (083 84) 271
junction of A85 and A82 £6

There can be long queues at the counter of this all-day self-service. There are good baps filled with salmon, beef or ham; a range of salads; and quiches. It is quick food rather than fast food. Hot meals include lamb hot-pot, chicken pie, and broths of all kinds. House French is £2·95.

CHEFS: Lesley Wilkie, Moira Brebner and Mary Smith
PROPRIETORS: Derek D. Wilkie, Lesley Wilkie and Lamond P. Gosden
OPEN: all week, L only CLOSED: Nov to Mar MEALS: 8.30 to 5.30
PRICES: £5 (£6), Snacks from 70p CARDS: Access, Amex, Diners, Visa
SEATS: 220. Car-park, 200 places. Vegetarian meals. Children's helpings. No-smoking area. Wheelchair access (also WC). Air-conditioned. Self-service

ULLAPOOL Highland map 8

▲ *Altnaharrie Inn* [14/20]

Ullapool IV26 2SS
DUNDONNELL (085 483) 230
on Loch Broom, opposite Ullapool.
Phone for ferry **Real Food** £5–£23

Strictly this is not on an island as we said last year, but you have to take the ferry from Ullapool to get there so it might as well be. You could walk, but it's a long way round. Fred Brown and Gunn Eriksen's tiny, solitary hotel on the shore of Loch Broom serves food unadulterated by modern science. She cooks using wild produce, such as nettle or elderflower soup, and employing one or two of her native Norwegian techniques, as in krum kaker – thin biscuit shells made in a special iron to form a cup that is then filled with cloudberries, cream and small meringues, and decorated with spun sugar. Langoustines are dropped off at the jetty before the boat docks at Ullapool; lamb comes from a farm that Fred Brown used to advise when he was a vet. His training has led him to avoid animals treated with hormones and antibiotics and he usually takes more mature animals than is general practice because, he argues, the flavour improves when you let them graze longer on the heather and in the forest. Alpha dishes are turbot in cream sauce, breast of pigeon with juniper sauce, and gravlax, but all the meals show the sheer vitality of the ingredients. As one reporter says, 'It was quite simply the best dinner either of us can recall', which underlines the basic point of the Real Food policy. Breakfasts, too, are superb. Mr Brown has been known to grill trout he has caught that morning, and even in this remote spot the orange-juice is freshly squeezed. There are 70-odd wines now, including

Entries are compiled from the unsolicited reports from readers and are checked by inspectors; each restaurant is asked to supply details of its operation. Report forms can be found at the back of the Guide.

classed growth clarets from good years. House claret is £6. CELLARMAN'S CHOICE: Ch. La Croix '76 at £15·20.

CHEF: Gunn Eriksen Brown PROPRIETORS: Fred and Gunn Brown
OPEN: all week, D only, L by arrangement only CLOSED: Oct to Apr MEALS: 12.30 to 2, 7.30
PRICES: Set L £1·50 (£5), Set D £17·50 (£23)
SEATS: 14. Private parties: 14 main room. Vegetarian meals by arrangement. Children's helpings. No children under 10. No smoking in dining-room. Classical music. One sitting
ACCOMMODATION: 4 rooms, 2 with bath/shower. B&B £50 for 2. Deposit: £20. No children under 10. Garden. Fishing. Scenic [GHG]

UPHALL Lothian — map 8

▲ *Houstoun House* [10/20]

Uphall EH52 6JS
BROXBURN (0506) 853831 — £14–£19

Houstoun House is notable for its wine. There is a carefully selected range of good châteaux and vintages from all the major Bordeaux communes, a spoilt-for-choice pick of Burgundy, first-rate Alsace, bull's-eye Spanish and Italian, well-ordered Germans, a nod to the New World, a few curiosities (whites from Vougeot and Musigny), and exemplary half-bottles. Pricing is generous enough to make a second bottle tempting. There is food too, of course: leafy spinach tart, sea-trout with mustard and yoghourt sauce, lamb with minted hollandaise, rhubarb and banana tart with custard.

CHEFS: Keith Knight and David Hamilton PROPRIETORS: Keith and Penny Knight
OPEN: all week CLOSED: 1 to 3 Jan MEALS: 12.30 to 2, 7.30 to 9.30
PRICES: Set L £10 (£14), Set D £14·75 (£19). Cheaper D available for residents. Service inc
CARDS: Access, Amex, Diners
SEATS: 75. Private parties: 40 main room, 25 and 16 private rooms. Car-park, 70 places. Children's helpings (L only). Smart dress preferred. No pipes in dining-room. Air-conditioned
ACCOMMODATION: 30 rooms, all with bath/shower. B&B £40 to £54. Children welcome. Pets welcome. Afternoon teas. Garden. Golf. Helicopter pad. TV. Phone

WALLS see SHETLAND

WESTER HOWGATE Lothian — map 8

Old Howgate Inn [9/20]

Wester Howgate EH26 8QB
PENICUIK (0968) 74244
on B7026, 2m SE of Penicuik — £6–£18

There is a choice of 36 different fillings to the open Danish sandwiches at this historic coaching-inn. Steaks are char-grilled, and Danish specialities include

The Guide *is always anxious to recruit new inspectors. If you would like to apply, write to the editor enclosing a) a detailed report on a restaurant where you have eaten and b) a comparative study of restaurants known to you.*

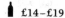

fondue and gravlax. The wine list is well chosen and annotated, though Trimbach's '83 Alsace wines will be better than the '82s. House French is £4·45.

CHEF: R.A.Reid PROPRIETORS: M.R.Inn Partnership
OPEN: all week CLOSED: 25 Dec and 1 Jan MEALS: 11.30 to 2.30, 6 to 10 (12.30 to 2.30, 6.30 to 10 Sun)
PRICES: £13 (£18), Set L and D from £2·50 (£6), Snacks from £1·45 (£1·60)
CARDS: Access, Amex, Diners, Visa
SEATS: 45. 4 tables outside. Private parties: 20 main room. Car-park, 30 places. Vegetarian meals. Children's helpings

WHITEBRIDGE Highland — map 8

▲ *Knockie Lodge* [10/20]

Whitebridge IV1 2UP
GORTHLECK (045 63) 276
on B862, 8m N of Fort Augustus — £15

A peaceful and relaxing 200-year-old shooting-lodge built by Lord Lovat, and overlooking Loch Ness – guests are encouraged to hunt, shoot and fish. There is a vast entrance hall with an open fireplace, and a comfortable lounge with help-yourself drinks from an Edwardian bookcase; the feel is of a private house. The five-course dinner with no choice before the pudding is good value for £12. Interesting soups, such as creamed spinach with turmeric and lemon, can be mopped up with good brown bread. Cooking is sound rather than fashionable, as befits this neck of the woods: chicken breast in a wine and mushroom sauce; orange and apricot mousse; and lemon griesetorte. Game, salmon and trout are of course local, and a few Taste of Scotland items appear from time to time: tomato soufflé with haggis, raspberry Cranachan, malt whiskies, and Alice brewery's real ale. The enterprising wine list includes Australian and South African wines and errs on the side of reds. House wines are £3·75.
CELLARMAN'S CHOICE: Fleurie '83 at £7·50.

CHEFS/PROPRIETORS: Mr and Mrs Ian Milward
OPEN: all week CLOSED: Nov to Easter MEALS: 8 to 8.45
PRICES: Set D from £12 (£15), Bar meals from £2·50 (£2·75) CARDS: Access, Amex, Visa
SEATS: 22. Private parties: 12 main room. Car-park, 30 places. No children under 10. Jacket and tie. One sitting
ACCOMMODATION: 10 rooms, all with bath/shower. B&B £25 to £45. No children under 10. Pets by arrangement. Garden. Fishing. Helicopter pad. Scenic [GHG]

Wales

ABERSOCH **Gwynedd** map 4

▲ *Porth Tocyn Hotel* [12/20]

Abersoch LL53 7BU
ABERSOCH (075 881) 2966 £10–£13

'In the past cooks have sometimes used Maggi soup bases and tinned artichokes but not for about five years' – hurrah! The Fletcher-Brewer family have been established in their hotel with a stunning view over Cardigan Bay since 1948. The parquet floor in the dining-room is spotless and the furniture antique. Fish is a feature – hot, potted haddock, poached salmon with vermouth sauce or cucumber dip, mullet, and turbot. Other good dishes have been the soups and a casserole of guinea-fowl before bread-and-butter pudding with whisky sauce, coffee meringues, or plum compote with honey. The biscuits with cheese are not exactly Real Food, which is a pity, because the Stilton has been in peak condition. Nor is the bought-in marmalade at breakfast Real Food, but the promotion by one point is correct. There is a trio of Alsace wines, from Sipp, on a conservative list. CELLARMAN'S CHOICE: House claret at £5.

CHEF: E.L. Fletcher-Brewer PROPRIETORS: The Fletcher-Brewer family
OPEN: all week CLOSED: Nov to Mar MEALS: 12.30 to 2, 7.30 to 9.30
PRICES: Set L £6·25 (£10), Set D from £9·50 (£13), Snacks from £1 (£1·10). Cheaper set D available CARDS: Access, Amex (only by agreement when booking)
SEATS: 60. 12 tables outside. Private parties: 60 main room. Car-park, 40 places. Vegetarian meals by arrangement. Children's helpings by arrangement. No children under 7 at D. Smart dress preferred. Wheelchair access (also WC)
ACCOMMODATION: 18 rooms, all with bath/shower. Rooms for disabled. B&B £22·50 to £35. Deposit: £30. Children welcome. Baby facilities. No pets in dining-room. Afternoon teas. Garden. Swimming-pool. Tennis. TV. Scenic. Doors close at 12 [GHG]

BRECHFA **Dyfed** map 4

▲ *Tŷ Mawr* [11/20]

Brechfa SA32 7RA
BRECHFA (026 789) 332 and 330
on B4310, 10m NE of Carmarthen £11–£13

An hospitable sixteenth-century house. Garlic bread is offered and there is good roast guinea-fowl, moist sewin, and generous-sized sole Véronique. The style is

Cordon Bleu and sweets can be excellent. The owners may sell up this year so it's best to check. House Bordeaux is £5·40.

CHEF: Jill Ross PROPRIETORS: Cliff and Jill Ross
OPEN: Tue to Sat, D only (L by arrangement) MEALS: 7 to 9.30
PRICES: £9 (£13), Set D £8·75 (£11). Service inc CARDS: Access, Diners, Visa
SEATS: 55. 3 tables outside. Private parties: 55 main room. Car-park, 60 places. Children's helpings. No-smoking area. Wheelchair access (also WC). Music. Air-conditioned
ACCOMMODATION: 5 rooms, all with bath/shower. B&B £21 to £39. Deposit: 10%. Children welcome. Baby facilities. Garden. Fishing. Shooting. Golf. Air-conditioning. Scenic. Doors close at 12. Confirm by 6

BROAD HAVEN Dyfed — map 4

▲ *Druidstone Hotel* [10/20]

Broad Haven SA62 3NG
BROAD HAVEN (043 783) 221
2m N of Broad Haven on National Park Coast Path

Real Food £11–£14

The Pembrokeshire Coast Path is a hard-surfaced narrow lane here. The hotel comes into view suddenly, perched high on a cliff looking west across St Brides Bay. The cliff falls away so steeply that the part of the house facing the sea has one more storey (underneath) than the east side of the house. Inside is unaffected and undecorated and the dining-room has the air of a boy scout camp. It is a place for outdoor people who are not keen on dressing up, but the food is honest and good value, and the cooking consistently above average. The menu changes daily with a given routine that takes in Kansas chicken and good casseroles from different countries. Thursday, for instance, is Mexican night. Bread is fresh from the oven, vegetables arrive in separate dishes for you to help yourself, cheeses come from Llangloffan farmhouse. The Pavlovas are the pick of the sweets. Bar meals are served downstairs. Fifty wines, with house French at £5·50.

CHEFS/PROPRIETORS: Rod and Jane Bell
OPEN: Mon to Sat D, Sun L CLOSED: Nov MEALS: 1 to 2, 7.30 to 9.30 (Bar 12.30 to 2.30, 9.30 to 10.30, 7.30 to 9.30 Sun)
PRICES: Set Sun L from £7·50 (£11), Set D from £10 (£14), Bar snacks from 80p (90p)
CARDS: Amex, Visa
SEATS: 40. 8 tables outside. Private parties: 45 main room, 12 private room. Car-park, 40 places. Vegetarian meals by arrangement. Children's helpings. Wheelchair access (also WC)
ACCOMMODATION: 19 rooms. Rooms for disabled in 4 cottages. B&B £15 to £30. Deposit: £10 per person. Children welcome. Baby facilities. Pets welcome. Afternoon teas. Garden. Helicopter pad. Scenic. Doors close at 12

CARDIFF South Glamorgan — map 4

BACKGROUND BRIEFING: *The South Wales fleet docks at Milford Haven and much of its catch goes to French buyers. Even so, the fish and chip shops in the city centre of Cardiff tend to use fresh fish from Brixham, Newlyn, Grimsby and Aberdeen. J. R. Dye in Llanrumney and the Divonia in Whitchurch Road both have nominations from readers. Butchers in the city's main market have cheap pork, offal and lamb, but for all west Wales's growth as a haven of organic farming the wholesale fruit and vegetable market is still heavily dependent on imported produce. Penclawdd cockles, the pride of the Welsh shellfish industry, reach the capital usually mid-week; other cockles are Dutch imports. Fresh laver-bread can be found in the covered market off St Mary's Street near the Working Street entrance, and in the fish section of Howells department store. For wine, there is Oddbins in the main drag of St Mary's Street. Chinese provisions can be found at Nam Kiu, 34 Tudor Street, and at number 30 there is Frank Gorno for Italian sausage. Madhav's Indian shop, 58 Lower Cathedral Road, has supplies of freshly made chevra. The coffee importers at 62 St Mary Street have particularly good Costa Rican. Savastano's in North Road, Gabalfa, has stucco walls, pine furniture and serves a good pasta Sophia Loren. Crumbs, in David Morgan's Arcade, has good, cheap, wholefood snacks. There are votes for Taste of India, 103–105 Woodville Road, Cathays.*

Armless Dragon [new entry, zero rated]

97 Wyvern Road, Cathays, Cardiff CF2 4BG
CARDIFF (0222) 382357 £14

A pair of converted terraced houses with a red and cream exterior and, inside, peach-coloured washed walls, red woodwork and farmhouse tables. The menu, with half a dozen choices per course, offers a good choice, and includes some out-of-the-rut dishes, often with oriental touches: gurnard served with a sauce of tamarind and coconut; shark curry; Persian meatballs with a walnut sauce. But there is a more bourgeois strain too, as in game pâté garnished with slices of gherkin and tomato, wild rabbit with ham and celery cream sauce, and rack of Welsh lamb. The champagne syllabub and the chocolate and rum wholewheat gateau are the pick of the sweets. Coffee is freshly ground. House vin de pays du Tarn or de l'Hérault at £4·50. CELLARMAN'S CHOICE: Rioja, Marqués de Cáceres, red and white, at £5·50. More reports, please.

CHEF: E.Smikle PROPRIETORS: M.Sharples and D.Richards
OPEN: Mon to Sat MEALS: 12.30 to 2.30, 7.30 to 10.30
PRICES: £10 (£14) CARDS: Access, Visa
SEATS: 50. Private parties: 50 main room. Vegetarian meals. Children welcome. Wheelchair access. Music

Blas-Ar-Cymru/A Taste of Wales [11/20]

48 Crwys Road, Cardiff CF2 4NN
CARDIFF (0222) 382132 £10–£15

Patricia and Meirion Dally's box-like, beamed dining-room is doing its best to resurrect Welsh cooking. There are a couple of Welsh wines from the Monnow Valley and the Croffta vineyard at Pontyclun, although these are less successful than the cooking itself. The traditional dishes are well executed, from laver-bread served with oatmeal and bacon to Lady Llanover's salt duck, which is marinated in salt for three days and then braised and served with onion sauce. Penclawdd cockles usually arrive on a Wednesday and are cooked with scrambled eggs or else go into a pie with bacon and onions for a copious main course. Salmon has been moist and served with a cucumber sauce. Sweets are rather in the mould of cherries in kirsch, but otherwise the theme is faithful to tradition, from the small loaves of hot brown bread to the hot and stodgy Welsh cakes served with coffee.

Mead is 75p a goblet, or there are some good French wines, including Gewürztraminer '83, from Louis Gisselbrecht, at £7·95 or CELLARMAN'S CHOICE: Ch. Millet'78 at £12·95.

CHEFS: Patricia Dally, Neil Baker and Michael Jones
PROPRIETORS: Patricia and Meirion Dally
OPEN: Mon to Sat, exc Sat L CLOSED: 2 weeks Jan MEALS: 12 to 2, 7 to 10.30
PRICES: £11 (£15), Set L from £5·95 (£10) CARDS: Access, Amex, Diners, Visa
SEATS: 50. Private parties: 50 main room. Car-park, 30 places. Vegetarian meals. Children welcome. Smart dress preferred. Wheelchair access (also ladies' wc). Classical music

La Brasserie [8/20]

60 St Mary Street, Cardiff CF1 2AT
CARDIFF (0222) 372164 £11

Order a bottle from the long oak bar; serve yourself with salad; go to the refrigerated cabinet and choose raw fish or meat which will then be charcoal-grilled and delivered to the table by waiters in dark green aprons. Brochette of lamb is large cubes of leg cooked pink with tomato, pepper and onions. A good place for women eating alone at lunchtime to feel comfortable. French house wine is £3·95.

CHEF: Mr Juan PROPRIETORS: K.Brenton and B.D.Martinez
OPEN: Mon to Sat MEALS: 12 to 2.45, 7 to 12.15
PRICES: £7 (£11). Service inc CARDS: Access, Amex, Diners, Visa
SEATS: 40. Children welcome. Smart dress preferred. French popular music

La Chaumière [new entry, zero rated]

44 Cardiff Road, Llandaff CF5 2DS
CARDIFF (0222) 555319 £18

A small, whitewashed brick building at the back of the Maltster's Arms pub and the betting shop. The entrance is in the car-park. Inside is green and pink, with a scrubbed pine bar and wall-benches, white bentwood chairs, and orange-trees painted on the white walls. The waiters wear black tail coats and pink bow-ties. Nevertheless, there is an honest attempt to cook carefully at a fairly ambitious level. The style of the food is modern, and there is an accent on presentation. The menu is sensibly short, with half a dozen choices for each course. Cream is the common denominator, neutralising the tomato in a soup that was saved only by a measure of fresh coriander; appearing with excellent rare beef with Roquefort and white wine sauce; and in a grapefruit soufflé. The fresh French bread does not come with cream, but the watercress soup, mushrooms in a pastry case, salmon with a herb sauce, a side serving of potatoes, and raspberry and hazel-nut meringue all do. A selective wine list of 12 bottles includes several *cru* Beaujolais; also a pretentious page called 'Directors' Bin' which has Ch. Haut-Brion '66 at

The Guide *is always anxious to recruit new inspectors. If you would like to apply, write to the editor enclosing a) a detailed report on a restaurant where you have eaten and b) a comparative study of restaurants known to you.*

The Guide *does not accept free meals.*

£120 and Gevrey-Chambertin '37 at £125. The carafe wine comes in an earthenware jug. More reports, please.

CHEF: Kay Morgan PROPRIETORS: Greenoak Ltd
OPEN: Mon to Sat, exc Mon D MEALS: 12 to 1.30, 7 to 9.30 (post-theatre by arrangement)
PRICES: £12 (£18). Service 10% CARDS: Amex, Diners
SEATS: 40. Private parties: 40 main room. Car-park, 30 places. Children's helpings. Classical music. Air-conditioned

Everest Indian Cuisine [10/20]

43–45 Salisbury Road, Cathays, Cardiff CF2 4AB
CARDIFF (0222) 374881 £9–£13

In the Cathays area of Cardiff, near the Civic Centre and the Students' Union. There is Bombay mix to nibble in the bar, among pink velvet and statues of Buddha. Of the two dining-rooms the upper one has less atmosphere; well, being Everest it would, wouldn't it? The menu avoids long lists of curries, and the spicing, never hot, is sometimes very underplayed: tandoori shashlik comes sizzling, with a mild creamy sauce; pakoras are golden and crispy; and nan and dhal are first-rate. There is also hot-and-sour mulligatawny soup; rogan josh with a cashew, almond and pistachio sauce; and vegetarian and non-vegetarian thalis. Much better than a standard curry house.

CHEF: Mathaur Rahman PROPRIETORS: Abdul Kowsor and Abdal Miah
OPEN: all week MEALS: 12 to 2, 6 to 11.45 (12.30 Fri and Sat)
PRICES: £7 (£13), Set L from £5·50 (£9), Set D from £6 (£9). Minimum £5. Service 10%
CARDS: Access, Amex, Diners, Visa
SEATS: 120. Private parties: 80 main room, 30 private room. Vegetarian meals. Children's helpings. Jacket and tie. Wheelchair access (also wc). Indian music

Gibsons [new entry, zero rated]

8 Romilly Crescent, Canton, Cardiff CF1 9NR
CARDIFF (0222) 41264 £13–£20

Irene Canning is serious about her food and has put the cooking on a surer footing than it was last year, when the *Guide* felt unable to support her. She hasn't had much luck finding locally grown vegetables, but has made use of free-range guinea-fowl and culled baby rooks in autumn. There are daily and weekly changes to the French regional menu, and dinner is more elaborate than lunch. Pâté and terrines figure prominently – chicken and walnut is accompanied by sweet, pink onion marmalade – and hand-made boudin blanc and boudin noir appear occasionally. Among fish dishes tarte de brochet is praised, and monkfish comes à l'armoricaine. Duck leg is boned and stuffed with pork, veal and truffle, and served with a potato and pasta salad. Home-made ravioli is stuffed with spinach and veal, or Gruyère and goats' cheese. The cheeseboard is kept in good condition, sorbets proliferate, and the ginger syllabub is very rich. The 60 wines, plus bin-ends, are as French as the menu, including house wine at £6. There are

We keep files on every restaurant, so reports of poor meals are just as valuable as reports of good meals because they save unnecessary inspections.

four Alsace, or the CELLARMAN'S CHOICE: Ch. Bonnet '83, a white from Entre-Deux-Mers, at £5·85.

CHEFS/PROPRIETORS: The Canning family
OPEN: Mon to Sat CLOSED: 1 week at Christmas MEALS: 12.30 to 2.30, 7.30 to 9.30
PRICES: £10 (£17), Set L from £7·50 (£13), Set D £13·95 (£20). Service 10%
CARDS: Access, Amex, Diners, Visa
SEATS: 38. Private parties: 12 main room. Car-park, 5 places. Children's helpings by arrangement

Harvesters [9/20]

5 Pontcanna Street, Canton, Cardiff CF1 9HQ
CARDIFF (0222) 32616 £9–£16

Vincenzo Biundo cooks British dishes with a Welsh flavour, such as pastai ty mawr – steak, kidney and mushroom pie with good pastry – and Welsh lamb cutlets with rosemary. There is fish, offal – brains in black butter – and copious quantities of well-cooked seasonal vegetables, with bread-and-butter pudding to finish. Forty wines with house French from £4·25. CELLARMAN'S CHOICE: Ch. Pontet-Canet '70 at £15·95

CHEF: Vincenzo Biundo PROPRIETORS: Vincenzo and Rosa Biundo
OPEN: Mon to Sat, exc Sat L CLOSED: 3 weeks Aug MEALS: 12 to 2.30, 6.30 to 11.30
PRICES: £10 (£16), Set L from £6 (£9), Set D from £6·75 (£10). Service 10% alc only
CARDS: Access, Amex, Diners, Visa
SEATS: 46. Private parties: 36 main room. Vegetarian meals. Children's helpings (D only). Wheelchair access. Air-conditioned

Riverside [10/20]

44 Tudor Street, Cardiff CF1 8RM
CARDIFF (0222) 372163 £10–£18

Wendy Chan has taken over the running of this upstairs Cantonese restaurant from her husband. She has redecorated the long room with flowers, birds and the occasional dragon, and generally given the place a big lift. The menu is the usual Cantonese accumulator, but all is done to order, and the flavours from the fresh ginger and scallions (available from their nearby Nam Kim supermarket) are distinct. Good dishes eaten have included pork and salt cabbage soup; squid with ginger; beef and cashew nuts; monks' vegetables, which have included interesting fungi; and well-cooked egg fried rice. A surprisingly good list of wines includes three from Alsace that merit exploration; there's also Chinese beer – Tsingtao.

CHEF: F.L. Yip PROPRIETOR: Wendy Chan
OPEN: all week MEALS: 12 to 11.45 (12.15 Fri and Sat)
PRICES: £11 (£18), Set L and D £6·50 (£10). Service 10% CARDS: Access, Amex, Diners, Visa
SEATS: 140. Private parties: 75 main room, 65 private room. Vegetarian meals by arrangement. Children welcome. Music. Air-conditioned

If you cannot honour a restaurant booking, always phone to cancel.

Yr Ystafell Gymraeg/The Welsh Room [10/20]

72–74 Whitchurch Road, Cardiff CF4 3LY
CARDIFF (0222) 42317 and 397660 £14

Judith Evans has been known to tell diners that the pastry for pies is actually made to order in her and husband David's Welsh restaurant. The unpretentious menu has Anglo influences of the prawn cocktail variety, but at the same time there is an admirable attempt to show off national cooking – laver-bread is rolled with oatmeal and served on toast with a thick rasher of bacon, and thick slices of excellent honey-roasted Welsh lamb are served with a gravy made from the pan-juices and ale. Vegetables have been over-cooked and the lemon syllabub is more bub than lemon. The decor is Welsh, from the dresser to the lace cloths to vases of daffodils. Some interesting French country wines on a list lacking detail, but there is also Welsh beer, wine and whisky.

CHEFS/PROPRIETORS: Judith and David Evans
OPEN: Mon to Sat, exc Sat L MEALS: 12 to 2, 7 to 11
PRICES: £9 (£14) CARDS: Access, Visa
SEATS: 50. Private parties: 50 main room. Vegetarian meals by arrangement. Children's helpings. Wheelchair access (also WC). Music

CARDIGAN Dyfed map 4

Blas-O-Ddyfed [8/20]

9 Black Lion Mews, High Street, Cardigan SA43 1HJ
CARDIGAN (0239) 612657 **Real Food** £6

Paul Nicholas was a consultant in worldwide food and drug safety before opening this Real Food delicatessen with an eating-area. He uses traditional recipes for bara Brith, Welsh cakes and oatcakes, fosters local cheese-makers and even uses 'organic' butter. There are salads, pasties and so on. We are rather less impressed by the cooking than by the ingredients, but it is a heroic little place. No licence; no corkage. Coffee is 35p.

CHEF: Huw Parsons PROPRIETORS: Paul and Elizabeth Nicholas
OPEN: Mon to Sat, daytime only MEALS: 9 (10.30 Mon) to 5
PRICES: £5 (£6), Snacks from 60p. Unlicensed, but bring your own: no corkage
CARD: Access
SEATS: 24. Private parties: 24 main room. Vegetarian meals. Children's helpings. No smoking in dining-room

▲ *Rhyd-Garn-Wen* [14/20]

Cardigan SA43 3NW
CARDIGAN (0239) 612742
on A487, 2¾m S of Cardigan at first crossroads £16

'I am one of the true amateurs,' says Susan Jones. Her kitchen, as in classic Cordon Bleu teaching, will not cook for more than 12. And she continues: 'the quality of the ingredients, as much as careful cookery, makes a good meal.' How then can this Welsh manor rate as high as 14? Simply because despite not having a huge menu, despite not having a thousand pounds' worth of curtains in the dining-room, despite not cooking to a cuisine that might remotely be called fashionable, what arrives on the plate is consistently rather better than what is served at restaurants scoring 13 or less. And the napery, from the lacy cloths to the glasses, is not second-hand. The menu is built of the finest local ingredients – even if the fish has to go up to Manchester and come back down again (such are the inanities that govern cottage food industries today). These translate into hot oysters and bacon on waffles; guinea-fowl with juniper and redcurrants; quiches; bobotie of lamb. Recent additions reflect an interest in historical recipes – a Tudor pudding of saffron, honey and cream, or another of chocolate and chestnut purée. The accent is on the old-fashioned and the natural. Huw Jones enjoys his 40, largely French wines, which are not overpriced. CELLARMAN'S CHOICE: Ch. Clos Beauregard '80 at £6·50.

CHEF: Susan Jones PROPRIETORS: Susan and Huw Jones
OPEN: all week, D only CLOSED: Nov to Easter MEALS: 7.30 to 9.30
PRICES: Set D £12 (£16) CARD: Access
SEATS: 10. 4 tables outside. Car-park, 10 places. Vegetarian meals by arrangement. No children under 12. Jacket and tie. No smoking in dining-room. Wheelchair access
ACCOMMODATION: 4 rooms, all with bath/shower. B&B £25 to £35. Children welcome. No dogs. Garden. Scenic [GHG]

CILGERRAN Dyfed — map 4

Castle Kitchen [new entry, zero rated]

Cilgerran SA43 2SG
CARDIGAN (0239) 615055
off A478, 2m SE of Cilgerran — £6–£8

'Nearly every item on the menu is home-made and we do not serve chips.' This old cottage is run by two sisters as an informal restaurant. The slate floor is covered with rush mats and the walls with the sisters' own watercolours. For lunch there are home-made soups from good stocks, fine pies and, occasionally, exotica like couscous and samosas. Dinner is by booking only. Traditional beef casserole with walnuts and vegetarian nut-roast with port sauce have both drawn enthusiasm. Sweets can be less accomplished. Limited wines, with house French at £3·30. More reports, please.

CHEFS/PROPRIETORS: Barbara and Elizabeth Moore
OPEN: all week CLOSED: daytime Nov to Easter, Mon to Thur D July and Aug
MEALS: 12 to 5, 7.30
PRICES: £4 (£6), Set D from £5·80 (£8), Snacks from 70p (80p)
SEATS: 25. Private parties: 16 main room. Vegetarian meals. Children's helpings (daytime only). Wheelchair access. Music

'The omelette was apparently born of at least six eggs, cooked to a consistency resembling a truck tyre, and accomplished by flaccid chips.' (On eating in Wales)

Prices quoted are for an average three-course meal including service and VAT and half a bottle of house wine (or the equivalent in an ethnic restaurant).

COWBRIDGE South Glamorgan map 4

Basil's Brasserie [10/20]

2 Eastgate, Cowbridge CF7 7DG
COWBRIDGE (044 63) 3738 £13

Bare wooden floors and tables create the atmosphere of a pub-cum-wine bar, and prints of horses echo the horse, dressed up as a waiter, on the sign outside. It is friendly, relaxed, informal, and regulars know each other. The blackboard menu travels Europe, picking up self-service starters of gravlax, bresaola, Neapolitan sausages, and hummus. Presentation is sophisticated, sometimes elaborate to the point of tomato rosebud garnishes, and the menu may include first-class rabbit terrine with Cumberland sauce; simple but well-flavoured cream and mustard sauce for less good kidneys; unpeeled new potatoes; and ordinary puddings. Fish is spanking fresh from Swansea – salmon with beurre blanc, monkfish, steamed sea-bass with ginger, or poached sewin with cucumber sauce. House wine from a basic list is £4·25. CELLARMAN'S CHOICE: Berry Bros Bourgogne Chardonnay at £6·75.

CHEF: Giampiero Fama PROPRIETORS: Giampiero and Virginia Fama
OPEN: Tue to Sat CLOSED: 2 weeks Aug, 1 week at Christmas MEALS: 12 to 2, 7 to 10.30
PRICES: £9 (£13), Snacks from £1·55 (£1·70) CARDS: Access, Visa
SEATS: 80. Private parties: 25 main room. Car-park, 10 places. Vegetarian meals. Children's helpings. No pipes in dining-room. Wheelchair access. Air-conditioned. Partly self-service

CRICKHOWELL Powys map 4

▲ *Bear Hotel* [10/20]

High Street, Crickhowell NP8 1BW
CRICKHOWELL (0873) 810408 £4–£17

A comfortable old coaching-inn with dark beams and pews, where the Welsh choir practises on Monday evenings. The menu runs from lasagne to lamb Crughywal (cooked in wine, honey, rosemary and thyme), with many standard dishes in between. There seems to be a conviction that eating out must be different from plain home cooking, judging by the elaborate nature of some dishes and the quantity and variety of vegetables. Beef Wellington is good, puddings less so, apart from a fine almond cream terrine. Simpler food is available in the bar. Three dozen wines include CELLARMAN'S CHOICE: Fleurie '83, from Loron, at £8·40.

CHEFS: J.L.Hindmarsh and Gary Hack PROPRIETOR: J.L.Hindmarsh
OPEN: D all week exc Sun, bar meals L and D exc Sun D MEALS: bar 12 to 2, 6.30 to 10, rest 7 to 9
PRICES: D £11 (£17), Bar meals from £3·25 (£3·60), Snacks from £1·40 (£1·60)
CARD: Access
SEATS: 58. Private parties: 70 main room. Car-park, 28 places. Children's helpings. No children under 5 in dining-room. Smart dress preferred. Wheelchair access (also men's wc). Music
ACCOMMODATION: 12 rooms, 9 with bath/shower. B&B £23 to £32. Children welcome. No pets in public rooms. Doors close at 12. Confirm by noon

DOLGELLAU Gwynedd map 4

La Petite Auberge [9/20]

2 Smithfield Street, Dolgellau LL40 1BS
DOLGELLAU (0341) 422870 £9

This restaurant has become a wine bar but the menu is in the same pattern, if a little cheaper. Fish is the major business – soupe de poisson, gravlax, and terrine of turbot. A short, unvintaged wine list. Vin de pays du Gard is £4·25.

CHEF: George Dewez PROPRIETORS: Evelyne and Yannick Tonnere, and George Dewez
OPEN: Mon to Sat, D only CLOSED: 31 Sept to 1 Apr MEALS: 7 to 9.30
PRICES: £6 (£9). Service inc
SEATS: 34. Private parties: 20 main room. Children's helpings

ERBISTOCK Clwyd map 4

Boat Inn [9/20]

Erbistock LL13 0DL
BANGOR-ON-DEE (0978) 780143
off A539, 7m S of Wrexham £11–£24

A sixteenth-century timbered building in a delightful riverside spot by the Dee. Locally caught salmon and trout are first-class, sole is poached in white wine with a tomato and lobster sauce, and sea-bass is done with a fennel sauce. Chicken Kiev is said to be better than in Kiev! Prices are not low. There are some old and classy wines, including claret and burgundy from the '60s, as well as some more affordable bottles. CELLARMAN'S CHOICE: Gewürztraminer '81, from Boeckel, at £9·50.

CHEF: Peter Highfield PROPRIETOR: John Chamberlain
OPEN: all week CLOSED: Sun D and Mon from Oct to Apr
MEALS: 12.15 to 2.15, 7.30 to 9.30
PRICES: £18 (£24), Set L £7 (£11), Snacks from 90p (£1) CARDS: Access, Amex, Diners, Visa
SEATS: 70. 9 tables outside. Private parties: 25 main room, 50 and 45 private rooms. Car-park, 40 places. Vegetarian meals by arrangement. Children's helpings. No pipes in dining-room. Wheelchair access (also WC)

GLANWYDDEN Gwynedd map 4

Queen's Head [9/20]

Glanwydden LL31 9JP
LLANDUDNO (0492) 46570 £11

Fish and the sweets are the things to eat in this pub that has two big open fires in winter. The Conway mussels, which everyone mentions, are cooked in garlic butter, topped with cheese and finished under the grill. Mentions also for the fudge pie and the treacle tart to finish – otherwise the long menu is filled out with salads, chicken Kiev and so on. Ind Coope ales.

CHEF/PROPRIETOR: Robert Cureton
OPEN: all week, exc Sun D MEALS: 12 to 2, 7 to 11
PRICES: £7 (£11)
SEATS: 120. 12 tables outside. Private parties: 14 main room. Car-park, 40 places. Vegetarian meals. Children's helpings. Music

HARLECH Gwynedd map 4

▲ *Castle Cottage* [10/20]

Pen Llech, Harlech LL46 2YL
HARLECH (0766) 780479 £14

Wales meets the Mediterranean head-on at the Yuills' cottage restaurant. On the one hand there is smoked goose breast with home-made chutney, or laver-bread with deep-fried cockles, and on the other steak with Roquefort or trout meunière. The sweets and sauces get mentions, though we have little information this year. Everyone is extremely friendly, but the rooms are said not to be of the standard of the food. The 60-strong wine list commendably tries to find good-value bottles for under £10 – white Hermitage, Le Chevalier de Sterimbourg '83, from Jaboulet, at £7·95, and white Châteauneuf-du-Pape, Domaine du Vieux Télégraphe '82 at £7·75 are bargain Rhônes.

CHEF: Jim Yuill PROPRIETORS: Jim and Betty Yuill
OPEN: all week for D, Easter to Oct; Tue, Thur, Fri and Sat D, Oct to Easter; Mon to Sat L at Easter, July and Aug MEALS: 12 to 2, 7 to 9.30
PRICES: £10 (£14), Bar meals from £2 (£2·20) CARDS: Access, Visa
SEATS: 35. 2 tables outside. Private parties: 40 main room. Vegetarian meals. Children's helpings. No smoking in dining-room. Wheelchair access. Music
ACCOMMODATION: 5 rooms, 4 with bath/shower. B&B £11 to £21. Deposit: 25%. Children welcome. Baby facilities. No pets in public rooms. Scenic

▲ *The Cemlyn* [13/20]

High Street, Harlech LL46 2YA
HARLECH (0766) 78425 **Real Food** £10–£13

This is a Real Food restaurant. Ken Goody will drive 30 miles to get scallops off the boat and risk the day's catch not being the best of the year, but will react and adjust the recipes to suit. He relies on freshness for effect; others would rather wait two days to select cleaned and graded scallops to fit their menus. That is the difference between cooking and catering. He has even dropped frozen prawns in favour of fresh ones held in brine.

The Cemlyn shines out in Gwynedd. Mr Goody's pride in his work shows through at his comfortable, homely, 36-seater restaurant and manifests itself in wholemeal pancakes stuffed with seafood; beautiful fish dishes, such as sea-bass with honey and sweet and sour leeks, grilled Dover sole, monkfish thermidor, and also magnificent shoulder of lamb stuffed with pork and herbs and cooked in white wine. Eggs are free-range, of course, and the cream sweets get a good measure of alcohol. The rating is happily raised to 13 as an example of first-class ingredients handled with the respect they deserve. Half the dining-room has become no-smoking. The wine list has been compiled with care and an eye for less expensive vineyards – the Alsace big four, Gewürztraminer, Tokay, Riesling

and Muscat, figure at £6 and £7 – and is a model for a small restaurant. There are good eaux-de-vie from Alsace, too.

CHEF/PROPRIETOR: Ken Goody
OPEN: Thur to Sat, Oct to Jan; all week, Easter to Oct. L by arrangement only
CLOSED: Jan to Easter MEALS: 7 to 10 (9.30 quiet season)
PRICES: £9 (£13), Set D from £6 (£10) CARDS: Amex, Diners
SEATS: 36. 3 tables outside. Private parties: 40 main room, 10 private room. Vegetarian meals. Children's helpings. Wheelchair access (also wc)
ACCOMMODATION: 2 rooms, 1 with bath/shower. B&B £8·50 to £21. No children. No pets. Afternoon teas. TV. Scenic. Doors close at 12. Confirm by 6

HAY-ON-WYE Powys — map 4

Lion's Corner House [new entry, zero rated]

39 Lion Street, Hay-on-Wye HR3 5AA
HAY-ON-WYE (0497) 820175 — £13

This is on the corner of Lion Street rather than part of Joe Lyons' empire. Ploughman's lunches are imaginative, soups home-made. Main courses often have fish, and there is Welsh lamb with garlic, honey and thyme. Excellent but rich chocolate mousse. Colin Thomson likes to cook vegetarian dishes according to what is in the kitchen. Good bread; not uninteresting wine list. More reports, please.

CHEFS: Colin Thomson and Bernice Brown PROPRIETOR: Colin Thomson
OPEN: all week, exc Sun L CLOSED: D Sun and Mon out of season MEALS: 11 to 2, 7 to 9.30
PRICES: £9 (£13). Cheaper L available
SEATS: 30. Private parties: 12 main room. Children's helpings. Wheelchair access. Music

LLANBERIS Gwynedd — map 4

Y Bistro [11/20]

43–45 High Street, Llanberis LL55 4EU
LLANBERIS (0286) 871278 — £14

A welcoming, family-run bistro. Nerys Roberts does all the cooking, her father grows the herbs and flowers. Ingredients are solid, from locally smoked fish and poultry to high-quality meats. Saucing is less successful. Cockle pie, lambs' livers, and kidneys in wine are typical. Fifty wines. CELLARMAN'S CHOICE: Ch. Chasse-Spleen '78 at £12·85.

CHEF: Nerys Roberts PROPRIETORS: Danny and Nerys Roberts
OPEN: Mon to Sat, D only MEALS: 7.30 to 9.30
PRICES: Set D £10·50 (£14)
SEATS: 48. Private parties: 36 main room. Vegetarian meals. Children welcome. Smart dress preferred. Wheelchair access (also wc). Music. Air-conditioned

An index of restaurants by name appears at the back of the Guide.

New restaurants that we have not been able to assess completely are given a zero rating for this year. We are particularly keen to have reports on these places.

LLANDDERFEL Gwynedd map 4

▲ *Palé Hall* [new entry, zero rated]

Llandderfel LL23 7PS
LLANDDERFEL (067 83) 285
on B4401, 8m SW of Corwen £12–£22

A honey-coloured stone house built in 1870 by Henry Robertson, a Scottish engineer. The entrance hall leads to a magnificent panelled reception room with a fire crackling in the grate, and a high-ceilinged dining-room with carvings, mirrors and lush velvet curtains. Chef David Atkinson takes time off to go fishing. He marinates trout, poaches salmon with cream and cucumber pearls, and cooks turbot with saffron and dill sauce. Lamb is local. Good-quality steak is served with red, green and black peppercorns. Butterscotch crème caramel is light, and toffee pudding is gooey. Cheeses need re-thinking. The five-course menu is imaginative, and good value. The ladies' has sumptuous upholstered sofas. Over a hundred wines include classic French and German bottles, with plenty under £10 from the Rhône, the Loire, Italy and Spain. More reports, please.

CHEFS: David Atkinson, Mark Wallace and Andrew Duffin PROPRIETORS: The Duffin family
OPEN: all week MEALS: 12 to 2, 7 to 9.30
PRICES: £15 (£22), Set L from £7·95 (£12), Set D £14 (£18), Bar snacks from £1·25 (£1·40). Minimum in dining-room £8 CARDS: Access, Amex, Diners, Visa
SEATS: 70 Private parties: 12 main room, 45 and 24 private rooms. Car-park, 40 places. Vegetarian meals. Children's helpings. Jacket and tie. Wheelchair access (also WC)
ACCOMMODATION: 17 rooms, all with bath/shower. B&B £34·50 to £46. Deposit: £10. Children welcome. Afternoon teas. Garden. Sauna. Exercise room. Sun-bed. Fishing. Lift. TV. Phone. Scenic. Confirm by 6 [GHG]

LLANDEWI SKIRRID Gwent map 4

Walnut Tree Inn [15/20]

Llandewi Skirrid NP7 8AW
ABERGAVENNY (0873) 2797
on B4521, 2½m NE of Abergavenny **Real Food** £26

Let's get this straight. This is a pub with a dining-room. It is best summed up by the reader who says: 'We went for a snack and ended up having a full meal.' The kitchen earns its rating by the breadth and quality of the menu, but there are no waiters in bow-ties, nor a sommelier, and there's no need to book for the bistro, which has a similar menu to the dining-room proper, if you get there early. The menu encompasses freshly made pasta with spinach and cottage cheese and a massive seafood platter, as well as classic roast guinea-fowl Rossini and more modern dishes, like the now-famous salmon with rhubarb. Mr Taruschio has his own truffle importing business near Venice, and in autumn his kitchen is pungent with the smell from a wicker basket packed high with little black and white golf-ball-sized nuggets. Have them grated on eggs. Of many alpha dishes there have been scallops en croûte, a starter of cold trout with vermouth and orange, and veal with orange and peppercorns. Sweets are consistently triumphant and belong to the middle-European school of calorie advancement – charlottes, tortes, emperor's gateau, and strawberry soup. The wine list apologises for the increase in prices and warns that white burgundy prices are rising just as claret and red burgundy prices have. The Rhône section offers some alternatives, as does the Alsace section, mainly supplied via Schleret. Tokay, Vendange Tardive '76, from Hugel, at £12·95 is said to go well with strawberries. The Italian section is less expensive and includes red Venegazzù '81 at £8·75, which is made from traditional claret grapes.

CHEF: Franco Taruschio PROPRIETORS: Franco and Ann Taruschio
OPEN: Mon to Sat, exc Mon L CLOSED: 12 to 24 Feb MEALS: 12 to 2.30, 7.15 to 10
PRICES: £20 (£26)
SEATS: 90. 5 tables outside. Private parties: 40 main room. Car-park, 30 places. Vegetarian meals. Children welcome. Wheelchair access (also WC). Air-conditioned

---

LLANDUDNO Gwynedd map 4

▲ *Bodysgallen Hall* [13/20]

WELSH HOTEL OF THE YEAR GFG '86

Deganwy, Llandudno LL30 1RS
DEGANWY (0492) 84466
on B5115, ½m E of Llandudno **Real Food** £11–£23

An immaculate hall with porters dressed in uniform and hardly a piece of gravel out of place. Entrance is straight into a large, elegant, low-ceilinged, stained oak-panelled room with an enormous fireplace, fine old oils and sofas and chairs. The two dining-rooms are formal and, like the bedrooms, irregularly shaped. David Harding's cooking, fuelled with the best of local produce as well as such extravagances as foie gras served on a salad with chicory and walnuts, is a fusion of the best of modern French cooking and the best of Welsh – witness excellent Anglesey mussel soup and sashimi-style chunks of salmon marinated carefully in lime, garlic and peppers. The quality of the meat holds up main courses of local lamb with anchovies and garlic, or beef with paprika and sour cream, though by London standards there is a tendency to overcook. Vegetables are first-class and unadulterated by saucing, while the cheeseboard includes wonderful Caerphilly and Welsh goats' cheese. Sweets are professionally done. A little more consistency and a rating of 14 would be in order. The rooms are enormous and elegantly furnished, and breakfasts feature free-range eggs as well as kidneys, haddock and croissants. Some of the wine pricing is inconsistent, but the list is copious, being strongest in expensive vintage clarets and burgundies. Nonetheless there are affordable halves, and the Alsace section features the four major grapes, including Tokay '82, from Wiederhirn, at £8·20. House wine is £6·30. CELLARMAN'S CHOICE: Coteaux des Baux-en-Provence, Domaine de Trévallon '80, at £10·50.

CHEF: David Harding PROPRIETORS: Historic House Hotels
OPEN: all week MEALS: 12.30 to 2, 7.30 to 9.45
PRICES: £16 (£23), Set L from £6·60 (£11), Set D from £15·50 (£21). Also cut-price menu. Service 10% CARDS: Access, Amex, Diners, Visa
SEATS: 62. Private parties: 48 main room, 30 private room. Car-park, 50 places. No children under 8. Jacket and tie. No cigars/pipes in dining-room. Wheelchair access (also WC). Pianist/harpist Sat only
ACCOMMODATION: 19 rooms, 9 with bath/shower. Also 9 cottage suites. Rooms for disabled. B&B £44·40 to £68·80. No children under 8. Afternoon teas. Garden. Tennis. Croquet. Helicopter pad. TV. Phone. Scenic. Confirm by 6 [GHG]

The Floral [12/20]

Victoria Street, Craig-y-Don, Llandudno LL30 1LJ
LLANDUDNO (0492) 75735 £11–£17

The decor looks rather like something out of *Homes and Gardens*, and Tony Muff sometimes extends this to his dishes, garnishing strawberries with orchids. It is a conservative menu, but it changes with the seasons and customers' whims, hence, for vegetarians, pancakes can be stuffed with laver-bread or mung beans and covered with mature Cheddar. There is fine fish including salmon, of course, but also halibut; avocados are served ripe filled with smoked fish, apple and cream; duck breasts are served pink; and there is even the extravagance of stuffing chicken with smoked salmon and serving it with a champagne sauce. Vegetables are varied and well cooked. Portions are large enough for many to fall at the sweets hurdle, where soufflé cheesecake and pineapple Fauntleroy lie in wait. Only the vanilla ice-cream is bought in, we are assured. A varied, well-spread list of 50 wines.

CHEF: Tony Muff PROPRIETORS: Tony Muff, Bill Johnson and Michael Ratcliff
OPEN: Tue to Sun, exc Sat L and Sun D CLOSED: 2 weeks Mar, 2 weeks Aug MEALS: 12 to 2, 7 to 10
PRICES: £12 (£17), Set Sun L £6·85 (£11)
SEATS: 60 Private parties: 34 main room, 14 private room. Vegetarian meals. Children's helpings. No children under 10 at D. Music

LLANDYBIE Dyfed map 4

The Cobblers [12/20]

3 Church Street, Llandybie SA18 3HZ
LLANDYBIE (0269) 850540 **Real Food** £13

A simple, unpretentious restaurant offering the best local produce served by unassuming young waitresses. The chickens and eggs are free-range, game comes from the local shoot, and cockles, laver-bread, home-cured hams and local cheeses are bought at market. The menu moves with the seasons, relying strongly on grills with colourful herb sauces. Local salmon is rolled in a herb mixture, wrapped in lettuce and poached with dry vermouth. Highlights have been the marinated beef with elderberry sauce, pork in white wine, excellent Cheddar, and the vegetables from the garden. There is good Sancerre to drink, as well as local wines. House French is £5·50.

CHEF: Margaret Rees PROPRIETORS: Hywel and Margaret Rees
OPEN: Tue, Wed, Fri and Sat MEALS: 12 to 1.30, 7 to 9.30
PRICES: £9 (£13), Snacks from 85p (95p) CARDS: Access, Visa
SEATS: 40. Private parties: 45 main room. Vegetarian meals. Children's helpings. Wheelchair access (also WC). Music

The 1987 Guide *will appear before Christmas 1986, so reports are particularly important in the spring. Report forms are at the back of this book, but just write a letter if you prefer. Address them to* The Good Food Guide, *Freepost, 14 Buckingham Street, London WC2N 6BR. No stamp is necessary if you post in the UK.*

LLANGOLLEN Clwyd map 4

Caesar's [11/20]

Castle Street, Llangollen LL20 7EH
LLANGOLLEN (0978) 860133 £13

'If the restaurant is open, I am cooking,' – Richard Hendey's maxim is a good one. He cooks a set-price menu which is served by local women. Salmon comes from the river at the back of the restaurant, and game from a hunter friend. Typical of many good dishes have been seafood pancakes; chicken breasts with a lightly curried sauce; prawns grilled with garlic butter; and the fillet steak with garlic sauce. More modern, but just as successful, has been the mix of salmon, mackerel, smoked haddock, prawns and cod in a chive sauce. To finish there are mousses – chocolate and rum; brandy and coffee. The list of 30 everyday wines is backed up by a few interesting bottles in the cellar, available on request. House Côtes du Rhône is £4·25.

CHEF/PROPRIETOR: Richard Hendey
OPEN: all week D MEALS: 7 (6.30 Sat and all week in summer) to 10
PRICES: Set D £10·95 (£13). Service inc CARDS: Access, Visa
SEATS: 30. Private parties: 28 main room. Children's helpings. Wheelchair access. Classical music

▲ *Gales* [8/20]

18 Bridge Street, Llangollen LL70 8PF
LLANGOLLEN (0978) 860089 £8

A small wine bar with good soups, salads, quiches, a single main course, and home-made ice-creams. Wines are very decently priced: Ch. Gazin '82 is £4·75. CELLARMAN'S CHOICE: Château La Coste rouge, from Provence, at £4·40, and Rioja Campo Viejo '73, Gran Reserva, at £7·50.

CHEFS: Jo Johnson, Gillie Gale and John Gopung PROPRIETORS: Richard and Gillie Gale
OPEN: all week CLOSED: 2 weeks in Nov; Sun and Mon Sept to May MEALS: 12 to 1.45, 6 (7 Sun) to 10.15
PRICES: £5 (£8)
SEATS: 50. 10 tables outside. Private parties: 14 private room. Wheelchair access. Classical music
ACCOMMODATION: 3 rooms. B&B £9 to £18. Children welcome. Baby facilities. No pets in public rooms. Doors close at 11. Confirm by 6

LLANGWM Gwent map 4

▲ *Bridge Inn* [11/20]

Llangwm NP5 1HG
WOLVESNEWTON (029 15) 249 £12

Llangwm is a hamlet of 20 houses, and its pub is a typical white plaster, slate-roofed and black-painted timber building. Inside are quarry-tiled floors and rough stone walls with animal skins and stuffed animals, with the feel of a good pub. Meals are served in the old bar or the modern annexe set with church pews and with large rusty enamel advertising signs. Bob Evans takes the orders from behind a glass counter displaying some fine examples of his pre-preparation – superb ham ('not that flabby, factory stuff'); gravlax; bresaola; plenty of smoked fish; and permutations of salad. The cooking is generally robust, such as rabbit with sweet mustard sauce, with vegetables served on a separate plate for you to help yourself. Bread is wholemeal. The baked potatoes with any number of fillings make inexpensive bar meals. The lemon cheesecake is excellent. Service is by young girls. The place gets very crowded – especially on Saturdays. Pub wines; draught Bass.

CHEFS/PROPRIETORS: Bob and Jane Evans
OPEN: all week, exc Sun D MEALS: 12.30 to 2 (12 to 1 Sun), 7 to 9.30
PRICES: £7 (£12), Snacks from 50p (55p)
SEATS: 50. 5 tables outside. Private parties: 12 main room. Car-park, 50 places. Vegetarian meals. Children's helpings. No children under 14. Wheelchair access
ACCOMMODATION: 3 rooms, all with shower. B&B £18 to £30. Garden. Scenic. Doors close at 12

LLANRWST Gwynedd map 4

▲ *Meadowsweet Hotel* [12/20]

Station Road, Llanrwst LL26 0DS
LLANRWST (0492) 640732 £10–£18

A comfortable, family-run hotel with a fabulous wine cellar and bedrooms that overlook the mountains. John Evans cooks a short, varied Welsh/French *carte* with *nouvelle cuisine* portions. Fish is fresh: sardines are grilled, skate is poached with an orange butter, or the delivery of the day may be poached in a fumet and served with a prawn and cream sauce. Good starters have been pear with tarragon cream, and the gravlax before chicken breast with cream. John Evans likes his sauces, and duck is marinated in lime juice, sauté and served with a gin and tomato sauce. Other sauces, however, have lacked virility. Lunches are cheaper and good value and breakfast eggs are free-range. Cheeses are very good. The pace is easy going and the rating reflects the current standards in Wales. It is a Goliath of a wine list, especially strong in vintage claret. The mark-ups are reasonable, and in the Alsace section there are five grape varieties from '83, all supplied by Blanck and around the £8 mark, but also four Gewürztraminer from the brilliant '76 vintage, including a Vendange Tardive, from Hugel, at £14·50 for half.

CHEF: John Evans PROPRIETORS: John and Joy Evans
OPEN: all week MEALS: 12.30 to 1.45, 6.30 to 9.30
PRICES: £13 (£18), Set L from £5·75 (£10), Set D £12·50 (£18), Snacks from £1·50 (£1·65) CARDS: Access, Amex, Visa
SEATS: 36. Private parties: 50 main room. Car-park, 10 places. Children's helpings. Smart dress preferred. No smoking in dining-room. Wheelchair access. Classical music
ACCOMMODATION: 10 rooms, all with bath/shower. B&B £20 to £34. Deposit: £3 per person. Children welcome. Baby facilities. No pets in dining-room. Afternoon teas. TV. Phone. Scenic. Doors close at 12. Confirm by 6.30 [GHG]

Restaurants are checked every year and their entries rewritten. The restaurant scene changes very rapidly so don't be caught with an out-of-date Guide.

LLANWDDYN Powys map 4

▲ *Lake Vyrnwy Hotel* [new entry, zero rated]

Llanwddyn, Shropshire SY10 0LY
LLANWDDYN (069 173) 244
on B4393, 35m W of Shrewsbury £8–£11

There are few concessions to modernity at Mrs Moir's shooting-lodge above the lake, which she has run since 1947. Good-value menus include home-made soups, mixed fish quiche, cold meats, traditional roasts, salads, marvellous chutneys and good old-style bread-and-butter pudding. Coffee is served in the sumptuous lounge. Game is shot on the estate – 1250 birds last year – and trout comes out of the lake – 2500 last year. Leave your muddy gumboots at the porch. The non-vintage and inexpensive wine list includes a few bargains, such as St Julien '80, from the Barton stable, at £7·50. More reports, please.

CHEF: N.Robinson PROPRIETOR: R.I.Moir and Lt-Col. Sir John Baynes
OPEN: all week CLOSED: Feb MEALS: 1, 7.30 (8 Easter to Oct)
PRICES: Set L £5 (£8), Set Sun L £8·25 (£11), Set D £8·75 (£11). Cheaper set L available. Service inc
SEATS: 50. Private parties: 14 main room. Car-park. Vegetarian meals. Children's helpings. No children under 3 at D. Jacket and tie at D. Wheelchair access (also wc). One sitting
ACCOMMODATION: 29 rooms, 11 with bath/shower. Rooms for disabled. B&B £14 to £55. Children welcome. Baby facilities. Afternoon teas. Garden. Tennis. Fishing. Lift. Scenic. Doors close at 11. Confirm by 7 [GHG]

LLANWRTYD WELLS Powys map 4

▲ *Llwynderw Hotel* [10/20]

Abergwesyn, Llanwrtyd Wells LD5 4TW
LLANWRTYDWELLS (059 13) 238 £10–£20

This small eighteenth-century manor house, with fittings and decor to match, is situated at the end of a wooded valley in remote walking country. Bedrooms are comfortable and spacious. Bread is home-made, and butter, eggs and Welsh mountain mutton and lamb come from local farmers. Good dishes have been the potage limousin; boneless quail with cherries; light spongy Black Cap pudding; and truckle Cheddar.

CHEF: Clive Brooks PROPRIETOR: Michael Yates
OPEN: all week CLOSED: Nov to Mar MEALS: 1, 8
PRICES: Set L £6 (£10), Set D £15 (£20)
SEATS: 21. Private parties: 21 main room, 12 private room. Car-park, 12 places. Vegetarian meals. Children's helpings by arrangement. No children under 10. Jacket and tie. Wheelchair access (also wc). One sitting
ACCOMMODATION: 10 rooms, all with bath/shower. B&B £50 to £100. No pets in public rooms. Afternoon teas. Garden. Scenic. Doors close at 11.30

All inspections are carried out anonymously as we accept no handouts.

Restaurant tricks (4): Charging for service but leaving the total on the credit card slip blank, thus inviting an extra tip.

LLANYCHAER Dyfed map 4

▲ *Penlan Oleu* [new entry, zero rated]

Llanychaer SA65 9TL
PUNCHESTON (034 882) 314
B4313 from Fishguard, through
Llanychaer, then R at Puncheston sign £12

Penlan Oleu means 'the light above the church'. It is a converted farmhouse 800 feet above Fishguard Bay and handily placed to stay at before catching the early ferry to Rosslare. On a clear day it is possible to see across the water to the mountains of Co. Wicklow, with a few bent hawthorn trees, some sheep and granite boulders to block the view. The dining-room is the pick of the rooms – small, with a sloping ceiling and a square hole in the white-painted, rough stone wall connecting it to the entrance hall. The menu is short. Portions are small, but fish is straight out of the harbour and there is always a steak. Mushrooms are cooked with garlic and served on waffles with fresh parsley, and scallops feature prominently for main course with plenty of vegetables. Coffee is unlimited. The Stuart-Lyons will do you a decent packed lunch, and breakfasts offer a wide selection of fruit, juices, cereals and cooked dishes, included in the price of a room. There are sometimes log fires in the main rooms. Twenty five wines. More reports, please.

CHEF: Ruth Stuart-Lyon PROPRIETORS: Andrew and Ruth Stuart-Lyon
OPEN: all week, exc Sun L MEALS: 12 to 1.45, 7.30 to 9.30 (9 Sun)
PRICES: £9 (£12), L snacks from £1. Service inc CARDS: Access, Visa
SEATS: 12. 4 tables outside. Private parties: 18 main room, 18 and 12 private rooms. Car-park. Vegetarian meals. No children under 7. Smart dress preferred. No smoking in dining-room. Wheelchair access (also WC)
ACCOMMODATION: 5 rooms, all with bath/shower. Rooms for disabled. B&B £14 to £28. Deposit: 10%. No children under 7. No pets. Garden. Scenic. Confirm by 6.30 [GHG]

MACHYNLLETH Powys map 4

Janie's [11/20]

57 Maengwyn Street, Machynlleth SY20 8EE
MACHYNLLETH (0654) 2126 £11–£14

During the summer Jane Mohamed cooks to order a short bistro menu of local produce. The salmon and sea-trout are wild, but not the trout. Marinating is the favoured preparation for kebabs of steak, lamb and pork, and for lamb steaks which are then char-grilled with rosemary. Good dishes from a Mediterranean-

All inspections are carried out anonymously as we accept no handouts.

The 1987 Guide *will appear before Christmas 1986, so reports are particularly important in the spring. Report forms are at the back of this book, but just write a letter if you prefer. Address them to* The Good Food Guide, *Freepost, 14 Buckingham Street, London WC2N 6BR. No stamp is necessary if you post in the UK.*

leaning menu have been vegetable soup, roast chicken, guinea-fowl cooked in red wine, and meringues with blackcurrant sauce. There are a dozen sensible wines.

CHEF: Jane Mohamed PROPRIETORS: Mr and Mrs Mohamed
OPEN: Tue to Sun CLOSED: Oct to Easter MEALS: 12.30 to 2, 7.30 to 10 (9.30 in winter)
PRICES: £10 (£14), Set Sun L £7·50 (£11). Minimum £4·95 at D
SEATS: 40. Private parties: 25 main room. Vegetarian meals by arrangement. Children's helpings by arrangement. Wheelchair access. Classical music

MAESYCRUGIAU Dyfed map 4

Bryn Martin [11/20]

Maesycrugiau SA39 9LU
MAESYCRUGIAU (055 935) 244 £14

Readers continue to find this a happy and satisfying place, and it continues to serve its unchanging menu: salade niçoise with walnuts; large, very peppered steaks; and crisp meringues. We cannot argue with anyone who keeps the food simple and does it well, and we may have been a little unfair with last year's score. So, despite out-of-season vegetables, the food and cooking warrant an extra rating point. Eggs are from the Martins' own free-range chickens, and locally fished trout sometimes appear. Donald Martin's interest in growing vegetables and breeding sheep may even make more of a difference soon. Good service. A short wine list.

CHEF: Fleur Martin PROPRIETORS: Donald and Fleur Martin
OPEN: Tue to Sat, D only MEALS: 7 to 8.30
PRICES: £9 (£14)
SEATS: 30. Private parties: 30 main room. Car-park, 30 places. Vegetarian meals by arrangement. Children's helpings. No children under 5. Wheelchair access

MORFA NEFYN Gwynedd map 4

Bryncynan Inn [10/20]

Morfa Nefyn LL53 6AA
NEFYN (0758) 720879 £8

There is a bit of a scrum during the tourist season, when they don't take bookings, but they serve plenty of salads, and fresh Porth Dinllaen crabs and lobsters (two or three nights a week to the sounds of live or disco music). It is quieter in winter for stew and hot-pots, and it may be necessary to order in advance if you want a roast. The village butcher and baker are pressed into service, and a van delivers the fruit and vegetables. Ind Coope and Tetley ales.

CHEF/PROPRIETOR: Alan Wilson
OPEN: Mon to Sat MEALS: 12 to 2.15, 7 to 9.30
PRICES: £6 (£8). Service inc
SEATS: 38. 6 tables outside. Private parties: 10 main room. Car-park, 80 places. Vegetarian meals. Children in dining-room only. Wheelchair access (also WC). Music

If you cannot honour a restaurant booking, always phone to cancel.

NEWPORT Dyfed map 4

The Pantry [10/20]

Market Street, Newport SA64 0PH
NEWPORT (0239) 820420 £13

The locals use this muted-brown little restaurant a lot. The menu is conservative, with a great deal of cream and butter. Sewin is served cold with cucumber and mayonnaise; the beef Stroganoff is obviously home-made. Plenty of vegetables, but sweets can be less good. Twenty-six wines. House French is £4.

CHEF: Robin Evans PROPRIETORS: Robin and Joan Evans
OPEN: Tue to Sat, D only (only Sat D in winter) MEALS: 7.15 to 9.30
PRICES: Set D £10 (£13). Service 10%. Licensed, plus bring your own: corkage £1·50
CARDS: Access, Visa
SEATS: 45. Private parties: 50 main room. Car-park, 15 places. Children's helpings. Wheelchair access (also wc). Music. Air-conditioned

PONTSHAEN Dyfed map 4

French Restaurant [new entry, zero rated]

Castell Howell, Pontshaen SA44 4TZ
PONTSHAEN (054 555) 341
off B4459, 5m N of Llandyssul £16

The tables are thick, two-inch wooden slabs in this restaurant attached to a leisure complex that offers horse riding, squash and so on. The lacquered-wood decor is reminiscent of a sauna but the conservative menu is cooked with flair. Soups of fish or pea, tomato and rosemary are well done; so is the duck and port house pâté. Both duck and lamb dishes are recommended, less so the chicken Kiev.The malakoff torte is not the most subtle of sweets but it tastes good. Twenty-eight wines, with house French at £5. More reports, please.

CHEF: Mr George PROPRIETOR: E. Atkinson
OPEN: all week, D only MEALS: 7.30 to 1
PRICES: £11 (£16)
SEATS: 45. 20 tables outside. Private parties: 50 private room. Car-park, 20 places. Vegetarian meals. Children's helpings. No children under 6. Music

PORT DINORWIC Gwynedd map 4

Seahorse [11/20]

20 Snowdon Street, Port Dinorwic LL56 4NQ
PORT DINORWIC (0248) 670546 £14

Snowdon Street is a steep hill: roll a marble and it will go straight into the Menai Straits. The Seahorse has been trading for 10 years, which is a testimony to the quality of Keith Rothwell's largely French-inspired cooking. Fish is the main business – local bass, sole, scallops and locally smoked salmon. Prawns are stir-fried with up to a dozen vegetables. Main courses of hare with junipers, veal with saffron, cream, tomato and garlic sauce, and duck with raspberry sauce have all been good. Sweets tend to be ice-cream, chocolate, or fruit. VAT is now included in the price of both the food and the list of 50-odd wines. The latter has some interesting vintages and is not as expensive as it might look at first glance, especially in the older clarets. House French is £4·65.

CHEF: Keith Rothwell PROPRIETORS: Rothwell and Robertson Ltd
OPEN: Mon to Sat, D only MEALS: 7.30 to 9.30
PRICES: £10 (£14) CARDS: Access, Visa
SEATS: 50. Private parties: 30 main room. Children's helpings. No children under 7

REYNOLDSTON West Glamorgan map 4

▲ *Fairyhill Country House* [new entry, zero rated]

Reynoldston SA3 1BS
SWANSEA (0792) 390139
between A4118 and B4295, 11m
W of Swansea £11–£17

Here is a place to eat the famous Penclawdd cockles served as a chowder, hot in their shells, or surrounding laver-bread and oatmeal. This large, stone country house set in 24 acres is being restored. The dining-room is decorated in pastel colours with a thick-pile traditional carpet. The short menu is changed on Wednesdays, and its pedigree is evident from the free-range chickens to the local fish. 'Nothing is frozen.' Good meals have started with deep-fried Camembert served in the bar with drinks, and there have been warm brown rolls, smoked haddock mousse, fine steaks, thick slices of loin of lamb with gravy flavoured with lemon and ginger, and new potatoes, which at inspection had not been out of the ground for more than a day. The coffee and brandy gateau is a good version, and cafetière coffee comes with home-made truffles. The 20-minute drive from Swansea is through some fine countryside. Twenty wines start with house French at £3·95. Buckley's ales and home-made sloe gin. More reports, please.

CHEF: Kate Spring PROPRIETORS: John and Margaret Frayne
OPEN: Mon to Sat D, Sun L MEALS: 12 to 1.45, 7 to 9.30
PRICES: Set L £7·50 (£11), Set D £12·95 (£17) CARDS: Access, Amex, Diners, Visa
SEATS: 60. Private parties: 32 main room, 20 private room. Car-park, 60 places. Vegetarian meals. Children's helpings. Smart dress preferred. No jeans. Wheelchair access (also WC). Classical music
ACCOMMODATION: 11 rooms, all with bath/shower. B&B £35 to £45. Deposit: 10%. Children welcome. No pets in public rooms. Garden. Sauna. Fishing. TV. Phone. Scenic

ROBESTON WATHEN Dyfed map 4

▲ *Robeston House* [new entry, zero rated]

Robeston Wathen SA67 8EU
NARBERTH (0834) 860 392
on A40, 8m E of Haverfordwest £9–£17

The fish comes up from Milford Haven quay to this elegant and spacious hotel. Other supplies come from local farmers or the kitchen garden. The menu is classically inclined and cooked to order. Quails roasted with apricots is a speciality, and other good dishes have been the prawn créole, steak au poivre, and the sole. There is home-made fudge cake to finish. Odd choice and pricing of 30 wines. More reports, please.

CHEF: Marlene Everest PROPRIETORS: David and Dorothy Watchman
OPEN: Mon to Sat D, Sun L MEALS: 12 to 2, 7 to 9.30
PRICES: £13 (£17), Set L £5·50 (£9), Set D from £8·50 (£13) CARDS: Access, Amex, Diners, Visa
SEATS: 50. Private parties: 55 main room. Car-park, 40 places. Children's helpings (Sun L only). No children under 12. No jeans. Wheelchair access (also WC). Classical music
ACCOMMODATION: 8 rooms, all with bath/shower. B&B £19 to £45. Deposit: £20. Garden. Outdoor swimming-pool. Fishing. Helicopter pad. TV. Scenic. Doors close at £12. Confirm by 6

ROSSETT Clwyd — map 4

Churtons [10/20]

Chester Road, Rossett LL12 0HW
ROSSETT (0244) 570163
on A483 — £13

This wine and food bar has a big local reputation and can be packed out. There is a dining-area, reached via a staircase hung with the heads of a buffalo, eland, bear, and a stag. There are good soups on the ever-changing and eclectic menu – it has included cod florentine and Indonesian chicken. The fine wine list has a full sweep of the Alsace grapes and plenty of good drinking in the £5 to £6 range.

CHEF: Susan Watson
PROPRIETORS: Nicholas Churton, James Churton and Richard Bowen-Jones
OPEN: Mon to Sat CLOSED: Christmas to New Year, and bank hols MEALS: 12 to 2.15, 7 to 10
PRICES: £9 (£13) CARDS: Access, Amex, Diners, Visa
SEATS: 60. Private parties: 12 main room. Car-park, 20 places. Children's helpings (Sat L only). No children under 10, exc Sat L. Wheelchair access (also WC). Music. Air-conditioned

SWANSEA West Glamorgan — map 4

BACKGROUND BRIEFING: *There are several fishmongers in the covered market in the town centre. One of the best, Coakley Greene, has a good range which on one spring day ran to haddock, cod, wrasse, conger, perch, scad, sardines, herring, mackerel, rainbow trout, Scottish kippers, oysters, bonito tuna, squid, red snapper, red mullet, skate and tilapia (St Peter's fish).* EEC *quotas restrict the amount of small plaice and Dover sole landed, leaving ray as the only local fish freely available to trawlermen. Laver-bread now mostly comes from the processors at Penclawdd and Crofty. It can be bought from some bread stalls and a cockle stall in the splendid glass-covered market. The price is 40p for eight ounces. Local cockles are now plentiful again along both sides of the Loughor estuary, following a few years of scarcity. Vegetable stalls in the market have fresh produce from Gower at the weekends, and there is one stall for exotica – pawpaw, mooli, bilberries, and so on. The cheese stall, Curds & Whey, has a good range of Welsh and continental cheeses. Of half a dozen wine bars 1266 at 1–2 St Mary's Street, and Corks, 39 Uplands Crescent, Uplands, are reliable. There are a number of old-fashioned bakers in the town – Davies in Uplands, Nancy Morgan in Bryn-y-mor Road, and*

T. & G. Davies in Mumbles. As we go to press Colin Pressdee is not sure how his involvement in the Drangway restaurant will be changing over the year, so with regret we have had to drop its entry. His canned food company continues to produce laver-bread (about four times the price of fresh) and has recently introduced three more dishes to join the range: seafood and cockle soup and cawl.

Heritage Restaurant [10/20]

2 Prospect Place, Swansea SA1 1QP
SWANSEA (0792) 473886 £13

A homely, good-value basement restaurant with white stucco walls, underneath a Welsh craft shop. Tasty, properly cooked food is served without frills: whatever fresh fish come in are usually grilled plainly, and there are tender steaks with a choice of four or five sauces. Home-made laver-bread pâté with chicken liver and herbs is the most Welsh dish on the menu, but Mrs Thomas makes good puddings, such as bread-and-butter, and light, spongy rhubarb and raspberry crumble. There are snacks at lunchtime, and two vegetarian dishes. Bulgarian house wine is £4.

CHEF/PROPRIETOR: Barbara Thomas
OPEN: all week MEALS: 8.30am to 5.30pm Mon to Fri, 7.30pm to 10pm Thur to Sat, 11 to 6 Sun
PRICES: £9 (£13), Snacks from 55p (65p) CARDS: Access, Amex, Diners, Visa
SEATS: 40. Private parties: 60 main room. Vegetarian meals. Children welcome. Music

TALSARNAU Gwynedd map 4

▲ *Hotel Maes-y-Neuadd* [11/20]

Talsarnau LL47 6YA
HARLECH (0766) 780200
off B4573, 3m N of Harlech £11–£16

Two couples run this centuries-old, granite and slate house in Snowdonia National Park. The menu is varied, drawing strongly on fish, mountain lamb and Welsh dishes, but with a few innovative touches. Good starters have been home-cured herring with cider and apple, the traditional Welsh mussel stew (though traditionally it is unlikely to contain garlic and sherry, surely) and prawn and salmon terrine. Halibut, lightly grilled and served with a wine sauce, and the duck breast with the ubiquitous green peppercorn sauce stand out as main courses. Vegetarian meals are available on request and rely on cheese for their zest – Brie pâté, and Stilton and vegetable pie. The cheeseboard is good. There are tarts to finish or puddings made with fruit from the orchard at the back of the

The Guide is always anxious to recruit new inspectors. If you would like to apply, write to the editor enclosing a) a detailed report on a restaurant where you have eaten and b) a comparative study of restaurants known to you.

New restaurants that we have not been able to assess completely are given a zero rating for this year. We are particularly keen to have reports on these places.

house. Plenty to brood over on the list of well-chosen, essentially French wines. CELLARMAN'S CHOICE: Ch. Chasse-Spleen '78 at £13·90.

CHEFS: Olive Horsfall, June Slatter and Andrew Price
PROPRIETORS: Michael and June Slatter, Malcolm and Olive Horsfall
OPEN: all week CLOSED: 3 to 24 Jan MEALS: 12.15 to 1.45, 7.30 to 9
PRICES: Set L from £7·25 (£11), Set D from £11 (£16) CARDS: Access, Amex, Diners, Visa
SEATS: 40. Private parties: 70 main room, 20 private room. Car-park, 50 places. Vegetarian meals. Children's helpings. No children under 5 at D. Smart dress preferred. Wheelchair access
ACCOMMODATION: 14 rooms, 12 with bath/shower. Room for disabled. B&B £22 to £52. Deposit: £20. No children under 7. Dogs by arrangement. Afternoon teas. Garden. Helicopter pad. TV. Scenic. Doors close at 11. Confirm by 6

TALYLLYN Gwynedd — map 4

▲ *Minffordd Hotel* [12/20]

Talyllyn LL36 9AJ
CORRIS (065 473) 665
at junction of A487 and B4405 — £12

The Pickles will accept non-resident diners at their comfortable hotel where, as they put it, the amenities are those of nature rather than of the electronic age: card games and conversation instead of television. It follows that the food tends to be fresh and local. The short menu changes from day to day and mixes popular hotel dishes, such as chilled honeydew melon and rainbow trout in Pernod sauce, with more solidly country cooking, such as smoked haddock soup and roast honeyed leg of Welsh lamb, or roast guinea-fowl in Normandy sauce. There is a selection of British cheeses. Wines are good value because the mark-up is a flat £2. CELLARMAN'S CHOICE: Gevrey-Chambertin, Domaine des Varoilles '80, at £11·20.

CHEF: Jonathan Pickles PROPRIETORS: Bernard and Jessica Pickles
OPEN: Tue to Sat, D only CLOSED: Jan and Feb, and weekdays Nov, Dec and Mar
MEALS: 7.30 to 8.30
PRICES: Set D £9·30 (£12). Service inc CARDS: Access, Diners, Visa
SEATS: 28. Private parties: 28 main room. Car-park, 12 places. Vegetarian meals. Children's helpings. No children under 3. Smart dress preferred. No smoking in dining-room
ACCOMMODATION: 7 rooms, all with bath/shower. B&B £24·50 to £43. No children under 3. No pets. Garden. Phone. Scenic [GHG]

TENBY Dyfed — map 4

Chinatown [new entry, zero rated]

Lower Frog Street, Tenby SA70 8BX
TENBY (0834) 3557 — £6–£9

A converted terraced house, now a Cantonese restaurant with red flock walls, hanging lanterns and Chinese pictures. Among the dishes that have impressed as being well above local standards are the lemon chicken, crispy duck and deep-fried beef with green peppers. Service is helpful. Licensed. More reports, please.

CHEF: Fu Kung Man PROPRIETOR: Yau Ken Chung
OPEN: all week MEALS: 12 to 2, 5 to 12
PRICES: £7 (£11), Set L from £3·30 (£6), Set D from £6·40 (£9). Service inc CARDS: Access, Amex, Visa
SEATS: 60. 15 tables outside. Private parties: 80 main room, 30 private room. Vegetarian meals. Children's helpings. No children under 5. Wheelchair access (also wc). Oriental music. Air-conditioned

THREE COCKS Powys — map 4

▲ *Three Cocks Hotel* [new owners, zero rated]

Three Cocks LD3 0SL
GLASBURY (049 74) 215
on A438 between Brecon and Hay-on-Wye — £18–£19

The Winstones now run this fifteenth-century inn with its view of the Black Mountains. Good ingredients have included scallops, vegetables, and duck, which is roasted and served with a cherry sauce. Garlic butter finds its way into lots of starters, and steak figures prominently among main courses. Service is pleasant. House claret from Luc Lacerre is £7·50, and Croffta, a dry white produced by John Bevan at Groes-faen in Mid Glamorgan from Müller-Thurgau, Seyve-Villard and Madeleine Angevine grapes, is £9. More reports, please.

CHEF: M.E. Winstone PROPRIETORS: Mr and Mrs M.E. Winstone
OPEN: all week CLOSED: Jan MEALS: 12 to 2, 7 to 9.30
PRICES: £14 (£19), Set L and D £14 (£18). Service inc CARDS: Access, Visa
SEATS: 40. Private parties: 40 main room. Car-park, 30 places. Children's helpings. Smart dress preferred. Classical music
ACCOMMODATION: 7 rooms. B&B £16 to £32. Children welcome. Baby facilities. Garden. Scenic

TUDWEILIOG Gwynedd — map 4

Dive Inn [10/20]

Tudweiliog LL53 8PB
TUDWEILIOG (075 887) 246 — £12–£18

This family-run restaurant specialises in fish, as well it might, since it is situated on a cliff-top 500 yards from the sea. At lunch-time there are fresh crab salads, but in the evening lobster features. Supplies are from local boats. Sauces are straightforward – mayonnaise and Mornay. The Williamses say we under-rated their sweets last year. House Italian is £5·60 a litre.

CHEFS: Mary and Stephen Williams PROPRIETORS: Edric and Mary Williams
OPEN: all week, exc Sun D MEALS: 12 to 2, 7 to 9.30
PRICES: Set D from £7·85 to £14·75 (£12 to £18), Bar L from £1·25 (£1·40)
SEATS: 65. Private parties: 40 main room, 18 private room. Car-park, 40 places. Children's helpings. Smart dress preferred. Wheelchair access (also wc)

Places rating 8 or 9 may not be restaurants at all but still serve very good food. In this category expect to find pubs, cafes, small hotels and wine bars.

WOLF'S CASTLE Dyfed map 4

▲ *Wolfscastle Country Hotel* [11/20]

Wolf's Castle SA62 5LZ
TREFFGARNE (043 787) 225
on A40, 7m S of Fishguard £16

Quite ambitious hotel cooking, from a kitchen that shows enthusiasm and respect for its ingredients, can be eaten in the bar for half the price of the main dining-room, but with half the poise, too. The dining-room is large, with the sweets trolley in the middle, and there are views of flowers and trees across the valley. The portions are large and there is a lot of cream. Kidneys are sauté and placed with a green peppercorn sauce inside a bouchée, which should be an improvement on the same dish that arrived with rice instead of pastry at one inspection. Another elaborate dish is crayfish tails sauté in garlic and served with prawns and scrambled eggs, but there are also classic dishes, like sewin with hollandaise or guinea-fowl vallée d'Auge. The rating is dropped a point because standards fluctuate, although the garnishing is consistent. A good wine list of nearly 50 well-annotated bottles; house French is £5·25.

CHEFS: Michael Lewis and Alex George PROPRIETOR: Andrew Maxwell Stirling
OPEN: Mon to Sat D, Sun L CLOSED: 23 to 30 Dec MEALS: 12 to 2, 7 to 9.30
PRICES: £11 (£16), Bar meals from 90p (£1) CARDS: Access, Amex, Visa
SEATS: 60. Private parties: 90 main room. Car-park, 60 places. Vegetarian meals. Children's helpings. Smart dress preferred. No pipes/cigars in dining-room. Wheelchair access. Pianist once a week. Air-conditioned
ACCOMMODATION: 12 rooms, 8 with bath/shower. B&B £22 to £33. Children welcome. Baby facilities. Pets welcome. Garden. Tennis. Squash. TV. Scenic. Doors close at 12. Confirm by 6 [GHG]

Northern Ireland

Most of the best hotels are just outside Belfast: the **Culloden** (Holywood 5223) beside BELFAST LOUGH, the **Conway** (Belfast 612101) in DUNMURRY, six miles to the south, which is Trusthouse Forte, and **Dunadry Inn** (Templepatrick 32474) in Co. Antrim.

For restaurants, Co. Down has a good selection, with several having been opened by enterprising young couples. About five miles from Comber is **Nick's**, 18 Kilmood Church Road, Killinchy, NEWTOWNARDS. The restaurant is in a converted nineteenth-century court-house and serves afternoon teas as well as dinner from Tuesday to Saturday. The atmosphere is informal, and good dishes prepared from fresh ingredients have been monkfish in hot plum sauce, and turbot hollandaise. Vegetables are extra, but imaginative: cauliflower with cucumber sauce, spinach and courgette soufflé. Puddings have included banoffi pie. Three miles away at KILLINCHY CROSS ROADS is the very popular **Balloo House** (Killinchy 541210), a recently redecorated old coaching-inn near the yachting area of White Rock, open for bistro lunches, à la carte dinners, and a Sunday buffet.

Just off the A7 about 10 miles south-west of Belfast, on the Monlough Road, is **The Barn** (Saintfield 510396). Robbie Wright cooks and his wife Jane runs the front of house at this converted barn; the menu is enterprising, though dishes are sometimes rather over-elaborate. Desserts are reported to be good. **Nutgrove**, at SEAFORDE (Seaforde 275), is a restaurant in Heather and Christopher Cowdy's own early-Victorian miller's house. Open from Easter to October, Wednesday to Saturday, it serves dinner only, with a short menu of original dishes finely presented. A similar style of establishment is **Woodlands**, Spa Road, BALLYNAHINCH (Ballynahinch 562650) where Alison and David Sandford serve good food – with the accent on local produce – in their small country house. Drinks are in the family drawing-room; game is often featured.

Outside Co. Down we have very few recommendations. **The Bramley Apple**, Main Street, LOUGHGALL, Co. Armagh, is a former schoolhouse with a menu along the lines of chef's pâté, pork Cordon Bleu, and chicken Véronique. At BALLYCASTLE, Co. Antrim, the **Rendezvous**, Main Street, is a friendly, simply decorated cafe serving generous portions of dishes such as pasty and peas and chips, with pots of excellent tea. **The Beach Hotel**, BALLINTRAE, Co. Antrim has had good, fresh plaice with green beans, followed by a fine Pavlova.

More reports, please, on the following restaurants. In Co. Down: The George, Crawfordsburn Road, Clandeboye, Bangor; The Grange, Main Street, Waringstown; Henry T's, 74 Hill Street, Newry; Lobster Pot, 11 The Square, Strangford; Schooner, 30 High Street, Holywood. Elsewhere: Ramore, The Harbour, Portrush, Co. Antrim; Strand, 12 Stranmillis Road, Belfast; MacDuff's, 112 Killeaugue Road, Blackhill, Coleraine, Co. Derry.

Channel Islands

Three firm Channel Islands favourites have emerged from reports received in the last year. At the top of most lists is **Longueville Manor**, ST SAVIOUR, JERSEY (0534 25501), a comfortable and well-appointed hotel in an originally thirteenth-century building, where John Dicken serves skilfully prepared Real Food. Some dishes are in the modern style, such as warm oysters with toasted sesame seeds or lattice of leek and salmon with warm scallop and a truffle vinaigrette, but there are salutes to the classic French tradition, as in Barquette Michel Bourdin – a pastry shell with duxelles, quail eggs and hollandaise – and touches of more homely cooking, with chicken pie and lamb navarin. VAT-free wine puts Riesling Réserve Personnelle '79, from Hugel, at £9·50. Hotel facilities include a heated outdoor pool, private stables and grounds stretching through a wooded valley.

The **Old Court House**, ST AUBIN, JERSEY (0534 41156), is an old inn in a superb location overlooking the harbour (as Bergerac viewers will know). Like most major establishments in these islands it specialises in seafood. The reasonably priced set lunch has included a mountain of fresh mussels to start, with a large crab per person to follow. Fresh sardines, turbot stuffed with seafood, and poached salmon are also approved. For non-fish eaters the gazpacho and rack of lamb have been good, too. There is a limited wine list with most bottles hovering at the £5 mark.

Apple Cottage, ROZEL, JERSEY (0534 61002), is a pink granite cottage fronted by an old-fashioned garden. The food is typical of Jersey's best – spankingly fresh seafood cooked simply and served in very large quantities. It is unwise to order anything to follow the platter, which has a crab, half a lobster, langoustines, prawns, mussels, clams and oysters with a salad garnish and home-made mayonnaise. The plaice meunière and sea-bass cooked with fennel have also been excellent. Pat and Setti Pozzi also serve strawberry and Jersey cream-teas in the garden. The **Sea Crest Hotel**, Petit Port, CORBIÈRE, JERSEY (0534 42687), has good sea views, and serves authentic pasta dishes and a seafood menu on which the scallops, sea-bass, plaice and lobster have all been exemplary. Sadly, locals say the fish and chip shops on the islands are all so poor that they use them as little as possible. The use of frozen fish, which is cheaper than fresh and so allows the chippies to 'price competitively', probably explains the lack of popularity. A tip is to look for the word 'Jersey' and a higher price on the list if you want fresh fish.

Georgian House, Victoria Street, ALDERNEY, serves the best food on the island. Sunday lunch is the meal of the week, and there are good-value barbecue meals served in the garden in the summer. The other reported restaurant on ALDERNEY is **Nellie Grays**, where you can sit in a luxurious dining-room in the Edwardian style, or have an inexpensive lunch in the garden. Portions have been excessive, but some dishes are above average standard, notably fisherman's bisque, lamb kebab, and chicken with honey and a sharp chilli sauce.

Also worth mentioning on GUERNSEY are three places in ST PETER PORT: **Le Nautique**, Quay Steps, which has well-reported dishes of vichyssoise, brill with a mushroom and cheese sauce, and crêpes Suzettes; **St Pierre Park**, which is especially good for lunches; and **La Frégate**, where the set three-course lunch at £7·25 has offered shrimp and endive salad, monkfish, and apple pastry. JERSEY has several more addresses to note. Two in ST HELIER are: **La Buca**, a jolly place with good seafood on the set menu; and **Gradees**, Colomberie Court, where the artichoke hollandaise, king prawns in black bean sauce, and hot rum baba have all been fresh and well prepared. At the **Moorings Hotel**, Gorey Pier, the local advice is to go for the saddle of lamb en voiture. **Château de la Valeuse**, St Brelade's Bay, has dishes along the lines of whole Jersey melon, plate of Parma ham, and Dover sole, grilled or meunière. More reports, please, on: White House Hotel, Herm; Villa Dante, St Peter Port, Guernsey; Hotel L'Horizon, St Brelade's Bay, Jersey; Victoria's, Grand Hotel, St Helier, Jersey; and Aval du Creux, Sark, now that the Hausers have left.

France
Twenty great restaurants

These great restaurants of France are not necessarily the best places, although some would appear on everybody's list, but they are all unique in their own way.

LES BAUX-DE-PROVENCE Bouches-du-Rhône

L'Oustaù de la Baumanière, 13520

Tel (90) 97.33.07

The abrupt, scrawny hills called les Alpilles stand in the triangle formed by Avignon, Arles and Salon-de-Provence. Les Baux, at the centre, after which bauxite (aluminium ore) is named, is within reach of the Pont du Gard and a handful of Roman theatres, the wild Camargue, the landscape that Cézanne painted, and Alphonse Daudet's windmill. It is also the setting for one of France's most prestigious restaurants, Raymond Thuilier's l'Oustaù de la Baumanière, which recently celebrated 30 years of three Michelin stars. This is where royalty comes for home-from-home comfort and food that retains the best of tradition, refreshed by the lightness of *cuisine moderne*, on an inventive but not fashion-conscious menu. Everything tastes of what it should: Mediterranean fish served simply with herbs or a red wine sauce; the best pigeons in France; incomparably fresh vegetables; a vanilla mille-feuille to end all mille-feuilles. There are good local wines among the classics. It is not, of course, cheap.

Carte 500fr-plus

BENOUVILLE Calvados

Manoir d'Hastings

18 av de la Côte de Nacre, 14970
Tel (31) 44.63.14

Six miles out of Caen and situated in a seventeenth-century priory is one of the best restaurants in Normandy, though the cooking is noticeably lighter and less showy than you might expect either in the region or from a French restaurant of calibre. Outstanding has been the lobster cooked in cider and served with slices of glazed and browned apples, a few shallots and marinated raisins, and also the sole with freshly made pasta and a sauce of coriander and tomatoes. The sweets trolley holds half a dozen confections, from chestnut bavarois to orange mousse, and a second trolley holds another half-dozen sorbets. The wine list is comprehensive in claret, but accessible because it concentrates less on the *grands crus* and more on the minor vineyards.

CLOSED: Sun D, Mon. Set meals 110fr, 290fr, 300fr, carte 300fr

LES BEZARDS Loiret

Auberge des Templiers, 45290

Tel (38) 31.80.01

Once an auberge maybe, but now a four-star hotel and proud of it. Huge signs on the N7 ensure you cannot miss it. It is a low, timbered building that trades on its age and charm – enormous beams, a flagstoned floor and Persian rugs; it is formal and old-fashioned in its attention to detail. Fear not that you might have to pull in your own chair following a trip to the lavatory, nor that the waiters might be a milli-second apart in their synchronised salver lifting. There is no cult of the big chef personality here. Christian Willer stays in the kitchen and is uncredited on the menus. His cooking, though, is fashionably light with a refreshing interest, for France, in the textures of unpurée vegetables and in regional dishes. It is elegant – foie gras pâté is served with baby turnips and endive; scallops, oysters and langoustines are put together to form a cassoulette flavoured with ginger; saddle of lamb is stuffed with its kidneys and is boldly underdone. The cheeseboard, as befits the locality, is a playground for goats' cheese enthusiasts, and the sweets are sweet – most indulgent of all is the croquante à la banane, crunchy with chocolate and swimming in coffee sauce.

CLOSED: 15 Jan to 15 Feb. Set meals 230fr, 350fr, carte 400fr to 500fr

BOULOGNE-SUR-MER Pas-de-Calais

Hostellerie de la Rivière

17 rue de la Gare, Pont-de-Briques, 62360
Tel (21) 32.22.81

A restaurant for serious eaters. The name conjures up relaxed riverside eating with views over the rolling plains of the Pas-de-Calais. Nothing could be further from the truth. In a suburb of Boulogne, off the main road to Paris, this hotel and restaurant is in a built-up street which does have a bridge but one of no importance. The service is friendly. Even arriving late for lunch, the welcome is open armed, and the waiters, who are pleased to use their fractured English, do not rush you through the meal. The menu is not too extensive, and the food is a mixture of *nouvelle cuisine* and good old bourgeois traditions. The portions are generous, and some of the sauces are rich in butter and cream. Typical are the feuilleté of snails and the sole with a mousse of seafood and a sabayon-style sauce. Foie gras and scallops are specialities. Main courses have included lamb with tarragon, and although the lamb is definitely not of the quality of English or Welsh, the sauce, full of tarragon flavour, makes up for it. Kidneys in a rich wine sauce are exceptional; juicy and still pink. Vegetables receive careful attention. There is a good selection of puddings, which is unusual for a French restaurant. A charlottine of orange with chocolate sauce has not only home-made sponge

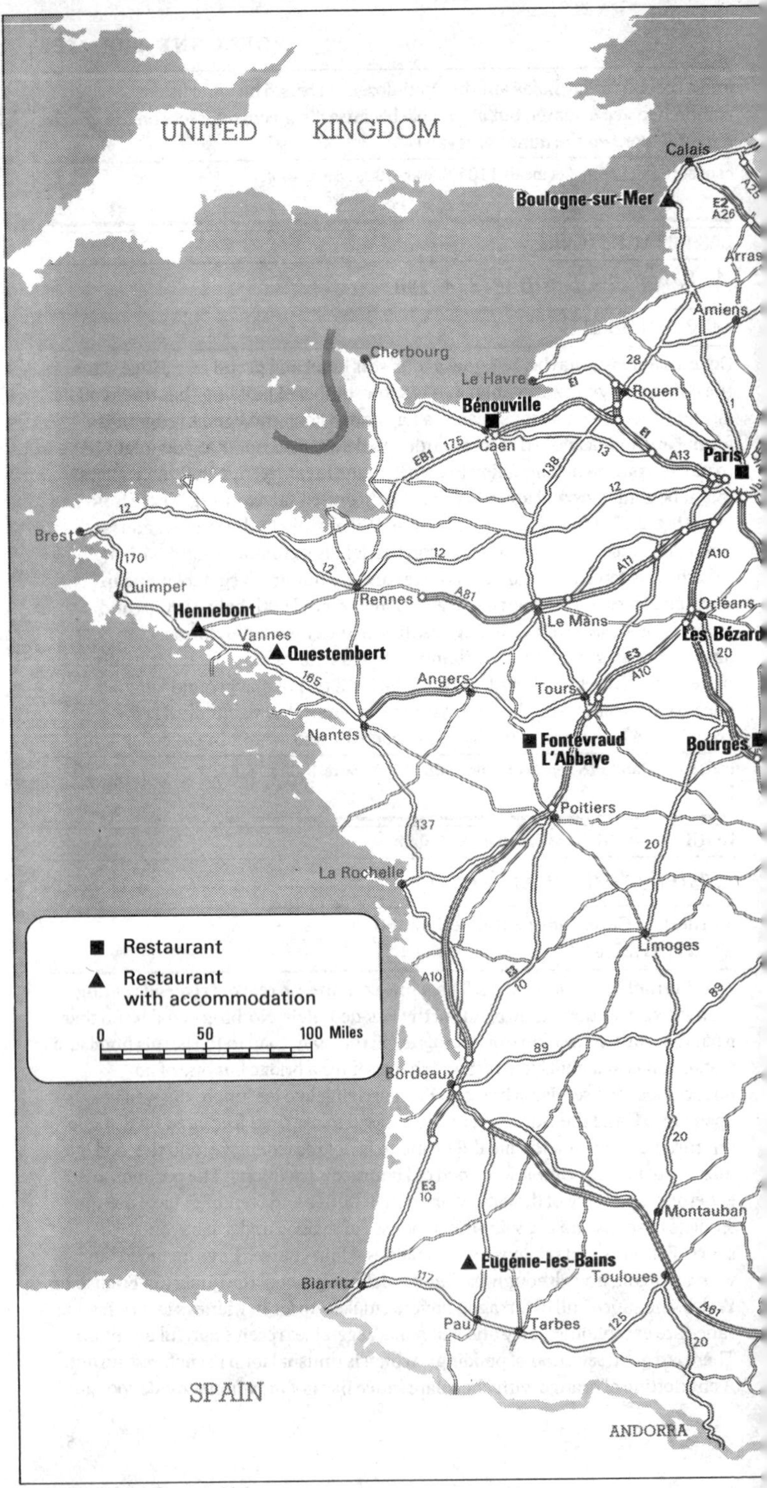
UNITED KINGDOM
Calais
Boulogne-sur-Mer
Arras
Amiens
Cherbourg
Le Havre
Rouen
Bénouville
Caen
Paris
Brest
Quimper
Hennebont
Vannes
Questembert
Rennes
Le Mans
Orleans
Les Bézard
Angers
Tours
Nantes
Fontevraud L'Abbaye
Bourges
Poitiers
La Rochelle
Limoges
Bordeaux
Montauban
Eugénie-les-Bains
Biarritz
Touloues
Pau
Tarbes
SPAIN
ANDORRA
Restaurant
Restaurant with accommodation
0
50
100 Miles

Cartographic Services (Cirencester) Ltd.

FRANCE: TWENTY GREAT RESTAURANTS

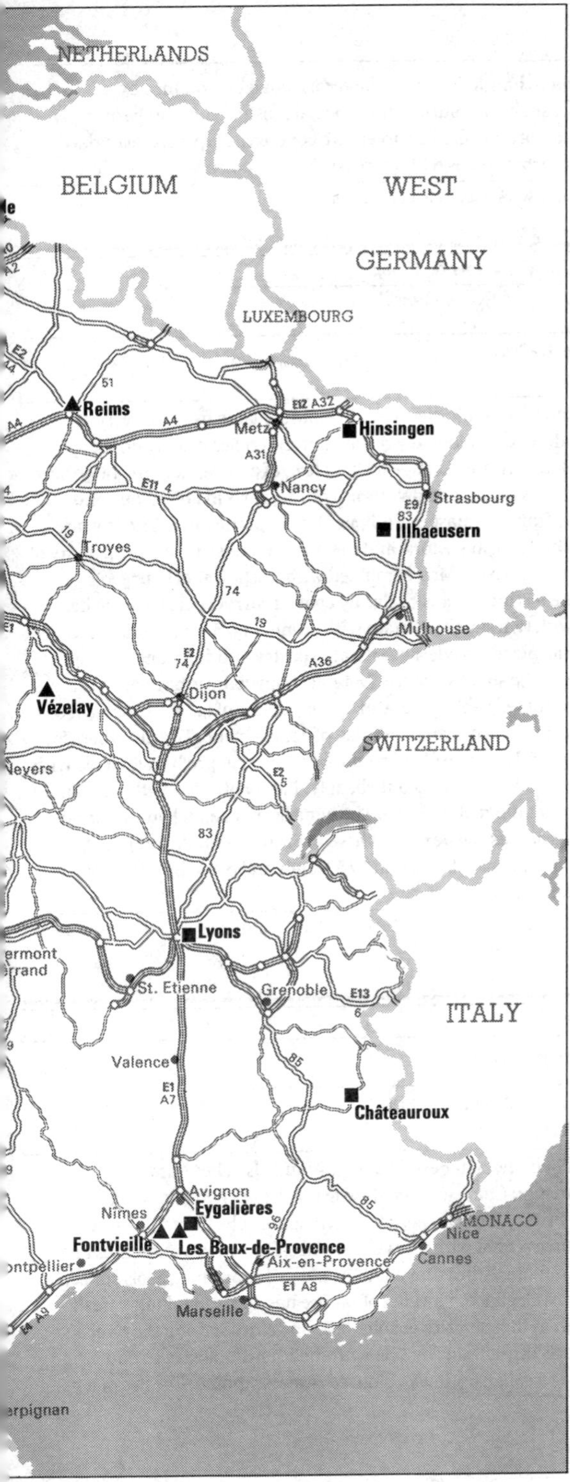

fingers and a lighter-than-light orange bavarois, but is surrounded by a chocolate sauce of such dark purity and chocolate taste that it can be an outstanding feature of a meal. The sorbets are covered in expensive eau-de-vie or marc. The lemon sorbet comes with marc de champagne, and plenty of it.

CLOSED: Sun D, Mon, 1 week Feb, Aug. Carte 180fr

BOULOGNE-SUR-MER Pas-de-Calais

La Matelote

80 bvd Ste Beuve, 62200
Tel (21) 30.17.97

Opposite the casino and ideally placed – a 10-minute walk from the ferry terminal – is this deceptively low-key restaurant that relies heavily on the strengths of the Boulogne markets – excellent fish, of course, from the huge fleet that docks a few yards away (and dwarfs its counterparts in Folkestone and Dover) and cheese from the master, Philippe Olivier, in the town. The staff are used to dealing with English visitors, and the menu is constructed using many of the good habits of modern cooking combined with the power of bourgeois traditions – a skate terrine lined with lightly cooked carrots held by a chicken jelly and served with two sauces, tomato with cumin and a pesto; or else the white flesh of a crab placed inside a giant hat of pastry and surrounded by an intense and aristocratic shellfish sauce. Notable main courses have been the steaks with a purée of red cabbage; gratin of sole; a plate of langoustines grilled with fennel seeds and served with a side dish of beurre blanc. To finish there is a spectacularly colourful array of fresh fruits and sorbets, or profiteroles filled with vanilla cream. The set lunch works out cheaply. Plenty of coffee with platefuls of petits fours and very little rush to leave. The wine list is splendid on clarets and burgundies – at a price, as is true everywhere in France – but its pedigree goes all the way down to the Muscadet at around 75 francs and even the minor house clarets at around 60 francs.

CLOSED: Sun D, Tue, 15 June to 1 July, 20 Dec to 15 Jan. Set meals about 150fr, carte 250fr. Euro, Visa

BOURGES Cher

Le Jardin Gourmand

20 rue Viala or 57 rue Mirebeau, 18000
Tel (48) 24.54.21

After stints at Michelin two-star establishments and also chez Bardet at Châteauroux, Christian Chaveau and his wife Colette opened their own restaurant last February. First meals have been admirable, from the croûtons of chicken liver mousse served with an eye-glassful of Pineau des Charentes as aperitifs to copious main dishes that combine old-fashioned bourgeois concepts with *nouvelle cuisine* elegance. The fillet of sandre has come spankingly fresh – infrequent enough in the majority of Loire-side hostelries serving the river's native fish – morsels of quail side by side with their hard-boiled eggs and artichoke hearts as a salad; a snowy coloured rascasse mousseline lies in a pond of particularly fine beurre blanc, liaised with Noilly Prat. Alpha main dishes are the bourgeois sauté shoulder of lamb and the farm rabbit served with an endive and shallot jam. The tarte solognote, a local speciality, is a variation of tarte tatin with ice-cream incorporated. Compliments for the wine list too, with a well-researched and reasonably priced variety of local wines purchased at the vineyards from individual growers – not the usual selection from a négociant's list.

CLOSED: Mon. Set meals 78fr, 120fr, carte 170fr

CHATEAUROUX Indre

Jean Bardet

1 rue Jean-Jacques Rousseau, 36000
Tel (54) 34.82.69

Jean Bardet is being hailed as one of the great new stars of French cooking. From the outside his restaurant looks like any other classy restaurant, only the prices are rather higher. The dining-room is hung with plants and set with padded chairs, and there is evidence of the overstated luxury that the French admire – more than two hundred goats' cheeses, and no fewer than three sweets served as part of the menu dégustation, which is quite a meal. After canapés and a meaty feuilleté, one evening's menu went through a meal underpinned with expensive wines in the sauces – a slice of foie gras marbled with yellow fat, served with a delicate Chasselas jelly and warm, thick pieces of toast; three Marennes oysters, barely cooked, sitting on tiny pools of hollandaise on a foam of purée cress sharpened with Muscadet; the next course, for contrast, was a ragout of scallops with a sweet sauce and ginger and minuscule shreds of mange-tout, broad beans, and tomato; and, justifiably after so many starters, there followed a sharp grapefruit sorbet. The main course was rabbit sliced with liver, surrounded by a purée of artichoke and its sauce of rosemary fused with rare Château-Chalon. After the massive classic cheeseboard came half a pear fried in butter and covered with caramelised nuts in a pool of Chantilly surrounded by chocolate fondant; *and then* a fan of mango glazed with lime and brushed with strawberry purée, served with a tuile and a lemon sorbet garnished with candied peel; *and then* a meringue split with semi-frozen cream in the same chocolate fondant as the pear; and finally, coffee and superb petits fours. The wine list is magnificent and viciously expensive, but there is local Quincy at around £10.

CLOSED: Sun, 3 weeks Feb, 17 to 27 Nov. Set meals 140fr, 280fr, carte 260fr to 300fr

EUGENIE-LES-BAINS Landes

Les Prés d'Eugénie

Geaune, 40320
Tel (58) 51.19.01

The sign at the entrance to the village proclaims Eugénie-les-Bains as the 'premier village minceur de France', but by some contradictory irony the next sign says, 'vente directe de foie gras'. Les Prés d'Eugénie stands well back from one end of the main and virtually only street of the tiny village and is set in a beautiful and impeccably kept park surrounded by tennis courts, swimming-pool and a fascinating herb and rose garden. In the hotel there is a formidable collection of antique clocks, but hardly any of them seems to work. The dining-room is set with pictures of food, game and gun-dogs. The staff are quite relaxed, except when they serve the napkin with a fork and spoon. Michel Guérard, perhaps the most influential of all the great French chefs of the last 20 years, persists with a *menu minceur*, relatively inexpensive at around 150 francs for three courses. But the real power of his cooking is to be found in the repas de ville (350 francs) and the repas des champs (320 francs). Here are such majestic dishes as a slice cut off a whole foie gras encased in a jelly made with Pomerol, garnished with a tart of fig conserve topped with lemon zest; half a lobster roasted and lightly smoked and served with a fabulous beurre blanc; grilled salmon with a sauce mousseuse lifted by the juice of oysters; a casserole of rabbit, pig's cheek and lamb's foot that becomes a gorgeous, sticky meat stew filled with vegetables and flanked by a ravioli filled with a meat farce. Believe that the pastry for the mille-feuille – flanked on one side by caramelised pears with an apricot sauce and on the other by a raspberry sauce – has wings and that even such gimmicky dishes as the little croûton-topped pots filled with a snail and a frog's leg are more than a conceit. There are an incredible 750-odd French wines of which 600 are red – the claret and white burgundy sections are the strongest – and some date from before the turn of the century. Monsieur Guérard's own Château de Sandmange has an unusual fruity tang and is 75 francs.

CLOSED: 4 Nov to 30 Mar. Set meals 230fr to 350fr, carte 400fr

EYGALIERES Bouches-du-Rhône

Auberge Provençale, 13810

Tel (90) 95.91.00

In contrast to the preceding entry, l'Auberge Provençale is a quiet country inn off the beaten track, with a courtyard for barbecues in summer. The limited menu is never the same from one meal to the next, apart from a large tray of hors d'oeuvres with a dozen items, including home-made onion confit, small calamares, red peppers and courgettes in oil and small brown lentils. The food is as simple and rustic as the surroundings: salad of hot chicken liver and raw duck breast with dandelion leaves, grapes and a sesame oil dressing; veal kidney, not just a few dainty slices but the entire organ in one piece, cooked pink, with smoked bacon and a rich peppery sauce; galette of grated potatoes; hot goats' cheese on toast with herbs and olive oil; prune tart with a slug of armagnac and a dollop of honey ice-cream. You will need a good appetite. A hundred and forty francs buys a large three-course lunch with one of ten wines on the list adding between 50 and 100 francs.

Set meals from 130fr

Restaurants are checked every year and their entries rewritten. The restaurant scene changes very rapidly so don't be caught with an out-of-date Guide.

An index of restaurants by name appears at the back of the Guide.

FONTEVRAUD L'ABBAYE Maine-et-Loire

Restaurant de l'Abbaye, 49590

Tel (41) 51.71.04

Set meals 47fr, 50fr, 76fr, carte 100fr

Restaurant la Licorne, 49590

Tel (41) 51.72.49

Our Plantagenet rulers are buried at Fontevraud, which has two restaurants, each providing good food, within the shadow of the abbey. Sunday is the most entertaining day to lunch at the unpretentious Restaurant de l'Abbaye. By one o'clock the large dining-room is packed with shoulder-to-shoulder citizenry; the overflow takes up the bar. The sauce-stained menus recall the glorious eccentricity produced by the late Louis Carini's vintage typewriter in the heyday of The Deanery in Ripon. Délice de grandmère figures on two of the set meals, and consists of large morsels of breadcrumbed deep-fried béchamel-cheese mixture. Steaks of grilled salmon are set off by shallot-packed beurre blanc, and massive portions of guinea-fowl forestière are succeeded by a generous frisée salad laced with a mordant, tasty vinaigrette, then cheese and various desserts, the most calorific of which is the giant omelette Norvegiènne (*sic*). Excellent local wines, such as Savennières, Clos St Yves, and Filliatreau's Saumur Champigny Vieilles Vignes, are modestly priced.

La Licorne, up the road, is a different sort of establishment. Local vignerons, not easily impressed by up-market eating houses, eat here. Jean Criton took on a young chef from the Prieuré, and the combination of perfectionist patron and gifted cook is irresistible. The ambience is confidence-inspiring: elegant and cool. The menu changes with the season, and has an emphasis on fish. The 120 franc meal is excellent value. Home-prepared pâté de foie gras (served with a glass of venerable Coteaux du Layon); smoked salmon à la julienne d'endives; bouillon of chicken with a hint of fresh ginger is a satisfying and delicate broth. These precede major creations such as colourful étuvée of sweetbreads with fresh lime; inspired fricassée of guinea-fowl with langoustine sauce – succulent joints of bird dressed with lozenges of courgette and large morsels of langoustine. Otherwise, turbot is served with oysters, and salmon is cooked with cider vinegar and apple. Of the puddings, a hot poached pear nestling in a new-cooked sponge of blow-away lightness served with fresh blackcurrant sauce stands out. Good locally attributed wines are the obvious choice compared with expensive less-identifiable *grands crus* from Burgundy or Bordeaux.

Set meals from 120fr

'The sartorial habits of the children of the family may cause offence to anyone who fought in the Second World War, i.e. a T-shirt advertising Hitler's tour of Europe 1939–1945.' (On staying at an expensive country house hotel in Scotland)

If you suspect that a restaurant is using processed food, always ask. It would be a contravention of the Trade Descriptions Act for the restaurant to lie.

FONTVIEILLE Bouches-du-Rhône

Auberge la Régalido

rue Frédéric Mistral, 13990
Tel (90) 97.60.22

Auberge la Régalido, between Les Baux and Arles, is the place to stay: a small, stylish hotel-restaurant with comfortable settees clustered around a big cheminée, and a dining-room that seems to have been carved out of the rock. Proprietor M. Michel is welcoming, courteous, attentive and everywhere at once, although he's probably best in the kitchen: starters and main courses both range from 50 to 100 francs, and the seasonally changing menu might include a pastry case of lamb sweetbreads with morel mushrooms in cream; Provençal Aïgo Sau (a variation of bouillabaisse); strips of sole and cabbage cooked with tagliatelle and mushrooms. Cheeses are good, and the sorbet made with marc is a knockout. House wine is young Châteauneuf-du-Pape, there are plenty from Provence, and the local Domaine de Trévallon '82 is first-rate. The food is taken seriously, but it is not a place that stands on ceremony.

CLOSED (Rest.): Mon, Tue L. Carte 200fr to 250fr

HENNEBONT Morbihan

Château de Locguénolé, 56700

4km S on the D781, Route de Port-Louis
Tel (97) 76.29.04

The château is not of the same stature as its setting or as the sunsets over the bay, but the cooking at meals we have eaten has been classy without the usual ensuing pretentions and flurry of other major French restaurants. The set menus at 340 and 420 francs start with an amazing course of appetisers – salmon pâté, an oyster, beautiful rough vegetable and ham terrine, choux pastry filled with mildly curried lobster, and onion tarts. Each menu contains genuine contrasts, from superb asparagus feuilleté to pigeon garnished with artichoke hearts, and a purée made from the bird's wings, grapes and carrots. Portions are not small. Sweetbread arrives as a single piece studded with cloves and is cut into slices. Alongside comes a sauce of carrots and more cloves in cream, and a blanched lettuce filled with chopped mushrooms. Langoustines come with sole in a fish stock sauce and garnished with a pancake filled with leeks and celery-flavoured custard, or else with a Sauternes sauce. Sweets are plentiful but have not been quite as good as the rest of the meal. There are some useful half-bottles on the wine list, which can ease the impact of the price of the *grand cru* clarets.

CLOSED: Mon and 15 Nov to 1 Mar. Set meals 185fr to 420fr, carte 300fr to 350fr

The 1987 Guide *will appear before Christmas 1986, so reports are particularly important in the spring. Report forms are at the back of this book, but just write a letter if you prefer. Address them to* The Good Food Guide, *Freepost, 14 Buckingham Street, London WC2N 6BR. No stamp is necessary if you post in the UK.*

HINSINGEN Bas Rhin

La Grange du Paysan

8 rue Principale, 67260
Tel (88) 00.91.83

Off the beaten track, but not too far from the Paris to Strasbourg autoroute and not difficult to find with a Michelin map, is the little farming village of Hinsingen (population 106). The Grange has been converted, just, from a clutch of old buildings: a small cowshed, a large conservatory and a fair-sized barn constitute the dining-areas. It is still convincingly rustic, despite the display of ersatz wooden farming tools. It serves unashamedly regional food: very farmhouse, very good and very cheap. It is largely a case of 'If that's choucroute, it must be Wednesday,' although there is a selection of fixed-price menus at about 60 francs upwards, and a carte as well. Pot-au-feu à l'alsacienne, potato pancakes, and their own grain-fed chicken feature at some time or other during the week. Bäckeofen on Fridays is a slow-cooked dish of bacon hock and trotter buried in sliced potatoes and sealed in the pot. At Sunday lunchtime, families troop in for the likes of a four-course menu for 90 francs, starting off with a generous platter of rough pork terrine (a whole bowl – help yourself to as much as you like), boudin noir and boudin blanc (ditto), as well as leeks, carrots, coleslaw, and so on and so forth. Don't be tempted to overdo it, because tarte flambée (a.k.a. Flammkuchen) comes next, a thin charcoal-crisp savoury pancake with onion, smoked bacon and crème fraîche, to be followed by the main course: slices from a whole roast suckling pig (whisked round on a wooden stretcher for oohs and aahs while you're tucking into your tart) come complete with crisp crackling and a stuffing made from all the unmentionable bits with which it was already stuffed, as it were, before its appointment at the abattoir, minced and slightly rearranged. Ordinary-looking mushrooms with a gloriously wild flavour, a baked potato, a jug of crème fraîche to pour over them, and a bowl of tossed green salad ensure that you don't go away short changed in either quantity or quality. Puddings of ice-cream, crème caramel and fruit tart are rather less exciting. Drink Alsace wine or Strasbourg beer. This is simple, straightforward food, but honest; it is overseen by an understanding proprietress, served at an unhurried pace (allow for that if you're treating it as a motorway stop), and at a price that almost makes up for the tolls.

CLOSED: Mon. Set meals 52fr, 63fr, 65fr, carte 130fr

ILLHAEUSERN Haut-Rhin

Auberge de L'Ill

Ribeauvillé, 68150
Tel (89) 71.83.23

This little village in the heart of Alsace could be overlooked on a map. The place itself might even be ignored – despite its charm and beauty, because after all Alsace has plenty of both – but for the fact that here the brothers Haeberlin run their restaurant, L'Auberge de L'Ill. The inn stands by the bridge, somewhat changed since 1882 when it started as a small tavern selling fried fish or crayfish fritters to the local gentry. Now, the garden creates a gentle ambience, being riverside, lawned, tree-lined, with small paved patios and pretty terraces. Floodlit at night, it is in full view through the dining-room picture windows, and before and after dinner drinks can be enjoyed there. Jean-Pierre Haeberlin is a competent painter and the menu shows one of his watercolours. He played a major role in redesigning the decor, the garden and the paraphernalia when the restaurant was rebuilt after the Second World War. He takes authoritative but gentle charge of the dining-room. Paul Haeberlin, now assisted by his son Marc (also a talented artist), cooks. The menu reflects Paul's traditional approach and Marc's classical training, but there are also innovative touches from Marc, inspired by oriental journeys of culinary discovery. For example, lobster comes with spices; medallions of veal with lemon and ginger. More conventionally there is turbot with tomato and tarragon, and fillet of beef with shallots.

The menu gastronomique at 780 francs illustrates the force of the cooking. Consommé de pigeonneau aux oeufs de cailles et aux aromates: deep-flavoured consommé garnished with tiny cubes of pigeon meat and carrots and containing three poached quails' eggs. Terrine de foie gras truffé: some say that foie gras d'Alsace is the finest in the world, and that the foie gras at L'Auberge de L'Ill is the finest in Alsace. Three fan-shaped slices are laid in a stoneware pot decorated with orchids – rich, pink and smooth, with the texture almost of butter. Mousseline de grenouilles et les filets de poissons de rivière: the smooth, moulded mousseline stands on a leaf of spinach garnished with chopped chives in a velvety sauce of cream sharpened with lemon. Surrounding it are fresh fillets of local carp, salmon and eel. When cut, the mousse reveals its contents of frogs' thighs. The local story is that Queen Elizabeth the Queen Mother had avoided eating frogs' legs until she came to L'Auberge de L'Ill – and reputedly, after sampling it here, regretted waiting so long. Well, that's their story and they're sticking to it. Ballotine de lapereau aux ris de veau: firm, rich pale meat of a young rabbit is rolled with soft, white veal sweetbreads and served with a rich truffle sauce made with stock and cream. Chinese-style noodles with strips of peppers, carrots and courgettes provide a refreshing contrast.

Cheeses are numerous. Sweets are listed on a separate menu, the front of which features a watercolour by Marc. You can even have a taste of all the sweets with an 'assiette gourmande': charlotte au caramel, mousse au chocolat, sorbet de champagne, sorbet de fraises, and an exquisite green rhubarb purée with Sauternes.

The wine list is appropriate to the food, with over 600 bottles that include, of course, a detailed selection from Alsace, and the 1983 champion sommelier of France is there to dispense them. The wines are not as expensive as their breeding might indicate, but if you wished you could pay between 1,000 and 5,000 francs for a Romanée-Conti, depending on vintage.

CLOSED: Tue, Mon in winter, 1 to 11 July, Feb. Set meals 220fr, 320fr, carte 380fr to 420fr

New restaurants that we have not been able to assess completely are given a zero rating for this year. We are particularly keen to have reports on these places.

All Guide *inspectors are anonymous. Anyone purporting to represent the* Guide *is an impostor.*

LILLE Nord

Le Flambard

79 rue d'Angleterre, 59000
Tel (20) 51.00.06

Lille is easily missed on journeys through France, being a little to the north for most travellers and easily passed by drivers who use the motorways. However, down a dingy cobbled street in the old part of the city a deep-blue awning marks the establishment of M. Robert Bardot, Maître Cuisinier de l'Académie Culinaire de France. Pass the carved wooden bar and in front of it is the mock façade of a large floodlit mansion. Eat in the courtyard, under the 'sky' of a blue painted ceiling. There is a *carte* and three *menus gourmands* from 180 to 360 francs, and a choice of some 350 wines of impeccable character. The 360-franc set meal is a feast. First, a selection of hors d'oeuvre, including sauté baby onion covered by an orange glaze with a garnish of julienne strips of orange peel. Then suprême of pigeon perfumed with Muscadet – rich young breast with a hint of nutmeg and a salad of asparagus, artichoke, julienne of carrot and celery – followed by firm white meat of baby lobster dressed in a delicate curry sauce with a tender wild mushroom alongside. Next comes a champagne sorbet, then a fillet of rich turbot with beurre de tomate, the turbot with a distinct, yet not overpowering flavour from the anchovy fillet which lies on top, the sauce a blend of clarified butter and purée tomato, delicate in taste and pastel-shaded. The entrée consists of four noisettes of young lamb in a glazed sauce, garnished with lamb sweetbreads and with a tiny portion of braised lambs' trotters diced and wrapped in spinach. The accompanying ravioli is filled with a sharp, but not bitter, goats' cheese. The cheeses themselves are numerous and include a Roquefort moulded with armagnac. Sweets and petits fours are equally impressive. Service is impeccable, from the proud presentation and announcement of the dishes, to the wine waiter who tastes each of the wines before offering them to the customer. There are *grand* and *premier cru* burgundies and a host of clarets, 10 or more listed from the many *cru* Châteaux.

CLOSED: Sun D, Mon, Aug, early Jan. Set meals 180fr to 360fr, carte 200fr to 300fr. Amex, Diners

LYONS Rhône

Léon de Lyon

1 rue Pleney, 69000
Tel (7) 828.11.33

There are a number of very good restaurants in Lyons, a city that might well lay claim to the title of the gastronomic capital of France. This is its figurehead – a vast, glowing shopfront hiding an elegant and unassertive Edwardian restaurant cooking traditionally lyonnais dishes and using lyonnais produce. Here it is possible to eat *gras-double émincé* – thin layers of tripe interspersed with cheese, covered with a tomato and onion confit; here it is possible to eat a simple salad of dandelion leaves with tiny pieces of hot bacon and soft sliced boiled egg, whose reputation rests only on its vinaigrette dressing; here it is possible to start with a simple steamed garlic sausage served with lentils and potatoes with oil. Most fundamental of all is the Lyonnaiseries – lamb's foot, layers of calf's foot, garlic sausage, pig's muzzle and black pudding neatly arranged on a single plate garnished with lentils. Elsewhere the menu manages to find a way between the rustic in the way that it uses blade steak cuts for main courses – sauté in red wine for a few minutes, served with salsify and bonemarrow and a little macaroni – and between some elegant flourishes, as in the hot sole soufflé with a sauce of white wine and also one of shellfish. The waiters in blue shirts and aprons are professional, the linen is faultless and the crockery durable rather than elegant. The dining-chairs are comfortably solid, designed to support the weightier lyonnais. There are Beaujolais on the wine list around 70 francs which will match the food.

CLOSED: Sun and Mon L, 23 Dec to 6 Jan. Set meals 130fr, 200fr, carte 300fr

PARIS

Robuchon (formerly *Jamin*)

32 rue Longchamp, 16e
Tel (1) 727.12.27

Book a month in advance. Joël Robuchon has established himself as the new champion of French cooking. The restaurant has even changed its name after him. Whether or not Robuchon will be able to handle the pressure that such a reputation brings remains to be seen, but his cooking can be a revelation. He comes from Poitiers and combines the *nouvelle* with the regional, but that is only a fraction of the story. He is a chef who cooks unto himself. The restaurant itself is chic without the usual Gallic flamboyance – indeed, he brought in a Japanese designer. His reputation comes from dishes such as the eye of a rack of lamb baked in salt with rosemary and served with a slightly curried sauce – made from the lamb bones and reduced to barely more than a couple of teaspoons – and with fresh noodles. Other dishes are the langoustine ravioli with a shredded cabbage garnish and a beurre blanc; mille-feuille of salmon; lime soufflé encased in freshly made pancakes and served with a strawberry sauce. Sometimes the descriptions make the reality sound more ordinary than it is, such as sweetbread and kidney fricasée with girolle, but after Robuchon's execution. . . . The memory of even his mashed potatoes lingers on in the mind, the result of his real art of cooking. There is a set lunch which is not extraordinarily expensive, and a section of the wine list, marked 'Divers', has some wines under 100 francs.

CLOSED: weekends July. Set meals 145fr, 350fr, carte 300fr to 500fr

QUESTEMBERT Morbihan

Hôtel de Bretagne

13 rue St Michel, 56230
Tel (97) 26.11.12

Madame resembles an escapee from an F. Scott Fitzgerald novel, and greets people in the bar area, which is bizarrely decorated with a wooden figure of Pan and modern brown corded-velvet, foam, armless, low sunken armchairs, whose curves mirror those of a four-feet-high wooden elephant. The dining-room is a sharp contrast, panelled in oak with an aquamarine ceiling and a slaty-blue coloured carpet. Georges Paineau specialises in Brittany cooking, but that in itself is in a confused state. Fish is the main subject. The speciality of the house is oysters from the bay of Quiberon, wrapped up in a spinach-beet leaf and served on a much reduced and very slightly thickened sauce of fumet of oyster. The sauces run through the menu as if they were an end in themselves – a thickened white wine and fish stock from the cheeks of monkfish served with fairly bloody chicken livers; an hollandaise-style sauce flavoured with a purée of celery for a gratin of langoustines; another fish stock and cream sauce, this time coloured with tomato for the goujons of sole and their little mound of mushrooms and garlic. The execution can be masterly, though it can also be careless, and there are some anomalies such as the strength of the Bordeaux wines for a fish restaurant – the Muscadet, though, is impeccable, as is the house cocktail – Muscadet with an orange liqueur, vanilla and a dash of vodka.

CLOSED: 3 Jan to 15 Mar, Sun and Mon, exc July and Aug. Set meals 140fr to 400fr, carte 300fr

RHEIMS Marne

Boyer 'Les Crayères'

64 bvd de Henri-Vasnier, 51100
Tel (26) 82.80.80

Gérard Boyer and his radiant wife Elyane, assisted by the Pommery Champagne house – Rheims is at the heart of the Champagne region – have converted this nineteenth-century château into one of the finest restaurants in France. Going through the 20-feet-tall iron gates into the walled garden you are struck by the elegant splendour of the magnificent, pure white, three-storeyed château with symmetrical arched windows and a four-columned doorway. At the rear, overlooking the 20 acres of tree-lined grounds, there is an open pebbled courtyard where you drink champagne and survey the menu. Indoors there is a marble stairway and mahogany reception desk. The dining-rooms are bare stone dressed with ancient tapestries and modern paintings, or covered from floor to 20-feet-high ceiling in restored wooden panels. Modern flush ceiling lights and silver candelabra carry on this theme of matching old and new.

The menu is seductive. There is a section offering fresh market produce and they will offer you several half portions as a menu de dégustation. Asparagus with puff pastry in a delicate truffle sauce is excellent, with soft and light, buttery layered pastry. Sea-bass comes as a small baked fillet, enriched with a buttery, well-seasoned creamy wine sauce, and garnished with chopped artichoke and julienne of red pepper. Most magnificent, however, is the duck with pears and ginger – succulent sliced breast of wild duck, not pink but a rich deep red, with deeply browned skin coated in a caramelised sauce made with the pear syrup and duck juices and with a julienne of sliced ginger as decoration. The pears are lightly poached and browned, their sweetness and softness complementing the richness of the rest of the dish. Another offering is last year's fashionable dish of fillet of lamb roast in a salt crust (originating from Joël Robuchon – see Paris). The crust is cut open at the table to reveal the deep red lamb which is then cut into thin slices and served with a rich brown stock and baby vegetables.

Cheeses are varied and served with fresh toasted bread. Gratin de fraises is poached strawberries served warm in a creamy custard and a hot syrup of strawberry purée, while the sweets trolley speciality is five sorbets spoon-moulded and arranged in a circle, the centre being filled with strawberries and stem ginger.

Choose from the encyclopaedic wine list – 130 champagnes and 35 white burgundies with at least three vintages from each. There is a small section of local reds from the Coteaux Champenois *appellation*; these are still wines, the better ones being produced from the *grand cru* and *premier cru* Champagne Villages; Bouzy is the best-known red and can be soft and elegantly fruity.

After dinner take a garden walk among the floodlit trees – white and pink horse-chestnuts, red-blossomed thorn, and deep bronze copper beech. A room costs between 700 and 900 francs; with views over the grounds, an enormous bed, a settee, walk-in wardrobe and marble-tiled bathroom, it is worth it for the experience. Breakfast – croissants, brioches, jams and marmalades, coffee, freshly pressed orange juice, goats' milk cheese and fresh fruit – a relative bargain at 46 francs, is served on a large circular table in your room with a pure white tablecloth and napkin.

CLOSED: Mon, Tue L, 23 Dec to 12 Jan. Carte 380fr to 400fr

VEZELAY Yonne

L'Espérance

à St-Père-sous-Vézelay, 89450
Tel (86) 33.20.45

Marc Meneau is one of the less famous of the elite of French chefs. To reach his restaurant you have to take the road from the ancient hilltop town of Vézelay to the unassuming village where his name is writ large. The dining-room is a glass dome with views on to the gardens. The tables, albeit well spaced on the tiled floors covered with rugs, are sizeable, as they need to be for the battery of napery. One of Meneau's achievements is his services to the petits fours: at the end of meals, the tables are suddenly cleared and refilled with plate upon plate upon plate of truffles, marzipan, fudge, pastries, nougat and a chocolate so soft it is served with a spoon. Some of his other dishes show more restraint – deep-fried cromesquis filled with purée foie gras; Loire salmon cooked almost blue, cut thick and served with a simple butter, tarragon, parsley, garlic and lemon sauce. Outstanding at two meals were the pastilles d'agneau Léonel – nuggets of lamb with a kidney and mushroom and served with a complementary creamy celery purée. Service is suave, and the wine list has a cornucopia of all that France offers, usually marked up in the region of three hundred per cent (par for the course), although the local wines are not bad – they're Chablis.

CLOSED: Tue and Wed L, Jan. Set meals 180fr, 280fr, 350fr, carte 300fr to 450fr

Channel ports

BOULOGNE-SUR-MER (Tel prefix 21)

The top restaurant is **La Matelote**, *80 bvd Ste Beuve*, and fish is what it does best: see Twenty great restaurants of France. A few doors along, at number 124, the busy **Hôtel Restaurant de la Plage** (Tel 31.45.35. Closed Mon, mid Dec to 20 Jan) is a down-market alternative serving straightforward food, useful if you've only a few francs left: fish soup, baby squid or brochette d'agneau with ratatouille.

In the centre of town, **La Liégeoise**, *10 rue Monsigny* (Tel 31.61.15. Closed Fri), takes the silver medal. Book, or get in early at lunchtime before the local businessmen, for succulent coquilles St Jacques with spinach; attractive salads; sole with lobster mousse; duck with mushrooms; and excellent sugar-spun puddings. The professional service is nearly as good as the cooking; not cheap, but worth the price.

The other restaurants can all be patchy, but you may strike lucky in *place Dalton* (number 24) at **Brasserie Alfred** (Tel 31.53.16. Closed Tue) with its long menu, big plateau de fruits de mer, and plentiful fish and shellfish, or (number 26–28) at the **Welsh Pub** (Tel 31.51.31) which is neither Welsh nor a pub but another brasserie serving stuffed mussels, coquilles St Jacques à la provençale, and decent cheeses. It's quiet, clean, professional, and very French. A few doors away, **La Charlotte**, at *11 rue du Doyen* (Tel 30.13.08) serves feuilleté de coquillages; mousse de foie de volaille au porto; mille-feuille de moules au curry. **L'Huîtrière**, *11 place Lorraine* (Tel 31.35.27. Closed Sun D, Mon), is both a shellfish shop and a clean, comfortable restaurant: buy fresh oysters to take away, or sit down to fillet of sole meunière.

By the quay on the corner of *rue Faidherbe* the **Hamiot** serves basic food to fishermen and tourists alike, and has a clean, comfortable but noisy hotel attached. Traffic also affects the **Hôtel Faidherbe**, *12 rue Faidherbe*, and the **Metropole**, *15 rue Thiers*, unless you get a room overlooking the garden. The **Lorraine**, *7 place Lorraine*, and the **Londres**, *22 place France*, are quieter and cheaper.

Philippe Olivier's cheese shop, *43–45 rue Thiers*, has an enthusiastic English following, not least among restaurateurs. Be prepared to queue, make sure you get at least one unpasteurised (lait cru) and one goats' cheese, and be specific about when you want to eat them. They also sell butter, fromage blanc and walnut bread, and will take sterling if you've spent all your francs.

On the same street the **Café Rous Seaux** sells freshly roasted coffee. In the *Grande Rue* charcuterie is good from **Derrien** (number 1), and pastry and chocolates from both **Lugand** (number 9) and **Au Cornet d'Amour**, *91 rue Thiers*.

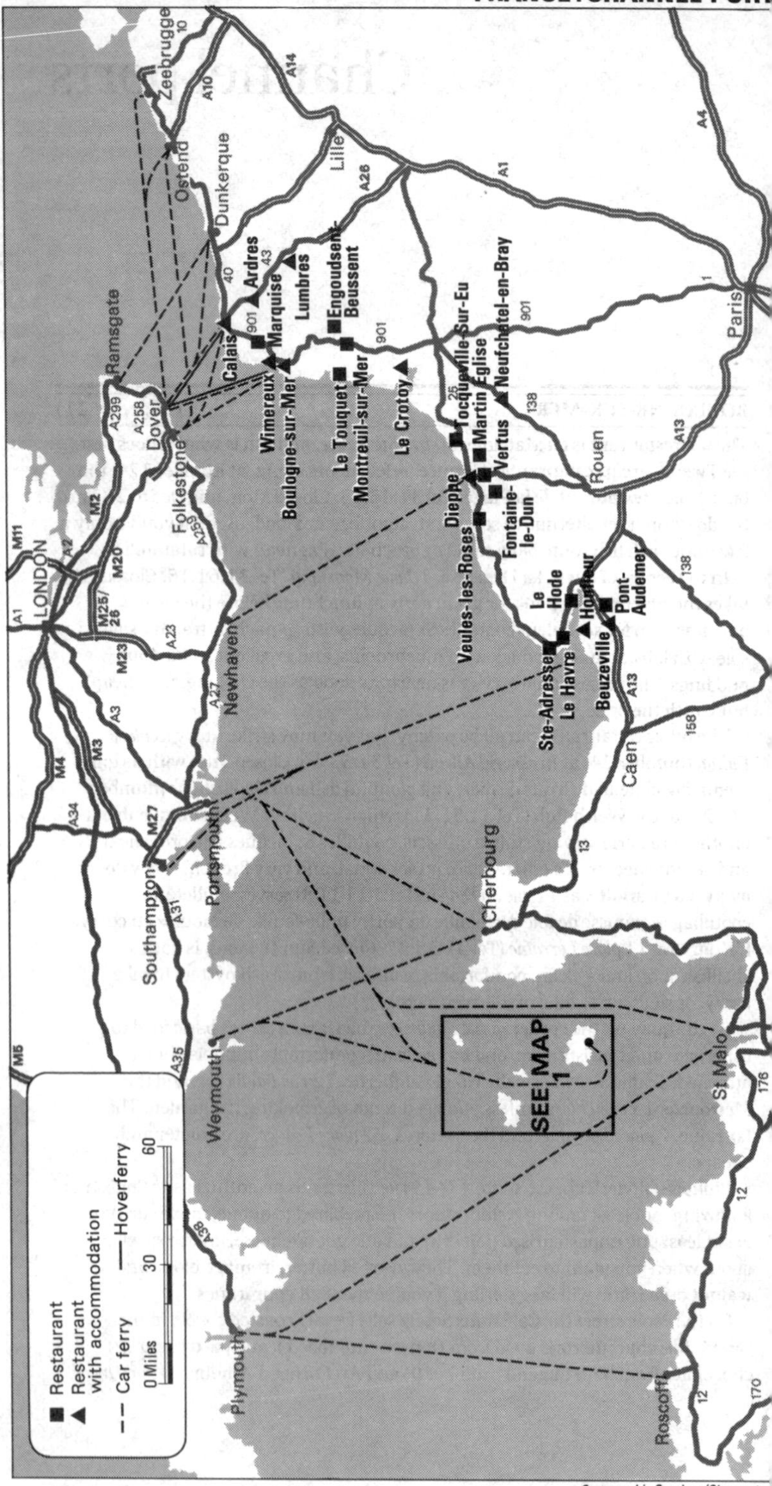

Cartographic Services (Cirencester)

Pick up wines from one of the branches of **Les Vins de France** at *13 rue Nationale, 4 rue de Lille*, or *34 rue de Brequerecque*. There is a **Nouvelles Galeries** in *rue Thiers* and a **Prisunic** at the corner of *rue Victor Hugo* and *Grande Rue*. The fish stalls line the quay opposite the ferry.

At WIMEREUX, 6km north along the D940 coast road, **Hôtel Restaurant du Centre**, *78 rue Carnot* (Tel 32.41.08. Closed Mon, 23 Dec to 20 Jan, 2 to 13 June), produces straightforward cooking with a few flourishes: soupe de poissons; moules marinière; coquilles St Jacques à la diable; saumon poché beurre blanc.

CALAIS (Tel prefix 21)

Hôtel des Dunes (Tel 34.54.30. Closed Mon) at *Blériot-Plage* is a 20-minute walk 2km west of town along the seafront esplanade, and is probably the best restaurant in Calais. Good-value fixed-price menus are served efficiently in a smart dining-room: generous and interesting hors d'oeuvres; good monkfish; rillettes de saumon; plateau de fruits de mer. The other restaurants are within easy reach of the *place d'Armes*, a large car-park surrounded by shops in the old town of Calais near the port. **Au Coq d'Or** (Tel 34.79.05. Closed Wed, 15 Jan to 1 Mar) at number 31 serves conventional, inexpensive dishes. Just around the corner, where the seafront joins the main street, at *1 bvd de la Résistance*, **La Sole Meunière** has a good and original selection of dishes using fish: they appear in couscous, choucroute and quiche; a *vivier* provides lobsters. Next door at number 3 there is traditional bourgeois cooking with a generous choice at **Le Channel**, with good langoustines mayonnaise, and turbot with mousseline sauce. **Le Touquet's** (Tel 34.64.18), on the main street, *57 rue Royale*, is a useful brasserie open from noon to 2am for couscous and plateau de fruits de mer, but the menu is basic enough for all the family, prices are attractive, and parties are catered for.

The *place d'Armes* has a market on Wednesday and Saturday (the one in *place Crèvecoeur* is on Thursday and Saturday), a supermarket called **Gro**, and two wine shops, **Le Cellier** and **La Feuillandine**. Close by, at *1 rue André-Gerschel*, is the **Maison du Fromage**, not perhaps the equal of Philippe Olivier (see Boulogne) but with a comprehensive selection of cheese nonetheless. The *rue Royale* is the place to buy charcuterie, from **Bellynck** (number 10), pastries, from **Au Croissant d'Or** (number 48) or **Outhier** (number 53), and coffee, from **Coffea** (number 65).

Continuing away from the port past the town hall into what used to be a separate town called St Pierre but is now Calais-sud, the main road becomes *bvd Jacquard* and its better shops include **A la Sole Berckoise** (number 55) for fish, **Lablanche** (number 41) for charcuterie, and **La Chocolaterie** (number 84) for guess what, as well as two department stores **Au Printemps** and **Prisunic**.

Near the big crossroads another restaurant, **Moulin à Poivre**, *10 rue Neuve*, serves imaginative dishes based on fish, duck and game. Turning left into *bvd Lafayette* brings you to the **Croissant Chaud**, another good fish shop, **Huîtrière Calaisienne** (number 12), and two charcuteries **Eng Davelou** and **Fin Bec** (number 30).

About 17km along the N43 from Calais towards St Omer, the **Grand Hôtel Clément** (Tel 82.25.25. Closed Mon) at ARDRES is a comfortable *relais du silence* where young François Coolen combines classical and *nouvelle* skills to produce a northern fish soup; hot pike pâté with sorrel; lapin aux pruneaux; langue de porc; noisettes d'agneau. It can be expensive. **Le Relais** (Tel 35.42.00) is much cheaper, serving cassolette d'escargots, rognons de veau, and first-class lamb.

At LUMBRES, near St Omer on the N42 to Boulogne, the **Moulin de Mombreux**, *route de Bayenghem* (Tel 39.62.44. Closed Mon), is a converted eighteenth-century watermill. Thin bedroom walls are a drawback, but in the near-circular restaurant the formal service delivers dishes such as fresh foie gras de canard, soufflé de turbot, and blanquette de lotte aux épinards from a frequently changing menu.

Half way between Calais and Boulogne on the NI, **Le Grand Cerf** (Tel 92.84.53. Closed Mon) at MARQUISE is another conversion of an eighteenth-century building, this time a coaching-inn, with imaginative *nouvelle*-style cooking from Jean-François Lemercier: feuilleté de filets de sole aux poireaux confites; aiguillettes de canard au miel et citron vert; as well as, not unexpectedly, good venison and chocolate marquise, from a choice of four fixed-price menus.

DIEPPE (Tel prefix 35)

Dieppe is a busy working port with a wide selection of plain, straightforwardly good restaurants serving a healthy variety of seafood, and is worth visiting out of season. **L'Armorique**, *17 quai Henri IV* (Tel 84.28.14. Closed Mon, 2 weeks June, 2 weeks Sept to Oct), has a *vivier*, a fine view of the port, and offers goujons of sole tartare, coquilles St Jacques and raie au beurre noir, while **La Marmite Dieppoise**, *8 rue St Jean* (Tel 84.24.26. Closed Sun D, Mon, Thur D, 2 weeks June to July), serves the dish of the same name – a big bowl of mussels, prawns, scallops, sole and turbot with a creamy sauce – plus tarte aux pommes, in a cheerful, busy atmosphere with good-natured service. Locals are particularly in evidence at the **Grand Duquesne**, *15 place St Jacques* (Tel 84.21.51. Closed Wed, Oct), which is run on friendly but efficient lines by three generations of women, who cook moules marinière and poisson à la crème. Market traders patronise **Le Jupiler**, *10–12 rue Duquesne* (Tel 84.35.65. Closed Thur D, Fri, 2 weeks June to July); it has an inexpensive fixed-price menu of freshly marinated mackerel, amandes farcies, gigot with pommes frites, commercial ice-cream and coffee. For about the same price the **Normandy** at number 16 (Tel 84.27.16. Closed Mon, 1 week June, 2 weeks Oct) might produce terrine de poissons, charcuterie, faux-filet garni, Camembert and coffee. As well as bouillabaisse and matelote, **Le Moderne**, *21 arcades de la Poissonnerie* (Tel 84.66.90.) also does a good magret de canard aux cèpes et échalottes, while at number 1 **La Marine** (Tel 84.17.54. Closed Tue D, Wed in winter) turns out succulent local squid, faux-filet, estouffade de boeuf, and apple tart with calvados. **Les Arcades**, *1–3 arcades de la Bourse* (Tel 84.14.12. Closed Wed D, Thur, Nov to Feb) is useful for a plateau de fruits de mer, velouté de poissons, terrine poivre vert, and andouillette grillée.

The **Municipal Poissonnerie** on the quay, or **Crustaces**, *15 arcades de la Poissonnerie* (just opposite), are the places to buy fresh fish, and there is a general food market on Saturday along *rue St Jacques* and the *Grande Rue*, with a smaller one on Tuesday and Thursday. **Prisunic** and **Au Printemps** are both in the *Grande Rue.*

If you're staying overnight, the old **L'Univers**, *10 bvd de Verdun* (Tel 84.12.55), or the clean and pleasant **Select**, *place de la Barre*, are worth considering.

Out of town, 24km west along the D925, there is a luxurious, modern, rather expensive restaurant, **Les Galets** (Tel 97.61.33. Closed Tue D, Wed, Feb) at

VEULES-LES-ROSES, where a talented chef produces good salads with langoustes and foie gras; arlequin de sole et turbot; blanquette de saumon aux pâtés fraîches avec un flan d'épinards; ris de veau braisé aux poireaux. About 8km south, by the D142, the **Auberge du Dun** (Tel 83.05.84. Closed Mon) at FONTAINE-LE-DUN is a small *logis de France* with a *nouvelle* menu: feuilleté d'écrevisses aux épinards frais; salade de ris de veau tiède; and magret de canard forestière.

Only 3.5km south of Dieppe, on the N27 at VERTUS, **La Bucherie** (Tel 84.83.10. Closed Mon, Feb, 3 weeks Sept to Oct) is a one-star Michelin restaurant where you can have foie gras, wild duck, strawberry crêpes and good sorbets, but at a price. About 6.5km outside Dieppe, on the Paris road, the **Auberge du Clos Normand**, *22 rue Henri IV* (Tel 82.71.01. Closed Mon D, Tue, Jan) at MARTIN-EGLISE is a dreamy little place with a pretty garden, a stream, a vine-covered barn, and good, if not cheap, provincial cooking: rich terrines; tarte aux moules; sauté of chicken or duck in cream and calvados; fruit tarts. Another 30km along the same road, at NEUFCHATEL-EN-BRAY, is a useful *relais routier* providing basic food at modest prices: **Chez Jean Pierre**, *8 Grand Rue St Jacques* (Tel 93.02.91) does avocado with prawn and egg dressing, contrefilet aux champignons, and pear tart, and doubles as a bar, hotel and *traiteur*. A journey of 15km along the coast road north-east of Dieppe brings you to TOCQUEVILLE-SUR-EU. Don't blink or you'll miss it. **Le Quatre Pain** (Tel 86.75.40. Closed Sun D, Mon, Feb, Aug) near the church is welcoming, and has vinaigrette de fraise de veau au chou vert; hure de saumon; filets d'agneau à la crème d'ail; and feuillantine glacée with a hot, bitter chocolate sauce.

LE HAVRE and HONFLEUR (Tel prefix 35, 31)

Le Havre station's **Buffet de France**, *28 cours République* (Tel 35-26.54.33) serves straightforward, old-fashioned food: rillettes; tête de veau vinaigrette; langue de boeuf sauce piquante; cervelle meunière; tarte aux pommes; crème caramel. **La Petite Auberge**, *32 rue Ste Adresse* (Tel 35-46.27.32. Closed Mon, 2 weeks Feb to Mar, Aug) is a tiny, rustic place with beams and charm. It is essential to book for the excellent set meals at reasonable prices. The cheaper one might include quenelles de brochet, salmon mousseline or rillettes, and stuffed hare, before cheese and dessert. The more expensive one has an extra course. **Marine Marchande**, *27 bvd Amiral-Mouchez* (Tel 35-25.11.77. Closed Sun, Sat L, 3 weeks Aug to Sept) may look less promising, but the fixed-price menu is good value: mussel soup or fish terrine; boeuf à la ficelle or salt cod in cream; a sweet; a kir; and a half-carafe of wine. The carte is first rate too, from sand-eels and turbot right down to the chips. **Le Cambridge**, *90 rue Voltaire* (Tel 35-42.50.24. Closed Sun, July) is also good for fish but posher and pricier: soupe de poissons; praires farcies à l'ail; blanquette de St Pierre aux petits légumes.

Lefèvre, *127 rue Victor Hugo*, is a well-stocked delicatessen. The charcuterie **Rondel**, *95 ave René-Coty*, makes lots of things with heads and feet, and for more charcuterie plus take-away dishes **Charcuteries des Ormeaux**, at number 136, **Delahaye** in *rue George Braque*, and **Jean-Luc Lebesne**, *18 rue de Guillaume-de-Marceilles* (off *rue de Paris*) are probably the best. **Duchemin**, *49 ave René-Coty*, sells bread and pastry. **Au Printemps** and **Nouvelle Galeries** are near *place Gambetta* and *place Hôtel-de-Ville*.

As for hotels, stay perhaps in the leafy STE ADRESSE suburb at cheap and cheerful, clean and comfortable **Hôtel des Phares**, *29 rue Général-De-Gaulle*.

About 18km east of Le Havre, just off the main road leading to the spectacular Pont de Tancarville, the **Restaurant Dubuc** (Tel 35-20.06.97. Closed Sun D, Mon, 2 weeks Aug) at LE HODE demonstrates what being a one-star Michelin restaurant is all about: home-prepared foie gras de canard with salad; feuilleté d'asperges sauce cerfeuil; magret de canard poivre vert; poire fondant au caramel. Drink cidre bouché, Muscadet or whatever you can afford. More traditional Norman food with plenty of cream is served at the **Auberge du Vieux Puits**, *6 rue Notre-Dame du Pré* (Tel 32-41.01.48. Closed Mon D, Tue, mid Dec to mid Jan,1 week July) at PONT-AUDEMER. It also has a good wine list.

HONFLEUR, facing Le Havre across the estuary of the Seine, and scene of much Impressionist activity, is many people's idea of what all little ports should be like, with its narrow cobbled streets and bobbing yachts. In order not to spoil the illusion it is best to eat at **Le Carlin**, *32 place Pierre-Berthelot* (Tel 31-89.39.69), which overlooks the quay. It has a relaxed atmosphere, in which to enjoy competent fricassée de volaille au cidre; blanquette de lotte aux primeurs; good salmon and cheeses. **La Ferme Saint-Siméon**, *rue Adolphe-Marais* (Tel 31-89.23.61) is expensive because you pay for the pleasure of dining where the Impressionists used to meet (and think what people fork out for the pictures) as well as for chausson de homard; râble de lapereau; navarin de sole et homard, prepared by a chef taught by Troisgros and Vergé. At the other extreme is **Le Tilbury**, *8 place Ste Catherine* (Tel 31-89.24.88. Closed Fri) with inexpensive moules, steak, cheese and fruit, or hamburgers, chicken and chips. Somewhere in between comes **L'Absinthe**, *10 quai de la Quarantaine* (Tel 31-89.39.00.), which the locals enjoy for its plateau de fruits de mer, veal kidneys, and unusually generous helpings of *nouvelle cuisine* dishes.

Inland fron Honfleur, near PONT L'EVEQUE, the **Auberge Cochon d'Or** (Tel 32-57.70.46) at BEUZEVILLE is a cheerful, relaxed, good-value place with large portions of poulet vallée d'Auge; jambon au cidre; light and creamy charlotte aux poires; cidre bouché. It has simple accommodation too.

MONTREUIL-SUR-MER and LE TOUQUET (Tel prefix 21)

At MONTREUIL-SUR-MER – no longer, in fact, sur mer – the well-appointed **Château de Montreuil**, *4 chaussée des Capucins* (Tel. 81.53.04) is the star attraction. It is a country house run by Christian Germain (who trained with the Roux brothers) and his English wife Lindsay, combining first-class raw materials and light sauces to produce a short menu including St Jacques grillées au beurre de noisettes, or fricassée de volaille aux écrevisses. Down a winding lane 2.5km from Montreuil on the D139, **La Grenouillère**'s (Tel 06.07.22. Closed Wed, exc July and Aug, Tue D, Feb) simple rustic setting by the river Canche belies Claudine and Roland Gauthier's professional service and sophisticated cooking of rognons de veau à la crème de poivron; panaché de poissons au coulis de persil; pastry dishes; and iced soufflés.

Off the beaten track in the attractive valley of the Course 10km north of Montreuil, the hamlet of ENGOUDSENT near the village of BEUSSENT is home to the Provin-Denoves' traditional restaurant **Au Bon Acceuil** (Tel 90.70.63). They serve a simple-sounding menu based on fine materials, where the assiette de charcuterie might even include fish; trout with brown butter and almond sauce;

first-class beef and chicken; and good apple tart.

LE TOUQUET is of course sur mer, and **Flavio-Club de la Forêt**, *1–2 ave du Verger* (Tel 05.10.22.) brings the point home with impeccably served fish and shellfish, including raw salmon in gros sel; sole homardine; bar soufflé coulis d'herbe à soupe; as well as pigeonneau rôti au miel; magret de canard; lamb; and kidneys. Dishes are as expensive as they sound, with wines to match. In the same avenue, **Hotel Westminster** (Tel 05.19.66) does super sauces on medaillons de boeuf and grilled turbot, and good almond pastries and crêpes; immaculate service. On the seafront at the northern end of town a friendly welcome awaits at **Le Chalut**, *7 bvd Jules-Pauget* (Tel 05.22.55. Closed Tue D, Wed, Jan) with fixed-price menus offering petit pâté de sole aux écrevisses; assiette de saumon sauvage aux limes; and good wines.

At LE CROTOY on the coast 26km north-west of Abbeville **Chez Mado** at **Hôtel de la Baie**, *quai Leonard* (Tel 22.27.81.22) produces spicy fish soup; large succulent scallops; rich sauces for moules and sole; and apple pie. The restaurant is better than the hotel.

Features

Eight centuries of the English restaurant

C. Anne Wilson

Eating out dates from the time of the earliest large towns. In some ancient Italian cities traces remain of the restaurants of 2,000 years ago, as in the bar at Ostia where seating for the guests survives inside the doorway, or the wine-shop at Pompeii which has a mural on the wall of a group of customers, still wrapped in their cloaks, sitting on stools around a three-legged table and enjoying their wine.

But there is another side to eating out, and that is the provision for travellers whose long journeys obliged them to eat away from home. Again there are precedents in the Roman Empire, for the *mansiones* which were built at intervals along the main roads (in England every 20 to 30 miles, like the motorway service stations of today) served as post-horse stations and hotels for the use of officials of the imperial postal service and other travelling officials. Their hospitality was also available to private travellers – though at some periods such people could enjoy the privilege only if they had first obtained a permit!

In England the city eating-places of the Romans have not left such distinctive traces as in Italy, nor have we direct evidence of the kind of fare offered to visitors to the inns attached to the *mansiones*. So it is perhaps true to say that the earliest forerunner of the modern English restaurant was the medieval cookshop, already well established in twelfth-century London. Local citizens brought their guests there, and foreigners, the knights from the shires, and small gentry who could not afford their own grand London houses would have stayed in lodgings and taken their dinners at these cookshops, where the food was laid out on a cloth spread over a trestle-and-board table.

As London grew, the number of cookshops increased. They served not only as restaurants, but also as take-aways. A price-list of the Guild of Cooks and Pastelers (Piemakers) in 1378 included: best roast pig, 8d; best roast goose, 7d; best roast capon, 6d; best roast river mallard (wild duck), 4½d; best roast dunghill mallard (farmyard duck), 3½d; 5 roast larks, 1½d; best roast heron, 18d. The best capon baked in a pasty was 8d. These roast or baked meats could either be consumed on the premises or taken home.

Standards of hygiene varied. In some shops pies were prepared from tainted meat, and civic regulations were issued from time to time to try to prevent the practice. In *The Canterbury Tales*, Chaucer's host taunted the cook in the party with misdeeds that were not unknown in contemporary cookshops. 'From many a pasty hast thou letten blood (i.e. drained out the gravy)/And many a Jack of Dover has thou sold/ That hath been twice hot and twice cold.' The Jack of Dover, like the French Jack of Paris, appears to have been the argot term for an old or hard meat pie.

Not all cookshops were like this, and some may have been able to attract customers by their good reputation alone. But it was more usual for the cooks and their servants to cry their wares: 'Hot pies, hot/Good gris (little pigs) and geese, go dine, go.' Sometimes it must have been quite difficult to avoid being drawn into a cookshop. Inside, pewter pots clattered and there might be music from harp, pipe and psaltery (a kind of zither) – which shows there is nothing new-fangled about the background music supplied by so many eating-places today.

Taverns existed primarily as drinking-houses for the consumption of ale and wine; but as cookshops proliferated in the city, some taverns brought in food from a neighbouring cookshop, while others began offering cooked dishes prepared in their own kitchens. There was a Dagger tavern in Shakespeare's time famous not only for its strong Dagger ale but also for Dagger frumenty (a pottage of hulled wheat with milk or butter, sometimes yellowed with saffron) and for Dagger pies, which were ornamented with a pastry representation of a dagger with a magpie on the point.

Some taverns had sleeping accommodation and were thus virtually inns. Outside London and the largest towns, inns could supply both meals and a sleeping-place for travellers. On a well-used route, like that taken by pilgrims who set out from Southwark bound for Canterbury, there was no shortage of inns. But in Lincoln the provision of inns was so sparse that the townspeople used to give pilgrims food and shelter in their own homes. During the Middle Ages, and even much later, travellers in remote places could depend upon hospitality offered by people living in the district, who undertook to look after strangers as an act of Christian charity. The medieval traveller could also seek meals and accommodation from the monks, if a religious house lay near his road. Of the monastery at Chester it was said: 'The seats are worn by reason of the many meals given to strangers. . . . There, travellers to and from Ireland find rest, companionship and shelter while waiting for wind and tide.'

The Elizabethan era saw the development of the 'ordinary'. This term at first meant a fixed-price table d'hôte meal. Later it was extended to the particular cookshops and taverns where such meals could be had, and they too became known as ordinaries. In the course of the seventeenth century some of the London ordinaries became fashionable resorts for men about town, who visited them not only to eat and drink, but also to gamble. Samuel Pepys went on 18 February 1668 to 'the Beare in Drury Lane, an excellent ordinary after the French manner, and there had a little fricasee'; and on 15 March 1669 he 'dined very handsome with a good soup and a pullet for 4s. 6d. the whole' at 'the Cocke at the end of Suffolk street, a great ordinary'.

The humbler cookshops still supplied meals for artisans, but now an alternative was to eat at an alehouse. A statute of 1604 allowed labourers and 'handicraftsmen' to stop work for an hour in the middle of the day 'to take their diet in an alehouse'. Alehouses were numerous in all cities and towns, and one or more was to be found in every village; within the towns they tended to be clustered in the poorer suburbs. They were not purpose-built, but were simply the home of the alehouse-keeper and his family. Some were too small to provide service in a separate room even, and the customers ate and drank in the kitchen where they could also enjoy the warmth of the fire. The fire was a great attraction for poorer people, who could not afford to have a fire and a hot meal in their own homes every day. The food most commonly available in alehouses was spiced bread, or buns or wigs (originally 'wedges' cut from a larger round breadcake), which were toasted and steeped in ale. But if a substantial meal was required, the customer was expected to bring along his own meat, which would be cooked for him in the alehouse – a practice that continued well into the eighteenth century. Some alehouse-keepers offered more ambitious fare. Peter Clark, in *The English Alehouse*, quotes the example of cheesecakes and apple pies on sale at a Leicester alehouse, and conger eels and mutton pies at one in Faversham. And during Lent alehouse-keepers were forbidden to sell meat, suggesting that some of them served it at other times of year. In London drinkers were able to purchase 'rashers on the coals, red herrings, anchovies and all sorts of saltmeat', though these thirst-inducing foods may have been on offer at inns and taverns rather than in humbler alehouses, where the patrons had less money to spend.

The better-off traveller outside London took his meal at an inn. Here, as at the London ordinary, he could expect a set-price meal from a choice of dishes offered by the proprietor; and it was usually eaten in his company.

Fynes Moryson, a keen tourist who journeyed through several European countries, has left us a long and interesting description of the service offered to travellers in England at the beginning of the seventeenth century. At its best it must have been welcoming and very pleasant. He wrote:

> . . . as soon as a passenger comes to an inn, the servants run to him, and one takes his horse and walks him till he be cold, then rubs him and gives him meat (i.e. food) . . . . Another servant gives the passenger his private chamber and kindles his fire; the third pulls off his boots and makes them clean. Then the host or hostess visits him, and if he will eat with the host, or at a common table with

others, his meal will cost him six pence, or in some places but four pence (yet this course is less honourable, and not used by gentlemen); but if he will eat in his chamber, he commands what meat he will according to his appetite, and as much as he thinks fit for him and his company, yea, the kitchen is open to him, to command the meat to be dressed as he likes. It is the custom and no way disgraceful to set up (i.e. put away) part of supper for his breakfast.

It is notable that the system had not yet spread to Scotland. There, the old medieval custom of offering private hospitality in the absence of any alternative still prevailed. Of his Scottish tour, Fynes Moryson wrote: 'I did not see or hear that they have any public inns, with signs hanging out, but the better sort of citizens brew ale, their usual drink (which will distemper a stranger's body); and the same citizens will entertain passengers upon acquaintance or entreaty.'

The principal inn in a substantial town was also a place where a man might invite friends or business associates to dine with him as his guests. William Russell, fifth Earl of Bedford, liked to pay visits to Cambridge, where he had connections with Trinity College. To entertain his Cambridge friends, he gave splendid dinners at the Red Lion Inn, where the guests were offered a multitude of dishes (served in only two separate courses, a practice that continued into the early nineteenth century), including such items as 'a dish of capons and sausage'; 'a stand of all sorts of pickle and collared eels'; 'a dish of tongues, udders and marrowbones with cauliflowers and spinach'; 'a couple of pullets with oysters'; 'a dish of whipped sillabubs'. The bill for two dinners and a supper on 15 and 16 October 1689 came to a total of £33 19s. 6d. This sum is followed in the account-book by the statement, 'Given to the house (i.e. the Red Lion), £1 10s. 0d', which indicates that tips in the seventeenth century were at a rather lower level than today's minimum of 10 per cent.

The first half of the eighteenth century was a time of good harvests in England, and for most people a time of plentiful food. Meat-eating was on the increase, and this was reflected in the type of meal offered to diners by the London cookshops. M Misson, a French visitor, described a typical cookshop meal in the early years of the century:

Generally, four spits, one over another, carry round each five or six pieces of butcher's meat, beef, mutton, veal, pork and lamb; you have what quantity you please cut off, fat, lean, much or little done; with this, a little salt and mustard upon the side of a plate, a bottle of beer and a roll; and there is your whole feast.

A variant on the cookshop was the chop-house, a new name in 1690 for an eating-place 'Where both boiled and roast mutton (in chops) are always ready', and likewise beefsteaks and other small cuts of meat. Chop-houses quickly became a regular part of the London scene; Sir Richard Steele wrote in *The Spectator* in 1712, 'I dine at the chophouse three days a week'.

Coffee-houses, which arrived in London in the 1650s, a year or two after the first had opened at Oxford, existed initially to supply simply the drink itself together with newspapers and a club-like ambience for their all-male clientele. But later many of them became eating-places too. In Georgian times they were supplemented by the establishments known as coffee-rooms, which, despite their name, were actually dining-rooms and from the start offered meals to precede the coffee. During the eighteenth century many clubs, too, came into existence, and for some of them dining was a major activity. A famous example was the 'Sublime Society of Beefsteaks' which lasted from 1732 to 1869 and had as its object the eating of beefsteaks of the finest quality, an activity carried out by the members with various elaborate mock ceremonies.

London also offered a good choice of inns and taverns for the fashionable diner-out. The London Tavern (built on the site of an earlier White Horse tavern which had been burned down) was one such; it was recorded that in 1782 the annual officers' dinners of 28 different regiments were held there. The following year the famous cookery book *The London Art of Cookery* was published by the Tavern's principal cook, John Farley, with his portrait as the frontispiece.

Outside London, inns were still the source of meals for travellers. The best of them were very good. The Hon. John Byng, touring through Sussex in 1788, had 'a comfortable meal on a loin of mutton and potatoes' with a bottle of port at the New Inn at Winchelsea. A few days later at the White Hart Inn at Godstone in Surrey he was served 'a fine boiled fowl, whose parentage and education I learnt of the landlady; with a fresh morello-cherry pie and good port-wine'.

During the eighteenth century a newer and grander type of inn made its appearance under the French name of hôtel. The grandeur had to be paid for; the earliest hotels were very expensive. But they had come to stay, and their numbers increased all through the nineteenth century, in London and the principal cities, in fashionable spas and watering-places, and eventually, when the railways arrived, in the vicinity of many railway stations.

Hotels supplied overnight accommodation and meals for travellers. But they were also a venue for the diner-out, where he might eat alone or take a party of friends. In general the food offered was 'English' rather than 'French'. A few hotels had a special reputation for particular foods, such as the Adelphi Hotel and the Waterloo Hotel at Liverpool, each of which became well known for serving turtle, both the soup and the flesh. They were appropriately situated for the purpose, since so many of the ships bearing turtles from the West Indies docked at Liverpool.

In London in the early nineteenth century Birch's in Cornhill was said to be the place for eating turtle; and Garraway's Coffee-house in Change Alley was recommended for midday snacks of cutlets and asparagus, or sandwiches and sherry. Gover's Coffee-house in Brook Street and Mount Coffee-house in Grosvenor Street were famous for their dinners; and around Leicester Square there were several French eating-houses of which La Sablonière was the most popular. By the middle of the century Dolly's chop-house in St Paul's Churchyard had a high reputation 'for a chop, or steak, or a cut direct from the joint, with well-boiled mealy potatoes', and the Ship and Turtle in Leadenhall Street for 'a plate of turtle and a grilled fowl done Indian fashion'.

Turtle recurs frequently in the choice menus of the period. Thomas Walker, writing in a periodical called *The Original* (1835), recommended the following meal, which was subsequently served to his party at Lovegrove's at Blackwall:

> Eight I hold to be the golden number (of guests). . . . The dinner is to consist of turtle, followed by no other fish but whitebait; which is to be followed by no other meat but grouse, which are to be succeeded by apple fritters and jelly. . . . With the turtle, of course, there will be punch, with the whitebait champagne, and with the grouse claret. I shall take care there is Cayenne with lemons cut in halves, not quarters, within reach of everyone for the turtle, and brown bread and butter in abundance for the whitebait. . . . The dinner will be followed by ices and a good dessert, after which coffee and one glass of liqueur each and no more.

Another favourite eating-place for the male diner-out of the period was the gentleman's club. Most of the eighteenth-century clubs had dwindled away, but the three that stayed the course through the nineteenth century – White's, Boodle's and Brooks's – were joined before long by a series of new clubs. By 1840 there were said to be 20 clubs in London's West End, all supplying excellent meals as well as such useful adjuncts as reading-rooms with daily newspapers, writing-rooms and libraries. There were often facilities for the country member to spend the night; and bachelors who lived in chambers or lodgings could dine daily at their club. Some famous nineteenth-century chefs worked at London clubs, for example Charles Francatelli at the Coventry Club, Alexis Soyer at the Reform, and Eustache Ude at Crockford's. A club not only supplied an excellent dinner to a regular member, but that member could also have a special meal served to a party of his guests by prior arrangement with the chef.

The success of the clubs affected eating patterns at other establishments in the metropolis. There certainly seems to have been some falling off in alternative provision for the diner-out during the middle years of the nineteenth century, and many of the city hotels had become antiquated, serving substantial but dull meals ('dinner from the joint and a pint of inferior wine') in their dining-rooms.

But the scene was even then beginning to change, following the arrival in London of the earliest restaurants and the growing importance of their role as places where gentlemen might take ladies out to dine. The restaurant, initially often called the 'restaurateur', reached the English capital from Paris. According to A. Hayward in *The Art of Dining*, the first Parisian restaurateur was *Champ d'Oiseau*, rue des

Poulies, which commenced business in 1770. By 1789 the number of Parisian restaurateurs had increased to a hundred, and in 1804 (the date of the first appearance of the *Almanach des Gourmands*) to five or six hundred. Curiously, the inspiration for these French eating-places came in part from England, at a time when things English were enjoying a great vogue in France: 'the English, as is well known, almost always take their meals in taverns', wrote the author of the *Almanach*. The French Revolution underwrote the growth of the restaurant trade; on the one hand, many of the new legislators did not have their permanent homes in Paris, so lived in lodgings and needed places where they could dine; on the other, the cooks of the rich nobility, both clerical and secular, were driven to seek a new occupation when their employers' establishments were broken up.

The earliest restaurants of London were attracting attention by the 1830s. For a long time they offered only dishes prepared in the French style. In about 1880 *Cassell's Domestic Dictionary* defined the word *restaurant* as 'a modern French name for an eating-house. . . . In our metropolis restaurants have been introduced, to which foreigners and other persons resort who prefer the French method of cooking.' By then the restaurant had come to stay, and by 1875 had already given its name to a new phenomenon of the age: the railway restaurant-car.

The restaurant also influenced other eating-places, even those that did not bear its name. When Lieutenant-Colonel N. Newnham-Davis took a young female teacher to Willis's Rooms, King Street, as his dinner guest, he told her that the interior was 'as close a transcript of a Paris restaurant as could be found in London; the white walls with great mirrors let into the shining wood, the scarlet couches by the wall, the chairs with their quaint backs and scarlet seats all savour of Paris'.

Newnham-Davis's book *Dinners and Diners: Where and How to Dine in London* (1899) was originally published as a series of articles in the *Pall Mall Gazette*, and was a sort of forerunner of *The Good Food Guide*. He tested a great variety of eating-places and visited several of them in the company of ladies of various ages and interests. That in itself was a sign that the presence of women in public dining-rooms was at last beginning to be a normal feature of life.

Hitherto, their expectations with regard to eating out had been very limited. It is true that at all periods a family party, or in medieval times a group of pilgrims of both sexes, had been able to visit the better type of inn or tavern. Again, men did, on occasion, take their wives to an alehouse. Nevertheless, as one scans the records through the centuries one is very much aware that eating out was far more of a male activity than a female one.

When women in the Middle Ages or in Tudor times ate and drank outside their own or their friends' homes, it tended to be in celebration of a special event. Thus, groups of wives gathered together at the alehouse for 'ales', or parties, for particular events during the year, such as Easter-ales, lamb-ales, tithe-ales, midsummer-ales, and scot-ales (at which each member contributed a share of the drink). But respectable women did not go alone to alehouses or to most of the taverns; any who did were regarded as women of loose morals, and were welcomed accordingly. The regular clientele of alehouses and taverns, ordinaries and inns, was almost exclusively male.

During the eighteenth century teashops were opened in London and provincial towns, and tea-gardens were also established on the outskirts of cities and towns. Both were venues where the beverage tea, which had become fashionable among the ladies of gentry families, could be enjoyed by women further down the social scale. That development represented the earliest example in the catering field of positive discrimination in favour of the female sex. But in other respects the situation changed only very slowly, and the problem of finding a suitable eating-place to which a lady might be taken to dine was still only partly solved by the middle of the nineteenth century.

By 1899 the situation had improved. Newnham-Davis matched his ladies carefully to the dining-places to which he took them: for a young American actress, Epitaux in the Haymarket; for a more mature English actress friend, Romano's on the Strand, and on another, summery occasion, the Ship Tavern, Greenwich, for a fish dinner; for a cosmopolitan society lady, Verrey's in Regent Street; for a débutante, the Hotel Continental, Regent Street; for his sister-in-law, daughter of a dean, the Cafe Royal, Regent Street (formerly rather Bohemian, but just entering upon a phase of greater gentility); and so on. He did not really regard women as serious diners-out. He made an exception for the cosmopolitan society lady ('for she understands the art of dining, and is, as well, a most excellent cook herself when she chooses'); but depicted several of his other female guests as prattling away to him when they should have been savouring their food in appreciative silence.

If by 1899 there was no shortage of places where gentlemen might take ladies to dine, places where females might dine alone were still very few. Newnham-Davis, commenting on the other diners at the Berkeley, Piccadilly, added the special point that 'two ladies going on to the opera were dining by themselves – the Berkeley is a place where ladies can dine and lunch without an escort'. That situation seems to have been rather exceptional, since it is not stated for any of his other eating-places, bar one. The one was unusual in another respect: it was a vegetarian restaurant. Newnham-Davis visited it alone, having failed to persuade any of his red-blooded male acquaintances to eat a meal that did not include meat. When he reached St George's Cafe, St Martin's Lane, he found that the service was entirely in the hands of waitresses (whereas waiters served him at all his other dining-places). The guests included women either alone or in pairs, as well as male vegetarians.

The menu was: Hors d'oeuvre; Mulligatawny soup or Carrot soup; Flageolets (a type of bean) with cream and spinach; Fried duck's egg and green peas; Lenten pie or stewed fruit; Mixed salad; Cheese; Dessert (an orange, raisins and nuts); Coffee. The price, 1s. 10d., was the lowest paid for a single meal in the whole book – but this was also the only dinner mentioned from which the author 'went forth feeling rather empty'.

He took many of his other dinners in the company of male friends, some in places from which women were excluded altogether, such as the downstairs dining-room at Simpson's (as a compromise, Simpson's, in common with some other restaurants, had an upstairs room where a lady could dine with her male escort), the Old Blue Posts in Cork Street, and, not surprisingly, the Freemasons' Tavern in Great Queen Street. A small point of differential diet may also be mentioned; at the two last-named, hot marrowbones wrapped in napkins were served just before the cheese and port, or dessert, and the diners regaled themselves on the rich hot marrow within.

To list all the menus in *Dinners and Diners* would take far too long. The dinner shared by the author with a middle-aged female friend from his Simla days in a private room at Pagani's in Great Portland Street may be quoted as an example. They had: Hors d'oeuvre variés; Potage Bortsch; Filets de sole Pagani; Tournedos aux truffes, Haricots verts sautés, Pommes croquettes; Perdreau Voisin; Salade; Soufflé au Curaçao.

A fish dinner downstairs at Simpson's (the alternative there to a dinner from the joint) comprised turbot with sauce; fried sole or stewed eels; whitebait or salmon; cheese and celery.

When Newnham-Davis dined with his editor and wife at the Berkeley in Piccadilly they all enjoyed: Melon Cantaloup; Crème d'or (soup); Truite froide au court bouillon, sauce verte; Caneton Nantais à la Drexel; Selle de pré-salé rôtie aux légumes; Petits pois à la française; Salade à la St-James; Ananas glace Sibérienne; Corbeille de petits fours; Croustade Victoria.

For the first menu the accompanying wine was champagne, for the second, Liebfraumilch, and for the third, hock cup. But it was the first that was the most representative dinner wine of the age. Newnham-Davis wrote:

> In Paris no man dreams of drinking champagne, and nothing but champagne for dinner; but in London, the climate and the taste of the fair sex go before orthodox rules. A tired man in our heavy atmosphere feels often that champagne is the one wine that will give him life again; and as the ladies as a rule would think a dinner at a restaurant incomplete without champagne, ninety-nine out of a hundred Englishmen, in ordering a little dinner for two, turn instinctively to the champagne page of the wine-card.

So much for dining out in London. Provincial dining out was on the whole less sophisticated, and less under the influence of French cuisine.

But eating out for pleasure was on the increase. One reason was the growth of the holiday trade following the development of the railways. The guidebooks of the 1870s and 1880s named the principal hotels of each resort, and soon began to add further details of the price of each hotel's table d'hôte luncheon and dinner. Holidaymakers who stayed at the hotels would naturally take most of their meals there. But some who put up at humbler lodgings elsewhere in the town could add to the pleasure of their holiday week by dining out once or twice at a hotel, for hotel dining-rooms were usually open to non-residents. In smaller towns the hotel was often an earlier inn brought a little more up to date. Again, the dining-room was open to passing travellers and to local visitors dining out with friends as well as to its residents.

With the twentieth century we have reached the point where living memory takes over from history. There have been further changes, of course. One is the increase in the number of foreign restaurants serving their own ethnic foods. A kosher restaurant figures in the late Victorian *Dinners and Diners*, but this was the only departure from the English or French *haute cuisine* of all the other eating-places mentioned. Sophisticated diners did not then venture into restaurants of any other national affiliation. Ethnic food was available in Victorian times, but mainly in small eating-places in port towns and in areas where groups of immigrants had settled.

Well before 1914 eating ethnic had begun to impinge on more fashionable diners-out in London. Schmidt's in Charlotte Street was founded near the beginning of the century, originally with four marble-topped tables reached through the delicatessen, but soon expanding into many more rooms. Other German restaurants followed. There were Italian restaurants, too – Bertorelli's was founded in 1913. After the First World War, more and more foreign restaurants arrived in London. The famous Hungaria Restaurant in Lower Regent Street began serving Hungarian food to Londoners in 1928. In Bon Viveur's *Where to Dine in London* (1937) examples are cited of Italian, Spanish, German, Russian, Swiss, Hungarian, Danish, Swedish, Indian, Chinese and Japanese restaurants in the capital, all supplying the dishes of their country.

A second big influence on twentieth-century eating-out habits has been the rise and rise of the motor-car. Between the Wars, road-houses flourished, usually close to important main roads, as the inns had been for centuries before. More recently the country restaurant has come into its own, sometimes established in a small town, but very often in a fine old building on the edge of a remote country village, to which customers will drive 20 or 30 miles.

It was only 40-odd years ago that the British Restaurants of the war years were serving snoek (whale-meat) or Woolton (vegetable) pie as part of a state-subsidised dinner. Today, happily, we have far more choice. . . .

Eating ethnic . . .

Chinese by Yan-kit So

So many people keen on Chinese food let loose in a Chinese restaurant are baffled when confronted with an apparently mile-long menu numbering anything up to 150 items (a short one, more likely a Peking/Szechuan restaurant) or even up to 300 (par for the course in a Cantonese restaurant), and they wonder what on earth they can order other than the sweet-and-sour and the chow mein dishes.

To eat an authentic meal in a Chinese restaurant involves having some understanding, however rudimentary, of Chinese food culture, as restaurants are a traditional part of that culture.

The Chinese everyday family meal, occurring at midday and in the evening, consists of a staple, ideally white rice or, in the wheat-growing north, steamed bread or noodles, and a few dishes served at the same time. The meal for entertainment – a banquet – at home or in a restaurant – and Chinese city dwellers visit restaurants frequently – comprises a number of dishes, usually no less than five but more likely eight and upwards to twelve and beyond, depending on the occasion and the wallet.

The contents of these dishes depend ultimately on the opposites of yin and yang. The Chinese philosophy of the two opposing forces, yin and yang, which make up the universe and all things in it, was well established long before the dawn of the Christian era in the West. Yin is cold, negative, gentle, and represented by the moon, the female, darkness, weakness; yang is hot, positive, aggressive, and represented by the sun, the male, light, strength. The ideal is to have a harmonious balance between these two forces. Since foodstuffs themselves are classified into possessing either the yin or the yang properties – red meats are yang food whereas fish are yin, for instance – it is vital to maintain a balance in what one eats to hold the hot and cold elements in harmony and thus ensure good health.

The Chinese do not reach for an abacus whenever they eat to work out the balance between yin and yang (there's no complete agreed list in any case). They simply try to ensure that in the same meal there is meat, fish or seafood (or both), and vegetables, besides rice or another grain food, all cooked by more than one method, and by doing so they hope to strike a balance between yin and yang.

Apart from harmony, the five flavours have reigned supreme in Chinese gastronomy – sweet, sour, bitter, spicy-hot and salty. (These are like the five elements – metal, wood, water, earth and fire – that dominate the Chinese world.) A balance of these flavours has always been desirable too.

Cantonese

The most varied and versatile of all Chinese regional cuisines is Cantonese, and the majority of Chinese restaurants in Britain are Cantonese. The variety is due to the rich resources of ingredients from both the land and the sea.

The climate in south China being sub-tropical, Cantonese soups by and large are clear-stock based, not served to precede the main course but often as a side dish to help quench the thirst and down the rice in the hot and humid weather.

If only two of you are eating together it is more difficult to reach the ideal balance, for after the starter and/or the soup, you can perhaps take no more than two or at most three more dishes. If there are four of you, you can have a very satisfactory meal with a balanced spread of dishes; if there are six or eight or more of you, you can really go to town and order the widest variety.

Whatever the number of people, you can do worse than start with steamed fresh scallops (two per person). Stir-fried crabs either with ginger and spring onion or with green pepper and black bean sauce are also delicious. When lobsters are in season, stir-fried lobster with ginger and spring onion is succulent and fragrant. Or try spare ribs, stuffed crab claws, prawn toasts, or one or two of the dim-sum categories such as siu-mai or har-gau or both, which some restaurants offer as a starter at dinner-time.

If you want soup other than egg-drop and sweet corn, try West Lake beef soup, bean curd soup, shredded pork with Szechuan cabbage soup, or fish soup. During the autumn/winter season, winter melon pond – the melon hollowed in the centre then stuffed with such delicacies as crab, duck, and mushrooms and filled with the best stock and then steamed for hours – is available in some restaurants, but only by order one or two days in advance. It is well worth spending the money, for you will eat one of the most subtle soups you can dream of. The best one I have had is at Fung Shing (see London). Unless you have arranged with the restaurant ahead of time or you are certain it is the restaurant's speciality, don't order shark's fin soup or you'll pay a lot of money for a string or two of the shark's fin in a bowl of consommé.

As to main dishes, bear in mind the harmonious balance between meat and vegetables and the different cooking methods – steamed, stir-fried, deep-fried, sauté and braised. Allow one dish per person but share them, as the Chinese always do. Beef with black bean sauce or with oyster sauce are famous Cantonese dishes. In fact, any dish with a black bean sauce (a characteristic of Cantonese cooking) – chicken, squid, clams and fish – will be good, as will the ingredients served in a bird's nest. This nest (*not* of bird's nest soup fame) is a deep-fried basket woven with strips of taro (actually more likely potato) in which are placed stir-fried chicken and scallop pieces accompanied by black Chinese mushrooms, bamboo shoots and the like, or chicken and prawns or beef. The nest is edible, and should be crisp.

Bean curd dishes are a forte of Cantonese restaurants. Try hung-shao bean curd (bean curd pieces deep-fried then cooked with vegetables and often served in a clay pot) and bean curd stuffed with prawns, sauté or steamed. Seafood dishes are another forte, especially prawn, scallop and squid. Prawns fried in the shell then finished with a little sauce – often tomato ketchup or/and Worcester sauce-based – or served with a dip of spiced salt are a true favourite of the Cantonese. Squid is often served with the strong, peasant shrimp sauce, with both fresh and dried squid stir-fried in the sauce. There is always sweet-and-sour pork which, at its best, is appetising and mouth-watering and fits nicely into the scheme of the five flavours. Many restaurants roast their own pork (char-siu) and ducks, and offer a plate of 'roasties' consisting of sliced char-siu or chopped pieces of duck or both, sometimes with wings, gizzard and liver as well.

Other famous Cantonese duck dishes worth a try are duckling steamed in plum sauce, and braised whole duck stuffed with various delicacies. Of the chicken dishes, besides those all-too-familiar ones stir-fried with bamboo shoots, mushrooms and cashew nuts, salt-baked chicken is one of the famous dishes of the East River area in Kwangtung province. The pièce de résistance of Cantonese chickens, however, must be crispy deep-fried chicken: the skin should be cracklingly crisp and traditionally it is served with crispy shrimp crackers. Few restaurants serve it as a regular feature, one exception being Tiger Lee (see London).

The most popular way to serve fish in Cantonese restaurants is to steam it. If there are fewer than four of you the fish, sea-bass, sole or grey mullet, to name the most popular, will probably be served together with the other dishes. But if you are a group of eight, ten or twelve having a banquet-style dinner of many dishes, the fish should be served as the last course. This is because of a punning symbolism beloved of the Chinese: the word fish is pronounced exactly the same as the word meaning to have surplus. You can also try eel, either steamed, stir-fried with chilli and black beans or, better still, braised in a clay pot with roast belly of pork and other delicacies.

No Chinese meal is complete without vegetables. In the south, the most sought-after is the green flowering cabbage, lightly blanched then laced with oyster sauce, or stir-fried with meat, fish or seafood. When available, Cantonese restaurants in England do serve it, but you'll have to ask for it, for it comes generally under the seasonal vegetables category. In the summer, when it is in season for a short while, try water spinach, which will be the peasant dish stir-fried with either strong shrimp paste or an equally strong fermented white chilli bean curd 'cheese'. Equally delicious is this bean curd cheese cooked with ordinary spinach. Chinese broccoli, again when available, is reminiscent of asparagus, and is delicious served blanched or stir-fried laced with fresh ginger juice, or with meat or seafood.

As a day-to-day meal, the Cantonese have plain-boiled white rice to go with their few dishes. When they have a banquet-style dinner, fried rice and sometimes noodles (soupy or fried) as well are served after the fish. Renowned for their hospitality as the Chinese have always been, it is their way of saying politely: 'Do forgive my humble fare; if you haven't had enough, please now fill up with rice.' Noodles are always served at this point if the dinner is to celebrate a birthday, for noodles, long in shape, are the symbol of longevity, and the dish is actually known as longevity noodles.

Szechuan

Save for very few exceptions – such as the Dragon Gate, the original Szechuan restaurant in London – Szechuan restaurants and Peking restaurants are hardly distinguishable from each other.

For starters, try deep-fried seaweed (in real life cabbage or spring greens), sesame prawn toast, edible jellyfish with cucumber, bang bang or pang pang chicken (cold chicken with a peppery hot sauce), smoked fish (cold and on the sweet side) or the cold platter (thinly sliced chicken, ham, braised beef, tongue and giblet, all decorously arranged). You can also opt for dumplings, the most common ones being those fried on one side and steamed on the other, or the Peking boiled or steamed dumplings served with chilli oil and vinegar. If you see it listed on the menu, try the Peking street food of spring onion cake and enjoy this oily and hearty fried pastry made fragrant by the spring onion inside.

For soups, definitely the hot-and-sour soup for local flavour. Shredded pork with Szechuan vegetable is also exciting because of the preserved vegetable (a species of mustard plant). If you don't like anything spicy, try the soup with chicken, ham and mushroom.

For main dishes, there is the pièce de résistance of the Peking duck for a Peking restaurant or the fragrant and crispy duck for a Szechuan restaurant. Peking duck must be ordered whole because of the way it is cooked, whereas Szechuan duck comes halved or even quartered. Peking duck is served sliced into pieces and accompanied by thin pancakes, cucumber sticks and shredded spring onion and sweet bean or hoisin sauce, and you wrap up everything inside the pancake and eat it. Szechuan duck should not be served in the same way, even though many restaurants do so, some probably out of ignorance, others claiming that it is out of deference to Westerners who have insisted on it. Be that as it may, this classic Szechuan dish is traditionally served with steamed buns, called lotus leaf buns, and a dipping salt spiced with ground Szechuan peppercorns.

The other Szechuan duck of renown is the camphor wood-smoked duck, smoked with tea in restaurants in Britain. Anywhere that serves a smoky, tasty and fragrant smoked duck with moist and succulent meat is a good Szechuan restaurant indeed.

Other famous Peking dishes you may like to order are sliced fish in wine sauce, paper-thin lamb with spring onion, barbecued Mongolian lamb, and chicken glazed in hoisin sauce. Famous Szechuan dishes are spicy hot Kung Pao chicken, dry-fried beef (which is in fact deep-fried with carrots), chilli bean curd and dry-fried four-season beans. There are also pork, prawn, and aubergine dishes with 'fish-fragrant' sauce: aubergine is a must.

Szechuan/Peking restaurants, unlike Cantonese restaurants which offer virtually no sweets, do offer one and sometimes two of note. The most famous Peking dessert is apples or bananas cooked in batter, and trailing the golden threads of their caramel glaze; these are known as toffee apples or bananas. The other is a pancake (sometimes made of glutinous rice flour) stuffed with date paste or the red azuki bean paste. Both are deep-fried and delicious, if you like sweet things.

Whatever the cuisine, decor, atmosphere, price range and location, one phenomenon universal to all Chinese restaurants is the use of monosodium glutamate (MSG), the fine white crystalline powder that enhances the savoury-sweet flavour of food. Even though of Japanese origin, it is an ingredient in all the major cookbooks published in China, and Chinese chefs all over the world use it. Since the 1960s, when the phrase 'the Chinese restaurant syndrome' was first coined in the United States to describe the symptoms of thirst, a tingling sensation around the cheekbones and temples and, in more severe cases, headaches after a deliciously tasty Chinese meal, much heated debate, especially in the West, has centred on the pros and cons of MSG, the cause of these discomforts, however temporary.

To be sure, the only substitute for MSG is genuinely good stock and fresh ingredients, which are labour-intensive and costly on both counts. While cheap take-aways may be forgiven their MSG-laden food, there is no reason why serious and expensive restaurants, with all the facilities, manpower and ingredients at their disposal, cannot make the stock essential to produce delicious dishes. After all, MSG became a standard ingredient only after the Second World War, but Chinese cooking had been established for centuries before that.

Over the last few years, less MSG has been detected in the dishes served in Chinese restaurants in Britain, if only out of deference to customers' wishes – a sure way to ensure better business. In the States, Chinese restaurants are starting to advertise that they do not use MSG. I sincerely hope that the same thing happens in Britain.

Indian by Jeremy Round

Indian food available to the British restaurant-goer is undergoing a change. After years of High Street restaurants and take-aways (run predominantly by Punjabis with Bengali cooks) simply serving hunks of protein in sauces varying only in their degree of chilli-heat, restaurants are now more likely to reflect the regional and cultural diversity of cooking south of the Himalayas. There is, for example, a broadening of the range of vegetarian Indian food that is on offer. More and more you may be able to order a thali – a complete vegetarian meal made up of a number of dishes served in small bowls on a metal tray.

Of course it is spice that characterises Indian food, but the subtlety of different uses of spice is one of the distinctions between styles of Indian cookery, and these can now be more readily sampled. Perhaps soon 'curry powder' will be used only in measly pinches by French chefs for their sauces 'à l'indienne'.

One of the prime influences on Indian cooking, giving it a broad scope of content and style, has been the various religious taboos and practices in the sub-continent. Among India's population of almost 700 million Hinduism is the predominant religion, and a proportion of the continent is Buddhist – especially on the northern and western fringes and in independent Sri Lanka. Islam is Pakistan's religion but there is also Sikhism in the north-west, Zoroastrianism – adhered to by the Parsees of the west coast around Bombay – a relatively small number of Jains, and a tradition of Christianity in the south-west, introduced by Portuguese Catholic colonists.

Orthodox Hindus do not eat meat, although advantage may be taken of the earth's bounty, so fish – the 'fruit of the sea' – is important to coastal diets. Kashmiri Hindus do not use onions or garlic in their cooking, believing them to inflame the passions. Buddhists and Jains are vegetarian, the latter so extreme that they will not eat beetroot or tomatoes because of their blood-like juices, nor do they eat root crops because of the violent way they are harvested. Parsees have a particular fondness for eggs, and Muslims will not eat pork or shellfish. Only Christians eat everything.

For a fuller idea of the variety of food to be found in the sub-continent, the sketch of dietary taboos must be overlaid with a plan of the different patterns of agriculture in this vast area of land, as it straddles latitudes shared in the north with Crete and in the south with Lagos, and encompasses the permanent snows of the world's highest mountain chain. There is also temperate rolling country that could be compared with the Sussex Downs (Simla is said to be not unlike Hindhead), vast fertile river flood-plains, sunbaked scrubland, desert, rocky plateaus, tropical rainforest and palm-fringed beaches.

Pulses are common to all regions, but the north has wheat as its staple and the south rice. The northern uplands also have apples, pears, strawberries, game and forest mushrooms while in the south you find bananas, mangoes, coconuts, tamarind, sugar-cane and the fish pomfret.

The strongest example of outside cultural influences on the cooking is the Mongol (Moghul, Moghlai) invasion in the sixteenth century that brought to India ingredients and methods of cooking recognisable throughout the Middle East. The tandoori, for instance, is not native to India: the Moghuls introduced it wherever they invaded and today Turkish villagers still use a clay oven they call a tandir.

Some dishes from all areas are fiercely hot, but Kashmiri food can be delicate and creamy, making use of many spices, like nutmeg and cinnamon, and of pulverised nuts. Moghlai dishes, also essentially northern, tend to the lavish – complicated pilaus and birianis, stuffed meats in rich sauces, with long marination and full spicing, using yoghourts, curds, cream or heavily reduced milk, especially in desserts. This contrasts with the simple grilled kebabs and tandoori meats (often colourfully dyed for decoration) suffused with spicy and tenderising marinades that are also characteristic of Moghul cooking. Delhi was the capital of the Moghul Shahs and the food of the surrounding area was greatly influenced by them. Much use is made of the 13 classic curry spices and flavourings – ginger, garlic, onion, cumin, coriander, turmeric, red and green chilli, cardamom, cinnamon, cloves, nutmeg and black pepper. The last five form the basis of the warmly fragrant garam masallah often sprinkled on dishes just before serving. For special occasions vark, leaves of thinly beaten gold or silver, are laid on top as an edible, extravagant garnish.

Northern dishes are often best eaten with bread: nan, leavened and tear-shaped, is often sprinkled with sesame seed or kalonji (black onion seed) before being cooked in the tandoor; chapatis are unleavened and griddle-cooked; parathas, sometimes stuffed with potatoes and peas or minced lamb, are fried; and puris, small puffed-up balls of wheat, are deep-fried. Dhals (stewed pulses) are the common accompaniment.

In the west there is the rich, distinctive Parsee cuisine, with its ekuri (scrambled egg with coriander and ginger) and sweet–sour dhansak stews based on lentils, and the vegetarian cookery of the Gujerat. Gujerati snack dishes include bhajias (vegetables dipped in chick-pea flour batter and deep fried), kachori (a ball of pastry-covered mung beans deep fried), patra (vine leaves rolled in spice and steamed), dhokra (a savoury chick-pea flour sponge cake), and more substantial dishes of potato, yam, or pulses in sour sauces with lime or tamarind, and aromatic vegetable stews served with pickles. The spicing of the region makes effective use of black mustard seed, fenugreek, asafetida, and, common in all regions, fresh, green coriander leaves. Bhel poori originated as the Bombay seaside snack of crunchy puffed cereals, chopped onion and chillies, tangy tamarind sauce, sweet chutney, coriander and yoghourt.

The vegetarian cookery of the south has strong similarities with that of Gujerat except for the emphasis on coconut and coconut milk which are used as a basic flavouring. Chilli-heat can be intense and a common part of a meal is rasam, a sour, pepper broth. Although fish is an interesting feature of the vegetarian-based cooking of the Kerala and Malabar coasts of southern India, it is also prominent in Bengali and Bangladeshi cuisine in more pungent dishes such as stewed fish-heads and vegetables. Unfortunately, very little of this cooking is found on the menus of British restaurants (except at London's Bombay and Moghlai Brasseries).

Other southern vegetarian dishes are iddly (a steamed rice-flour dumpling served with coconut chutney), dhosa (a crisp ground-rice and lentil pancake sometimes stuffed with spiced vegetables), and uttapom (a thicker pancake with onion and chilli in the batter). A typical southern thali may consist of perhaps a couple of vegetable curries, some bhajias, a bean curry, a lentil dhal, and a pudding (often shrikhand – a creamy yoghourt reduction flavoured with lemon and cardamom) served with bread and rice. Thalis are also catching on in non-vegetarian restaurants, where a selection of meat curries, kebabs and tandoori meat might be served.

From the south-west comes vindaloo, Goa's most famous contribution. Originally a sour, vinegared pork stew, it reflects the influence of the colonising Portuguese. The spicy chourisam sausage is also a direct descendant of the Iberian chorizo.

Like medieval British cookery, Indian cooking uses spices to sanitise and disguise the flavour of none-too-fresh ingredients. The tradition of preparing a meal with various small dishes, rather than basing it European-style on a centrepiece, comes from the acceptance that no one ingredient may be in prime condition. It is not important in which order dishes are eaten. Drinks are not considered a vital component of a meal. Lassi (yoghourt and water with either salt or a sweetener) goes well with the less rich vegetarian dishes. Of the Western drinks, lager, coke and even champagne seem to suit well.

Indonesian and Malaysian by Aileen Hall

'Unity in diversity,' Indonesia's national motto, could well be applied to all of south-east Asia. The area may have a common climate and vegetation, but history and culture ensure many variations. Because Indonesia and Malaysia have each shared traders and invaders from China, India, the Middle East, Portugal, Spain, Holland, and Britain – as well as having Hindu and Islamic influences in turn – it is no surprise to find common eating patterns in the two.

Marco Polo called Indonesia 'the spice islands', and the Arabs supplemented the rich local harvest (ginger, nutmeg, cloves, cinnamon, pepper, to name but a few) with Indian and Middle Eastern additions, such as cumin, caraway and coriander. Rice is the staple, and appears three times a day. Other characteristic flavours come from coconut, chillies, sereh (lemon grass), laos (galingale), kecap (soy sauce), citrus fruits and tamarind. Most startling to the uninitiated, and definitely an acquired taste, is terasi, or blachan – salted and dried shrimps that are then allowed to rot. Vegetables include the familiar cabbage, lettuce, tomatoes, green beans, aubergines and bean sprouts, and there is of course a wealth of tropical fruit.

Within Indonesia there are many variations: Sumatran dishes are highly spiced, with ginger a favourite flavour. The Javanese love sweet things and produce delicious sweet-and-sour sauces. Bali shows a Hindu influence in its use of pork, and Borneo dishes are most like Malay.

Malaysia produces three main styles of cooking: Malay, Indian (mainly southern Indian or Tamil) and Nonya, a blend of Chinese and Malay, which is a mere five generations old. Nonya is especially popular in Singapore, where its hot and spicy dishes, cooked slowly in coconut milk, compete with every other style – and even rival the fame of the many street vendors.

The confusion of Indonesian and Malaysian styles is compounded in Britain by restaurateurs, trying to please everyone with a mixture of dishes, so that you may eat Balinese, Nonya, Sumatran, Chinese and Tamil food all at one sitting.

What we are discussing is peasant cooking, not *haute cuisine*. All the food for a meal is put on the table at the same time, diners help themselves and – as in most hot countries – the temperature of the food is not considered crucial. Eating with the fingers (right hand only) is common, although spoon and fork are always provided for Westerners and chopsticks if the style is Chinese.

There may well be a set meal, but if you wish to compose your own, remember that a party of six will probably want four or five cooked dishes of meat, fish or vegetables, as well as salads and pickles, and perhaps soup to sip throughout and fresh fruit to finish. Aim at a contrast in texture, taste and degree of chilli-heat. Don't stint on the rice, which acts as protection against the searing heat of the spices. Meat and fish are served in small quantities. It is easy to put together a tasty vegetarian meal in Indonesian restaurants. Advice is generally freely given both on the suitability of your choice and on the chilli-heat of the various dishes. Beware sambal, a chilli-relish which appears in or with many dishes.

Start, perhaps, with satay: tiny skewers of marinated chicken, lamb, beef or pork, barbecued and served with a peanut sauce containing terasi, sugar, garlic and chillies. Continue with a selection of other favourites: pergedel (spiced potato cakes); laksa (coconut-based soup with noodles, prawns, chicken, tamarind, bean curd and vegetables – a good one-dish meal if you are eating alone); ayam goreng (fried chicken); nasi goreng (fried rice with all sorts of additions); rendang (Sumatran beef stew, cooked to tenderness in coconut milk and spices until the sauce has evaporated); kare kambing (lamb curry); Singapore chilli crab; lumpia (spring roll); sambal terong (aubergine with chilli sauce); mee goreng (fried noodles with squid, beef, and shrimps); martabak (stuffed pancake rolls); acar campur (pickled vegetable salad); gado-gado (vegetable salad with peanut sauce); udang assam manis (sweet-and-sour prawns); rujak, or rojak (spicy fruit and vegetable salad with peanut sauce).

There are occasional sago-based sweets, brightly coloured pancakes with a coconut filling, and even banana fritters (pisang goreng). But fresh fruit is more common. You could settle for a sweet and lurid drink: chendol (coconut milk, sweet bean paste and chunks of coloured jelly), or the similar ais kachan. Otherwise drink tea, fruit juices or water. Lager tends to be expensive in Indonesian restaurants here.

The rijsttafel, with its overtones of Dutch colonialism, is unpopular in Indonesia nowadays, but you may still meet it in tourist spots: a banquet of coloured rice and innumerable side dishes making a dazzling display. Malaysia's more modest contribution to party fun is the steamboat, a simmering moat of stock in which you cook your meat, fish and vegetables, finishing off with the gloriously enriched broth.

Japanese by Lesley Downer

Japanese restaurants in England opened initially to serve the needs of the growing Japanese community. Eating out is an essential part of Japanese life, not just for pleasure but as part of the tradition of hospitality: important guests are never entertained in the home. Crucial business decisions are often made after working hours over a bottle of saké (rice wine) and a good meal. A Japanese wife would be surprised and rather worried if her husband arrived home before 10 or 11 at night.

Of London's 30 or so Japanese restaurants, eight, including Suntory and Shogun, are extremely expensive and enjoy considerable prestige in the Japanese community. They offer a luxurious environment, superb and rather formal service, and food which is a delight to the eye – matters that are of more importance to many Japanese than the actual quality of the food. Unlike French food, say, Japanese food is classical, and the art is seen in fulfilling traditions rather than innovating. For an ordinary meal, the cheaper restaurants like Kitchen Yakitori, which serve a less rarefied range of dishes, are popular among Japanese, and offer a means of tasting Japanese food and experiencing the Japanese atmosphere without breaking the bank.

Japanese cookery relies not on complex cooking methods or intricate spicing, but on the natural flavour of its ingredients. Historically, the basis of the Japanese diet is fish, seafood and seaweeds supplemented by vegetables, including wild foods such as burdock root and a wide variety of fresh and dried mushrooms, and soya bean products such as tofu (bean curd). Meat and dairy foods have only recently become popular in Japan, and still play a minor role: until the end of the Second World War the Japanese themselves would not eat meat apart from chicken, and older people still do not eat meat. Dishes like sukiyaki are modern inventions. The only place meat was eaten was Nagasaki, a trading post where a few outside influences percolated through prior to the end of the last century.

Rice is served at every meal, including breakfast. The rice grown in Japan is short grain, not the long-grain rice used in Chinese and Indian cookery, and it is cooked until it clings together. Rice is quite a celebrated food in Japan; it is eaten alone, not mixed with other foods, and the word 'rice' (gohan) actually means 'a meal'.

The four main flavouring agents in Japanese cookery are dashi, soy sauce, cooking wines, and miso. Dashi is a very light, delicately flavoured stock made from kelp and shavings of dried bonito fish, and is used for soups, sauces, and for simmering fish and vegetables. Japanese soy sauce is sweeter and less salty than Chinese, and has quite a different flavour; a particularly pale soy sauce is used to avoid changing the colour of some dishes. Saké is used to enrich simmered and steamed dishes and to tenderise fish and meat. Mirin, a sweet golden rice wine with a mild flavour and very low alcohol content, is used only for cooking and gives a fine glaze to grilled foods. Miso is a salty paste made by fermenting cooked soya beans, and appears at the end of nearly every meal in the form of miso soup; it is also used in sweet dressings and as a pickling medium. Other flavourings include wasabi (a sort of fresh horseradish, which is stingingly hot and is served with raw fish), fresh root ginger, sesame seeds and sesame oil, and mild rice vinegar.

Japanese chefs select the finest and freshest fish, meat and vegetables of the season, cooking them simply and lightly without a great deal of seasoning or spicing so as to alter their basic character as little as possible. The flavours of Japanese dishes tend to be subtle, with stronger flavours reserved for the sauces and condiments which accompany the main dish, such as the rich sesame sauce served with shabu shabu (paper-thin slices of beef and vegetables simmered in light stock) and the miso dressings served with grilled tofu and vegetables.

The cooking methods are simple, standard and traditional. It is in the presentation of the meal that the skill of the chef is revealed, and Japanese customers judge a dish by its appearance and visual appeal rather than by its flavour. The individual ingredients are selected as much for their perfection of form and colour as for their flavour, and cut with impeccable skill. While cooking is regarded as simple, cutting is a fine art, and Japanese home cooks would never venture to cut their own beef for sukiyaki or fish for sashimi, but buy it ready cut. The ingredients for each dish are rapidly cooked, so that the colour is conserved and intensified, and then artistically arranged in small bowls and plates, with a garnish to provide a contrast of colour and to give a pleasing reference to the season. A slice of carrot or a quail's egg may be transformed into a plum blossom to garnish a spring dish, while a chestnut or a cucumber 'pine cone' is appropriate for autumn. The style of cooking and the menu changes with the seasons. Dishes cooked at table by the customers themselves are popular in winter; these include sukiyaki, slices of beef and vegetables fried at table and seasoned with sweetened soy sauce, and a variety of fish-based casseroles. Chilled dishes, such as cold buck-wheat noodles served on a slatted bamboo tray, or cold tofu, are served in summer.

A Japanese meal is served in many small dishes of various shapes, sizes and colours to harmonise with the colour and shape of the food; the one rule is that the plates and bowls at each setting should never match, so that they form an interesting design on the table. Traditionally, an odd number of dishes is served, representing different cooking methods.

The simplest meal consists of a soup and three dishes each cooked by a different method, usually raw fish, a grilled or fried dish and a simmered dish, followed by rice, pickles and tea. The basic set meals in Japanese restaurants are often made up in this way.

For a banquet or a very formal meal the dishes are served one by one in a set order. The appetisers are followed by a delicate clear soup in which float a few decoratively cut morsels of seafood and vegetables, and a plate of sashimi, raw fish, beautifully cut and presented and served with a little soy sauce and wasabi. It is on these that the chef lavishes his attention. Fine sashimi is a mark of respect from your host and a sure sign of a good meal to follow. Raw fish has a most delicate, unfishy taste and silky texture, and any fish, roe or shell fish – if it is totally fresh – can be served raw. Dark red tuna (magoro), particularly rich belly of tuna (toro), chewy octopus (tako) and squid (ika), pink salmon (sake) which melts in the mouth, scallops (hotategai) and prawns (ebi) are some of the most popular sashimi available in England.

In a formal banquet, soup and sashimi are followed by a succession of small dishes, first grilled fish or meat, followed by a steamed dish, often chawan mushi, a soft savoury custard served in a small lidded cup. Next comes a dish of fish or vegetables simmered in a richly seasoned stock, and finally there will be a deep-fried dish. In the winter these four dishes are often replaced by a large casserole cooked at table. A small, cooked vegetable salad is usually served. The meal ends with rice, some pickled vegetables and a bowl of thick miso soup. Dessert consists of small portions of fresh fruit, exquisitely carved.

Usually only a selection of the above dishes is served, and most restaurants in Japan specialise in a particular style of cooking, such as tempura – small pieces of fish, prawns and vegetables deep-fried in a very light batter – or sashimi; noodles; dishes cooked at table; or grilled foods such as yakitori (chunks of chicken on skewers with a rich sweet glaze) or teriyaki (glazed steak), which are often cooked in front of the customers on a charcoal brazier. In London, restaurants offer a range of the most popular dishes. Some London restaurants have sushi bars, where you order directly from the chef, who then cuts thin slices of fish from the great slabs in a glass cabinet on the counter, and presses each slice on to a small ball of vinegared rice; two make one serving. Sashimi and sushi rolls (rice and slices of tuna or cucumber rolled in nori seaweed) are also served in sushi bars.

Traditionally, saké accompanies the meal. Some Japanese prefer beer, whisky or wine – Japanese Suntory whisky is said to be particularly light and mild and suitable for Japanese food. The correct procedure is to fill your neighbour's cup but never your own, in the expectation that he will then fill yours. When receiving saké hold the cup in both hands. The toast is 'Campai!' ('make dry your little cup') and the saké should be downed in one.

Jewish by Claudia Roden

Jewish restaurants serve the kind of food that grandmothers used to make in Eastern Europe and Russia. Most, but not all, are kosher, which means that they observe the religious dietary laws under rabbinical supervision. Because of these laws, if they serve meat they cannot serve dairy products, and vice versa. They are generally meat restaurants, so you cannot expect to have cheese, cream, butter or milk with your tea. The meat comes from animals that have been slaughtered according to laws, and it will have been salted before cooking.

It is basic, homely food, simply cooked – boiled or roast chicken, turkey, steaks and hamburgers, grilled or fried fish (fried fish in a matzo meal coating is usually eaten cold). There are also the specially 'Jewish' dishes brought to this country by Russian and Polish immigrants at the turn of the century.

The traditional menu is still exactly as it was in the 1920s, when the first Jewish restaurants opened in the East End of London. Favourite hors d'oeuvre are gefilte fish (minced fish balls, and the most Jewish of foods), chopped (chicken) liver and chopped herring. But there are also meat-filled pancakes called blintzes, egg and onion, and calves-foot jelly. (You will not be served meat and fish on the same plate as they are not meant to be eaten together.) Particularly popular with Jewish people is soup. Borshch, barley soup and one with ravioli-like dumplings called kreplach are especially good.

Perhaps the best Jewish food, though, is salt beef (the fat in the brisket gives this pickled meat a special flavour) which, like tongue, can be eaten hot or cold. Other traditional entrees are meat balls in a sauce, liver and onion, and schnitzel. Jewish-style vegetables are sweetened carrots called tzimmas, sweet-and-sour cabbage, and latkes, which are crisp fried potato cakes.

At lunchtime these days people like to have a snack, such as a salt beef sandwich, frankfurters, or worsht (salami) and eggs. Pickled cucumber is a must with everything, and horseradish sauce is a piquant garnish.

For dessert there is apple strudel, or try the sweet noodle lockshen pudding, which cannot be had elsewhere.

Korean by Deborah Buzan

The first Korean restaurant in Britain opened 11 years ago. Five years ago there were two. Today there are ten, and there are also four speciality food shops. They are all but one in London.

Korea, like Japan, remained isolated through most of it history. In 1876 the country's isolation was broken by Japan, and in 1910 the Japanese absorbed Korea into their empire. Korea remained under Japanese rule until 1945, when the North was occupied by the Soviet Union and the South by the United States. The border was agreed in 1953 and the nation became two states: the Communist-ruled North, and the pro-Western South. South Korea is now part of the international scene.

Korean food has elements of both Japanese and Chinese cooking. Koreans revere both yin and yang and pay tribute to the Oriental rule of five flavours: salt (salt, soy sauce and salty bean paste), spicy-hot (chillies and mustard), bitter (ginger), sweet (honey and sweet potatoes), and sour (vinegar), and also five colours: red, green, yellow, white, and black. It is a health-conscious diet: meals are often designed according to the restorative and curative properties of the ingredients.

Rice and soy-bean products figure prominently, hardly any dairy products or eggs are used, and vegetables are raw or barely cooked. Food is chopped into small pieces before steaming, grilling or frying. This means that less time and fuel are needed to cook – enforced features of the cuisine because of the nomadic nature of the society in the past and because of the scarcity of fuel. Most Koreans use metal knitting-needle-sized chopsticks, traditionally silver, which were handy in the old days for identifying poisoned or tainted food as they changed colour on contact with it.

Korean food is spicy, especially in the far south of the country where the climate is hot. Sauces tend to be thin rather than glutinous. Where the Chinese favour pork, Koreans eat beef, and tend to grill their meat, where the Chinese wok-fry. Bean paste and chillies go into many dishes; rice often comes mixed with barley or beans, and many vegetables are pickled to keep through the winter. Traditionally with food Koreans drink water or rice tea made with the crusty dregs of the rice pan. The barley tea served gratis in restaurants is a habit acquired after the Second World War.

Koreans, like the Japanese, hold ritualised feasts and food-orientated festivals. But meals are informal and unstructured. They eat less fish than the Japanese, though they too like it raw or marinated.

Traditionally, breakfast is rice-based, and typically the main meal of the day. Lunch is composed of noodles or rice mixed with red beans, nuts and seeds. Dinner in wealthy homes is an elaborate affair of nine to twelve dishes around a central bowl of rice. A normal family dinner consists of three to seven dishes with rice.

Most restaurants in Britain serve typically Korean food. There are a few concessions to the Western palate, notably the restrained use of chillies. And whereas Koreans are used to eating everything more or less at the same time, restaurants here have turned some of the pickles and soup dishes into appetisers. Most Korean restaurants in London offer set meals that are more accessible to the uninitiated than the sometimes daunting and many-paged *carte*. But almost without exception the staff will be extremely helpful and anxious to encourage experiment.

Classic dishes feature beef, fish, shellfish, or soya bean cake – or a combination of them all. Bean sprouts, cabbage, radish, mushrooms, green, red and yellow peppers, turnips and seaweed are the most commonly added vegetables. Primary flavourings include soy sauce, chillies, garlic, spring onions and sesame seeds (or sesame oil), and many dishes are made sweet and sour with vinegar and sugar. Rice-flour dumplings, usually meat-filled, are similar to the Chinese, but the bintakok (called 'Korean pizza' but more pancake-like) is a dish unto its own, made of ground green-coloured beans mixed with oysters, meat, fish and spring onions, then fried and served with a sesame, spring onion and soy sauce. Kim-chee is a spicy, fermented pickled vegetable, usually cabbage, which accompanies every Korean meal, including breakfast. No Korean household is complete without its large kim-chee jar buried in the garden to keep dark and cool. It is often listed as an appetiser, though it complements every other dish. The offering of a stick of chewing gum or mint at the end of a meal is meant to counteract the kim-chee's garlic pungency.

If anything may be called Korea's national dish, it's bulgogi, thin strips of beef marinated in soy sauce, garlic, sesame oil, sugar, and then grilled, often at the table. Shin-sol-lo is a classic soup of the kings, which contains everything but the royal sink. Yuk kwe is Korea's answer to steak tartare, though flavourings consist of pears, pine nuts, soy sauce and sesame oil.

To drink, jung-jong is an aromatic version of rice wine. Ginseng spirits and ginseng tea may be excellent revitalising tonics, but Koreans say most Westerners need three tries before appreciating them. Ginseng root is also used in cooking, but the flavour is masked as much as possible. Koreans prize it for its medicinal properties rather than its taste.

Fruit is the usual dessert, but sticky cakes made from wheat, bean or rice flour are popular too, but rarely found in restaurants here.

Lebanese by Claudia Roden

The Lebanese are the only people in the Arab world who have developed a restaurant trade. Their menu, based on meze (appetisers), was born in the region of Zahle, in the north-east of the country, as an accompaniment to the local anis-flavoured grape spirit, arak.

There was a time when Zahle was known as a mountain paradise, the Switzerland of the Middle East. In 1920 two cafes opened by the river Bardaouni, which cascaded down the mountain. They gave away assorted nuts, seeds, olives, bits of cheese and raw vegetables with the arak. Gradually the entire valley became filled with open-air cafes, each larger and more luxurious than the last, and vying to attract the customers who flocked from all over the Middle East with ever more varied meze (they created 40). The reputation of dishes such as tabouleh (parsley, mint and cracked wheat salad) and different kinds of kibbeh (cracked wheat and meat dishes), which were local village specialities, spread far afield. Meze became a national institution which was allied with all kinds of grilled foods (the other traditional part of the Lebanese menu). Open-air restaurants opened in the capital and on the coast in idyllic surroundings. Where there was no river or sea, a fountain was installed to increase the feelings of well-being and good humour.

Now, the main thing in dealing with a Lebanese menu is to order small amounts of as wide a variety of meze as possible. It is a good idea to go in a group and to divide up dishes into twos and fours. Eat them with arak and take your time to pick at them. You are not meant to hurry.

Choose a balanced selection of at least four or five hot and cold items, preferably with an emphasis on vegetables (menus tend to be too meaty these days). Have refreshing tabouleh, yoghourt and cucumber salad, or the strained and thickened yoghourt called labne, or try mashed aubergine, pickles, hummus or tahina (sesame meal). There may be aubergine slices and fried courgettes, and there are usually stuffed vine leaves, falafel (bean rissoles), broad beans, all sorts of pies, raw or stuffed fried kebbeh (a must), and sometimes also brain and tongue salads, stuffed spleen, fried liver and meat balls. Dressings of olive oil and lemon juice and chopped garlic will be there for you to add to taste. If you like them, put on plenty, as flavours should be sharp and strong.

You may like to follow the meze with a soup – the best is lentil – though I think it is superfluous. Go on to the main course, which will be charcoal-grilled fish, chicken or meat – mostly lamb, of which there are many kinds. If there are no radishes, peppers, cucumbers and tomatoes (usually placed on the table) for you to cut up, order a side salad. Restaurants occasionally offer a few other main dishes, such as meat and vegetable stews, combined wheat, rice or pasta dishes (those cooked in yoghourt are especially good), fish cooked with rice and onions, or chicken stuffed with rice.

To end the meal there are fruit and milk puddings, or simply try the nutty, syrupy sweets, followed by Turkish coffee.

Thai by Drew Smith

Thailand is a fertile country laced with rivers and surrounded on three sides by warm shallows. It is rich in fish and vegetables.

Over the centuries it has become home for refugees from neighbouring countries and for traders from across the seas, and all have brought with them culinary traditions and practices that the Thais have adopted. The Chinese largely introduced pork and poultry, as well as a liking for noodles, omelettes and duck. Some experts (including Jennifer Brennan, whose *Thai Cooking*, published by Jill Norman & Hobhouse at £7.95, is one of the best books on the subject) hold that the Thai liking for hot, spicy foods derives from the cooking of the Szechuan and the Hunan regions of China.

Settlers from India brought subtle influences on the spicing and encouraged changes to the traditional curry. The Muslims probably introduced beef, and Arab traders may well have brought what is today one of the best-known Thai dishes, the satay stick. This variation on a Middle Eastern kebab is char-grilled and served with a hot peanut sauce. From southern India came the use of coconut milk to dilute the power of the spices. The coconut – its leaves, flesh and milk – is intrinsic to Thai cooking. Dishes would originally have been fired with black peppers, but later, around the early 1500s, the Portuguese brought from the Americas the chilli, which has become the hall-mark of Thai cooking. Many Western palates find that much of the food in Thailand today is just too hot to eat.

There are also similarities between Thai and southern Malaysian cooking, most obviously in the use of fermented fish. A classic dish that Westerners may find difficult but which is usually found on good Thai restaurant menus in this country is nam prik, a viciously powerful sauce that may accompany a number of tit-bits. Although the Thais share with the French a high regard for saucing, the Thais virtually elevate it to be the centrepiece of a meal. In Thailand nam prik will almost always be served. Its constituents vary, but in essence it will be made up of fermented fish sauce, dried shrimps or shrimp paste, fresh and dried chilli, lime juice, garlic and tamarind. Tame it is not.

As for the cooking, the wok is the prime utensil and improvisation the main technique, because recipes are rarely written down.

Most meals will include soup and a rice dish; soup is eaten even for breakfast. Meat may feature as the centrepiece of a banquet, but it is the fish and vegetables that show the true colours of the cooking, the fish often strongly spiced with chillies. In London Thai restaurants will tend to use a combination of local vegetables, dried fish from Chinese supermarkets, and ingredients flown in each week from Thailand.

In the classic cuisine, now dying out because of the expense of the labour involved, the vegetables and fruits are ornately carved and presented with the same kind of visual artistry as is found in Japanese and also imperial Peking cooking. Chillies will be fashioned into flower shapes, spring onions into chrysanthemum shapes, and cucumbers hollowed out as vessels for other foods.

One curiosity is the durian, reputedly the most expensive fruit in the world, which has a uniquely pungent, almost fetid taste.

Thais will usually drink iced tea, coffee or fruit juices in the heat of their native country. Thai beer is a relatively new addition of this century, and there is also a local distillation that tastes like bourbon. As in other parts of the East, guests bringing whisky are well appreciated, and some hold that the best drink of all with the food is Johnny Walker Black Label.

The Thai shop at 3 Craven Terrace, London W2 (01-723 2358) is open from 11 to 6 every day of the week and stocks not only Thai foodstuffs brought directly from Bangkok but also made-up dishes. A new shop, Tawanna, has opened at 18 Chepstow Road, London W2 (01-221 6316). And the Matahari supermarket at 11 Hogarth Road, London SW5 (01-370 1041) has a range of Thai groceries, including durian in season.

The view from the kitchen

Raymond Blanc

My father, a firm atheist, would mark a symbolic cross over the bread before each meal – not in accordance with any Christian belief, but as a mark of respect for what the bread represented. Of course no one at the table was allowed to help themselves before this ritual. Then came the ragout, simmered gently and lovingly by my mother for hours. Its aroma would engulf the table and the conversation would spill over. The family bond was once again renewed. The second half of the twentieth century has not been kind to this traditional way of life. And in Britain this period has been marked by a lack of education at an early age about good food and what it stands for.

For many years now cooks have been taken into the industry for the wrong reasons. Academic failures have turned to catering, or else it has been the last resort for students without personality or even standards of personal hygiene. The result has been an apathetic, non-performing industry. Even now finding efficient, courteous waiters who pride themselves on their work is practically impossible. Fawlty Towers was not so much a comedy as a tragedy, because it was so true to the realities of life. I blame the catering schools. They have processed 'catering' students with little knowledge of what today's cuisine is about. They have made little or no attempt to recognise that standards can be achieved. Of course fast-food businesses need man-power and this they have provided. But there has been no real selection of young people of talent whose way forward has been blocked by the many others who are just in it for a job, nothing more or less. The quality of craftsmanship has been lost in the schools.

Also, the raw materials used in the catering colleges are just not good enough. The textbooks on which lessons are based are out of date. Is it any wonder that the results are questionable? The schools are not prepared for the realities of today, let alone those of tomorrow, when our growing tourist trade must become an industry of increasing importance. Something must be done nationally to attract quality students and to set up a new order if we are to build a successful industry.

For too long it has been true that to eat well in Britain you must eat breakfast three times a day. For example, a fourteen-year-old memory is planted in my mind that sums up the state of British poultry. It is of a big, white, flabby, fatty Aylesbury duck which when cooked shrunk to a ridiculous size, leaving in the roasting tray a pond of fat. When served it was a pale unappetising colour, although I have to admit that it was tasty. Disgusted, I went to Aylesbury to find a real Aylesbury duck – one that had been fed on corn and maize, that had strutted around the farmyard and eaten its fill from what lay on the ground. I imagined it with its short, meaty legs, a thin layer of skin with a slight yellow tinge covering graciously a fleshy breast. Once carved it would show a tender, juicy, reddish breast whose aroma could send the senses reeling. The first butcher gave me the address of a second who he thought might have such a duck. The second butcher gave me the name of a third. The third butcher laughed mockingly. 'It does not exist. It did once but that was a long time ago,' he said. I understood then that English regional cuisine did not exist any more.

Like many chefs I was presented with a problem. To solve this problem we had to find the freshest and the highest-quality ingredients that were available – and the meat, game and fish in Britain are of a very high standard, even if some of the fish is transported across the country in unrefrigerated vans – and build up our new cooking from there. To call this catering *nouvelle cuisine* is misleading. It is an arrogant term that suggests the condemnation of the work of many centuries by great chefs who were innovators and who, without proper recognition or status, and often working in the most appalling conditions, established the classical structures on which we lean today.

There is no doubt that the so-called *nouvelle cuisine* has had, and still has, a dramatic influence on our perception of today's cooking. Even so, many customers had to suffer a lot of abuse from the men in white who were overtaken by a delirium of fashionable inventiveness, most often of extravagant originality, who created little monsters of dishes. Carême, Escoffier and Point, God bless them, must have turned in their graves. It was they, rather than the exponents of *nouvelle cuisine*, who were the initiators of today's movement, who gave us the armoury and the understanding with which to meet the new demands. Like any art form or industry, catering evolves slowly. It was the technology that provided the trigger – polytunnels, refrigeration, conservation, rapidity of transport, new exotic products brought from across the world, and of course the new awareness of the health factor.

The modern chef is not a creator, as such, but a renovator. The classic cuisine had to change. The useless artifices imposed by high society had to go, and so did the unacceptable disguises and the codified rigidity of received ideas. These were anachronisms from another age. We have our own anachronisms today. We condemn the use of flour . . . and yet cream and butter are indulged in heavily, which is even worse. Perhaps the health factor should not dictate what we eat, but at least it ought to influence us. There is nothing worse than to feel 'full' after a lovely meal.

Today's cooking offers a freedom – to be enjoyed within the basic rules which must be respected. Only the best can be used to obtain the best results. And already we can see the signs of such a renaissance both in the kitchens and among producers. I believe that within the next decade a new generation of young chefs will open their own restaurants and take today's cooking to new heights. But they will need the suppliers. When I opened Les Quat' Saisons in Oxford I imported all my poultry from France. Now, however, for the first time a British firm has decided to breed real squabs and the result is outstanding – they are even better than the pigeonneaux de Bresse, supposedly the best in the world. This company is now considering breeding chickens and ducks, maybe even for sale to France. And why not?

Why is it that growers have not felt the need to produce better-quality products and raw materials? Why do growers produce hundreds of acres of cabbages and fields of lettuce wrapped in plastic bags, force-fed on chemicals and insecticides to obtain those 'magnificent-sized vegetables' that taste of nothing? It is not the climate or the soil. In my own garden I can grow artichokes, aubergines, red and green peppers, cherry tomatoes, cavaillon, melons, all my herbs, eight varieties of lettuce. At last a few adventurous people are beginning to grow vegetables organically. If you choose your seeds carefully the results can be exceptionally good. The use of polytunnels and greenhouses can extend the seasons. It is a mystery why this is not being done on a large scale across the country. At least in Scotland they have realised the high gastronomic value and financial potential of wild mushrooms. For the first time in years these natural assets are being commercialised in Britain. Hundreds of restaurateurs are crying out for such supplies. And the consumer has had a bad deal for too long in this country. We can change it. Let us make it happen.

The best restaurant in the world?

Drew Smith

The old Hôtel de Ville sign still hangs on the front of the big square building at the crossroads opposite the grocer's shop and down from the church. At each window there is a flower box on the sill filled with flowers. The tiled roof sits atop as if on a big cuckoo clock.

Crissier is a small town of 4,000 people, 40 minutes down the motorway from Geneva or longer if you take the winding road by the lake. It is a town where people walk their dogs along the roads that do not border the industrial estates and where the hoardings are taken up by Marlboro cigarette adverts.

Through the heavy wooden door is an empty hallway, and at the far end is a glass door with the letters 'fg' inscribed on it. A waiter comes out to greet. There are two dining-rooms connected by a corridor, in which are located the reception desk and the automatic doors into the kitchen. The dining-room to the left is the larger; it has orange banquettes and bigger paintings than the other.

The room to the right has roughly worked stone walls, some covered with a cream velour cloth; the oil-paintings on the walls, of a sunset over fields of snow, a village street in sunlight, and a white boat moored on blue water, are by local artists. The ceiling has been lowered, and looks like the undersurface of a billiard table inlaid with spotlights. The opened bottles of claret lie in silver baskets, like loaded artillery, waiting to be summoned. The chairs are bamboo, and on each table is a fat brown oriental-style bowl filled with blazes of orchids. The tablecloths are olive and cream; in the centre are embroidered the initials 'fg'. The napkins match. Three glasses are lined up for each setting, and the table silver is heavy and well used, scratched from the washing and polishing. Knives and forks last three years, when the constant use by 60 diners twice a day from Tuesday to Saturday begins to show.

What is remarkable is what is not there. No sorbets pop up in the middle of meals as palate cleansers, no trolley crammed with ostentatious vintages of armagnac and cognac is wheeled about the dining-room, no bevy of waiters hovers like gnats around the tables, no framed certificates of merit hang on the walls, no thick-pile carpet covers the floor – just large brown washed, almost industrial tiles. Diners eat in shirt sleeves. The butter on the table is unfashionably sweetcream, lightly salted, and sits in an unfashionable brown pot. Only a duck press in the far corner announces to the casual eater that anything about this restaurant might just be out of the ordinary for anywhere other than Crissier. There is no pomp in the atmosphere. Just this food . . .

Frédy Girardet is probably the greatest discovery of the French guidebook *Gault Millau*. They rate him 19.5 out of 20 on their points system. 'Only the good Lord can score 20, and he has not much time for cooking,' is how they put it, which is a nice line they may come to regret. Michelin ignores him: Geneva figures in the French edition, but not Lausanne, let alone Crissier. If their coverage extended to Crissier they might give only two stars and not the coveted three because of the things that aren't there and because of the lack of formality. On the *Guide*'s rating system I would rate him 17 but would want to eat a few more meals before being certain that he warrants 18.

His style and his importance to restaurant cooking are summed up in the title of one of his books, *Cuisine Spontanée*. He is not a chef who has created a few dishes that have become his trademarks. He uses the best produce, the suppliers of which he has fostered over the years, with a strong local bias among them. The wine list contains a substantial section of Swiss wines as well as clarets and burgundies in magnums and bottles. Ingredients are brought to the kitchen and cooked to order, and at the end of each evening the larder is virtually bare. The waiters will suggest alternative meals according to what is in the kitchen. 'Why don't you try some of this? I would not have that with that because they both have lettuce. This is very good tonight: you should have a taste.' They speak English.

Girardet himself is a grey-haired paternal figure, now 50, who walks around the dining-room in his chef's whites, chatting in a laconic growl in French to diners as if they were his children. He is in the modern idiom of the hero, a working-class figure, almost humbled by his talent, resisting the lures of fame in favour of continuing his work in the restaurant. He shares with people in other spheres, like Bruce Springsteen or Jimmy Connors or even Richard Branson the sense that the work ethic dominates and is recognised and respected as the single, all-important fact of life. He does not swan around opening supermarkets when he can be doing what he does best, cooking. 'My work is my obsession,' he has said, which is very much a 1980s phenomenon.

He wanted to be a professional footballer, but when his father died when he was 19 he reluctantly had to take over the family bistro in Crissier. The great gastronomy did not exactly come pouring out of the kitchen straight away. Ten years later, on a trip to Burgundy, a wine grower friend took him to lunch at the Troisgros brothers' restaurant in Roanne. By this time the brothers were in their heyday creating what we now usually casually term *nouvelle cuisine*. 'I realised I had slept through life until then. I suddenly understood that there was an art called gastronomy and that I had a talent for it.'

After three years of experimentation he went to the bank for a loan to take over the ground floor of the local town hall. Five years later, in 1973, *Gault Millau* first ate there. He was hardly an overnight sensation.

In the kitchen there are now 18 chefs. It is a live cuisine. The taste of his poultry is a revelation. The breast and legs of quail are spatchcocked out on the plate and tucked up with a heap of cabbage, sliced carrots and some wild mushrooms, whose lactic juices run into the sauce, giving it a peppery taste.

The creativity is seen more in the technique and approach than in the individual dishes, which can nonetheless be magnificent. On a single plate are arranged the claws of a lobster with a mound of mashed potato topped with crushed tomato and a pair of langoustines, with a faint taste of smoking, and some diced, fried courgette with garlic.

On another plate is a strip of grilled turbot, surrounded by sauté scallops, each with a sauce, one of purée leek and another of endive and then an embracing beurre blanc is added as well.

The plates do not swim with sauces but just have little smears and puddles. Two fillets of silky red mullet sit in what looks like a cream sauce decorated with a huge sprig of young rosemary, but hidden in the sauce are the tastes of the fish livers, the rosemary, and the juices of the fish stock and the herb stock that dilute the cream.

The dishes are not always perfect, but some of his failures are almost as glorious as his successes – like the monkfish, seared with spices on the outside, sitting in a fennel sauce so vivid that it eventually overpowered the whole dish.

Swiss steaks might not bear comparison with the best Aberdeen Angus but come with a red wine, vinegar and shallot sauce and a ragout of vegetables, including cauliflower topped with sieved egg yolk.

At the back of the menu is a list of dishes that have been in the repertoire. It reads like a Greatest Hits album – the lobster and saffron minestrone; roast veal kidneys with thyme and cream sauce; pigeon pot-au-feu with foie gras; caramelised apple tart with ice-cream of almond milk; and more.

There is a stretcher of a cheeseboard bearing mainly hard Swiss cheeses plus a corner of goats'. There are four types of Gruyère – mild, semi-salted, salted and superb montagne – but like others Girardet has had difficulty finding it with holes lately. There are fine Sauternes on the wine list to go with them.

The ice-creams are a performance. Out of great silver vats with flip-over lids come little sorbets which the waiter moulds into little torpedoes using a hot spoon – melon, kiwi, peach, banana, prune, and so on, and then on another plate come the ice-creams fashioned in the same way – a bread ice-cream, a caramel ice-cream, a Charentais melon ice-cream, all of superb smoothness and depth of flavour.

And then there is a sweets trolley, loaded with fruits in syrups and alcohols, or plain, and naturally, because after all this is Switzerland, mille-feuilles, clafoutis . . . With coffee come impeccable petits fours from chocolate truffles to exquisite little custard tarts to beautiful raspberry tarts. The pastry-work throughout is sublime.

To end meals, Girardet has his own-label eaux-de-vie which are remarkable for possessing the same intensity and clarity of taste which are the hallmarks of the food. (They are for sale at his shop next door, which also has some food produce – at a price.)

The wine list is fitting. It opens with around 60 Swiss wines with interesting variations on different themes, such as a choice of seven Dézaleys and an interesting Pinot Noir de Saillon at 42 Swiss francs. The whites are in the main the better bet, particularly in terms of value because most are around 30 to 40 francs.

Given the current exchange rate meals are not cheap by any standards. The set meal is 140 francs and off the *carte* bills of £60-plus a head are the order of the day, even more if you drink the fine clarets – no fewer than five Ch. Pétrus; Ch. Latour '70 (310 francs); Ch. La Mission-Haut-Brion '61 (680 francs) – or the '76 and '78 Côte de Nuits burgundies. The Alsace section is mainly from Beyer and does not seem to be as strong as the Swiss wines. The Rhônes concentrate on the '79s and are accessible at around 50 francs.

Tables in the evening are at a premium and have to be booked months in advance; lunch is less congested and the menu no different.

How far ahead is Girardet of the field? It is a Carved Angel (see Dartmouth) rather than a Gavroche (see London) of a dining-room. There are perhaps 10 chefs in Britain today who might aspire to this level – Raymond Blanc, Pierre Koffman, Nico Ladenis in particular. But too much of their energy is still taken in building up the kind of suppliers that are needed to produce food of such dazzling invention. But if such supplies can be got to a small town like Crissier, then there is reason to hope it could be done here. But for a kitchen to start creating on its feet like Girardet's, it must, after all, have the produce to cook. . . .

Eating out in Ireland

A letter to the Editor

Having returned to live in Ireland I was saddened to find that Ireland no longer has full status in your *Guide*, but sad indeed is the restaurant situation confronting the traveller in Ireland, whether he or she is a gourmet or someone simply seeking good value and good cooking. There are a number of background factors, but the major problem would seem to be caused by the villain VAT. The very high VAT rate of 23 per cent is to a large extent crippling the restaurant industry. People who regularly dined out at least once a week can no longer afford that treat, and generally the Irish person who loves good food is well advised to cook it at home from our excellent raw materials, or visit friends with the same idea.

This leaves eating-out to those who have money to spend but who may not be very discerning, to the traveller who needs to fill a gap and stops where he or she wants, to expense-account diners who may not always be very discerning either, and to the special occasion customer who finds it increasingly difficult to find a standard worthy of a celebration.

Apart from VAT, another chronic problem is besetting the good food scene in Ireland, and this arises from some of our own national characteristics. Your average Irish customer is not often a good, *constructive* critic. The beleaguered restaurateur, in his struggle to keep ahead, may well try to cut back in all areas while still trying to keep his share of the market, ending up with problems, like the inexcusable but common unhygienic kitchens, slovenly, disagreeable staff, bad food or exorbitant prices – sometimes all together! If the customer accepts such a situation in silence, pays for it and even says, 'Thank you' and comes again, who is to blame the more unscrupulous managements if they think anything goes? Whose fault is it if a bored chef continues to produce an ignorant and mis-spelt menu as long as nobody comments or asks an informed question? Who would bother to produce careful cooking for a customer who spends an hour or two drinking in the bar before the meal? And who can blame an establishment that finds it easier to make money on drink? Here we are with land, seas and climate which can produce among the best ingredients in the world, yet we can be our own worst enemies in exploiting them.

That said, there is a ray of hope in the movement around the country to provide either 'real' food in the form of local produce well cooked and presented in quite small, simple surroundings, often by a husband-and-wife team, or good, attractive snacks in a clean, self-service establishment. At the other end of the scale is the Irish Country House, well maintaining its object of providing accommodation and dining for those in search of high standards. Experience of the establishments in the Irish Country Houses and Restaurants Association has proved that they offer excellent food in gracious and elegant surroundings – at high prices, yes, but they are special places. Here and there, also, is the occasional, independent, distinguished restaurant. In the middle range, alas, there is something of a black hole. Not to be scorned, of course, is the Irish bed-and-breakfast house with its fortifying breakfast. Good pub grub is not a tradition in our country (and package soup lurks in the most unexpected places), but there is good smoked salmon and brown bread to be found in many pubs.

So what do I advise friends coming to Ireland?

Well, if they arrive at Dublin, sightseers and shoppers would do well to eat at Caesar's in Dame Street, confident of getting good food, good service and good value, or for delicious lunches in interesting surroundings they could take in the Cellar Restaurant in the Hugh Lane Gallery in Parnell Square, or (if they have no objection to queuing at busy times) they could find good, attractive dishes at the self-service Kilkenny Kitchen in the absorbing Kilkenny Shop in Nassau Street. South of the city, in the port town of Dun Laoghaire, they would be safe in going to Barrels Steak and Wine Bar, a mews in Lower Great George's Street, or at Russells, in Glasthule (good value but rushed). On Dublin's westerly outskirts, in Lucan, Henri's, on the Mall, has upheld its standards for many years now, and the traveller who could afford a big night out could try the fish at the King Sitric in Howth on the north side, or the superb cooking of John Howard at Le Coq Hardi in Pembroke Road, Ballsbridge, a southerly suburb. If they had time to book well in advance, and travel north-west towards Navan, they should not miss a really super dinner at Dunderry Lodge, five miles outside the town.

Those bound across the Midlands could find log fires, a welcome and a good dinner at Crookedwood House outside Mullingar. On the north-west coast around Sligo, there is the pleasure of good food at the Knockmuldowney House Restaurant (provided you like sauces), and peace and delight at dinner at the no-choice, but superb Drumlease Glebe House, hidden near Dromahair, Co. Leitrim. Then there is the choice of turning northwards towards Co. Donegal and the excellence of Rathmullan House near the northern tip of the county, and the possibility of hunting for the new crop of small, good places to eat in the touring area around Donegal. Those who go on down the west coast towards the Connemara region could eat well at Letterfrack in Co.

Galway, either with an elegant and good dinner at Rosleague Manor or a lunch snack in a craft-shop. They should certainly try to plan their itinerary to include a meal at Cashel House Hotel near Clifden. South of Galway there is pub grub, including fresh oysters, to be had in Moran's of the Weir, or at Burke's in Clarenbridge.

The hungry in Ennis, Co. Clare, could try Lady Gregory's Restaurant in Abbey Street and then, if they take the ferry to Co. Kerry, they must not miss Dingle and the famous Doyle's Seafood Bar, or the nearby Half-Door, or Whelan's. In Dingle also is the delightfully special Café Liteartha, where you can enjoy delicious coffee and home-made goodies while you browse through the newspapers, books and records. Further south, on the next peninsula, there is the new and good little French restaurant Dominique's at Catherdaniel, or those who can afford the luxury will be well rewarded at the Park Hotel in Kenmare. There is engaging ambience as well as good cooking in Irene Maes' no-glamour restaurant in the middle of Killarney, Gaby's (no booking, so arrive early).

Co. Cork has long had a good share of fine restaurants, with top place going to the Ryans' outstanding Arbutus Lodge Hotel at Montenotte in Cork city. Still in Cork there is Lovetts for fine food and service, or the traveller could step back in time at the Allens' famous, gracious Yeats' Room at Ballymaloe House near Shanagarry and Midleton. Out amid the beauty of west Cork there is Courtmacsherry House at Courtmacsherry, the O'Connors have a good seafood place in Bantry's main square, and there is Blair's Cove Restaurant nearby at Durrus. The food is good at the Overdraught Bar at Tracton, Minane Bridge, and another good stop, near Carrigaline, is Roberts Cove Inn. In Kinsale, which is noted for its wealth of restaurants, the visitor could choose The Vintage, Blue Haven and Man Friday and do well in all of them, or on the back road at Ballinhassig they will find Bawnlee House. On the east side of Cork there is the splendour and good cooking of Longueville House and its President's Restaurant at Mallow, while on the coast road, in Youghal, there is the welcome Aherne's Seafood Bar Restaurant in the town, long a leader in the field, and still first-class.

Coming inland through Co. Tipperary, there is the Cashel Palace Hotel in Cashel, a haven of quiet in an interesting town, and a restaurant with superb food and service in elegant surroundings. For the traveller going on through Co. Waterford, it is worth taking the car ferry from the flower-filled little town of Passage East (which offers its own reasonable little seafood pub, the Farleigh, as well as access to the Suir Inn, an English-style pub with an excellent seafood platter at tiny Cheekpoint). The ferry lands at Ballyhack in Co. Wexford, and beside the little harbour, with all the benefits therefrom, at the Neptune the McAuliffs are producing first-class soups, fish and trimmings from real local produce. For anyone who would like to dine on the water, the

Galley Cruising Restaurant offers quite good food and value – in cramped quarters, but with superb views as you cruise up or down the river from New Ross, Co. Wexford. Near the port of Rosslare, in Co. Wexford, one could enjoy the fresh food and intimate atmosphere of the seaside restaurant the Bakehouse, at Carne, or in the high season one could try tracking down the French cooking of Claude Kelly in his tiny restaurant Le Gourmet at Rosslare Strand.

The traveller driving towards Dublin from the south-east must not miss the famous Marlfield House, Mary Bowe's restaurant outside Gorey, where food, presentation and surroundings have maintained a high standard of excellence over the years. For those who head inland, a trip should be made over the mountain to Borris, Co. Carlow, to find truly excellent food and careful cooking at the Step House, an old house in the centre of this pretty village. While studying all that is of interest in Kilkenny, pangs of hunger could be allayed in Kilkenny Kitchen at the fascinating Design Centre opposite the castle. Beyond Carlow, towards Dublin, there is another worthwhile stop for a good and unusual menu at the mildly eccentric Schoolhouse in Castledermot.

There must be many more good stops, and the traveller would be wise to ask, when he finds a good one, about recommendations for other areas – Ireland is small when it comes to knowledge of this kind! He or she should always check first that the place recommended is still there, its opening hours and days, and usually should book in advance. The fast food monster spreads itself far and wide and the ubiquitous tin, freezer and microwave may reign for a time, but the winds of change are blowing in other directions too, and perhaps 1986 will see lower taxes and better standards taking over again.

Your hungry, hopeful Irish correspondent

Alsace wines

James Ainsworth

Alsace has at different times belonged to France and Germany. Albert Schweitzer was born among the half-timbered houses and cobbled streets of Kaysersberg in the southern part of Alsace, near Colmar, in 1875 when the region was annexed by Prussia. Had he been born five years earlier he would have been French; by the time he died Alsace had changed ownership three more times, ending up French. The wines have not escaped the effects of this Franco-German tug of war any more than the people, the language or the cooking, and display some characteristics of each country.

After the First World War the Alsace wine producers, keen to put quality first, grubbed up the common Chasselas vines which the Germans had cultivated, and replanted with better German grape varieties, such as Riesling, Gewürztraminer and Sylvaner, more suitable to the northerly location than are most native French vines. They then proceeded to make wine in the French style. Where German wines are normally low in alcohol – around 8° to 10° – Alsace wines reach the normal French level of 10° to 12° and even more in exceptional years. German wines are typically sweet, but Alsace follows the more customary French tradition of producing dry wines. Whereas German wines are light in body, Alsace are more full-bodied. Summed up, this means that Alsace wines, like those from the rest of France, are more appropriate to drink with savoury foods than their sweet German counterparts.

The modern success story of Alsace wines dates from the end of the Second World War. They have come from nowhere to produce 20 per cent of France's white *appellation* wine; according to CIVA – the Comité Interprofessionnel du Vin d'Alsace – they account for nearly half of all white *appellation* wine drunk by the French.

What the French consumer has cottoned on to is that, despite differing styles among producers, the overall quality of Alsace wine is amazingly high. There are few duffers, plenty of crisp, distinctive surprises, and most of them sell for ridiculously reasonable prices, making them the best-value whites available from just about anywhere.

The crisp, refreshing acidity is easy to produce in a region which is even further north than the Loire. The effect of a long, slow growing season is further enhanced by many producers who deliberately stop the malo-lactic fermentation – that springtime conversion of sharp malic into soft lactic acid. This helps to preserve the wines, and although most are delicious when young, they will generally mature and keep well. Some wines from particularly good vintages will need sitting on for a few years until they reach their full potential.

Despite the fact that 95 per cent of Alsace wine is white, the tremendous range of styles means that there is no shortage of choice when it comes to matching wine to foods as different as snails in garlic butter, onion quiche, cheese, and fish from smoked salmon to pike quenelles. There are, of course, no hard and fast rules about which wines to drink when, where, or with what. The delight is in experimenting rather than trying to find a definitive answer to the conundrum.

There is only one *appellation* in the region and that is Alsace. Apart from permitted blends such as Edelzwicker, the wines must be made purely from one of seven grape varieties, which must be specified on the label.

Gewürztraminer has a distinctive, unforgettable aroma and mouth-filling flavour. Wine-tasters note 'spice and lychees.' In Chinese restaurants it will take on most dishes you are likely to come across. Otherwise think of it particularly for smoked foods and cheese, especially for strong varieties such as Münster, Roquefort, and blue cheeses in general.

If Alsatians (the human kind) were to vote in a wine election, they would probably elect Riesling for president. It is suave, sophisticated and goes well with a wide variety of foods, especially classier dishes made with fish and white meats. It is particularly useful in restaurants and can, for instance, put up with just about everything on a *nouvelle cuisine* menu.

With Muscat, unlike other wines made from the Muscat grape, the flavour is unobscured by sweetness – except perhaps in exceptional years like 1983 when the sugar levels in the harvest were very high – and its pure, flowery aroma jumps out of the glass while you sip it as an aperitif.

The last of the big four is Tokay. Because European lawmakers feel it could be confused with Hungarian Tokay (a totally different drink) it may appear as Pinot Gris. But because Alsace producers have used the original name for centuries and don't easily give in to Brussels, be prepared for either name on the label. Tokay is unjustly neglected, but is a rich, opulent, supple wine which is equally at home with fine foie gras or a multitude of red meats.

The one bottle in twenty that is not white is Pinot Noir, the same grape as red burgundy is made from. It is not a full-bodied macho red, but neither is it always rosé. While red Sancerre, also made from Pinot

Noir, becomes increasingly trendy, this light, quaffable but stylish red is its equal. It can be very good value, and can be served slightly chilled.

To complement the *haute couture* whites there are a couple of off-the-peg versions, Pinot Blanc and Sylvaner. Both are simple wines for which no great claims are made, the Sylvaner even being noted for its oddly neutral quality. But would that all white wines were as inexpensive, clean and soundly made. They have a place as a foil to precede more individual wines, as well as an ability, by virtue of their unobtrusiveness, to partner a wide variety of dishes.

Although the words have no legal status, producers often label their better wines Cuvée Tradition, Réserve Personnelle or some such. These wines have greater power and more class than the otherwise good, but standard bottles in the range, and they are usually well worth the difference in price.

Certain Alsace vineyards have been awarded the special status of *Grand Cru*, but beware of paying too much over the odds for the privilege of drinking them. There is also a sparkling Crémant d'Alsace, pioneered by Dopff au Moulin; some co-operatives now also produce it.

In particularly fine years, such as 1976 and 1983, the grapes can achieve a much higher sugar level than usual, particularly if they are left on the vine for longer, one of the practices that Alsace wine-makers do share with German producers. A few producers occasionally make a rich, concentrated, late-picked or Vendange Tardive (VT) wine, which will generally have some residual sweetness and will take a long time to mature. Even rarer is a super-concentrated Sélection de Grains Nobles (SGN) made from individually picked grapes affected by *botrytis cinerea* or 'noble rot'.

What year?

1984 was an average sort of year for quality; the lesser wines can be drunk now, but the better ones have a lot of acidity and good fruit and will keep going for a while. Locals almost cross themselves in reverence when talking of **1983**, and they have to go back a long way to find anything quite as good; these are magnificent wines, rich, concentrated, balanced, and many are very attractive to drink now. This is a pity because too many will be drunk too soon: Vendange Tardive and Sélection de Grains Nobles will last for decades.

Plentiful **1982**, very good **1981**, plain **1980** and fair to middling **1979** are all drinkable now, but the lesser wines will more than likely be disappearing over the hill, so choose the best that you can afford, particularly from Réserve Personnelle and similar quality levels. **1978** was a first-rate vintage and is drinking extremely well now. **1977** is best avoided. **1976** was getting all the accolades for rich, long-lasting wines until 1983 came along; choose a 1976 if you want to treat yourself to a special bottle. **1975** was a classic year and the better bottles are still doing extremely well.

Recommended producers

Apart from vintage and grape, the other key to finding a good bottle is the name of the producer, which provides a useful clue to the style of wine to expect. These are the main exporters:

Léon Beyer, Eguisheim. Full-bodied, firm, steely wines, particularly good with food: famous for being in all the top restaurants in France. Special wines: Riesling Cuvée des Ecaillers and Gewürztraminer des Comtes d'Eguisheim. Recommeded: '83 Pinot Blanc.

E. Boeckel, Mittelbergheim. Reliable producer in traditional style, best known for Riesling Wibelsberg, Gewürztraminer Zotzenberg and Château d'Isembourg, and producing a good Sylvaner.

Dopff au Moulin, Riquewihr. Pioneers of sparkling Crémant d'Alsace. They have a wide range of styles on the market, including non-vintage, and produce most of them in half-bottles too. Best vineyard wines are Riesling Schoenenberg and Gewürztraminer Eichberg or the unusual Sporen. Recommended: '83 Muscat and Riesling Réserve.

Dopff & Irion, Riquewihr. One of the largest houses, whose wines need time to develop. Best are Riesling Les Murailles, Gewürztraminer Les Sorcières, and particularly Muscat Les Amandiers.

Théo Faller, Domaine Weinbach, Kaysersberg. Superb, well-structured wines with lots of fruit and acidity, which are meant to age. Réserve Particulière and Cuvée Ste Catherine Rieslings and Gewürztraminers are best. Also some excellent Vendange Tardive. Recommended: '83 Tokay, Riesling and Gewürztraminer.

Louis Gisselbrecht, Dambach-la-Ville. Honest, straightforward style, light to medium-bodied, rounded. Particularly good Rieslings. Recommended: '83 Riesling.

Willy Gisselbrecht, Dambach-la-Ville. Larger of the two firms, which went their separate ways in 1936. Good Rieslings, medal-winning Gewürztraminers.

Heim, Westhalten. The wines retain their own label and identity despite the acquisition of a majority shareholding by the Westhalten Co-operative in 1980. Modern, technical wine-making combines with tradition to produce elegance and style with an intensity of fruit in the top wines which may take a few years to develop. Best wines are Pinot Blanc from Clos de Strangenberg and Gewürztraminer from Zinnkoepflé.

Hugel & Fils, Riquewihr.They account for nearly half the market for Alsace wine in the UK. Distinctively rich, full, round wines with finesse and style, perhaps even a little overpowering for some tastes, but tip-top quality, especially Réserve Personnelle. Specialists in Riesling and Gewürztraminer and in making Vendange Tardive and Sélection de Grains Nobles wines. Recommended: most wines.

Domaine Klipfel, Barr. A firm with a high reputation for well-structured but approachable wines, also acting as a *négociant* under the André Lorentz label. Gewürztraminer Clos Zisser is particularly good.

Kuehn, Ammerschwihr. Although now part of the Ingersheim co-operative, the firm still carries on in the traditional way, making balanced, attractive wines, some from the famous Kaefferkopf vineyard. Gewürztraminer St Hubert is good. Recommended: '83 Gewürztraminer.

Kuentz-Bas, Husseren-les-Châteaux. A very good-quality small producer well known in the UK, with good Muscat and Réserve Personnelle.

Maison Laugel, Marlenheim. Probably the largest, and still expanding, *négociant* in Alsace. Sound, well-made light wines with wide appeal, which include Pichet d'Alsace, a blend of largely Pinot Blanc with some Riesling and a little Gewürztraminer. Also Crémant d'Alsace.

Gustave Lorentz, Bergheim. A 150-year-old family firm producing Riesling and Gewürztraminer from their own *grand cru* vineyards, and making other wines from bought-in grapes. Recommended: '83 Gewürztraminer and Riesling.

A & O Muré, Rouffach. A particular combination of microclimate and soil in their Clos St Landelin vineyard makes for big, intense wines that are for very long keeping. Recommended: '83 Muscat and Gewürztraminer.

Preiss-Henny, Mittelwihr. A large firm using modern methods. Riesling Cuvée Marcel Preiss and Gewürztraminer Camille Preiss are best.

Preiss-Zimmer, Riquewihr. Consistently top-class wines, rather steely and firm, clean, with excellent Riesling and Gewürztraminer.

Charles Schleret, Turckheim. A small grower-producer with medal-winning wines made in a rich style. Recommended: '83 Gewürztraminer.

Schlumberger, Guebwiller. Distinguished for having the largest single *domaine* in Alsace. The style is rich, weighty, full, round, and the best wines are from the Kitterlé vineyard.

Pierre Sparr, Sigolsheim. A plain, direct style, firm and with good fruit, characterises these reliably good wines. Single-vineyard Riesling Schlossberg and Gewürztraminer Mambourg.

Sick-Dreyer, Ammerschwihr. Never mind the name, the wines have good fruit and freshness, and the best Rieslings and Gewürztraminers come from the Kaefferkopf vineyard.

F.E. Trimbach, Ribeauvillé. An old family firm with an outstanding reputation for consistently fine quality. The wines are delicate if a little austere. Unusually, they mature the bottles until the wine is ready for drinking. Best Rieslings are Cuvée Frédéric Emile and the excellent Clos Ste Hune; best Gewürztraminer,

Cuvée des Seigneurs de Ribeaupierre. Recommended: most wines including '83 Gewürztraminer.

A. Willm, Barr. A sound producer of Riesling and Sylvaner.

Zind-Humbrecht, Mittelbergheim. Specialist in single-vineyard wines using modern vinification, the best being Riesling Clos St Urbain.

Co-operatives. Alsace has the distinction of having formed the first wine co-operative in France in 1895 at Ribeauvillé, whose best wines come from old vines in their Clos du Zahnacker. The largest is at Eguisheim, and it makes a Crémant, a good Gewürztraminer Cuvée St Léon, and Riesling Cuvée des Seigneurs. Top-quality wines are made at Bennwihr: Riesling Rebgarten and Gewürztraminer Côtes de Bennwihr. Other co-operatives include Orschwiller, whose wines are dubbed Faîtières, with a good showing in Gewürztraminer; Kientzheim which produces Riesling Schlossberg and Gewürztraminer Kaefferkopf; Sigolsheim which makes a Crémant; Westhalten; Turckheim; Hoen at Beblenheim; Ingersheim; and Pfaffenheim.

Supermarkets. Some supermarkets have wines bottled under their own label. Particularly recommended are '83 Gewürztraminer from British Home Stores and Sainsbury.

Vintage report

Kathryn McWhirter

*Look out especially for double-starred (**) vintages to drink this year, or single-starred (*) vintages if **wines are not available or are too expensive. Vintages that are highly unlikely to appear on any restaurant list do not appear here. Countries are listed alphabetically, wine-growing regions alphabetically within their countries.*

Argentina

Drink **whites** as young as possible, and remember that, being in the southern hemisphere, the Argentinians pick their grapes six months earlier than Europe does in a given year – in February or March. Vintages from 1983 back are now too old. You may see **red** Argentine Cabernet Sauvignon back to **1975** on the occasional restaurant list. It should still be a very good, full-bodied wine, as should any younger vintages available. All the reds will need to be drunk with food.

Australia

Whites
Drink the youngest you can find of all grape varieties, including Chardonnays, but especially Rieslings, which tire very quickly. Some very good ****1985s** will be around already, and ***1984s** will be enjoyable, though some will start to tire during the course of 1986.

Reds
Practically any reds you come across will be big and fruity, and a good match for full-flavoured food. ****1980** was a particularly successful year, and the lighter wines of the cooler **1984** vintage are delicious now. That said, Australian wine styles depend much more on the producer than on the vintage.

Austria

In dry wines, buy ***1984s**, which are sometimes a bit acid, sometimes very good, or ***1981**; in sweet wines, go for ***1981**, and ***1979**.

Bulgaria

Reds

***1981** Good. The 1981 Cabernet is a big, fat but fruity wine.

***1979** Some 1979 Cabernet will still be on wine bar lists; it is a rounded, fruity wine.

***1980** Good Bulgarian Merlot will be on sale in 1986.

***1976** The superior Sakar Mountain Cabernet of this vintage is still very good.

Whites

***1983** Chardonnay is good and inexpensive. The 1984 Chardonnay had not arrived in Britain as we went to press.

California

Whites

***1984** Best vintage for most Chenin Blanc and Sauvignon Blanc.

1983 Lighter, more elegant Chardonnays than in previous years. Other whites of this vintage should be enjoyable.

***1982** The best vintage of Chardonnay for drinking this year; Sauvignon can be too fat (though Mondavi Sauvignon is delicious).

1981 Some top Chardonnays are still good, as is Mondavi Reserve Sauvignon.

1980 Many whites are tiring, though some top Chardonnay is still good.

Reds

1982 OK now with food if you like rich, fairly tough young reds.

***1981** Light Cabernet Sauvignon is ready now, as are the other reds.

****1980** Excellent year for reds and Cabernet in particular, with intense flavour, good to drink now.

****1978** Splendid Cabernets, now at their best.

Chile

Drink **whites** as young as possible – you may find some ***1984** vintage whites by the end of 1985. Earlier vintages will be tiring. Chilean **reds** tend to be very big, fruity but fairly hard and alcoholic wines when young, though the youngest on the market, a **1982**, is perfectly drinkable with food. The exception is the soft, fruity Cabernet Sauvignon from Torres. You may find Chilean Cabernet Sauvignons back to **1975**, which are still in fine form, and have become much softer with age.

France

Alsace

1984 Rather thin and weedy, except for the special wines.

***1983** Excellent vintage. Pinot Blanc and Sylvaner are better flavoured than usual, Rieslings becoming very good during 1986, while Gewürztraminer, mostly deliciously spicy, is often off-dry, and always extremely alcoholic, as in the delicious, meaty Tokay – not really for lunch-time drinking. Muscats can be over-soft and disappointing.

1982 Except for very special wines (such as Réserve Personnelle), 1982s are becoming tired and flabby.

1981 Tired, except for the special wines.

1980 Tired.

1979 Ordinary wines are tired. Special wines from good producers (Réserve Personnelle, Vendange Tardive, etc.) are still very good.

***1978** Excellent Réserve Personnelle and Vendange Tardive Rieslings.

***1976** Excellent Vendange Tardive Rieslings and Gewürztraminers.

Beaujolais

1984 Much 1984 Beaujolais has an unpleasant, rhubarb-like acidity; all are fairly light. Some have quite pleasant fruit. Top merchants like Duboeuf and some individual estates made some easier-to-drink wines.

** **1983** The *crus* (Chiroubles, Fleurie, Moulin-à-Vent, Brouilly, Côte de Brouilly, St-Amour, Morgon, Chénas, Juliénas) are extremely rich and fruity; look out especially for wines labelled Domaine de .... or Château de .... Beaujolais-Villages will be lighter, but should still be good and fruity, and a lot of ordinary Beaujolais will still be very enjoyable, too.

1982 Even the top wines are past their best.

1981 *Cru* wines should still be pleasurable.

1980 Too old.

1979 Too old.

1978 *Cru* wines are mature, with an old spiciness quite different from the flavours of young Beaujolais. Worth trying.

Bergerac

Drink the youngest possible dry whites and rosés; the same applies to the ordinary reds. Côtes de Bergerac reds from the excellent ***1983** and especially the ****1982** vintage are worth looking out for, however.

Bordeaux

Reds

Red Bordeaux (claret) ranges from very simple, inexpensive wine for drinking young to the world's finest wines, much too tough to drink for many years. Clarets at the bottom end of the restaurant price range, labelled Ch.... and, in the small print underneath, simply **AC Bordeaux**, **Bordeaux Supérieur**, or even **house claret**, fit, of course, into the first category. Look especially for the rich and fruity ****1983** and ****1982** vintages, with the harder, thinner but still fruity ***1981** for second best.

For more expensive wines labelled **Cru Bourgeois**, **St-Emilion Grand Cru**, **Montagne St-Emilion**, **St-Georges-St-Emilion**, **Fronsac** or **Lalande de Pomperol:**

1982 Nice with well-flavoured food, but big and not quite ready.

***1981** Some is very good (with food), some still too hard.

***1980** Light, clean-cut, fresh, fruity wines, good now.

***1979** Well-balanced, medium-weight, fruity wines.

1978 Good, but still fairly hard and needs food.

Avoid any earlier vintages.

Classed growths

** **1980** Best value this year, since it has matured to drinkability very early, and so is still reasonably priced. Even the very top 1980 clarets are enjoyable this year.

***1979** Good, firm and fruity.

1978 Still too tough.

1977 Not always so bad as its reputation. Quite high acidity, light in body, but it may be worth trying the

top wines if they are not too expensive.
1976 Many top châteaux' wines are now tasting old and fruitless with drily astringent tannin. Avoid except on very good advice.
1975 Pomerols and St-Emilions are good, and much more approachable than Médocs, which are mostly still very tough.
1974 Avoid.
1973 Mostly too old.
1972 Avoid: hard and astringent.
** **1971** Ready. Elegant claret, particularly good from St-Emilion and Pomerol.
** **1970** The top 1970s are still too young, but the rest are delicious now.
In the **1960s**, anything but the ***1966** (top wines only) and ****1961** vintages are for gamblers only; **1955** and **1953** are the safest bet in the **1950s**, and *may* be delicious if you like your claret very mature.

Dry whites
Anything white from Bordeaux at the cheaper end and middle of the price range of a restaurant list is for drinking young – **1984s** are the vintage to go for in late 1985 and the first part of 1986. In *very* expensive and very good dry white Bordeaux (such as Ch. Haut-Brion Blanc), anything younger than **1978** is too young. If you find them, ****1978** and ****1969** are the years to go for, and should be delicious, rich and complex. **1970s** may be good, or may be past it.

Sweet whites – Sauternes, Barsac
1982 Fair and reasonably priced.
1981 Fair.
1980 Good, moderately rich.
1979 Fair.
***1978** Very sweet and rich, without being exciting, because the grapes were not 'nobly rotted', so the wines lack concentration of flavour.
1977 Avoid.
1976 Rich but sometimes too soft. Some very fine wines.
1975 Rich and well balanced
1974 Very poor.
1973 Disappointing, light.
1972 Poor.
***1971** Attractive, ready.
***1970** Attractive, ready.
1969 Variable.
** **1967** Fine rich wines.
** **1962** Excellent balance and flavour, still going strong.
1959 Very mature now, some too mature. A risk.
** **1955** Very good indeed, and delicious now.
1953 Mixed, may still be attractive.
1952 May still be attractive.
1949 Some are still attractive, ripe and balanced.
** **1945** Excellent, concentrated wines.
1943 Some good, some tiring.
***1942** Good, rich wines.
** **1937** Great wines, delicious now.
***1934** Very good, very mature wines.

Burgundy

Reds
1984 Light-bodied wines, pleasant to drink now.
1983 Big, hard wines, still much too young.
1982 Mostly ready for drinking. Many are light, pale and thin. From good growers and merchants, they can be delicious. Worth taking a chance.
1981 Mostly hard, acid and short of fruit. *Some* exceptionally good growers made tasty wines.
1980 Ready-for-drinking wines that are now fairly soft after a few years of tasting unpleasantly tart.
1979 Simple, attractive wines. The best are good now, though some simpler wines are beginning to taste rather dull. Worth taking a chance.
1978 The most recent 'great' vintage. A few of the simpler wines may be tiring,

but on the whole it's hard to go wrong. Very many **1978s** are absolutely delicious, concentrated and complex.

1977 Mostly acid and metallic-tasting. *Very* good producers made good wines.

1976 Impossible to generalise with this vintage. *Some* are soft and mature, but many are tough and unpleasant, while some have lost all their fruit. A vintage to avoid, except on good advice.

If you want to pay the high price, you might still find some good **1972s** and **1971s**, especially Côte de Nuits. Other vintages whose red wines may be still alive are: **1970, 1969, 1966, 1964, 1961**; very generally, Côte de Nuits wines are more likely to have survived than Côte de Beaune. But buying old Burgundy is a very expensive risk.

Whites

*1984 Pleasant wines for drinking young – that means now.

*1983 Untypical of Burgundy in their rich fatness and high alcohol, but usually very pleasant, if not really refreshing. To be avoided at lunchtime for fear of afternoon snoozing.

1982 Soft wines, most of which are now too old.

1981 Some good, some bad. Impossible to generalise, so probably best avoided unless there's nothing else, or you can rely on good advice.

1980 A bad, acid year when rotten grapes tainted the wine.

1979 Now mostly dull.

** 1978 Delicious!

Of older vintages, you may still find some of the big, fat **1976** whites enjoyable, or the very tip-top **1973s**. The safest bet is **1971**, though it's still a risk.

Buzet

Look for **1983** and **1982**. Only the co-operative's Côtes de Buzet, Cuvée Napoléon, ages well: vintages of that particular wine from **1978** to **1981** are lovely now.

Cahors

*1983 Some are good and fruity, some too hard. Worth a try.

1982 Big and tannic.

1981 Big and tannic.

*1980 Good year, fruity.

1979 Mediocre.

** 1978 Excellent.

Chablis

*1984 Poor, acidic – and expensive. Avoid.

1983 Some good wines, but many are too soft and not really refreshing.

1982 Soft wine, much of it now dull and flabby.

*1981 A good year.

1980 Bad vintage.

1979 Now mostly dull.

** 1978 Delicious *premiers* and *grands cru*

Pre-1978, look out for **1975** and **1971**, but only the very top wines from the very top growers.

Champagne (vintage)

** 1979 Good, fresh wines.

*1978 Fairly good.

1976 Most are now tired, flabby and fruitless.

1975 Some are now too old, some are good if you like your champagne well matured.

Loire

Dry whites – Muscadet, Anjou, Touraine, Sancerre, Pouilly-Fumé, Sauvignon du Haut Poitou

1984 A rather thin and acid vintage, though Sancerre and Pouilly-Fumé, Sauvignon du Haut Poitou, Sauvignon de Touraine and Sauvignon, Vin de Pays du Jardin de la France, are enjoyable.

1983 Quite full-bodied wines, some very good, though best drunk before mid-1986, after which many may be too flabby. Vouvray and some Pouilly-Fumé will keep longer.

1982 Flabby and flat, though Vouvray is better balanced.

1981 Still good for Vouvray, Savennières and Montlouis, and some Pouilly-Fumé is still pleasant.

Reds – Cabernet d'Anjou, Saumur, Bourgueil, St-Nicolas de Bourgueil, red Sancerre

1984 Rather thin and acid, to be avoided.

** **1983** Excellent vintage for all these appellations, and even the red Sancerre is very much better than usual.

1982 Short of acidity, so many are becoming flabby, though the top Anjou Rouge, Chinon and Bourgueil are still good.

1981 Good Cabernet Rouge d'Anjou, Bourgueil and Chinon.

1980 Pale and uninteresting.

1979 Pleasant Chinons and Bourgueils.

1978 Pleasant Chinons and Bourgueils.

1976 Delicious, spicily full Chinons and Bourgueils.

Rosé

1984 Thin and acid.

1983 Tiring already, and too old after mid-1986.

Rhône

Northern reds – Crozes-Hermitage, Hermitage, Côte-Rôtie, St-Joseph, Cornas

***1982** Big, soft wines to be drunk with food.

1981 A light year, often disappointing, except from the best producers. Best avoided except on good advice.

***1980** Good, well-balanced wines. Crozes-Hermitage and St-Joseph are easy to drink, the others still a bit tough, though drinkable with gutsy food.

***1979** Pleasant wines, most of them ready to drink.

1978 Big, concentrated wines, too young.

1977 Light wines, quite pleasant.

***1976** Good and ready to drink.

If you come across older vintages, **1973** Hermitage should still be good, as will **1972**, though probably tasting a bit too old for some people. **1971s** should still be good from Cornas, Hermitage and Côte-Rôtie, while **1969s** from Hermitage and Côte-Rôtie should be worth a try.

Southern reds – Châteauneuf-du-Pape, Gigondas, Côtes du Rhône, Vacqueyras

1984 Light-bodied, often acid wines.

***1983** Good, deep red wines, though Châteauneuf-du-Pape is still too tough.
1982 Pleasant, soft, sweet or jammy-tasting Châteauneuf, but the lighter wines, Côtes-du-Rhône, etc., now taste a bit tired.
1981 Châteauneuf and some Gigondas is too tough at the moment to drink. Côtes-du-Rhône *domaine* wines, Côtes-du-Rhône-Villages and Vacqueyras can be very good.
1980 Châteauneuf tends to be unpleasantly hard. Gigondas and Vacqueyras can be good.
***1979** Châteauneuf is good, though the more expensive ones are still a bit too tough. Good for Gigondas, and for *domaine* Côtes-du-Rhône.
***1978** Look out for the simpler, cheaper Châteauneufs – the more expensive ones are still overpoweringly tough.

Germany

1984 A disappointing vintage, to be avoided while you can still buy 1983.
** **1983** Excellent vintage. The best vintage to buy in ordinary QbA wines (including the usually poor value Liebfraumilch, Niersteiner Gutes Domtal, etc.), but look out for excellent Kabinett wines for something rather better and still not too expensive, or the slightly sweeter Spätlesen.
1982 Mostly getting tired and flabby, except for top estate wines.
1981 Avoid any remaining ordinary QbA 1981s, but Kabinett and Spätlesen are likely to be attractively mature.
1979 The more expensive Rieslings should still be alive and flavoursome.
** **1976** Sweet Riesling wines labelled Spätlese, Auslese, Beerenauslese and Trockenbeerenauslese should be rich, mature and delicious.
** **1975** Only Rieslings from the best producers are worth the risk: firm, mature wines.

Italy

Whites

** **1984** Unusually cool, so that the grapes were less ripe than usual (a plus-point in Italy since it leads to fresher, more acid wines) and a small vintage, making the flavours more concentrated. Wines labelled Trentino, Friuli, South Tyrol/Alto Adige, Riesling, Traminer, Gewürztraminer – occasionally to be found on restaurant lists – should be very good. Soave, Verdicchio, Frascati, etc. are better than usual.
1983 Mostly tired.
1982 Some are still fresh, but best to choose 1984 if you can. Avoid anything older, except on very sound advice.

Reds – Chianti
For ordinary Chianti, labelled just Chianti, avoid the poor and expensive **1984** vintage when it arrives. ***1983** and **1982** Chiantis are the best choice. Chianti Riserva vintages are:

***1982** Excellent. Some are too young.
1981 Fair to good. Some are ready.
1980 Fair. Ready.
***1979** Very good.
***1978** Good.

Reds – Barolo and Barbaresco
Anything younger than **1980** is too young.
1980 Good, and some are ready to drink, some much too tough.
***1979** Very good. Some are ready.
***1978** Very good.
1977 Avoid.
1976 Avoid.
1975 Avoid.
***1974** Good.
***1971** Good.
***1970** Good.

Valpolicella and any other inexpensive reds you are likely to find on a restaurant list should be drunk as young as possible: drink ***1984** or ***1983**.

Lebanon

Anything you see on a restaurant list (and there are some fairly old vintages around of the only Lebanese wine available in Britain, Château Musar) should be enjoyable. **1980** is still a bit too young. The best vintages otherwise are ***1978** and ***1972**.

New Zealand

Anything before **1983**, red or white, is likely to be tiring. Look for **1983s**, and if you can find them ***1984s**, which will be fresher.

Port

All **late-bottled** and **tawny** ports on the list will be ready for drinking.

Vintage and single quinta ports
Anything younger than **1975** will cause severe headaches!
** **1975** The perfect vintage for restaurant drinking, because it has reached maturity astonishingly early, and because it's young and therefore relatively cheap. Attractive, light and fruity.
***1974** Not an 'official' vintage, but there are some 1974 crusting ports which are good value and ready.
1972 Unexceptional wines, ready now.
***1970** Big, full, fruity wines, very drinkable now, though some may still be rather tough.
***1968** Not an officially declared vintage, but you may find some pleasant, fruity single quinta wines (Quinta de. . . .) on restaurant lists at reasonable prices.
***1967** Light and rounded single quinta wines.
** **1966** Absolutely delicious now, full and luscious.
** **1963** All are enjoyable, all are expensive, some may still be rather too young, though drinkable. An excellent, concentrated vintage.
** **1960** Good, and ready.
***1958** Mature, light, ready.
** **1955** Very good wines, at their peak.

Portuguese table wines

Vinho Verde is more often than not sold without vintage. If a vintage is listed, leave it alone if it's older than **1984**.

Dão
The older, the softer, and possibly more pleasant to drink. You're unlikely to find anything *too* old on a restaurant list. Wines of the **1980s** are likely to be very tough and will certainly need gutsy food.

Spain

Whites
For almost all Spanish whites, you should be buying the ***1984** vintage, and the **1985** vintage in preference as soon as it appears. The exceptions you may find on restaurant lists are **Torres Gran Viña Sol**, of which the **1983** is good, as is the **1981 Gran Viña Sol Green Label** and white **Riojas** from **Marqués de Murrieta**, **López de Heredia**, and **CVNE** (**Dry Monopole**), whose older vintages should be good, firm, oaky wines.

Reds – Rioja
***1983** Soft, fresh wines with little or no taste of oak.
***1982** Good.
***1981** Good. Look for Reservas.
***1980** Soft, fairly full. Look for Reservas.
1979 Not very good.
***1978** Good now for Reservas and Gran Reservas.
1976 Some Reservas are now tasting a bit feeble.
1973 Some Gran Reservas are very good, some are nearly past it.

Diners' rights

A restaurant is legally obliged to provide you with a meal and service which are of a reasonable standard, and a failure to do so may give you the right to sue for breach of contract. Having said this, it is important to remember that the reasonableness or otherwise of both the meal and the service must be judged on the type of restaurant in question.

Dining out should be a pleasurable experience. However, it is as well to be aware of your basic legal rights just in case you find yourself in a sticky situation, like one of these:

1. *You arrive at the restaurant only to find that it is full, and there is no table for you.*
If you've booked a table, this situation is a breach of contract on the part of the restaurant and you are entitled to be compensated by the restaurant. In practice, unless it's a special occasion such as a wedding party, it would be best to forget it, except that you would probably never go there again – and you should write to the *Guide*.

2. *What if you can't keep the booking?*
This is a breach of contract on your part and the restaurant could claim for its loss of profit. This is unlikely to happen, but as a matter of law as well as of courtesy you should let the restaurant know if you can't make it, even if it is at the last minute.

3. *You arrive at the restaurant, to be told that you aren't suitably dressed and that you won't be served.*
If you haven't made a prior reservation then there is little that you can do. A restaurant can refuse to serve anyone, as long as it doesn't do so on the grounds of your colour, sex, race or ethnic origin. If you have made a reservation, the restaurant is obliged to provide a table. However, if your attire is sufficiently out of keeping with the standards of the restaurant – and who can say whether that's the case? – it would probably be justified in law in refusing to serve you.

4. *You arrive at the restaurant to discover that it is less than hygienic.*
If you think that this is the type of place where you might well find something nasty in your soup – don't risk it. Just send us a report and we'll inspect the establishment. Or alternatively inform the public health inspectorate.

5. *Your meal arrives but you don't want to eat it because:*
. . . it wasn't what you ordered.
You don't have to accept it (although you can if you want to), and you can insist on your original order.

. . . you've changed your mind since ordering.
Tough luck. You'll have to accept it or order again – but if you do, you'll have to pay for both.
. . . it looks/tastes/smells strange and unappealing.
Your meal must be edible and composed of ingredients that conform to strict, well-defined standards. Failure to do so by the restaurant can be a criminal offence under the Food Act 1984 and the matter should be reported to the local environmental health officer. If the meal is edible but is cold, unattractively served or whatever, and is clearly of an unreasonable standard for that type of restaurant, you would be entitled to deduct a fair sum from the restaurant's bill for food and service, or even to send the meal back and not pay for it at all.

6. Your wine tastes like vinegar.
The wine, like the food, ought to be of reasonable standard. The trouble is that not everyone who would recognise a bad meal will recognise an equally dubious bottle of wine. If you order a particular wine but your waiter/waitress presents you with something else, send it back.

7. 'Waiter – There's a fly in my soup.'
The discovery of foreign bodies lurking in your meal can be a most daunting experience. Such discoveries *could* amount to a criminal offence under the Food Act if it renders the meal unfit for human consumption.

8. The meal isn't as described on the menu.
The menu must be accurate in describing the food and drink served. If not, the restaurant may be guilty of a criminal offence under the Trade Descriptions Act. Wrong descriptions should be reported to the local trading standards department.

9. The bill arrives but you think that you've been overcharged.
Always check your bill carefully. If it doesn't add up, query it immediately. If the bill charges the correct amount according to the menu, but the food or service were so bad as not to justify those prices, you can consider knocking something off the bill. If the restaurant insists that the bill is correct and threatens to call the police unless you pay up – don't be put off. Contrary to popular belief, deducting from the bill is a matter of civil, not criminal law, and unless a breach of the peace is involved the police won't be interested (making off without payment is something quite different and *is* a criminal offence). You should offer your name and address as an act of good faith, and leave it up to the restaurant to sue you. If things do get difficult, you can pay 'under protest' but you would then have to sue to get your money back.

10. The meal and/or service were not up to scratch and you don't want to leave a tip.
If a service charge isn't included (check the menu for this) you don't have to tip even if the meal and service were first class. If a service charge is included then you must pay it, unless the restaurant is itself in breach of contract, i.e. the food and/or service were below standard. If this is the case, you can deduct the service element from the bill.

11. The restaurant wants your table.
The meal is over and you are having coffee, liqueurs and an after-dinner chat. The art of eating may involve eating slowly but not, it seems, when the next

party has arrived and your waiter is anxiously trying to get you to shift so that he can get the next lot seated and served. Any good restaurant will allow you ample time between courses and after your meal, and you should not allow yourself to be rushed. On the other hand, it might be unreasonable if you sat down at 7.00pm and you are still drinking coffee at 11.00pm. It all depends on the type of restaurant, the price paid for the meal and all the other circumstances. If you are planning a long, late evening, make it clear when you book.

12. The waiter/waitress spills food on your clothes.
Waiters/waitresses are all part of the service. Careless waiters/waitresses mean bad service and you can deduct the service charge accordingly. Clothes ruined by sloppy service would entitle you to compensation. This could be the cleaning bill or the cost of replacing the damaged article.

13. The waiter/waitress is rude.
Indifferent or positively rude service merits witholding a tip or a service charge – remember that you are entitled to expect food *and* service of a reasonable standard. You should also complain to the management about the individual concerned.

14. You want to pay by cheque/credit card.
A restaurant can refuse to accept payment by cheque or credit card, although most restaurants will accept them. Make sure that you know about acceptable methods of payment in advance.

Glossary *of cooking terms*

A rough-and-ready description of some of the dishes frequently encountered on restaurant menus and in the pages of the *Guide*.

Amer	American	*Fr*	French	*Mid East*	Middle Eastern
Arab	Arabian	*Ger*	German	*Pek*	Pekinese
Aust	Austrian	*Gk*	Greek	*Rus*	Russian
Austral	Australian	*Indo*	Indo-Pakistani	*Scot*	Scottish
Canton	Cantonese	*Ital*	Italian	*Span*	Spanish
Eng	English	*Jap*	Japanese	*Swed*	Swedish
Flem	Flemish	*Mex*	Mexican	*Sw*	Swiss

afelia (*Gk*) pork stewed or casseroled with red wine and coriander

agrodolce (*Ital*) sweet-sour sauce, usually accompanying game or duck

aïoli (*Fr*) mayonnaise with crushed garlic and sometimes mashed potato

Atholl brose (*Scot*) originally a thick drink made from oatmeal, water, honey and whisky. The modern version is normally a dessert of double cream whipped with whisky and honey or sugar until thick

avgolemono (*Gk*) chicken broth with rice, eggs and lemon

baklava (*Gk*) paper-thin filo pastry layered with nuts, honey, cinnamon and often breadcrumbs, baked in the oven, cooled in syrup and served cold

ballotine (*Fr*) (ballottine) small bird or leg, boned and stuffed or rolled before cooking. Generally served hot, but glazed if cold (see galantine)

béarnaise, sauce (*Fr*) hollandaise sauce (*qv*) flavoured with a strained reduction of chopped shallots, vinegar and tarragon and with the addition of chopped fresh tarragon leaves and often chervil

béchamel, sauce (*Fr*) a white sauce made with butter, flour and milk that has been infused with bay leaf, onion and black peppercorns

beurre blanc (*Fr*) unsalted butter beaten into a warm reduction of shallots, white wine and vinegar until the consistency of cream

bhajia (*Indo*) usually pieces of vegetable (onion, aubergine, etc) deep-fried in gram (chickpea) flour, but can also mean any vegetable cooked in chilli and spices

bhel poori (*Indo*) small deep-fried breads and noodles served with chopped onion, puffed rice, coriander, chutney and sometimes cubed potatoes, lemon juice and garlic

biriani (*Indo*) spiced rice cooked with pieces of meat, chicken, prawns or vegetables

blanquette (*Fr*) a 'white' stew, usually of veal, the sauce thickened with cream and egg yolks

bordelaise (*Fr*) cooked in or served with a red wine sauce, strictly with beef marrow

börek (*Mid East*) small pastry

envelopes or rolls, usually made of paper-thin filo dough, filled with a meat, vegetable or cheese mixture. Normally deep-fried and served hot. It is possible but less common to have a sweet version

borshch (*Rus*) beetroot soup, often garnished with sour cream and usually served chilled

bouillabaisse (*Fr*) a fish soup originating from the south of France. There are so many versions of the 'authentic' recipe that the only guarantee is that you may be sure you will never get the same soup twice. However, generally it is agreed that rascasse is essential and that the fish is served with its head. Olive oil and saffron are equally essential and, contrary to most fish recipes, the liquid must be furiously boiled so that the olive oil and water (or wine) amalgamate

bouillon (*Fr*) broth or uncleared stock

boulangère (*Fr*) braised onions and potatoes, served as a garnish or sliced and braised in stock as a separate vegetable dish

bourguignonne, à la (*Fr*) cooked with onions, mushrooms, diced bacon and red wine (traditionally burgundy)

brandade de morue (*Fr*) a purée of poached salt cod mixed with oil, milk, garlic and sometimes mashed potatoes

burfi (*Indo*) fudge-like sweet flavoured with coconut, rose-water, almonds, etc

cacciatore (*Ital*) sauce, usually for chicken, of white wine, mushrooms, tomatoes and herbs

carbonara (*Ital*) a sauce for pasta, usually spaghetti, of beaten eggs, chopped fried bacon, Parmesan cheese and sometimes cream

cassoulet (*Fr*) a thick white haricot bean stew originating from the Languedoc region, with pieces of pork, preserved goose (*confit d'oie*), garlic sausage, onions, garlic and tomatoes. Ingredients vary and may include lamb, partridge or preserved duck

ceviche (*Mex*) strips of raw fish or shellfish marinated in lime or lemon juice and mixed with chopped onion, tomato, chilli and avocado

chaat (*Indo*) hot or cold salty/sour snack of meat or vegetables

chasseur (*Fr*) sauce based on meat stock with the addition of mushrooms, tomatoes and white wine

cheung-fun (*Canton*) envelopes of noodle paste (from rice flour) with shrimp or pork stuffing and a soy-based sauce. Served as part of dim-sum (*qv*)

Choron (*Fr*) garnish for beef of artichoke bottoms filled with peas and butter-browned potato balls

Choron, sauce (*Fr*) tomato-flavoured sauce béarnaise (*qv*)

choucroute (*Fr*) finely shredded pickled white cabbage (Sauerkraut) flavoured with juniper berries and white wine. Generally served as a bed under smoked-pork products and served with plain boiled potatoes

choux (*Fr*) a thick paste, made from heated water and butter, flour and eggs, is piped or spooned into balls or a large round and baked until puffed up and golden. Usually used for desserts (such as chocolate profiteroles) but can be savoury (*see* gougère)

clafoutis (*Fr*) pancake batter poured over fruit (usually cherries) and baked in the oven until firm

coquilles St Jacques (*Fr*) literally the French for scallops, but on an 'international' hotel-type menu usually taken to mean cooked in white wine and cream with sliced mushrooms, surrounded by piped mashed potato

coulibiac *see* **koulibiaca**

couscous (*Arab*) meat (usually mutton) and vegetables are boiled in the lower half of a double boiler; grain (wheat semolina) is steamed above, thus acquiring the flavour of whatever is below: the grain is piled on to a dish, the meat and vegetables set on top and a sauce is poured over before serving

crème pâtissière (*Fr*) a thick vanilla-flavoured custard made by cooking eggs, milk and flour, used to fill pastries, often as a base to a fruit flan

crespolini (*Ital*) pancakes filled with spinach and cream cheese and covered with a béchamel sauce (*qv*) and baked in the oven

croustade (*Fr*) a small baked bread or pastry case served with a savoury filling

croûte (*Fr*) a slice of bread, often circular, fried or toasted until golden, used as a garnish or as a base under meat (e.g. game) or for a savoury (e.g. devils on horseback)

croûte, en (*Fr*) cooked in a pastry case

croûton (*Fr*) golden fried or toasted cubes or discs of bread used as a garnish (e.g. sprinkled on soup), sometimes flavoured with garlic, cheese or herbs

Cullen skink (*Scot*) fish soup made from smoked haddock, milk, onion and potato (named after a village in Morayshire)

darne (*Fr*) a fish steak

dauphine, pommes/gratin (*Fr*) mashed potatoes mixed with egg and unbaked choux paste, formed into balls or cork-like shapes, rolled in breadcrumbs and deep-fried or sometimes baked

dauphinoise, pommes (*Fr*) layers of thinly sliced raw potatoes slowly baked in a garlic-buttered dish, with cream poured over, until soft and the top golden. Cheese (which should be Gruyère) is sometimes added between the layers or sprinkled on top

dhal (*Indo*) a generic name for split pulses or légumes, but more commonly a purée of cooked lentils

dhansak (*Indo*) a Parsee curry of lamb or chicken in dhal (*qv*)

dijonnaise (*Fr*) a sauce, often mayonnaise, containing Dijon mustard

dim-sum (*Canton*) snack food, usually of filled dumplings, often served from trays or trolleys in the bamboo baskets in which they were steamed

dolmades (*Gk*) vine leaves stuffed with meat and/or rice and herbs

dopiaza (*Indo*) lamb cubes stir-fried with onion and chillies then simmered until tender before more grated or pulverised onions are added to give contrast to the cooked onions

Doria (*Fr*) cucumber, often boiled, used as a garnish or in a sauce or soup

Dubarry (*Fr*) cauliflower, whether as garnish or in a cream soup

duxelles (*Fr*) a thick dry paste of open black field-mushrooms finely chopped or minced and cooked in butter with chopped shallots and sometimes parsley. Used as a stuffing, or added to a rich brown sauce with white wine. Sometimes cream is stirred in

émincés (*Fr*) sliced, chopped (traditionally leftover) cooked meat reheated in a sauce or gravy

escalope (*Fr*) thin slice of fish or meat (usually veal or pork) cut from the leg or fillet, often beaten out to make it thinner and larger

estouffade (*Fr*) marinated meat fried in hot fat to brown all surfaces before braising

fondue (*Sw*) melted cheese, wine and kirsch, served in a communal pot into which are dipped chunks of crusty bread on long forks

fondue bourguignonne (*Sw*) cubes of raw meat cooked by each diner by frying them on long forks in hot oil from a central pot on the table and eaten with a selection of sauces

friandises (*Fr*) little biscuits or cakes, often iced and quite elaborately decorated, served at the end of a meal

fumet (*Fr*) strong flavoured stock, usually much reduced, used to flavour sauce. Normally the liquid in which fish has been poached, but can also refer to meat- or truffle-flavoured stock

galantine (*Fr*) classically the breast, leg or a whole bird, or loin or breast of veal, boned, stuffed, cooked and served cold coated with a white sauce set with gelatine (chaudfroid sauce)

gazpacho (*Span*) a cold soup made by

soaking raw chopped tomatoes, onions, sweet peppers and cucumber in vinegar and then mixing them with oil, breadcrumbs and crushed garlic. Liquid is provided by crushed ice, often added just before serving. Sometimes the soup is pureed until smooth

gougère (*Fr*) diced Gruyère cheese added to choux paste (*qv*) before being shaped and baked, usually served hot as a starter

gratin, au (*Fr*) the thin crust formed when a dish is browned under the grill or in the oven – often breadcrumbs are sprinkled on top, sometimes having been fried in butter; cheese is often added to the crumbs

gravlax (*Swed*) marinated or pickled salmon, the term 'buried salmon' originating from when the salmon was buried in the ground with its marinade. A salmon is filleted into two, one fillet is placed skin side down in a dish and covered with a mixture of granulated sugar, coarse salt (the proportion varies) and chopped dill. This is sometimes moistened with alcohol. The second fillet is placed on top, skin side up, the fish is weighted down and left to marinate for at least 24 hours but often three days or more. Either thick slices are cut vertically, in which case the skin is removed before serving, or thin slices are cut almost parallel to the skin, like smoked salmon. Usually served with a mustard and dill mayonnaise or similarly flavoured soured cream

grecque, à la (*Fr*) applied to vegetables boiled in water flavoured with parsley stalks, celery, thyme, bay leaf, coriander, fennel, black peppercorns, olive oil and lemon juice or white wine, drained and allowed to cool. The water is often reduced and made into a sauce with the addition of tomato purée, poured over the vegetables and chilled

guacamole (*Mex*) a thick purée of mashed avocado, oil, garlic and chillies, served as a dip for raw vegetables or savoury biscuits, or to fill tortillas

gulab jamun (*Indo*) deep-fried sponge balls made from flour, butter, yoghourt and sometimes ground almonds, soaked in syrup and served cold

halva (*Indo*) heavy sweetmeat made by reducing cereal (usually semolina) and sugar, with almonds, fruit or vegetables, then cooking in either ghee (clarified butter) or milk

hollandaise sauce (*Fr*) a rich liaison made by beating unsalted butter into warm egg yolks until thick. A strained reduction of vinegar and peppercorns is often added together with lemon juice

hummus (*Mid East*) a thick purée of cooked chickpeas with the addition of crushed garlic, lemon juice, sesame paste and olive oil. Used as a dip for pitta bread or vegetables

Kir (*Fr*) chilled white wine (strictly Bourgogne Aligoté) flavoured with blackcurrant liqueur (crème de Cassis)

kleftiko (*Gk*) (kleftikon) large pieces of lamb (usually shoulder) seasoned and braised slowly with onions until the meat falls from the bones

kofta (*Indo*) spiced meat or vegetable balls, cooked in curry sauce and served with rice, or deep-fried and served with a curry sauce

korma (*Indo*) mild meat curry, braised in yoghourt and/or cream

koulibiaca (*Rus*) pastry filled with cooked rice, hard-boiled eggs, sometimes chopped vegetables and with flaked or fillets of fish, usually salmon

kromeski (*Rus*) (cromesquis) cutlets made from finely minced meat, deep-fried in batter or egg and breadcrumbs

kulfi (*Indo*) ice-cream, often with pistachios or almonds

macédoine (*Fr*) mixed diced fruit or vegetables

meunière (*Fr*) usually fish fillets lightly coated with flour and fried gently in butter which then has lemon juice added. The butter is served over the fish

meze (*Mid East*) (mezze, mezedes) any titbit served with drinks between meals or as an hors d'oeuvre (nuts, cheese, salads, dips, pastries, meats, pickles, etc). When it includes hot dishes too it is often taken as a whole meal

mille-feuille (*Fr*) layers of puff pastry and cream, crème pâtissière (*qv*) and/or fruit or jam. A savoury filling is now quite common

monosodium glutamate (MSG) white crystalline food additive, supposedly (but not really) tasteless, which accentuates the flavour of a dish

Mornay (*Fr*) cheese sauce

moules marinière (*Fr*) mussels cooked in white wine and chopped shallots, served in their cooking liquid with the addition of butter, lemon juice and chopped parsley

moussaka (*Gk*) layers of sliced fried aubergines alternating with a mixture of cooked minced lamb (although beef is often now used), onions, tomatoes, herbs and spices. Often sliced potatoes are added. A thick cheese sauce with added eggs is poured over the top and the dish is baked, the eggs in the sauce setting it like a custard

mousseline (*Fr*) a mixture of pureed raw fish, chicken or veal, kept very cold while double cream and egg white are incorporated, baked as a terrine for slicing, or in individual moulds, or shaped and poached as for quenelles (*qv*). Can be served hot or cold

mousseline, sauce (*Fr*) hollandaise sauce (*qv*) to which whipped cream is added

nan (*Indo*) flat, leavened bread baked in a clay oven (tandoor)

Nantua (*Fr*) béchamel sauce (*qv*) blended with crayfish purée, cream and sometimes with the addition of chopped or minced lobster and/or crayfish tails

noisettes (*Fr*) lamb: cutlets from the best end, boned and tied. Veal: miniature escalopes (*qv*) (sometimes called médaillons). Pork: cut from the chump end of the loin, boned

normande (*Fr*) a garnish of shrimps, mussels and mushrooms, or a creamy sauce containing cider, calvados and sometimes apples

osso buco (*Ital*) knuckle or shin of veal sawn into thick pieces with the marrow intact, braised in white wine, tomatoes and garlic, often also with chopped lemon rind and parsley

paella (*Span*) named after the heavy iron frying-pan in which it is cooked: rice mixed with sauté fish, shellfish, vegetables and meats, usually chicken. Ingredients vary enormously, but usually include garlic, tomatoes, onions and sweet peppers

paloise, sauce (*Fr*) hollandaise sauce (*qv*) or béarnaise sauce (*qv*) to which chopped mint is added

papillote, en (*Fr*) usually fish baked inside a sealed packet of greaseproof paper or foil

Parmentier (*Fr*) ingredients include potatoes

Parmentier, pommes (*Fr*) half-inch cubes of potato cooked in butter

paupiette (*Fr*) a thin slice of meat or fish fillet spread with a soft stuffing, rolled up and cooked, usually in stock

pavé (*Fr*) 'paving-stone'; usually means a thick steak

persillade (*Fr*) a mixture of chopped parsley with shallots or garlic, usually added as a flavouring during the final stages of cooking

pesto (*Ital*) olive oil, freshly chopped basil, pine nuts, garlic and Parmesan cheese, pounded until smooth and used as a sauce for pasta or added to soup

pilaff (*Fr*) (pilaf, pilau) rice cooked in stock, often flavoured and coloured with saffron, with meat, vegetables or fish added (pulao: *Indo*)

pipérade (*Basque*) sliced sweet peppers, tomatoes and onions, cooked slowly in oil until very soft, into which eggs are scrambled

pissaladière (*Fr*) the French equivalent to a pizza – a yeast dough topped with sliced onions, tomatoes, anchovy fillets, olives and herbs

pistou, soupe au (*Fr*) vegetable soup,

sometimes with vermicelli, flavoured with a sauce of pounded fresh basil, garlic and olive oil

pitta (*Mid East*) round or oval bread, only slightly leavened, with a pocket in the centre. Served in strips with hummus (*qv*) and taramosalata (*qv*) or halved and filled with kebabs and salad

pizzaiola (*Ital*) highly seasoned sauce, with tomatoes and garlic, generally served with meat

poivre vert (*Fr*) unripe green peppercorns, softer and with a milder flavour than ripe black or white ones

polenta (*Ital*) maize flour boiled in water until thick and stodgy, cooled and cut into pieces for frying, baking or grilling

pommes soufflées (*Fr*) thin, square slices of potato, fried in deep fat until partly cooked, removed and plunged into hotter fat so that they puff up

portugaise (*Fr*) ingredients include tomatoes and often red peppers

provençale (*Fr*) ingredients include olive oil, tomatoes, onions and garlic

quenelles (*Fr*) light dumplings made by binding a purée of raw fish, veal or chicken with a béchamel sauce (*qv*) or breadcrumbs, shaped into ovals and poached. Served with a cream sauce. Modern restaurants may use the name to describe a mousseline mixture (*qv*)

rasgulla (*Indo*) curd cheese balls in rose-water syrup

ratatouille (*Fr*) a stew (in oil) of aubergines, courgettes, tomatoes, green and red peppers and onions, served hot or cold

rémoulade (*Fr*) mayonnaise sauce with mustard, chopped capers, parsley, herbs, and sometimes gherkins and anchovy essence

rillettes (*Fr*) potted pork, seasoned with herbs or spices

risi e bisi (*Ital*) a Venetian dish of rice with green peas, onion, bacon or ham and Parmesan cheese

rogan josh (gosht) (*Indo*) so named because of its rich, red appearance: lamb pieces fried with yoghourt, ginger and chillies

rösti (*Sw*) grated potato, mixed with onions and seasoning, and fried as a cake

rouille (*Fr*) garlic, pimento and chilli peppers pounded with cooked potato or breadcrumbs until smooth before olive oil is added slowly to make a thick sauce. Traditionally served with (or in) fish soups

sabayon (*Fr*) egg yolks, sugar and white wine whisked in a bowl over hot water until thick and creamy. Occasionally refers to a savoury egg-yolk-based sauce

saké (*Jap*) Japanese rice wine served warm in tiny cups

salmis (*Fr*) duck or game, roasted, jointed and served in a strongly flavoured sauce made with stock from the carcase. Usually garnished with croûtons (*qv*)

saltimbocca (*Ital*) 'jump in the mouth': veal escalope (*qv*) covered in ham and sage leaves, cooked in butter with Marsala

sashimi (*Jap*) thinly sliced raw fish (mackerel, salmon, tuna, bream, etc) served with soy sauce, grated horseradish, hot mustard and fresh root ginger

satay (*Indo*) (saté) cubes of meat, or less often seafood, coated with spices and barbecued on bamboo skewers. Served with a hot peanut sauce

scaloppine (*Ital*) thin veal escalope (*qv*)

sewin (*Welsh*) sea trout

shabu shabu (*Jap*) principally the same idea as sukiyaki (*qv*) except that the ingredients are simmered in stock rather than fried. The vegetables usually include cabbage and either the stock or a separate dipping sauce flavoured with soy, red peppers and sesame oil and/or seeds

shashlik (*Mid East*) lamb, onions and mushrooms marinated and grilled on skewers (same as kebabs)

sheftalia (*Gk*) minced lamb (or lamb and pork) in sausage shapes, grilled or barbecued

shrikhand (*Indo*) a curd cheese or yoghourt sweet, spiked with lemon

and cardamom
smokies (*Scot*) Scottish oak-smoked haddock, originally from Arbroath
soubise (*Fr*) a purée of cooked onions combined with rice or béchamel sauce (*qv*)
spätzle (*Ger*) Swabian noodles made out of an egg and flour dough, usually cut into strips and dropped into soup to cook for a few minutes before serving
stifado (*Gk*) beef, hare, veal or chicken casseroled with button onions, tomatoes and red wine
stracciatella (*Ital*) chicken broth into which egg and grated Parmesan have been beaten
sugo (di carne) (*Ital*) standard Italian meat and tomato sauce to serve with pasta
sukiyaki (*Jap*) a one-dish meal in which thin slices of meat – usually beef, sometimes chicken – transparent noodles, sliced onions, mushrooms and bean curd are cooked on a hot plate at the table, seasoned with soy, saké and sugar, then dipped into raw beaten egg to cool before eating
suprême (*Fr*) the breast and wing fillets of a chicken, removed raw in one piece
sushi (*Jap*) small thin circles or rectangles of rice cooked with seaweed, bound together with vinegar, salt and sugar, and covered with a variety of morsels – raw fish, omelette, mushrooms – and served with ginger and horseradish
syllabub (*Eng*) traditionally a dessert made by milking a cow into a pan of white wine, it is now made by whipping double cream with lemon juice and grated rind, sugar and white wine or sherry
tahini (*Mid East*) an oily paste of ground roasted sesame seeds, used in dishes such as hummus (*qv*)
tandoori chicken (*Indo*) marinated in yoghourt, lemon juice, garlic and spices, cooked in a tandoor (clay oven) or over a charcoal grill
tapénade (*Fr*) named after the word for caper, a Provencal purée of pounded olives, anchovy fillets, capers and lemon juice, to which olive oil is slowly added, resulting in a smooth thick sauce. Used as a dip for crudités or to stuff hard-boiled eggs
taramosalata (*Gk*) smoked grey mullet roe, or more usually cod's roe, pounded to a paste with garlic, lemon juice and olive oil. Served as a dip with pitta (*qv*)
tempura (*Jap*) deep-fried morsels of thinly battered seafood, vegetables or meats, served with a sauce of soy, rice wine and dried fish paste
teriyaki (*Jap*) small slices or strips of meat or fish marinated in soy sauce, rice wine, ginger and garlic before being quickly sauté
tsatsiki (*Gk*) chopped or grated cucumber stirred into yoghourt with crushed garlic, served as a dip with pitta (*qv*)
vacherin (*Fr*) rounds of meringue sandwiched together with whipped cream and fruit, sometimes with ice-cream and liqueur
vallée d'Auge (*Fr*) ingredients include calvados, apples and cream
veal Cordon Bleu (*Fr*) veal escalopes (*qv*) sandwiched with ham and Gruyère cheese, covered with breadcrumbs and shallow-fried
vichyssoise (*Amer*) a creamy cold leek and potato soup
vigneronne (*Fr*) ingredients, or garnish, include grapes
wun-tun (*Canton*) (won ton) thin wrappers of dough ('Chinese ravioli') filled with minced pork, shrimp, vegetables or dates; served either as dumplings (dim-sum, *qv*), in soup or deep-fried
zabaglione (*Ital*) egg yolks, sugar and Marsala whipped in a bowl over hot water until a thick, frothy cream. Usually served warm, sometimes cold

General lists

General lists

Real Food

These restaurants do not normally serve processed foods, and they encourage cottage industries.

LONDON

British Harvest, Hilton Hotel, W1
Capital Hotel, SW3
Cherry Orchard, E2
Connaught Hotel, W1
Food for Thought, WC2
Le Gavroche, W1
Gavvers, SW1
Gay Hussar, W1
Inigo Jones, WC2
Interlude de Tabaillau, WC2
Neal Street Restaurant, WC2
Le Poulbot, EC2
Tante Claire, SW3

ENGLAND

Alderminster Ettington Park Hotel
Ashburton Country Garden
Askrigg Rowan Tree
Bakewell Fischer's
Barwick Little Barwick House
Bath Popjoy's
Beanacre Beechfield House
Bradfield Combust Bradfield House
Bray Waterside Inn
Brighton & Hove Food for Friends
Bristol Bistro Twenty One
Broadway Hunters Lodge
Bromsgrove Grafton Manor
Burghfield Knights Farm
Burnham Market Fishes'
Canterbury Restaurant 74
Waterfields
Chagford Gidleigh Park
Teignworthy Hotel
Chelmsford Melissa
Chipping Norton La Madonette
Clun Old Post Office
Corse Lawn Corse Lawn House
Dartmouth Carved Angel
Dedham Terrace Restaurant, Dedham Vale Hotel
Derby Restaurant 524
Elsworth Meadow Farm
Evershot Summer Lodge
Fadmoor Plough Inn
Farrington Gurney The Old Parsonage
Glastonbury No. 3
Glemsford Weeks Restaurant
Grasmere White Moss House
Great Dunmow The Starr
Great Milton Le Manoir aux Quat' Saisons
Grimston Congham Hall
Guist Tollbridge
Hambleton Hambleton Hall
Helford Riverside
Heswall Les Bougies
Hinton Charterhouse Homewood Park
Hungerford Bear Hotel
Ilkley Box Tree
Olive Tree
Ipswich Singing Chef
Isle of Wight Peacock Vane
Kirkby Fleetham Kirkby Fleetham Hall
Knaresborough Schwallers
Lacock At the Sign of the Angel
Ledbury Hope End Country House Hotel
Lewes Kenwards
Lifton Arundell Arms
Lincoln White's
Lower Brailes Feldon House
Malvern Wells Croque-en-Bouche
Melmerby Village Bakery
Mersham Stone Green Hall
Orford Butley-Orford Oysterage
Oundle Tyrrells
Oxford Le Petit Blanc
Padstow Seafood Restaurant
Penrith Passepartout
Pickworth Manor House
Polperro The Kitchen
Pool in Wharfedale Pool Court
Pulborough Stane Street Hollow
Richmond Lichfield's
Romsey Old Manor House
Ross-on-Wye Pengethley Hotel
Roxwell Farmhouse Feast
Rye Simmons
St Austell Boscundle Manor
Salisbury Crane's
Sharpthorne Gravetye Manor
Sheffield Toffs
Shipdham Shipdham Place
Shrewsbury Delany's
Spark Bridge Bridgefield House
Stonham Mr Underhill's
Taunton Castle Hotel
Thornage The Black Boys
Thornbury Thornbury Castle

Ullswater Sharrow Bay Hotel
Veryan Treverbyn House
Walton-on-the-Hill Ebenezer Cottage
Warwick Randolph's
Wath-in-Nidderdale Sportsman's Arms
Whitney-on-Wye Rhydspence Inn
Williton White House Hotel
Windermere Miller Howe
Witherslack Old Vicarage
Wrightington The High Moor
Wymondham Adlard's

SCOTLAND

Achiltibuie Summer Isles Hotel
Anstruther The Cellar
Blair Drummond Broughton's
Colonsay Isle of Colonsay Hotel
Drumnadrochit Polmaily House Hotel
Drybridge The Old Monastery
Dunblane Cromlix House
Edinburgh Champany Inn Town
Eriska Isle of Eriska Hotel
Fort William Inverlochy Castle
Gullane La Potinière
Harris Scarista House
Kentallen The Holly Tree
Kingussie The Cross
Osprey House
Linlithgow Champany Inn
Moffat Beechwood Country House Hotel
Mull Ardfenaig House
Nairn Clifton Hotel
Peat Inn Peat Inn
Peebles Cringletie House Hotel
Port Appin The Airds Hotel
Portsonachan Portsonachan Hotel
Scone Balcraig House
Shetland Burrastow House
Tweedsmuir Crook Inn
Ullapool Altnaharrie Inn

WALES

Cardigan Blas-O-Ddyfed
Harlech The Cemlyn
Llandewi Skirrid Walnut Tree Inn
Llandudno Bodysgallen Hall
Llandybie The Cobblers

Exceptional wine cellars

These restaurants, marked with a bottle symbol in the text, have outstanding wine cellars.

LONDON

Capital Hotel, SW3
Mabileau, SE1
Mijanou
Pollyanna's, SW11
RSJ, SE1
Tate Gallery, SW1

ENGLAND

Alfriston Moonrakers
Ambleside Rothay Manor
Aston Clinton The Bell
Barnsley Brooklands
Bath Priory Hotel
Beanacre Beechfield House
Boroughbridge Fountain House
Bournemouth Crust
Bourton-on-the-Water Rose Tree
Brockenhurst Le Poussin
Bromsgrove Grafton Manor
Burghfield Knights Farm
Chagford Gidleigh Park
Chedington Chedington Court
Chittlehamholt Highbullen Hotel
Christchurch Splinters
Coggeshall White Hart
Epworth Epworth Tap
Fressingfield Fox and Goose
Glastonbury No. 3
Glemsford Weeks Restaurant
Great Dunmow The Starr
Helford Riverside
Hinton Charterhouse Homewood Park
Horton French Partridge
Hungerford Bear Hotel
Kintbury Dundas Arms
Kirkby Fleetham Kirkby Fleetham Hall
Knaresborough Schwallers
Ledbury Hope End Country House Hotel
Lewes Kenwards
Lincoln Harvey's Cathedral Restaurant
White's
Malvern Wells Croque-en-Bouche
Matlock Riber Hall
Norwich Marco's
Padstow Seafood Restaurant
Painswick Painswick Hotel
Pangbourne Copper Inn
Pickworth Manor House
Pinner La Giralda
Pool in Wharfedale Pool Court
Richmond Lichfield's
Ross-on-Wye Pengethley Hotel
Sharpthorne Gravetye Manor
Shepton Mallet Bowlish House
South Godstone La Bonne Auberge
Southwold Crown
Spark Bridge Bridgefield House
Ston Easton Ston Easton Park
Streatley Swan Hotel
Taunton Castle Hotel
Thornbury Thornbury Castle
Tiverton Hendersons
Ullswater Sharrow Bay Hotel

Uppingham Lake Isle
Wallingford Brown & Boswell
Williton White House Hotel
Witherslack Old Vicarage

SCOTLAND

Drybridge The Old Monastery
Glasgow Ubiquitous Chip
Gullane La Potinière
Harris Scarista House
Kingussie Osprey House
Linlithgow Champany Inn
Moffat Beechwood Country House Hotel
Newton Stewart Kirroughtree Hotel
Peat Inn Peat Inn
Port Appin The Airds Hotel
Scone Balcraig House
Selkirk Philipburn House Hotel
Uphall Houstoun House

WALES

Llandewi Skirrid Walnut Tree Inn
Llandudno Bodysgallen Hall
Llanrwst Meadowsweet Hotel

No smoking

The following restaurants all place some restriction on cigarette smoking in the dining-room (restrictions on cigar and pipe smoking are so commonplace now that such places are not listed). In some, smoking is not allowed at all. Check the entry for details.

LONDON

Al Khayam, W2
Cherry Orchard, E2
Country Life, W1
Fleet Tandoori, NW3
Food for Thought, WC2
Govinda's, W1
Mijanou, SW1
Monsieur Thompsons, W11
Olive Branch, NW6
Quincy's '84, NW3
RSJ, SE1
Le Soufflé, W1
Tate Gallery, SW1
Tiger Lee, SW5

ENGLAND

Ambleside Kirkstone Foot Country House Hotel
Rothay Manor
Sheila's Cottage
Applethwaite Underscar Hotel
Bath Hole in the Wall
Belbroughton Bell Inn
Birtle Normandie
Bishop's Lydeard Rose Cottage
Blackpool Danish Kitchen
Brampton Tarn End
Brighton Food for Friends
Bristol Michael's
Brockdish Sheriff House
Bromsgrove Grafton Manor
Buckden Low Greenfield
Cambridge Free Press
Canterbury Restaurant Seventy Four
Cartmel Uplands
Chagford Teignworthy Hotel
Chelmsford Melissa
Chester Abbey Green
Chittlehamholt Highbullen Hotel
Coatham Mundeville Hall Garth
Cockermouth Wythop Mill
Croydon Hockneys
Durham Undercroft
Glemsford Weeks
Grasmere Michaels Nook
White Moss House
Grimston Congham Hall
Guildford Rumwong
Harrogate Bettys
Herstmonceux Sundial
Hinton Charterhouse Homewood Park
Ilkley Bettys
Box Tree
Olive Tree
Ixworth Theobalds
Kilsby Hunt House
Kirkby Lonsdale Eaveslea
Knaresborough Schwallers
Langley Marsh Langley House Hotel
Ledbury Hope End
Louth Mr Chips
Manchester Gaylord
On the Eighth Day
Tandoor
Melmerby Village Bakery
Nantwich Cellars Bistro
Rookery Hall
Newton Tabuteau's
Northallerton Bettys
Northampton Royal Bengal
Nottingham Pagoda
Oxford Browns
Pickworth Manor House
Pool in Wharfedale Pool Court
Powburn Breamish House
Scotsdike March Bank Country House
Sharpthorne Gravetye Manor
Shepton Mallet Bowlish House
Shipdham Shipdham Place
Shrewsbury Delanys
Old Police House
Spark Bridge Bridgefield House
Stonham Mr Underhill's
Temple Sowerby Temple Sowerby House
Thornage Black Boys
Totnes Elbow Room
Trebarwith Trebarwith Strand Hotel
Ullswater Sharrow Bay
Underbarrow Greenriggs Country House
Walford Walford House
Wallingford Lamb Wine Vault
Walton-on-the-Hill Ebenezer Cottage

Wetheral Fantails
Winchcombe Corner Cupboard Inn
Windermere Miller Howe
Winkleigh Kings Arms
Witherslack Old Vicarage
Wooler Ryecroft Hotel
Wotton under Edge Ellerncroft
Wrelton Huntsman
York Bettys
St. Williams
Taylors Tea Rooms

SCOTLAND

Achiltibuie Summer Isles
Arisaig Arisaig House
Ballater Tullich Lodge
Callander Roman Camp Hotel
Canonbie Riverside Inn
Cromarty Le Chardon
Cupar Ostler's Close
Dunblane Cromlix House
Dunoon Ardenslate Hotel
Edinburgh Kalpna
Pompadour Room (Caledonian Hotel)
Fort William Inverlochy Castle
Gullane La Potinière
Harris Scarista House
Inverness Dunain Park
Kentallen Holly Tree
Killiecrankie Killiecrankie Hotel
Kingussie The Cross
Osprey Hotel
Moffat Beechwood Country House
Mull Ardfenaig House
Tiroran House
Nairn Clifton Hotel
Newton Stewart Kirroughtree Hotel
Peat Inn Peat Inn
Peebles Cringletie House
Port Appin Airds Hotel
Portsonachan Portsonachan Hotel
Shetland Burrastow House
Busta House
St Andrews Grange Inn
Tarbert West Loch Hotel
Tyndrum Clifton Coffee House
Ullapool Altnaharrie Inn

WALES

Brechfa Ty Mawr
Cardigan Blas-O-Dyfed
Rhyd-Garn-Wen
Harlech Castle Cottage
Llanrwst Meadowsweet Hotel
Llanychaer Penlan Oleu
Talyllyn Minffordd Hotel

Afternoon teas

These hotels serve afternoon teas to non-residents.

LONDON

Brittania Hotel (Best of Both Worlds), W1
Blakes Hotel, SW7
British Harvest (Hilton Hotel), W1
Capital Hotel, SW3
Connaught, W1
Dorchester (Grill Room & Terrace), W1
Ninety Park Lane (Grosvenor House), W1
Le Soufflé (Inter-Continental Hotel), W1

ENGLAND

Alderminster Ettington Park
Ambleside Kirkstone Foot Country House
Rothay Manor
Applethwaite Underscar
Bainbridge Riverdale House
Barkston Barkston House
Bath Priory Hotel
Beanacre Beechfield House
Bishops Tachbrook Mallory Court
Blanchland Lord Crewe Arms
Blockley Lower Brook House
Bosham Millstream Hotel
Bournemouth New Ambassadors Hotel
Brampton Farlam Hall
Broadway Lygon Arms
Broxted Whitehall
Buckland Buckland Manor
Bury St Edmunds Angel Hotel
Chagford Gidleigh Park
Thornworthy House
Chester Grosvenor Hotel
Cirencester Fleece Hotel
Clun Old Post Office
Coatham Mundeville Hall Garth
Crackington Haven Crackington Manor
Evesham Evesham Hotel (Cedar Restaurant)
Faringdon Bell Hotel
Flitwick Flitwick Manor
Hambleton Hambleton Hall
Harrogate Russell Hotel (Hodgson's)
Hawes Cockett's
Hinton Charterhouse Homewood Park
Huntingdon Old Bridge
Ipswich Marlborough
Kildwick Kildwich Hall
Kingham Mill Hotel
Lacock Red Lion
Leighton Buzzard Swan Hotel
Lifton Arundell Arms
Ludlow Feathers Inn
Lymington Stanwell House (Railings)
Lytham St Annes Dalmeny Hotel (C'Est la Vie)
Matlock Riber Hall
Middle Wallop Fifehead Manor
Nantwich Rookery Hall
Northam Grays
Painswick Painswick Hotel
Pangbourne Copper Inn
Pickering Forest & Vale
Poole Mansion House
Powburn Breamish House
Redlynch Langley Wood
Ross-on-Wye Pengethley Hotel
Rothley Rothley Court
Shepton Mallet Bowlish House

Shipdham Shipdham Place
Shipton gorge Innsacre Farmhouse
Slaidburn Parrock Head Farm
South Molton Stumbles
Southwold Crown
Stamford George
Ston Easton Ston Easton Park
Streatley Swan Hotel
Sway Pine Trees
Taunton Castle Hotel
Temple Sowerby Temple Sowerby House
Tetbury Gentle Gardener
Thorpe-le-Soken Thorpe Lodge
Tickton Tickton Grange
Tregony Tregony House
Ullswater Sharrow Bay
Underbarrow Greenriggs Country House
Veryan Treverbyn House
Walberswick Mary's
Walford Walford House (Le Cedre)
Watermillock Leeming Country House
Wath-in-Nidderdale Sportsman's Arms
West Mersea Blackwater Hotel (Le Champenois)
Willerby Willerby Manor (Le Restaurant Francais)
Windermere Miller Howe
Windsor Oakley Court
Woodstock Feathers
Wooler Ryecroft Hotel
Yalding Walnut Tree
York Middlethorpe Hall

SCOTLAND

Achiltibuie Summer Isles
Ardeonaig Ardeonaig Hotel
Bellochantuy Putechan Lodge
Colonsay Isle of Colonsay Hotel
Dirleton Open Arms
Dunblane Cromlix House
Edinburgh Caledonia Hotel (Pompadour Room)
Inverness Dunain Park
Kelso Sunlaws House
Kentallen Holly Tree
Kilchrenan Ardanaseig Hotel
Taychreggan Hotel
Kildinan Kilfinan Hotel
Killiecrankie Killiecrankie Hotel
Kingussie Osprey Hotel
Kirkmichael Log Cabin Hotel
Lybster Bayview Hotel
Moffat Beechwood Country House
Nairn Clifton Hotel
Newton Stewart Kirroughtree Hotel
Orkney Foveran
Peebles Cringletie House
Port Appin Airds Hotel
Portsonachan Portsonachan Hotel
Scone Balcraig House
Selkirk Philipburn House
Shetland Busta House
Skye Harlosh Hotel
Kinloch Lodge
Skeabost House
Tarbert West Loch Hotel
Tweedsmuir Crook Inn
Uphall Houstoun House

WALES

Abersoch Porth Tocyn
Broad Haven Druidstone Hotel
Harlech The Cemlyn
Llandderfel Palé Hall
Llandudno Bodysgallen Hall
Llanrwst Meadowsweet Hotel
Llanwddyn Lake Vyrnwy Hotel
Llanwrtyd Wells Llwynderw Hotel
Talsarnau Hotel Maes-y-Neuadd

Fine views

These restaurants offer particularly fine views. Check entry for details.

LONDON

Ninety Park Lane (Grosvenor Hotel), W1
Le Soufflé (Inter-Continental Hotel), W1

ENGLAND

Alderminster Ettington Park
Alston High Fell
Ambleside Kirkstone Foot
Rothay Manor
Wateredge Hotel
Applethwaite Underscar Hotel
Aston Clinton Bell
Bainbridge Riverdale House
Barnsley Brooklands
Barwick Little Barwick House
Birtle Normandie
Bodinnick Old Ferry Inn
Bosham Millstream Hotel
Bournemouth New Ambassadors Hotel
Bradford Restaurant 19 (Belvedere Hotel)
Brampton Farlam Hall
Branscombe Masons Arms
Broadway Collin House
Buckden Low Greenfield
Buckland Buckland Manor
Cartmel Uplands
Chagford Gidleigh Park
Thornworthy House
Chedington Chedington Court
Chester Grosvenor Hotel
Chittlehamholt Highbullen Hotel
Clun Old Post Office
Corse Lawn Corse Lawn House
Crackington Haven Crackington Manor
Dedham Terrace Restaurant (Dedham Vale Hotel)
Flitwick Flitwick Manor
Grasmere White Moss House
Great Milton Le Manoir Aux Quat' Saisons
Gulworthy Horn of Plenty
Halifax Holdsworth House
Hambleton Hambleton Hall

Harrogate Hodgson's (Russell Hotel)
Shrimps (Studley Hotel)
Hassop Hassop Hall
Helford Riverside
Hintlesham Hintlesham Hall
Hinton Charterhouse Homewood Park
Huntingdon Old Bridge Hotel
Isle of Wight Peacock Vane
Kildwick Kildwick Hall
Kingham Mill Hotel
Kintbury Dundas Arms
Kirkby Lonsdale Eaveslea
Lacock At the Sign of the Angel
Red Lion
Langley Marsh Langley House Hotel
Ledbury Hope End
Lifton Arundell Arms
Lytham St Annes C'Est La Vie (Dalmeny Hotel)
Matlock Riber Hall
Mersham Stone Green Hall
Mullion Old Inn
Nantwich Rookery Hall
Nayland Bear
Neasham Newbus Arms Hotel
Northam Grays
Painswick Painswick Hotel
Penzance Abbey
Poughill Reeds
Powburn Breamish House
Reeth Burgoyne Hotel
Rothley Rothley Court
St Margaret's at Cliffe Wallett's Court
Scotsdike March Bank Country House
Shipton Gorge Innsacre Farmhouse
Shurdington Greenway
Spark Bridge Bridgefield House
Staddlebridge McCoy's
Ston Easton Ston Easton Park
Streatley Swan Hotel
Sturminster Newton Plumber Manor
Tarrant Monkton Langtons
Temple Sowerby Temple Sowerby House
Thornage Black Boys
Thornton-Le-Fylde River House
Tickton Tickton Grange
Trebarwith Trebarwith Strand Hotel
Ullswater Sharrow Bay
Underbarrow Greenriggs Country House
Veryan Treverbyn House
Walford Walford House
Wareham Kemps
Watermillock Leeming Country House
West Bexington Manor House Hotel
West Mersea Le Champenois
Whitney-on-Wye Rhydspence Inn
Wickham Old House
Windermere Miller Howe
Windsor Oakley Court
Witherslack Old Vicarage
Woolacombe Little Beach Hotel
Wooler Ryecroft Hotel
Woolhope Butchers Arms
Yalding Walnut Tree
York Middlethorpe Hall

SCOTLAND

Achiltibuie Summer Isles Hotel
Ardeonaig Ardeonaig Hotel
Arisaig Arisaig House
Ballater Green Inn
Tullich Lodge
Bellochantuy Putechan Lodge
Callander Roman Camp Hotel
Colonsay Isle of Colonsay Hotel
Dirleton Open Arms Hotel
Drumnadrochit Polmaily House
Dulnain Bridge Muckrach Lodge
Dunoon Ardenslate Hotel
Edinburgh Pompadour Room (Caledonia Hotel)
Eriska Isle of Eriska Hotel
Fort William Inverlochy Castle
Haddington Browns Hotel
Harris Scarista House
Inverness Dunain Park
Kentallen Holly Tree
Kilchrenan Ardanaiseig Hotel
Kilfinan Kilfinan Hotel
Killiecrankie Killiecrankie Hotel
Kirkmichael Log Cabin
Moffat Beechwood Country House
Mull Ardfenaig House
Tiroran House
Nairn Clifton Hotel
Newton Stewart Kirroughtree Hotel
Old Meldrum Meldrum House
Orkney Foveran
Port Appin Airds Hotel
Portsonachan Portsonachan Hotel
Scone Balcraig House
Selkirk Philipburn House
Shetland Burrastow House
Busta House
Skye Harlosh Hotel
Kinloch Lodge
Skeabost House
St Andrews Grange Inn
Stewarton Chapeltown House
Tarbert West Loch Hotel
Tweedsmuir Crook Inn
Ullapool Altnaharrie Inn
Whitebridge Knockie Lodge

WALES

Abersoch Porth Tocyn Hotel
Brechfa Ty Mawr
Broad Haven Druidstone Hotel
Harlech Cemlyn
Llandderfel Palé Hall
Llangwm Bridge Inn
Llanrwst Meadowsweet Hotel
Llandwddyn Lake Vyrnwy Hotel
Llanwrtyd Wells Llwynderw Hotel
Llanychaer Penlan Oleu
Reynoldston Fairyhill
Robeston Wathen Robeston House
Talsarnau Hotel Maes-y-Neuadd
Talyllyn Minffordd Hotel
Three Cocks Three Cocks Hotel

Jacket and tie

These restaurants insist that their gentlemen customers wear a jacket and tie.

LONDON

L'Arlequin, SW8
Best of Both Worlds (Britannia Hotel), W1
Boulestin, WC2
Connaught, W1
Defune, W1
Dorchester (Grill Room & Terrace Restaurant), W1
Le Gavroche, W1
Masako, W1
Ninety Park Lane (Grosvenor House), W1
Le Poulbot, EC2
Red Fort, W1
Simpson's In The Strand, WC2

ENGLAND

Alderminster Ettington Park
Badminton Bodkin House
Battle Blacksmith's
Belbroughton Bell Inn
Berkswell Nailcote Hall
Bishops Tachbrook Mallory Court
Braintree Braintree Chinese
Broadway Lygon Arms
Brockdish Sheriff House
Brockenhurst Le Poussin
Bromsgrove Grafton Manor
Bury St Edmunds Angel Hotel
Chester Grosvenor Hotel
Grimston Congham Hall
Hawkhurst Osborn House
Huntingdon Old Bridge Hotel
Husbands Bosworth Fernie Lodge
Kimbolton La Côte D'Or
Kingham Mill Hotel
Littlewick Green Warrener Restaurant
Manchester Assam Gourmet
Matlock Riber Hall
Nantwich Rookery Hall
New Milton Marryat Room (Chewton Glen Hotel)
Newcastle upon Tyne Le Roussillon
Rupali
Poole Mansion House
Ross-on-Wye Pengethley Hotel
Rothley Rothley Court
Spurstow Rembrandt
Staveley Royal Oak
Ston Easton Ston Easton Park
Tregony Tregony House
Walford Walford House
Windsor Oakley Court
York Middlethorpe Hall

SCOTLAND

Ardeonaig Ardeonaig Hotel
Ballater Tullich Lodge
Dunblane Cromlix House
Edinburgh Pompadour Room (Caledonia Hotel)
Eriska Isle of Eriska Hotel
Fort William Inverlochy Castle
Kilchrenan Ardanaiseig Hotel
Moffat Beechwood Country House
Mull Ardfenaig House
Tiroran House
Newton Stewart Kirroughtree Hotel
Skye Skeabost House
Whitebridge Knockie Lodge

WALES

Cardiff Everest
Cardigan Rhyd-Garn-Wen
Llandderfel Palé Hall
Llandudno Bodysgallen Hall
Llanwddyn Lake Vyrnwy Hotel
Llanwrtyd Wells Llwynderw Hotel

Vegetarian meals

These restaurants have stated that they offer fully vegetarian meals on their standard menu. However, we have not been able to verify all of them, so double check when you book.

LONDON

Al Diwan, W2
Al Khayam, W2
Anarkali, W6
Anna's Place, N1
Arirang, W1
Ark, W8
L'Arlequin, SW8
Au Bois St Jean, NW8
L'Aventure, NW8
Aziz, W6
Bahn Thai, W8
Balzac Bistro, W12
Bambaya, N8
Bayleaf Tandoori, N6
Beau-Rivage, NW6
Beccofino, SW3
Bengal Lancer, NW5
Le Bistroquet, NW1
Bloom's, E1
Bombay Brasserie, SW7
Brewer Street Buttery, W1
Le Café du Jardin, WC2
Café Pelican, WC2
Le Caprice, SW1
Cap's (Pembridge Court Hotel), W11
Chaglayan Kebab House, NW4
Champagne Exchange, W1
Charco's Wine Bar, SW3
Le Chef, W2
Cherry Orchard, E2
Chiang Mai, W1
Christian's, W4

Chuen Cheng Ku, W1
Colombina, SW1
La Coree, WC2
Cork & Bottle, WC2
Country Life, W1
Crowns, SW1
Crowthers, SW14
Daphne, NW1
Defune, W1
Desaru, W1
Dewaniam, SE23
Diamond, WC2
Dining Room, SE1
Ealing Tandoori, W5
Ebury Wine Bar, SW1
Equatorial, W1
L'Estanquet, SW5
Fleet Tandoori, NW3
Food for Thought, WC2
Fox and Anchor, EC1
Frith's, W1
Ganpath, WC1
Good Friends, E14
Gordon's Wine Bar, WC2
Govinda's, W1
Grahame's Seafare, W1
Green Cottage 11, NW3
Green Leaves, W1
Han Kuk Hoe Kwan, W1
Hard Rock Café, W1
Hee's, NW7
R.S. Hispaniola, WC2
Ho-Ho, E18
Hoults, SW17
Hung Toa, W2
Ikkyu, W1
India Palace, E12
Inigo Jones, WC2
Jack's Place, SW11
Joy King Lau, WC2
Justin De Blank, W1
Kalamaras, W2
Kettners, W1
Kitchen Yakitori, W1
Knoodles, W2
Korea House, W1
Koto, NW1
Lal Bhag, NW6
Lal Qila, W1
Lantern, NW6
Last Days of the Raj, WC2
Lemonia, NW1
Light of Kashmir, NW3
Luigi's, SE19
Mabileau, SE1
Magno's Brasserie, WC2
Maharajah, W2
Malabar, W8
Mandalay, SE10
Mandeer, W1
Maroush, W2
Maroush 11, SW3
Maxim, W13
Maxim Wine Bar, W7
Le Mazarin, SW1
Methuselah's, SW1
Le Metro Wine Bar, SW3
Mi Mi, W1
Mon Plaisir, WC2
Montpeliano, SW7
Mr Kong, WC2
Mr Liu, SE22
Mr Lu, SW14
Mr Tang, W1
M'sieur Frog, N1
M'sieur Frog's Bistro, N8
New Bengal, W2
New Friends, E14
New World, W1
Nosherie, EC1
Old Budapest, W1
Olive Branch, NW6
One Hampstead Lane, N6
192, W11
One Two Three, W1
Ormes, SW4
Il Passetto, WC2
Paulo's, W6
Peachey's, NW3
Perfumed Conservatory, SW6
Le Petit Prince, NW5
Phoenicia, W8
Pollyanna's, SW11
Ponte Nuovo, SW3
Porte de la Cite, WC1
Le Poulbot, EC2
Quincy's, NW2
Ragam, W1
Rajput, W12
Red Fort, W1
The Restaurant and Brasserie, SW1
Rudland & Stubbs, EC1
Rue St Jacques, W1
Sabras, NW10
Saga, W1
San Frediano, SW3
San Lorenzo, SW3
Semiramis, W2
Shapla, SW9
Shireen Tandoori, W12
Soho Brasserie, W1
South Kensington Pasta Bar, SW3
Spread Eagle, SE10
Sree Krishna, SW17
Tate Gallery, SW1
Thierry's, SW3
Tiger Lee, SW5
Topkapi, W1
Treasure of China, SE10
Twenty Trinity Gardens, SW9
Wakaba, NW3
Woodlands, W1
Yung's, W1
Zen, SW3

ENGLAND

Alfriston Moonrakers
Applethwaite Underscar Hotel
Ashby de la Zouch Mews Wine Bar
Barford St Martin Michel's
Barnard Castle Market Place Teashop
Barnet Wings
Barnstaple Lynwood House
Bath Chikako's
Clos Du Roy
Hole in the Wall
Moon and Sixpence
Woods
Beaconsfield China Diner
Beaminster Nevitt's
Berkswell Nailcote Hall
Biddenden Three Chimneys
Birkenhead Beadles
Birmingham Los Andes
Chung Ying
Franzl's
Ho Tung
Maharaja
Rajdoot
Bishop's Cleeve Cleeveway House
Bishop's Lydeard Rose Cottage
Blackburn Foxfields
Blackpool Danish Kitchen
Jasmine Cottage
Blanchland Lord Crewe Arms
Blockley Lower Brook House
Bognor Regis Costellos
Boroughbridge Fountain House
Botley (Hants) Cobbett's
Botley (Oxon) Bilash Tandoori
Tong San
Bournemouth Crust
Bradford Shiraz Sweet House
Braintree Braintree Chinese
Bridgnorth Haywain
Old Colonial
Brighton Eaton Restaurant
Food for Friends
Le Français
Muang Thai

Bristol Berkeley Brasserie
Edwards
Ganges
Michael's
Vintner Wine Bar
Broadstairs Marchesi Bros
Broadway Hunters Lodge
Lygon Arms
Brockenhurst Le Poussin
Bromley Carioca
Peking Diner
Broxted Whitehall
Burghfield Knights Farm
Burnham on Crouch Contented Sole
Polash
Buxton Nathaniel's
Cambridge Free Press
Campsea Ash Old Rectory
Canterbury Tuo e Mio
Cartmel Uplands
Chagford Teignworthy Hotel
Chelmsford Melissa
Cheltenham Retreat
Chesham Chesham Tandoori
Chester Abbey Green
Pippa's in Town
Chesterton Woods
Chilgrove White Horse Inn
Chinnor Crickets
Sir Charles Napier Inn
Chipping Norton Anarkali
Christchurch Splinters
Cirencester Fleece Hotel
Rajdoot Tandoori
Clun Old Post Office
Coatham Mundeville Hall Garth
Cockermouth Wythop Mill
Colchester Bistro Nine
Congleton Oddfellows Wine Bar
Constable Burton Wyvill Arms
Corse Lawn Corse Lawn House
Cotherstone Fox and Hounds
Coventry Herbs (Trinity House Hotel)
Crackington Haven Crackington Manor
Croydon Hockneys
Munbhave
Dedham Marlborough Head Hotel
Terrace Restaurant (Dedham Vale Hotel)
Derby Golden Pheasant
Restaurant 524
Disley Ginnel
Diss Salisbury House
Donhead St Andrew Le Radier
Dorking River Kwai
Durham Undercroft Restaurant
East Bergholt Fountain House
East Horsley Tudor Rose
Eastry Coach and Horses
Elland Berties Bistro
Esher Les Deux Amis
Eton Eton Wine Bar
Evershot Summer Lodge
Evesham Cedar Restaurant (Evesham Hotel)
Eynsham Edwards
Faringdon Bell Hotel
Farnham Tirolerhof
Farnley Tyas Golden Cock
Fawley Walnut Tree
Felsted Rumbles Cottage
Fleetwood Trafalgar
Flitwick Flitwick Manor
Folkestone India
Fowey Restaurant Cordon Bleu
Fowlmere Chequers Inn
Glastonbury No. 3
Rainbows End Café
Grays R. Munford & Son
Great Dunmow Indian Village Tandoori
Starr
Great Milton Le Manoir aux Quat' Saisons
Guildford Three Kingdoms
Gulworthy Horn of Plenty
Gunthorpe Mr Toad's
Hadleigh Weaver's
Hambleton Hambleton Hall
Harrogate Bettys
Shabab
Shrimps (Studley Hotel)
William & Victoria Wine Bar
Hassop Hassop Hall
Hatfield Salisbury
Hemel Hempstead Casanova
Henfield Kents
Herstmonceux Sundial
Hildenborough Gate Inn
Holt Flask
Huddersfield Shabab
Husbands Bosworth Fernie Lodge
Huxham Barton Cross
Ilford Bolaka
Mandarin Palace
Sharon's
Da Umberto
Ilkley Bettys
Olive Tree
Sangster's Wine Bar
Ipswich Marlborough
Singing Chef
Jevington Hungry Monk
Kenilworth Romano's
King's Lynn Riverside Rooms
Knaresborough Schwallers
Knutsford La Belle Epoque
Lacock Red Lion
Leeds Mandalay
Salvo's
Sang Sang
Shabab
Waterhole
Leicester Water Margin
Leighton Buzzard Swan Hotel
Lewes Kenwards
La Cucina
Sussex Kitchen (Pelham Arms)
Lifton Arundell Arms
Limpsfield Old Lodge
Lincoln Harvey's Cathedral Restaurant
White's
Liphook Lal Quilla
Liverpool Armadillo
Beaujolais
Carrageen Café
Casa Italia
Far East
La Grande Bouffe
Lostwithiel Trewithen
Ludlow Dinham Weir
Feathers Inn
Penny Anthony
Lympstone River House
Lytham St Anne's Bennett's Bistro
Macclesfield Harlequin's
Manaccan New Inn
Manchester Armenian Taverna
Assam Gourmet
Café Istanbul
Connaught
Gaylord
Happy Gathering
Hung Chun
Kai's
Kathmandu Tandoori
Kosmos Taverna
Market Restaurant
Mina Japan
Moss Nook
Mr Kuks
Mulberry's
On the Eighth Day

Rajdoot
Tandoor
Terrazza
That Café
Truffles
Woo Sang
Matlock Riber Hall
Mayfield Old Brew House
Melmerby Village Bakery
Mersham Stone Green Hall
Morpeth Gourmet
Nantwich Cellars Bistro
Jade House
Neasham Newbus Arms
Newark Gannets
Newcastle upon Tyne
Jade Garden
Rupali
Sachins
Wan Ton House
Newent Soutters
Newton Tabuteaus
Newtown in St Martin Anthea's
North Weald Bassett Wo Ping
Northallerton Bettys
Northampton Royal Bengal
Norwich Brasted's
Greens Seafood
Marco's
Tatlers
Nottingham Les Artistes Gourmands
Chand
Pagoda
Oswestry Good Companion Wine Bar
Ottery St Mary Lodge
Oxford Browns
Gees
Munchy Munchy
Le Petit Blanc
Padiham Le Jardin Bistro
Pangbourne Copper Inn
Penzance Abbey
Enzo
Pinner La Giralda
Plumtree Perkins Bar Bistro
Plymouth Hosteria Romana
Mister Barretts
Polperro Kitchen
Pool in Wharfedale Pool Court
Poole Gullivers
Preston Tiggis
Redlynch Langley Wood
Richmond Red Lion
Ripon Old Deanery
Rochford Renoufs
Rockley Loaves & Fishes
Ross on Wye Pengethley Hotel
Roxwell Farmhouse Feast
Saffron Walden Old Hoops
St Albans Diomides
St Austell Boscundle Manor
St Margaret's at Cliffe Wallett's Court
Scarborough Lanterna
Scotsdike March Bank Country House
Seatoller Yew Tree
Sheffield Nirmals
Toffs
Zing Vaa
Shepshed Turtles
Shepton Mallet Blostin's
Bowlish House
Shere La Chaumière
Shildon Rajah Tandoori
Shipdham Shipdham Place
Shipley Aagrah
Shipston-on-Stour White Bear
Shipton Gorge Innsacre Farmhouse
Shrewsbury Delanys
Old Police House
Shurdington Greenway
Sileby Old School
Smarden Bell
South Molton Stumbles
Southall Brilliant
Southampton Pearl Harbour
Southend-on-Sea Pipe of Port
Spark Bridge Bridgefield House
Spilsby Buttercross
Spurstow Rembrandt
Staddlebridge McCoy's
McCoy's Bistro
Stamford George
Stapleton Bridge Inn
Stoke Bruerne Butty
Ston Easton Ston Easton Park
Stonham Mr Underhill's
Stonor Five Horseshoes
Stony Stratford Bekash Tandoori
Storrington Manleys
Stourport-on-Severn Severn Tandoori
Stratford Upon Avon Rumours
Strete Laughing Monk
Sudbury Fords Bistro
Tamworth Kealeys
Tarrant Monkton Langtons
Taunton Castle Hotel
Thornton Heath Bunga Raya
Thornton-Le-Fylde River House
Thorpe Mandeville Three Conies
Thorpe-Le-Soken Thorpe Lodge
Tisbury Garden Room
Tiverton Hendersons
Torquay Green Mantle
Torrington Rebecca's
Trebarwith Trebarwith Strand Hotel
Ullswater Sharrow Bay
Uppingham Lake Isle
Wadhurst Spindlewood Hotel
Walberswick Potter's Wheel
Wallingford Brown & Boswell
Lamb Wine Vault
Walton-on-the-Hill Ebenezer Cottage
Warminster Agra
Cooper's
Wath-in-Nidderdale Sportsman's Arms
Wembley Moghul Brasserie
West Bexington Manor House Hotel
West Clandon Onslow Arms
Westerham Shapla Tandoori
Wetheral Fantails
Weybourne Gasche's
Weybridge Gaylord Gourmet
Whitby Magpie Café
Whitehaven Bruno's
Whitney-on-Wye Rhydspence Inn
Windsor Oakley Court
Woburn Crispins
Paris House
Woodbridge Royal Bengal Wine Bar
Woodstock Feathers Hotel
Woolhope Butchers Arms
Worcester Brown's Cornucopia
Wotton Under Edge Ellerncroft
Yalding Walnut Tree
York Bettys
Middlethorpe Hall
St William's
Taylors Tea Rooms

SCOTLAND

Auchterhouse Old Mansion House
Ballater Green Inn
Colonsay Isle of Colonsay Hotel
Cromarty Le Chardon
Cullipool Longhouse Buttery
Dirleton Open Arms Hotel
Dunblane Cromlix House
Dundee Raffles
Edinburgh Aye
Kalpna
Martins
Maxies Bistro
New Edinburgh Rendezvous
Shamiana
Vito's
Waterfront Wine Bar
Gattonside Hoebridge Inn
Glasgow Amritsar Tandoori
Asha
La Bavarde
Café Gandolfi
Loon Fung
Pavarotti
Poachers
Preet Palace
Shish Mahal
Ubiquitous Chip
Killiecrankie Killiecrankie Hotel
Kingussie Cross
Osprey Hotel
Kirkmichael Log Cabin Hotel
Moffat Beechwood Country House
Mull Ardfenaig House
Nairn Clifton Hotel
Perth Timothys
Selkirk Philipburn House Hotel
Shetland Burrastow House
Skye Harlosh Hotel
Three Chimneys
St Andrews Grange Inn
Tyndrum Clifton Coffee House
Wester Howgate Old Howgate Inn

WALES

Broad Haven Druidstone Hotel
Cardiff Armless Dragon
Blas-ar-Cymru
Everest
Harvesters
Cardigan Blas-O-Ddyfed
Cilgerran Castle Kitchen
Cowbridge Basil's Brasserie
Glanwydden Queen's Head
Harlech Castle Cottage Cemlyn
Llanberis Y Bistro
Llandderfel Palé Hall
Llandewi Skirrid Walnut Tree Inn
Llandudno Floral
Llandybie Cobblers
Llangwm Bridge Inn
Llanwddyn Lake Vyrnwy Hotel
Llanwrtyd Wells Llwynderw Hotel
Llanychaer Penlan Oleu
Morfa Nefyn Bryncynan Inn
Pontshaen French Restaurant
Reynoldston Fairyhill
Swansea Heritage
Talsarnau Hotel Maes-y-Neuadd
Talyllyn Minffordd Hotel
Tenby Chinatown
Wolfs Castle Wolfscastle Country Hotel

Bring your own wine

These restaurants allow customers to bring their own wine. Some charge corkage. See the entry for details.

LONDON

Cherry Orchard, E2
Chuen Cheng Ku, W1
Food for Thought, WC2
Good Friends, E14
Hung Toa, W2
Lampwicks, SW8
Nanten Yakitori Bar, W1
Paulo's, W6
Ragam, W1
Rogue's Kitchen, SE16
Sabras, NW10
Seashell, NW1
Seashell, E8
Seashore, NW3
Sidi Bou Said, W1

ENGLAND

Birmingham Los Andes
Le Biarritz
Brighton Twenty One
Chelmsford Melissa
Croydon Hockneys
Derby Restaurant 524
Eastbourne Qualisea
Great Dunmow The Starr
Gunthorpe Mr Toad's
Limpsfield Old Lodge
Lincoln White's
Liverpool Carrageen Cafe
Lower Brailes Feldon House
Manchester Hung Chun
Kai's
Kathmandu Tandoori
On the Eighth Day
Newtown-in-St. Martin Anthea's
Oxford Munchy Munchy
Le Petit Blanc
Rockley Loaves & Fishes
Shipston-on-Stour White Bear
Southend-on-Sea Slassor's
Walberswick Potter's Wheel
Whitby Magpie Café
Wickham Old House

SCOTLAND

Glasgow Poachers
Shish Mahal
Ubiquitous Chip
Wester Howgate Old Howgate Inn

WALES

Cardigan Blas-O-Ddyfed
Newport The Pantry

Restaurants with tables outside

These restaurants all have at least two tables outside in fine weather. Check the entry for details.

LONDON

Al Hamra, W1
Anna's Place, N1
Ark, W8
L'Aventure, NW8
Bagatelle, SW10
Bayleaf Tandoori, N6
Beccofino, SW3
Le Bistroquet, NW1
Brasserie St Quentin, SW3
Café Pelican, WC2
Café Rouge, EC1
Champagne Exchange, W1
Chanterelle, SW7
Charco's Wine Bar, SW3
Le Chef, W2
Cherry Orchard, E2
Christian's, W4
Colombina, SW1
La Croisette, SW10
Daphne, NW1
Fox & Anchor, EC1
La Frimousse, NW6
Genevieve, W1
Gordon's Wine Bar, WC2
Govinda's, W1
Green Leaves, W1
Hard Rock Café, W1
R.S. Hispaniola, WC2
Ho-Ho, E18
Hoults, SW17
Malean Chinese, SW16
Martin's, SW10
Masako, W1
Methuselah's, SW1
Mijanou, SW1
Montpeliano, SW7
Olive Branch, NW6
One Hampstead Lane, N6
One Two Three, W1
Ormes, SW4
Peachey's, NW3
Perfumed Conservatory, SW6
Pollyanna's, SW11
Ponte Nuovo, SW3
La Preferita, SW11
Le Quai St Pierre, W8
Quincy's, NW2
Read's, SW5
Rogue's Kitchen, SE16
Soho Brasserie, W1
Le Suquet, SW3
Twenty Trinity Gardens, SW9
Wine Gallery, SW10

ENGLAND

Arundel Pink'n'Green
Barford St Martin Michels'
Barnsley Brooklands
Bath Moon & Sixpence
Battle Boxers
Beanacre Beechfield House
Belbroughton Freshman's
Biddenden Three Chimneys
Birtle Normandie
Bishop's Lydeard Rose Cottage
Blackpool Jasmine Cottage
Blockley Lower Brook House
Bognor Regis Costellos
Bosham Millstream Hotel
Botley Tong San
Bourton-on-the-Water Rose Tree
Branscombe Masons Arms
Brightlingsea Jacobe's
Brighton Eaton
Restaurant Chardonnay
Brightwell Baldwin Lord Nelson Inn
Broadstairs Marchesi Bros
Broadway Collin House
Hunters Lodge
Broxted Whitehall
Buckland Buckland Manor
Cambridge Free Press
Cattawade Bucks
Chagford Teignworthy Hotel
Thornworthy House
Chappel Swan Inn
Cheam Mandarin
Cheltenham Retreat
Chester Abbey Green
Chesterton Woods
Chilgrove White Horse Inn
Chinnor Crickets
Sir Charles Napier Inn
Chittlehamholt Highbullen Hotel
Cirencester Fleece Hotel
Clun Old Post Office
Coatham Mundeville Hall Garth
Cobham Plough
Coggeshall White Hart
Congleton Oddfellows Wine Bar
Constable Burton Wyvill Arms
Corse Lawn Corse Lawn House
Coventry Herbs (Trinity House Hotel)
Coxwold Fauconberg Arms
Dedham Marlborough Head Hotel
Terrace Restaurant (Dedham Vale Hotel)
Diss Salisbury House
East Bergholt Fountain House
East Stoke Kemps
Ely Old Fire Engine House
Esher Les Deux Amis
Eton Eton Wine Bar
Evershot Summer Lodge
Ewhurst Windmill Inn
Faringdon Bell Hotel
Farnley Tyas Golden Cock
Faversham Read's
Fawley Walnut Tree
Flitwick Flitwick Manor
Fotheringhay Falcon Inn
Fowlmere Chequers Inn
Glastonbury No. 3
Rainbows End Cafe
Great Milton Le Manoir aux Quat' Saisons
Guist Tollbridge
Gulworthy Horn of Plenty
Hadleigh Weaver's
Hawes Cockett's
Haydon Bridge General Havelock Inn
Herstmonceux Sundial
Holt Flask
Hook Whitewater House
Hopton Wafers Crown Inn
Horncastle Magpies
Hungerford Bear Hotel
Huntingdon Old Bridge Hotel
Ilkley Sangster's Wine Bar
Inkpen Swan Inn
Ipswich Marlborough
Singing Chef
Ixworth Theobalds
Jevington Hungry Monk

Kimbolton La Cote d'Or
King's Lynn Riverside Rooms
Kintbury Dundas Arms
Lacock Red Lion
Leighton Buzzard Swan Hotel
Limpsfield Old Lodge
Lytham St Annes C'est La Vie (Dalmeny Hotel)
Macclesfield Harlequin's
Manaccan New Inn
Manchester Moss Nook
March Acre
Mawgan Yard Bistro
Melmerby Village Bakery
Mersham Stone Green Hall
Middle Wallop Fifehead Manor
Mullion Old Inn
Nayland Bear
Newark Gannets
Newcastle Upon Tyne Fisherman's Lodge
Sachins
New Milton Marryat Room (Chewton Glen)
Newtown in St Martin Anthea's
Nottingham Les Artistes Gourmands
Staropolska
Oundle Tyrells
Oxford Browns
Cherwell Boathouse
Padstow Seafood Restaurant
Painswick Painswick Hotel
Pangbourne Copper Inn
Peasmarsh Flackley Ash
Pickering Forest & Vale
Plumtree Perkins Bar Bistro
Plymouth Clouds
Hosteria Romana
Poole Gulliver's
Priors Hardwick Butchers Arms
Reeth Burgoyne Hotel
Ripon Old Deanery
Romsey Old Manor House
Ross on Wye Pengethley Hotel
Rothley Rothley Court
Saffron Walden Saffron Hotel
Salisbury Crane's
Scarborough Lanterna Ristorante
Scotsdike March Bank Country House
Seatoller Yew Tree
Shepton Mallet Bowlish House
Shere La Chaumiere
Shipston on Stour White Bear
Shipton Gorge Innsacre Farmhouse
Shurdington Greenway
Smarden Bell
South Godstone La Bonne Auberge
South Molton Stumbles
Southwold Crown
Spilsby Buttercross
Staddlebridge McCoy's
Stamford George
Stapleton Bridge Inn
Staveley Royal Oak
Steeple Aston Red Lion
Stockbridge Game Larder
Stoke Bruerne Butty
Ston Easton Ston Easton Park
Stonor Five Horseshoes
Tetbury Gentle Gardener
Thaxted Recorder's House
Thorpe-le-Soken Thorpe Lodge
Three Legged Cross Bull
Tiverton Hendersons
Totnes Elbow Room
Tunbridge Wells, La Galoche (Mount Edgecombe Hotel)
Thackeray's House
Walberswick Mary's
Walford Walford House
Warminster Cooper's
Washington George's Carvery
Waterhouses Old Beams
Watermillock Leeming Country House
Wath in Nidderdale Sportsman's Arms
West Bexington Manor House Hotel
West Clandon Onslow Arms
West Mersea Le Champenois (Blackwater Hotel)
Whitney on Wye Rhydspence Inn
Windsor Oakley Court
Woburn Crispins
Paris House
Woodstock Feathers Hotel
Woolhope Butchers Arms
Wotton under Edge Ellerncroft
Yalding Walnut Tree
York St Williams

SCOTLAND

Arisaig Arisaig House
Auchterhouse Old Mansion House
Ballater Green Inn
Bellochantuy Putechan Lodge
Canonbie Riverside Inn
Colonsay Isle of Colonsay Hotel
Dunblane Cromlix House
Dunoon Ardenslate Hotel
Edinburgh Pompadour Room (Caledonia Hotel)
Waterfront Wine Bar
Glasgow Poachers
Inverness Dunain Park
Kelso Sunlaws House
Kilchrenan Taychreggan Hotel
Kilfinan Kilfinan Hotel
Linlithgow Champany Inn
Moffat Beechwood Country House
Newton Stewart Kirroughtree Hotel
Portsonachan Portsonachan Hotel
Selkirk Philipburn House
Skye Three Chimneys
Wester Howgate Old Howgate Inn

WALES

Abersoch Porth Tocyn Hotel
Brechfa Ty Mawr
Broad Haven Druidstone Hotel
Cardigan Rhyd-Garn-Wen
Erbistock Boat Inn
Glanwydden Queen's Head
Harlech Castle Cottage
Cemlyn
Llandewi Skirrid Walnut Tree Inn
Llangollen Gales
Llangwm Bridge Inn
Llanychaer Penlan Oleu
Morfa Nefyn Bryncynan Inn
Pontshaen French Restaurant
Tenby Chinatown

Cover charge blacklist

These restaurants still have a separate cover charge, which is added as an extra to the bill. Check the entry for details.

LONDON

Al Diwan, W2
Al Hamra, W1
L'Amico, SW1
Ark, W8
L'Aventure, NW8
Aziz, W6
Bagatelle, SW10
Bahn Thai, W8
Beau-Rivage, NW6
Beccofino, SW3
Bengal Lancer, NW5
Beotys, WC2
Boot and Flogger, SE1
Brasserie St. Quentin, W3
Bunny's, NW3
Café Rouge, EC1
Le Caprice, SW1
Il Cavaliere, NW11
Chaglayan Kebab House, NW4
Chalcot's, NW1
Le Chef, W2
Chez Gerard, W1
Christian's, W4
Colombina, SW1
Corney & Barrow, EC2
Desaru, W1
Don Pepe, NW8
Eatons, SW1
Ebury Wine Bar, SW1
L'Estanquet, SW5
La Frimousse, NW6
Fuji, W1
Gay Hussar, W1
Golden Chopsticks, SW7
Grahame's Seafare, W1
Greenhouse, W1
R.S. Hispaniola, WC2
Inigo Jones, WC2
Jason's, SW11
Kalamaras, W2
Langan's Bistro, W1
Langan's Brasserie, W1
Luigi's, SE19
Ma Cuisine, SW3
Magno's Brasserie, WC2
Malabar, W8
Mandalay, E10
Maroush, W2
Maroush II, SW3
Masako, W1
Mijanou, SW1
Mon Plaisir, WC2
Neal Street Restaurant, WC2
Odins, W1
L'Olivier, SW10
One Hampstead Lane, N6
One Two Three, W1
Ormes, SW4
Il Passetto, WC2
Peachey's NW3
Phoenicia, W8
Ponte Nuovo, W3
La Preferita, SW11
Le Quai St Pierre, W8
The Restaurant & Brasserie, SW1
Saga, W1
San Frediano, SW3
San Lorenzo, SW3
Santini, SW1
Sheekey's, WC2
Shireen Tandoori, W12
Sidi Bou Said, W1
Simpson's in the Strand, WC2
69 Westow Hill, SE19
Soho Brasserie, W1
Le Suquet, SW3
Thierry's, SW3
Topkapi, W1
Tower Grill Restaurant, W1
Viareggio, NW6
Village Restaurant, SW19
White Tower, W1
Wine Gallery, SW10
Zaki's, NW11

ENGLAND

Ashburton Country Garden
Ashford Terrazza
Barnet Wings
Battle Blacksmith's
Birmingham Rajdoot
Brightlingsea Jacobe's
Bristol Les Semailles
Canterbury Tuo e Mio
Christchurch Splinters
Cookham Peking Inn
East Molesey Lantern
Vecchia Roma
Eynsham Edwards
Faversham Read's
Folkestone India
Fowlmere Chequers Inn
Grayshott Woods
Hemel Hempstead Casanova
Horton French Partridge
Huntingdon Old Bridge Hotel
Ilford Da Umberto
Isle of Man La Rosette
Manchester Gaylord
Rajdoot
Tandoor
Terrazza
Melbourn Pink Geranium
Mersham Stone Green Hall
St Albans Diomides
Shardlow La Marina
Stamford George
Woburn Paris House
Wye Wife of Bath

London restaurants by cuisine

AFRICAN

Afric-Carib, N4
Sidi Bou Said, W1

BISTRO

Ark, W8
Balzac Bistro, W12
Barnaby's, SW13
Le Bistroquet, NW1
Le Café du Jardin, WC2
Café Pelican, WC2
Cap's, W11
Le Chef, W2
Crowns, SW1
Ebury Wine Bar, SW1
Lantern, NW6
Magno's Brasserie, WC2
Le Metro Wine Bar, SW3
Monkeys, SW3
M'sieur Frog, N1
M'sieur Frog's Bistro, N8
192, W11
Ormes, SW4
Wine Gallery, SW10

BRAZILIAN

Paulo's, W6

BURMESE

Mandalay, SE10

CARIBBEAN & WEST INDIAN

Bambaya, N8

CHINESE (non-Cantonese)

Dragon Gate, W1
Green Leaves, W1
Hee's, NW7
Ho-Ho, E18 & W1
Malean, SW16
Maxim, W13
Maxim's Wine Bar, W7
Mr Liu, SE22
Mr Lu, SW14
Treasure of China, SE10
Zen, SW3

CHINESE (Cantonese)

Chuen Cheng Ku, W1
Diamond, WC2
Fung Shing, WC2
Golden Chopsticks, SW7
Good Earth, NW7
Good Friends, E14
Hung Toa, W2
Joy King Lau, WC2
Mr Kong, WC2
Mr Tang, W1
New Friends, E14
New World, W1
Poons, WC2
Tiger Lee, SW5
Wong Kei, W1
Yung's W1

ENGLISH

Boot & Flogger, SE1
British Harvest (Hilton Hotel), W1
Corney & Barrow, EC2
Dorchester Grill, W1
Fox & Anchor, EC1
Pollyanna's, SW11
Simpson's in the Strand, WC2
Spread Eagle, SE10
Tate Gallery, SW1

FISH

La Croisette, SW10
Green's Champagne & Oyster Bar, SW1
Mr Fish, SW15
Le Quai St Pierre, W8
Rudland & Stubbs, EC1
Sheekeys, WC2
Le Suquet, SW3

FISH & CHIPS

Seashell, E8 & NW1
Seashore, NW3
Upper Street Fish Shop, N1

FRENCH

L'Arlequin, SW8
L'Auberge, SE22
L'Aventure, NW8
Boulestin, WC2
Brasserie St Quentin, SW3
Bunny's, NW3
Café Rouge, EC1
Chalcot's, NW1
Chanterelle, SW7
Chez Moi, W11
Ciboure, SW1
L'Estanquet, SW5
La Frimousse, NW6
Frith's, W1
Le Gavroche, W1
Gavvers, SW1
Hilaire, SW7
Interlude de Tabaillau, WC2
Ma Cuisine, SW3
Martin's, SW10
Le Mazarin, SW1
Mon Plaisir, WC2
Monsieur Thompson's, W11
Le Muscadet, W1
Ninety Park Lane (Grosvenor House), W1
L'Olivier, SW10
Peachey's, NW3
Le Poulbot, EC2
Quinns, E2
RSJ, SE1
Rue St Jacques, W1
Soho Brasserie, W1
Tante Claire, SW3
Twenty Trinity Gardens, SW9

GREEK

Beotys, WC2
Daphne, NW1
Jason's, SW11
Kalamaras, W2
Lemonia, NW1
Nontas, NW1
Semiramis, W2
White Tower, W1

HUNGARIAN

Gay Hussar, W1
Old Budapest, W1

INDIAN

Al Khayam, W2
Anarkali, W6
Aziz, W6
Bayleaf Tandoori, N6
Bengal Lancer, NW5
Bombay Brasserie, SW7
Dewaniam, SE23
Ealing Tandoori, W5
Fleet Tandoori, NW3
Ganpath, WC1
India Palace, E12
Lal Bhag, NW6
Lal Qila, W1
Last Days of the Raj, WC2
Light of Kashmir, NW3
Maharajah, W2
Malabar, W8
New Bengal, W2
Ragam, W1
Rajput, W12
Red Fort, W1
Shapla, SW9
Shireen Tandoori, W12

INDONESIAN-MALAY

Desaru, W1
Equatorial, W1
Melati, W1

ITALIAN

L'Amico, SW1
Beccofino, SW3
Il Cavaliere, NW11
Colombina, SW1
Knoodles, W2
Luigi's, SE19
Montpeliano, SW7
Il Passetto, WC2
Ponte Nuovo, SW3
La Preferita, SW11
San Frediano, SW3
San Lorenzo, SW3
Santini, SW1
69 Westow Hill, SE19
South Kensington Pasta Bar, SW3
Viareggio, NW6

JAPANESE

Defune, W1
Fuji, W1
Ginnan, EC4
Gonbei, WC1
Hana Guruma, EC4
Ikkyu, W1
Kitchen Yakitori, W1
Koto, NW1
Masako, W1
Nanten Yakitori Bar, W1
One Two Three, W1
Saga, W1
Wakaba, NW3
Yamato, NW4

JEWISH

Bloom's, E1
Grahame's Seafare, W1
Nosherie, EC1
Zaki's, NW11

KOREAN

Arirang, W1
La Coree, WC2
Han Kuk Hoe Kwan, W1
Korea House, W1
Mi Mi, W1
Seoul, EC3

MIDDLE EAST (Gulf)

Al Diwan, W2

MIDDLE EAST (Lebanese)

Al Hamra, W1
Maroush, W2
Maroush II, SW2
Phoenicia, W8

POLISH

Brewer Street Buttery, W1
Daquise, SW7

PORTUGUESE

Ports, SW3

SCANDINAVIAN

Anna's Place, N1

SPANISH

Don Pepe, NW8
Rebato's, SW8

THAI

Bahn Thai, W8
Chiang Mai, W1
Oh Boy, SW17

TURKISH

Chaglayan Kebab House, NW4
Efes Kebab House, W1
Hodja Nasreddin, N1
Topkapi, W1

VEGETARIAN

Cherry Orchard, E2
Country Life, W1
Dining Room, SE1
Food for Thought, WC2
Govinda's, W1
Green Cottage II, NW3
Mandeer, W1
Sabras, NW10
Sree Krishna, SW17
Woodlands, W1

VIETNAMESE

Saigon, W1

London restaurants open on Sunday

The following restaurants are open for both lunch and dinner on Sundays.

Afric-Carib, N4
Al Diwan, W2
Al Hamra, W1
Al Khayam, W2
Anarkali, W6
Au Bois St Jean, NW8
L'Aventure, NW8
Bayleaf Tandoori, N6
Bengal Lancer, NW5
Le Bistroquet, NW1
Blakes Hotel, SW7
Bloom's, E1
Bombay Brasserie, SW7
Brasserie St Quentin, SW3
British Harvest (Hilton Hotel), W1
Bunny's, NW3
Café Pelican, WC2
Capital Hotel, SW3
Le Caprice, SW1
Il Cavaliere, NW11
Champagne Exchange, W1
Chanterelle, SW7
Chez Gerard, W1 (Charlotte Street)
Chiang Mai, W1
Chuen Cheng Ku, W1
Connaught Hotel, W1
Cork & Bottle, WC2
La Croisette, SW10
Daquise, SW7
Desaru, W1
Dewaniam, SE23
Diamond, WC2
Don Pepe, NW8
Dorchester (Grill Room), W1
Dragon Gate, W1
Ealing Tandoori, W5
Ebury Wine Bar, SW1
Equatorial, W1
Fleet Tandoori, NW3
Fung Shing, WC2
Golden Chopsticks, SW7
Good Friends, E14
Green Cottage II, NW3
Hard Rock Café, W1
Hee's, NW7
R.S. Hispaniola, WC2
Hodja Nasreddin Kebab House, N1
Ho-Ho, E18
Hoults, SW17
Hung Toa, W2
India Palace, E12
Joy King Lau, WC2
Kettners, W1
Korea House, W1
Lal Bhag, NW6
Lal Quila, W1
Lantern, NW6
Light of Kashmir, NW3
Maharajah, W2
Malabar, W8
Maroush, W2
Maxim Wine Bar, W7
Melati, W1
Mr Fish, SW15
Mr Kong, WC2
Mr Tang, W1

New Bengal, W2
New Friends, E14
New World, W1
Ormes, SW4
Phoenicia, W8
Pollyanna's, SW11
Ponte Nuovo, SW3
La Preferita, SW11
Ragam, W1
Rajput, W12
Red Fort, W1
Sabras, NW10
Santini, SW1
Shapla, SW9
Shireen Tandoori, W12
Le Soufflé (Inter-Continental Hotel), W1
South Kensington Pasta Bar, SW3
Sree Krishna, SW17
Le Suquet, SW3
Topkapi, W1
Treasure of China, SE10
Waltons, SW3
Wine Gallery, SW10
Wong Kei, W1
Woodlands, W1
Yamato, NW4
Yung's, W1
Zaki's, NW11
Zen, SW3

The following restaurants are open for Sunday lunch only.

L'Auberge, SE22
Chalcot's, NW1
Crowthers, SW14
Jack's Place, SW11
Le Metro Wine Bar, SW3
Monkeys, SW3
Mr Lu, SW14
One Hampstead Lane, N6
192, W11
Le Papillon, SE10
Quincy's '84, NW2
Read's, SW5
Rudland & Stubbs, EC1
69 Westow Hill, SE19

The following restaurants are open for Sunday dinner only.

Ark, W8
Ark, W8
Bambaya, N8
Beau-Rivage, NW6
Best of Both Worlds (Britannia Hotel), W1
Christian's, W4
Fuji, W1
Ikkyu, W1
Last Days of the Raj, WC2
Malean Chinese, SW16
Maxim, W13
Mr Liu, SE22
Olive Branch, NW6
One Two Three, W1
Le Petit Prince, NW5
Semiramis, W2
Tiger Lee, SW5
Viareggio, NW6
Wakaba, NW3

London restaurants open after midnight

These restaurants all take last orders after midnight. Check the entry for details.

Beau-Rivage, NW6
Bengal Lancer, NW5 (Fri & Sat only)
Café Pelican, WC2
Diamond, WC2
Don Pepe, NW8
L'Estanquet, SW5
Hard Rock Café, W1
R.S Hispaniola, WC2
Hodja Nasreddin, N1 (Fri & Sat only)
India Palace, E12
Langan's Brasserie, W1 (Sat only)
Maroush, W2
Maroush II, SW3
Maxim, W13 (Fri & Sat only)
Mr Kong, WC2
Yung's, W1

The Good Food Club 1985

Many thanks to all the following people who contributed, in one way and another, rather more than usual to this year's *Guide* . . .

Mr & Mrs N.T.Abbott
Richard Abington
Dr Sidney Abrahams
Mr R.W.Ackernley
Dr David Adams
Mr Richard Adams
C.G.Adamson
Mrs A.F.Adamson
Frank & Mary Adcock
Ian Adley
William Aherne
Mrs Joan Aikman
Dr J.B.Ainscough
Mr John R.Aird
Mrs C.Alcock
C.E.Aldam
Mrs E.Alder
Mr Alan Alexander
Mr M.Alge
Dr E.J.Allaway
Ms Christine Allen
Mr John Allen
Mr & Mrs S.Alley
Mr C.Allfree-Reid
Mr D.Allsopp
Mr & Mrs M.J.Almond
D.J.Alsford
Mr Henry Altszuler
Mr Tony Alyen
G.D.Amos
Dr M.Anand
C. & D.Anderson
J.H.Anderson
Mr C.F.Anderson
Mr N.H.Andrew
Mrs Anne Andrews
Dr Peter Andrews
Mrs Angel
Mr D.A.Angless
Mr David W.T.Angwin
Mr John Anness
Mr F.H. & Mrs J.M.Annett
Mr M.Appleby
Mr D.Appleton
Mr F.J.Apps
Mr & Mrs D.Archer
C.Arkwright
Revd M.Armitage
Mrs D.Arthur
C.E.Arthur
Mrs S.E.Ash-Edwards
Mrs H.G.Ashburn
Mr & Mrs P.Ashley
Mrs G.Ashley
Mr Andrew Ashwin
Dr A.Ashworth
A.E.Asker
Mr H.D.Astley
Dr P.Aston
Mr G.B.Atkinson
Mr P.N.Atterby
Mr Martin Attewell
Mr Alan Attwood
Mr G.Avery
Julian Aviss
Dr M.A.Awty
Dr A.T.R.Axon
Mr R. K. Baardwaj
Mrs A. H. Bachner
Cynthia Bacon
D.I.Baddeley
Mrs S.E.Badman
W.Bailey
Mr Steven Bailey
Ian C.Baillie
Mr A.J.V.Baker
Gerard Baker
Paul & Margaret Baker
Mr P.J.Baker
R.W.Baker
Mr R.J.Baker
A.J.Baker
Mrs Peggy Balaam
Mr R.Baldock
Mrs J.Ball
Bruce Ballard
Mr D.C.Ballard
Mrs J.Bamforth
D.B.Bancroft
Miss Sara Bancroft
Mrs E.M. Banham
Mr John Banks
Mr J.Banks
P.Bann
Ms Diana Bannister
Mr P.C.Barber
Mr R.Barber
Mr E.E.Barber
Dr M.C.Barchard
D.W.Barker
Mr J.E.Barker
Ms Celia Barlow
Paul Barnard
Ms Pamela Barnes
Mr A.M.Barnes
Mrs R.Barnets
Alan & Jean Barnett
Ms Erica Barnett
Peter Barnsley
Mr Nigel Barnsley
Mr P.Barraclough
Mr Douglas J.Barrington
R.Barrington Brock
Mrs B.J.Barry
Miss E.M.Barsham
C.R.Bartholomew
Mr Leslie J.Bartholomew
Mr G.E.Bartlett
Mr B.E.Barton
J. R. Bate
P.R.G.Bates
Mrs Jean Bates
Mr Ted Bather
John R.Batty
M.Bavage
Helen & Michael Baws
K.Baxter
L.D.Beamish
Mr Paul Beard
Mr L.F.Beattie
Mr Ian Beattie
Mr P.J.Beck
E.B.Beck
R. L. Beckh
Lindsay Beckman
Mr Simon J.Beckwith
Mr & Mrs Bedeman
Mr & Mrs W.E.Bedford
M.J.Beese
Ms Sally Bell
Ms Elizabeth Bell
Mrs A. Bellerby
Nick Bellis
Mr S.U.Belsey
L.Benavides
A.J.Benbow
Mr Haydn Bendall
Mr R.Bendon
M.J.Benenson
Rosemary Beney
Mr G.G.Bennett
Mrs Barbara Bennett
W.Bennett
Mrs Bennett
Mr Clive Bennett
Ms Gillian Bennett
Mrs L.S.Bennett
R.S.Bennett
Paul Benson
Mrs Marjorie Bentham
Dr Brian Bentley
Mr R.G.Bentley

Mr William Bentsen
Professor M.W.Beresford
J. & C.Beresford
W.Bergman
Mr & Mrs H.I. Berkeley
Mr Robin L.Berkson
Mr J.H.Bermon
Derek Bernard
Mr John Bernstein
Michelle Berriedale-Johnson
Mr P.G.Berry
Mrs Valerie Berry
Mrs Anne Bevan
Mr A.K.Beverton
Homi K.Bhabha
Mr & Mrs Bianco
Mr E.Bickerstaff
Alan P. Bigg
Dr & Mrs J. Biggs
Mr Peter Biles
Ms Rosemary Billam
Martin Billingsley
Miss J.Bingham
Ms Ann Binnie
Mr R.G.Birch
Mrs M.Birch
Mr Charles L.Birch
Mr M.Bird
R.N.Bird
Ms J.Bird
Mr Michael Birt
Mrs T.J.H.Bishop
A.C.Bishop
Mrs V.Bishop
Ms Julie Bishop
Mr S.V.Bishop
Mr H.W.Bitton
Donald Black
Victor & Avril Blackburn
Ms Jane E. Blackledge
Ms L.Blackwell
Mr E.Blades
Mrs H.Blair
Mr J.Blair
Mr Timothy Blake
Diana Blake
Miss C.A.Blackeney
Mrs Audrey Blakey
Mr Lionel M. Blanche
Muriel Blandford
Mr J.Bloom
Mrs M.V.Blyth
K.W.Bogle
Ms Elizabeth Boisseau
Mr Bolter
Ms Iris J.Bolton
Mr C.T.Bolton
Mr B.A.W.Bond
Dr Jane V.Bond
Mr L.Bonner
E.Bonner-Maurice
Mr & Mrs Booker
R.D. & H.Booker
Mr Paul Booker
Mr & Mrs Boothman
Dr P.Booton
Mr A.Bordeau
Mr & Mrs E. Borgonzolo
G.Boris
Mrs Kathleen M. Borland
Mr & Mrs D.A.C. Borrett
Dr A.Borthwick-Clarke
T.Bostwick
Mr E.M.Boswell
Mr & Mrs Bottomley
Mr John J.Boulter
Ms Sue Boulton
Tim Bouquet
Revd M.A. Bourdeaux
Dr H.Bourne
Robin & Mary Bourne
Ms Anne Boustred
Miss June Bowden
Paul Bowden
Mr Richard Bowden
Mrs E.C.Bowden
Mr Anthony S. Bowell
Mr A.J.Bowen
Dr S.Bower
H.L.Bower
Mr D.Bowles
Mrs Margaret Box
Mr N.H.C.Boxer
Mr G.Boyer
Dave Brabants
Keith & Glenys Bradbury
Earl of Bradford
Mr W.O.Bradley
Robert Bradshaw
Aileen Brady
Mr W.Brady
Joan Brady
Mr Peter Brady
Mrs D.Bragg
K.S.Bragman
Dr A.Bratt
Dr A.M.Braverman
N.P.Bray
Mrs B.J.Brayshaw
Mr F.E.Braziel
Mrs J.E.Brazier
W.T.Brennan
Mr D.H.Brett
Ms Frances Brew
Dr T.B.Brewin
Mr & Mrs J.R.Bridge
Mrs J.Bridges-Adams
Mr Alan Brien
N.N.Brien
J.B.Brierley
Mr T.G.Brierly
Major & Mrs C.F. Briggs
Ms Susanne Bright
Miss L.A.Brimble
Mr K.H.Brining
Miss M.C.Brinton
Mr B.Brittain
Mr Richard Britton
Mr R.Britton
Mr M.Broady
Mr A.A.Brodie
William Brodsky
David Brokensha
Roy Y.Bromell
Mr C.E.Bromilow
Dr Brooke
Ms Susan Brooke Jackson
Mary Brookes
Ms Joan Brookman
Mr M.W.L.Brooks
Mr M.P.Brooks
Mr Oliver Brooks
Mr Paul Brooks
Douglas Brooks
K.B.Brotchie
Mrs J.C.Broughton
Alaisdair & Moira Brown
Audrey & Chris Brown
Mr Ceridwen Brown
Bob & Alison Brown
R.M.Brown
Mr R.Brown
Mrs Diane Brown
Mr D.Brown
R.L.Brown
Ms S.Brown
G. F. Brown OBE
Mr Alan Brown
Mrs E.Brown
Mr Lawrence Brown
Mrs R.Brown
Mr R.M.Brown
Mrs Lorraine Browne
Mr W.G.Browning
L.P.R.Browning
Barbara Brownjohn
Mr David Brownlee
Miss M.M.Bruce
N.D.Bruce
Mr Bruce Ballard
Robert Bruh
Mr J.R.Brumpton
Mr M.P.M.Brunwin
Mr Oscar V.Bryan
Mr Ian Bryant
Mr John Bryant
Mr Roberto Buccafusca
Robert Buchanan-Michaelson
Hadley & Heather Buck
Mrs Patricia Buckeridge
Mrs Anne Bucket
N.Buckley
Mrs Caroline Buckley
Ms Julia Budd
K.A.Bulgin
Mrs Ruth R.Bullock
Philip Bullus
Roger Bunner
Mr D.J.Bunter
Professor P.R.J. Burch
Mr M.L.Burch
Mrs J.Burford
Mrs Anne Margaret Burke
Mrs M.Burman
Mrs B.Burns
Mr D.C.Burrows
C.M.Burton
Mr J.Bushell
Peter Bushell
Mr R.Butcher
Mr R.P.Butland
The Rt Revd R.C.Butler
Mr G.Butler
Mr C.Butterfield
Mr J.M.Butterfield
B.L.Butterworth
D.G.Buxton
Noel Buxton
Mr Peter Byes
Mr Robert Byng
Kevin Byrne
Paul E.Byrne
Mr T. Byrne
C.H.Byron
Miss Gill Caddox
S.P.Cadwallader
Prof. Robert Cahn
Canon Douglas Caiger

Rob and Vivien Caird
Mr Robert Caldicott
Mr J.S.Caley
M.G.Callan
Mr Paul Callick
Marianne Calmann
Keith Calnan
Mr J.Calnpen
Mr M.J.Calvert
Lady Campbell of Alloway
Mrs Alison J.Campbell
Mr J.R.D.Campbell
Mrs Campbell
Caroline Campbell
Ms Thyra Campbell
Ms Carol M.Campbell
Mr & Mrs H.Campbell
Mr R.A.Campbell-Gibson
G.W.Canham
Mr & Mrs A.P.Cant
Mr Peter F.Carey
Mr G.M. Carmichael
P.Carpenter
Mrs Betty Carr
Mr M.D.Carr
Mr E.J.Carruthers Smith
Mr R.G.Carson
Mrs Susan Carson
Mr Liam Carson
Mrs J.F.Carter
Mr P.E.Carter
Mr N.Carter
Mr J.A.H. Cartwright
Ms Judith Cartwright
Mr Derek Carver
Mr H.J.Case
Mr V.Casel
John B.Cass
Mrs Barbara K.Cassels
Thomas and Irene Cassidy
Mrs S.Casson
J.J.Catchpole Jnr
Mr Walter Cattermole
Mr F.H.Chaffer
Mr Richard Chagford-Stoneman
Mr H.J.Challenger
Louise Challis
Mr William Chalmers
Ms Veronica Chamberlain
Ms Linda Chamberlain
Mrs B.Chamberlain
Andrew M.Chambers
Khee Chan
Dr L.Chan
Mr Philip C.Chandler
Mr John Chandos
Mrs F.Chaplin
Clare Chapman
Mr C.H.G.Chapman
Mrs Clare Chapman
Mr R.E.Chapple
Mr James F.D.Charles
Mr Alan Charlesworth
Ms Maureen Charlton
Mr A.Chasan
E.M.Chatten
Canon P.C.Chawker
Mr C.Chen
Miss Joan Chenhalls MBE
Mr L.V.R.Chiappini
Mr Steven Chichlin
Mrs F.Chinellato
Dr S.Chinnapha
Mr C.M.Chisnall
Mr M.Y.Chowdrey
Ms Karen Christensen
Mr R.D.Christie
Mr N.K.Christie
Mrs S.Christopher
Peter S.Y.Chu
A.V.Chute
Ms Janet Ciana
Mr Norman Civval
Ms Jane Clack
Mr S.A.Clancy
J.A. & L.Clare
Dr David H.Clark
D.J. & S.A.Clark
Pamela Clark
Mrs P.M.Clark
Ms Elizabeth Clark
Mr S.R.Clark
Mr M.D.Clark
E.R.Clark
Major J.J.Clarke
D.A. & P.F.Clarke
Mrs P.Clarke
Mrs Yvette Anne Clarke
Mrs Clarke
Derek & Pauline Clarke
Mrs M.Clarke
A.C.Clarke
Mr David Clarke
Ms Barbara Clauson
Mr S.J.Clayman
Mr R.John Clayton
Mr Alan M.Clegg
T.A.Clegg
Dr M.H.Clement
Miss M.A.Clennett
Mr Kenneth Cleveland
Mrs E.Clifton-Brown
J.N.Clogstoun-Willmott
Mr Philip A.Clough
Mr Brian Clowes
Mr L.A.Clowry
E.Clyne
Ms S.P.Coates
Ms Lucy Coats
Mr Ian A.C.Cobbold
Mr E.H.M. Cochrane
Ms I.M.Cocking
Ms Maddy Cockram
Mr I.Codrington
Mr Michael Codron
Dr & Mrs Coe
Richard Coe
Mrs Roberta Coffer
Colin Cohen
G.J. & M.E.Cohen
Mr Donald D.Cohen
H.A.Cohen
Professor V.Cohen
Mrs S.Cohen
Mr Alan Cohen
M.Cohen
Lauren Cohn
Steven F.Cohn
Mr C.H.Cole
P.M.Colebrook
B.Colegrave
Mr & Mrs G.Coleman
The Rt Revd Peter Coleman
Mrs Lisa Coleridge
Ms Joanna Coles
Mr C.Colley
Mrs M.C.Collie
Derrick Collier
Mrs J.Collins
Mr Robert Collins
Mr Paul Collins
W.A.Collins
Mr Duncan Collins
Rodney Collins
A.R.Collinson
J.E.Collinson
Professor M.Coltheart
Ms Cressida Connolly
Desmond Connolly
Ms V.M.Conrad
Mrs D.Cook
Mr T.G.R.Cook
Mrs J.Cook
Mr & Mrs G.G.Cook
J.P.F.Cooke
L.Cooklin
Mrs J.Cookson
Mr & Mrs Coomber
Mr Paul G.Cooney
Ms Elspeth Cooper
Mr Paul Cooper
Ms Catherine Cooper
Dr Christine Cooper OBE
Mr David Cooper
M.Cope
Ms Anne Copp
J.H.Copping
Mr R.C.Corbett
Ms Susan Corby
Mr & Mrs K.Cordell
Mrs Carl F.Cori
Mr B.C.Cornelius
A.D.Corner
Dr C.D.Cossar
Ms Helen Coster
Ms Jill Cotgrove
A.L.Cotterell MBE
Mr Michael Coulthurst
Stephen E.Coupe
Lady Couper
B.H.Cousins
Mrs S.Cousins
Mrs F.Couzens
W.H.Covington
Mr T.S.Cowan
Mr A.Cowan
H.L.Cowdy
Mr Ian Cowen
Mrs R.S.Cowie
Mr T.A.Cox
Mr Andrew Cox
Mr & Mrs M.Cox
Tony Cox
Mr Brian Cox
Peter Cox
R.M.Cox
Mrs A.M.Craig
Mr & Mrs S.R.T.Craig
Mr Craig

R.D.Cramond
Mr & Mrs G.Crane
Peter Crane
Ron Crank
Mr Philip Cranmer
Esler Crawford
Mrs S.Crawford
Mrs Beryl Crawford
Mr A.S.Crawley
James Creagh
Mrs R.M.Crichton
Mr Quintin T.Crichton
Lady Helen Crichton-Stuart
Mr J.G.Cridlan
Ms Anthea Cridlan
A.B.Crilly
Julian Critchley
G.S.Crockett
Mr & Mrs Croft
Mrs J.Crompton
Mr Robert J.Crosby
Mr P.R.Crosland
Dr W.G.Cross
Mr J.Cross
Mary Cross
W.Crossland
G.Crossley
Mrs W.W. Crosthwaite
Dr & Mrs A.L.Crowther
Mr J.D.Crowther
Mr John Cruickshank
Mrs Ruth Crusham
Mrs Cubitt
Dr John Cule
Elizabeth Cullen
Mr A.C.Cullum
Robert Cumberford
Miss Rosemary Cumming
Frank Cummins
Dr A.C.Cunliffe
Mrs Jean Cunningham
Mrs C.M.Currie
Mr & Mrs Curtis
Sir John Curtis
Mr W.R.Curtis
Mr J.A.Cushman
Mr Mike Cushman
Mrs R.B.Custerson
Mr H.Cusworth
Mr A.Cutler
J.E.Cuvall
Mr J.P.d'Ambra
Caroline d'Cruz
Mr John D'Oliveira
Mrs M.A.Dachtler
Mrs Robert Daigneault
Lady Gloria Dale
Mrs P.M.Dalton
Mr J.L.Danciger
Mr V.J.Daniel
Sarah Danny
Ms Hazel Darbyshire
Mrs R.D.Darwin
Mr & Mrs R.Dathan
Wg Cdr K.Dauncey
Ms Helen V.Davenport
R.S.Davenport
Mr Paul Davenport-Brown
Mrs Heather Daves
Dr T.J.David
Mrs J.Davidson
Mrs Caroline Davidson
Ron & Jan Davidson
M.Davies
Mr I.Davies
P.J.Davies
Mrs L.P.Davies
Mr E.M.Davies
Mr Humphrey Davies
C.V.Davies
Frances Davies
Mrs Margaret Davies
Mr L.G.Davies
Mr O.M.Davies
Mrs J.Davies
Dr R.J. & Mrs K.B.Davies
Mr P.I.Davies
Ms G.Davies
Sydney Davis
H.L.Davis
R.A.Davis
Brian L.Davis
Mr M.Davis
Dr William Davison
Mr D.J.Davison
Mr Philip S.Davison
Dr & Mrs R.P.R.Dawber
Margaretta Dawson
Mr H.G.Dawson
Mr J.Dawson
Ms J.Dawson
Mr & Mrs K.Dawson
Mr R.Dawson-Smith
Mr John Day
Ms Tamasin Day-Lewis
Dr Paul de Berker
Mr G. De Luca
I.B.P.De Minvielle-Devaux
Mrs S.de Mont
S.H.de Wild
Michael De-la-Noy
Mr A.G.B.Deacon
Roger H.Deal
Dr G.De Lisle Dear
Deborah Price
Mr N.C.Dee
Conrad Dehn
David Delany
Dr A.J.Dell
Dr A.R.Delmar
Mr W.Delong
Mrs Susan Demont
Mr & Mrs M.Dempsey
Mr A.Denney
Mr P.Denning
F.Dentico
John F.Derbyshire
Muriel Derry
Mrs A.Desmond
Mr J.Devane
Louise K.Devaney
I.C.Dewey
Mr Charles Dewhurst
Dr P.B.Dias
Mr & Mrs O.Dickinson
Mrs R.P.Dickinson
G.C.Dickson
Mr M.T.R.Digwell
Mr John Dillingham
M.Djokic
Mrs M.R.Dobbins
A.Docherty
Mr S.W.Dodd
M.L.Dodd
Mr Simon Dodds
Mrs R.Dodwell
A.J.Donaldson
Mrs M.Donot
Michael S.G.Dougall
Mr & Mrs Geoffrey Dove
Mrs J. Downes
Catherine Downing
Mr Charles Doxat
Mr Alan Draper
Mr P.E.Dresel
Mr Garth Drinkwater
Mr Jeff Driver
Mrs N.J.Drucquer
Mr Mervyn Druian
Mr & Mrs R.Drumheller
Mr D.Drummond
Capt S.H.Drummond
Mr E.M.Duckworth
Sqdn Ldr & Mrs M.G.Dudgeon
Mr A.A.Dudman
Mrs Jane A.Duffin
Mr Terence Duffy
Mr C.Duggan
M.Duhy
Miss E.M.Duke
M.Duky
N.B.Duncan
The Revd James Duncan
Mrs G.Dundas
Ms Leslie Dunn
David & Eileen Dunn
Mr A.Dunn
Mr Michael H.Dunn
Mr A.Dunn
Mr J.Dunne
Mr W.T.Dunne
Mr Francis Durham
Dr A.M.Duthie
Pembroke Duttson
Anthony Dux
Mr F.Dvorak
Mrs S.A.Dyer
J.J.Dynes
R.S.Eades
Mr Peter Earl
Jim Earle
Mr J.Earney
Mr & Mrs B.O.Earp
Louise Eastwood
Peter Eaton
Nicole Eddison
Mr Mark Edelson
Dr S.Eden
Mrs S.Edmonds
The Hon Mrs A.Edmondson
Bishop of Edmonton
M.B. & R.J.Edwards
Ms Elizabeth Edwards
Mr K.Edwards
Rosemary Joan Edwards
Mr J.B.R.Edwards
Mr E.Eisenhandler
Lt Col & Mrs R.A.Ekert
Myra & Ray Elderfield
Neville D.Eldridge
Mr R.S.Elegant
Mr D.Eliot
Mrs P.Ellerman

Mr Jack K.Elliot, Exec. V.P.
Mr A.M.Elliot
Tom Elliot
Ms Karen Elliott
L.C.Elliott
Mr Ian Elliott
Lady Joan Elliott
D.R.Ellis
Mr & Mrs John Ellis
Mrs M.Ellis
Prof Lewis Elton
Mr John Elvidge
J.V.Elvin
T.Elwell
Mr J.W.Elwin
Lord Elyston Morgan
Michael & Anita Emmott
Professor H.E.Emson
Dr & Mrs T.H.English
Patrick Ensor
Professor M.A.Epstein CBE FRS
Mrs Kathryn Erickson
Mr R.Erskine
Mr H.Escott
Mr R.A.Escoffey
Mr P.Evans
P.G.Evans
Susan Evans
Mrs Jean Evans
Miss Y.M.Evans
R.G.Evans
Mr D.E.Evans
Mr A.E.Evans
J.S.Evans
Mr & Mrs M.Everett
D.J.Eynon
Mrs Sybil Eysenck
Mr Christopher J.Fahey
Mrs Veronica Fair
Mr J.Fairley
Mr Quentin Falk
Mr Falkender
Mrs J.R.Farmer
Mr D.M.Farquhar
Edward Farquhar
Mr R.A.Farrand
Mr Farrer Brown
R.W.Farrington
Mr R.H.Farrington
Mrs A.M.Fasson
Mr David Faulkner
Mr & Mrs Faust
Miss E.Fawcett
Mr D.J.Fawthrop
Mr D.A.Fearney
Dr Eleanor J.Feldman
Mrs K.Felix
F.Feller
Ms K.Ferguson
Julia Ferguson
Mrs J.Ferrett
Mr & Mrs K.G.Ferris
Mr H.Fessler
Mr J.B.Fidler
Alan Field
Mr H.W.Field
Ms Gretta Finer
Dr N.B.Finter
Mr Richard M.Firth
Mr Alan Firth
Mr P.J.Fischer
Mr R.P.Fisher
H.J.Fisher
K.S.Fischer
Dr M.J.Fisher
Mrs H.Fisher
Mr J.M.Fisher
Mr Paul Fishpool
Mr Fish PR
E.Fitchett
S.Fitzgerald
Dr H.B.Fiwzer & T.Eswell
J.Flatau
G.E.Fletcher
Dr J.Fletcher
Ron Fletcher
P.D.J.Fletcher
Mrs Susan Fletcher
Mr & Mrs J.Fletcher
D.C.Flint
Geoff & Brenda Float
Nigel Foley
T.P.Folwell
Mr D.G.Foot
Mr J.Forbes
J.G.Ford
Nick Forde
Mr Christopher Forman
Mr A.Forrest
Mrs Mary Foster
Mrs B.Foster
A.Fotheringham
J.Foulston
Mr Terence Fowler
Mr Paul J.Frain
Dr A.Frank
Mr W.Frankland
M.J.Franklin
Mr Eric Fraser
Mrs J.P.Fraser
Mr P.N.Freel
Mr R.G.Freeman
Mr Brian R.Freeman
R.Freeman
Ms Jane A.N.Freeman
Mr S.E.Freere
Dr Malcolm Freeth
Robert Freidus
Mr Brian French
Mr David Frentzel
Mr D.G.J.Frewin
Mr K.J.Friar
Mr Jack Friedman
Mrs D.Frith
Mr Bob Fromer
Mr T.D.Frost
Mr G.Froyd
Ms Eva Frumin
Mr C.Fry
Dr R.Fry
Dr E.H.K.Fui
Mr H.Fulton
Mr Stephen Gaastra
Mr I.A.Gabb
Mr D.G.Galloway
Mr & Mrs P.Galt
Revd Peter Gamble
Mr & Mrs Patrick Gammell
Mr & Mrs Peter Gammie
Gp Capt T.Garden
Ms Fiona Gardiner
R.J. & C.Gardiner
Mr S.Garman
Mr Robert C.Garner
R.G.Carson
Mr J.L.Gaskell
Mrs S.J.Gassaway
Mrs M.Gates
Dr R.A.P.Gaubert
Graham Gauld
Dr Ian Gavin
Mr P.R.Gawn
Mr S.Gee
R.M.Gelber
Mr P.Gallatley
Nancy & Herb Geller
Mr & Mrs G.N.Georgano
Mr Peter George
Mr L.Gerber
Ms Christine Gerezdi
Mr Rueben Gerling
Mr A.Ghiara
Mr Austin Gibbons
Alan C.C.Gibbs
Mr B.Gibson
Mrs S.C.Gibson
Mr & Mrs J.W.Gibson
Derek Gifford
Mr W.Gilbertson
Ms Mary Giles
Mr M.W.K.Gill
John Gillett
Mrs Sarah S.Gillings
Peter Gillman
Mrs I.D.Gilmour
Richard Gilpin
Mr L.Ginger
D.Gladwell
C.T.Glass
N.Glasser
Professor Duncan Glen
Mr S.W.Glenister
James P.M.Glinchey
Mrs Joy Glover
Mr H.Glover C.B.
Mrs J.Godfrey
J.G.Goldby
Mr John A.J.Golding
Sheila Goldstone
M.P.Goldwater
Mr R.Gollin
Tom Gondris
Mr David Goodbrand
Mr M.Goode
Suzanne Goodhew
Mr D.Goodridge
Mr James M.Goodsman
Mrs P.Goodson
Mrs K.Goodwin
Mr Godfrey Goolden
E.Gordon
Paul Gordon-Saker
Lt J.Gore
Sir Donald Gosling
Mary F.Gough
P.Gould
Mr J.Gourley
Mr P.L.Gower
B.Ramayansingh Gowreesunker
Brian & Catherine Gowthorpe
Ms Anne Goady
Mr J.M.Graham
Capt J.B.Graham
Mr George Graham
Mr J.Graham
Mrs B.Graham
Mrs J.M.Graham
H.Graham Cave
Mr Maurice Gran
Miss Isabella Granger
Miss J.Valerie Grant
Mr Richard Grant-Rennick

Mr E. Grantham
Mr A. G. Grau
Brigadier T. I. G. Gray
Mr Ronald Gray
D. W. Gray
Mrs Patricia Gray
Mr Alan Gray
Rebecca Gray
Mr C. Gray
Colin Gray
H. C. Greaves
S. Green
Mrs M. Green
Mr R. Green
Mrs Hazel Green
Ken Green
D. K. Green
Mrs Green
P. H. Green & J. Thompson
Mr A. Greenwood
J. Greenwood
Mr & Mrs K. Greenwood
A. H. Gregory
Sqn Ldr A. J. Gregory
Mr M. A. Gregory
Mrs Marjorie Gregory
Mrs S. Grenfell
Colin Grey
A. K. Grice
I. S. Grier
Mr & Mrs B. Grieve
Mr John Griffith
Mrs M. Griffiths
Mr William Griffiths
Dr M. J. Griffiths
Mr S. Griffiths
P. Grimsdale
Mr N. M. Grimwood
Mrs Shirley Grimwood
Mr Don Grisbrook
Mrs Rita Gromb
E. & E. Grossi
Mr Alan Grounds
Lieut K. R. Groves
Mr V. Guereca
Mrs D. M. Guest
Mrs S. A. Gugen
Mrs E. Guiness
Kim Gumbley
Mrs V. Gundry
Mr A. Gunn
Mr & Mrs Gunton
C. A. Gurney
Mr H. Gutfreund
Ian Guthrie
P. J. Guy
Mrs G. Hadden
Sir Douglas Haddow
Mrs A. G. T. Hadley
R. J. Haerdi
Mr Guy Halahan
Mr J. D. Hale
Richard Hales
Mrs W. T. Halford
Mr J. P. Hall
Mr & Mrs D. G. Hall
Mr J. M. Hall
I. Hall
W. J. Hallett
Mrs Hilary Halpin
Mr Michael Hambi
Mr M. V. Hambling
Mr W. B. Hamilton
Mrs P. Hamlyn
Dr Richard Hamm
Mr J. Hammerton
Mr Geoffrey Hammond
Mrs A. Hancock
C. J. Hancock
J. R. Hancock
E. J. Hand
Mr G. Handley
Mr Eugene T. Handley
Mr Walter Hanlon
Mr Tony Hanmer
Mrs Dorothy Hannan
Dr & Mrs P. W. Hannay
The Revd R. F. Hannay
J. C. G. Hannigan
G. H. Hanson
Ellen Haragan
Mrs Carol Hardinge
Michael & Mollie Hardwick
A. Harel
Mr W. E. Harknett
Mr Trevor Harley
M. Harling
Ms Sheila Harper
M. J. Harper
Mrs B. A. Harra
Mr R. W. Harries
Mrs Joan Harris
Mr Raymond Harris
Lewis Harris
L. M. Harris
Mr B. Harris
Mr P. G. Harris
Mrs J. Harris
R. J. & D. Harris
Malcolm Harris
Ms K. Harris & Mr B. Derrick
Mr B. Harrison
Valerie & Colin Harrison
P. R. Harrison
Z. Harrison
M. J. Harrison
J. G. Harrison
F. Harrison
Professor & Mrs Harrison
D. Harrop
Mr Iain Harrow
A. C. W. Hart
Mr Mark Hart
Mr K. J. Hart
A. C. W. Hart
M. B. & V. A. Hart
Mr & Mrs T. Hart
Mr J. D. Hartley
Mr P. Hartley
G. J. Hartley
J. & A. Hartley
Mr Norman W. Hartman
Mr D. Hartog
Mr & Mrs A. Harvey
Mr J. K. Hassell
P. Hasswell
C. H. Hastie
Mr Rochard Hatcher
L. M. Hatchwell
Canon P. C. Hawker
Mr Maurice Hawker
Mr N. T. Hawson
N. Hay
Mr S. M. Hay
Mr John Hayes
Mrs S. Hayes
Mr S. Hayes
Mr O. Hayward
Mr Nicholas Hayward
Ms Caroline Hayward
Mr C. Haywood
Mr M. Hazell
S. B. Hazzard
A. C. Head
David Head
Mrs A. V. Heap
Roger Heathcote
O. S. Heavens
Mrs J. Heavey
T. P. Heavisides
Mrs R. V. Hebdon
Mr & Mrs Heber-Percy
Capt P. A. Heckingbottom
Mr J. A. Hedges
Piers Hedley
Mr D. Hedworth
Miss A. Hegarty
Mrs H. Heideman
Mr H. Heimer
Karen Helliwell
Mrs P. A. Heminway
Mrs J. Hemmingway
John R. Henderson
Fiona Henderson
Mr Colin Henderson
Ms F. Hendley
Dr George Hendry
Liz Hendry
Mr C. Q. Henriques
Ms Charlotte Henry
Dr M. Henry
Mr H. E. Henry
R. A. Hepher
Mr Jacques R. Herbert
R. Herd
Mr M. J. Herrick
Mrs Avril Herriot
Ms Victoria Herriott
Mr W. M. Herten
Mr C. R. Heseltine
Mrs V. Heseltine
Mr John Heskell
Miss A. Hessayon
Mr & Mrs C. Hewitt
Mrs A. E. Hewitt
R. Hewlett
Mrs O. E. Hewlett
Edward Hibbert
Mr David Hicks
Mr Edward A. Hickson
Mrs P. Higginson
K. Highley & B. Collins
F. R. Hilborne
Mr H. O. A. Hill
Mr & Mrs Mark Hill
Mr R. C. S. Hill
J. M. M. Hill
Mr M. R. Hill
J. R. M. Hill
Mr R. Hill
Mr J. R. Hill
Mrs H. Hill-Jenkins
Ms Wendy Hillary
Mrs J. M. Hillery Robinson
Mr L. C. Hillier
Mr H. J. Hillyer
Mrs Hind
Ronald & Maureen Hinde
Dr B. P. Hindle
Jane Hirons
J. K. Hirst
Michael Hjort
Mr Neil Hoad

Ms J. Hobson
Mr A. J. Hobson
Mr C. N. Hobson
Mr Richard Hobson
Mr Brian W. G. Hodds
Mrs B. M. Hodgson
Mrs H. Hodgson
Mr R. A. Hogg
Mr John Hogg
Mrs P. R. Hoggard
Mr Michael Hoggett
Mr Peter Hokes
Mrs B. E. Holden
Fr James Holdroyd
Sqdn Ldr & Mrs J. C. Holdway
Mr C. Hollamby
Ms Lesley Holland
T. R. Holland Esq
Mrs P. V. A. Holland
Mr Nick Hollis
Mr J. F. Holman
Mr & Mrs R. Holmes
A. M. Holmes
Dr R. L. Holmes
Mr & Mrs R. Holmes
A. M. Holmes
Dr R. L. Holmes
Mr A. E. Holmes
A. M. Holmes
Mr Robin Holmes
Mr G. I. Holt
Mr & Mrs M. R. Holt
Mr Ramsay Homa
Mr Nigel Honey
Mr A. Hood
R. A. Hood
E. Hoodless
Drs R. A. & S. L. Hope
D. H. Hope
Mrs B. M. Hopewell
A. G. Hopkins
Mr David Hopkins
Mr C. J. Hopkinson
Mr Frank Hoppe
Mr E. E. Hopwell
Mr & Mrs R. H. Horncastle
Ms Rita Horridge
W. Horsfield
Mrs S. P. Horsley
T. W. Hoskins
Mr J. A. Houldsworth
Mr D. Howard
J. H. Howard
Mr C. Howe
Mr John P. Howes
R. Howgego
Mrs Kirsteen Howie
Dr G. M. Howie
Mrs Diane Howlett
J. Howse
T. A. Hoyle
Mr Miles Huddleston
Ms C. Huddleston
Joan & Peter Hudson
Mr Derrick Hudson
Mr A. M. Hudson
Dr Stephen Huggett
R. L. Hughes
D. W. Hughes
Christopher Hughes
Diane Hughes
Mrs G. M. Hughes
Mr C. Hughes
Mr R. J. Hughes
Mr R. N. Hughes
Mr R. J. A. Hughes
F. M. Hughes & B. P. L. Higgs
Mr Gwilym C. Hughes
R. J. Hughes
Naomi Hull
D. Hulls
G. G. Hulme
Mrs Delia Hume
F. C. Hummel
Doreen Anne Hummer
Mr J. L. Humphries
R. J. & D. M. B. Humphries
Mrs Elizabeth Humphris
Andrew Hunt
Mrs Harold Hunt
Mr & Mrs J. Hunt
Mr & Mrs Hunter
C. R. Hunter
Hugh C. Hunter
Mr N. R. Hunter
Mr K. Hurd
Jules Hurry & Alan Griffiths
Mrs I. M. Hurst
Sylvia Hurst
Mr & Mrs C. R. Hurtley
Mrs C. A. Hutton
Mike Hutton
Mr James Hyde
Mr W. D. Hyde
Ms Caroline A. Hyde-Price
Mr T. J. Hypher
Mr & Mrs B. Igra
Mr & Mrs F. D. Iles
David & Maureen Iliffe
Mr Brian Ingram
Mrs Brenda Innes
V. R. Ireland
Mr J. Ireland
Mr Hugh M. Irvine
Mr Peter Isaac
Mr & Mrs Philip Ison
Ms P. Izzard
Mrs B. W. Jack
Mr S. Jackson
S. J. M. Jackson
Mrs L. Jackson
A. J. Jackson
C. Jackson
Mr James McG. Jackson
Mr Paul Jackson
Ms E. E. Jackson
Mr Andrew Jacobs
K. Jacobs
Mrs I. Jacobs
Mr Anthony Jacobs
Ms Sue Jacobs
Mr P. H. Jacobsen
Mrs J. Jaffe
B. W. Jaffe
C. B. James
Mrs B. C. James
Mr W. J. L. James
Wendy James
Dr Alastair Jamieson
Mr & Mrs B. G. W. Jamieson
Mr M. D. Janson
Mr P. R. Jarvis
Mr Patrick Jefferson
Mr & Mrs Jefferys
Mr Jeffrey
Mr Mark Jeffries
Mr D. L. Jelley
Brian Jenkins
I. J. Jenkins
Mrs H. G. Jenkins
Drs Howard & Pat Jenkins
R. Jenkins
Mr G. Jenkins
B. H. Jenkinson
Mr Clive Jenkinson
Ms M. G. Jenkinson
Mrs Margaret Jennings
J. C. Jennings
Paul Jerome
Miss E. N. D. Jervie
Mr David Jervois
Mr H. D. Jewitt
Mr Brian Jobson
Miss Iris Johnson
Mr Ian Johnson
Dr C. D. Johnson
Alison Johnson
Mr R. T. Johnson
Rex Johnson
Mr & Mrs B. T. Johnson
Mrs D. G. Johnson
Mr A. R. C. Johnston
Anne Johnston
Dr I. H. D. Johnston
Mr D. T. Johnston
Mr J. C. Johnston
Mr Ernest Jones
G. M. Jones
Mr Terence Jones
Terry Jones
Mr Alan Jones
Mrs L. Jones
Ian Jones
C. E. Jones
T. L. Jones
Mrs Sheilagh Jones
Canon Ronald Jones
Mrs N. E. Jones
Peter Jones
Mr Melvyn Jones
Robert & Heather Jordan
Mr & Mrs D. Jordan
Mr D. Joseph
Mr Charles S. Joseph
Paul L. Joslin
Mr A. H. Jowett
Mr Jozwiak
Mr & Mrs C. S. Juneman
Dr Tom Keeble
Mr M. Keeling
G. D. Keelon
Caroline Keely
Mrs Sheila Keene
Ms S. E. Keighley
John C. Keighley
Mr & Mrs A. Kelly
Mr John Kelly
Dennis Kelly
Ms J. Kelly
Mr H. S. Kemp
R. Kempsey
Mr H. D. Kenley
Dr D. A. Kennard
Mr Andrew R. Kennedy
Mr D. Kennedy
Ms Grace Kenny
Mrs M. Kenny
John Kenward
Mr R. B. Kenyon
S. M. Kenyon
Mrs B. Keown
Mr C. C. Kerridge
A. D. Keswani
Mr H. D. Kette

Ms Elizabeth Key
Nicholas P. Khan
Mr Derrick Kidson
E. Kiefer
B. J. Kilbride
Mr John A. Kilpatrick
Mrs C. T. Kilvington
Mrs R. M. Kimmins
Paul A. King
Revd A. B. King
Miss A. M. King
Ms Suzanne H. King
Mr E. B. King
Prof Anthony King
Janey King
C.R. & T. King-Farlow
Mr R. Kinnon
M.E. Kirk
Mrs J. Kirk
Mr John Kitchen
Mr John Kleeman
Mrs C. Kleiner
Mr Simon Knapp
Mr R. Knapp
Mrs C. M. Knibb
E. J. Knifton
R. A. Knight
Eveline Knight-Jones
Chris Knowles & Wanda Rossiter
Mr Peter Knowles
Ms Wyn Knowles
David Kolbrook
Ms Sally A. Korda
Jack Krelle
Dr D. W. Kyle
James R. Laidlaw
Miss Dinah Lambert
Mr Derek Lambert
Mr A. J. Lambert
M.S. Lambert
Mr J. Lancaster
Mike & Lorna Lane
Mr C. H. R. Lane
Robert Lane
Fred Lang
Victor J. Lang Jnr
Mr R. C. Lang
Mr Jack Lang
Mrs A. Langdon
D. Langdon
Gina Langford-Allen
Mr A. F. Langham
Mr Michael Langridge
Mr J. Lanham
Mr W. Lansley
Mrs Jane Larsen-Collinge
Muriel Laskin M.D.
Dr R. D. Last
Mrs B. Lauffer
Mrs P. A. Laurie
Mr & Mrs Law
Dr Derek Lawford
Mrs M. E. Lawrence
Mr M. J. Lawrence
Mrs B. Lawrence
Mr & Mrs A. Lawson
Mr G. M. Lawson
Mr E. W. Laycock
Dr G. Leach
Mrs E. Leach
Ms Jeanette Leach
Major & Mrs N. H. Leadsom
Mr Ian Leaman
Miss M. P. Learmonth
B. A. Ledger
Mr & Mrs A. Ledsham
Mrs S. A. Lee
Mr Ming San Lee
Dyanne Lee
A. & J. Leeming
John Lees
Mr C. G. Leigh-Bennett
Clay Leitch
Mrs P. J. Lesbirel
V. Leser
Seth Lesser
Mrs Alexandra R. G. Lethbridge
J. M. Leuw
Mr L. Leventhal
Mr M. Lever
David Levin
Mr B. P. Levitt
Jan Lewartowski
Meg Lewis
R. H. Lewis
Mr Lewis
Mr D. J. B. Lewis
Mr D. N. Lewis
Mr David Lewis
Mr D. J. Lewis
Mr V. J. Lewis
D. J. Lewis
Ms Janet Lewis
M. Lewis
Mary Lewis
Desmond Leyden
Mr Timothy Leyland
Mrs M. A. Leyland
Mr K. M. Li
W. I. Light
Mr Peter G. Lilley
D.R. & A. J. Limmell
Mr Herbert Lindenberger
Mrs M. L. Lindley
Mr Peter Line
Mr & Mrs Lingley
Anne Lingley
D.R. & A. J. Linnell
Miss E. A. Linton
Ms Joan Lipkin-Edwards
Mrs J. Lipman
Adrian & Ann Lisney
Mr Peter Little
Mr G. Livesey
E. Livesey
Mr J. R. Lloyd
Mr R. T. Lloyd
Mr I. David Lloyd
Paul R. H. Lock
Mr J. A. Lock
Mr Jack M. Lockwood
David Lodge
Mr A. Logan Petch
Ms Victoria Logue
Mr T. Lomas
Martin Lone
Garry & Pat Longden
Mr H. J. Lott
Ms Jean Louis
Mr Love
James Lovely
Mr P. A. Lovick
Mrs Anne Low-Beer
P.A. & J.B,. Lowater
Mr E. J. Lowe
Ronald A. Lowe
C. P. Lowell
Cecily Lowenthal
H. P. Lowit
Mr G. W. Lubin
Mr Edwin R. Lucas
Ms Maureen Lucas
Dr John Lunn
The Revd Dr Philip Luscombe
Ian Lush
Mr D. C. Luther
Mr & Mrs P. R. Lynch
Mr G. Angus Lyon
Mr S. Lyons
Andrew Macallan
Mr James Macdonald
Mr I. A. J. Macdonald
Mr Alan Bell Macdonald
A. S. Mace
Dr B. E. W. Mace
Mrs S. Macfarlane
J. B. Macgill
Mrs D. Mack
John Mackay
Margaret-Anne Mackay
M. A. E. Mackenzie
Michael Mackenzie
Mr D. Mackenzie
Martin MacKeown
Mr & Mrs D. Mackey
The Lord Machie of Benshie
Mr Melvin Mackie
Ms Marcia MacLeod
Mr A. Macleod
Mr Howard Macnamara
Dr D. Macphail
William Macquitty
Mr & Mrs P. Magentie
Mr & Mrs K. R. A. Maggs
Professor I. A. Magnus
Mr Stanley Maguire
Dr James Mair
Ms Katherine Maisey
Robert Maitland
Mr G. S. Makin
D. C. Makin
Mrs J. W. Makinson
Ms Barbara Maletz
Rita Mangat
Mr D. Manley
Ms Margaret Mann
Mr & Mrs R. Mann
Martin & Jane Manning
E. J. Mansell
Mr J. C. Mansfield
Wilhelmina Maguire
Mr A. C. M. Marano
M. Alain Marcesche
Barnaby Marder QC
Mr Jonathan P. Margolis
Ms Anne & D. L. Mariano
D. Markham
Mr R. W. Marshall
R. F. D. Marshall
Tricia & Barry Marshall
Mrs M. L. Martin
Mr Eric Martin
Mrs Belinda Martin
Mrs R. Martin
Miss Margaret J. Martin

Jennifer Martin
Mrs J.Martin
Mrs Joan Martin JP
Mr Brian Martin
Mrs R.N.Martineau
Mr M.Masefield
Mr George E.Maslen
Mr Andrew Mason
Mr John H.Mason
Ms K.Ruth Mason
Mr & Mrs G.Mason
G.Masonparry
Rita Masseron
Dexter Masters
Mr T.C.Masters
Graham & Wiescka Masterton
Mr Hugh Matheson
Mrs Evelyn Matheson
Dr & Mrs A.M.Mathewson
Mrs L.Mathieson
Dr B.R.Matthews
Miss K.R.Matthews
Mr Michael Matthews
M.Maxwell & M.Wohrle
Kenneth & Suzanne May
Mr R.I.McAllister
Mr J.B.McAndrew
Mrs Gillian McAndrew
P.McArdle
Miss Joy McCann
Mr J.S. & Mrs C.P.McClelland
Mrs Diana McClure
Mrs D.G.McConnell
William McCracken
M.G.McCullagh
Sir Charles McCullough
David William McDonald
Kate McDowall
Maryanne & William McEvoy
Mrs J.McGetrick
Colin & Lilian McGhee
Ms Moira McGhie
Ms Susan McGorrigan
Mrs J.M.McGrenra
W.McHaffie
G.J.McKean
Patricia McKechnie
Mr K.Muir McKelvey
C.W.McKerrow
J.A.McKinnell
G.S.McKnight
Jan L.M.McLachlan
Ms E.McLoughlin
Mr R.K.McMahon
Mr M.McMorrie
Helen McMurray
J.M.McNab
Mr T.P.NcNamara
Mrs Dorothy McRae
Jonathan Meades
Mr M.R.Medcalf
Dr Ted Megan
M.E.L.Mellvish
Mr S.E.Mercer
Mr M.E.Mercer
Mr William Mercer
Mr R.Merchant
Mr Andrew Metcalfe
E.F.P.Metters
Mr C.G.Metters
Mr J.B.Meyer
Mr Siraj Miah
Mrs J.E.Michael
Mr J.R.Michaelis
Mr G.Middleton
Mr P.M.Middleton
Mr Robin Middleton
Henry Midwinter
Mr & Mrs Mignano
Mr Ken Millar
Mr A.Miller
Mr J.Miller
Sandra M.Miller
Mr & Mrs J.D.Miller
Christian Miller
Mr Vernon Mills
R.O.Millson
Mr David Millward
Mrs F.Millward
Sarah Milne
Mr G.Milner
D.J.Milner
Mr J.B.Miners
Mr J.A.Mirrlees
Mr Martin Mistlin
Dr M.J.Mitchell
Geoffrey Mitchell
Mr R.E.Mitchell
Ms Sandra Mitchell
Prof J.M.Mitchison
Mrs J.M.Moffat
Mr John Mole
Ms Linda Moller
Ms Jennifer Mollison
Mr J.W.Molloy
Sandy Molloy
Dr P.R.Monk
Hugh Montefiore
R.N.Montgomery
P.Monzeglio
T.L.Moody
D.Moon-Parvin
Mr R.H.Moore
Mr Anthony Moore
Timothy Moore
Ms Hazel Morgan
Mrs Elizabeth Morgan
Dr W.T.W.Morgan
Mr & Mrs C.Morgan
Dr Bryn Morgon
D.P.Morland
C.P.Morley
Mr F.Morrell
Mr Norman Morris
Mrs B.E.Morris
G.Morrison
Mr & Mrs I.Morrison
Mr D.Morrison
Mr D.C.Mort
Vivika Mortensen
W.V.Moseley
A.B.Moss
P.J.Moss
Paul Moulton
Mr J.Mountain
A.W.Mowbray
Mr & Mrs Moyes
D.Moyse
Ms Philippa Muggridge
Ms S.T.Muir
Mr Robert Muir
Mr Ian Mukherjee
Frank Mullery
Mr D.E.Mullinger
Mr D.E.Mullinger
Ms Amanda Mulvey
Mr F.G.Mulvihill
Mr A.Munford
Mr W.D.Munro
Mr Anthony Murlay
Mr Brian Murphy
Mrs M.Murray
Mr M.H.Murray
Mrs O.A.Murray
Mrs E.M.Murray
Mr A.L.Murray
Mr & Mrs J.B.Murray
Mrs M.L.Murray Smith
Eileen & Peter Murton
Mr J.Mustarde
Mr R.V.Myott
Dr N.Naunton Davies
D.A.Naylor
Dr A.Neder
P.N.Negretti
Mrs M.K.Nelles
R.D.Nesbitt
S.W.Nesbitt
Julia Neuberger
Dr Richard Neville
Ms Deborah Newman
M.L.W.Newman
B.M.Newman
S.C.Newman
Mr Newton
Dr J.Newton
Mr S.Newton
Mr Jeffrey Ng
Dr C.W.Nicholls
D.J.B.Nicholls
Ms Sarah Nicholls
Mr Tom Nicholls
Mrs T.Nichols
Mrs Nickalls
Mr D.Nicola
J. & R.A. Nightingale
Mr B.Nimian
Dr Angela Ning
Mr D.Nisbet
Dr J.Nixon
Mr David Hobbs
Mrs D.A.Noble
Mr Ian Noble
P.Noel
Geoff Normile & Sue Taylor
Ms Carolyn Norris
J.Nott
Mr Keith C.Noutch
Mr J.E.Nurse
Mr David Nutt
Mr L.S.Nuttall
Ms Patricia O'Brien
Mrs K.O'Connell
A.S.O'Connor
Mr M.O'Dowd
Ms Sandra J.O'Mera
W.B.O'Neill
Mr G.O'Reilly
Mr G.M.O'Reilly
Mr H.D.O'Reilly
P.L.Oakley
Mr David Obree
Mr Oddey
Mr J.Oddy
Peter & Jillian Oglesby-Ede
R.A.L.Ogston
Dr Catherine Ogus
Neil Oldfield
A.J.Oliver
R.Oliver-Tasker
Ms Joan Olivier
Mrs I.Olty
N.J.Olympitis

Ir R. Ongley
Is Lindsay Oram
Ir D. W. Orchard
erek C. Orgles
.G. Ormiston
Irs C. S. Osborn
Osborn-Clark
Ir Bernard Osborne
Is Enid Osborne
Irs Ostrowska
Irs W. J. Osuji
Ir G. J. Otter
lizabeth Owen
Irs R. W. Owen
Irs B. Owen
r E. E. L. Owens
nn Owston
Irs A. Owston
ichard Pach
.J. Page
Ir & Mrs D. E. Pain
onathan
P. R. Palfrey
rani Pallas
Ir J. Pallot
Ir D. Palmer
Ir A. Palmer
ndrew & Laurella
Parffrey
tephen Parish
Ir G. Parker
Ir H. T. Parker
.E. Parker
Irs Zoe Parkhouse
Ir Chris Parkin
Ir Steve Parr
Irs F. Parr
Ir Michael Parry
Ir & Mrs D. Parsons
Ir C. J. Parsons
Ir J. W. Parsons
Ir Roger Pask
Ir George Pate
irti B. J. Patel
Iartin Paterson
he Very Revd John
Paterson
Is Judith Paterson
Ir David Patient
Is Fiona J. Paton
Ir B. Pattenden
.S. Patterson
Irs M. G. Patterson
Ir Thomas
Patterson
Ir S. J. Paul
Is Odette Pauy
Ir & Mrs F. I. Pavey
Iiss J. Paxton
Ir T. M. Payne
Ir & Mrs L. Payne
Is C. Payne

A. & R. Peace
Joy Peach
F. G. Peach
Mr & Mrs D. V. Pean
Mrs M. Pearlman
Mr & Mrs
A. Pearman
Mr John Pearson
Dr R. Pearson
Mr Jonathan Peck
Mrs S. Peckover
The Countess Peel
Stephen Pegler
M. Pegson
A. Peill
Miss L. R. Pelican
Mr Pembroke
Duttson
Mr W. S. Penfold
Jane Penton
Anne & Mike Pentz
Mr Roy Pepper
Mrs G. S. Perkins
Mr Paul Perlin
Mr J. A. Perreur-
Lloyd
B. Perryman
Mrs L. Persand
Bishop of
Peterborough
Mr J. F. Peters
Mr D. Petter
Mr Andrew Pettitt
D. R. G. Philip
Mr D. Philips
Ms V. Phillips
Mr John W. Philips
Mrs D. Phillips
Mrs K. Phillips
Robert & Susan
Phillips
Ms Jane Phillips
Mr B. J. E. Phillips
Dr & Mrs
R. M. Phillips
Mrs I. L. Phillipson
A. J. Phillipson
David & Jacqui
Phipps
Martin Pick
Dr A. D. Picton
F. J. Pidgeon
Mr J. B. Pierpoint
Mrs V. Pilling
Mr T. Pilt
B. R. Pinches
A. Pinder
Mr J. Piper
Mr Michael Pitel
Mrs T. V. M. Pitman
J. S. Pitt-Brooke
Michael Pitts

Mrs J. Plachta
Mr Roger Plant
Mr R. Plastow
Jack Pleasant
Mrs A. Plummer
Alexander Poliakoff
Ben Pollard
Mrs Lucy Pollard
Mr G. Pollard
Richard Polo
Mr Nicola
Pomponio
Giovani Pomponio
D. L. Pope
Mrs John Pope
S. J. Popham
Neil Popplewell
Ms Pamela Porter
Mr J. A. Porter
Mrs Mary Porter
Mrs Christine Porter
Mrs Porter
Mr David Potter
Mr & Mrs A. J. Potts
Ms Sophie Poulain
Mr A. M. Pountney
Mr C. N. P. Powell
Joan A. Powell
Ms Catherine
Powell
Mr Bruce M. Powell
Mrs R. Powell-
Thomas
Mrs V. J. Power
Mrs M. Poynton
Mrs M. Pratt
Mr P. Preston
Pat Preston
Mrs Sandra M. Price
Mrs Valerie Price
Mr M. K. Price
Ms Deborah Price
Mrs M. Priday
Ms Colleen Prince
Keith Pring
Miss Karen Pringle
Mr & Mrs
C. B. Pringle
Peter J. Prior
Mr Tim Pritchard
E. M. Probyn
Mr D. Procter
J. F. Procter
Anne Proctor
Mr Stewart
A. Prodger
Mr Gordon
W. Provis
Mr J. Pruggmayer
Mrs Monica Pudney
Mr B. Pugh
Hilary Pugh

Dr Oscar Puls
Mr M. Puran
Mr John Purcell
Mr & Mrs Reg
Pycroft
Mr & Mrs D. L. Pye
Simon Pyle
Eric Pysden
R. Anthony
Goodchild
Mr M. J. Radcliffe
Peter & Jackie
Radford
Marian Radley
N. A. Rae
Ms Ruby Rae
Mr Ian Ragg
Mr M. R. Railston
Ghislaine Raku
Mrs P. Raman
Mr D. S. Rampton
Mr A. Rampton
Mrs Jean Randell
William Rankin
Mrs H. C. Ranson
Mr C. W. Raper
D. T. Rasey
Dr R. J. Rathbone
Mrs Pamela Ratoff
Mrs I. M. Raven
Mrs Margaret
Ravenshaw
Michael Rawling
Ms Susan Rawlins
Mrs K. Rawson
Mr Cyril Ray
Mr N. H. Ray
Mary Rayner
J. Read
Mr K. Reader
Mr & Mrs
W. J. Reader
J. M. Reason
Mr D. Reay
C. W. E. Redman
Mr T. F. Redman
Bernard Redshaw
Mr Jeffrey J. Reed
Dr Reed
Dr J. Reed
M. A. Reed
L. Reeve
Mr & Mrs P. Reid
Ms Hilary Reid
A. S. Reid
Mrs Frances
Remington
Mr P. Rendell
Mr A. L. Rennie
M. Revell
Mr & Mrs W. Rex
Ms Rosalind Rey

Mrs M.H.Reynolds
Joanna Reynolds
Mr Guy Rhodes
Melvin R.Rhodes
M.W.Richard
Mrs R.B.Richards
Ms Kay Richards
Miss S.P.Richards
C.J.Richardson
Frank Richardson
Mrs E.Richardson
Mr W.E.G. Richardson
Ms Sue Riches
Mr & Mrs B.R.Richmond
Mr J.Rickard
C.J.Ricketts
Mrs Carol Riddick
J.Riddleston
Mr & Mrs A.Rieck
Joshua Rifkin & Helen Palmer
Mr Brian Rigden
Mrs Linda Riley
Frances Rimington
Ms V.Ringham
Mr Gordon Ringrose
Mrs O.Rippon
Alison Ritchie
Dr B.Ritson
B.A.Rivett
M.Roach
Mr James Robbins
Mr A.J.Roberson
Mr A.T.Roberts
Ms Sally Roberts
Mr B.L.Roberts
Brig Gen & Mrs N.J.Roberts
Miss E.Roberts
Mr J.P.Roberts
Mr David Roberts
Mrs Patricia Roberts
Mr C.Roberts
E.Roberts
Miss M.F.Robertson
Mr William Robertson
Mrs Marjory A.Robertson
M.Robertson
Dr A.John Robertson
Charlie Robertson
Morag Robertson
Mr J.C.Robertson
Mrs H.G.Robertson
Mrs I.Robertson
Mrs Anne Robiette
Mr D.Robins
Moira & Dick Robinson
Roderick Robinson
Mrs P.N.Robinson
Mr Derrick Robinson
Mr Robinson
Mrs W.Robinson
Mr Derek Robinson
Dr N.D.P.Robinson
Mr & Mrs P.Robinson
Mr I.P.Robson
Mr John Robson
Dr G.A.Robson
Mr A.G.Roby
George K.Rock-Evans
Mr C.H.Rodeck
Mrs Anne Rodewig
Mr Alan Rodger
Mr P.N.Rodgers
William Rodgers
Mrs B.P.Roetter
Mr & Mrs D.Rogers
Barry Rogers
Frank J.Rodgers
Mr C.C.Rogers
Mr Frank Rogers
T.B.Rogers
Mrs M.L.Rogers
Susan Rollings
G.C.Ronco
Mr John Rooke
Mr D.F.Roper
H.D. & A.L.Rose
W.Rose
Mr M.H.Rose
L.Rose
Mr John Rose
William Rose & Susan Lawe
J.L.Roselaar
Mr Richard Ross
Dr H.E.Ross
Stephen Ross
Ms Nicola J.Ross
A.W.Ross
Mrs D.Rosser Jenkins
Mrs A.Rossiter
Mr Anthony Rota
Mr P.D.Rouse
Mr B.Routledge
Miss N.Rowan-Kedge
H.D. & A.C.Rowe
Mr J.Rowe
H.Rowe
Michael D.B.Rowe
Mr Michael Rowland
David & Diana Rowlands
Margaret Rowlett
Mr P.W.Rowley
Mr D.H.Rowley
Keith Rowley
Mr G.Rowntree
T.R.Roydon
P.Rozee
Mrs J.Rubens
Mr Peter Rudd
Dr Diana Rudd
J.Rudd
Mr Simon Rudd-Clarke
Ms Jean E.M.Ruffer
John Rumsey
Dr I.J.Runcie
Mr D.P.Russell
Mr Archibald Russell
Mrs J.Russell
I.A. & J.A.Russell
Ms Gillian A.Russell
Mrs M.Rutherford-Hall
Mr Duncan Rutter
Mr & Mrs L.W.Rutter
Mr J.S.Rutter
Mr J.M.Ryan
Mr Richard L.Ryan
R.S.Ryder
Mr A.A.Ryner
Mr R.Sacker
Mr L.Saffron
M.Sahid
Mr Ron Salmon
N.L.Salmon
Mr Iain G.K.Sample
O.W.Samuel
Mr M.Samuel
Mrs G.A.Samuels
D.N.Samuels
Ms Katherine Sand
Mr James C.Sanders
Mr E.S.Sanders
Ms Jennifer Sanderson
R.J.Sandry
L.Sands
Mrs Rachel Sanger
Mr A.Saunders
Mr Vincent Saunders
Ms E.Saunders
Mr J.R.Saunders
C.A.Saunders
M.S.M.Saux
Mr M.Savage
Mr N.Savva
Dr Derek Say
Mrs F.Scarr
Mr P.J.Scherer
Professor P.J.Scheuer
Dr & Mrs Schmedding
Mr Michael Scholfield
H.Scholes
Mr R.Schwartz
Mrs J.Scothern
Mr P.D.Scott
Michael Scott
Mr W.A.Scott
Mr J.G.J.Scott
Mr G.F.Scott
Mr John Scott
Major J.K.C.Scott
Mr J.Scott
Mr E.Scott
Mr & Mrs G.Scott-Campbell
Mr David Scott-Holte
C.G.P.Scott-Malden
Mr David Scott-Moncrieff
Mr J.Scott-Smith
Peter Searle
Mrs Petra Searle
Dr P.S.Sebel
Mr & Mrs D.Seel
Mr R.N.Seeman
Paul Seligman
Mrs J.Seller
D.Sellwood
Mrs V.E.Senior
Mr J.M.Sennett
Mrs E.M.Shanks
Mr John F.Shapley
Anne E. Sharp
R.T.Sharpe
Mr John G.Sharpe
Mrs Frances Shaw
Mr T.Shearer
Mr Edward Sheehan
Dr R.P.Sheldon
Mr R.W.Shelton
Mr D.R.E.Shephard
F.L.Shepley
Mr J.Shepperd
Mr & Mrs H.Sherwood
Mr Peter Shier
Mr D.H.Shillitto
Ms Carla Shimeld
Mrs S.M.Shorrock
Mr J.Shorrocks
Mr & Mrs G.Short
J.H.Short
Professor M.F.Shutler

Mr Peter Shuttleworth
an Sier
M.Silverman
Dr P.Silverstoone
Mr Daniel Silverstone
Mr Robert C.Sim
Mr R.Simon
Mr H.Simon
Mr P.H.Simon
R.L.Simonds
Mrs Anne Simons
Miss Christine Simons
Mr William Simpson
D.G.Simpson
Mr S.Simpson
W.F.Simpson
P.F.Simpson
R.E.C.Sims
.Sinclair
I.Sinclair
Mr R.Sinclair-Taylor
Mr E.Singer
Mr J.F.Sinnott
Mr Howard D.Sirak
Mr G.Sivewright
Mr & Mrs A.Skaliotis
Mrs M.Skippings
F.R.Sladden
Mr D.H.Slade
Mr P.R.Slade
A.F.S.Slaymark
Mr G.S.Sloman
Mr Simon Small
Simon Small
Ms Susan E.Smalldridge
M.Smart
Mr T.Smart
Mr Michael H.W.Smart
Mr N.E.Smith
Mr J.H.Smith
Ms B.Smith
A.F.M.Smith
Mr Malcolm Smith
I.B.Smith
Dr L.M.Smith
Mrs Ann Smith
Dr D.A.Smith
Beverly J.Smith
M.D.Smith
Mr & Mrs D.F.Smith
Mr D.G.Smith
.S.Smith
Mr S.E.Smith
M.A.Smith
Mr David Smith
Mr B.D.Smith
Arthur J.Smith
Mr D.E.C.Smith
Mr G.S.Smith
Ms H.Smith
Mrs Helen Smith
Kenneth E.Smith
J.D.Smith
Mr Wayland G.Smith
Ms Barbara H.Smith
Mr Peter Smith
Mrs Margaret Smith
Mr Smith
Professor J.A.S.Smith
Mr Simon T.Smith
Mrs Kay Smith
Alan H.Smith
Ms Pamela Smith
Mr A.W.Smith
Mr J.Smith
Mr S.R.Smith
Mr S.G.Smith
Dr Bernard Smits
Mr Andrew Smy
Iain Smyth
Mr & Mrs Snell
J.W.E.Snelling
Mrs G.M.Soane
Mrs J.Soden
Mr P.J.Solomon
Rosemary Somers
Mrs B.M.Somerset-Jones
C.Sonnex
Julian Soper
Mr E.C.South
Ms Alison L.Sparkes
Ms Esme Speakman
Geoff Speed & Liz Hollister
Mr J.Spencely
M.B.Spencer
Mr Anthony Spencer
Dr Seymour Spencer
Mr F.E.V.Spencer
Arthur F.Spencer-Bolland
Miss P.A.Spink
Mr & Mrs Sprent
Mr & Mrs Jack Springett
J.F.Kirby
S.M.St John
Mr David St John Thomas
Robin Stainer
B.H.Stamp
Mr J.Stanley-Smith
Mrs Vera Stanton
Mrs E.Stanton
L.Stead
Mr John Stead
Barrie & Millicent Stead
Miss E.Steele
Mrs M.Steele
Mr & Mrs R.Stein
Mr F.M.M.Steiner
Mrs Kathryn Stephen
P.Stephens
Mrs J.Stephens
Mr K.Stephenson
Mr A.M.Stephenson
Maxwell Stern
Ms Angela Sternwood
Mrs M.A.Sterton
Frank & Marlene Stettner
J.M.Stevens
Mr D.R.Stevens
Mr A.Stevens
Mr & Mrs A.J.Stevens
Mrs M.Stevenson
John Stevenson
D.R.Stevenson
Sylvia Stevenson
Ms Jill Steventon
Mr D.Steward
Ms Sally Stewart
Mrs Stewart
Mr S.A.Stewart
Dr J.B.Stewart
Capt & Mrs J.S.Stewart
Mr A.J.Stewart
Ms Christine Stewart
Mr C.R.Stirling
Mr G.W.Stitt
Ivor C.Stock
D.Stockfis
R.H.Stockton
Lt Stokes
Mr A.J.Stone
Mr M.Stone
Rod Stoneman & Susan Clarke
Mr A.Stones
Mr R.Storey
Mr Ivor C.Storey
H.Storr
John Stothert
Laura Stout
Mr M.Strange
Mrs Rosemary Stratford
J.W.Straw
Mr A.M.Street
John Streets
Hilary & Malcom Strong
Mrs G.Struthers
Mr Stuart
Charles Stuart
Andrew Stuart-Lyon
Major D.W.Stubbs
John Sullivan
Ms L.Sumiga
Ms Hilary Sunman
John Surbey
Mr & Mrs Simon Surtees
Dr N.H.Sutcliffe
A.R.Sutherby
George & Margaret Sutherland
Mr D.C.Sutherland
Dr Arthur M.Sutherland
A.M.Sutton
Ms Kathleen M.Swales
Dr M.Swan
Mrs J.K.M.Swift
Mr Simon Swift
Ms Linda Swindale
N.P.Sykes
R.Sykes
Ms Brenda Symes
Mr Frederic Symonds
Mr & Mrs K.N.Symons
Mrs Elizabeth Syrett
Mr Louis Szathmary
Professor J.F.Tait FRS
Mr Paul Tait
Dr L.S.Taitz
Susan Tamlyn
Mr J.A.Tarrant
Ms Jacqueline Tarrant
Mr Denis W.Tate
Mr C.J.Tatham
Dr P.H.Tattersall
Mrs S.Tatton
Mr & Mrs G.Tayar
Mr Alan Taylor
Anthony Taylor
Mr J.Grigor Taylor
Mrs S.R.Taylor
Mr J.A.Taylor
Mrs Wendy Taylor
Mrs Alison J.Taylor
Ms Jean Taylor
Mr T.G.Taylor
Mr & Mrs L.Tayne

Mr M.P.Tebutt
Mr Richard Temple
M.Temple
Mrs B.Temple
Ms Isabel Tennant
Mrs G.Terry
Mrs P.Tester
Mr J.C.Thackray
Mr Frank Thackray
Miss Thatcher
Mr B.Theobald
Marcel Theunis
M.Thierens
R.E.Thomas
R.Thomas
Mr A.W.Thomas
Richard & Carol Thomas
Mr Thomas
Ms S.Thomas
Mr A.J.Thomas
Mr B.M.Thomas
David St John Thomas
Mr P.Thompson
Mrs S.Thompson
Mr W.Thompson
Ms Jacqueline Thompson
Mr Barrie Thompson
Mr W.Thompson
Peter Thompson
Ms Dawn Thompson
Dr C.S.Thomson
Dr M.Thomson
R.Thomson
Drs M.Thomson & A.J.E.Clapper
David Thornber
Mr G.E.Thorne
Mr D.Thornton
Margaret Thorson
Mrs M.S.Thubron
Mr James A.Tice
Dr P.Tidswell
Mrs M.Tillotson
Mr P.Tilsley
Mrs R.E.Timpson
Elizabeth Tindall
Mr Benjamin Tindall
Mr F.A.Tinker
H.Tint
Mr & Mrs A.Tobey
Mr & Mrs J.Todd
Mr H.Todman
Mr J.E.A.Tonkin
Mr P.C.Tomkins
Mr A.G.Tomkins
Dr J.S.Tomkinson CBE
Mr M.Tomlinson
Cmdr Michael Hastings Toone
Mrs Jean Toper
Brian Tora
Mr & Mrs M.T.Torne
M.Tosh
Dr G.Tottie
Miss A.M.Towers
Dr M.Townend
J.A.H.Townsend
Ms Jane Tracy-Forster
Mr G.Tragen
Ms Valerie Tramontano
N.Tree
Alison Treneer
Mr H.W.Trickett
Mr H.Trill
Dr Ennio Troili
T.J.Trotman
David C.Truram
Mr David Tuddenham
Mr Simon Tulitt
Ms Cathie Tuohy
Mr G.S.E.Turnbull
Mr K.Dudley Turner
Mr & Mrs G.Turner
C.Turner
Mr Anthony P.Turner
Dr H.Turner
Ms C.Turner
P.J.Turner
J.S.Turpin
K.C.Turpin
Ms Andrea Turrell
Mrs Elizabeth Tweddle
Mrs C.Twomey
Mrs C.A.Tyas
Alan Tye
Mr & Mrs J.Tynan
I. Tysh
M.K.Uddin
Mr C.J.Uncles
Mr A.G.Underwood
Ms R.M.Underwood
Mr Adrian Underwood
Mrs R.Upson
Mrs S.Usiskin
Mr R.Utley
Mr B.Van Gulik
Mrs J.van Huet
D.Vardy
Anne Vasse & A.Raines
Mr Max Velody
H.Velt
Mr J.P.Verdonck
A.W.Vernon-Harcourt
Paul Veysey
H.Vickers
Major & Miss Vines
Ms Carolyn Voss
Mr Michael Wace
Mrs Judith Wadsworth
Kenneth D.Wadsworth
Mark Waghorn
Mrs J.Wainwright
Christopher H.Waite
Helen A.Wakefield
Mrs Mavis Wakemouth
Christopher Wakley
Tom & Angela Walford
Patricia Walker
Alan & Rae Walker
Caroline Walker
Mrs E.Walker
H.V.Walker
Mr J.D.Walker
Mr A.K.F.Walker
Mr G.R.Walker
Mrs C.J.Wall
Mathew Wallis
Mr A.J.Walsh
Mr A.D.Walsh
R.V.Walsh
P.K.Walsh
Mr W.H.Walsh & Mr P.C.Brooks
O.Walston
David G.Walters
Emily Walters
H.Walton
Mr D.Walton
Hayward Wane
Dr Ian Wang
Mr D.Ward
Mr H.A.Ward
Ms J.Ward
Dr S.C.Ward
St John F.Ward
Mr Anthony J.Ward
Mr A.J.Wardrop
Mr A.B.Warner
Mr John R.Warren
Mr D.R. & Mrs M.D.Warry
Mrs P.A.Warwick
P.H.Wass
Mr Toshio Watanabe
Mrs P.M.Waterlow
Ms N.Waters
J.Waterson
Mrs Mavis Waterworth
J.Watling
T.M.Watson
Mr D.Watson
Sheila Watson
Mr James A.V.Watson
Mrs B.Watson
Dr Kenneth Watters
J.M.Watts
Mr John Watts
Mr A.Weaving
Dr T.Webb
Ms Valerie Webb
Mrs J.C.Webb
Mrs Jennifer Webb
Mrs Jean Webb
Mrs J.Webb
Mr John L.Webb
Ann Webb
Miss R.H.Webster
Dr D.E. & Mrs E.Webster
Mr J.R.Webster
Mr John F.N.Wedge
A.C.Wehner
Ms Paula Wiedeger
Mr Al Weil
Ms Libby Weir-Breen
Mr Edric A.Weld
Mrs David Wenman
Mr J.F.M.West
I.E.West
Mr T.West
Mr A. Westmoreland
Simon & Victoria Wethered
Mr B.B.Weyland
Mr S.Y.Whang
David Wharry
R.D.Wharton
Mr John E.Whatley
Dina Wheatcroft
Mrs R.J.Wheeler
T.Whelan
Dr J.Whiston
Mr J.W.Whitaker
E.H.Whitaker
G.M.Whitaker
Ms Susie Whitcombe
Mrs D.White
Sqn Ldr R.R.G.White

ᴚ.White
rs V.P.White
White
H.White
rs D.White
ıth M.Whitehead
r D.Whitehouse
r P.R.Whitelock
r E.V.M.
Whiteway
ephen & Susan
Whittle
eville T.Whittle
rs L.S.
Whitworth
r A.D.Whyte
Widdows
r N.J.Wikeley
B.Wilbraham
rs L.Wild
s Jean Wilding
rs M.S.Wildman
r M.Wiley
r Michael Wilkes
ridget Wilkins
rs R.D.Wilkinson
rofessor Yorick
Wilks
r P.Willer
R.Willett
s Annwyl
Williams
rs G.Williams
r T.Williams
D.Williams
r R.Williams
E.Williams
rian Williams
r T.C.Williams
r John Williams
rian B.Williams
David & Gillie
Williams
Mrs E.M.Williams
Mr P.A.Williams
Mr David Williams
R.H.Williams
Mr John Williams
B.Williams
Dr Simon Williams
Mr B.W.Williams
Ms S.Williams
N.M.Williamson
Gillian Williamson
A.Wills
Mrs Audrey
Willsher
Mrs Willson
Mrs Jean Willson
Mr A.Wilson
Mr Ian T.Wilson
Mr T.M.Wilson
Ian S.Wilson
Mr R.D.Wilson
Mr E.Wilson
Ms R.E.P.Wilson
Susan Cooper
Wilson
Dr P.Wilson
M.R.Wilson
Mr Alan Wilson
Mr Douglas
F.Wilson
Mr G.H.Wilson
Mr John M.Wilson
Mrs Marjorie
Wilson
Miss R.Wilson
Dr H.P.M.
Winchester
John C.Windon
J.C.Window
Mr N.Windridge
Roy Winston
Mrs Margaret
Winter
Mr & Mrs
P.A.S.Wise
Dr Martin Wiseman
Alan Wiseman
Roger & Julie
Wiseman
Mr David Wolfens
Dr B.Wolman
Mrs S.Wonnacott
Sue Wood
Ms J.E.R.Wood
Mr Ralph Wood
Mr C.F.Wood
Dr F.Peter
Woodford
M.Woodgate
Ms. Margaret
Woodham-Jones
Mr J.Woods
Mr Andrew Woods
Mr Lawrence
Woodward
Mrs M.J.Woodward
Mrs Vera Woolf
Mrs M.C.Woolff
Dr M.J.Woolley
Geoffrey Wormald
Mr G.Wormald
Mr Paul Worsley
Mr Josh Wort
Mr A.Worthington
Bryan & Diana
Wren
Tony Wren
S.H.Wright
D.Wright
Mrs S.R.Wright
Mr A.Wright
G.A.Wright
Mr & Mrs I.Wright
A.C.H.Wright
Mrs N.G.Wright
Mr & Mrs C.Wright
Mr G.A.Wright
Ms Sylvia Wright
Mrs S.Wright
Mr Robin Wright
Ms M.Wuidart
Mr D.Wurtzel
Mrs Jill L.Wyatt
Mr & Mrs K.Wyatt
Mr Richard Wybell
R.A.Wyld
Mr James Wyllie
Mr S.N.Wynde
E.J.C.Wynne
Mr John Wythe
Mr G.Yardley
Mr D.J.Yeo
Rev D.S.Yerburgh
Miss A.C.Youds
Sir Richard & Lady
Young
Mrs Sandra
D.Young
Mrs Maureen
Young
G.Young
P.T.Young
Mr D.J.Young
Mr A.Yousuf
Mr N.J.Yull
Mr & Mrs
P.Zacharias
Dr J.Zammit-Lucia
Mr Robert Zara
Dr & Mrs J.A.Ziesler
Mr A.D.Zucher

Alphabetical list of entries

London restaurants are indicated by their postal district.

Aagrah, Shipley
Abbey, Penzance
Abbey Green, Chester
Acre, March
Adlard's, Wymondham
Afric-Carib, N4
Agra, Warminster
Airds Hotel, Port Appin
Al Diwan, W2
Al Hamra, W1
Al Khayam, W2
Alp Horn, Edinburgh
Altnaharrie Inn, Ullapool
Alvaro's, Southend
L'Amico, SW1
Amritsar Tandoori, Glasgow
Anarkali, W6
Anarkali, Chipping Norton
Los Andes, Birmingham
Andres, Felixstowe
Angel Hotel, Bury St Edmunds
Angel Inn, Hetton
Anna's Place, N1
Anthea's, Newtown in St Martin
Ardanaiseig Hotel, Kilchrenan
Ardenslate Hotel, Dunoon
Ardeonaig Hotel, Ardeonaig
Ardfenaig House, Mull
Arirang, W1
Arisaig House, Arisaig
Ark, W8
Ark, W8
L'Arlequin, SW8
Armadillo, Liverpool
Armenian Taverna, Manchester
Armless Dragon, Cardiff
Les Artistes Gourmands, Nottingham
Arundell Arms, Lifton
Asha, Glasgow
Assam Gourmet, Manchester
At the Sign of the Angel, Lacock
L'Auberge, SE22
Auberge de L'Ill, Illhaeusern
Auberge Provençale, Eygalières
Auberge la Regalido, Fontvielle
Auberge des Templiers, Les Bézards
Au Bois St Jean, NW8
L'Aventure, NW8
Aye, Edinburgh
Aynsome Manor, Cartmel
Ayudhya, Kingston upon Thames
Aziz, W6

Bagatelle, SW10
Bahn Thai, W8
Balcraig House, Scone
Balzac Bistro, W12
Bambaya, N8
Barkston House, Barkston
Barnaby's, SW13
Barton Cross, Huxham
Basil's Brasserie, Cowbridge
La Bavarde, Glasgow
Bayleaf Tandoori, N6
Bayview Hotel, Lybster
Beadles, Birkenhead
Bear, Nayland
Bear Hotel, Crickhowell
Beau-Rivage, NW6
Beaujolais, Liverpool
Beccofino, SW3
Beechfield House, Beanacre
Beechwood Country House, Moffat
Bekash Tandoori, Stony Stratford
Bell, Aston Clinton
Bell, Smarden
Bell Hotel, Faringdon
Bell Inn, Belbroughton
La Belle Epoque, Knutsford
Belvedere Hotel (Restaurant 19), Bradford
Bengal Lancer, NW5
Bennett's Bistro, Lytham St Annes
Beotys, WC2
Berkeley Brasserie, Bristol
Berties Bistro, Elland
Best of Both Worlds (Britannia Hotel), W1
Bettys, Harrogate
Bettys, Ilkley
Bettys, Northallerton
Bettys, York
Le Biarritz, Birmingham
Bilash Tandoori, Botley
Bistro Montparnasse, Southsea
Bistro Nine, Colchester
Le Bistroquet, NW1
Bistro Twenty One, Bristol
Black Boys, Thornage
Black Bull, Moulton
Blacksmith's, Battle
Black Swan, Ravenstonedale
Blackwater Hotel (Le Champenois), West Mersea
Blakes Hotel, SW7
Blas-O-Ddyfed, Cardigan
Blas-ar-Cymru, Cardiff
Bloom's, E1
Blostin's, Shepton Mallet
Boat Inn, Erbistock
Bodkin House, Badminton
Bodysgallen Hall, Llandudno
Bolaka, Ilford
Bolton Castle, Castle Bolton
Bombay Brasserie, SW7
Boncompte's, Isle of Man
La Bonne Auberge, Heald Green
La Bonne Auberge, South Godstone

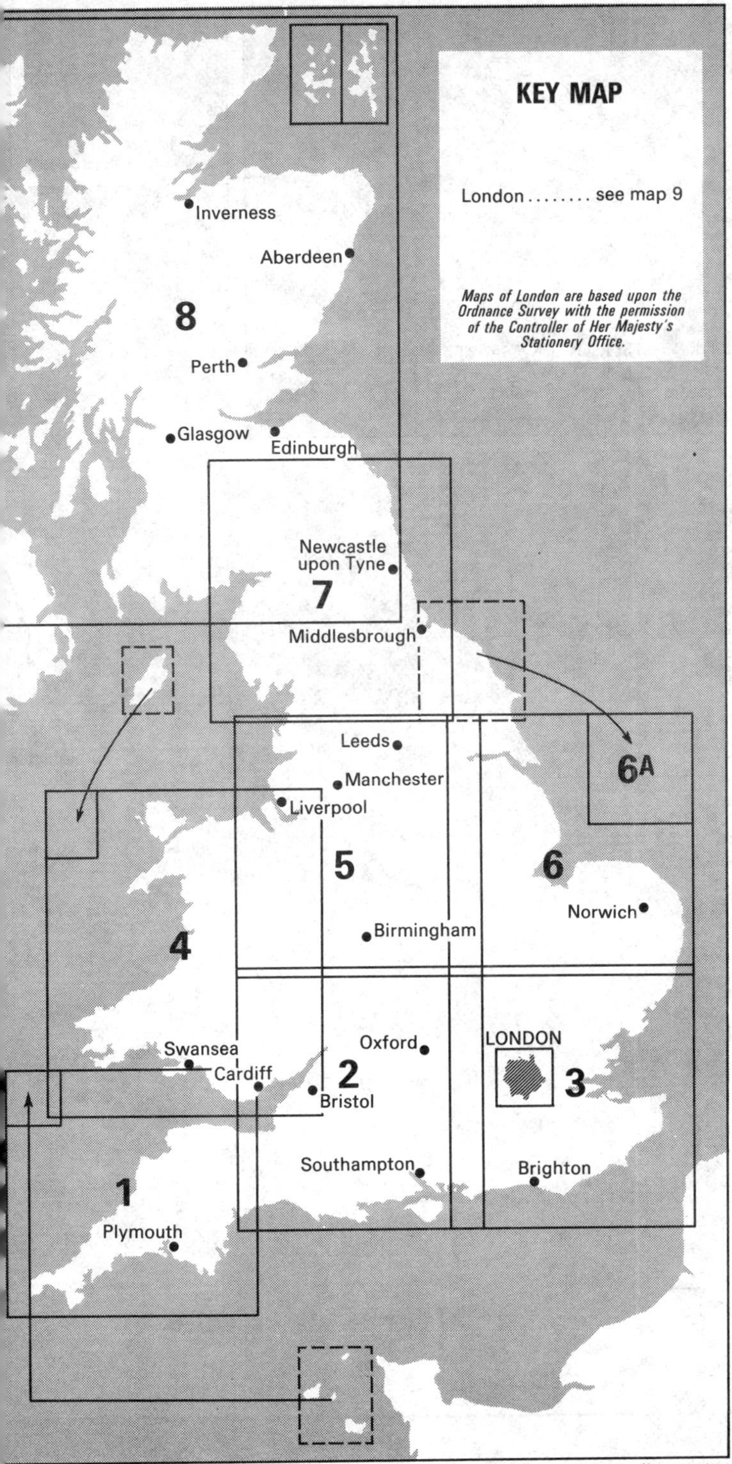

Cartographic Services (Cirencester) Ltd.

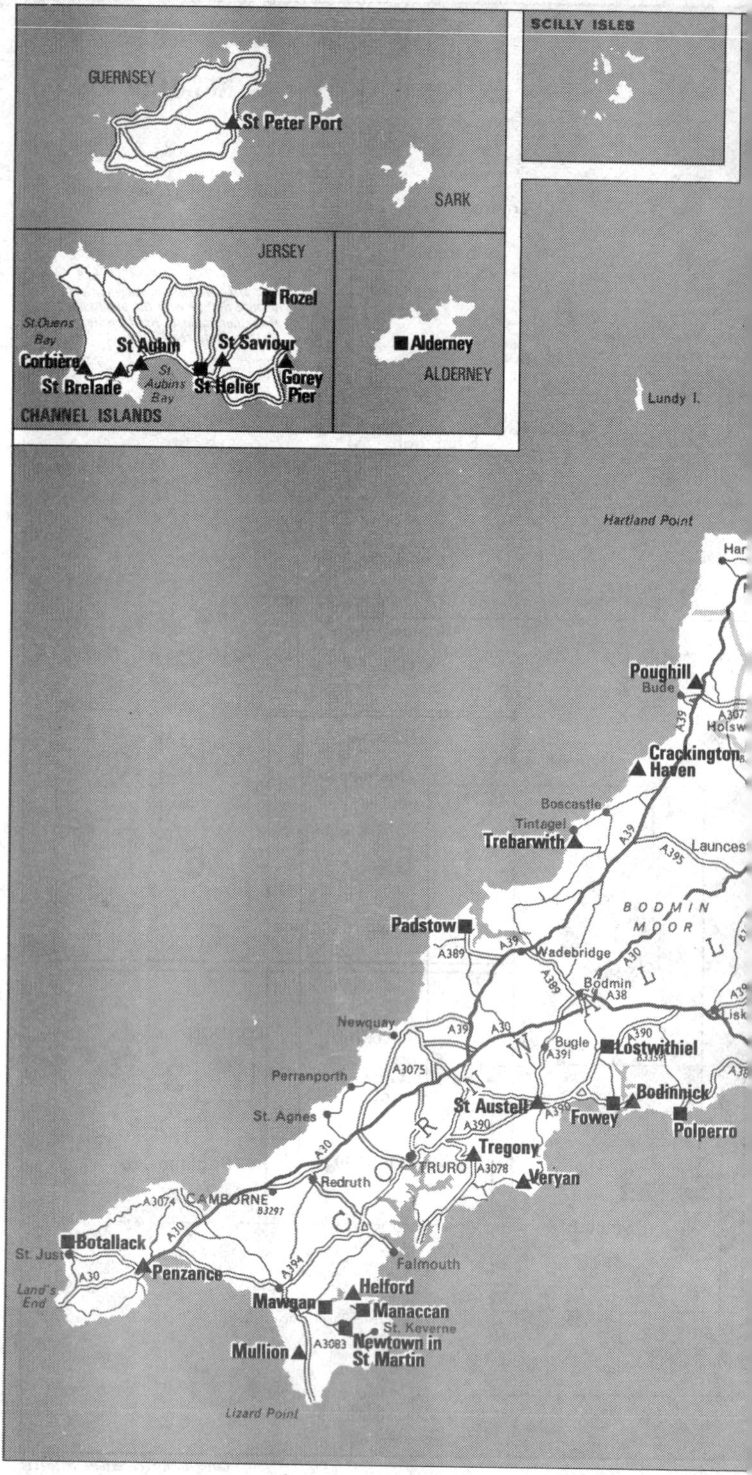

GUERNSEY
St Peter Port
SARK
SCILLY ISLES
JERSEY
Rozel
St.Ouens Bay
St Aubin
St Saviour
Corbière
St Brelade
St Aubins Bay
St Helier
Gorey Pier
CHANNEL ISLANDS
Alderney
ALDERNEY
Lundy I.
Hartland Point
Poughill
Bude
Holsw
Crackington Haven
Boscastle
Tintagel
Trebarwith
Launces
BODMIN MOOR
Padstow
Wadebridge
Bodmin
Newquay
Bugle
Lostwithiel
Perranporth
St. Agnes
St Austell
Bodinnick
Fowey
Polperro
Tregony
TRURO
Veryan
Redruth
CAMBORNE
CORNWALL
Botallack
St. Just
Penzance
Land's End
Falmouth
Helford
Mawgan
Manaccan
St. Keverne
Newtown in St Martin
Mullion
Lizard Point
A39
A30
A38
A389
A395
A390
A391
A3075
A3078
A3074
A394
A3083
B3297

1

DEVON and CORNWALL

CHANNEL ISLANDS

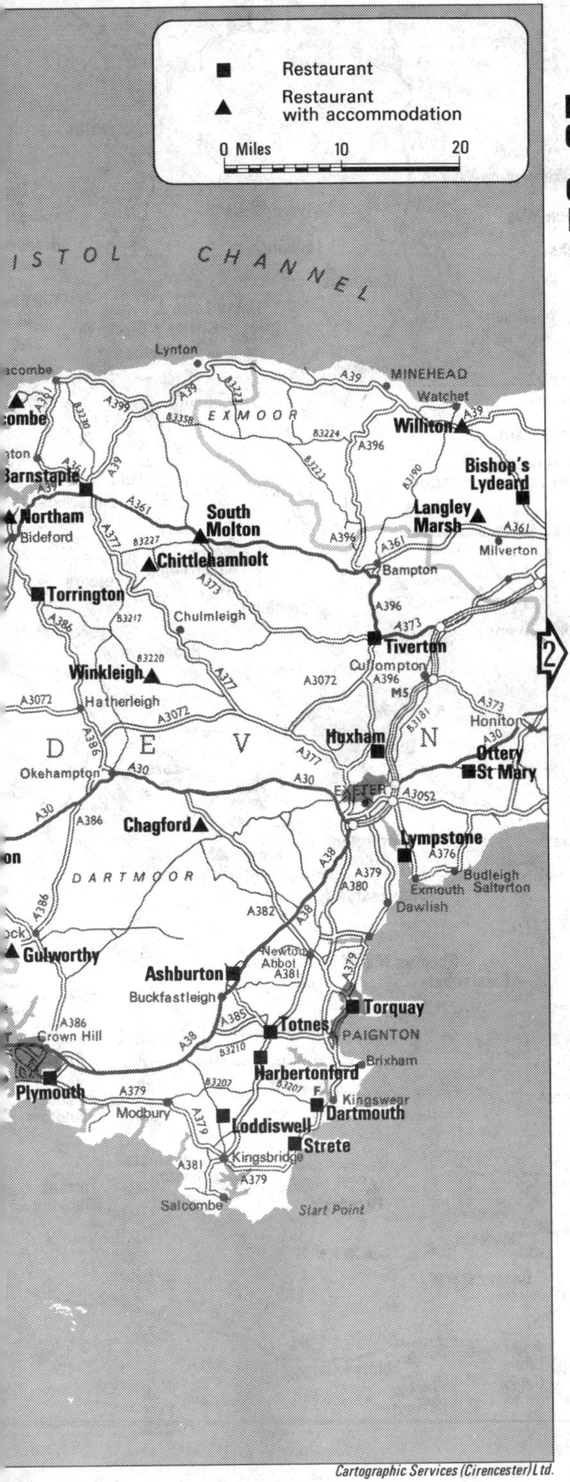

Cartographic Services (Cirencester) Ltd.

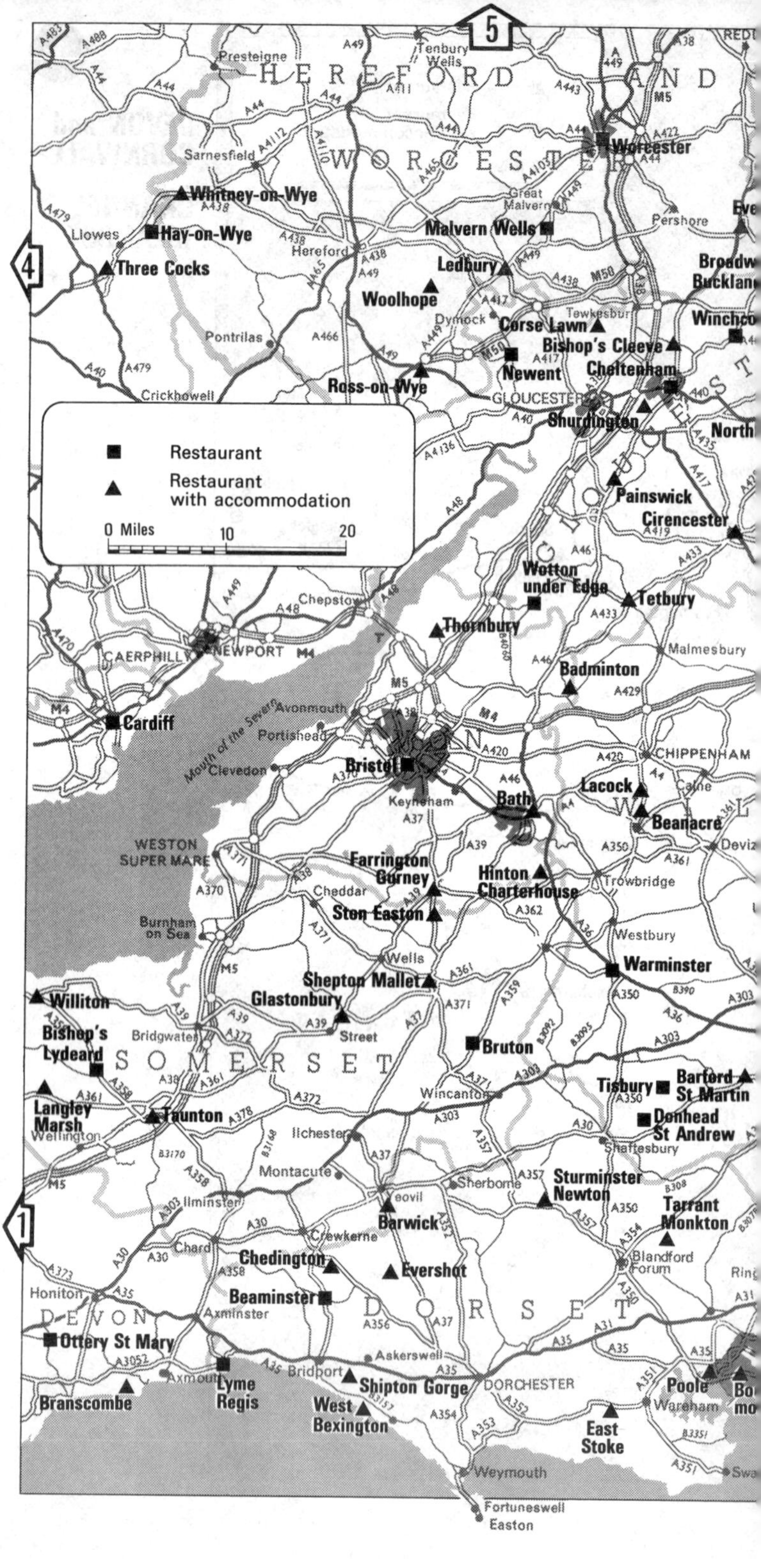

5
4
1
HEREFORD AND
WORCESTER
SOMERSET
DORSET
DEVON
AVON
Restaurant
Restaurant with accommodation
0 Miles 10 20
Presteigne
Tenbury Wells
Worcester
Sarnesfield
Whitney-on-Wye
Hay-on-Wye
Llowes
Three Cocks
Hereford
Great Malvern
Malvern Wells
Pershore
Ledbury
Woolhope
Dymock
Tewkesbury
Corse Lawn
Bishop's Cleeve
Broadway
Buckland
Winchcombe
Pontrilas
Crickhowell
Ross-on-Wye
Newent
Cheltenham
GLOUCESTER
Shurdington
Northleach
Painswick
Cirencester
Wotton under Edge
Tetbury
Chepstow
Thornbury
Malmesbury
CAERPHILLY
NEWPORT
Badminton
Cardiff
Mouth of the Severn
Avonmouth
Portishead
Clevedon
Bristol
Keynsham
CHIPPENHAM
Calne
Lacock
Bath
Beanacre
Devizes
WESTON SUPER MARE
Farrington Gurney
Hinton Charterhouse
Trowbridge
Cheddar
Ston Easton
Burnham on Sea
Westbury
Wells
Warminster
Shepton Mallet
Williton
Glastonbury
Street
Bishop's Lydeard
Bridgwater
Bruton
Langley Marsh
Wellington
Taunton
Wincanton
Tisbury
Barford St Martin
Donhead St Andrew
Ilchester
Shaftesbury
Montacute
Sherborne
Sturminster Newton
Ilminster
Yeovil
Barwick
Tarrant Monkton
Chard
Crewkerne
Chedington
Evershot
Blandford Forum
Honiton
Beaminster
Axminster
Ottery St Mary
Askerswell
Bridport
Axmouth
Lyme Regis
Shipton Gorge
DORCHESTER
Branscombe
West Bexington
Poole
Bournemouth
Wareham
East Stoke
Weymouth
Fortuneswell
Easton
M5
M4
M50
A38
A44
A49
A40
A48
A46
A30
A35
A37
A39
A303

2

ENGLAND: SOUTH WEST

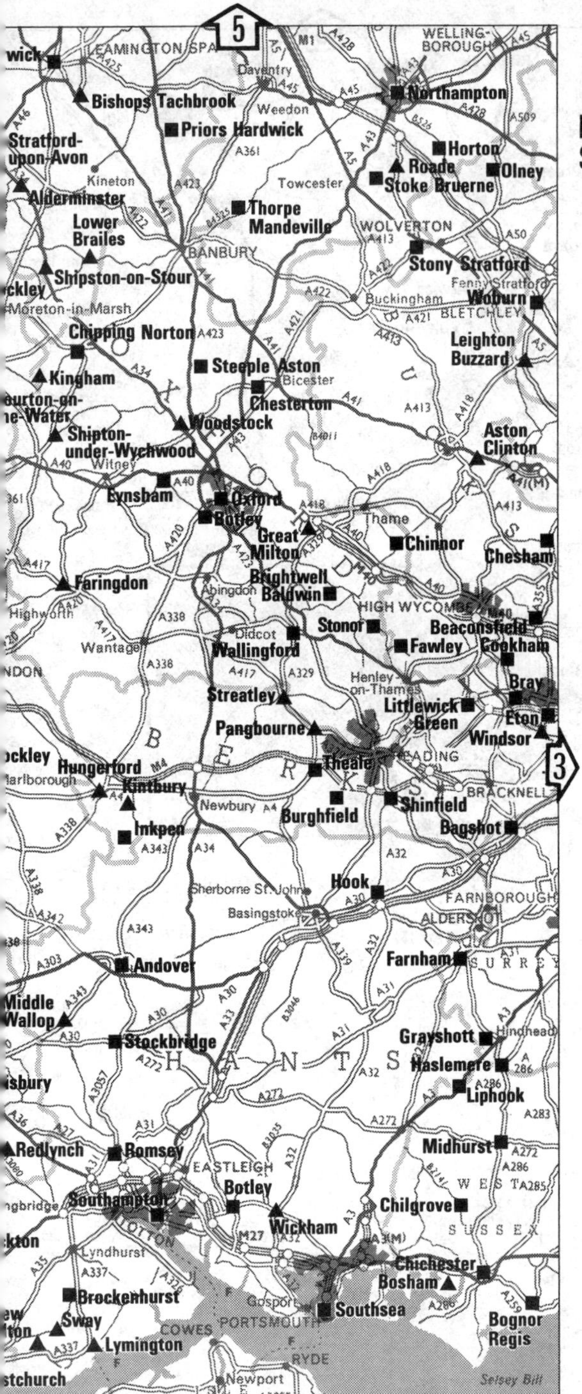

Cartographic Services (Cirencester) Ltd.

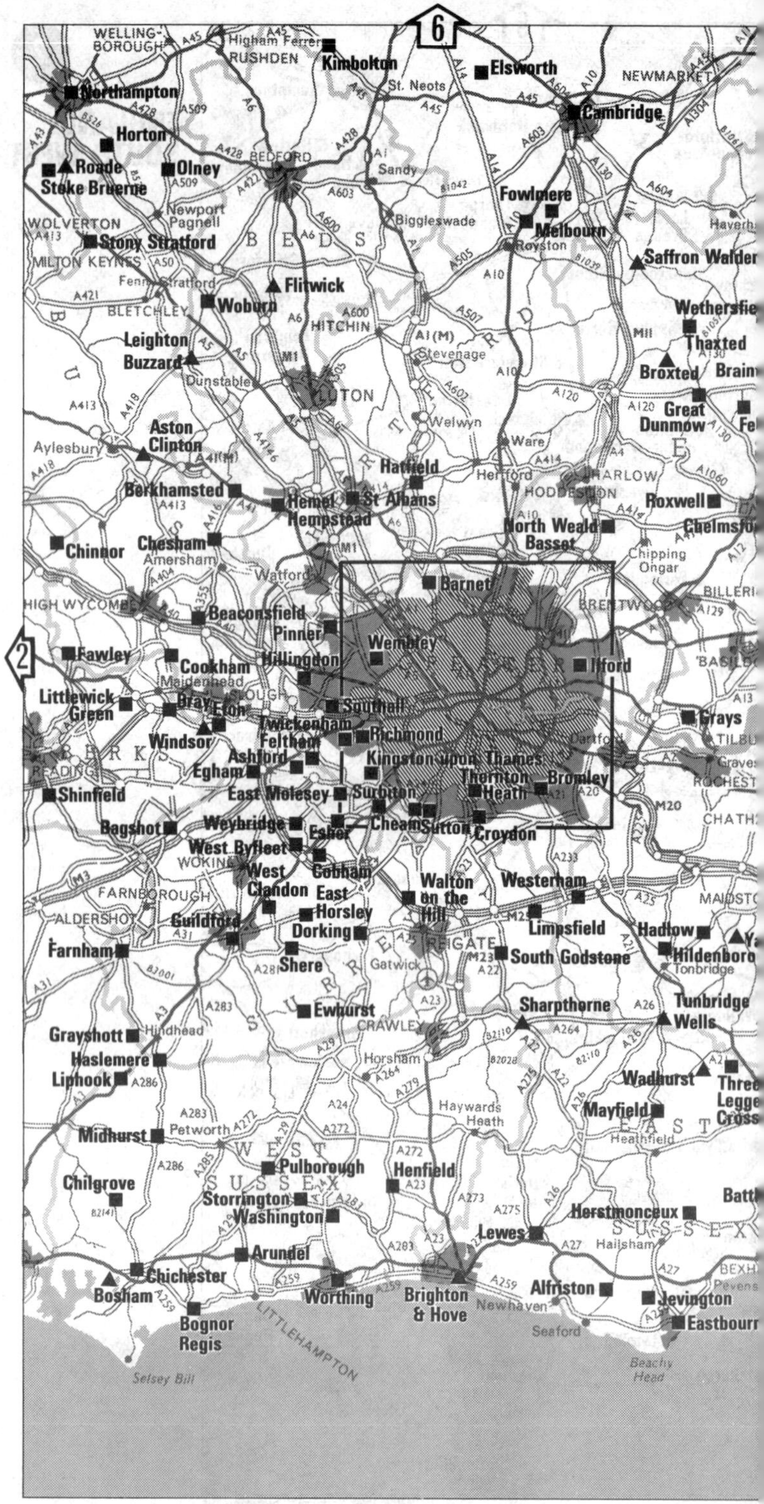
6
2
WELLING-
BOROUGH
Higham Ferrers
RUSHDEN
Kimbolton
Elsworth
NEWMARKET
Northampton
St. Neots
Cambridge
Horton
BEDFORD
Sandy
Roade
Stoke Bruerne
Olney
Newport
Pagnell
Fowlmere
WOLVERTON
Biggleswade
Melbourn
Stony Stratford
Royston
Saffron Walden
MILTON KEYNES
B E D S
Fenny Stratford
Flitwick
BLETCHLEY
Woburn
HITCHIN
Wethersfield
Leighton
Buzzard
Stevenage
Thaxted
Broxted
Dunstable
LUTON
Great
Dunmow
Aston
Clinton
Welwyn
Aylesbury
Ware
Hatfield
Hertford
HARLOW
Berkhamsted
HODDESDON
Roxwell
Hemel
Hempstead
St Albans
North Weald
Basset
Chelmsford
Chinnor
Chesham
Amersham
Chipping
Ongar
Watford
Barnet
HIGH WYCOMBE
BRENTWOOD
Beaconsfield
Pinner
Wembley
Fawley
Cookham
Hillingdon
Ilford
Maidenhead
Littlewick
Green
Bray
Eton
Southall
Grays
Windsor
Twickenham
Feltham
Richmond
Dartford
READING
Ashford
Egham
Kingston upon Thames
Thornton
Heath
Bromley
Shinfield
East Molesey
Surbiton
Cheam
Sutton
Croydon
Bagshot
Weybridge
Esher
West Byfleet
WOKING
West
Clandon
Cobham
Walton
on the
Hill
Westerham
FARNBOROUGH
East
Horsley
Limpsfield
ALDERSHOT
Guildford
Dorking
REIGATE
Hadlow
Farnham
Shere
Gatwick
South Godstone
Hildenborough
Tonbridge
Ewhurst
Sharpthorne
Tunbridge
Wells
CRAWLEY
Grayshott
Hindhead
Haslemere
Horsham
Liphook
Wadhurst
Haywards
Heath
Mayfield
Midhurst
Petworth
Heathfield
Pulborough
Henfield
Chilgrove
W E S T
S U S S E X
Storrington
Washington
Herstmonceux
Lewes
Hailsham
Arundel
Chichester
Alfriston
Bosham
Worthing
Brighton
& Hove
Newhaven
Jevington
Bognor
Regis
Seaford
Eastbourne
LITTLEHAMPTON
Selsey Bill
Beachy
Head
M1
M11
M20
M25
M23
M3
A1(M)
A10
A120
A23
A22
A26
A27
A259
A272
A283
A286
A29
A31
A413
A418
A5
A6
A505
A507
A602
A603
A604
A14
A45
A428
A509
A421
A404
A355
A414
A25
A21
A264
A24
A279
A281
A273
A275
A285
A13
A2
A129
A130
A1060

ENGLAND: SOUTH EAST

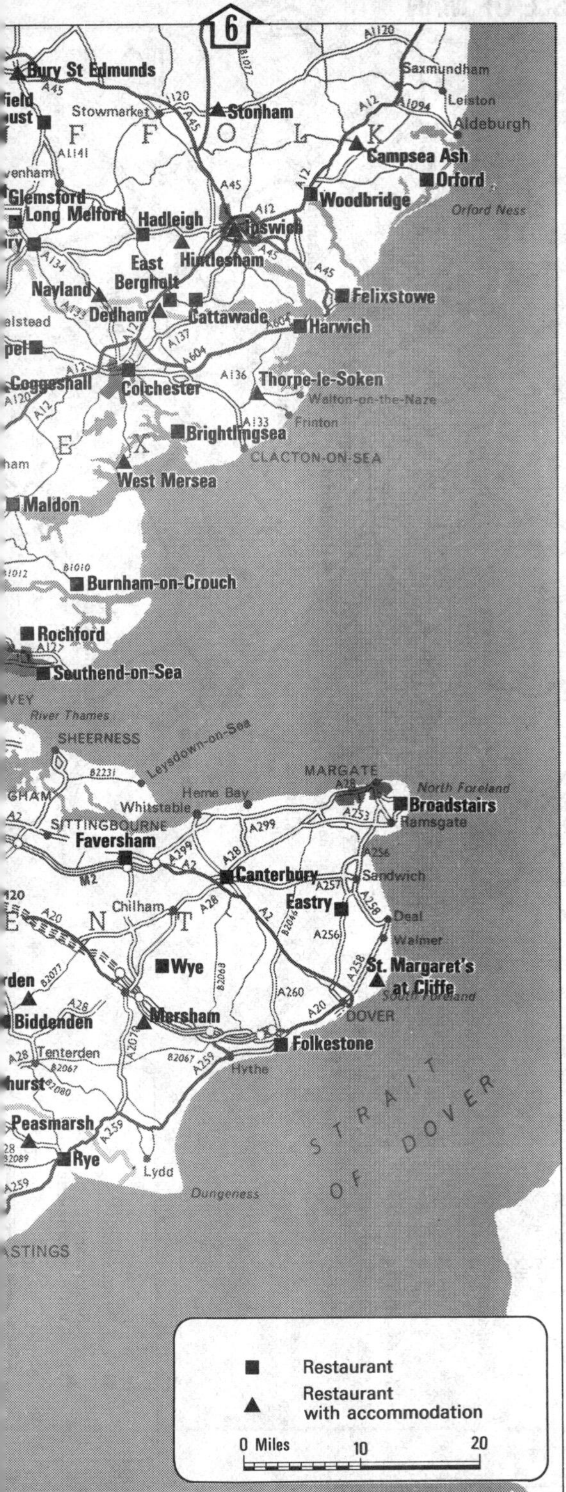

Cartographic Services (Cirencester) Ltd.

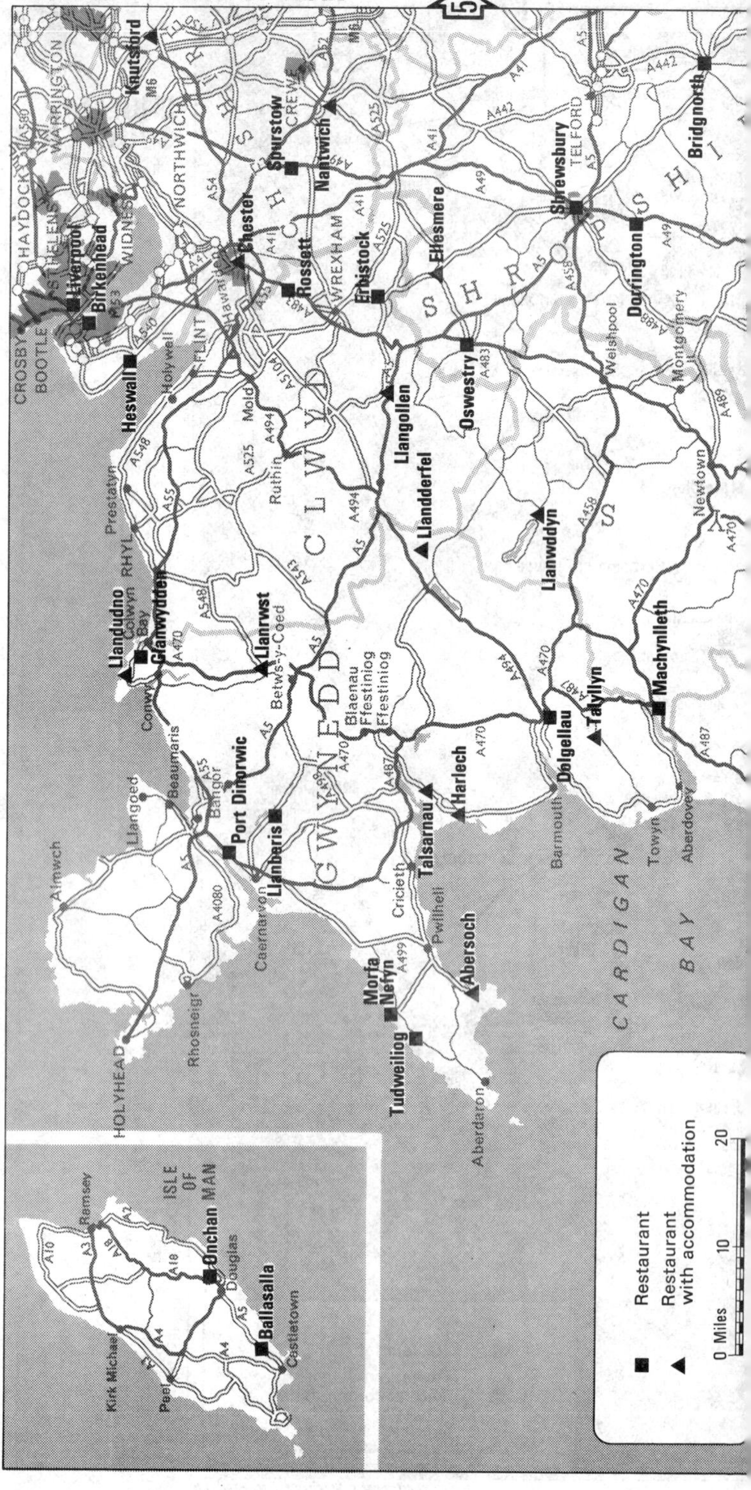
5
Liverpool
Birkenhead
Heswall
Knutsford
Chester
Spurstow
Nantwich
Rossett
Erbistock
Ellesmere
Shrewsbury
Bridgnorth
Dorrington
Oswestry
Llangollen
Llandderfel
Llanwddyn
Machynlleth
Tal-y-llyn
Dolgellau
Harlech
Talsarnau
Abersoch
Morfa Nefyn
Tudweiliog
Llanberis
Port Dinorwic
Llanrwst
Llandudno
Glanwydden
Ballasalla
Onchan
ISLE OF MAN
Douglas
Castletown
Peel
Kirk Michael
Ramsey
CLWYD
GWYNEDD
SHROPSHIRE
CARDIGAN BAY
HOLYHEAD
Restaurant
Restaurant with accommodation
0 Miles 10 20

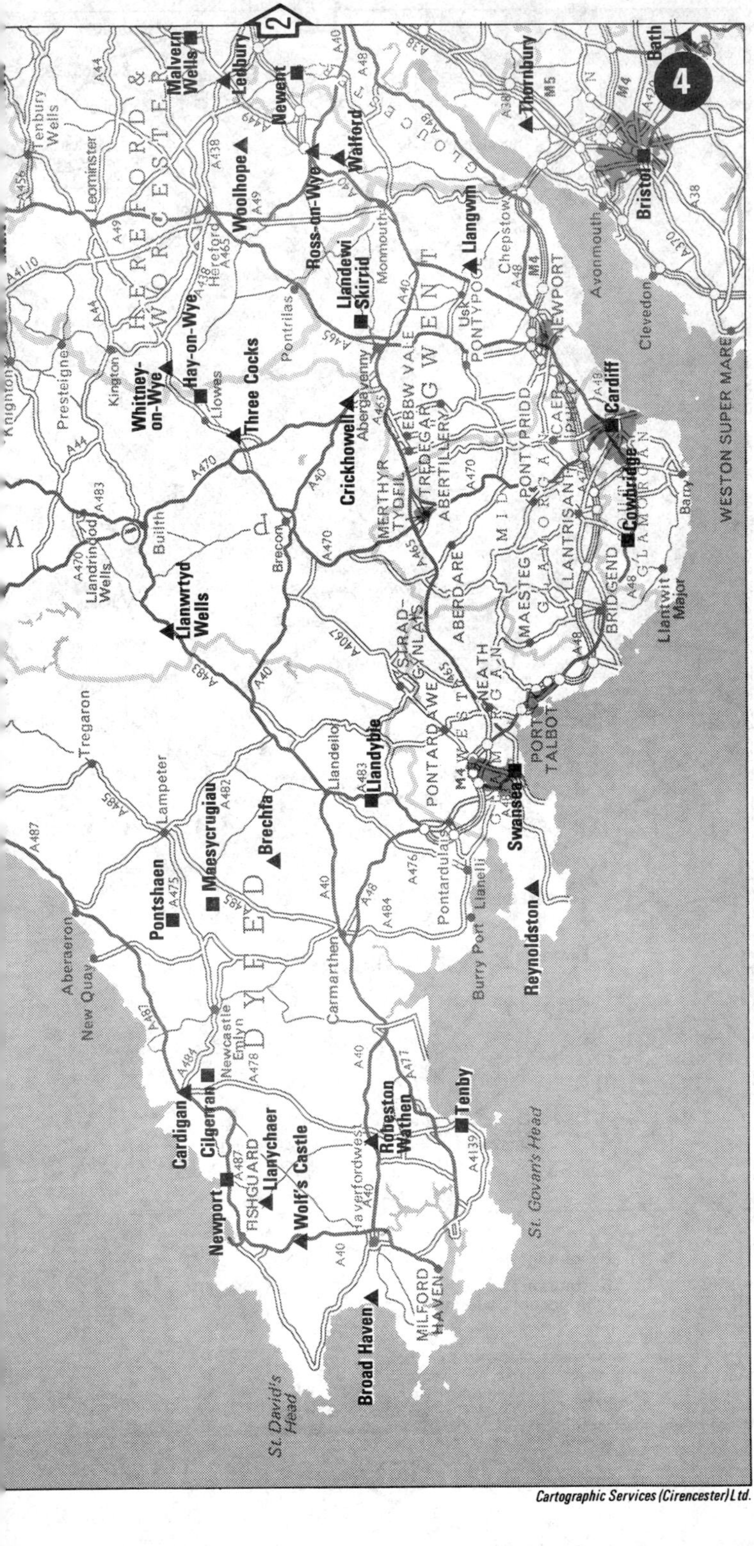

Cartographic Services (Cirencester) Ltd.

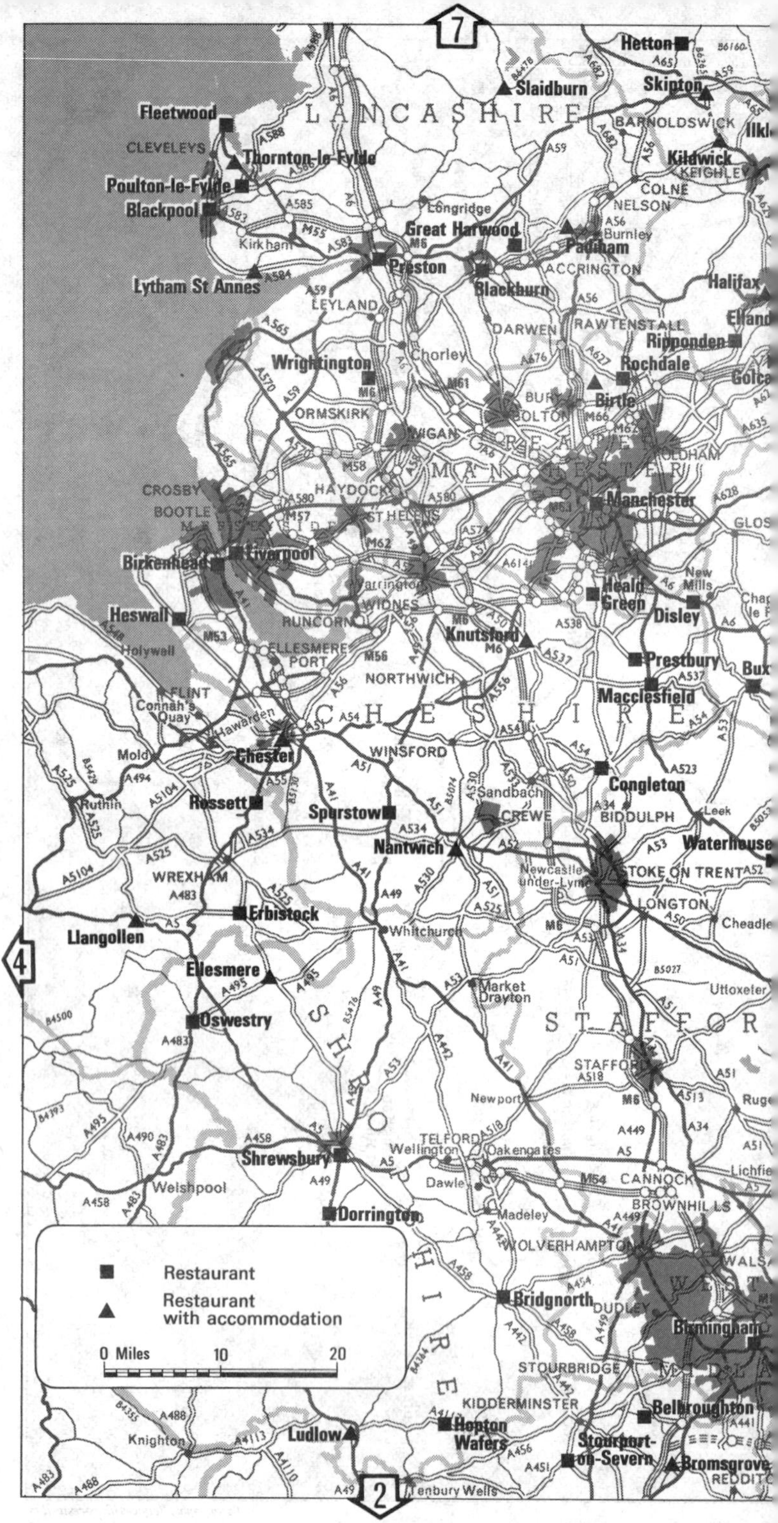
7
4
2
LANCASHIRE
GREATER MANCHESTER
MERSEYSIDE
CHESHIRE
STAFFORDSHIRE
SHROPSHIRE
WEST MIDLANDS
Hetton
Slaidburn
Skipton
Fleetwood
CLEVELEYS
Thornton-le-Fylde
Poulton-le-Fylde
Blackpool
Kirkham
Lytham St Annes
Longridge
Great Harwood
Preston
Blackburn
Padiham
ACCRINGTON
BARNOLDSWICK
Kildwick
KEIGHLEY
COLNE
NELSON
Burnley
Halifax
Elland
Ripponden
LEYLAND
DARWEN
RAWTENSTALL
Wrightington
Chorley
Rochdale
Birtle
BURY
BOLTON
ORMSKIRK
WIGAN
OLDHAM
Manchester
CROSBY
BOOTLE
HAYDOCK
ST HELENS
Liverpool
Birkenhead
Warrington
WIDNES
Heald Green
New Mills
Disley
Heswall
RUNCORN
Knutsford
Holywell
ELLESMERE PORT
NORTHWICH
Prestbury
Macclesfield
FLINT
Connah's Quay
Hawarden
Mold
Chester
WINSFORD
Congleton
Ruthin
Rossett
Spurstow
Sandbach
CREWE
BIDDULPH
Leek
Waterhouses
Nantwich
WREXHAM
Newcastle under-Lyme
STOKE ON TRENT
LONGTON
Erbistock
Llangollen
Whitchurch
Cheadle
Ellesmere
Market Drayton
Uttoxeter
Oswestry
STAFFORD
Newport
TELFORD
Wellington
Oakengates
Shrewsbury
Dawley
CANNOCK
BROWNHILLS
Lichfield
Welshpool
Dorrington
Madeley
WOLVERHAMPTON
WALSALL
Bridgnorth
DUDLEY
Birmingham
STOURBRIDGE
KIDDERMINSTER
Belbroughton
Knighton
Ludlow
Hopton Wafers
Stourport-on-Severn
Bromsgrove
REDDITCH
Tenbury Wells
Restaurant
Restaurant with accommodation
0 Miles 10 20

ENGLAND: MIDLANDS and NORTH WEST

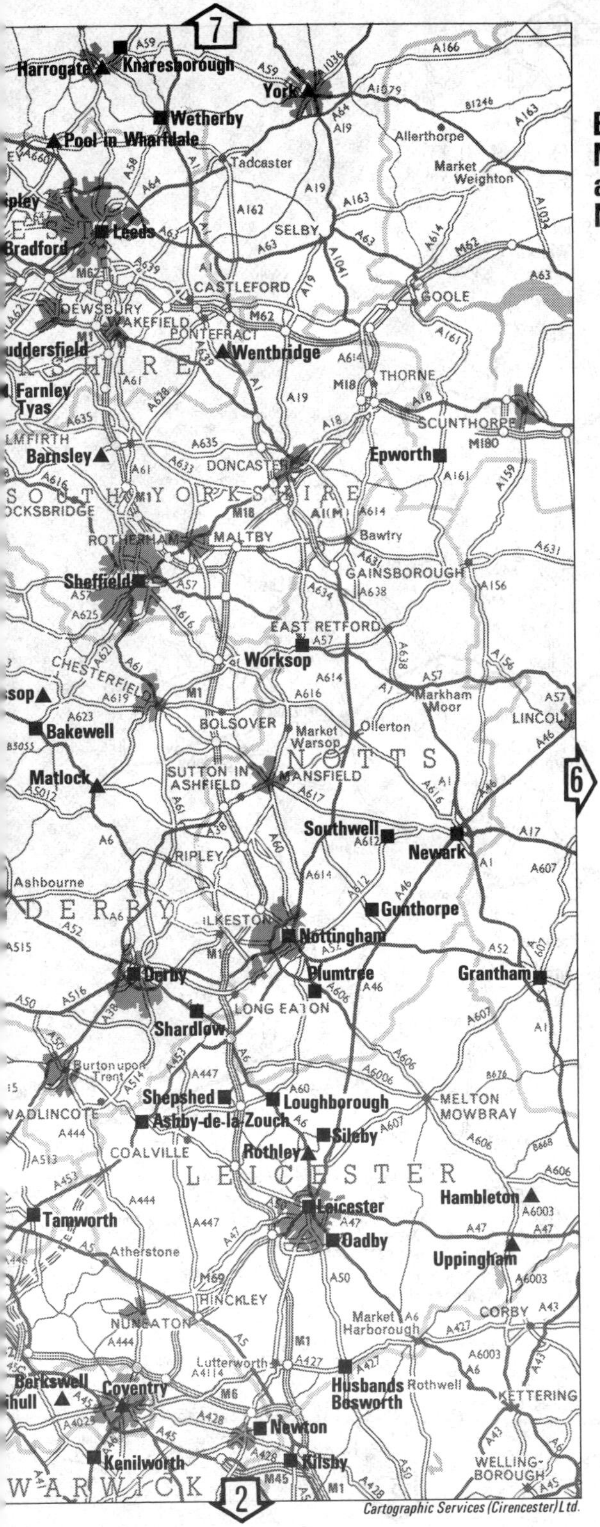

Cartographic Services (Cirencester) Ltd.

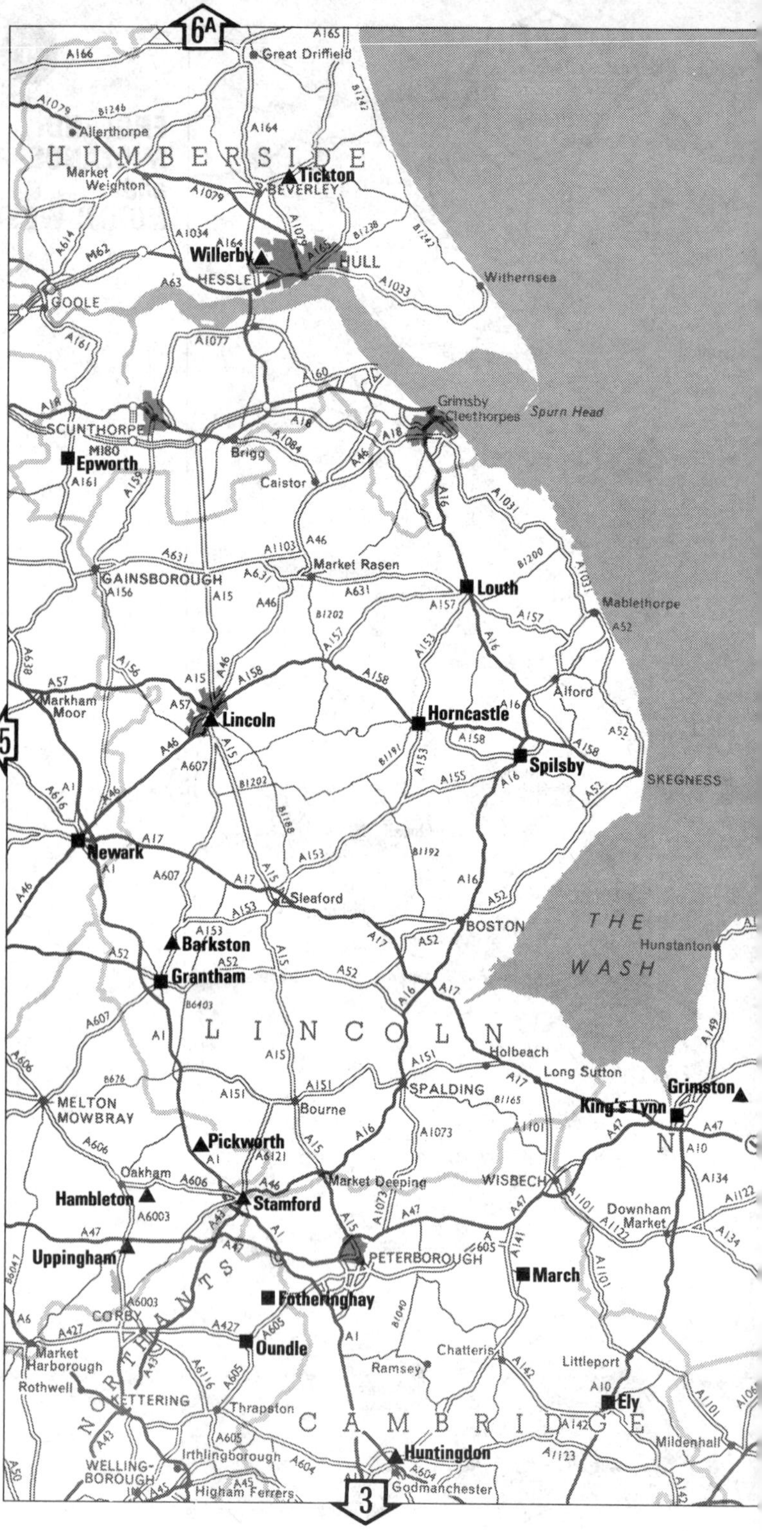

6A
5
3
HUMBERSIDE
LINCOLN
NORTHANTS
CAMBRIDGE
THE WASH
Great Driffield
Allerthorpe
Market Weighton
Tickton
BEVERLEY
Willerby
HULL
HESSLE
GOOLE
Withernsea
Grimsby
Cleethorpes
Spurn Head
SCUNTHORPE
Epworth
Brigg
Caistor
GAINSBOROUGH
Market Rasen
Louth
Mablethorpe
Alford
Markham Moor
Lincoln
Horncastle
Spilsby
SKEGNESS
Newark
Sleaford
BOSTON
Hunstanton
Barkston
Grantham
Holbeach
Long Sutton
SPALDING
Grimston
King's Lynn
MELTON MOWBRAY
Bourne
Pickworth
Oakham
Hambleton
Stamford
Market Deeping
WISBECH
Downham Market
Uppingham
PETERBOROUGH
March
Fotheringhay
CORBY
Oundle
Market Harborough
Rothwell
KETTERING
Chatteris
Ramsey
Littleport
Ely
Thrapston
Irthlingborough
WELLINGBOROUGH
Huntingdon
Mildenhall
Higham Ferrers
Godmanchester

ENGLAND: EAST

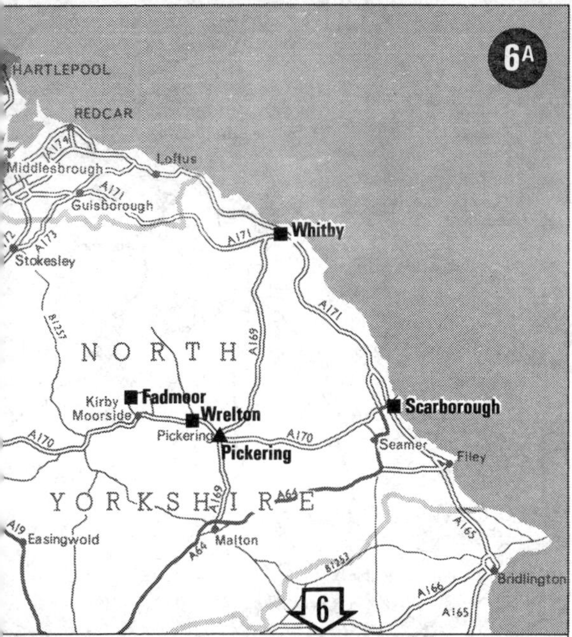

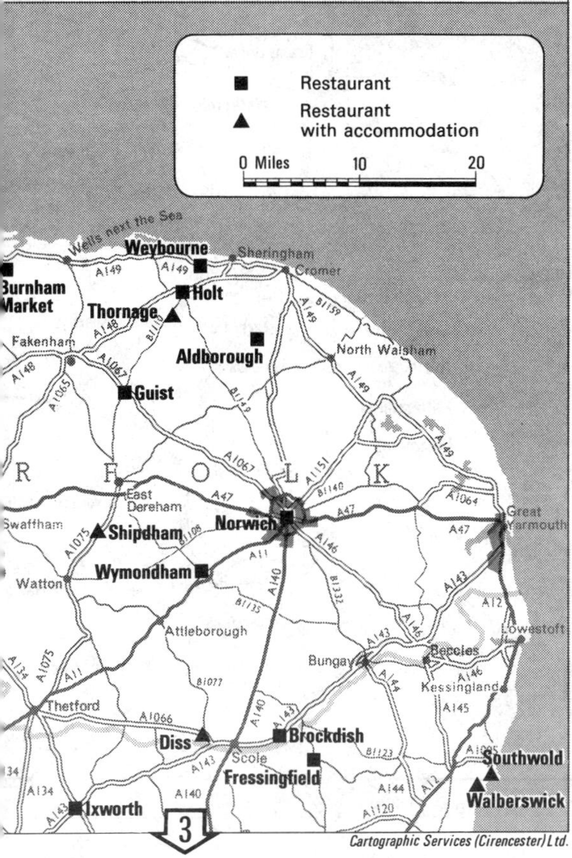

Cartographic Services (Cirencester) Ltd.

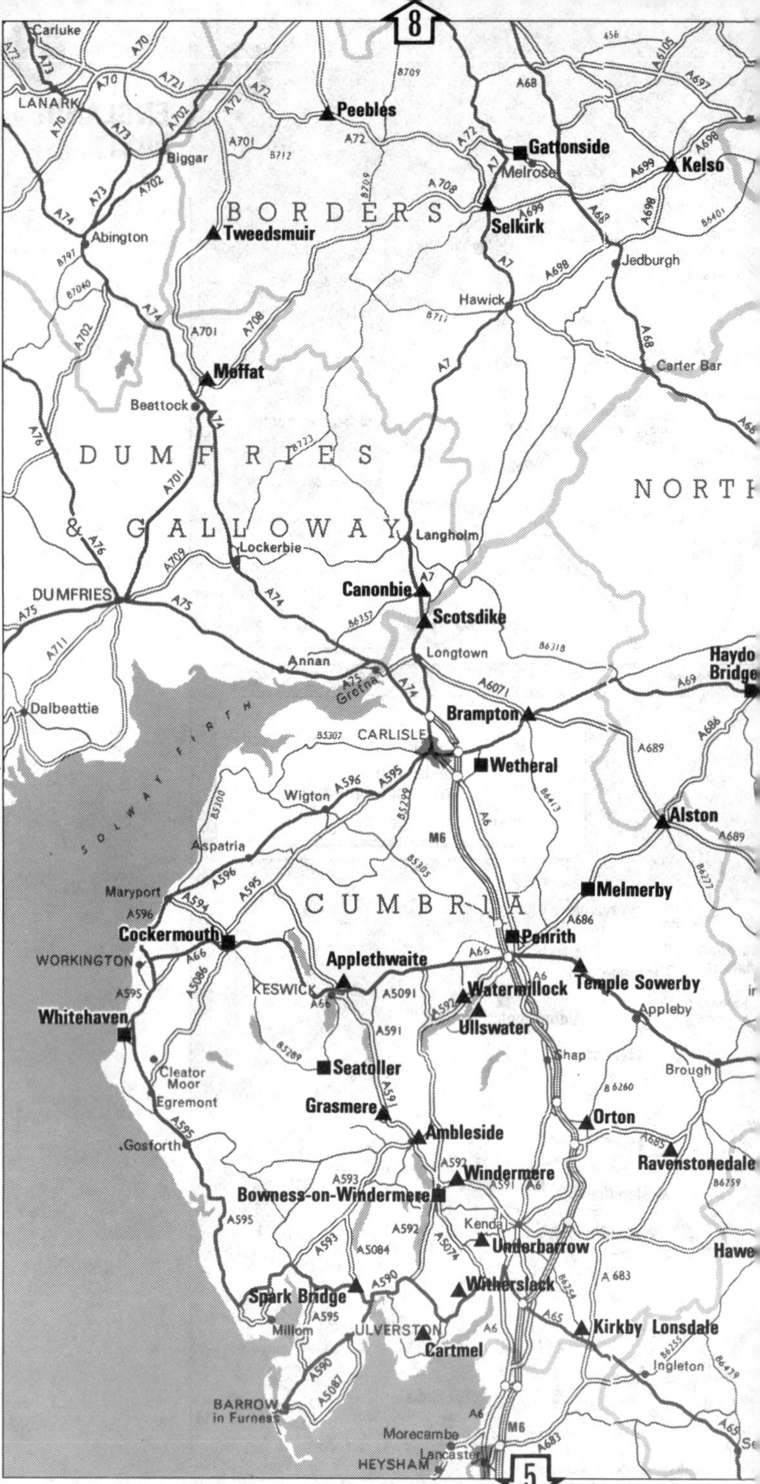

8
Carluke
LANARK
Biggar
Peebles
Gattonside
Melrose
Kelso
BORDERS
Selkirk
Tweedsmuir
Abington
Jedburgh
Hawick
Carter Bar
Moffat
Beattock
DUMFRIES
& GALLOWAY
NORTH
Langholm
Lockerbie
Canonbie
Scotsdike
DUMFRIES
Longtown
Annan
Gretna
Haydon Bridge
Brampton
Dalbeattie
SOLWAY FIRTH
CARLISLE
Wetheral
Wigton
Alston
Aspatria
Melmerby
Maryport
CUMBRIA
Cockermouth
Penrith
WORKINGTON
Applethwaite
Temple Sowerby
KESWICK
Watermillock
Whitehaven
Ullswater
Appleby
Shap
Seatoller
Brough
Cleator Moor
Egremont
Grasmere
Orton
Ambleside
Gosforth
Ravenstonedale
Windermere
Bowness-on-Windermere
Kendal
Underbarrow
Hawes
Spark Bridge
Witherslack
Millom
ULVERSTON
Kirkby Lonsdale
Cartmel
Ingleton
BARROW in Furness
Morecambe
Lancaster
HEYSHAM
5

ENGLAND: NORTH

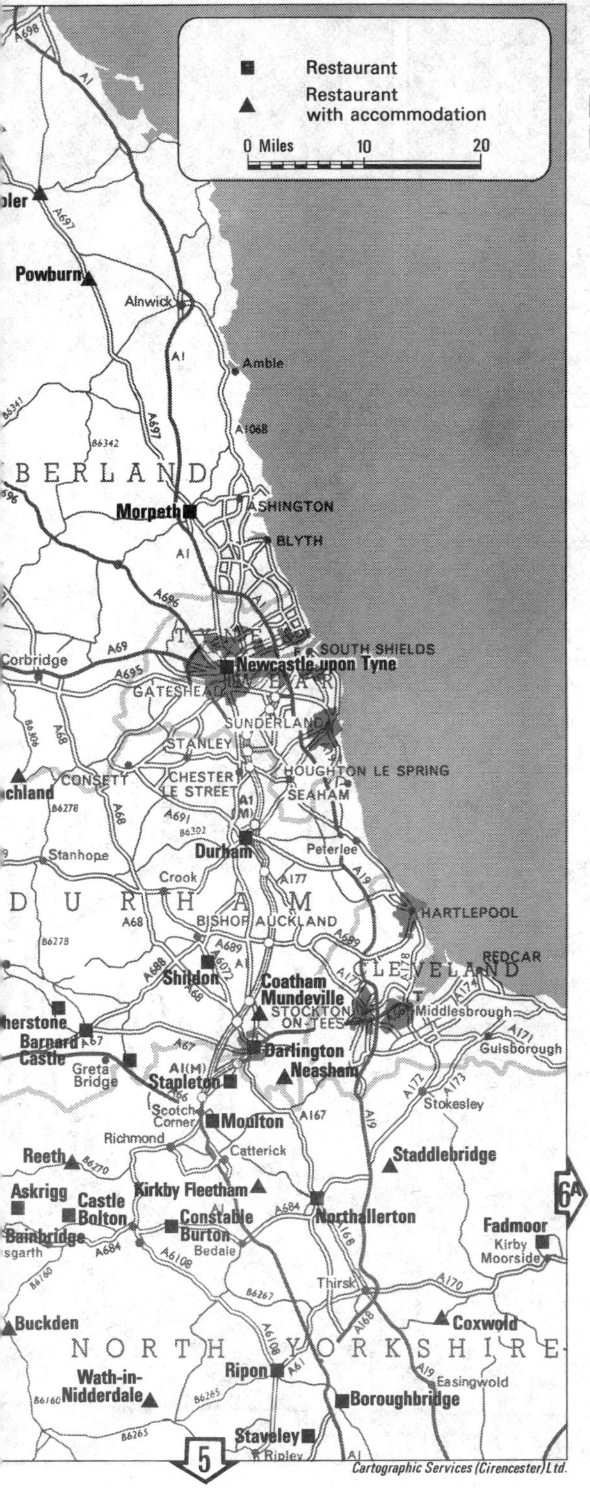

Cartographic Services (Cirencester) Ltd.

SCOTLAND

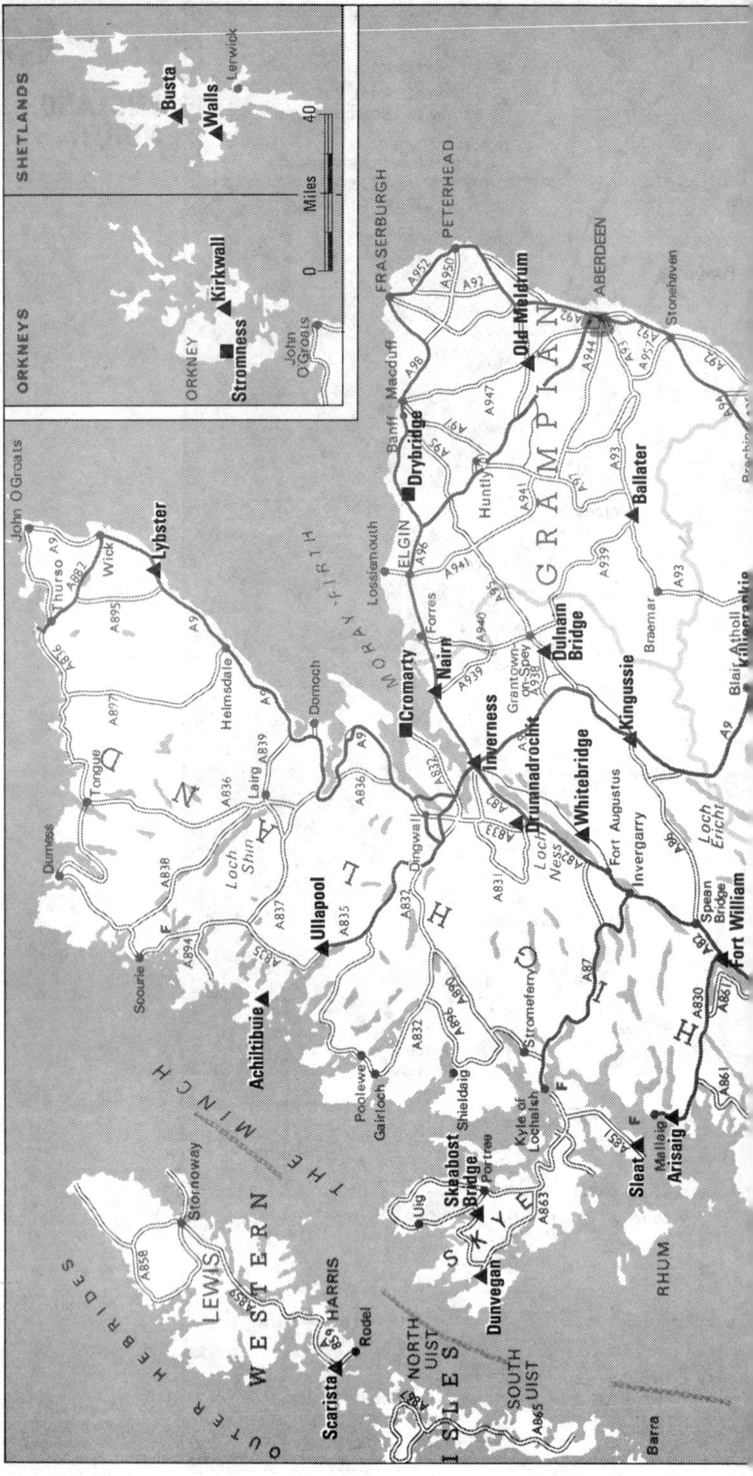
ORKNEYS
SHETLANDS
Lerwick
Busta
Walls
Kirkwall
Stromness
ORKNEY
John O'Groats
Miles
0
40
FRASERBURGH
PETERHEAD
ABERDEEN
Stonehaven
Old Meldrum
Macduff
Banff
Drybridge
Huntly
Ballater
Braemar
Blair Atholl
Killiecrankie
GRAMPIAN
Lossiemouth
ELGIN
Forres
Nairn
Cromarty
Dulnain Bridge
Grantown-on-Spey
Kingussie
Inverness
Drumnadrochit
Whitebridge
Fort Augustus
Invergarry
Loch Ness
Loch Ericht
Spean Bridge
Fort William
MORAY FIRTH
John O'Groats
Thurso
Wick
Lybster
Helmsdale
Dornoch
Tongue
Lairg
Durness
Loch Shin
Scourie
Ullapool
Achiltibuie
Dingwall
HIGHLAND
Poolewe
Gairloch
Shieldaig
Stromeferry
Kyle of Lochalsh
Mallaig
Arisaig
Sleat
Skeabost Bridge
Portree
Uig
SKYE
Dunvegan
RHUM
THE MINCH
Stornoway
LEWIS
HARRIS
Rodel
Scarista
NORTH UIST
SOUTH UIST
Barra
OUTER HEBRIDES
WESTERN ISLES
A9
A882
A836
A895
A897
A839
A838
A837
A835
A894
A832
A896
A890
A87
A830
A861
A851
A863
A858
A859
A865
A867
A831
A833
A82
A86
A96
A941
A939
A940
A938
A95
A97
A98
A947
A920
A93
A944
A92
A950
A952
A957
A94

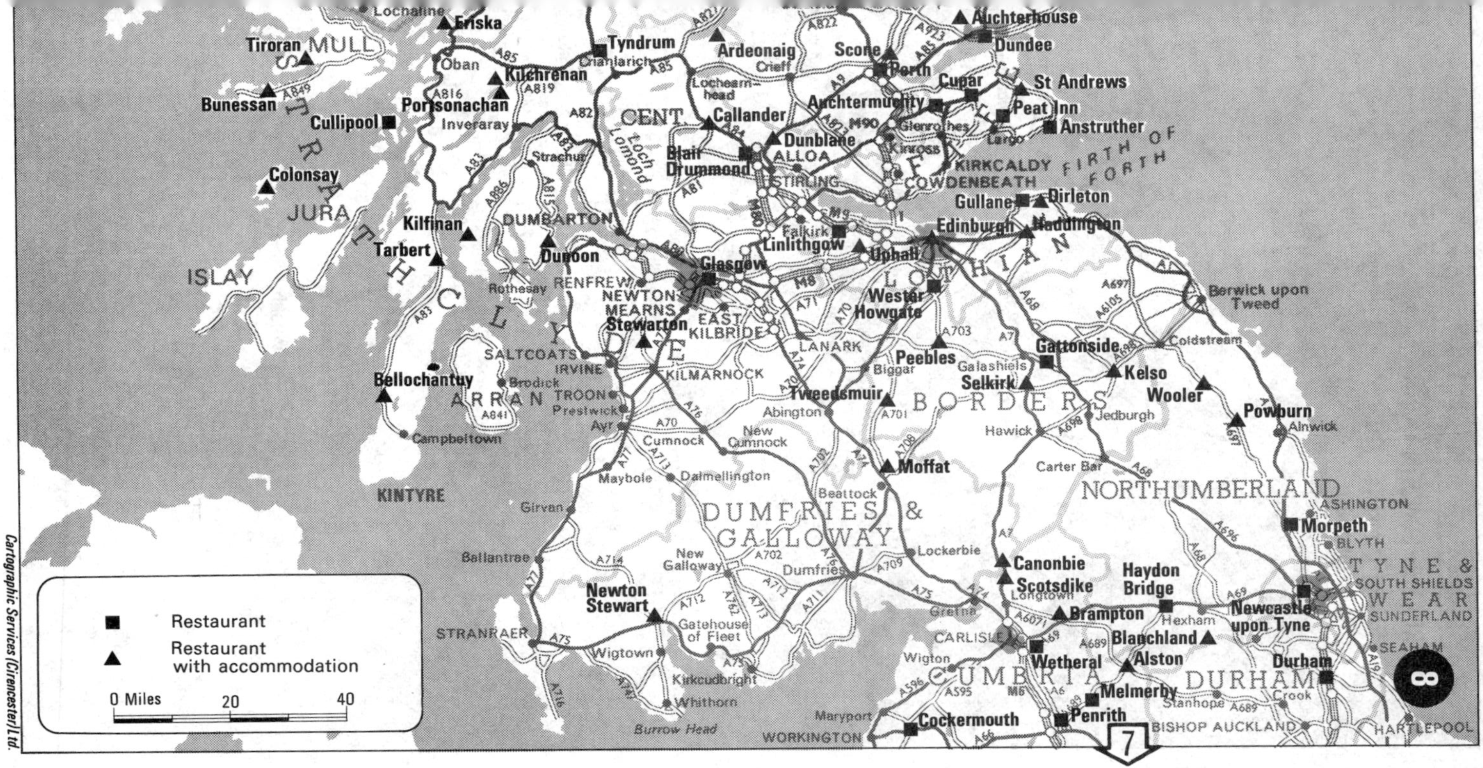

Cartographic Services (Cirencester) Ltd.

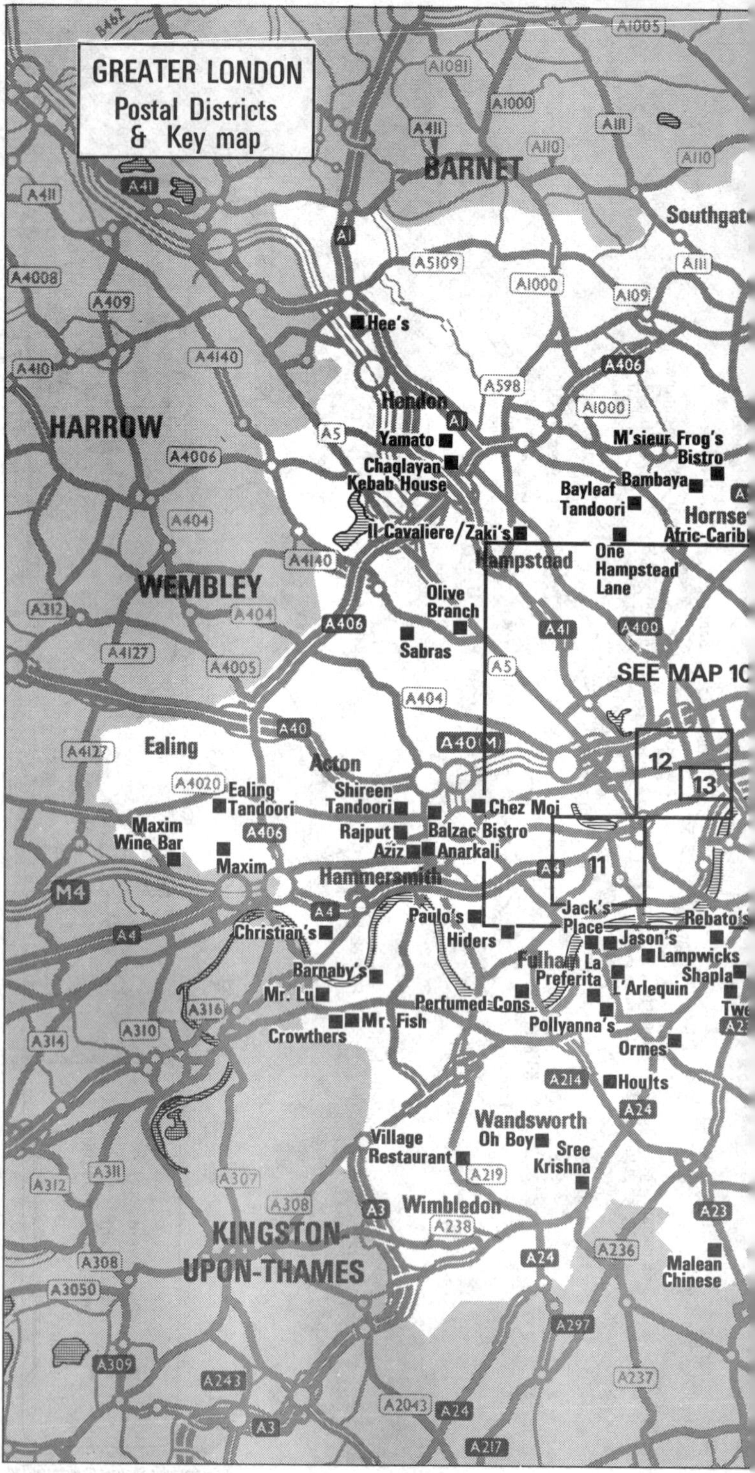
GREATER LONDON
Postal Districts
& Key map
BARNET
Southgate
HARROW
WEMBLEY
Hendon
Hee's
Yamato
Chaglayan Kebab House
Il Cavaliere/Zaki's
M'sieur Frog's Bistro
Bambaya
Bayleaf Tandoori
Hornsey
Afric-Carib
Hampstead
One Hampstead Lane
Olive Branch
Sabras
SEE MAP 10
12
13
11
Ealing
Acton
Ealing Tandoori
Shireen Tandoori
Chez Moi
Maxim Wine Bar
Maxim
Rajput
Balzac Bistro
Aziz
Anarkali
Hammersmith
Paulo's
Hiders
Jack's Place
Jason's
Rebato's
Lampwicks
Shapla
Christian's
Barnaby's
Fulham
La Preferita
L'Arlequin
Mr. Lu
Perfumed Cons.
Mr. Fish
Crowthers
Pollyanna's
Ormes
Hoults
Wandsworth
Oh Boy
Sree Krishna
Village Restaurant
Wimbledon
KINGSTON-UPON-THAMES
Malean Chinese
M4
A1
A41
A5
A40
A406
A4
A3
A24
A23
A214
A219
A238
A236
A297
A237
A217
A2043
A243
A309
A3050
A308
A312
A311
A307
A314
A310
A316
A4127
A4020
A404
A4005
A4140
A4006
A410
A409
A4008
A411
A5109
A1000
A598
A109
A111
A110
A1081
A1005
A400
A307
A308

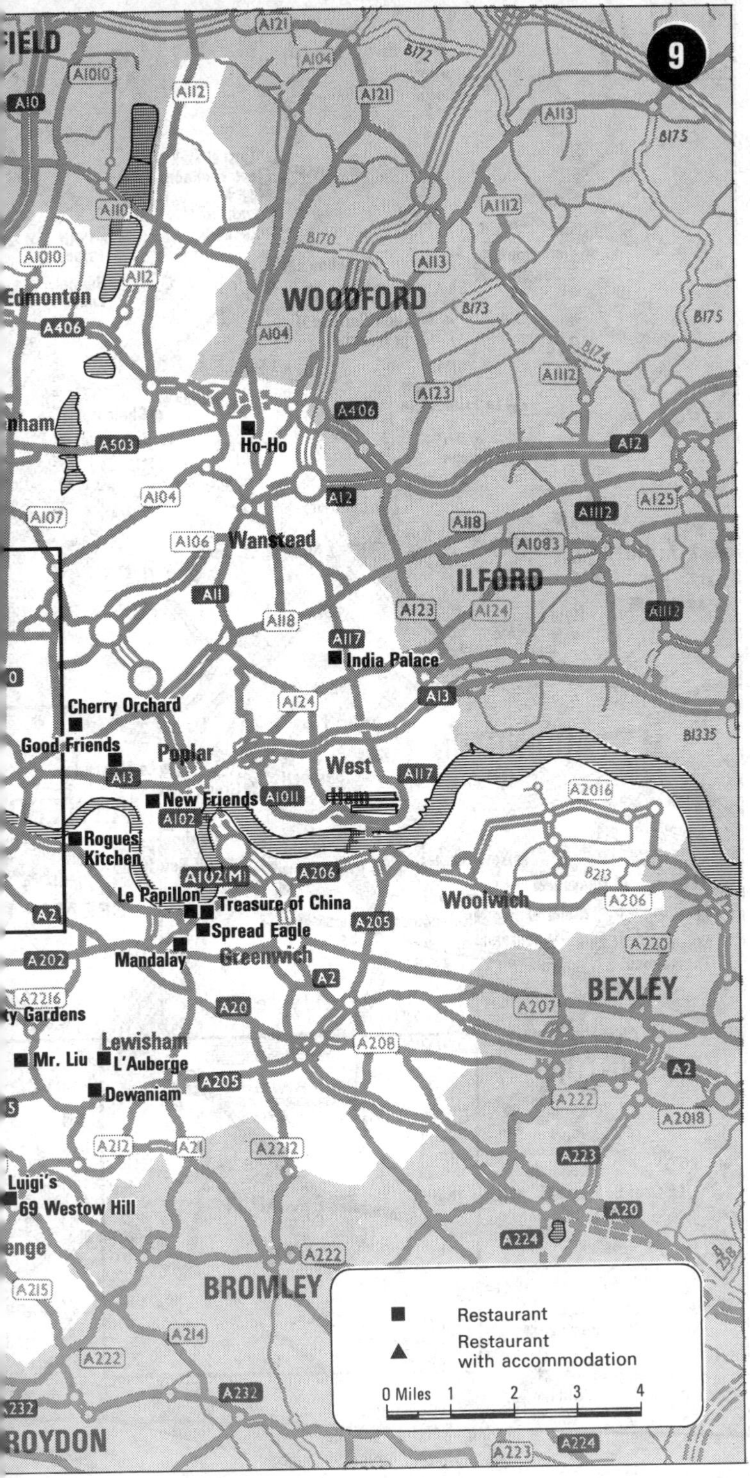
9
FIELD
WOODFORD
Edmonton
Ho-Ho
Wanstead
ILFORD
India Palace
Cherry Orchard
Good Friends
Poplar
West Ham
New Friends
Rogues Kitchen
Le Papillon
Treasure of China
Spread Eagle
Mandalay
Greenwich
Woolwich
BEXLEY
Gardens
Lewisham
Mr. Liu
L'Auberge
Dewaniam
Luigi's
69 Westow Hill
BROMLEY
ROYDON
Restaurant
Restaurant with accommodation
0 Miles 1 2 3 4

Child's Hill
Quincy's '84
Fortune Green
Hampstead Heath
Gospel Oak
Bunny's
Fleet Tandoon
Light of Kashmir
Le Petit Prince
Bengal Lancer
Viareggio
Seashore
Peachey's
HAMPSTEAD
Green Cottage II
Wakaba
Swiss Cottage
La Frimousse
Lemonia
Chalcot's
Le Bistroquet
Primrose Hill
Beau-Rivage
Koto
Nontas
Lalbhag
L'Aventure
Kilburn
Au Bois St. Jean
The Lantern
Regents Park
Maida Vale
PADDINGTON
Don Pepe
Seashell
La Muscadet
Green Leaves
ST. MARYLEBO
Daphne
New Bengal
Al Diwan
Knoodles
Sidi Bou Said
Maroush
192
Al Khayam
Hung Toa
Maharajah
Kalamaras
Le Chef
SEE MAP 1
Monsieur Thompsons
Cap's
Semiramis
Mayfair
Malabar
Hyde Park
Kensington Gardens
Clarke's
Ark
KENSINGTON
KNIGHTSBRIDGE
Ark
Phoenicia
Le Quai St Pierre
Bahn Thai
SEE MAP 11
Santini
Ciboure
CHELSEA
Le Mazarin
Tiger Lee
La Croisette
L'Olivier
Martin's
Bagatelle

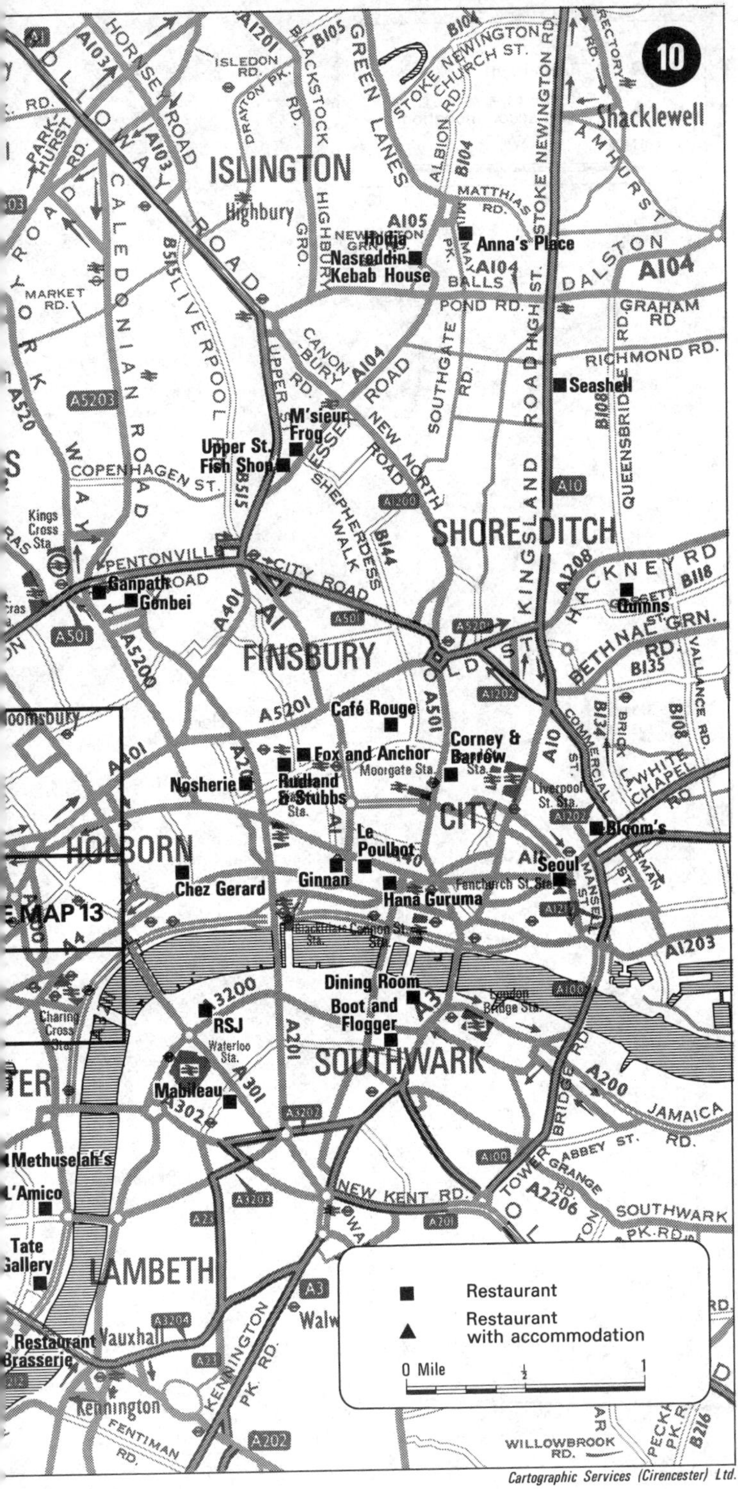

Cartographic Services (Cirencester) Ltd.

CENTRAL LONDON: South-West

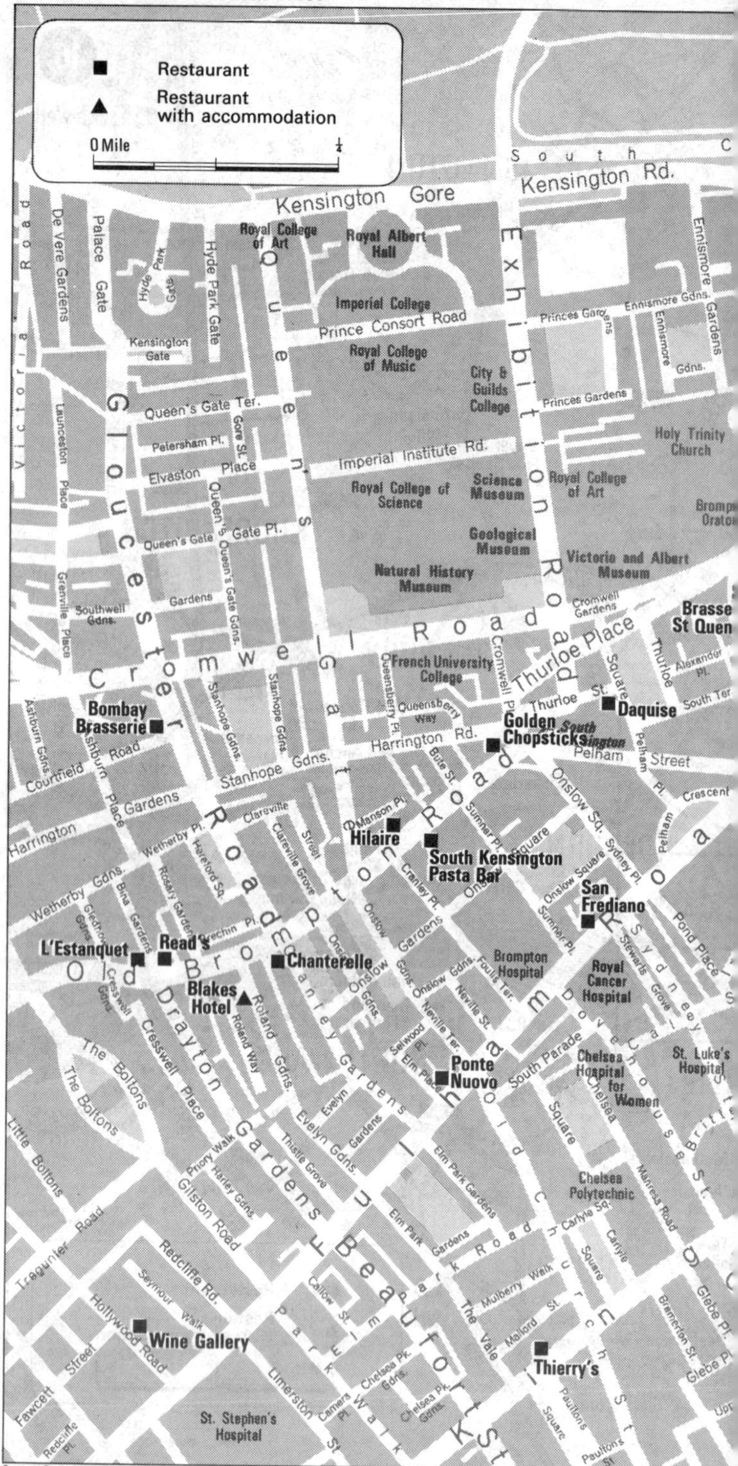

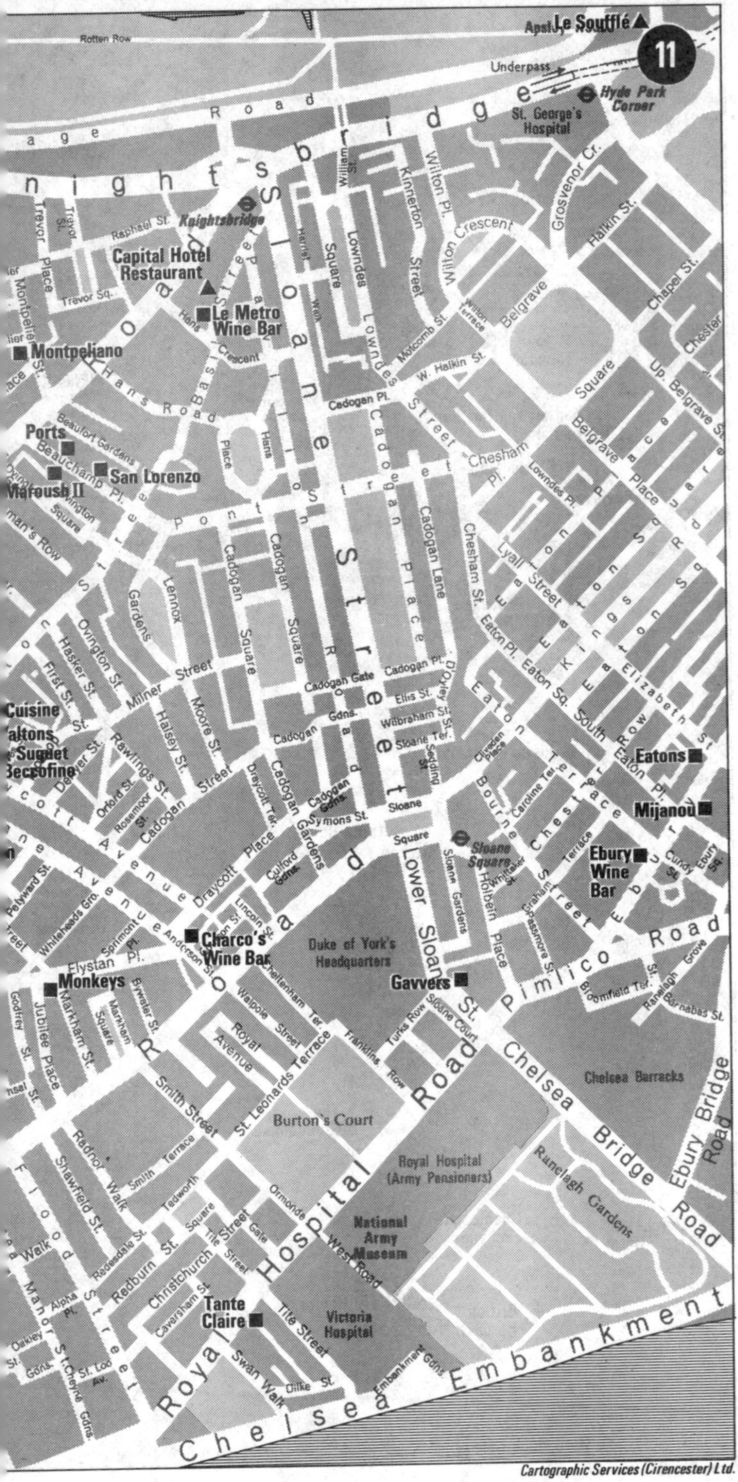

Cartographic Services (Cirencester) Ltd.

CENTRAL LONDON : West End

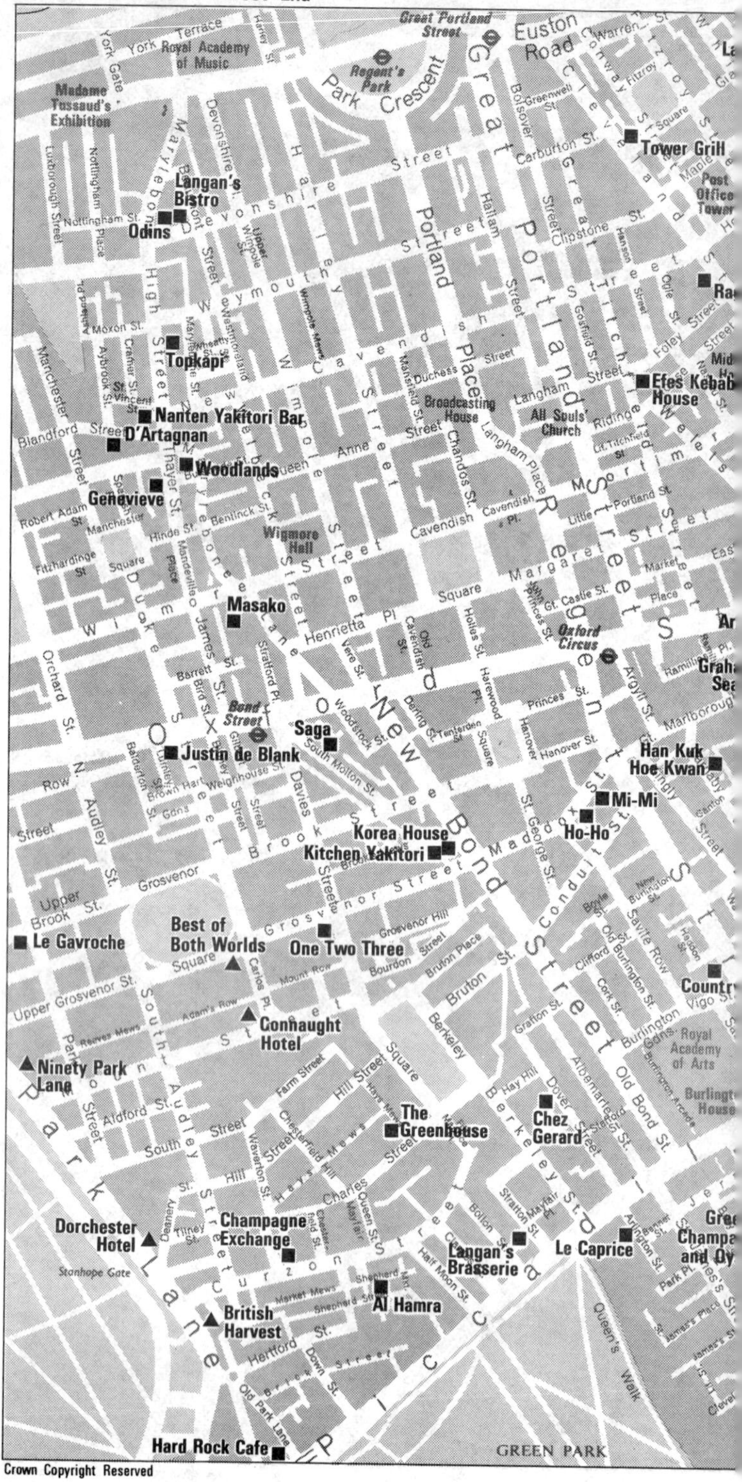

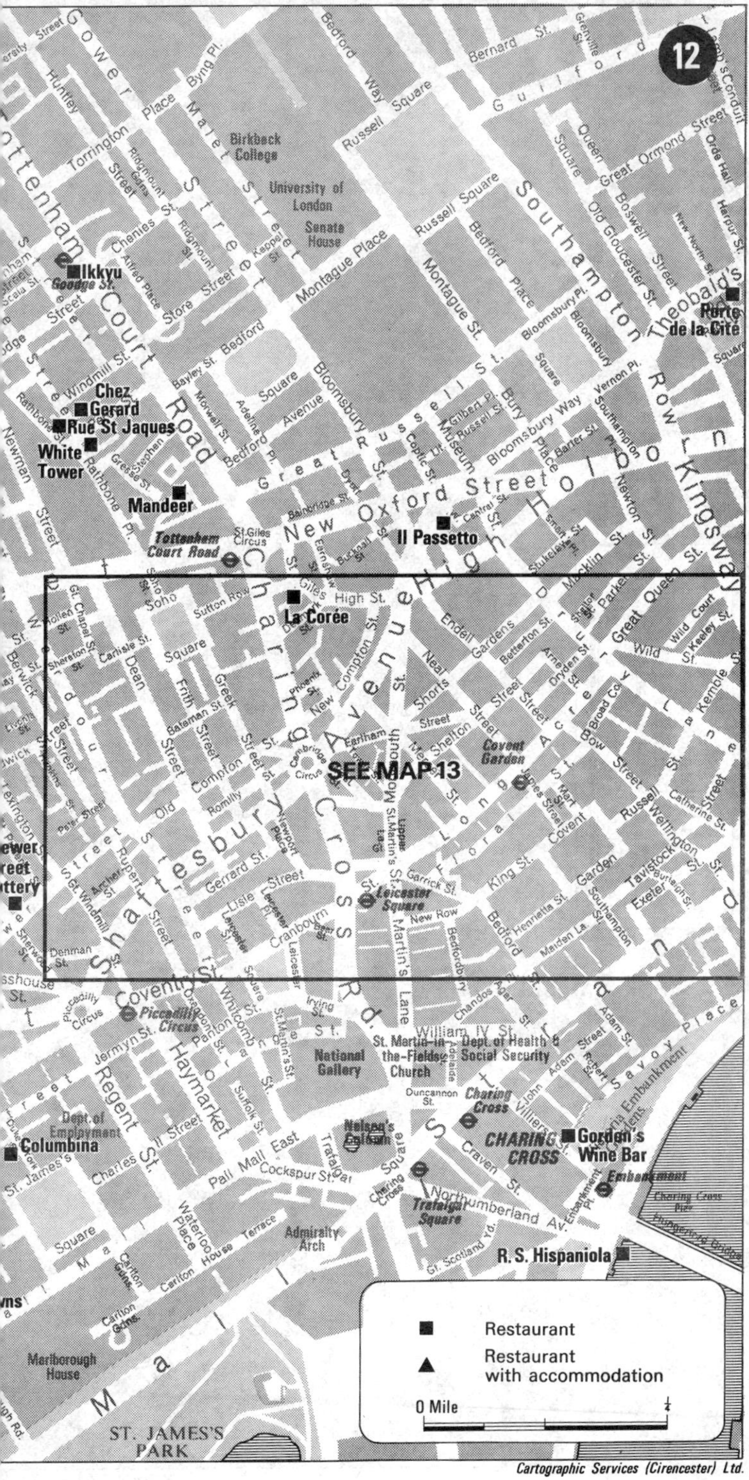

Cartographic Services (Cirencester) Ltd.

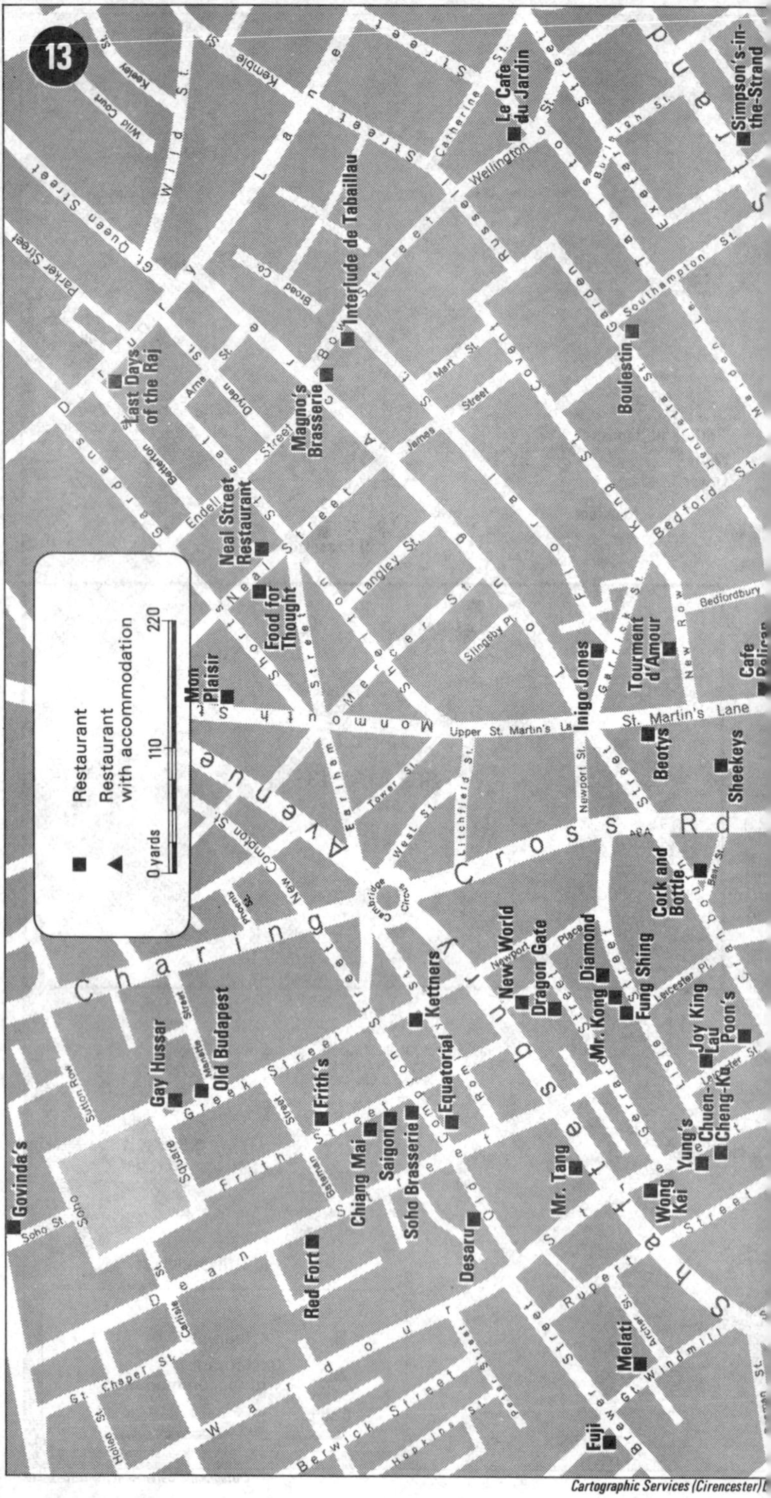

Cartographic Services (Cirencester) L

Report forms

Please use a separate report form (or sheet of paper if you prefer) for each restaurant or hotel, so that we can file each report separately in its own restaurant file.

Tell us, if you can, exactly what you ate and drank, what it cost and whether or not it was good, and what the service was like. Mention the surroundings, the decor, the music. Was the place friendly? Clean? Quiet? Was it good value for money?

If you report on a hotel you have stayed at, tell us also something about the standard of accommodation – whether or not it was comfortable and pleasant, and if it was good value for money. But please: food first and foremost; comfort and hotel facilities second.

The 1987 Guide will appear before Christmas 1986 so reports are needed particularly in spring. Everyone who reports on a restaurant in April and May will receive an acknowledgement letter containing a list of new addresses of restaurants and up-dated information on any changes that have taken place between the Guide's going to press and Easter. Let us have your report as soon as you can after your meal or stay.

Write – and sign – as clearly as possible: we hate misprinting names.

Ask us for more forms, which we will send free from Freepost, *The Good Food Guide*, 14 Buckingham Street, London WC2N 6DS (unfortunately Freepost facilities are not available in Ireland and the Isle of Man).

And above all, please do report to us. Do not let the villain who half-poisoned you get away unmarked; do not deprive the excellent people who served you so well of the reputation and custom they deserve.

Report forms

To the Editor *The Good Food Guide*
FREEPOST 14 Buckingham Street, London, WC2N 6DS

From my personal experience the following establishment should/ should not be included in the *Guide*

____

____

Telephone ____________

I had lunch/dinner/stayed there on ____________ 198____

I would rate this establishment _____/20

please continue overleaf

My meal for ____ people cost £__________ *Attach bill where possible*

☐ Please tick if you would like more report forms

I am not connected in any way with management or proprietors

Name and address (BLOCK CAPITALS)

Signed ______________________________

To the Editor *The Good Food Guide*
FREEPOST 14 Buckingham Street, London, WC2N 6DS

From my personal experience the following establishment should/ should not be included in the *Guide*

____

____

Telephone ____________________

I had lunch/dinner/stayed there on ____________________ 198____

I would rate this establishment ______/20

______________________________________ *please continue overleaf*

My meal for ____ people cost £__________ *Attach bill where possible*

☐ Please tick if you would like more report forms

I am not connected in any way with management or proprietors
Name and address (BLOCK CAPITALS)

____

____

Signed ____